NO POSTAGE
NECESSARY
IF MAILED
IN THE
UNITED STATES

BUSINESS REPLY MAIL
FIRST CLASS   **PERMIT NO.3376**   **QUINCY, MA**

POSTAGE WILL BE PAID BE ADDRESSEE

NATIONAL FIRE PROTECTION ASSOCIATION
1 BATTERYMARCH PARK
PO BOX 9101
QUINCY, MA 02269-9904
ATTN : CUSTOMER SERVICE

NO POSTAGE
NECESSARY
IF MAILED
IN THE
UNITED STATES

BUSINESS REPLY MAIL
FIRST CLASS   **PERMIT NO.3376**   **QUINCY, MA**

POSTAGE WILL BE PAID BE ADDRESSEE

NATIONAL FIRE PROTECTION ASSOCIATION
1 BATTERYMARCH PARK
PO BOX 9101
QUINCY, MA 02269-9904
ATTN : CUSTOMER SERVICE

NO POSTAGE
NECESSARY
IF MAILED
IN THE
UNITED STATES

BUSINESS REPLY MAIL
FIRST CLASS   **PERMIT NO.3376**   **QUINCY, MA**

POSTAGE WILL BE PAID BE ADDRESSEE

NATIONAL FIRE PROTECTION ASSOCIATION
1 BATTERYMARCH PARK
PO BOX 9101
QUINCY, MA 02269-9904
ATTN : CUSTOMER SERVICE

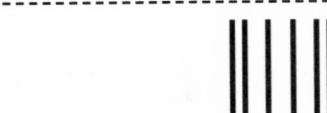

National Electrical Code® Handbook

Sixth Edition

National Electrical Code Handbook

Sixth Edition

Based on the 1993 Edition of the
National Electrical Code®

Mark W. Earley, P.E.
Editor-in-Chief

Richard H. Murray
Editor

John M. Caloggero
Editor

Jean A. O'Connor
Editorial Assistant

National Fire Protection Association
1 Batterymarch Park
P.O. Box 9101
Quincy, Massachusetts 02269-9101

This sixth edition of the *National Electrical Code® Handbook* is based on the 1993 edition of NFPA 70, *National Electrical Code*. The nation's most authoritative and comprehensive document on electrical safety, the code addresses safety from fire and electrocution. The code is developed by NFPA's National Electrical Code Committee. This committee consists of a broad range of representatives from the electrical industry, including electricians, engineers, electrical product manufacturers, electric utilities, code enforcers, research and testing organizations, and insurers.

Like other NFPA code handbooks, the *National Electrical Code Handbook* explains code requirements, especially changes to the code from the last edition. It also serves as a helpful guide in applying code provisions. The handbook contains the complete text of the code, along with explanatory commentary, which is integrated between the code requirements.

All NFPA codes and standards are processed in accordance with NFPA's *Regulations Governing Committee Projects*. The commentary in this handbook is the opinion of the author(s), recognized experts in the field of electrical safety. It is not, however, processed in accordance with the NFPA *Regulations Governing Committee Projects*, and therefore shall not be considered to be, nor relied on as, a Formal Interpretation of the meaning or intent of any specific provision or provisions of NFPA 70. The language contained in NFPA 70, rather than this commentary, represents the official position of the National Electrical Code Committee and the NFPA.

All of the commentary material has been researched, written, and reviewed by experts in the field of electrical safety — NFPA staff and members of the National Electrical Code Committee.

This handbook is a must for inspectors, electricians, engineers, building and fire officials, safety personnel, and all others whose responsibilities include electrical safety.

®Registered trademarks of the National Fire Protection Association

National Electrical Code® and *Life Safety Code®* are registered trademarks of the National Fire Protection Association.

Project Manager: Jennifer Evans

Project Editor: Dana Richards

Composition: Louise Grant, Cathy Ray, Claire McRudin, Nancy Maria

Art Coordinator: Laurie Beaulieu

Illustrations: George Nichols

Cover Design: Cameron, Inc.

Production: Donald McGonagle and Stephen Dornbusch

NFPA No. 70HB93

ISBN 0-87765-384-4

Library of Congress Catalog Card Number 89-63606

Printed in the United States of America

First Printing, November 1992

Contents

Preface

The *National Electrical Code* is the most widely adopted code in the world. The *National Electrical Code* is a nationally accepted guide for the safe installation of electrical conductors and equipment and is, in fact, the basis for all electrical codes used in the United States. It is also used extensively outside of the United States, particularly where American-made equipment is installed.

The *National Electrical Code Handbook* is published by the National Fire Protection Association in order to assist those concerned with electrical safety in understanding the intent of the 1993 edition of the *Code*. A verbatim reproduction of the 1993 *National Electric Code* is included, and added where necessary are comments, diagrams, and illustrations that are intended to clarify further some of the intricate requirements of the *National Electrical Code*.

The editors have worked very closely with members of the National Electric Code Committee in discussions that have led to the various revisions that have been incorporated in the 1993 edition of the *Code*. The assistance and cooperation of the Code-Making Panel Chairmen and various Committee members are herein gratefully acknowledged.

This edition of the *Handbook* would not have been possible without the invaluable technical assistance of Mark C. Ode, Senior Electrical Specialist. His contributions are appreciated.

The editors acknowledge with thanks the manufacturers and their representatives who generously supplied photographs, drawings, and data upon request. Special thanks, too, go to the editors and contributors to past editions.

Appreciation is expressed to the NFPA staff members who attended to the countless details that went into the preparation of this *Handbook*, and especially to Dana Richards, project editor; Louise Grant, Cathy Ray, Claire McRudin, Nancy Maria, composition; Jennifer Evans, project manager; George Nichols, illustrator; Angela J. Murphy, typing; and Donald McGonagle and Stephen Dornbusch, production.

Finally, the editors wish to express their sincere appreciation to Stanley Kaufman, Peter Schram, Ray Mullin, Phil Cox, Roger Sanstedt, Jim Pauley, Paul Duks, and Floyd DeVore for special help on specific articles. The editors also wish to thank E. C. Lawry of the State of Wisconsin Department of Industry and Human Relations, Safety and Buildings Division for a number of excellent suggestions for this edition.

Mark W. Earley, *Editor-In-Chief*

Richard H. Murray, *Editor*

John M. Caloggero, *Editor*

Concise History of the National Electrical Code

In 1881, the National Association of Fire Engineers met in Richmond, Virginia. From this meeting came a proposal that served as a basis for the first *National Electrical Code*, covering items such as the use of insulated conduit, the use of single disconnect devices, and the identification of the white wire. The first nationally recommended electrical code was published by the National Board of Fire Underwriters (now the American Insurance Association) in 1895. (The National Board of Fire Underwriters continued to publish the *National Electrical Code* until 1962, thus contributing greatly to its current universality.) With this 1895 code as a basis, in 1897 the *National Electrical Code* was drafted, the product of the combined labors of architectural, electrical, insurance, and allied interests which, through the National Conference on Standard Electrical Rules, composed of delegates from various national associations, unanimously voted to recommend it to their respective associations for approval or adoption.

In 1911, the National Fire Protection Association (NFPA) assumed sponsorship and control of the *National Electrical Code*, the National Conference on Standard Electrical Rules having disbanded in that very same year. Since 1920, the *National Electrical Code* has also been officially endorsed by the American National Standards Institute (formerly the United States of America Standards Institute and the American Standards Association), and the NFPA has maintained its capacity as Administrative Sponsor. Since that date, the Committee has been identified as "ANSI Standards Committee C1" (formerly "USAS C1" or "ASA C1").

In 1923, the *National Electrical Code* was rearranged and rewritten; in 1937 it was editorially revised so that all of the general rules would appear in the first chapters followed by supplementary rules in the following chapters; and, in 1959, it was editorially revised again, this time in order to incorporate a new numbering system under which each section of each article is identified by the article number preceding the section number. The National Fire Protection Association has been publishing and distributing the *National Electrical Code* since 1951.

It does so through its own office and through the American National Standards Institute. In addition, the *National Electrical Code* is found in Volume Three of the NFPA's annual *National Fire Codes*. The *National Electrical Code* is acknowledged to be the most widely adopted code of standard practices in the U.S.A.

1993 Edition of the National Electrical Code

This 1993 edition of the *National Electrical Code* (NFPA 70-1993) was adopted by the National Fire Protection Association at its 1992 Annual Meeting held in New Orleans, Louisiana. It was approved by the American National Standards Institute on August 14, 1992, and is known as ANSI/NFPA 70-1993. It supersedes all previous editions of the *National Electrical Code*, the most recent previous edition being 1990.

This *Code* is purely advisory as far as the NFPA and ANSI are concerned but is offered for use in law and for regulatory purposes in the interest of life and property protection. Anyone noticing any errors should please notify the NFPA Executive Office, the Chairman and the Secretary of the Committee.

Development of the National Electrical Code

In accordance with the provisions of the NFPA Regulations Governing Committee Projects, a National Electric Code Technical Committee Report containing proposed amendments to the 1990 *National Electrical Code* was published by the NFPA in June 1991. This report recorded the actions of the various Code-Making Panels and the Correlating Committee of the National Electrical Code Committee on each proposal that had been made to revise the 1990 *Code*. The report was circulated to all members of the National Electrical Code Committee, and was made available to other interested NFPA members and to the public for review and comment. Following the close of the public comment period, the Code-Making Panels met, acted on each comment, and reported their action to the Correlating Committee. The NFPA published the National Electrical Code Technical Committee Documentation in April 1992, which recorded the actions of the Code-Making Panels and the Correlating Committee on each public comment to the National Electrical Code Technical Committee Report. The National Electrical Code Technical Committee Report and National Electrical Code Technical Committee Documentation were presented to the 1992 NFPA Annual Meeting for adoption.

Coincident with the above processing procedures, each of the Code-Making Panels and the Chairman of the Correlating Committee reported their recommendations to meetings of the Electrical Section at the 1992 NFPA Annual Meeting.

The Electrical Section thus had opportunity to discuss and review the report of the National Electrical Code Committee prior to the adoption of this edition of the *Code* by the Association.

The *Electrical Code for One- and Two-Family Dwellings*, NFPA 70A-1993, is an abridged version of the 1993 text, edited only as dictated to eliminate extraneous material not of concern to this type of occupancy, and to place in the text only the more popular types of wiring methods, not to exclude any other type authorized by the complete *Code*.

Part 1
1993 National Electrical Code and Commentary

The text and illustrations that make up the commentary on the various sections of the *National Electrical Code* are printed in black. The text of the *Code* itself is printed in blue.

The Formal Interpretations included in this *Handbook* were issued as a result of questions raised on specific editions of the *Code*. Formal Interpretations apply to all other editions in which the text remains substantially unchanged, unless deemed inappropriate by the committee. Formal Interpretations are not part of the *Code* and therefore are printed in a shaded blue box.

Material identified by the superscript letter *x* was extracted from other NFPA documents. Those documents are identified in Appendix A.

ARTICLE 90　Introduction

Contents

90-1. Purpose.

(a) Practical Safeguarding. The purpose of this Code is the practical safeguarding of persons and property from hazards arising from the use of electricity.

The *National Electrical Code* (*NEC*) is prepared by the NFPA *National Electrical Code* Committee. The scope of this Committee is as follows:

Scope: This Committee shall consist of a Correlating Committee and Code-Making Panels. It shall have primary responsibility for preparing documents on minimizing the risk of electricity as a source of electric shock and as an ignition source of fires and explosions. It shall also be responsible for developing requirememts to minimize the propagation of fire and explosions due to electrical installations.

The *National Electrical Code* is the most widely adopted set of electrical safety requirements in the world and is offered for use in law and for regulatory purposes in the interest of life and property protection. NFPA has available a model state law on inspection of electrical installations entitled "The Model Law Providing for Inspection of Electrical Installations" (formerly NFPA 70L). The model law was prepared by the NFPA Advisory Committee on the

Adoption and Use of the *National Electrical Code* and Related Documents (formerly the Electrical Field Service Advisory Committee) as a guide for those jurisdictions that do not have formalized electrical inspection procedures or those that desire to amend their electrical inspection laws, and as a guide to adoption of the *National Electrical Code*. The model law is intended for use by states as well as municipalities.

(b) Adequacy. This Code contains provisions considered necessary for safety. Compliance therewith and proper maintenance will result in an installation essentially free from hazard but not necessarily efficient, convenient, or adequate for good service or future expansion of electrical use.

(FPN): Hazards often occur because of overloading of wiring systems by methods or usage not in conformity with this Code. This occurs because initial wiring did not provide for increases in the use of electricity. An initial adequate installation and reasonable provisions for system changes will provide for future increases in the use of electricity.

Consideration should always be given to future expansion in the use of electricity. Future expansion may not be likely in some occupancies, but in others it is wise to plan an initial installation comprised of service-entrance conductors and equipment, feeder conductors, and panelboards that will allow for future additions, alterations, designs, etc.

(c) Intention. This Code is not intended as a design specification nor an instruction manual for untrained persons.

The *National Electrical Code* is intended for use by capable engineers and electrical contractors in the design and/or installation of electrical equipment; by inspection authorities exercising legal jurisdiction over electrical installations; by property insurance inspectors; by qualified industrial, commercial, and residential electricians; and by instructors of electrical apprentices or students.

90-2. Scope.

(a) Covered. This Code covers:

(1) Installations of electric conductors and equipment within or on public and private buildings or other structures, including mobile homes, recreational vehicles, and floating buildings; and other premises such as yards, carnival, parking, and other lots, and industrial substations.

(FPN): For additional information concerning such installations in an industrial or multibuilding complex, see the National Electrical Safety Code, ANSI C2-1990.

Industrial and multibuilding complexes (for example, some universities) often include substations and other installations employing construction and wiring similar to electric utility installations. Although such nonutility installations are within the scope of the *National Electrical Code*, the *NEC* requirements may not always be sufficient or complete, for example, in such cases as clearances of conductors or clearance from buildings or structures for nominal voltages over 600 volts. In such cases, the user can find additional information in the *National Electrical Safety Code*, published by the Institute of Electrical and Electronics Engineers, Inc., P.O. Box 1331, 445 Hoes Lane, Piscataway, NJ 08855-1331.

(2) Installations of conductors and equipment that connect to the supply of electricity.

(3) Installations of other outside conductors and equipment on the premises.

(4) Installations of optical fiber cable.

See Article 770 for the installation requirements for optical fiber cable and Article 690 regarding solar photovoltaic systems.

(b) Not Covered. This Code does not cover:

(1) Installations in ships, watercraft other than floating buildings, railway rolling stock, aircraft, or automotive vehicles other than mobile homes and recreational vehicles.

Requirements for floating buildings will be found in Article 553.

(2) Installations underground in mines and self-propelled mobile surface mining machinery and its attendant electrical trailing cable.

(3) Installations of railways for generation, transformation, transmission, or distribution of power used exclusively for operation of rolling stock or installations used exclusively for signaling and communications purposes.

(4) Installations of communications equipment under the exclusive control of communications utilities located outdoors or in building spaces used exclusively for such installations.

(5) Installations under the exclusive control of electric utilities for the purpose of communications or metering; or for the

generation, control, transformation, transmission, and distribution of electric energy located in buildings used exclusively by utilities for such purposes or located outdoors on property owned or leased by the utility or on public highways, streets, roads, etc., or outdoors by established rights on private property.

(FPN): It is the intent of this section that this Code covers all premises wiring or wiring other than utility-owned metering equipment, on the load side of the service point of buildings, structures, or any other premises not owned or leased by the utility. Also, it is the intent that this Code cover installations in buildings used by the utility for purposes other than listed in Section 90-2(b)(5) above, such as office buildings, warehouses, garages, machine shops, and recreational buildings that are not an integral part of a generating plant, substation, or control center.

See Figure 90-1.

NEC does not apply

NEC applies

Figure 90-1. A typical electric utility complex indicating those facilities subject to the provisions of the NEC.

(c) **Special Permission.** The authority having jurisdiction for enforcing this Code may grant exception for the installation of conductors and equipment that are not under the exclusive control of the electric utilities and are used to connect the electric utility supply system to the service-entrance conductors of the premises served, provided such installations are outside a building or terminate immediately inside a building wall.

90-3. **Code Arrangement.** This Code is divided into the Introduction and nine chapters. Chapters 1, 2, 3, and 4 apply generally; Chapters 5, 6, and 7 apply to special occupancies, special equipment, or other special conditions. These latter chapters supplement or modify the general rules. Chapters 1 through 4 apply except as amended by Chapters 5, 6, and 7 for the particular conditions.

The reference to the Introduction and Chapter 9 Tables and Examples is made with the intention that Article 90 and Chapter 9 be included in the application of this *Code*.

Chapters 1 through 4 apply generally, except as amended or specifically referenced in Chapters 5, 6, and 7 (Articles 500 through 780). For example, Section 300-22 (Chapter 3) is modified by Sections 725-2(b), 760-2(b), and 770-2(b) (Chapter 7) and specifically referenced in Section 800-52(c) (Chapter 8). In addition, see commentary following Section 300-1.

Chapter 8 covers communications systems and is independent of the other chapters except where they are specifically referenced therein.

Chapter 9 consists of tables and examples.

Material identified by the superscript letter "x" includes text extracted from other NFPA documents as identified in Appendix A.

90-4. **Enforcement.** This Code is intended to be suitable for mandatory application by governmental bodies exercising legal jurisdiction over electrical installations and for use by insurance inspectors. The authority having jurisdiction for enforcement of the Code will have the responsibility for making interpretations of the rules, for deciding upon the approval of equipment and materials, and for granting the special permission contemplated in a number of the rules.

Section 90-4 advises that an authority must grant approval for all materials and equipment used under the requirements of the *Code* in its area of jurisdiction. The text of Sections 90-7, 110-2, and 110-3, along with the definitions of "approved," "identified," "listed," and "labeled," are intended to provide a basis for the authority having jurisdiction to make the judgments that fall within its area of responsibility.

See commentary following Section 90-1(a).

The authority having jurisdiction may waive specific requirements in this Code or permit alternate methods where it is assured that equivalent objectives can be achieved by establishing and maintaining effective safety.

It is the responsibility of the local authority enforcing the *Code* to interpret the specific rules of the *Code*.

The second paragraph to Section 90-4 is included to allow the authority having jurisdiction the option of permitting alternative methods where specific rules are not established in the *Code*. For example, this allows the local authority to waive specific requirements in industrial occupancies, research and testing laboratories, and other occupancies where the specific type of installation is not contemplated in the *Code* rules.

Some localities do not adopt the *National Electrical Code*, but even in those localities installations meeting the current *Code* are prima facie evidence that the electrical installation is safe.

This Code may require new products, constructions, or materials that may not yet be available at the time the Code is adopted. In such event, the authority having jurisdiction may permit the use of the products, constructions, or materials that comply with the most recent previous edition of this Code adopted by the jurisdiction.

The third paragraph of Section 90-4 permits the authority to waive a new *Code* requirement during the interim period between the acceptance of a new edition of the *NEC* and the availability of a new product, construction, or material redesigned to comply with the increased safety required by the new *Code* edition. It is difficult to establish a viable future effective date in the *NEC* because the time needed to change existing products and standards, and to develop new materials and test methods, is not usually known at the time of adoption of the new requirement in the *NEC*.

90-5. Mandatory Rules and Explanatory Material. Mandatory rules of this Code are characterized by the use of the

word "shall." Explanatory material is in the form of Fine Print Notes (FPN).

In addition to printing explanatory material in fine print (small type), the material is further identified in the *Code* by the term "(FPN)" preceding the paragraph. Footnotes to tables, although also in fine print, are not explanatory material unless identified by the term "(FPN)"; the footnotes are part of the tables and are necessary for the proper use of the tables. For example, see the footnotes to Table 310-16.

The material in Appendices A and B is also explanatory. Appendix A is a reference list of text that has been extracted from other NFPA documents. Appendix B provides guidance on the use of the general formula in Section 310-15(b).

90-6. Formal Interpretations. To promote uniformity of interpretation and application of the provisions of this Code, Formal Interpretation procedures have been established.

(FPN): These procedures may be found in the "NFPA Regulations Governing Committee Projects."

The procedures for formal interpretations of the provisions of the *National Electrical Code* are outlined in the Regulations Governing Committee Projects, which may be obtained from the Secretary of the Standards Council of the National Fire Protection Association. These regulations are included in the NFPA *Annual Directory*. The formal interpretations procedure can be found in Section 16 of the *Directory* and has been reprinted in its entirety in the appendix to this Handbook. Additional information on interpretations contained in the *NEC* Operating Procedures is included.

The *National Electrical Code* Committee cannot be responsible for subsequent actions by authorities enforcing the *NEC* that accept or reject its findings. The authority having jurisdiction has responsibility for interpreting the *Code* rules and should attempt to resolve all disagreements at the local level.

Two general forms of Formal Interpretations are recognized: (1) those making an interpretation of the literal text and (2) those making an interpretation of the intent of the Committee at the time the particular text was issued.

Interpretations of the *NEC* not subject to processing are those that (1) involve a determination of compliance with a design, installation, product, or equivalency of protection, including the suitability of isolation or guarding; (2) involve a review of plans or specifications or require judgment or knowledge that can only be acquired as a result of on-site inspection, including the degree and extent of a hazardous (classified) location; (3) involve text that clearly and decisively provides the requested information; or (4) involve subjects that were not previously considered by the committee or that are not addressed in the document.

Formal Interpretations of *Code* rules are published in the NFPA *Fire News*, the NFPA Electrical Section News Bulletin (Current Flashes), and the National Fire Codes Subscription Service, and sent to interested trade publications.

Most interpretations of the *NEC* are rendered as the personal opinion of NFPA Electrical Department staff, or of the involved member of the *National Electrical Code* Committee, because the request for interpretation does not qualify for processing as a Formal Interpretation in accordance with the Regulations Governing Committee Projects or the *NEC* Committee policy. Such opinions are rendered in writing only in response to written requests. The responses are identified as personal opinions, and indicate that the opinion shall not be considered the official position of the NFPA or of the *National Electrical Code* Committee and shall not be considered to be, nor be relied upon as, a Formal Interpretation.

90-7. **Examination of Equipment for Safety.** For specific items of equipment and materials referred to in this Code, examinations for safety made under standard conditions will provide a basis for approval where the record is made generally available through promulgation by organizations properly equipped and qualified for experimental testing, inspections of the run of goods at factories, and service-value determination through field inspections. This avoids the necessity for repetition of examinations by different examiners, frequently with inadequate facilities for such work, and the confusion that would result from conflicting reports as to the suitability of devices and materials examined for a given purpose.

Testing laboratories, inspection agencies, or other organizations concerned with product evaluation publish lists of equipment or materials that have been tested and meet nationally recognized standards or that have been found suitable for use in a specified manner. The *Code* does not

contain detailed information on equipment or materials but refers to the products as "listed," "labeled," or "identified." See Article 100, "Definitions," for explanation of these terms.

The National Fire Protection Association does not approve, inspect, or certify any installations, procedures, equipment, or materials nor does it approve or evaluate testing laboratories. In determining the acceptability of installations or procedures, equipment, or materials, the authority having jurisdiction may base acceptance on compliance with NFPA or other appropriate standards. In the absence of such standards, the authority may require evidence of proper installation, procedure, or use. The authority having jurisdiction may also refer to the listings or labeling practices of an organization concerned with product evaluations that is in a position to determine compliance with appropriate standards for the current production of listed items.

It is not intended that the *Code* apply to the internal factory-installed wiring or to the construction of listed equipment at the time of installation unless damage or alterations are detected.

It is the intent of this Code that factory-installed internal wiring or the construction of equipment need not be inspected at the time of installation of the equipment, except to detect alterations or damage, if the equipment has been listed by a qualified electrical testing laboratory that is recognized as having the facilities described above and that requires suitability for installation in accordance with this Code.

(FPN No. 1): See Examination, Identification, Installation, and Use of Equipment, Section 110-3.

(FPN No. 2): See definition of "Listed," Article 100.

90-8. **Wiring Planning.**

(a) **Future Expansion and Convenience.** Plans and specifications that provide ample space in raceways, spare raceways, and additional spaces will allow for future increases in the use of electricity. Distribution centers located in readily accessible locations will provide convenience and safety of operation. See Sections 110-16 and 240-24 for clearances and accessibility.

The requirement for providing the exclusively dedicated space required by Section 384-4 supports the intent of Section 90-8 regarding future increases.

(b) Number of Circuits in Enclosures. It is elsewhere provided in this Code that the number of wires and circuits confined in a single enclosure be varyingly restricted. Limiting the number of circuits in a single enclosure will minimize the effects from a short-circuit or ground fault in one circuit.

The heating effects inherently present wherever current-carrying conductors are grouped together will be minimized by these limitations. See Section 384-15. Distribution centers should contain additional space and capacity for future additions and should be conveniently located for accessibility.

Figure 90-2. Spare raceways or "pull lines" allow for adding additional circuits for future loads to the distribution system.

Where distribution equipment is installed so that easy access cannot be achieved, a spare raceway(s) or pull line(s) should be run at the initial installation.

90-9. **Metric Units of Measurement.** For the purpose of this Code, metric units of measurement are in accordance with the modernized metric system known as the International System of Units (SI).

Values of measurement in the Code text will be followed by an approximate equivalent value in SI units. Tables will have a footnote for SI conversion units used in the table.

Conduit size, wire size, horsepower designation for motors, and trade sizes that do not reflect actual measurements, e.g., box sizes, will not be assigned dual designation SI units.

(FPN): For metric conversion practices, see Standard for Metric Practice, ANSI/ASTM E380-1984.

In addition, warning signs stating specific clearances, such as required in Section 513-11(a), do not include metric equivalents.

An example of an application of SI conversion units as used in Table 110-16(a) follows:

$$3 \text{ ft} = 36 \text{ in.} \times 25.4 \text{ mm} = 914 \text{ mm}$$
$$3\tfrac{1}{2} \text{ ft} \times 0.3048 \text{ m} \qquad = 1.07 \text{ m}$$
$$4 \text{ ft} \times 0.3048 \text{ m} \qquad = 1.22 \text{ m}$$

Generally, dimensions up to 36 inches are expressed in millimeters, and those over 36 inches are expressed in meters. Footnotes to tables involving dimensions in feet are expressed as "one foot = 0.3048 meter." However, throughout the *Code* text the metric equivalent has been converted to millimeters and rounded off to 305 millimeters.

1

General

ARTICLE 100   Definitions

Contents
A. General
B. Over 600 Volts, Nominal

Scope. This article contains only those definitions essential to the proper application of this Code. It is not intended to include commonly defined general terms or commonly defined technical terms from related codes and standards. In general, only those terms used in two or more articles are defined in Article 100. Other definitions are included in the article in which they are used but may be referenced in Article 100.

Commonly defined general terms include those terms defined in general English language dictionaries that are not used in a unique or restricted manner in the *NEC*. Commonly defined technical terms such as "volt" and "ampere" will be found in the IEEE dictionary.

Other definitions are included in the following sections:

333-1. (Type) AC Cable.
513-1. Aircraft Hangars.
504-2. Associated Apparatus.
210-8(b)(1). Bathroom.
440-2. Branch-Circuit Selection Current.
515-1. Bulk Storage Plants.
364-2. Busways.
800-2. Cable.
800-2. Cable Sheath.
318-2. Cable Tray System.
365-1. Cablebus.
358-2. Cellular Concrete Floor Raceways.
356-1. Cellular Metal Floor Raceways.
725-3. Circuits, Class 1, 2, and 3, Remote Control.
410-76(b), FPN Combustible Low-Density Cellulose Fiberboard.
324-1. Concealed Knob-and-Tube Wiring.
504-2. Control Drawing.
240-12, FPN Coordination.
680-4. Cord- and Plug-Connected Lighting Assembly.
Table 300-5. Cover.
240-11. Current-Limiting Overcurrent Protective Device.
665-2. Dielectric Heating Equipment.
210-8(a)(3). Direct Grade Level Access.
502-1. Dust-Ignitionproof.

Part A of this article contains definitions intended to apply wherever the terms are used throughout this Code. Part B contains definitions applicable only to the parts of articles covering specifically installations and equipment operating at over 600 volts, nominal.

A. General

Accessible: (As applied to wiring methods.) Capable of being removed or exposed without damaging the building structure or finish, or not permanently closed in by the structure or finish of the building. (See "Concealed" and "Exposed.")

Wiring methods located behind removable panels designed to allow access are not considered permanently enclosed and are considered exposed as applied to wiring methods. See Figure 100-1. See also Section 300-4(c).

Figure 100-1. Busways and junction boxes are considered accessible where located above hung ceilings having lift-out panels.

Accessible: (As applied to equipment.) Admitting close approach: not guarded by locked doors, elevation, or other effective means. (See "Accessible, Readily.")

Accessible, Readily: (Readily Accessible.) Capable of being reached quickly for operation, renewal, or inspections, without requiring those to whom ready access is requisite to climb over or remove obstacles or to resort to portable ladders, chairs, etc. (See "Accessible.")

This definition does not preclude the use of a locked door for service equipment or rooms containing service equipment, provided those for whom ready access is necessary have a key (or lock combination) available. For example, Section 230-70(a) requires the service disconnecting means to be readily accessible. It is common practice to locate this disconnecting means in the electrical equipment room of an office building or large apartment building and to keep the door to this room locked to prevent access by unauthorized persons. See also Section 240-24(b), Exception.

Figure 100-2. This figure illustrates some exceptions to the provisions of Section 380-8(a). See also Section 364-12, which permits ropes, chains, or hook sticks as suitable for operating disconnecting means mounted on busways.

Ampacity: The current in amperes that a conductor can carry continuously under the conditions of use without exceeding its temperature rating.

The definition of "ampacity" recognizes that the maximum current a conductor can carry continuously varies with the conditions of use as well as with the temperature rating of the conductor insulation. For example, ambient temperature is a condition of use. A conductor with insulation rated at 60°C installed near a furnace where the ambient temperature is continuously maintained at 60°C has no current-carrying capacity. Any current flowing through the conductor will raise its temperature above the 60°C insulation rating. Therefore, the ampacity of this conductor, regardless of its size, is zero. See the ampacity correction factors following Tables 310-16 through 310-19, or see Appendix B.

Another condition of use is the number of conductors in a raceway or cable. See Note 8(a) to Tables 310-16 through 310-19.

Appliance: Utilization equipment, generally other than industrial, normally built in standardized sizes or types, that is installed or connected as a unit to perform one or more functions such as clothes washing, air conditioning, food mixing, deep frying, etc.

Appliance Branch Circuit: See "Branch Circuit, Appliance."

Approved: Acceptable to the authority having jurisdiction.

The phrase "authority having jurisdiction" is used in NFPA documents in a broad manner since jurisdictions and "approval" agencies vary, as do their responsibilities. Where public safety is primary, the authority having jurisdiction may be a federal, state, local, or other regional department or individual such as a fire chief, fire marshal, chief of a fire prevention bureau, labor or health department official, building official, electrical inspector, or other having statutory authority. For insurance purposes, an insurance inspection department, rating bureau, or other insurance company representative may be the authority having jurisdiction. In many circumstances, the property owner or the owner's designated agent assumes the role of the authority having jurisdiction; at government installations, the commanding officer or departmental official may be the authority having jurisdiction.

Askarel: A generic term for a group of nonflammable synthetic chlorinated hydrocarbons used as electrical insulating media. Askarels of various compositional types are used. Under arcing conditions, the gases produced, while consisting predominantly of noncombustible hydrogen chloride, can include varying amounts of combustible gases depending upon the askarel type.

Attachment Plug (Plug Cap) (Cap): A device that, by insertion in a receptacle, establishes connection between the conductors of the attached flexible cord and the conductors connected permanently to the receptacle.

Fuseless attachment plugs are available with a switch, and with overload protection. Attachment plugs with built-in ground-fault circuit-interrupters are also available.

Attachment plug contact blades have specific shapes, sizes, and configurations so that a receptacle or cord connector will not accept an attachment plug of a different voltage or current rating than that for which the device is intended.

Automatic: Self-acting, operating by its own mechanism when actuated by some impersonal influence, as for example, a change in current strength, pressure, temperature, or mechanical configuration. (See "Nonautomatic.")

Bare Conductor: See under "Conductor."

Bonding: The permanent joining of metallic parts to form an electrically conductive path that will assure electrical continuity and the capacity to conduct safely any current likely to be imposed.

Bonding Jumper: A reliable conductor to assure the required electrical conductivity between metal parts required to be electrically connected.

See Figure 100-3.

Figure 100-3. *A bonding jumper installed around a concentric or eccentric knockout is required by Section 250-76 for circuits over 250 volts to ground.*

Bonding Jumper, Circuit: The connection between portions of a conductor in a circuit to maintain required ampacity of the circuit.

Bonding Jumper, Equipment: The connection between two or more portions of the equipment grounding conductor.

Bonding Jumper, Main: The connection between the grounded circuit conductor and the equipment grounding conductor at the service.

See Figure 100-4.

Branch Circuit: The circuit conductors between the final overcurrent device protecting the circuit and the outlet(s).

See Figure 100-5.

Branch Circuit, Appliance: A branch circuit supplying energy to one or more outlets to which appliances are to be connected; such circuits to have no permanently connected lighting fixtures not a part of an appliance.

Small appliance branch circuits supplying receptacle outlets in kitchens, pantries, etc., as required in Section 210-52(b) and (c) and for laundry areas as required in Section 220-4(c), are not permitted to have any other outlets or permanently connected lighting fixtures connected to them. There are however some exceptions for the small appliance circuits as provided for in Section 210-52(b).

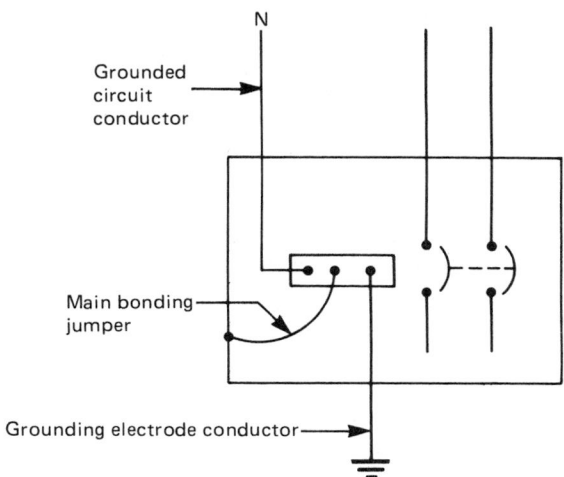

Figure 100-4. *The main bonding jumper provides the connection between the equipment ground and the grounded circuit conductor. It may consist of a wire, busbar, or screw.*

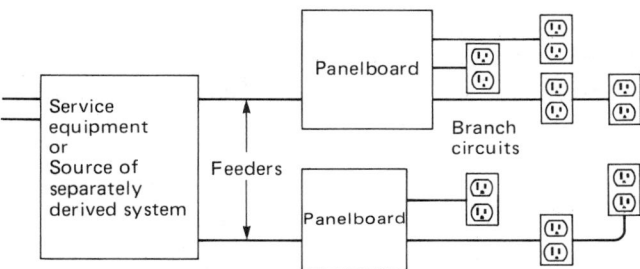

Figure 100-5. *Conductors between the overcurrent device in the panelboards and the duplex receptacles are branch-circuit conductors. Conductors between the service equipment, or source of separately derived systems, and the panelboards are feeders.*

Branch Circuit, General Purpose: A branch circuit that supplies a number of outlets for lighting and appliances.

Branch Circuit, Individual: A branch circuit that supplies only one utilization equipment.

An individual branch circuit is a circuit that supplies *only* one utilization equipment; for example, one range, one space heater, or one motor. See Section 210-23.

It supplies *only* one single receptacle for the connection of a single attachment plug. See Section 210-21(b).

A branch circuit that supplies one duplex receptacle that can accommodate two cord- and plug-connected appliances

or similar equipment is not an individual branch circuit. See Figure 100-6.

Figure 100-6. *A single receptacle intended for the connection of one utilization equipment. This single receptacle is required to have an ampere rating not less than the branch circuit. See Section 210-21(b)(1).*

Branch Circuit, Multiwire: A branch circuit consisting of two or more ungrounded conductors having a potential difference between them, and a grounded conductor having equal potential difference between it and each ungrounded conductor of the circuit and that is connected to the neutral or grounded conductor of the system.

See Sections 210-4, 240-20(b), and 300-13(b).

Building: A structure that stands alone or that is cut off from adjoining structures by fire walls with all openings therein protected by approved fire doors.

A building is a structure that may be used or intended for supporting or sheltering any use or occupancy. It may also be a separate structure such as a pole, billboard sign, or water tower. Definitions of the terms "fire walls" and "fire doors" are the responsibility of the municipal and/or state building codes and interpretations of building terms have been avoided by *NEC* committees. "Fire resistance rating" is defined as the time, in minutes or hours, that materials or assemblies have withstood a fire exposure.

Cabinet: An enclosure designed either for surface or flush mounting and provided with a frame, mat, or trim in which a swinging door or doors are or may be hung.

Both cabinets and cutout boxes are covered in Article 373. Cabinets are designed for surface or flush mounting with a trim to which a swinging door(s) is hung. Cutout boxes are designed for surface mounting with a swinging door(s) secured directly to the box. Panelboards are electrical assemblies designed to be placed in a cabinet or cutout box. See definitions of "Cutout Box" and "Panelboard."

Circuit Breaker: A device designed to open and close a circuit by nonautomatic means and to open the circuit automatically on a predetermined overcurrent without damage to itself when properly applied within its rating.

(FPN): The automatic opening means can be integral, direct acting with the circuit breaker, or remote from the circuit breaker.

Adjustable: (As applied to circuit breakers.) A qualifying term indicating that the circuit breaker can be set to trip at various values of current, time, or both, within a predetermined range.

Instantaneous Trip: (As applied to circuit breakers.) A qualifying term indicating that no delay is purposely introduced in the tripping action of the circuit breaker.

Inverse Time: (As applied to circuit breakers.) A qualifying term indicating that there is purposely introduced a delay in the tripping action of the circuit breaker, which delay decreases as the magnitude of the current increases.

Nonadjustable: (As applied to circuit breakers.) A qualifying term indicating that the circuit breaker does not have any adjustment to alter the value of current at which it will trip or the time required for its operation.

Setting: (of circuit breaker.) The value of current, time, or both at which an adjustable circuit breaker is set to trip.

Concealed: Rendered inaccessible by the structure or finish of the building. Wires in concealed raceways are considered concealed, even though they may become accessible by withdrawing them. [See "Accessible — (As applied to wiring methods)."]

Raceways and cables supported or located within hollow frames or permanently closed in by the finish of buildings are considered "concealed." Open-type work, such as raceways and cables in exposed areas; in unfinished basements; in accessible underfloor areas or attics; attached to the surface of finished areas; or behind, above, or below panels designed to allow access and that may be removed without damage to the building structure or finish are not considered "concealed." See definition of "Exposed" (as applied to wiring methods).

Conductor:

Bare: A conductor having no covering or electrical insulation whatsoever. (See "Conductor, Covered.")

Covered: A conductor encased within material of composition or thickness that is not recognized by this Code as electrical insulation. (See "Conductor, Bare.")

A typical covered conductor is the green-colored covered equipment grounding conductor in nonmetallic-sheathed cable or the uninsulated grounded system conductor in Type SE cable. A covered conductor should be treated as a bare conductor for working clearances, etc.

Insulated: A conductor encased within material of composition and thickness that is recognized by this Code as electrical insulation.

Conduit Body: A separate portion of a conduit or tubing system that provides access through a removable cover(s) to the interior of the system at a junction of two or more sections of the system or at a terminal point of the system.

Boxes such as FS and FD or larger cast or sheet metal boxes are not classified as conduit bodies.

Conduit bodies are a portion of a raceway system with removable covers to allow access to the interior of the system. They include the "short radius" type as well as capped elbows and service entrance elbows.

Some conduit bodies are referred to in the trade as "condulets" and include the LB, LL, LR, C, T, and X designs. Sections 300-15, 331-13, 345-14, 346-14, 347-16, and 348-14, and Article 370 may be referred to for rules on the usage of conduit bodies.

Type FS or FD boxes are not classified as conduit bodies; they are listed with boxes in Table 370-16(a).

Connector, Pressure (Solderless): A device that establishes a connection between two or more conductors or between one or more conductors and a terminal by means of mechanical pressure and without the use of solder.

Continuous Duty: See under "Duty."

Continuous Load: A load where the maximum current is expected to continue for three hours or more.

Controller: A device or group of devices that serves to govern, in some predetermined manner, the electric power delivered to the apparatus to which it is connected.

A controller may be a remote-controlled magnetic contactor, switch, circuit breaker, or device normally used to start and stop motors and other apparatus and, in the case of motors, is required to be capable of interrupting the stalled-rotor current of the motor. Stop and start stations and similar control circuit components are not considered controllers.

Cooking Unit, Counter-Mounted: A cooking appliance designed for mounting in or on a counter and consisting of one or more heating elements, internal wiring, and built-in or separately mountable controls. (See "Oven, Wall-Mounted.")

Copper-Clad Aluminum Conductors: Conductors drawn from a copper-clad aluminum rod with the copper metallurgically bonded to an aluminum core. The copper forms a minimum of 10 percent of the cross-sectional area of a solid conductor or each strand of a stranded conductor.

Covered Conductor: See under "Conductor."

Cutout Box: An enclosure designed for surface mounting and having swinging doors or covers secured directly to and telescoping with the walls of the box proper. (See "Cabinet.")

Damp Location: See under "Location."

Dead Front: Without live parts exposed to a person on the operating side of the equipment.

Demand Factor: The ratio of the maximum demand of a system, or part of a system, to the total connected load of a system or the part of the system under consideration.

Device: A unit of an electrical system that is intended to carry but not utilize electric energy.

Components, such as switches, circuit breakers, fuseholders, receptacles, attachment plugs, and lampholders, that distribute or control but do not consume electricity are termed "devices." See commentary following Section 210-4(b).

Disconnecting Means: A device, or group of devices, or other means by which the conductors of a circuit can be disconnected from their source of supply.

For disconnecting means for service equipment, see Part F of Article 230; for fuses, see Part D of Article 240; for circuit breakers, see Part G of Article 240; for appliances, see Part D of Article 422; for space heating equipment, see Part C of Article 424; for motors and controllers, see Part I of Article 430; and for air-conditioning and refrigerating equipment, see Part B of Article 440. See also references for "Disconnecting Means" in the Index.

Dry Location: See under "Location."

Dustproof: So constructed or protected that dust will not interfere with its successful operation.

Dusttight: So constructed that dust will not enter the enclosing case under specified test conditions.

(FPN): For test conditions other than for rotating equipment, see Enclosures for Electrical Equipment (1000 Volts Maximum), Clause 6.5, ANSI/NEMA 250-1985.

Reference to the ANSI/NEMA Standard will permit the user to evaluate the enclosure with regard to actual conditions of use. See Section 430-91 for some of the motor controller enclosure types.

Duty:

Continuous Duty: Operation at a substantially constant load for an indefinitely long time.

Intermittent Duty: Operation for alternate intervals of (1) load and no load; or (2) load and rest; or (3) load, no load, and rest.

Periodic Duty: Intermittent operation in which the load conditions are regularly recurrent.

Short-Time Duty: Operation at a substantially constant load for a short and definitely specified time.

Varying Duty: Operation at loads, and for intervals of time, both of which may be subject to wide variation.

For the protection of intermittent, periodic, short-time, and varying-duty motors against overload, see Section 430-33.

Dwelling:

Dwelling Unit: One or more rooms for the use of one or more persons as a housekeeping unit with space for eating, living, and sleeping, and permanent provisions for cooking and sanitation.

Where dwelling units are referenced throughout the *Code*, it is important to note that rooms of motels, hotels, and similar occupancies could be classified as dwelling units where they satisfy the requirements of the definition. A mobile home may be considered a dwelling unit. See Figure 100-7.

Multifamily Dwelling: A building containing three or more dwelling units.

One-Family Dwelling: A building consisting solely of one dwelling unit.

Two-Family Dwelling: A building consisting solely of two dwelling units.

Electric Sign: A fixed, stationary, or portable self-contained, electrically illuminated utilization equipment with words or symbols designed to convey information or attract attention.

Enclosed: Surrounded by a case, housing, fence, or walls that will prevent persons from accidentally contacting energized parts.

Enclosure: The case or housing of apparatus, or the fence or walls surrounding an installation to prevent personnel from accidentally contacting energized parts, or to protect the equipment from physical damage.

(FPN): For enclosure types, see Enclosures for Electrical Equipment (1000 Volts Maximum), ANSI/NEMA 250-1985.

Figure 100-7. A motel or hotel room with eating, living, and sleeping areas and areas having permanent provisions for cooking and sanitation meets the definition of a "dwelling unit."

Equipment: A general term including material, fittings, devices, appliances, fixtures, apparatus, and the like used as a part of, or in connection with, an electrical installation.

Equipment Grounding Conductor: See "Grounding Conductor, Equipment."

See Section 250-91(b) for types of equipment grounding conductors.

Explosionproof Apparatus: Apparatus enclosed in a case that is capable of withstanding an explosion of a specified gas or vapor that may occur within it and of preventing the ignition of a specified gas or vapor surrounding the enclosure by sparks, flashes, or explosion of the gas or vapor within, and that operates at such an external temperature that a surrounding flammable atmosphere will not be ignited thereby.

(FPN): For further information, see Explosion-Proof and Dust-Ignition-Proof Electrical Equipment for Use in Hazardous (Classified) Locations, ANSI/UL 1203-1988.

Exposed: (As applied to live parts.) Capable of being inadvertently touched or approached nearer than a safe distance by a person. It is applied to parts not suitably guarded, isolated, or insulated. (See "Accessible" and "Concealed.")

See Section 110-17 for guarding of live parts.

Exposed: (As applied to wiring methods.) On or attached to the surface or behind panels designed to allow access. [See "Accessible — (As applied to wiring methods)."]

See Figure 100-1.

Externally Operable: Capable of being operated without exposing the operator to contact with live parts.

Feeder: All circuit conductors between the service equipment or the source of a separately derived system and the final branch-circuit overcurrent device.

See Figure 100-5.

Fitting: An accessory such as a locknut, bushing, or other part of a wiring system that is intended primarily to perform a mechanical rather than an electrical function.

Items such as condulets, conduit couplings, EMT connectors and couplings, and threadless connectors are considered fittings.

Garage: A building or portion of a building in which one or more self-propelled vehicles carrying volatile flammable liquid for fuel or power are kept for use, sale, storage, rental, repair, exhibition, or demonstrating purposes, and all that portion of a building that is on or below the floor or floors in which such vehicles are kept and that is not separated therefrom by suitable cutoffs.

(FPN): For commercial garages, repair, and storage, see Section 511-1.

General-Purpose Branch Circuit: See "Branch Circuit, General Purpose."

General-Use Snap Switch: See under "Switches."

General-Use Switch: See under "Switches."

Ground: A conducting connection, whether intentional or accidental, between an electrical circuit or equipment and the earth, or to some conducting body that serves in place of the earth.

Grounded: Connected to earth or to some conducting body that serves in place of the earth.

Grounded, Effectively: Intentionally connected to earth through a ground connection or connections of sufficiently low impedance and having sufficient current-carrying capacity to prevent the buildup of voltages that may result in undue hazards to connected equipment or to persons.

Grounded Conductor: A system or circuit conductor that is intentionally grounded.

Grounding Conductor: A conductor used to connect equipment or the grounded circuit of a wiring system to a grounding electrode or electrodes.

Grounding Conductor, Equipment: The conductor used to connect the noncurrent-carrying metal parts of equipment, raceways, and other enclosures to the system grounded conductor, the grounding electrode conductor, or both, at the service equipment or at the source of a separately derived system.

Grounding Electrode Conductor: The conductor used to connect the grounding electrode to the equipment grounding conductor, to the grounded conductor, or to both, of the circuit at the service equipment or at the source of a separately derived system.

The grounding electrode conductor is required to be copper, aluminum, or copper-clad aluminum. It is used to connect the equipment grounding conductor or the grounded conductor (at the service equipment or at the separately derived system) to the grounding electrode for either grounded or ungrounded systems. See Figure 100-4.

The grounding electrode conductor is sized by using Table 250-94. See also Article 250, Parts H and J.

Ground-Fault Circuit-Interrupter: A device intended for the protection of personnel that functions to deenergize a circuit or portion thereof within an established period of time when a current to ground exceeds some predetermined value that is less than that required to operate the overcurrent protective device of the supply circuit.

See Figures 210-9 through 210-18. See also references for "Ground-Fault Circuit-Interrupters" in the Index.

Ground-Fault Protection of Equipment: A system intended to provide protection of equipment from damaging line-to-ground fault currents by operating to cause a disconnecting means to open all ungrounded conductors of the faulted circuit. This protection is provided at current levels less than those required to protect conductors from damage through the operation of a supply circuit overcurrent device.

See commentary on Section 230-95.

Guarded: Covered, shielded, fenced, enclosed, or otherwise protected by means of suitable covers, casings, barriers, rails, screens, mats, or platforms to remove the likelihood of approach or contact by persons or objects to a point of danger.

Hoistway: Any shaftway, hatchway, well hole, or other vertical opening or space in which an elevator or dumbwaiter is designed to operate.

See Article 620 for the installation of electric equipment and wiring methods in hoistways.

Identified: (As applied to Equipment.) Recognizable as suitable for the specific purpose, function, use, environment, application, etc., where described in a particular Code requirement. (See "Equipment.")

(FPN): Suitability of equipment for a specific purpose, environment, or application may be determined by a qualified testing laboratory, inspection agency, or other organization concerned with product evaluation. Such identification may include labeling or listing. (See "Labeled" and "Listed.")

In Sight From (Within Sight From, Within Sight): Where this Code specifies that one equipment shall be "in sight from," "within sight from," or "within sight," etc., of another equipment, one of the equipments specified is to be visible and not more than 50 feet (15.24 m) distant from the other.

See Figures 430-18, 430-20, and 600-1.

Individual Branch Circuit: See "Branch Circuit, Individual."

Insulated Conductor: See under "Conductor."

Intermittent Duty: See under "Duty."

Interrupting Rating: The highest current at rated voltage that a device is intended to interrupt under standard test conditions.

(FPN): Equipment intended to break current at other than fault levels may have its interrupting rating implied in other ratings, such as horsepower or locked rotor current.

Interrupting ratings are essential in the coordination of electrical systems so that available fault currents can be properly controlled.

Isolated: Not readily accessible to persons unless special means for access are used.

See definition of "Accessible, Readily" in Article 100.

Labeled: Equipment or materials to which has been attached a label, symbol, or other identifying mark of an organization acceptable to the authority having jurisdiction and concerned with product evaluation, that maintains periodic inspection of production of labeled equipment or materials and by whose labeling the manufacturer indicates compliance with appropriate standards or performance in a specified manner.

Equipment and conductors required or permitted by this *Code* are acceptable only where approved for a specific

environment or application by the authority having jurisdiction. See Section 110-2.

"Listing" or "labeling" by a qualified testing laboratory will provide a basis for approval. See Section 90-7.

Lighting Outlet: An outlet intended for the direct connection of a lampholder, a lighting fixture, or a pendant cord terminating in a lampholder.

Listed: Equipment or materials included in a list published by an organization acceptable to the authority having jurisdiction and concerned with product evaluation, that maintains periodic inspection of production of listed equipment or materials, and whose listing states either that the equipment or material meets appropriate designated standards or has been tested and found suitable for use in a specified manner.

(FPN): The means for identifying listed equipment may vary for each organization concerned with product evaluation, some of which do not recognize equipment as listed unless it is also labeled. The authority having jurisdiction should utilize the system employed by the listing organization to identify a listed product.

See comments that follow the definition of "Labeled."

Location:

Damp Location: Partially protected locations under canopies, marquees, roofed open porches, and like locations, and interior locations subject to moderate degrees of moisture, such as some basements, some barns, and some cold-storage warehouses.

Dry Location: A location not normally subject to dampness or wetness. A location classified as dry may be temporarily subject to dampness or wetness, as in the case of a building under construction.

Wet Location: Installations underground or in concrete slabs or masonry in direct contact with the earth, and locations subject to saturation with water or other liquids, such as vehicle washing areas, and locations exposed to weather and unprotected.

It is intended that the inside of a raceway in a wet location or where installed underground be considered a wet location. Therefore, any conductors contained therein would be required to be suitable for wet locations.

See Section 517-3 under definition for "Patient Care Area" for a definition of a wet location in a patient care area.

See Section 300-6(c) for examples of some wet locations and Section 410-4(a) for information on fixtures in wet locations.

Multioutlet Assembly: A type of surface or flush raceway designed to hold conductors and receptacles, assembled in the field or at the factory.

In dry locations, metallic and nonmetallic multioutlet assemblies are permitted; however, they are not permitted to be installed where concealed. See Article 353 for details on recessing these assemblies.

Multiwire Branch Circuit: See "Branch Circuit, Multiwire."

Nonautomatic: Action requiring personal intervention for its control. (See "Automatic.")

(FPN): As applied to an electric controller, nonautomatic control does not necessarily imply a manual controller, but only that personal intervention is necessary.

Nonincendive Circuit: A circuit in which any arc or thermal effect produced, under intended operating conditions of the equipment or due to opening, shorting, or grounding of field wiring, is not capable, under specified test conditions, of igniting the flammable gas, vapor, or dust-air mixture.

(FPN): For test conditions, see Electrical Equipment for Use in Class I, Division 2 Hazardous (Classified) Locations, ANSI/ISA-S12.12.

Outlet: A point on the wiring system at which current is taken to supply utilization equipment.

For example, a lighting outlet or a receptacle outlet.

Outline Lighting: An arrangement of incandescent lamps or electric-discharge lighting to outline or call attention to certain features such as the shape of a building or the decoration of a window.

See Article 600, Part B (1000 Volts, Nominal, or Less) and Part C (Over 1000 Volts, Nominal).

Oven, Wall-Mounted: An oven for cooking purposes designed for mounting in or on a wall or other surface and consisting of one or more heating elements, internal wiring, and built-in or separately mountable controls. (See "Cooking Unit, Counter-Mounted.")

Overcurrent: Any current in excess of the rated current of equipment or the ampacity of a conductor. It may result from overload (see definition), short circuit, or ground fault.

(FPN): A current in excess of rating may be accommodated by certain equipment and conductors for a given set of conditions. Hence the rules for overcurrent protection are specific for particular situations.

Overload: Operation of equipment in excess of normal, full-load rating, or of a conductor in excess of rated ampacity that, when it persists for a sufficient length of time, would cause damage or dangerous overheating. A fault, such as a short circuit or ground fault, is not an overload. (See "Overcurrent.")

Panelboard: A single panel or group of panel units designed for assembly in the form of a single panel; including buses, automatic overcurrent devices, and equipped with or without switches for the control of light, heat, or power circuits; designed to be placed in a cabinet or cutout box placed in or against a wall or partition and accessible only from the front. (See "Switchboard.")

See Article 384.

Periodic Duty: See under "Duty."

Plenum: A compartment or chamber to which one or more air ducts are connected and that forms part of the air distribution system.

This definition is essentially the same as the definition of plenum in NFPA 90A-1989, *Standard for the Installation of Air Conditioning and Ventilating Systems.* This definition is not intended to apply to the space above a suspended ceiling used for environmental air. See Section 300-22(c) FPN. See Section 300-22(b) for permitted wiring methods in plenums used for environmental air.

Power Outlet: An enclosed assembly that may include receptacles, circuit breakers, fuseholders, fused switches, buses, and watt-hour meter mounting means; intended to supply and control power to mobile homes, recreational vehicles, or boats; or to serve as a means for distributing power required to operate mobile or temporarily installed equipment.

See Figures 305-1 and 550-1.

Premises Wiring (System): That interior and exterior wiring, including power, lighting, control, and signal circuit wiring together with all of their associated hardware, fittings, and wiring devices, both permanently and temporarily installed, that extends from the service point of utility conductors or source of a separately derived system to the outlet(s). Such wiring does not include wiring internal to appliances, fixtures, motors, controllers, motor control centers, and similar equipment.

For the 1993 *Code*, this definition has been clarified by adding "service point," the point at which the electrical supply conductors are considered premises wiring. Separately derived systems on the load side of the service point are considered premises wiring. An example is an on-premises privately owned transformer supplying all building loads. The transformer would be considered part of the premises wiring system.

On the other hand, in the above example, the premises wiring system would not include the internal wiring of electrical equipment including that of the transformer. See Article 645.

Qualified Person: One familiar with the construction and operation of the equipment and the hazards involved.

Raceway: An enclosed channel designed expressly for holding wires, cables, or busbars, with additional functions as permitted in this Code.

(FPN): Raceways may be of metal or insulating material, and the term includes rigid metal conduit, rigid nonmetallic conduit, intermediate metal conduit, liquidtight flexible conduit, flexible metallic tubing, flexible metal conduit, electrical nonmetallic tubing, electrical metallic tubing, underfloor raceways, cellular concrete floor raceways, cellular metal floor raceways, surface raceways, wireways, cablebus, and busways.

Cable trays (see Article 318) are not considered raceways in the *NEC*.

Rainproof: So constructed, protected, or treated as to prevent rain from interfering with the successful operation of the apparatus under specified test conditions.

Testing laboratories perform tests that are used to evaluate equipment under specified test conditions. These tests are well known to manufacturers of electrical products as well as to users of these products. Descriptions of the tests are available from the testing laboratories. Users of the *NEC* should be aware of these tests.

Raintight: So constructed or protected that exposure to a beating rain will not result in the entrance of water under specified test conditions.

Raceways on exterior surfaces of buildings are required to be made raintight. See Sections 225-22 and 230-53.
For boxes and cabinets, see Section 300-6.
See comments following definitions of "Rainproof" and "Wet Location."

Readily Accessible: See "Accessible, Readily."

Overcurrent devices are required to be readily accessible. See Section 240-24(a). A high degree of safety exists where switches or circuit breakers can be disconnected quickly without being hindered by obstacles. See Section 230-70(a) for services. See also the exceptions to this rule for busways, Section 364-12; and for supplementary overcurrent protection, Section 240-10.

Receptacle: A receptacle is a contact device installed at the outlet for the connection of a single attachment plug.

(FPN): A single receptacle is a single contact device with no other contact device on the same yoke. A multiple receptacle is a single device containing two or more receptacles.

The basic receptacle is a single contact device for the connection of a single attachment plug. A multiple receptacle is a contact device containing two or more receptacles for the connection of two or more attachment plugs. A duplex receptacle is a multiple receptacle. See Figure 100-8.

Receptacle Outlet: An outlet where one or more receptacles are installed.

See Figure 100-8.

See commentary following Section 220-3(c).

Remote-Control Circuit: Any electric circuit that controls any other circuit through a relay or an equivalent device.

See Figure 100-9.

One receptacle   Multiple receptacles

Figure 100-8.

Figure 100-9. A remote-control circuit for starting and stopping an electric motor.

Sealable Equipment: Equipment enclosed in a case or cabinet that is provided with a means of sealing or locking so that live parts cannot be made accessible without opening the enclosure. The equipment may or may not be operable without opening the enclosure.

Separately Derived System: A premises wiring system whose power is derived from generator, transformer, or converter windings and that has no direct electrical connection, including a solidly connected grounded circuit conductor, to supply conductors originating in another system.

Service: The conductors and equipment for delivering energy from the electricity supply system to the wiring system of the premises served.

Service Cable: Service conductors made up in the form of a cable.

Service Conductors: The supply conductors that extend from the street main or from transformers to the service equipment of the premises supplied.

See Figures 100-10 and 100-11 for illustrations of service conductors. Note the service conductors include the service entrance conductors and the service drop or lateral.

Service conductors from an overhead distribution system originate at the utility pole, or wires attached to it, and terminate at the service equipment.

Service conductors from an underground distribution system originate at the utility manhole and terminate at the service equipment. Where utility-owned primary conductors are extended to outdoor pad-mounted or underground transformers on private property, the service conductors originate at the secondary connections of the transformers. See Figure 100-10.

See Article 230, Part H, and commentary following Section 230-200 for service conductors exceeding 600 V, nominal.

Service Drop: The overhead service conductors from the last pole or other aerial support to and including the splices, if any, connecting to the service-entrance conductors at the building or other structure.

See Figure 100-11.

Service-Entrance Conductors, Overhead System: The service conductors between the terminals of the service equipment and a point usually outside the building, clear of building walls, where joined by tap or splice to the service drop.

See Figure 100-10.

Service-Entrance Conductors, Underground System: The service conductors between the terminals of the service equipment and the point of connection to the service lateral.

See Figure 100-11.

Figure 100-10. Overhead system showing a service drop from a utility pole to attachment on the house and service-entrance conductors from point of attachment (spliced to service-drop conductors), down the side of the house, through the meter socket, and terminating within the service equipment.

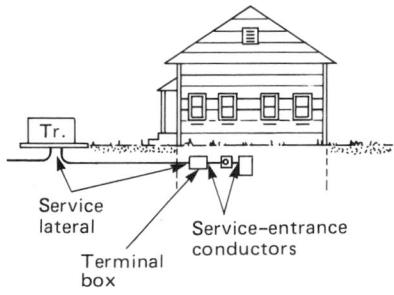

Figure 100-11. Service laterals (underground systems) may be run from poles or from transformers and with or without terminal boxes.

(FPN): Where service equipment is located outside the building walls, there may be no service-entrance conductors, or they may be entirely outside the building.

Service Equipment: The necessary equipment, usually consisting of a circuit breaker or switch and fuses, and their accessories, located near the point of entrance of supply conductors to a building or other structure, or an otherwise defined area, and intended to constitute the main control and means of cutoff of the supply.

Service equipment may consist of circuit breakers or fused switches provided to disconnect all ungrounded conductors in a building or other structure from the service-entrance conductors.

The disconnecting means at any ONE location is not allowed to consist of more than six circuit breakers or six switches and is required to be readily accessible either outside the building or structure or inside nearest the point of entrance of the service-entrance conductors. See Section 230-6 and Article 230, Part F.

Service Lateral: The underground service conductors between the street main, including any risers at a pole or other structure or from transformers, and the first point of connection to the service-entrance conductors in a terminal box or meter or other enclosure with adequate space, inside or outside the building wall. Where there is no terminal box, meter, or other enclosure with adequate space, the point of connection shall be considered to be the point of entrance of the service conductors into the building.

See Figure 100-11.

Service Point: Service point is the point of connection between the facilities of the serving utility and the premises wiring.

Setting (of Circuit Breaker): See under "Circuit Breaker."

Short-Time Duty: See under "Duty."

Show Window: Any window used or designed to be used for the display of goods or advertising material, whether it is fully or partly enclosed or entirely open at the rear and whether or not it has a platform raised higher than the street floor level.

See Figure 220-5.

Sign: See "Electric Sign."

Signaling Circuit: Any electric circuit that energizes signaling equipment.

Solar Photovoltaic System: The total components and subsystems that, in combination, convert solar energy into electrical energy suitable for connection to a utilization load.

See Article 690 for requirements for solar photovoltaic systems.

Special Permission: The written consent of the authority having jurisdiction.

The authority having jurisdiction for enforcement of the *Code* is responsible for making interpretations and granting special permission contemplated in a number of the rules. For examples, see Section 110-16(a), Exception No. 2; Section 230-2, Exception Nos. 3, 4c., and 5; and Section 426-14.

Switchboard: A large single panel, frame, or assembly of panels on which are mounted, on the face or back, or both, switches, overcurrent and other protective devices, buses, and usually instruments. Switchboards are generally accessible from the rear as well as from the front and are not intended to be installed in cabinets. (See "Panelboard.")

Busbars are to be arranged to avoid inductive overheating. Service busbars are required to be isolated by barriers from the remainder of the switchboard.

Most modern switchboards are totally enclosed to minimize the probability of spreading fire to adjacent combustible materials and to guard live parts.

Switches:

Bypass Isolation Switch: A bypass isolation switch is a manually operated device used in conjunction with a transfer switch to provide a means of directly connecting load conductors to a power source, and of disconnecting the transfer switch.

See Sections 700-6 and 701-7.

General-Use Switch: A switch intended for use in general distribution and branch circuits. It is rated in amperes, and it is capable of interrupting its rated current at its rated voltage.

General-Use Snap Switch: A form of general-use switch so constructed that it can be installed in flush device boxes or on outlet box covers, or otherwise used in conjunction with wiring systems recognized by this Code.

Isolating Switch: A switch intended for isolating an electric circuit from the source of power. It has no interrupting rating, and it is intended to be operated only after the circuit has been opened by some other means.

Motor-Circuit Switch: A switch, rated in horsepower, capable of interrupting the maximum operating overload current of a motor of the same horsepower rating as the switch at the rated voltage.

Transfer Switch: A transfer switch is a device for transferring one or more load conductor connections from one power source to another.

(FPN): A transfer switch may be either automatic or nonautomatic.

Thermal Protector: (As applied to motors.) A protective device for assembly as an integral part of a motor or motor-compressor that, when properly applied, protects the motor against dangerous overheating due to overload and failure to start.

(FPN): The thermal protector may consist of one or more sensing elements integral with the motor or motor-compressor and an external control device.

Thermally Protected: (As applied to motors.) The words "Thermally Protected" appearing on the nameplate of a motor or motor-compressor indicate that the motor is provided with a thermal protector.

Utilization Equipment: Equipment that utilizes electric energy for electronic, electromechanical, chemical, heating, lighting, or similar purposes.

Varying Duty: See under "Duty."

Ventilated: Provided with a means to permit circulation of air sufficient to remove an excess of heat, fumes, or vapors.

See commentary following Section 110-13(b).

Volatile Flammable Liquid: A flammable liquid having a flash point below 38°C (100°F), or a flammable liquid whose temperature is above its flash point, or a Class II combustible liquid having a vapor pressure not exceeding 40 psia (276 kPa) at 38°C (100°F) whose temperature is above its flash point.

The flash point of a liquid is the minimum temperature at which it gives off sufficient vapor to form an ignitible mixture with the air near the surface of the liquid or within the vessel used to contain the liquid. An "ignitible mixture" is a mixture within the explosive or flammable range (between upper and lower limits) that is capable of the propagation of flame away from the source of ignition when ignited. Some emission of vapors takes place below the flash point but not in sufficient quantities to form an ignitible mixture.

Voltage (of a Circuit): The greatest root-mean-square (effective) difference of potential between any two conductors of the circuit concerned.

(FPN): Some systems, such as 3-phase 4-wire, single-phase 3-wire, and 3-wire direct-current may have various circuits of various voltages.

A 3-phase, 4-wire wye system has two voltages (for example, 277/480 or 120/208). The "voltage of the circuit" is the highest voltage between any two conductors, i.e., 480 V and 208 V. The voltage of the circuit of a 2-wire feeder or branch circuit (one phase and the grounded conductor) derived from the above systems would be the voltage between the two conductors at the lower voltage, i.e., 277 V and 120 V.

The same applies to dc or single-phase, 3-wire systems where there are two voltages.

Voltage, Nominal: A nominal value assigned to a circuit or system for the purpose of conveniently designating its voltage class (e.g., 120/240, 480Y/277, 600).

See Section 220-2.

The actual voltage at which a circuit operates can vary from the nominal within a range that permits satisfactory operation of equipment.

(FPN): See Voltage Ratings for Electric Power Systems and Equipment (60 Hz), ANSI C84.1-1989.

Voltage to Ground: For grounded circuits, the voltage between the given conductor and that point or conductor of the circuit that is grounded; for ungrounded circuits, the greatest voltage between the given conductor and any other conductor of the circuit.

The voltage to ground of a 277/480 V wye system would be 277 V; of a 120/208 V wye system, 120 V; and of a 3-phase, 3-wire ungrounded 480 V system, 480 V.

For a 3-phase, 4-wire delta system with the center of one leg grounded, there are two voltages to ground. For example, on a 240-volt system, two legs would have 120 V to ground and the third or "high" leg would have 208 V to ground. See Sections 215-8, 230-56, and 384-3(e) for special marking on such circuits.

Watertight: So constructed that moisture will not enter the enclosure under specified test conditions.

(FPN): For test conditions other than for rotating equipment, see Enclosure for Electrical Equipment (1000 Volts Maximum), Section 250-5.07, Hosedown Test, NEMA Standards Publication No. 250-1979.

Unless the enclosure is hermetically sealed, it is possible for moisture to enter the enclosure. The ANSI/NEMA Standard alerts the user to the possibility of condensation in the enclosure and contains widely used testing procedures for enclosures for electrical equipment.

Weatherproof: So constructed or protected that exposure to the weather will not interfere with successful operation.

(FPN): Rainproof, raintight, or watertight equipment can fulfill the requirements for weatherproof where varying weather conditions other than wetness, such as snow, ice, dust, or temperature extremes, are not a factor.

Wet Location: See under "Location."

B. Over 600 Volts, Nominal

Whereas the preceding definitions are intended to apply wherever the terms are used throughout this Code, the following definitions are applicable only to parts of the article specifically covering installations and equipment operating at over 600 volts, nominal.

Circuit Breaker: See under "Switching Devices."

Cutout: See under "Switching Devices."

Disconnect (Isolator): See under "Switching Devices."

Disconnecting Means: See under "Switching Devices."

Fuse: An overcurrent protective device with a circuit opening fusible part that is heated and severed by the passage of overcurrent through it.

(FPN): A fuse comprises all the parts that form a unit capable of performing the prescribed functions. It may or may not be the complete device necessary to connect it into an electrical circuit.

Expulsion Fuse Unit (Expulsion Fuse): A vented fuse unit in which the expulsion effect of gases produced by the arc and lining of the fuseholder, either alone or aided by a spring, extinguishes the arc.

Power Fuse Unit: A vented, nonvented, or controlled vented fuse unit in which the arc is extinguished by being drawn through solid material, granular material, or liquid, either alone or aided by a spring.

Vented Power Fuse: A fuse with provision for the escape of arc gases, liquids, or solid particles to the surrounding atmosphere during circuit interruption.

Nonvented Power Fuse: A fuse without intentional provision for the escape of arc gases, liquids, or solid particles to the atmosphere during circuit interruption.

Controlled Vented Power Fuse: A fuse with provision for controlling discharge circuit interruption such that no solid material may be exhausted into the surrounding atmosphere.

(FPN): The fuse is designed so that discharged gases will not ignite or damage insulation in the path of the discharge or propagate a flashover to or between grounded members or conduction members in the path of the discharge where the distance between the vent and such insulation or conduction members conforms to manufacturer's recommendations.

Interrupter Switch: See under "Switching Devices."

Multiple Fuse: An assembly of two or more single-pole fuses.

Oil (Filled) Cutout: See under "Switching Devices."

Power Fuse: See under "Fuse."

Regulator Bypass Switch: See under "Switching Devices."

Switching Device: A device designed to close, open, or both, one or more electric circuits.

Switching Devices:

Circuit Breaker: A switching device capable of making, carrying, and breaking currents under normal circuit conditions, and also making, carrying for a specified time, and breaking currents under specified abnormal circuit conditions, such as those of short circuit.

Cutout: An assembly of a fuse support with either a fuseholder, fuse carrier, or disconnecting blade. The fuseholder or fuse carrier may include a conducting element (fuse link), or

may act as the disconnecting blade by the inclusion of a nonfusible member.

Disconnecting (or Isolating) Switch (Disconnector, Isolator): A mechanical switching device used for isolating a circuit or equipment from a source of power.

Disconnecting Means: A device, group of devices, or other means whereby the conductors of a circuit can be disconnected from their source of supply.

Interrupter Switch: A switch capable of making, carrying, and interrupting specified currents.

Oil Cutout (Oil-Filled Cutout): A cutout in which all or part of the fuse support and its fuse link or disconnecting blade is mounted in oil with complete immersion of the contacts and the fusible portion of the conducting element (fuse link), so that arc interruption by severing of the fuse link or by opening of the contacts will occur under oil.

Oil Switch: An oil switch is a switch having contacts that operate under oil (or askarel or other suitable liquid).

Regulator Bypass Switch: A specific device or combination of devices designed to bypass a regulator.

ARTICLE 110 Requirements for Electrical Installations

Contents

A. General

(c) Integrity of Electrical Equipment and Connections.

110-13. Mounting and Cooling of Equipment.

    (a) Mounting.

    (b) Cooling.

110-14. Electrical Connections.

    (a) Terminals.

    (b) Splices.

    (c) Temperature Limitations.

110-16. Working Space about Electric Equipment (600 Volts, Nominal, or Less).

    (a) Working Clearances.

    (b) Clear Spaces.

    (c) Access and Entrance to Working Space.

    (d) Front Working Space.

    (e) Illumination.

    (f) Headroom.

110-17. Guarding of Live Parts (600 Volts, Nominal, or Less).

    (a) Live Parts Guarded Against Accidental Contact.

    (b) Prevent Physical Damage.

    (c) Warning Signs.

110-18. Arcing Parts.

110-19. Light and Power from Railway Conductors.

110-21. Marking.

110-22. Identification of Disconnecting Means.

B. Over 600 Volts, Nominal

110-30. General.

110-31. Enclosure for Electrical Installations.

    (a) Indoor Installations.

    (b) Outdoor Installations.

    (c) Metal-Enclosed Equipment Accessible to Unqualified Persons.

110-32. Work Space about Equipment.

110-33. Entrance and Access to Work Space.

    (a) Entrance.

    (b) Access.

110-34. Work Space and Guarding.

    (a) Working Space.

    (b) Separation from Low-Voltage Equipment.

    (c) Locked Rooms or Enclosures.

    (d) Illumination.

    (e) Elevation of Unguarded Live Parts.

A. General

110-2. **Approval.** The conductors and equipment required or permitted by this Code shall be acceptable only if approved.

(FPN): See Examination of Equipment for Safety, Section 90-7 and Examination, Identification, Installation, and Use of Equipment, Section 110-3. See definitions of "Approved," "Identified," "Labeled," and "Listed."

Section 110-2 of the *Code* requires that all equipment be approved as defined in Article 100 and, as such, be acceptable to the authority having jurisdiction. Section 110-3 provides guidance for the judging of equipment and recognizes listing or labeling as a means of establishing suitability.

Approval of equipment is the responsibility of the electrical inspection authority, and many such "approvals" are based on tests and listings of testing laboratories.

110-3. **Examination, Identification, Installation, and Use of Equipment.**

    (a) **Examination.** In judging equipment, considerations such as the following shall be evaluated:

        (1) Suitability for installation and use in conformity with the provisions of this Code.

(FPN): Suitability of equipment use may be identified by a description marked on or provided with a product to identify the suitability of the product for a specific purpose, environment, or application. Suitability of equipment may be evidenced by listing or labeling.

        (2) Mechanical strength and durability, including, for parts designed to enclose and protect other equipment, the adequacy of the protection thus provided.

        (3) Wire-bending and connection space.

        (4) Electrical insulation.

        (5) Heating effects under normal conditions of use and also under abnormal conditions likely to arise in service.

        (6) Arcing effects.

        (7) Classification by type, size, voltage, current capacity, and specific use.

        (8) Other factors that contribute to the practical safeguarding of persons using or likely to come in contact with the equipment.

For wire-bending and connection space in cabinets and cutout boxes, see Section 373-6, Tables 373-6(a) and 373-6(b), and Sections 373-7, 373-9, and 373-11. For wire-bending and connection space in other equipment, see the appropriate *NEC* article and section. For example, see Section 370-28 for outlet, device, pull and junction boxes, and conduit bodies; Sections 380-3 and 380-18 for switches; Section 384-3(g) for switchboards and panelboards; and Section 430-10 for motors and motor controllers.

(b) Installation and Use. Listed or labeled equipment shall be used or installed in accordance with any instructions included in the listing or labeling.

Installation instructions are usually supplied with equipment by the manufacturer for use by the general contractor, erector, electrical contractor, electrical inspector, and others concerned with the installation. It is very important to consider the listing or labeling installation instructions. For example, Section 210-52(a), Exception, permits permanently installed electric baseboard heaters to be equipped with receptacle outlets that meet the requirements for the wall space utilized by such heaters. Installation instructions for such permanent baseboard heaters indicate that these heaters should not be mounted beneath a receptacle. In dwelling units, it is very common to use low-density heat units that may measure in excess of 12 feet in length. Therefore, to meet the provisions of Section 210-52(a), first paragraph, and also the installation instructions, a receptacle must either be part of the heating unit or be installed in the floor close to the wall but not above the heating unit. See Section 210-52(a), Exception, FPN, and Figures 210-26 and 210-27.

This section does not, in itself require listing or labeling. It does, however, require considerable evaluation of equipment. Section 110-2 requires that equipment be acceptable only if approved. The term "approved" is defined in Article 100 as "acceptable to the authority having jurisdiction." Before issuing approval, the authority having jurisdiction may require evidence of compliance with Section 110-3(a). The most common form of this evidence considered acceptable by authorities having jurisdiction is a listing or labeling by a third party.

There are some sections in the *Code* that require listed or labeled equipment, such as Section 250-114(a), which includes the term "listed grounding device."

110-4. **Voltages.** Throughout this Code, the voltage considered shall be that at which the circuit operates.

Voltages used for computing branch-circuit and feeder-loads are nominal voltages as listed in Section 220-2. See definitions of "Voltage (of a Circuit)," "Voltage, Nominal," and "Voltage to Ground" in Article 100.

See also Sections 300-2 and 300-3.

110-5. **Conductors.** Conductors normally used to carry current shall be of copper unless otherwise provided in this Code. Where the conductor material is not specified, the material and the sizes given in this Code shall apply to copper conductors. Where other materials are used, the size shall be changed accordingly.

(FPN): For aluminum and copper-clad aluminum conductors, see Section 310-15.

See Section 310-14 for aluminum conductor material.

110-6. **Conductor Sizes.** Conductor sizes are expressed in American Wire Gage (AWG) or in circular mils.

For copper, aluminum, or copper-clad aluminum conductors up to size No. 4/0, this *Code* uses the American Wire Gage (AWG) for size identification, which is the same as the Brown and Sharpe Gage (BS).

Conductors larger than 4/0 are sized in circular mils, beginning with 250,000 circular mils. Prior to the 1990 edition, a 250,000 circular mil conductor was labeled "250 MCM." In the 1990 edition, the notation was changed to "250 kcmil." The term MCM was defined as 1,000 circular mils ("M" is the Roman numeral designation for 1,000). The notation was changed to recognize the accepted convention that "k" indicates 1,000. ANSI/IEEE Standard 100-1988, *The IEEE Standard Dictionary of Electrical and Electronic Terms*, 4th Edition, recent UL standards, and new IEEE standards now use the notation "kcmil" rather than "MCM."

The circular mil area of a conductor is equal to its diameter in mils squared (1 in. equals 1,000 mils).

Example: The diameter of a No. 8 solid conductor is 0.1285 inches.

$$0.125 \text{ in.} \times 1,000 = 128.5 \text{ mils}$$
$$128.5 \times 128.5 = 16,512.25 \text{ CM}$$

or 16,510 CM, as rounded off by Table 8 of Chapter 9.

This represents the circular mil area for one conductor. Where stranded conductors are used, the circular mil area of each strand must be multiplied by the number of strands to determine the circular mil area of the conductor (see Table 8 of Chapter 9).

110-7. **Insulation Integrity.** All wiring shall be so installed that, when completed, the system will be free from short circuits and from grounds other than as required or permitted in Article 250.

Insulation is the material located between points of different potential in an electrical system that prevents the flow of electricity between those points. Failure of the insulation system is one of the most common causes of problems in electrical installations. This is true in both high-voltage and low-voltage systems.

Insulation tests are performed on new or existing installations to determine the quality or condition of the insulation of conductors and equipment.

The principal causes of insulation failures are heat, moisture, dirt, and physical damage (abrasion or nicks) occuring during installation. Insulation can also fail due to chemical attack, sunlight, and excessive voltage stresses.

Insulation integrity must be maintained during overcurrent conditions. Overcurrent protective devices must be selected and matched (time and current) to the insulation thermal withstand ability. For example, 75° insulated copper conductors have a safe withstand rating of one ampere . . . for 5 seconds . . . for every 42.25 circular mils. To exceed this value under fault conditions will damage the conductor insulation. The copper conductor will melt off at one ampere. . . for 5 seconds . . . for every 16.2 circular mils. Cable manufacturer's technical data and the Electrical Engineers Handbook provide this information. See Section 110-10.

In an insulation resistance test, an applied voltage ranging from 100 to 5,000 V (usually 500 to 1,000 V for systems of 600 V or less), supplied from a source of constant potential, is applied across the insulation. A hand-generated megohmmeter is the usual potential source, and it indicates the insulation resistance directly on a scale calibrated in megohms. The quality of the insulation is evaluated based on the level of the insulation resistance.

The insulation resistance of many types of insulation is quite variable with temperature, so the data obtained should be corrected to the standard temperature for the class of equipment under test.

The megohm value of insulation resistance obtained will be inversely proportional to the volume of insulation being tested. As an example, a cable 1,000 feet long would be expected to have one tenth the insulation resistance of a cable 100 feet long, if all other conditions were identical.

The insulation resistance test is relatively easy to perform and is useful on all types and classes of electrical equipment. Its main value lies in the charting of data from periodic tests, corrected for temperature, over a long period so that deteriorative trends can be detected.

Excellent manuals on this subject are available from instrument manufacturers. Thorough knowledge in the use of insulation testers is essential if the test results are to be meaningful.

See Figure 110-1 for a typical megohmmeter insulation tester.

Figure 110-1. Multivoltage multirange insulation tester. (James G. Biddle Co.)

110-8. **Wiring Methods.** Only wiring methods recognized as suitable are included in this Code. The recognized methods of wiring shall be permitted to be installed in any type of building or occupancy, except as otherwise provided in this Code.

The scope of Article 300 applies generally to all wiring methods, except as amended, modified, or supplemented by Chapter 5 (Special Occupancies), Chapter 6 (Special Equipment), and Chapter 7 (Special Conditions).

Chapter 8 (Communication Systems) is independent of the other chapters, except where some other section is specifically referenced in Chapter 8 of the *Code*. For example, see Section 800-40(b).

110-9. Interrupting Rating. Equipment intended to break current at fault levels shall have an interrupting rating sufficient for the nominal circuit voltage and the current that is available at the line terminals of the equipment.

Equipment intended to break current at other than fault levels shall have an interrupting rating at nominal circuit voltage sufficient for the current that must be interrupted.

Section 110-9 states that all fuses and circuit breakers intended to break the circuit at fault levels must have an adequate interrupting rating wherever they are used in the electrical system. Fuses or circuit breakers that do not have adequate interrupting ratings could rupture while attempting to clear a short circuit.

Interrupting rating is determined under standard test conditions. It is important that the test conditions match the actual installation needs.

The term "interrupting rating" is generally understood to refer to fuses and breakers. But the term is much broader in scope, including equipment such as disconnect switches. Disconnect switches also have some maximum value of current that they can safely interrupt.

The ability of an overcurrent device to safely interrupt high levels of fault current does not necessarily mean that the downstream connected equipment is capable of "withstanding" the let-through value of current.

For example, a component has been tested and listed at 5,000 amperes rms symmetrical fault current. The overcurrent device ahead of the component has a 42,000 amperes interrupting rating. The available fault current is 25,000 amperes. This is an improper match, unless the overcurrent protective device has the ability to limit the let-thru fault current to a value of less than 5,000 amperes. Testing laboratories evaluate the withstand rating of equipment as part of the listing evaluation. See commentary following Section 110-10.

The interrupting rating may include a series combination of an upstream overcurrent protective device in series with a downstream circuit breaker. The downstream breaker may have an interrupting rating less than that of the combina-

tion. UL 489 and UL 67 include tests for such series combinations. See Sections 240-83(c) and 110-22 for required marking.

Instructions for calculating available short-circuit currents are provided in ANSI/IEEE Std. C37.010b-1984 Supplement, *Application Guide for AC High-Voltage Circuit Breakers Rated on a Symmetrical Current Basis*. Additional details are provided in IEEE Std. 141-1986, *Recommended Practice for Electric Power Distribution for Industrial Plants*, Chapter 6; and ANSI/IEEE Std. 241-1990, *Recommended Practice for Electric Power Systems in Commercial Buildings*, Chapter 9.

110-10. Circuit Impedance and Other Characteristics. The overcurrent protective devices, the total impedance, the component short-circuit withstand ratings, and other characteristics of the circuit to be protected shall be so selected and coordinated as to permit the circuit protective devices that are used to clear a fault without the occurrence of extensive damage to the electrical components of the circuit. This fault shall be assumed to be either between two or more of the circuit conductors, or between any circuit conductor and the grounding conductor or enclosing metal raceway.

The basic purpose of overcurrent protection is to open the circuit before conductors or conductor insulation are damaged when an overcurrent condition occurs. An overcurrent condition can be the result of an overload, a ground fault, or a short circuit and must be eliminated before the conductor insulation damage point is reached.

Overcurrent protective devices (such as fuses and circuit breakers) should be selected that ensure the short-circuit withstand rating of the system components will not be exceeded should a short circuit or high-level ground fault occur.

System components include wire, bus structures, switching, protection and disconnect devices, distribution equipment, etc., all of which have limited short-circuit ratings and would be damaged or destroyed if these short-circuit ratings are exceeded. Merely providing overcurrent protective devices with sufficient interrupting rating will not ensure adequate short-circuit protection for the system components. When the available short-circuit current exceeds the withstand rating of an electrical component, the overcurrent protective device must limit the let-through energy to within the rating of that electrical component.

Utility companies usually determine and provide information on available short-circuit current levels at the service equipment. Literature on how to calculate short-circuit currents at each point in any distribution can generally be obtained by contacting manufacturers of overcurrent protective devices or by referring to the IEEE "Red Book" (IEEE Standard 141-1986).

For a typical one-family dwelling with a 100-ampere service using No. 2 aluminum supplied by a 1.72 percent, 37½ kVA transformer at a distance of 25 feet, the available short-circuit current would be approximately 6,000 amperes.

Available short-circuit current to multifamily structures, where pad mount transformers are located very close to the multimetering location, can be relatively high. For example, the line-to-line fault current values close to a low impedance transformer could exceed 22,000 amperes. At the secondary of a single-phase, center tapped transformer, the line-to-neutral fault current is approximately 1½ times that of the line-to-line fault current. The short-circuit withstand rating of utilization equipment located and connected near the service-equipment should be known. For example, HVAC equipment is tested at 3,500 amperes through a 40-ampere load rating, and 5,000 amperes for loads rated more than 40 amperes.

Adequate short-circuit protection can be provided by fuses, molded case circuit breakers, and low-voltage power circuit breakers depending on specific circuit and installation requirements.

FUSES

The following information on fuses is based on the UL "Guide Card" information on fuses Guide No. JCQR, in the UL Electrical Construction Material Directory for Cartridge Nonrenewable Fuses (Guide Card JDZZ) and Cartridge Renewable Fuses (Guide Card JDRX), and special purpose fuses (Guide Card JFHR).

FUSES
CARTRIDGE NONRENEWABLE

Fuses designated as Class K1, K5, K9 (0-600 amp, 250 V, ac, or 600 V, ac) are classified as to interrupting capacity and in terms of maximum clearing ampere squared seconds and maximum peak let-through current. They incorporate dimensional features equivalent to, and are interchangeable with, other nonrenewable cartridge fuses intended for installation in conventional designs of equipment recognized by the *National Electrical Code* for branch circuit, service, and motor overload use. They are not marked "Current-Limiting."

Fuses designated as Class RK1 and RK5 (0-600 amps, 250 V, ac or 600 V, ac) are high-interrupting capacity types and are marked "Current-Limiting." They are classified in terms of maximum clearing ampere squared seconds and maximum peak let-through current at 50, 100, and 200 thousands rms symmetrical amperes. They incorporate features that permit their insertion into holders for other nonrenewable cartridge fuses intended for installation in conventional designs of equipment recognized by the *National Electrical Code* for branch circuit, service, and motor overload use. They are provided with a feature that allows their insertion into rejection-type fuseholders designed to accept only Class RK1 or RK5 fuses.

The rejection-type fuseholders are used in equipment as covered in the *National Electrical Code*.

Fuses designated as Class CC (0-30 amp, 600 V, ac) are high-interrupting capacity types and are marked "Current-Limiting." They are not interchangeable with fuses of higher voltage or interrupting rating or lower current rating.

Fuses designated as Class G (0-60 amp, 300 V, ac) are high-interrupting capacity types and are marked "Current-Limiting." They are not interchangeable with other fuses mentioned above and below.

Fuses designated as Class J (0-600 amp, 600 V, ac) or Class L (601-6000 amp, 600 V, ac) are high-interrupting capacity types and are marked "Current-Limiting." They are not interchangeable with other fuses such as those mentioned above and below.

Fuses designated as Class T (0-1200 amp, 300 V and 0-800 amp, 600 V, ac) are high-interrupting capacity types and are marked "Current-Limiting." They are not interchangeable with other fuses mentioned above.

The term "Current-Limiting" indicates that a fuse, when tested on a circuit capable of delivering a specific short-circuit current (rms amperes symmetrical) at rated voltage, will start to melt within 90 electrical degrees and will clear the circuit within 180 electrical degrees (½ cycle).

Because the time required for a fuse to melt depends on the available current of the circuit, a fuse that may be current-limiting when subjected to a specific short-circuit current (rms amperes symmetrical) may not be current-limiting on a circuit of lower maximum available current.

The performance of a fuse as determined by the ability of the fuse to open and clear a circuit is indicated by the following maximum permissible let-through values, which are obtained when fuses of the Class K designs are connected to circuits having an available current of up to 100,000 amp maximum (rms symmetrical) but not greater than the marked interrupting rating of the fuse if it is less than 100,000 amps, when fuses of the Class G design are connected to circuits having an available current of 100,000 amps maximum (rms symmetrical), and when fuses of the Class CC, J, L, RK, and T designs are connected to circuits having available currents of 50,000, 100,000, and 200,000 amps maximum (rms symmetrical).

Some Class J, L, and RK1 fuses have been "Special Purpose Listed" at 300,000 amperes maximum rms symmetrical. No industry standard values have yet been established for I_p and I^2t.

Class K-1, K-5, and K-9 fuses are marked, in addition to their regular voltage and current ratings, with an interrupting rating of 200,000, 100,000, or 50,000 amps (rms symmetrical).

Class CC, RK 1, RK5, J, L, and T fuses are marked, in addition to their regular voltage and current ratings, with an interrupting rating of 200,000 amps (rms symmetrical).

Class G fuses are marked, in addition to their regular voltage and current ratings, with an interrupting rating of 100,000 amps (rms symmetrical).

A Class H fuse has an interrupting rating of 10,000 amps, ac. In addition, a Class H fuse may be rated 10,000 amp dc.

A Class CC, G, J, K, or R fuse and a Class T fuse rated 600 A or less may have an interrupting rating of 10,000, 20,000, 50,000, or 100,000 amp dc. A Class T fuse rated 601 - 1200 A and a Class L fuse may have an interrupting rating of 20,000, 50,000, or 100,000 amp dc.

When a fuse has a dc rating, it is marked with the dc voltage and interrupting rating.

Equipment (switches, motor starters, panelboards, etc.) that has been investigated and found suitable for use with these fuses is marked with the class of fuse intended to be used in the equipment and the available current rating applicable to that piece of equipment.

The equipment, when so marked, with these fuses installed, is considered to be suitable for use on circuits that can deliver currents under short circuit conditions up to the available current rating of the equipment or the interrupting rating of the fuse, whichever is lower.

An interrupting rating on a fuse included in a piece of equipment does not automatically qualify the equipment in which the fuses are installed for use on circuits with higher available currents than the rating of the equipment itself.

Class L fuses are designed for use in equipment to which line and load connections are made by means of solid busbars. For this reason temperature rises on Class L fuse blades may exceed those observed in connection with other cartridge fuse designs. Terminal connections for wires in such equipment must be designed to avoid excessive temperatures on the wire insulation.

Class CC, G, H, J, K, L, and RK fuses may be marked as having a time delay characteristic. For the Class CC, G, H, J, K, and RK fuses, this characteristic (a minimum clearing time under a particular overcurrent condition) has been investigated. Class G or CC fuses, which can carry 200 percent of rated current for 12 seconds or more, and Class H, J, K, or RK fuses, which can carry 500 percent of rated current for 10 seconds or more, may be marked with "D," "Time Delay," "Dual Element," or some equivalent designation. Class "L" fuses are permitted to be marked "Time Delay," but have not been evaluated for such performance. Class T fuses are not permitted to be marked "Time Delay."

A Class K or R fuse, which has been investigated for use in protecting trailing cables in dc circuits in mines, is marked "Mine Duty" and has an interrupting rating of 20,000 amp, dc.

The basic standards used to investigate products in this category are UL198B, "Class H Fuses"; UL198C, "High-Interrupting-Capacity Fuses, Current-Limiting Types"; UL198D, "Class K Fuses"; UL198E, "Class R Fuses"; UL198H, "Class T Fuses"; UL198L, "DC Fuses for Industrial Use"; and UL198M, "Mine-Duty Fuses."

CARTRIDGE RENEWABLE

Renewable fuses of a given voltage rating or current rating range are not interchangeable in the same fuseholder with fuses of a different voltage rating or current rating range.

Each line of renewable links has been investigated only with the same line of fuses from the same manufacturer.

The basic standard used to investigate products in this category is UL198B, "Class H Fuses."

Nonrenewable Cartridge Fuses

Class CC Fuses
Maximum Peak Let-Through Current (lp-amperes) and Clearing
I^2t (ampere squared seconds)

Rating Amps	Between Threshold and 50KA		100KA		200KA	
	I^2tx10^3	$lpx10^3$	I^2tx10^3	$lpx10^3$	I^2tx10^3	$lpx10^3$
0-15	2	3	2	3	3	4
16-20	2	3	3	4	3	5
21-30	7	6	7	7.5	7	12

Class G Fuses (480 V)
Maximum Peak Let-Through Current

Cartridge Size Amps	Ampere X 10^3	Maximum Clearing I^2T (Amp-Squared Seconds X 10^3)
0-15	4.0	3.8
16-20	5.0	5.0
21-30	7.0	7.0
31-60	10.5	25.0

Class J and 600 Volt T Fuses
Maximum Peak Let-Through Current (lp-amperes) and Clearing
I^2t (ampere squared seconds)

Cartridge Size Amps	Between Threshold and 50KA		100KA		200KA	
	I^2tx10^3	$lpx10^3$	I^2tx10^3	$lpx10^3$	I^2px10^3	$lpx10^3$
0-30	7	6	7	7.5	7	12
31-60	30	8	30	10	30	16
61-100	60	12	80	14	80	20
101-200	200	16	300	20	300	30
201-400	1000	25	1100	30	1100	45
401-600	2500	35	2500	45	2500	70
601-800	4000	50	4000	55	4000	75

300 Volt T Fuses
Maximum Peak Let-Through Current (lp-amperes) and Clearing
I^2t (ampere squared seconds)

Cartridge Size Amps	Between Threshold and 50KA		100KA		200KA	
	I^2tx10^3	$lpx10^3$	I^2tx10^3	$lpx10^3$	I^2px10^3	$lpx10^3$
0-30	3.5	5	3.5	7	3.5	9
31-60	15	7	15	9	15	12
61-100	40	9	40	12	40	15
101-200	150	13	150	16	150	20
201-400	550	22	550	28	550	35
401-600	1000	29	1000	37	1000	46
601-800	1500	37	1500	50	1500	65
801-1200	3500	50	3500	65	4000	80

Nonrenewable Cartridge Fuses, continued

Class K Fuses

	Maximum Peak Let-Through Current Ampere X 10³			Maximum Clearing I²T (Amp-Squared Seconds X 10³)		
Cartridge Size Amps	K1	K5	K9	K1	K5	K9
30	10	11	14	10	50	50
60	12	21	28	40	200	250
100	16	25	35	100	500	650
200	22	40	60	400	1,600	3,500
400	35	60	80	1,200	5,000	15,000
600	50	80	130	3,000	10,000	40,000

Class L Fuses
Maximm Peak Let-Through Current (lp-amperes) and Clearing I²t (ampere squared seconds)

	50KA or Threshold Current-Whichever is Greater		100KA		200KA	
Cartridge Size Amps	I²tx10⁶	lpx10³	I²tx10⁶	lpx10³	I²tx10⁶	lpx10³
601-800	10	80	10	80	10	80
801-1200	12	80	12	80	15	120
1201-1600	22	100	22	100	30	150
1601-2000	35	110	35	120	40	165
2001-2500	—	—	75	165	75	180
2501-3000	—	—	100	175	100	200
3001-4000	—	—	150	220	150	250
4001-5000	—	—	350	—	350	300
5001-6000	—	—	350	—	500	350

Cartridge Nonrenewable
Class RK1 Fuses
Maximum Peak Let-Through Current (lp-amperes) and Clearing I²t (ampere squared seconds)

	Between Threshold and 50KA		100KA		200KA	
Cartridge Size Amps	I²tx10³	lpx10³	I²tx10³	lpx10³	I²tx10³	lpx10³
0-30	10	6	10	10	11	12
31-60	40	10	40	12	50	16
61-100	100	14	100	16	100	20
101-200	400	18	400	22	400	30
201-400	1200	33	1200	35	1600	50
401-600	3000	43	3000	50	4000	70

Class RK5 Fuses
Maximum Peak Let-Through Current (lp-amperes) and Clearing I²t (ampere squared seconds)

	Between Threshold and 50KA		100KA		200KA	
Cartridge Size Amps	I²tx10³	lpx10³	I²tx10³	lpx10³	I²px10³	lpx10³
0-30	50	11	50	11	50	14
31-60	200	20	200	21	200	26
61-100	500	22	500	25	500	32
101-200	1600	32	1600	40	2000	50
201-400	5000	50	5000	60	6000	75
401-600	10000	65	10000	80	12000	100

CIRCUIT BREAKERS

When using circuit breakers, "current-limiting" can be accomplished by using a current-limiting molded-case circuit breaker, a fused circuit breaker having integrally mounted current-limiting fuses, or by current limiters designed to be used in conjunction with specific circuit breakers.

The following information on circuit breakers is based on the UL "Guide Card" information on molded-case circuit breakers, Guide No. DIVQ, in the UL *Electrical Construction Materials Directory*.

Listed circuit breakers are intended for use in listed enclosures, or as part of other listed equipment, or without enclosures where acceptable.

Listed circuit breakers are rated 600 V or less. A circuit breaker is marked ac or dc or both ac and dc. The frequency is included if other than 60 Hz.

Class CTL circuit breakers may be identified by the words "Class CTL" or "CTL" on the circuit breaker as part of the marking.

Class CTL circuit breakers have physical size, configuration, or other means that, in conjunction with the physical means provided in a Class CTL assembly, are designed to prevent the installation of more circuit breaker poles than the number for which the assembly is designed and rated.

Some circuit breakers are not provided with a means to prevent their installation in Class CTL assemblies. These circuit breakers are for use in old style, non-Class CTL equipment and are marked "For Replacement Use Only, Not CTL Assemblies."

Circuit breakers marked "SWD" are suitable for switching 120 or 277 volt fluorescent lighting at their rated voltage on a regular basis.

Three-pole circuit breakers having provision for two poles to be connected to a bus structure and a third isolated pole (commonly referred to as Delta breakers) are marked "For Replacement Use Only."

Some circuit breakers include a pole intended to disconnect the grounded circuit conductor of a branch circuit. These poles open simultaneously.

Single-pole circuit breakers rated 120 volts ac or 120/240 volts ac and multipole independent trip circuit breakers rated 120/240 volts ac are suitable for use in a single phase multiwire circuit with the neutral connected to the load where the voltage to ground does not exceed 120 volts.

Single-pole circuit breakers rated 125 volts, 125 volts dc, 125/250 volts, or 125/250 volts dc and multipole independent trip circuit breakers rated 125/250 volts or 125/250 volts dc are suitable for use in a single phase and dc multiwire circuit with the neutral connected to the load where the voltage to ground does not exceed 125 volts.

Some independent trip circuit breakers are marked "Independent Trip," "No Common Trip," or with equivalent wording.

Multipole common trip circuit breakers rated 120/240 volts ac are suitable for use in a single-phase multiwire circuit with or without the neutral connected to the load where the voltage to ground does not exceed 120 volts.

Multipole common trip circuit breakers rated 125/250 volts or 125/250 volts dc are suitable for use in a single phase and a dc multiwire circuit with or without the neutral connected to the load where the voltage to ground does not exceed 125 volts.

Circuit breakers that are capable of correct operation where the temperature of the ambient air within the enclosure housing the circuit breaker attains 40 degrees Celcius are marked "40° C."

Unless otherwise marked, circuit breakers should not be loaded in excess of 80 percent of their current rating where in normal operation the load will continue for 3 hours or more.

Circuit breakers that have an interrupting rating higher than 5,000 amperes are marked to indicate the higher rating(s).

Circuit breakers are tested under overload conditions at six times rating to cover motor circuit applications and are suitable for use as motor circuit disconnects per Section 430-109 of the *National Electrical Code*.

An interrupting rating on a circuit breaker included in a piece of equipment does not automatically qualify the equipment in which the circuit breaker is installed for use on circuits with higher available currents than the rating of the equipment itself.

A circuit breaker that includes an accessory device, whether attached to the circuit breaker by the manufacturer or by others, is marked to indicate the presence of that accessory.

Where the accessory is a shunt trip device that is suitable for operation with ground fault sensing and relaying equipment, such suitability is indicated in the marking of the circuit breaker.

Two-pole circuit breakers that are marked to indicate use on 3-phase circuits have been investigated and found suitable for controlling three-phase, end-grounded delta circuits.

Three-pole circuit breakers are suitable for use only on 3-phase circuits unless marked to indicate otherwise.

Circuit breakers rated 50 amperes or less and 125/250 volts or less are tested with tungsten-filament lamp loads to determine that inrush current will not cause nuisance tripping or contact welding.

Listed circuit breakers may be mounted in any position unless marked to indicate otherwise.

In a switchboard where the circuit breaker handle is operated vertically rather than rotationally or horizontally, the up position of the handle shall be the "on" position.

Line and load markings on a circuit breaker are intended to limit connections there to as marked.

Circuit breaker enclosures that are suitable for use as service equipment are marked accordingly.

Circuit breaker enclosures marked for service equipment use may also be used to provide the main control and means of cutoff for a separately derived system or a second building.

Circuit breaker enclosures that are rainproof or raintight are marked accordingly.

Circuit breaker enclosures that have a short circuit current rating are marked accordingly.

For additional information, see Circuit Breakers.

The Marine Listing Mark identifies those circuit breakers that have been investigated and found suitable for use in a marine environment.

For additional information see Circuit Breakers, Molded-Case and Circuit Breaker Enclosures, Marine (DKTY) in the *Marine Products Directory*.

Circuit breakers that have been found suitable for use with heating, air conditioning, and refrigeration equipment comprising multimotor or combination loads bear the Listing Mark "Listed HACR Type." Such circuit breakers are suitable for use with heating, air conditioning, and refrigerating equipment marked for use with an HACR-Type circuit breaker. Use of these circuit breakers with heating, air conditioning, and refrigerating equipment is limited to installations where the equipment is marked as suitable for use with any properly sized circuit breaker, or is marked for use with an HACR-type circuit breaker, or is not limited by any

marking as to the type of branch-circuit, short-circuit, and ground-fault protective device.

A current-limiting circuit breaker is one that does not employ a fusible element and that when operating within its current-limiting range, limits the let-through I^2t to a value less than the I^2t of a $1/2$-cycle wave of the symmetrical prospective current.

Current-limiting circuit breakers are marked "current-limiting" and are marked either to indicate the let-through characteristics or to indicate where such information may be obtained.

The basic standard used to investigate products in this category is UL 489, "Molded-Case Circuit Breakers and Circuit-Breaker Enclosures."

CIRCUIT BREAKER CURRENT LIMITERS

The following information is based on the UL "Guide Card" information on Circuit Breaker Current Limiters, Guide Card No. DIRW in the UL *Electrical Construction Materials Directory*.

Circuit breaker current limiters are designed to be used in conjunction with specific circuit breakers and to be directly connected to the load terminals of the circuit breakers. They contain fusible elements that function only to increase the fault current interrupting ability of the combination that is intended for use in the same manner as circuit breakers where installed at the service and as branch circuit protection. The limiters are rated 600 V or less.

The fusible elements in circuit breaker current limiters are so coordinated that they function at currents below those specified in short-circuit test requirements for circuit breakers. Except for this feature of short-circuit operation, combinations of circuit breakers and circuit breaker current limiters meet all requirements applicable to branch-circuit and service circuit breakers and, in addition, are required to clear circuits up to and including 25 times their ampere rating, and circuits of 1,000 amperes or less regardless of ampere rating, without causing operation of the fusible elements in the current limiter.

Circuit breaker current limiters are marked to indicate the breakers with which they are intended to be used.

Circuit breaker current limiters that are marked "Current-Interrupting Rating(s), MAXIMUM RMS SYM, AMPERES _____VOLTS _____" have been investigated in conjunction with the circuit breaker and found suitable for the marked interrupting rating.

An interrupting rating on a circuit breaker current limiter included in a piece of equipment does not automatically qualify the equipment in which the combination is installed as suitable for use on circuits with higher available currents than the rating of the equipment itself.

The combination of circuit breaker and circuit breaker current limiter is intended to be mounted in listed enclosures.

Equipment (such as panelboards, service equipment, and dead-front switchboards) that has been investigated and found suitable for use with the combination of circuit breaker and circuit breaker current limiter is marked to indicate that both may be used.

Circuit breaker current limiters as listed herein are for use with copper conductors unless marked to indicate which terminals are suitable for use with aluminum conductors. Such marking shall be independent of any marking on terminal connectors and shall be readily visible.

Unless the circuit breaker current limiter is marked to indicate otherwise, the wiring space and current-carrying capacity are based on the use of 60° C wire in circuits rated 100 amperes or less, and the use of 75° C wire for higher ampere-rated circuits.

The basic standard used to investigate products in this category is UL 489, "Molded-Case Circuit Breakers and Circuit-Breaker Enclosures."

The listing mark of Underwriters Laboratories Inc. on the product is the only method provided by UL to identify products manufactured under its Listing and Follow-Up Service. The Listing mark for these products includes the name and/or symbol of Underwriters Laboratories Inc. (as illustrated in the Introduction of this Directory) together with the word "Listed," a control number, and the following product name: "Circuit Breaker Current Limiter."

(FPN): For circuit breakers, see Section 240-83(c).

110-11. **Deteriorating Agents.** Unless identified for use in the operating environment, no conductors or equipment shall be located in damp or wet locations; where exposed to gases, fumes, vapors, liquids, or other agents having a deteriorating effect on the conductors or equipment; nor where exposed to excessive temperatures.

(FPN No. 1): See Section 300-6 for protection against corrosion.

(FPN No. 2): Some cleaning and lubricating compounds can cause severe deterioration of many plastic materials used for insulating and structural applications in equipment.

Equipment approved for use in dry locations only shall be protected against permanent damage from the weather during building construction.

110-12. **Mechanical Execution of Work.** Electric equipment shall be installed in a neat and workmanlike manner.

(a) **Unused Openings.** Unused openings in boxes, raceways, auxiliary gutters, cabinets, equipment cases, or housings shall be effectively closed to afford protection substantially equivalent to the wall of the equipment.

(b) **Subsurface Enclosures.** Conductors shall be racked to provide ready and safe access in underground and subsurface enclosures, into which persons enter for installation and maintenance.

This regulation calling for "neat and workmanlike" installations has appeared in the *NEC* as currently worded for over a half century. It stands as a basis for pride in one's work and has been emphasized by persons involved in the training of apprentice electricians for many years.

Many *Code* conflicts or violations have been cited by the authority having jurisdiction based on the authority's interpretation of "neat and workmanlike manner."

Many electrical inspection authorities use their own experience, or precedents in their local areas, as the basis for their judgments. Any ruling, however, should be based on uniformity as intended by the *National Electrical Code* Committee.

Examples of installations that do not qualify as "neat and workmanlike" are exposed runs of cables or raceways that are improperly supported, that is, sagging between supports or using improper support methods; field-bent and kinked, flattened, or poorly measured raceways; or cabinets, cut-out boxes, and enclosures that are not plumb or that are not properly secured.

(c) **Integrity of Electrical Equipment and Connections.** Internal parts of electrical equipment, including busbars, wiring terminals, insulators, and other surfaces shall not be damaged or contaminated by foreign materials such as paint, plaster, cleaners, or abrasives.

110-13. Mounting and Cooling of Equipment.

(a) Mounting. Electric equipment shall be firmly secured to the surface on which it is mounted. Wooden plugs driven into holes in masonry, concrete, plaster, or similar materials shall not be used.

(b) Cooling. Electrical equipment that depends upon the natural circulation of air and convection principles for cooling of exposed surfaces shall be installed so that room airflow over such surfaces is not prevented by walls or by adjacent installed equipment. For equipment designed for floor mounting, clearance between top surfaces and adjacent surfaces shall be provided to dissipate rising warm air.

See Sections 430-14(a) and 430-16 for motor locations, and Sections 450-9 and 450-45 for transformer locations.

Electrical equipment provided with ventilating openings shall be installed so that walls or other obstructions do not prevent the free circulation of air through the equipment.

For example, a ventilated busway must be located where there are no walls or other objects that might interfere with the natural circulation of air and convection principles for cooling. See definition of "Ventilated" in Article 100.

Some types of equipment, such as panelboards and transformers, are adversely affected if enclosure surfaces normally exposed to room air are covered or tightly enclosed. Ventilating openings in equipment are provided to allow the circulation of room air around internal components of the equipment, and the blocking of such openings can cause dangerous overheating.

110-14. Electrical Connections.

Because of different characteristics of copper and aluminum, devices such as pressure terminal or pressure splicing connectors and soldering lugs shall be identified for the material of the conductor and shall be properly installed and used. Conductors of dissimilar metals shall not be intermixed in a terminal or splicing connector where physical contact occurs between dissimilar conductors (such as copper and aluminum, copper and copper-clad aluminum, or aluminum and copper-clad aluminum), unless the device is identified for the purpose and conditions of use. Materials such as solder, fluxes, inhibitors, and compounds, where employed, shall be suitable for the use and shall be of a type that will not adversely affect the conductors, installation, or equipment.

(FPN): Many terminations and equipment are marked with a tightening torque.

Section 110-3(b) applies where terminations and equipment are marked with tightening torques.

TIGHTENING TORQUES

Figures 110-2, 110-3, 110-4, and 110-5 provide information on the tightening torques used by Underwriters Laboratories Inc. when testing wire connectors unless the manufacturer assigns another value appropriate for the design. This information should be used for guidance only where no tightening information on the specific wire connector is available. It should not be used to replace manufacturer's instructions, which should always be followed. This information was taken from the edition of UL Standard 486B that was in effect at the time of the printing of this Handbook. Similar information can be found in UL 486A and UL 486C.

(a) Terminals. Connection of conductors to terminal parts shall ensure a thoroughly good connection without damaging the conductors and shall be made by means of pressure connectors (including set-screw type), solder lugs, or splices to flexible leads.

Exception: Connection by means of wire binding screws or studs and nuts having upturned lugs or equivalent shall be permitted for No. 10 or smaller conductors.

Terminals for more than one conductor and terminals used to connect aluminum shall be so identified.

(b) Splices. Conductors shall be spliced or joined with splicing devices identified for the use or by brazing, welding, or soldering with a fusible metal or alloy. Soldered splices shall first be so spliced or joined as to be mechanically and electrically secure without solder and then soldered. All splices and joints and the free ends of conductors shall be covered with an insulation equivalent to that of the conductors or with an insulating device identified for the purpose.

Field observations and trade magazine articles indicate that failures of electrical connections have been determined as the cause of many equipment burnouts and fires. Many of these failures are attributable to improper terminations, poor workmanship, the differing characteristics of dissimilar metals, and improper binding screws or splicing devices.

Tightening Torques for Screws—Pound Inches[a]

Wire Size	Slotted Head No. 10 and Larger				Hexagonal Head—External Drive Socket Wrench	
	Slot Width—Inches[b]		Slot Length—Inches[b]			
	to $^3/_{64}$	over $^3/_{64}$	to $^1/_4$	over $^1/_4$	Split-Bolt Connectors	Other Connectors
18-10AWG	20	35	20	35	80	75
8	25	40	25	40	80	75
6	35	45	35	45	165	110
4	35	45	35	45	165	110
3	35	50	35	50	275	150
2	40	50	40	50	275	150
1	—	50	—	50	275	150
1/0	—	50	—	50	385	180
2/0	—	50	—	50	385	180
3/0	—	50	—	50	500	250
4/0	—	50	—	50	500	250
250 MCM	—	50	—	50	650	325
300	—	50	—	50	650	325
350	—	50	—	50	650	325
400	—	50	—	50	825	325
500	—	50	—	50	825	375
600	—	50	—	50	1000	375
700	—	50	—	50	1000	375
750	—	50	—	50	1000	375
800	—	50	—	50	1100	500
900	—	50	—	50	1100	500
1000	—	50	—	50	1100	500
1250	—	—	—	—	1100	600
1500	—	—	—	—	1100	600
1750	—	—	—	—	1100	600
2000	—	—	—	—	1100	600

a. Clamping screws with multiple tightening means: for example, for a slotted hexagonal head screw, use the torque value associated with the tool used in the installation. UL uses both values when testing.

b. For values of slot width or length other than those specified, select the largest torque value associated with conductor size.

Figure 110-2. *Tightening torques for screws in pound-inches. (Underwriters Laboratories Inc.)*

Torques in Pound-Inches for Slotted Head Screws[a] Smaller than No. 10, for Use with No. 8 AWG or Smaller Conductors

Screw-Slot Length in Inches[b]	Screw-Slot Width Less than $3/64$ in.	Screw-Slot Width $3/64$ in. and Larger
to $5/32$	7	9
$5/32$	7	12
$3/16$	7	12
$7/32$	7	12
$1/4$	9	12
$9/32$	—	15
above $9/32$	—	20

a. Clamping screws with multiple tightening means: for example, for a slotted hexagonal head screw, use the torque value associated with the tool used in the installation. UL uses both values when testing.

b. For slot lengths of intermediate values, select torques pertaining to next shorter slot length.

Figure 110-3. Tightening torques for slotted head screws in pound-inches. (Underwriters Laboratories Inc.)

Torques for Socket Head Screws[a]

Socket Size Across Flats—Inches	Torque, Pound-Inches
$1/8$	45
$5/32$	100
$3/16$	120
$7/32$	150
$1/4$	200
$5/16$	275
$3/8$	375
$1/2$	500
$9/16$	600

a. Clamping screws with multiple tightening means: for example, for a slotted hexagonal head screw, use the torque value associated with the tool used in the installation. UL uses both values when testing.

Figure 110-4. Tightening torques for socket head screws in pound-inches. (Underwriters Laboratories Inc.)

Underwriters Laboratories Inc. requirements for listing solid aluminum conductors in sizes No. 12 and No. 10 AWG and for listing snap switches and receptacles for use on 15- and 20-A branch circuits incorporate stringent tests that take the factors listed in the previous paragraph into account. See Sections 380-14(c) and 410-56(b).

Lug Bolting Torques for Connection of Wire Connectors to Busbars, etc.

Bolt Diameter— Inches	Tightening Torque Pound-Feet
No. 8	1.5
No. 10	2.0
$1/4$ or less	6
$5/16$	11
$3/8$	19
$7/16$	30
$1/2$	40
$5/8$ or more	55

Figure 110-5. Lug bolting torques in pound-feet for connection of wire connectors to busbars, etc. (Underwriters Laboratories Inc.)

Screwless pressure terminal connectors of the conductor push-in type are for use with copper and copper-clad aluminum conductors only.

Instructions describing proper installation techniques and emphasizing the need to follow these techniques and practice good workmanship are required to be included with each coil of No. 12 and No. 10 AWG insulated aluminum wire or cable. Also, see commentary on tightening torque under Section 110-14, FPN.

New product and material designs that provide for increased levels of safety of aluminum wire terminations have been developed by the electrical industry.

To assist all concerned parties in the proper and safe use of solid aluminum wire in making connections to wiring devices used on 15- and 20-A branch circuits, the following information is presented. Understanding and utilizing this information is essential to proper application of materials and devices now available.

For New Installations

The following is based on a report that was prepared by the Ad Hoc Committee on Aluminum Terminations: Comply with Section 110-14(a) of the *NEC* where aluminum wire is used in new installations.

New Materials and Devices

a. For direct connection, use only 15- and 20-A receptacles and switches marked "CO/ALR" and connected as described under "Installation Method."

The "CO/ALR" marking is on the device mounting yoke or strap. The "CO/ALR" marking means the devices have been tested to stringent heat cycling requirements to determine their suitability for use with UL-labeled aluminum, copper, or copper-clad aluminum wire.

b. Use listed solid aluminum wire, No. 12 or No. 10 AWG, marked with the aluminum insulated wire label, as shown in Figure 110-6. Follow the installation instructions packaged with the wire.

Installation Method

1. Wrap the freshly stripped end of the wire two-thirds to three-quarters of the distance around the wire-binding screw post, as shown in Step A of Figure 110-6.

The loop is made so that rotation of the screw in tightening will tend to wrap the wire around the post rather than unwrap it.

2. Tighten the screw until the wire is snugly in contact with the underside of the screw head and with the contact plate on the wiring device, as shown in Step B of Figure 110-6.

3. Tighten the screw an additional one-half turn, thereby providing a firm connection. Where torque screwdrivers are used, tighten to 12 pound-inches. See Step C of Figure 110-6.

4. Position the wires behind the wiring device so as to decrease the likelihood of the terminal screws loosening when the device is positioned into the outlet box.

Figure 110-7 illustrates incorrect methods for connection and should not be used.

Existing Inventory

When labeled solid aluminum wire No. 12 and No. 10 AWG not bearing the new aluminum wire label is used, it should be used with wiring devices marked "CO/ALR" and connected as described in "Installation Method." This is the preferred and recommended method for using such wire.

In the following types of devices, the terminals shall not be directly connected to aluminum conductors but may be used with labeled copper or copper-clad conductors:

Receptacles and snap switches marked "AL-CU";

Receptacles and snap switches having no conductor marking;

Step A: Strip and wrap wire

Step B: Tighten screw to full contact

Step C: Complete connection

Figure 110-6. Correct method of terminating aluminum wire at wire-binding screw terminals of receptacles and snap switches. (Underwriters Laboratories Inc.)

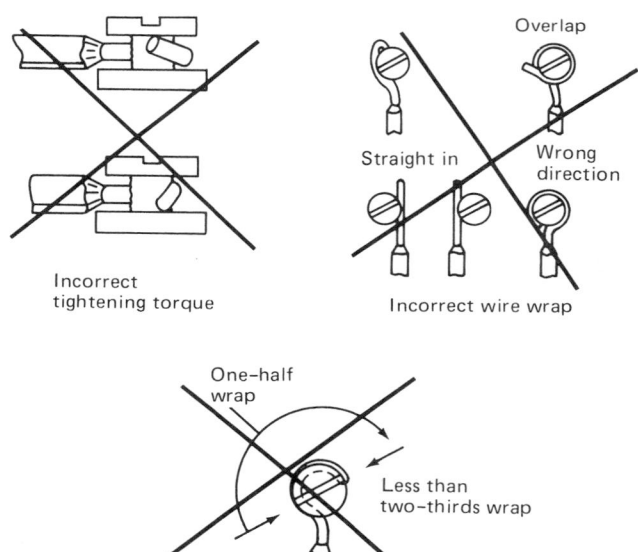

Figure 110-7. Incorrect methods of terminating aluminum wire at wire-binding screw terminals of receptacles and snap switches. (Underwriters Laboratories Inc.)

Receptacles and snap switches having backwired terminals or screwless terminals of the push-in type.

For Existing Installations

If examination discloses overheating or loose connections, the recommendations described under "For New Installations-Existing Inventory" should be followed.

WIRE NUTS

Effective January 2, 1987, UL 486C was revised with regard to the performance requirements for wire connectors for use with aluminum and copper-clad aluminum conductors. The effect of this change is that twist-on type wire connectors, often called "wire nuts," are required to meet new performance requirements if listing is to be continued. As of the writing of this handbook, no wire nuts have been listed as having met these requirements. However, listed connectors of other designs that can be used for connecting aluminum and copper-clad aluminum conductors to copper conductors are still available.

Pigtailing, either field or factory wired, as illustrated in Figure 110-8 is recognized by the NEC.

As of the writing of this handbook, listed connectors only in the tool-applied crimp-type construction are available for pigtailing to 15 and 20 amp wiring devices.

Note: Detailed installation instructions provided with pressure wire connectors must be followed

Branch–circuit wiring

Branch–circuit wiring

Aluminum wire No. 12–10 AWG

Insulated copper lead (pigtail) No. 14–12 AWG connected to wiring device

Listed AL/CU tool–applied crimp–type insulated wire connector provided in carton marked "FOR DRY LOCATIONS ONLY" and for the aluminum–to–copper combinations for which it is suitable

Figure 110-8. *Pigtailing copper to aluminum conductors.*

(c) Temperature Limitations. The temperature rating associated with the ampacity of a conductor shall be so selected and coordinated as to not exceed the lowest temperature rating of any connected termination, conductor, or device.

(1) Termination provisions of equipment for circuits rated 100 amperes or less, or marked for Nos. 14 through 1 conductors, shall be used only for conductors rated 60°C (140°F).

Exception No. 1: Conductors with higher temperature ratings shall be permitted to be used, provided the ampacity of such conductors is determined based on the 60°C (140°F) ampacity of the conductor size used.

Exception No. 2: Equipment termination provisions shall be permitted to be used with higher rated conductors at the ampacity of the higher rated conductors, provided the equipment is listed and identified for use with the higher rated conductors.

(2) Termination provisions of equipment for circuits rated over 100 amperes, or marked for conductors larger than No. 1, shall be used only with conductors rated 75°C (167°F).

Exception No. 1: Conductors with higher temperature ratings shall be permitted to be used, provided the ampacity of such conductors is determined based on the 75°C (167°F) ampacity of the conductor size used.

Exception No. 2: Equipment termination provisions shall be permitted to be used with the higher rated conductors at the ampacity of the higher rated conductors, provided the equipment is listed and identified for use with the higher rated conductors.

(3) Separately installed pressure connectors shall be used with conductors at the ampacities not exceeding the ampacity at the listed and identified temperature rating of the connector.

(FPN): With respect to Sections 110-14(c)(1), (2), and (3), equipment markings or listing information may additionally restrict the sizing and temperature ratings of connected conductors.

The maximum load at terminations, based on the device terminal temperature rating, has been misunderstood by many *Code* users, regardless of the requirements in Section 110-3(b).

Section 110-14(c) has been revised by adding requirements pertaining to load current limitations based on the temperature rating for which the device terminal was tested.

110-16. **Working Space About Electric Equipment (600 Volts, Nominal, or Less).** Sufficient access and working space shall be provided and maintained about all electric equipment

QO LOAD CENTER
CAT. NO. Q020-30M150
SERIES G1
BOX CAT. NO. Q0B20-30M150
USE WITH INTERIOR CAT. NO.
USE COVER CAT. NO.
Q0C20UF OR Q0C20US
MAINS 150 AMP. MAX.
SEE MAIN OR SERVICE DISCONNECT
RATING IF INSTALLED.
120/240V. AC 1PH. 3W.
▲ 240V. AC 3PH. 3W.,
MAIN LUGS ONLY.

TYPE 1 ENCLOSURE

SUITABLE FOR USE WITH
75° C COPPER OR ALUMINUM
MAIN CONDUCTORS.
SEE BRANCH BREAKERS FOR
BRANCH WIRE RATINGS.
MAIN TERMINALS SUITABLE
FOR NO. 4 TO 250KCMIL WIRE.
USE ONLY SQUARE D CLASS CTL TYPES
Q0, Q0A, Q0C, Q1, Q1A AND Q0T
BRANCH CIRCUIT BREAKERS, QOM2 MAIN
CIRCUIT BREAKER AND REPLACEMENT
PARTS WITH THIS PRODUCT. USE OF
OTHER COMPONENTS VOIDS THE WARRANTY,
MAY VOID THE UL LISTING AND MAY
RESULT IN PROPERTY LOSS OR
PERSONAL INJURY.

Figure 110-9. Examples of termination temperature markings on a circuit breaker and panelboard. (Square D Co.)

to permit ready and safe operation and maintenance of such equipment.

(a) **Working Clearances.** Except as elsewhere required or permitted in this Code, the dimension of the working space in the direction of access to live parts operating at 600 volts, nominal, or less to ground and likely to require examination, adjustment, servicing, or maintenance while energized shall not be less than indicated in Table 110-16(a). Distances shall be measured from the live parts if such are exposed or from the enclosure front or opening if such are enclosed. Concrete, brick, or tile walls shall be considered as grounded.

Table 110-16(a). Working Clearances

Voltage to Ground, Nominal		Minimum Clear Distance (feet)		
	Condition:	1	2	3
0-150		3	3	3
151-600		3	3 1/2	4

For SI units: one inch = 25.4 millimeters; one foot = 0.3048 meter.

In addition to the dimensions shown in Table 110-16(a), the work space shall not be less than 30 inches (762 mm) wide in front of the electric equipment. The work space shall be clear and extend from the floor or platform to the height required by this section. In all cases, the work space shall permit at least a 90-degree opening of equipment doors or hinged panels.

Note that the 30-inch wide dimension is intended to be clear all the way to the floor or platform. See new (FPN No. 4) following Section 384-4 and Figures 110-10 and 110-11.

These requirements apply to equipment that is likely to require examination, adjustment, servicing, or maintenance. Some examples of such equipment include panelboards, switches, circuit breakers, controllers, and controls on heating and air conditioning equipment.

The equipment must not be installed so close to walls, etc., that the equipment door or hinged panel cannot open at least 90°. Where the doors or hinged panels are wider than 3 feet, more than a 3-foot wide work space must be provided. Sufficient depth in the work space must be provided to allow the panel or door to open 90°. See Figure 110-10.

The minimum working clearances of Section 110-16(a) are not required if the equipment is such that it is not likely to require examination, adjustment, servicing, or maintenance while energized. However "sufficient" access and working space is still required by the first paragraph of Section 110-16. Also, see commentary following Section 384-4. Examples of equipment that do not require these clearances include junction boxes and some terminal boxes.

Figure 110-10. *Equipment doors are required to open a full 90° to ensure a safe working space.*

Where the "Conditions" are as follows:

1. Exposed live parts on one side and no live or grounded parts on the other side of the working space, or exposed live parts on both sides effectively guarded by suitable wood or other insulating materials. Insulated wire or insulated busbars operating at not over 300 volts shall not be considered live parts.

2. Exposed live parts on one side and grounded parts on the other side.

3. Exposed live parts on both sides of the work space (not guarded as provided in Condition 1) with the operator between.

Exception No. 1: Working space shall not be required in back of assemblies such as dead-front switchboards, or motor control centers where there are no renewable or adjustable parts such as fuses or switches on the back and where all connections are accessible from locations other than the back.

Exception No. 2: By special permission, smaller spaces may be permitted (1) where it is judged that the particular arrangement of the installation will provide adequate accessibility or (2) where all uninsulated parts are at a voltage no greater than 30 volts RMS, 42 volts peak, or 60 volts dc.

(b) Clear Spaces. Working space required by this section shall not be used for storage. When normally enclosed live parts are exposed for inspection or servicing, the working space, if in a passageway or general open space, shall be suitably guarded.

(c) Access and Entrance to Working Space. At least one entrance of sufficient area shall be provided to give access to the working space about electric equipment.

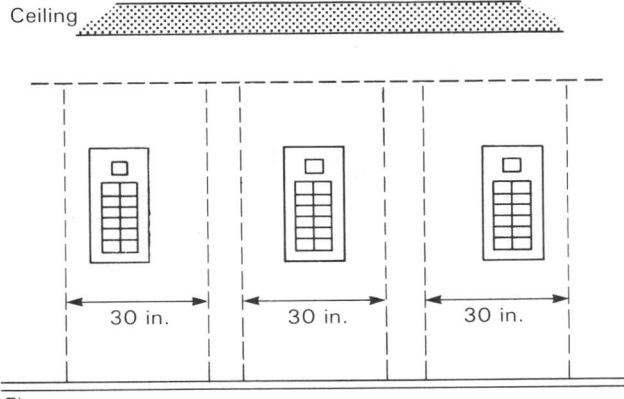

Figure 110-11. *The 30-inch wide front working space is not required to be directly centered on the electrical equipment where it can be assured that the space is sufficient for safe operation and maintenance of such equipment.*

For equipment rated 1200 amperes or more and over 6 ft (1.83 m) wide, containing overcurrent devices, switching devices, or control devices, there shall be one entrance not less than 24 inches (610 mm) wide and 6½ feet (1.98 m) high at each end.

Prior to the 1990 *Code,* the second paragraph of Section 110-16(c) applied only to switchboards and control panels. The paragraph was revised to apply to any equipment rated 1,200 amperes or more and, in addition, 6 feet or more in length if the equipment contains overcurrent devices, switching devices, or control devices.

Exception No. 1: Where the location permits a continuous and unobstructed way of exit travel.

Condition 1. Space would remain at 3 feet for 151–600 volts.

Condition 2. Space would increase to 3½ feet for 151–600 volts.

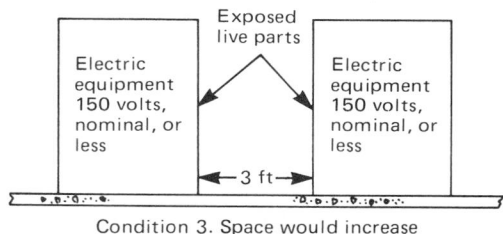

Condition 3. Space would increase to 4 feet for 151–600 volts.

Figure 110-12. *Distances are measured from the live parts if such are exposed or from the enclosure front if live parts are enclosed. If any assemblies, such as switchboards or motor-control centers, are accessible from the back and expose live parts, the working clearance dimensions would be required at the rear of the equipment as illustrated above. Note: For condition 3 where there is an enclosure on opposite sides of the work space, the clearance for only ONE work space is required.*

See Figure 110-16.

Exception No. 2: Where the work space required by Section 110-16(a) is doubled, only one entrance to the working space is required.

Working space with one entrance provided shall be so located that the edge of the entrance nearest the equipment is the

Figure 110-13. *Section 110-16(c), Basic Rule, first paragraph. At least one entrance is required to provide access to the working space around electric equipment. The installation shown in the sketch on the bottom would not be acceptable if the electric equipment was a switchboard over 6 feet wide and rated 1,200 amperes or more.*

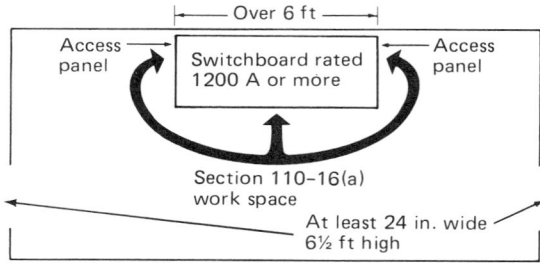

Figure 110-14. *Section 110-16(c), Basic Rule, second paragraph. For equipment rated 1,200 amperes or more, and over 6 feet wide, one entrance not less than 24 inches wide and 6½ feet high is required at each end.*

minimum clear distance given in Table 110-16(a) away from such equipment.

See Figure 110-17.

(d) Front Working Space. In all cases where there are live parts normally exposed on the front of switchboards or motor

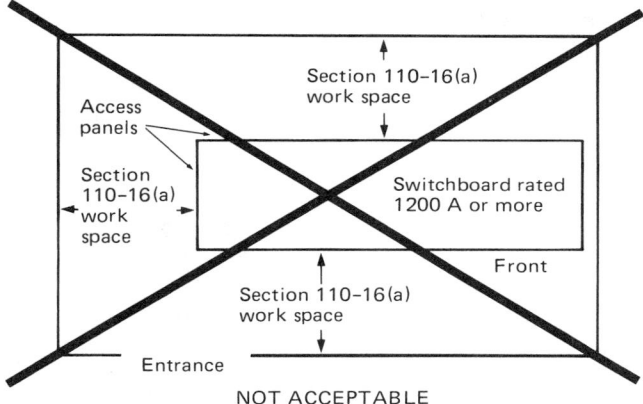

Figure 110-15. *Unacceptable arrangement of large switchboard. A person could be trapped behind arcing electric equipment.*

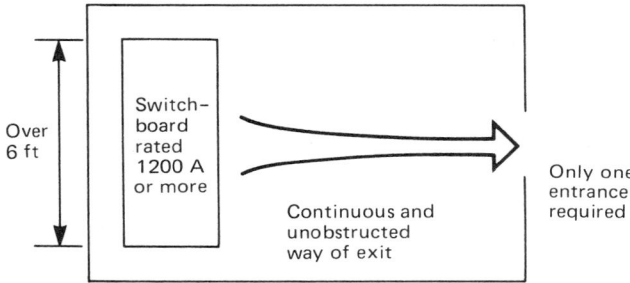

Figure 110-16. *Where the equipment location permits a continuous and unobstructed way of exit travel.*

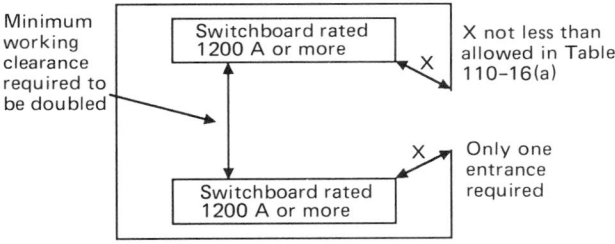

Figure 110-17. *Where the work space required by Section 110-16(a) is doubled, only one entrance to the working space is required.*

control centers, the working space in front of such equipment shall not be less than 3 feet (914 mm).

(e) Illumination. Illumination shall be provided for all working spaces about service equipment, switchboards, panelboards, or motor control centers installed indoors.

(FPN): Additional lighting fixtures are not intended where the workspace is illuminated by an adjacent light source.

(f) Headroom. The minimum headroom of working spaces about service equipment, switchboards, panelboards, or motor control centers shall be 6½ feet (1.98 m).

See commentary on Section 384-4. Note the increase in headroom in the 1993 *Code* from 6¼ feet to 6½ feet.

Exception: Service equipment or panelboards, in existing dwelling units, that do not exceed 200 amperes.

(FPN No. 1): For higher voltages, see Article 710.

(FPN No. 2): As used in this section, a motor control center is an assembly of one or more enclosed sections having a common power bus and principally containing motor control units.

110-17. Guarding of Live Parts (600 Volts, Nominal, or Less).

(a) Live Parts Guarded Against Accidental Contact. Except as elsewhere required or permitted by this Code, live parts of electric equipment operating at 50 volts or more shall be guarded against accidental contact by approved enclosures or by any of the following:

(1) By location in a room, vault, or similar enclosure that is accessible only to qualified persons.

(2) By suitable permanent, substantial partitions or screens so arranged that only qualified persons will have access to the space within reach of the live parts. Any openings in such partitions or screens shall be so sized and located that persons are not likely to come into accidental contact with the live parts or to bring conducting objects into contact with them.

(3) By location on a suitable balcony, gallery, or platform so elevated and arranged as to exclude unqualified persons.

(4) By elevation of 8 feet (2.44 m) or more above the floor or other working surface.

For example, see the requirements of Sections 610-13, Exception No. 2 and 610-21(a). Although contact conductors obviously have to be bare in order for contact shoes on the moving member to make contact with the conductor, it is possible to place guards near the conductor to prevent its accidental contact with persons and still have slots or spaces through which the moving contacts can operate. Note that the *Code* also recognizes the guarding of live parts by elevation.

(b) Prevent Physical Damage. In locations where electric equipment would be exposed to physical damage, enclosures or guards shall be so arranged and of such strength as to prevent such damage.

(c) Warning Signs. Entrances to rooms and other guarded locations containing exposed live parts shall be marked with conspicuous warning signs forbidding unqualified persons to enter.

(FPN):   For motors, see Sections 430-132 and 430-133. For over 600 volts, see Section 110-34.

Live parts of electric equipment should be covered, shielded, enclosed, or otherwise protected by covers, barriers, mats, or platforms to prevent the likelihood of contact by persons or objects. See definitions for "Dead Front," "Guarded," and "Isolated" in Article 100.

110-18. **Arcing Parts.** Parts of electric equipment which in ordinary operation produce arcs, sparks, flames, or molten metal shall be enclosed or separated and isolated from all combustible material.

(FPN):   For hazardous (classified) locations, see Articles 500 through 517. For motors, see Section 430-14.

An example of electric equipment that produces sparks during "ordinary" operation is an open motor having commutators or collector rings. Adequate separation from combustible material is necessary where open motors are used.

110-19. **Light and Power from Railway Conductors.** Circuits for lighting and power shall not be connected to any system containing trolley wires with a ground return.

Exception: Car houses, power houses, or passenger and freight stations operated in connection with electric railways.

110-21. **Marking.** The manufacturer's name, trademark, or other descriptive marking by which the organization responsible for the product may be identified shall be placed on all electric equipment. Other markings shall be provided indicating voltage, current, wattage, or other ratings as are specified elsewhere in this Code. The marking shall be of sufficient durability to withstand the environment involved.

The *Code* requires that the rating of equipment be marked on the equipment and that such markings be located so as to be visible or easily accessible during or after installation.

110-22. **Identification of Disconnecting Means.** Each disconnecting means required by this Code for motors and appliances, and each service, feeder, or branch circuit at the point where it originates, shall be legibly marked to indicate its purpose unless located and arranged so the purpose is evident. The marking shall be of sufficient durability to withstand the environment involved.

Where circuit breakers or fuses are applied in compliance with the series combination ratings marked on the equipment by the manufacturer, the equipment enclosure(s) shall be legibly marked in the field to indicate the equipment has been applied with a series combination rating. The marking shall be readily visible and state "Caution — Series Rated System A Available. Identified Replacement Component Required."

(FPN):   See Section 240-83(c) for interrupting rating marking for end-use equipment.

Note that proper identification is to be specific. For example, the marking is not merely to indicate "motor," but rather "motor, water pump"; not merely "lights," but rather "lights, front lobby." Consideration should also be given to the form of identification. Marking often fades or is covered by paint after installation.

The second paragraph requires series rated overcurrent devices to be legibly marked. The equipment manufacturer can mark the equipment that may be used with series combination ratings. If the installer installs equipment in the field at its marked series combination rating, the equipment must have an additional label as specified in this section to indicate that the series combination rating has been utilized.

B. Over 600 Volts, Nominal

110-30. **General.** Conductors and equipment used on circuits over 600 volts, nominal, shall comply with all applicable provisions of the preceding sections of this article and with the following sections, which supplement or modify the preceding sections. In no case shall the provisions of this part apply to equipment on the supply side of the service conductors.

See "Over 600 Volts" in the Index for various articles, sections, and parts that include requirements for installations over 600 volts.

Equipment on the supply side of service conductors is outside of the scope of the *National Electrical Code*. Such equipment is covered by the National Electrical Safety Code (ANSI C2), published by the Institute of Electrical and Electronic Engineers (IEEE).

110-31. Enclosure for Electrical Installations. Electrical installations in a vault, room, or closet or in an area surrounded by a wall, screen, or fence, access to which is controlled by lock and key or other approved means, shall be considered to be accessible to qualified persons only. The type of enclosure used in a given case shall be designed and constructed according to the nature and degree of the hazard(s) associated with the installation.

A wall, screen, or fence shall be used to enclose an outdoor electrical installation to deter access by persons who are not qualified. A fence shall not be less than 7 feet (2.13 m) in height.

(FPN No. 1): Article 450 covers minimum construction requirements for transformer vaults.

(FPN No. 2): Isolation by elevation is covered in paragraph (b) of this section and in Section 110-34.

(FPN No. 3): A fence made of a combination of 6 feet (1.80 m) or more of fence fabric and a 1-foot (300-mm) or more extension utilizing three or more strands of barbed wire is equivalent to a 7-foot (2.13-m) fence.

(a) **Indoor Installations.**

(1) **In Places Accessible to Unqualified Persons.** Indoor electrical installations that are open to unqualified persons shall be made with metal-enclosed equipment or shall be enclosed in a vault or in an area access to which is controlled by a lock. Metal-enclosed switchgear, unit substations, transformers, pull boxes, connection boxes, and other similar associated equipment shall be marked with appropriate caution signs. Openings in ventilated dry-type transformers or similar openings in other equipment shall be designed so that foreign objects inserted through these openings will be deflected from energized parts.

(2) **In Places Accessible to Qualified Persons Only.** Indoor electrical installations considered accessible to qualified persons only in accordance with this section shall comply with Sections 110-34, 710-32, and 710-33.

(b) **Outdoor Installations.**

(1) **In Places Accessible to Unqualified Persons.** Outdoor electrical installations that are open to unqualified persons shall comply with Article 225.

(FPN): For clearances of conductors for system voltages over 600 volts, nominal, see National Electrical Safety Code, ANSI C2-1990.

(2) **In Places Accessible to Qualified Persons Only.** Outdoor electrical installations having exposed live parts shall be accessible to qualified persons only in accordance with the first paragraph of this section and shall comply with Sections 110-34, 710-32, and 710-33.

(c) **Metal-Enclosed Equipment Accessible to Unqualified Persons.** Ventilating or similar openings in equipment shall be so designed that foreign objects inserted through these openings will be deflected from energized parts. Where exposed to physical damage from vehicular traffic, suitable guards shall be provided. Metal-enclosed equipment located outdoors and accessible to the general public shall be designed so that exposed nuts or bolts cannot be readily removed, permitting access to live parts. Where metal-enclosed equipment is accessible to the general public and the bottom of the enclosure is less than 8 feet (2.44 m) above the floor or grade level, the enclosure door or hinged cover shall be kept locked.

110-32. Work Space about Equipment. Sufficient space shall be provided and maintained about electric equipment to permit ready and safe operation and maintenance of such equipment. Where energized parts are exposed, the minimum clear work space shall not be less than 6½ feet (1.98 m) high (measured vertically from the floor or platform), or less than 3 feet (914 mm) wide (measured parallel to the equipment). The depth shall be as required in Section 110-34(a). In all cases, the work space shall be adequate to permit at least a 90-degree opening of doors or hinged panels.

110-33. Entrance and Access to Work Space.

(a) **Entrance.** At least one entrance not less than 24 inches (610 mm) wide and 6½ feet (1.98 m) high shall be provided to give access to the working space about electric equipment.

On switchboard and control panels exceeding 6 feet (1.83 m) in width, there shall be one entrance at each end of such board.

Section 110-33(a) coordinates with Section 110-16(c). See commentary following Section 110-16(c). However, because of the high voltages involved, Section 110-33(a) includes minimum work space entrance dimensions, even for switchboards 6 feet or less in width.

Exception No. 1: Where the switchboards and control panels location permits a continuous and unobstructed way of exit travel.

See commentary following Section 110-16(c), Exception No. 1.

Exception No. 2: Where the work space required in Section 110-34(a) is doubled.

Working space with one entrance provided shall be so located that the edge of the entrance nearest the switchboards and control panels is the minimum clear distance given in Table 110-34(a) away from such equipment.

See commentary following Section 110-16(c), Exception No. 2.

Where bare energized parts at any voltage or insulated energized parts above 600 volts, nominal, to ground are located adjacent to such entrance, they shall be suitably guarded.

(b) Access. Permanent ladders or stairways shall be provided to give safe access to the working space around electric equipment installed on platforms, balconies, mezzanine floors, or in attic or roof rooms or spaces.

110-34. Work Space and Guarding.

(a) Working Space. The minimum clear working space in front of electric equipment such as switchboards, control panels, switches, circuit breakers, motor controllers, relays, and similar equipment shall not be less than specified in Table 110-34(a) unless otherwise specified in this Code. Distances shall be measured from the live parts, if such are exposed, or from the enclosure front or opening if such are enclosed.

Table 110-34(a). Minimum Depth of Clear Working Space in Front of Electric Equipment

Nominal Voltage to Ground	Conditions		
	1	2	3
	(Feet)	(Feet)	(Feet)
601-2500	3	4	5
2501-9000	4	5	6
9001-25,000	5	6	9
25,001-75 kV	6	8	10
Above 75 kV	8	10	12

For SI units: one foot = 0.3048 meter.

Where the "Conditions" are as follows:

1. Exposed live parts on one side and no live or grounded parts on the other side of the working space or exposed live parts on both sides effectively guarded by suitable wood or other insulating materials. Insulated wire or insulated busbars operating at not over 300 volts shall not be considered live parts.

2. Exposed live parts on one side and grounded parts on the other side. Concrete, brick, or tile walls will be considered as grounded surfaces.

3. Exposed live parts on both sides of the work space (not guarded as provided in Condition 1) with the operator between.

Exception: Working space is not required in back of equipment such as dead-front switchboards or control assemblies where there are no renewable or adjustable parts (such as fuses or switches) on the back and where all connections are accessible from locations other than the back. Where rear access is required to work on deenergized parts on the back of enclosed equipment, a minimum working space of 30 inches (762 mm) horizontally shall be provided.

(b) Separation from Low-Voltage Equipment. Where switches, cutouts, or other equipment operating at 600 volts, nominal, or less, are installed in a room or enclosure where there are exposed live parts or exposed wiring operating at over 600 volts, nominal, the high-voltage equipment shall be effectively separated from the space occupied by the low-voltage equipment by a suitable partition, fence, or screen.

Exception: Switches or other equipment operating at 600 volts, nominal, or less, and serving only equipment within the high-voltage vault, room, or enclosure shall be permitted to be installed in the high-voltage enclosure, room, or vault if accessible to qualified persons only.

(c) Locked Rooms or Enclosures. The entrances to all buildings, rooms, or enclosures containing exposed live parts or exposed conductors operating at over 600 volts, nominal, shall be kept locked.

Exception: Where such entrances are under the observation of a qualified person at all times.

Equipment used on circuits over 600 volts, nominal, containing exposed live parts or exposed conductors is required to be located in a locked room or enclosure. The provisions for locking are not required where the location is under observation at all times, as in the case of some engine rooms.

Where the voltage exceeds 600 volts, nominal, permanent and conspicuous warning signs shall be provided, reading substantially as follows: "Danger—High Voltage—Keep Out."

(d) Illumination. Adequate illumination shall be provided for all working spaces about electrical equipment. The lighting out-lets shall be so arranged that persons changing lamps or making repairs on the lighting system will not be endangered by live parts or other equipment.

The points of control shall be so located that persons are not likely to come in contact with any live part or moving part of the equipment while turning on the lights.

(e) Elevation of Unguarded Live Parts. Unguarded live parts above working space shall be maintained at elevations not less than required by Table 110-34(e).

Table 110-34(e).   Elevation of Unguarded Live Parts above Working Space

Nominal Voltage Between Phases	Elevation
1001-7500	8'6"
7501-35,000	9'
Over 35kV	9' + 0.37" per kV above 35

For SI units: one inch = 25.4 millimeters; one foot = 0.3048 meter.

2

Wiring and Protection

Contents

200-1. **Scope.** This article provides requirements for (1) identification of terminals; (2) grounded conductors in premises wiring systems; and (3) identification of grounded conductors.

(FPN): See Article 100 for definitions of "Grounded Conductor" and "Grounding Conductor."

200-2. **General.** All premises wiring systems shall have a grounded conductor that is identified in accordance with Section 200-6.

Exception: Circuits and systems exempted or prohibited by Sections 210-10, 215-7, 250-3, 250-5, 250-7, 503-13, 517-63, 668-11, 668-21, and 690-41, Exception.

Isolated circuits are required in flammable anesthetizing locations. The ungrounded conductors of these circuits are colored orange and brown (for 3-phase systems, the third conductor is yellow) and are provided with a continually operating "line isolation monitor." See Sections 517-63, 517-160, and NFPA 99-1990, *Standard for Health Care Facilities.* Isolated circuits are also required if interruption of power cannot be tolerated. See Section 517-20.

In some installations, the colors brown, orange, and yellow may be used to identify grounded 480Y/277 volt systems in other than health care facilities.

The grounded conductor, where insulated, shall have insulation (1) that is suitable, other than color, for any ungrounded conductor of the same circuit on circuits of less than 1000 volts, or (2) rated not less than 600 volts for solidly grounded neutral systems of 1 kV and over as described in Section 250-152(a).

200-3. **Connection to Grounded System.** Premises wiring shall not be electrically connected to a supply system unless the latter contains, for any grounded conductor of the interior system, a corresponding conductor that is grounded.

For the purpose of this section, "electrically connected" shall mean connected so as to be capable of carrying current as distinguished from connection through electromagnetic induction.

Grounded conductors of premises wiring (other than separately derived systems) are required to be connected to the supply system grounded conductor to ensure a common, continuous, grounded system.

200-6. **Means of Identifying Grounded Conductors.**

(a) Sizes No. 6 or Smaller. An insulated grounded conductor of No. 6 or smaller shall be identified by a continuous white or natural gray outer finish along its entire length.

Exception No. 1: Multiconductor varnished-cloth-insulated cables.

Exception No. 2: Fixture wires as outlined in Article 402.

Exception No. 3: Where the conditions of maintenance and supervision assure that only qualified persons will service the installation, grounded conductors in multiconductor cables shall be permitted to be permanently identified at their terminations at the time of installation by a distinctive white marking or other equally effective means.

Exception No. 4: The grounded conductor of a mineral-insulated, metal-sheathed cable shall be identified at the time of installation by distinctive marking at its terminations.

For aerial cable, the identification shall be as above, or by means of a ridge so located on the exterior of the cable as to identify it.

Wires having their outer covering finished to show a white or natural gray color but having colored tracer threads in the braid,

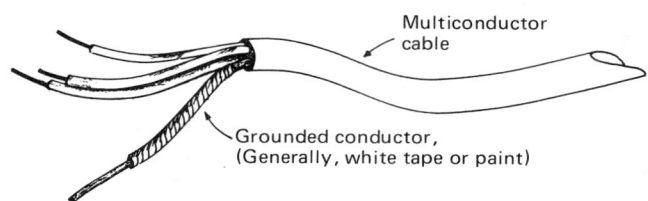

Figure 200-1. The grounded conductor of a multiconductor cable is permitted to be identified at the time of installation by qualified persons, generally in commercial or industrial locations where supervision and maintenance are assured. This method is permitted for all sizes of conductors of multiconductor cables. See Section 200-6(b), Exception for conductors larger than No. 6.

identifying the source of manufacture, shall be considered as meeting the provisions of this section.

(b) Sizes Larger than No. 6. An insulated grounded conductor larger than No. 6 shall be identified either by a continuous white or natural gray outer finish along its entire length or at the time of installation by a distinctive white marking at its terminations. Multiconductor flat cable No. 4 or larger shall be permitted to employ an external ridge on the grounded conductor.

See Figure 200-2.

Figure 200-2. Conductors are required to be white or natural gray for their entire length or identified at terminations as shown above. The term "larger than No. 6" in Section 200-6(b) applies to all conductor materials including multiconductor flat cable No. 4 or larger, which is permitted to employ an external ridge to identify the grounded conductor.

Exception: Where the conditions of maintenance and supervision assure that only qualified persons will service the installation, grounded conductors in multiconductor cables shall be permitted to be permanently identified at their terminations at the time of installation by a distinctive white marking or other equally effective means.

(c) Flexible Cords. An insulated conductor intended for use as a grounded conductor, where contained within a flexible cord, shall be identified by a white or natural gray outer finish or by methods permitted by Section 400-22.

(d) Grounded Conductors of Different Systems. Where conductors of different systems are installed in the same raceway, box, auxiliary gutter, or other type of enclosure, one system grounded conductor, if required, shall have an outer covering conforming to Section 200-6(a) or (b). Each other system grounded conductor, if required, shall have an outer covering of white with an identifiable colored stripe (not green) running along the insulation, or other and different means of identification as allowed by Section 200-6(a) or (b).

This section corresponds to Section 210-5(a) and applies in general to all grounded conductors including feeder conductors. See Figure 210-4.

Article 200 contains the grounded circuit identification requirements. The grounded circuit conductor is referred to throughout the *Code* as the "grounded conductor." It is often, but not always (as in corner-grounded delta systems), the neutral conductor.

Section 215-8, which covers 3-phase, 4-wire, delta-connected systems with the midpoint of one phase grounded, requires that the conductor with the higher phase-to-ground voltage be identified by the color orange, by tagging, or by some other effective means at every point of connection where the grounded conductor is also present. The high leg of 120/240 V 4-wire, 3-phase, delta systems is 208 V to ground (120 V /d 1.73).

Section 200-6(a) and (b) contains exceptions introducing a concept for identifying grounded conductors of multiconductor cables. These exceptions allow the identification of conductors at the time of installation by the use of a distinctive white marking or other equally effective means. A variety of other schemes that are equally effective include numbering, lettering, or tagging. These exceptions are intended to apply in locations where a regulated system of maintenance and supervision ensures that only qualified persons will service the installation.

For the identification of branch-circuit conductors, see Sections 210-4(d) and 210-5. For the identification of the high leg (delta-system) conductor, see Sections 215-8, 230-56, and 384-3(e).

200-7. **Use of White or Natural Gray Color.** A continuous white or natural gray covering on a conductor or a termination marking of white or natural gray color shall be used only for the grounded conductor.

Exception No. 1: An insulated conductor with a white or natural gray finish shall be permitted as an ungrounded conductor where permanently reidentified to indicate its use, by painting or other effective means at its termination, and at each location where the conductor is visible and accessible.

Exception No. 2: A cable containing an insulated conductor with a white or natural gray outer finish shall be permitted for single-pole, 3-way, or 4-way switch loops where the white or natural gray conductor is used for the supply to the switch, but not as a return conductor from the switch to the switched outlet. In these applications, reidentification of the white or natural gray conductor shall not be required.

Exception No. 3: A flexible cord for connecting an appliance, having one conductor identified by a white or natural gray outer finish or by any other means permitted by Section 400-22, shall be permitted whether or not the outlet to which it is connected is supplied by a circuit having a grounded conductor.

Exception No. 4: A white or natural gray conductor of circuits of less than 50 volts shall be required to be grounded only as required by Section 250-5(a).

200-9. **Means of Identification of Terminals.** The identification of terminals to which a grounded conductor is to be connected shall be substantially white in color, The identification of other terminals shall be of a readily distinguishable different color.

Exception: Where the conditions of maintenance and supervision assure that only qualified persons will service the installations, terminals for grounded conductors shall be permitted to be permanently identified at the time of installation by a distinctive white marking or other equally effective means.

See the commentary following Section 200-6.

200-10. **Identification of Terminals.**

(a) Device Terminals. All devices provided with terminals for the attachment of conductors and intended for connection to more than one side of the circuit shall have terminals properly marked for identification.

Exception No. 1: Where the electrical connection of a terminal intended to be connected to the grounded conductor is clearly evident.

Exception No. 2: The terminals of lighting and appliance branch-circuit panelboards.

Exception No. 3: Devices having a normal current rating of over 30 amperes other than polarized attachment plugs and polarized receptacles for attachment plugs as required in Section 200-10(b).

(b) Receptacles, Plugs, and Connectors. Receptacles, polarized attachment plugs and cord connectors for plugs and polarized plugs shall have the terminal intended for connection to the grounded (white) conductor identified.

Identification shall be by a metal or metal coating substantially white in color or the word "white" located adjacent to the identified terminal.

This paragraph permits the identification of the terminal for the grounded conductor by use of the word "white." It also permits the terminal to be otherwise identified by a distinctive white color on all devices, including those with binding head screws. These permitted methods allow plating of all screws and terminals to meet requirements of specific applications, such as corrosion-resistant devices.

If the terminal is not visible, the conductor entrance hole for the connection shall be colored white or marked with the word "white."

Exception: Terminal identification shall not be required for 2-wire nonpolarized attachment plugs.

(FPN): See Section 250-119 for identification of wiring device equipment grounding conductor terminals.

This exception coordinates with Section 410-42(a) and makes it clear that two-wire nonpolarized attachment plugs are not required to have the grounded terminal identified.

(c) Screw Shells. For devices with screw shells, the terminal for the grounded conductor shall be the one connected to the screw shell.

(d) Screw-Shell Devices with Leads. For screw-shell devices with attached leads, the conductor attached to the screw shell shall have a white or natural gray finish. The outer finish of the other conductor shall be of a solid color that will not be confused with the white or natural gray finish used to identify the grounded conductor.

(e) Appliances. Appliances that have a single-pole switch or a single-pole overcurrent device in the line or any line-connected screw-shell lampholders, and that are to be connected (1) by permanent wiring methods; or (2) by field-installed attachment plugs and cords with three or more wires (including the equipment grounding conductor) shall have means to identify the terminal for the grounded circuit conductor (if any).

The means for identifying the terminal for the grounded conductor may be by metal or metal coating substantially white in color or by the word "white" located adjacent to the terminal to be so identified. It may also be identified by marking on a wiring diagram.

200-11. **Polarity of Connections.** No grounded conductor shall be attached to any terminal or lead so as to reverse designated polarity.

ARTICLE 210   Branch Circuits

Contents

A. General Provisions

A. General Provisions

210-1. **Scope.** This article covers branch circuits except for branch circuits that supply only motor loads, which are covered in Article 430. Provisions of this article and Article 430 apply to branch circuits with combination loads.

Exception: Branch circuits for electrolytic cells as covered in Section 668-3(c), Exception Nos. 1 and 4.

Section 668-3(c), Exception Nos. 1 and 4 indicate that electrolytic cell line conductors, cells, cell line attachments, and the wiring of auxiliary equipment and devices within the cell line working zone are not required to comply with the provisions of Article 210.

210-2. **Other Articles for Specific-Purpose Branch Circuits.** Branch circuits shall comply with this article and also with the applicable provisions of other articles of this Code. The provisions for branch circuits supplying equipment in the following list amend or supplement the provisions in this article and shall apply to branch circuits referred to therein:

	Article	Section
Air-Conditioning and Refrigerating Equipment		440-6
		440-31
		440-32
Busways		364-9
Circuits and Equipment Operating at Less than 50 Volts	720	
Central Heating Equipment Other than Fixed Electric Space Heating Equipment		422-7

	Article	Section
Class 1, Class 2, and Class 3 Remote-Control, Signaling, and Power-Limited Circuits	725	
Closed-Loop and Programmed Power Distribution	780	
Cranes and Hoists		610-42
Electronic Computer/Data Processing Equipment		645-5
Electric Signs and Outline Lighting		600-6
Electric Welders	630	
Elevators, Dumbwaiters, Escalators, Moving Walks, Wheelchair Lifts, and Stairway Chair Lifts		620-61
Fire Protective Signaling Systems	760	
Fixed Electric Space Heating Equipment		424-3
Fixed Outdoor Electric Deicing and Snow-Melting Equipment		426-4
Infrared Lamp Industrial Heating Equipment		422-15 424-3
Induction and Dielectric Heating Equipment	665	
Marinas and Boatyards		555-4
Mobile Homes and Mobile Home Parks	550	
Motion Picture and Television Studios and Similar Locations	530	
Motors, Motor Circuits, and Controllers	430	
Pipe Organs		650-6
Recreational Vehicles and Recreational Vehicle Parks	551	
Sound-Recording and Similar Equipment		640-6
Switchboards and Panelboards		384-32
Theaters, Audience Areas of Motion Picture and Television Studios, and Similar Locations		520-41 520-52 520-62
X-Ray Equipment		660-2 517-73

210-3. Rating. Branch circuits recognized by this article shall be rated in accordance with the maximum permitted ampere rating or setting of the overcurrent device. The rating for other than

individual branch circuits shall be: 15, 20, 30, 40, and 50 amperes. Where conductors of higher ampacity are used for any reason, the ampere rating or setting of the specified overcurrent device shall determine the circuit rating.

Conductors of higher ampacity may be necessary to compensate for voltage drop. For example, a branch circuit of No. 10 AWG Type TW copper conductors with a 30-ampere ampacity protected by a 20-ampere overcurrent device is rated as a 20-ampere branch circuit.

Exception: Multioutlet branch circuits greater than 50 amperes shall be permitted to supply nonlighting outlet loads on industrial premises where maintenance and supervision indicate that qualified persons will service equipment.

It is common in industrial establishments to provide several single receptacles of 50-ampere or higher rating on a single branch circuit to allow quick relocation of equipment for production and/or maintenance use, such as in the case of electric welders. Generally, only one piece of equipment is operated at a time. The type of receptacle used is generally of the non-ANSI-type configuration, known as a pin-and-sleeve receptacle, although the *Code* does not so limit the design. These receptacles may or may not be horsepower rated.

210-4. Multiwire Branch Circuits.

(a) General. Branch circuits recognized by this article shall be permitted as multiwire circuits. A multiwire branch circuit shall be permitted to be considered as multiple circuits. All conductors shall originate from the same panelboard.

(FPN): A 3-phase, 4-wire power system used to supply power to computer systems or other similar electronic loads may necessitate that the power system design allow for the possibility of high harmonic neutral currents.

The power supplies for equipment such as computers, printers, and variable speed motor drives may introduce third and higher order integral harmonic currents in the system neutral conductor. The total harmonic distortion current that results can exceed the load current of the device itself.

(b) Dwelling Units. In dwelling units, a multiwire branch circuit supplying more than one device or equipment on the same yoke shall be provided with a means to disconnect simultaneously all ungrounded conductors at the panelboard where the branch circuit originated.

A "device" is defined in Article 100 as "a unit of an electrical system that is intended to carry but not utilize electric energy." The term "device" includes receptacles, switches, and lampholders. These are the three types of devices normally used on dwelling unit switch-and-receptacle yokes. The term "or equipment" includes such items as pilot lights, which do utilize electric energy.

Many 125-volt, 15- and 20-ampere duplex receptacles have a break-off tab (Section 210-4) that permits each of the two receptacles to be supplied from a different polarity and the single grounded conductor of a 3-wire (multiwire) branch circuit. This is commonly called a "split-wired" receptacle, i.e., one half of the duplex receptacle is supplied by one circuit and the other half on another circuit. The simultaneous opening of both "hot" conductors at the panelboard will effectively protect personnel from inadvertent contact with an energized conductor or device terminal. The simultaneous disconnection can be secured by a 2-pole circuit breaker or by two single-pole circuit breakers with a handle tie. Where fuses are used, a 2-pole disconnect switch is required. See Figure 210-1.

Figure 210-1. These multiwire branch circuits supply more than one device or equipment on the same yoke. For dwelling units, Section 210-4(b) requires simultaneous disconnection of all ungrounded conductors at the panelboard where the branch circuits originate. This can be accomplished with a 2-pole disconnect, handle ties, or a 2-pole circuit breaker.

(c) Line to Neutral Load. Multiwire branch circuits shall supply only line to neutral load.

Exception No. 1: A multiwire branch circuit that supplies only one utilization equipment.

Exception No. 2: Where all ungrounded conductors of the multiwire branch circuit are opened simultaneously by the branch-circuit overcurrent device.

(FPN): See Section 300-13(b) for continuity of grounded conductor on multiwire circuits.

Combination receptacle

Figure 210-2. Section 210-4(c) does not permit a multiwire branch circuit to supply other than line-to-neutral loads. However, Exception No. 2 permits line-to-line loads if the ungrounded conductors are opened simultaneously by the branch-circuit overcurrent device. See also Figure 210-1.

Article 100 defines "branch circuit, multiwire" as "two or more ungrounded conductors having a potential difference between them, and a grounded conductor having equal potential difference between it and each ungrounded conductor of the circuit and that is connected to the neutral or grounded conductor of the system."

The circuit most commonly used as a multiwire branch circuit consists of two ungrounded conductors and one grounded conductor supplied from a single-phase, 3-wire system. Multiwire branch circuits have many advantages, such as three wires doing the work of four (in place of two 2-wire circuits), less raceway fill, easier balancing and phasing of a system, and less voltage drop. See commentary following Section 215-2, FPN.

Other multiwire branch circuits are 3-phase, 4-wire; 2-phase, 3-wire; and 2-phase, 5-wire. It is always advisable to properly balance all multiwire branch circuits. See Section 220-4(d). In a 3-phase, 4-wire circuit, the neutral could be called upon to carry a current equal to that carried by each of the 3-phase conductors and should, therefore, be sized the same. The neutral for a 2-phase, 3-wire or 2-phase,

5-wire circuit must be sized to carry 140 percent of the ampere rating of the circuit. See Section 220-22. See commentary following Section 210-4(a), FPN.

Where loads are connected "line-to-line" (utilization equipment connected between two or three phases), 2-pole or 3-pole circuit breakers are required to disconnect all ungrounded conductors simultaneously. In testing 240-V equipment, it is quite possible not to realize that the circuit is still energized with 120 V if one overcurrent device is open. See Sections 210-10 and 240-20(b). Other precautions concerning device removal on multiwire branch circuits are found in the commentary following Section 300-13(b).

(d) Identification of Ungrounded Conductors. Where more than one nominal voltage system exists in a building, each ungrounded system conductor shall be identified by phase and system.

The means of identification shall be permanently posted at each branch-circuit panelboard.

(FPN): The means of identification of each system phase conductor, wherever accessible, may be by separate color coding, marking tape, tagging, or other equally effective means. See Sections 215-8, 230-56, and 384-3(e) for high leg marking.

See Figure 210-3.

210-5. Color Code for Branch Circuits.

(a) Grounded Conductor. The grounded conductor of a branch circuit shall be identified by a continuous white or natural gray color. Where conductors of different systems are installed in the same raceway, box, auxiliary gutter, or other types of enclosures, one system grounded conductor, if required, shall have an outer covering of white or natural gray. Each other system grounded conductor, if required, shall have an outer covering of white with an identifiable colored stripe (not green) running along the insulation or other and different means of identification.

See Figure 210-4.

Exception No. 1: The grounded conductors of mineral-insulated, metal-sheathed cable shall be identified by distinctive marking at the terminals during the process of installation.

See Figure 330-1 illustrating Type MI cable.

Figure 210-3. *An example of accessible phase conductors identified by marking tape. A notice indicating the means of identification has been permanently located at each panelboard. It should be noted that this requirement applies only to multiwire branch circuits.*

Figure 210-4. *Grounded conductors of different systems in the same enclosure.*

Exception No. 2: As permitted in Exception No. 3 of Section 200-6(a) and the Exception to Section 200-6(b).

See Figure 200-1 illustrating the identification of the grounded conductor of a multiconductor cable.

(b) Equipment Grounding Conductor. The equipment grounding conductor of a branch circuit shall be identified by a continuous green color or a continuous green color with one or more yellow stripes unless it is bare.

Exception No. 1: As permitted in Section 250-57(b), Exception Nos. 1 and 4 and Section 310-12(b), Exception Nos. 1 and 2.

Exception No. 2: The use of conductor insulation having a continuous green color or a continuous green color with one or more yellow stripes shall be permitted for internal wiring of equipment if such wiring does not serve as the lead wires for connection to branch-circuit conductors.

The color-coding requirements for grounded and grounding conductors are given in Section 210-5. Section 210-5(a) covers installations where more than one grounded branch-circuit conductor is carried in a raceway, box, or other enclosure. It requires that one grounded conductor have an outer covering of white or natural gray, and each other grounded conductor in the raceway, etc., where required, have an outer coloring of white with an identifiable colored stripe (not green) to provide a means of identifying the grounded conductors of each different system. See Section 200-6(d) for the equivalent requirement for other than branch-circuit conductors.

Although the *Code* does not require the use of specific colors for phase (ungrounded) conductors of a circuit, some means of identification is required. See Section 210-4(d). It is extremely important that multiwire branch circuits and their grounded circuit conductors (neutral conductors) be identified in the course of installation to ensure that the phase conductors are connected to the proper circuit breakers to avoid overloading the grounded circuit conductors.

210-6. Branch Circuit Voltage Limitations.

(a) Occupancy Limitation. In dwelling units and guest rooms of hotels, motels, and similar occupancies, the voltage shall not exceed 120 volts, nominal, between conductors that supply the terminals of:

"Similar occupancies" include sleeping rooms in dormitories, nursing homes, etc.

(1) Lighting fixtures.
(2) Cord- and plug-connected loads 1440 volt-amperes, nominal, or less, or less than 1/4 horsepower.

Small loads such as those of 1440 volt-amperes or less and motors of less than 1/4 horsepower are limited to 120-volt circuits. High wattage cord- and plug-connected loads

such as electric ranges, clothes dryers, and some window air conditioners are permitted to be connected to a 208-volt or 240-volt circuit.

(b) 120 Volts Between Conductors. Circuits not exceeding 120 volts, nominal, between conductors shall be permitted to supply:

(1) The terminals of medium-base screw-shell lampholders or lampholders of other types applied within their voltage ratings.

"Lampholders of other types" include fluorescent lampholders, screw-shell lampholders of the admedium- and mogul-base type, and special lampholders such as those intended for pin-type and blade-type lamp bases and those intended for tubular-type quartz-iodine (incandescent) lamps. See also commentary following Section 210-6(c)(2).

(2) Auxiliary equipment of electric-discharge lamps.

This includes ballasts for fluorescent and high-intensity-discharge (mercury vapor, etc.) lamps.

(3) Cord- and plug-connected or permanently connected utilization equipment.

(c) 277 Volts to Ground. Circuits exceeding 120 volts, nominal, between conductors and not exceeding 277 volts, nominal, to ground shall be permitted to supply:

(1) Listed electric-discharge lighting fixtures equipped with medium-base screw-shell lampholder.

Lighting fixtures equipped with smaller (intermediate-base, candelabra-base, etc.) screw-shell lampholders are not permitted to be connected to circuits exceeding 120 volts, nominal, to ground (480-volt and 277-volt circuits, for example). See Section 225-7(c) and (d) for additional restrictions for installation of outdoor lighting fixtures on 277-volt and 480-volt circuits. See Figure 210-5.

(2) Listed incandescent lighting fixtures equipped with medium-base screw-shell lampholder, where supplied at 120 volts or less from the output of a stepdown autotransformer that is an integral component of the fixture, and the outer screw-shell terminal is electrically connected to a grounded conductor of the branch circuit.

This section is new in the 1993 *NEC*. It permits a medium-base screw-shell incandescent fixture on 480Y/277V circuit. However, it must be a listed fixture that has an integral autotransformer. In this application, the autotransformer limits the voltage supplied to the screw shell to 120 volts. This application is similar to a branch-circuit derived from an autotransformer, except that the 120-volt circuit is internal wiring of the fixture.

(3) Lighting fixtures equipped with mogul-base screw-shell lampholders.

(4) Lampholders other than the screw-shell type applied within their voltage ratings.

(5) Auxiliary equipment of electric discharge lamps.

(6) Cord- and plug-connected or permanently connected utilization equipment.

The equipment listed above is permitted to be connected to circuits not exceeding 277 volts to ground. This includes 480-volt grounded systems in general; however, 480-volt corner grounded delta systems do not qualify. Typical examples of cord- and plug-connected equipment listed under item 6 are through-the-wall heating and air-conditioning units and restaurant fryolators operating at 480 volts, 3-phase from a grounded wye system.

(d) **600 Volts Between Conductors.** Circuits exceeding 277 volts, nominal, to ground and not exceeding 600 volts, nominal, between conductors shall be permitted to supply:

(1) The auxiliary equipment of electric-discharge lamps mounted in permanently installed fixtures where the fixtures are mounted in accordance with one of the following:

a. Not less than a height of 22 feet (6.71 m) on poles or similar structures for the illumination of outdoor areas, such as highways, roads, bridges, athletic fields, or parking lots.

b. Not less than a height of 18 feet (5.49 m) on other structures, such as tunnels.

Figure 210-5. Some examples of lighting units permitted to be connected to branch circuits. Medium-base screw-shell lampholders are not permitted to be directly connected to 277-volt branch circuits. Connecting the 277-volt branch circuit to a listed electric discharge fixture or a listed autotransformer-type incandescent fixture with a medium-base screw-shell lampholder is permitted.

See Figure 210-6.

(2) Cord- and plug-connected or permanently connected utilization equipment.

(FPN): See Section 410-78 for auxiliary equipment limitations.

Exception No. 1 to (b), (c), and (d) above: For lampholders of infrared industrial heating appliances as provided in Section 422-15(c).

Exception No. 2 to (b), (c), and (d) above: For railway properties as described in Section 110-19.

Figure 210-6. Minimum mounting heights are required to be maintained for circuits exceeding 277 volts to ground and not exceeding 600 volts between conductors where supplying auxiliary equipment of electric discharge lampholders.

210-7. Receptacles and Cord Connectors.

(a) Grounding Type. Receptacles installed on 15- and 20-ampere branch circuits shall be of the grounding type. Grounding-type receptacles shall be installed only on circuits of the voltage class and current for which they are rated, except as provided in Tables 210-21(b)(2) and (b)(3).

A single receptacle installed on an individual branch-circuit is required to have an ampere rating of not less than that of the branch-circuit. That is, a single receptacle on a 20-ampere circuit must be rated at 20 amperes; however, a 15-ampere duplex or two or more 15-ampere rated receptacles would be permitted on a 20-ampere general-purpose branch-circuit. See also Section 210-21.

Exception: Nongrounding-type receptacles installed in accordance with Section 210-7(d), Exception.

(b) To Be Grounded. Receptacles and cord connectors having grounding contacts shall have those contacts effectively grounded.

Exception No. 1: Receptacles mounted on portable and vehicle-mounted generators in accordance with Section 250-6.

Exception No. 2: Ground-fault circuit-interrupter replacement receptacles as permitted by Section 210-7(d), Exception.

See commentary following Section 210-7(d), Exception.

(c) Methods of Grounding. The grounding contacts of receptacles and cord connectors shall be grounded by connection to the equipment grounding conductor of the circuit supplying the receptacle or cord connector.

(FPN): For installation requirements for the reduction of electrical noise, see Section 250-74, Exception No. 4.

The branch circuit wiring method shall include or provide an equipment grounding conductor to which the grounding contacts of the receptacle or cord connector shall be connected.

(FPN No. 1): Section 250-91(b) describes acceptable grounding means.

(FPN No. 2): For extensions of existing branch circuits, see Section 250-50.

(d) Replacements. Grounding-type receptacles shall be used as replacements for existing nongrounding types and shall be connected to a grounding conductor installed in accordance with Section 210-7(c).

Ground-fault circuit-interrupter protected receptacles shall be provided where replacements are made at receptacle outlets that are required to be so protected elsewhere in this Code.

This paragraph is new in the 1993 *NEC*. It requires replacement receptacles to be GFCI protected if GFCI protection is required in the current *Code*. For example, if a kitchen was designed in accordance with the 1984 *NEC*, GFCI-protected receptacles were not required. However, if a replacement receptacle is now required that is within 6 feet of the kitchen sink, the replacement receptacle would be required to be a GFCI type or connected to the load side of a GFCI-type receptacle, or be protected by a GFCI-type circuit breaker.

Exception: Where a grounding means does not exist in the receptacle enclosure, either a nongrounding or a ground-fault circuit-interrupter-type of receptacle shall be used. A grounding conductor shall not be connected from the ground-fault circuit-interrupter-type receptacle to any outlet supplied from the ground-fault circuit-interrupter-type receptacle. Existing nongrounding-type receptacles shall be permitted to be replaced with grounding-type receptacles where supplied through a ground-fault circuit-interrupter. These receptacle locations shall be marked "GFCI protected."

Where existing nongrounding-type receptacles are replaced, only grounding-type receptacles are permitted where a grounding means exists in the receptacle enclosure. Where a grounding means does not exist in the receptacle enclosure, there are four choices: (1) a nongrounding-type receptacle can be used, thereby indicating to the user that a grounding means for an appliance is not available; (2) a grounding-type receptacle can be used as permitted by Section 250-50(b), Exception; (3) a ground-fault circuit-interrupter type of receptacle can be used, or (4) a GFCI-type circuit breaker may be used to supply the branch circuit. If the ground-fault circuit-interrupter type of receptacle is used, it can either be the nonfeed-through type, or a feed-through type wired so that the equipment grounding conductor is not connected to any outlet supplied by this receptacle. However, outlets supplied by a GFCI-type receptacle are permitted to connect to grounding-type receptacles.

The ability of the GFCI to provide shock hazard protection is independent of whether the tool, appliance, etc., to which it is connected is grounded. A nongrounding-type receptacle provides no shock hazard protection.

If the ungrounded GFCI-type receptacle is used, care should be exercised in the installation to ensure that an equipment grounding conductor is not connected between the GFCI grounding terminal and any grounding type receptacle on the load side of the GFCI-type receptacle.

Existing nongrounding-type receptacles may be replaced with a grounding type without an equipment grounding where supplied through a GFCI-type receptacle or GFCI-type circuit breaker. However, the receptacles must be marked "GFCI Protected."

(e) Cord- and Plug-Connected Equipment. The installation of grounding-type receptacles shall not be used as a requirement that all cord- and plug-connected equipment be of the grounded type.

(FPN):   See Section 250-45 for type of cord- and plug-connected equipment to be grounded.

Over the years there has been a requirement that grounding-type receptacles be used as replacements for nongrounding types. See Section 210-7(d). It is intended that grounding-type receptacles be conveniently located for use with utilization equipment that is required to be grounded. For cord- and plug-connected equipment that is required to be grounded, see Section 250-45.

Many appliances are not required to be grounded, for example, toasters, flat irons, and some heating equipment [see commentary following Section 210-7(b)], and there are still many nongrounding-type receptacles in use. The use of an adapter or other approved means is necessary where grounding is required. Distinctively marked, listed, double-insulated tools and appliances are not required to be grounded.

(f) Noninterchangeable Types. Receptacles connected to circuits having different voltages, frequencies, or types of current (ac or dc) on the same premises shall be of such design that the attachment plugs used on these circuits are not interchangeable.

See Figures 210-7 and 210-8.

Figure 210-7. *Configuration chart for general-purpose nonlocking plugs and receptacles; reproduced from NEMA WD 6-88, Wiring Devices-Dimensional Requirements (Revision and Redesignation of ANSI C73-73).*

Figure 210-8. Configuration chart for specific-purpose locking plugs and receptacles; reproduced from NEMA WD 6-88, Wiring Devices-Dimensional Requirements (Revision and Redesignation of ANSI C73-73).

210-8. Ground-Fault Circuit-Interrupter Protection for Personnel.

Additional Requirements for Location of Ground-Fault Circuit-Interrupter Protection for Personnel

Location	Section
Fountains	680-51(a)
Commercial Garages	511-10
Construction Sites	305-6
Marinas	555-3
	550-8(b)
Mobile Homes	550-23(d)
Permanently Installed Pools	680-6(a)
Storable Pools	680-31
Recreational Vehicles	551-41
Recreational Vehicles Parks	551-71

(a) Dwelling Units.

(1) All 125-volt, single-phase, 15- and 20-ampere receptacles installed in bathrooms shall have ground-fault circuit-interrupter protection for personnel.

The requirement for ground-fault circuit-interrupters for receptacles in bathrooms was originally included in the *Code* because data supplied with the *Code* proposal for GFCIs indicated that a number of accidents occurring in bathrooms could be prevented by GFCIs. See Figures 210-9 and 210-10.

(2) All 125-volt, single-phase, 15- or 20-ampere receptacles installed in garages shall have ground-fault circuit-interrupter protection for personnel.

Exception No. 1 to (a)(2): Receptacles that are not readily accessible.

A ceiling-mounted receptacle installed for connection of a garage door opener is exempt. See Figure 210-11.

Exception No. 2 to (a)(2): A single receptacle or a duplex receptacle for two appliances located within dedicated space for each appliance that in normal use is not easily moved from one place to another, and that is cord- and plug-connected in accordance with Section 400-7(a)(6), (a)(7), or (a)(8).

This section has been revised for the 1993 *NEC*. It now recognizes the use of a duplex receptacle where there are two cord- and plug-connected appliances occupying the dedicated space. Where there is only a single cord- and plug-connected appliance occupying the dedicated space, a single receptacle must be used.

One duplex receptacle

GFCI

Two basins

Closet

Or Two single or Two duplex receptacles

GFCI   GFCI

Two basins

Closet

Figure 210-9. *Section 210-8(a)(1) indicates that all 125-V, single-phase, 15- and 20-A receptacles in bathrooms are to have GFCI protection for personnel. This includes any such receptacles located for a clothes washer, clothes dryer (gas), integral with a lighting fixture, and, of course, the wall-mounted receptacles adjacent to the basin. The definition of bathroom refers to an area that includes the entire area shown above, whether a separating door (as illustrated) is present or not. Where receptacles are provided in bathroom areas of hotels and motels, commercial, industrial, and all other nondwelling occupancies, ground-fault circuit-interrupter protection for the receptacles is required. See Figure 210-10. Section 210-52(d) requires that a receptacle be located adjacent to each basin location. Where the basins are adjacent and in close proximity, one receptacle outlet may satisfy the requirement.*

Receptacles installed under exceptions to Section 210-8(a)(2) shall not be considered as meeting the requirements of Section 210-52(g).

Figure 210-10. *Typical motel bathroom as defined at the end of Section 210-8 includes the wash basin located outside the door to the room containing the tub, toilet, and (other) wash basin.*

The purpose of GFCIs in garages is to provide a degree of safety for persons using portable hand-held tools, gardening appliances, snow blowers, etc. that might be connected to receptacles in garages since they are often the location of the closest receptacle. Also, auto repair work and general workshop electrical tool usage are protected. GFCIs are not required in dedicated spaces for appliances such as freezers or refrigerators. See Figure 210-11.

(3) All 125-volt, single-phase, 15- and 20-ampere receptacles installed outdoors where there is direct grade level access to the receptacles shall have ground-fault circuit-interrupter protection for personnel.

(FPN): See Section 215-9 for feeder protection.

For the purposes of this section, "direct grade level access" is defined as being located not more than 6 feet, 6 inches (1.98 m) above grade level and being readily accessible.

(4) All 125-volt, single-phase, 15- and 20-ampere receptacles installed in crawl spaces at or below grade level and in unfinished basements shall have ground-fault circuit-interrupter protection for personnel.

Figure 210-11. *Receptacles that are not readily accessible (e.g., door opener) or are located for appliances occupying dedicated space (e.g., food freezer) are not required to have GFCI protection for personnel.*

Figure 210-12. *The three receptacles located outdoors at a dwelling unit are considered to be at direct grade level access and must have GFCI protection for personnel. See also commentary following Section 210-52(e) and Section 410-57.*

For purposes of this section, unfinished basements are defined as portions or areas of the basement not intended as habitable rooms and limited to storage areas, work areas, and the like.

Exception No. 1: A single receptacle supplied by a dedicated branch circuit that is located and identified for specific use by a cord-and plug-connected appliance, such as a refrigerator or freezer.

Basement (plan)

Figure 210-13. An unfinished basement is limited to storage areas, work areas, and the like. Section 210-8(a)(4) does not apply to areas of sleeping rooms or family rooms in basements. Therefore, GFCI protection of these receptacles is not required. The freezer and laundry receptacles do not require GFCI protection in accordance with the exceptions to Section 210-8(a)(4).

Exception No. 2: The laundry circuit as required by Sections 210-52(f) and 220-4(c).

Exception No. 3: A single receptacle supplying a permanently installed sump pump.

(5) All 125-volt, single-phase, 15- and 20-ampere receptacles to serve counter top surfaces, installed within 6 feet (1.83 m) of a wet bar sink or kitchen sink, shall have ground-fault circuit-interrupter protection for personnel.

Most kitchen appliances are ungrounded, and the presence of water and grounded surfaces contributes to a hazardous environment, leading to this requirement for GFCI protection around the kitchen sink or a wet bar sink. See Figure 210-14 for wet bar sinks and 210-29 for kitchens. The requirement is intended for receptacles serving the counter top. Receptacles installed for disposals, dishwashers, and trash compactors, as permitted in Section 422-8(d), are not required to be protected by a GFCI.

Family room

Figure 210-14. Receptacles within 6 feet of a wet bar sink are required to be GFCI protected.

(FPN): The intent of this subsection is to permit the exemption of receptacles that are located specifically for appliances such as refrigerators and freezers from ground-fault circuit-interrupter protection for personnel.

(6) All 125-volt, single-phase, 15- or 20-ampere receptacles installed in boathouses shall have ground-fault circuit-interrupter protection for personnel.

(b) Other than Dwelling Units.

See commentary following Section 210-8(a)(1) and Figure 210-10.

The requirement for ground-fault circuit-interrupter protection for receptacles on construction sites is covered under Section 305-6.

(1) All 125-volt, 15- and 20-ampere receptacles installed in bathrooms of commercial, industrial, and all other nond-welling occupancies shall have ground-fault circuit-interrupter protection for personnel.

This requirement has been expanded in the 1993 *NEC* to include all bathrooms of all occupancies covered by the *Code*.

Bathroom: As used in this article, a bathroom is an area including a basin with one or more of the following: a toilet, a tub, or a shower.

Figure 210-15 shows a typical circuit arrangement of a GFCI for personnel protection. The line conductors are passed through a toroidal coil and connected to a shunt-trip device.

Figure 210-15. The circuitry and components for a typical ground-fault circuit-interrupter.

As long as the current in each conductor remains equal, the device remains in a closed position. If one of the conductors comes in contact with a grounded object, either directly or through a person's body, some of the current returns by an alternative path and an unbalanced current results. The unbalanced current is sensed by the toroidal coil, and a circuit is established to the shunt-trip that reacts and opens the circuit. Note that the design technology does not require the presence of an equipment grounding conductor, which is the reason the exception to Section 210-7 permits their use as replacements for receptacles where a grounding means does not exist. Ground-fault circuit-interrupters operate on currents of 5 mA. Evaluation standards permit a differential of 4 to 6 mA. At trip levels of 5 mA (the instantaneous current could be much higher), a

shock can be felt during the time of the fault, leading to involuntary reactions that may cause secondary accidents such as falls. GFCIs will not protect personnel from shock hazards where contact is between phase and neutral or phase-to-phase.

A variety of GFCIs are available, including portable and plug-in types and circuit-breaker types, types built into attachment plug caps, and receptacle types. Each has a test switch so that the unit can be checked periodically to ensure proper operation. See Figures 210-16 and 210-17.

Figure 210-16. A portable plug-in-type ground-fault circuit-interrupter. (Square D Co.)

(2) All 125-volt, single-phase, 15- and 20-ampere receptacles installed on roofs shall have ground-fault circuit-interrupter protection for personnel.

This requirement is new in the 1993 *Code*. It requires all rooftop 15- and 20-ampere receptacles in nondwelling occupancies to be GFCI protected. See Section 210-63 for placement of rooftop receptacles.

Figure 210-17. *A 15-ampere duplex receptacle with integral ground-fault circuit-interrupter that also protects downstream loads. (Pass & Seymour/Legrand, Inc.)*

Figure 210-18. *Leakage of the neutral conductor to ground and ground-fault leakage current from the hot conductor can be measured by this GFCI tester. (Gould Inc.)*

210-9. **Circuits Derived from Autotransformers.** Branch circuits shall not be derived from autotransformers unless the circuit supplied has a grounded conductor that is electrically connected to a grounded conductor of the system supplying the autotransformer.

Figures 210-19 and 210-20 illustrate autotransformers used to derive 120-V and 240-V systems from 240-V and 208-V systems. In Figure 210-19 the grounded conductor of the primary system is electrically connected to the grounded conductor of the secondary system.

Exception No. 1 allows an autotransformer (without an electrical connection to a grounded conductor) to extend or add an individual branch circuit in an existing installation where transforming (boosting) 208 V to 240 V as shown in Figure 210-20. Transforming (bucking) 240 V to 208 V for use with appliances would also be allowed for applications; such as ranges, air conditioners, heating elements, and motors.

In industrial locations, Exception No. 2 allows the use of an autotransformer to supply a 600 V load from 480-V systems, provided there are qualified personnel to service the installation. It also allows 480 V loads to be supplied through an autotransformer supplied by a 600 V system.

It is also possible to increase 240 V to 277 V for lighting systems, and 440 V to 550 V for power equipment. A single unit is used to boost or buck single-phase voltage, but two or three units are used to boost or buck 3-phase voltage. An autotransformer requires little physical space, is economical, and, above all, efficient.

A buck-boost transformer is a means of raising or lowering (boosting or bucking) a supply line voltage by a small amount (no more than ± 20 percent). It is an insulating transformer with two primary (input) windings, both rated at 120 V, or 240 V and two secondary (output) windings, both rated at either 12 V, 16 V, or 24 V. Its primary and secondary windings can be connected together so that the electrical characteristics are changed from an insulating transformer to those of a "boosting" or "bucking" autotransformer, correcting voltage up to ± 20 percent.

Literature containing diagrams for connection and application of autotransformers is available from manufacturers.

Figure 210-19. *The circuitry for an autotransformer used to derive a 2-wire, 120-V system for lighting from a 240-V corner-grounded delta power system.*

Figure 210-20. *The circuitry for an autotransformer used to derive a 240-V system from a 208-V supply.*

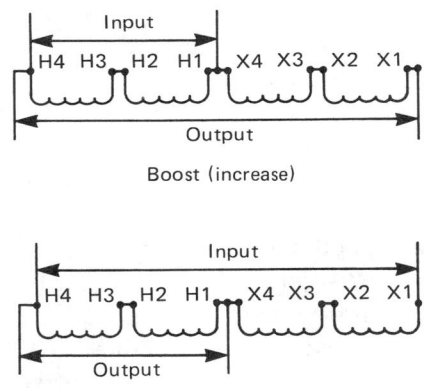

Figure 210-21. *Typical hookups for buck or boost transformers connected as autotransformers to change 240 V single-phase to 208 V or vice versa.*

Figure 210-22. *Typical hookups for buck or boost transformers connected in 3-phase open delta as autotransformers to change 240 V to 208 V or vice versa.*

Exception No. 1: An autotransformer shall be permitted to extend or add a branch circuit for an equipment load without the connection to a similar grounded conductor when transforming from a nominal 208 volts to a nominal 240-volt supply or similarly from 240 volts to 208 volts.

Exception No. 2: In industrial occupancies, where conditions of maintenance and supervision ensure that only qualified persons will service the installation, autotransformers shall be permitted to supply nominal 600-volt loads from nominal 480-volt systems, and 480-volt loads from nominal 600-volt systems, without the connection to a similar grounded conductor.

210-10. **Ungrounded Conductors Tapped from Grounded Systems.** Two-wire dc circuits and ac circuits of two or more ungrounded conductors shall be permitted to be tapped from the ungrounded conductors of circuits having a grounded neutral conductor. Switching devices in each tapped circuit shall have a pole in each ungrounded conductor. All poles of multipole switching devices shall manually switch together where such switching devices also serve as a disconnecting means as required by Section 410-48 for double-pole switched lampholders; Section 410-54(b) for electric-discharge lamp auxiliary equipment switching devices; Section 422-21(b) for an appliance; Section 424-20 for a fixed electric space heating unit; Section 426-51 for electric de-icing and snow-melting equipment; Section 430-85 for a motor controller; and Section 430-103 for a motor.

Figures 210-23 and 210-24. Branch circuits tapped from ungrounded conductors of multiwire systems.

Two-wire ungrounded branch circuits may be tapped from ac or dc circuits of two or more ungrounded conductors having a grounded neutral conductor. Figure 210-23 (top) illustrates ungrounded 2-wire branch circuits tapped from the ungrounded conductors of a dc or single-phase system to supply a small motor. Figure 210-24 (bottom) illustrates a 3-phase, 4-wire wye system.

Circuit breakers or switches used as the disconnecting means for a branch circuit are required to open all poles simultaneously. This requirement involves only the manual operation of the disconnecting means; thus, where switches and fuses are used and one fuse blows, or where circuit breakers (two single-pole circuit breakers with a "handle-tie") are used and one breaker trips, one pole could remain closed. The intention is not to provide a common trip of fuses or circuit breakers but to disconnect "manually" the ungrounded conductors of the branch circuit with one manual operation. It should be understood that circuit breakers, where used as overcurrent devices as well as switching devices, are required to be of the double-pole type. Handle ties are not permitted. See Section 240-20(b).

B. Branch-Circuit Ratings

210-19. Conductors — Minimum Ampacity and Size.

(a) General. Branch-circuit conductors shall have an ampacity not less than the maximum load to be served. In addition, conductors of multioutlet branch circuits supplying receptacles for cord- and plug-connected portable loads shall have an ampacity of not less than the rating of the branch circuit. Cable assemblies where the neutral conductor is smaller than the ungrounded conductors shall be so marked.

Only multioutlet branch-circuit conductors supplying receptacles for cord- and plug-connected portable loads are required to have an ampacity not less than the rating of the circuit (the rating of the overcurrent device per Section 210-3), because the loading of such circuits is unpredictable.

(FPN No. 1): See Section 310-15 for ampacity ratings of conductors.

(FPN No. 2): See Part B of Article 430 for minimum rating of motor branch-circuit conductors.

(FPN No. 3): See Section 310-10 for temperature limitation of conductors.

(FPN No. 4): Conductors for branch circuits as defined in Article 100, sized to prevent a voltage drop exceeding 3 percent at the farthest outlet of power, heating, and lighting loads, or combinations of such loads and where the maximum total voltage drop on both feeders and branch circuits to the farthest outlet does not exceed 5 percent, will provide reasonable efficiency of operation. See Section 215-2 for voltage drop on feeder conductors.

Improper voltage is a major source of trouble and inefficient operation of electrical equipment. Both overvoltage and undervoltage reduce the capability and reliability of motors, lighting sources, heaters, and solid-state equipment.

(b) Household Ranges and Cooking Appliances. Branch-circuit conductors supplying household ranges, wall-mounted ovens, counter-mounted cooking units, and other household cooking appliances shall have an ampacity not less than the rating of the branch circuit and not less than the maximum load to be served. For ranges of 8¾ kW or more rating, the minimum branch-circuit rating shall be 40 amperes.

For a minimum 40-A branch-circuit rating, for example:
No. 8 AWG copper, Type TW = 40 A
No. 6 AWG aluminum, Type TW = 40 A

See Table 310-16 for other applications.

Exception No. 1: Tap conductors supplying electric ranges, wall-mounted electric ovens, and counter-mounted electric cooking units from a 50-ampere branch circuit shall have an ampacity of not less than 20 and shall be sufficient for the load to be served. The taps shall not be longer than necessary for servicing the appliance.

This exception permits a 20-ampere tap conductor from a range, oven, or cooking unit to be connected to a 50-ampere branch circuit provided: the taps are no longer than necessary for servicing or for permitting accessibility to the junction box; the taps to each unit are properly spliced; the junction box is adjacent to each unit; and the taps are of sufficient size for the load to be served. See Figure 210-25.

Figure 210-25. *Tap conductors are permitted to be sized smaller than the branch-circuit conductors, but they are to be no longer than necessary for servicing.*

Exception No. 2: The neutral conductor of a 3-wire branch circuit supplying a household electric range, a wall-mounted oven, or a counter-mounted cooking unit shall be permitted to be smaller than the ungrounded conductors where the maximum demand of a range of 8¾ kW or more rating has been computed according to Column A of Table 220-19, but shall have an ampacity of not less than 70 percent of the branch-circuit rating and shall not be smaller than No. 10.

Column A of Table 220-19 and Section 220-19 indicate that the maximum demand for one range (not over 12 kW rating) is 8 kW (8 kW = 8,000 volt-amperes; 8,000 volt-amperes ÷ 240 V = 33.3 A). The allowable ampacity of a No. 8 TW copper conductor is 40 A (see Table 310-16) and may be used for the range branch circuit. According to this computation, the neutral of this 3-wire circuit can be smaller than No. 8 but not smaller than No. 10, which has an allowable ampacity of 30 A (30 A is more than 70 percent of 40 A, as per the exception). The maximum demand for a neutral of an 8 kW range circuit seldom exceeds 25 A since current is drawn from the neutral only for lights, clocks, timers, and heating elements when in the low-heating position.

(c) Other Loads. Branch-circuit conductors supplying loads other than cooking appliances as covered in (b) above and as listed in Section 210-2 shall have an ampacity sufficient for the loads served and shall not be smaller than No. 14.

Exception No. 1: Tap conductors for such loads shall have an ampacity not less than 15 for circuits rated less than 40 amperes and not less than 20 for circuits rated at 40 or 50 amperes and only where these tap conductors supply any of the following loads:

a. Individual lampholders or fixtures with taps extending not longer than 18 inches (457 mm) beyond any portion of the lampholder or fixture.

b. A fixture having tap conductors as provided in Section 410-67.

c. Individual outlets with taps not over 18 inches (457 mm) long.

d. Infrared lamp industrial heating appliances.

e. Nonheating leads of de-icing and snow-melting cables and mats.

Exception No. 2: Fixture wires and cords as permitted in Section 240-4.

Tap conductors are required to be suitable for the temperature encountered and, where the conductors supply loads as specified in subparts a. through e. of Exception No. 1, are required to have an ampacity of 15 A or more (No. 14 AWG copper conductors) for circuits rated less than 40 A, and an ampacity of 20 A or more (No. 12 AWG copper conductors) for circuits rated 40 or 50 A. See Section 240-4 for special requirements for the overcurrent protection of flexible cords and fixture wires.

210-20 . Overcurrent Protection. Branch-circuit conductors and equipment shall be protected by overcurrent protective devices having a rating or setting (1) not exceeding that specified in Section 240-3 for conductors; (2) not exceeding that specified in the applicable articles referenced in Section 240-2 for equipment; and (3) as provided for outlet devices in Section 210-21.

Exception No. 1: Tap conductors as permitted in Section 210-19(c) shall be permitted to be protected by the branch-circuit overcurrent device.

Exception No. 2: Fixture wires and cords as permitted in Section 240-4.

(FPN):   See Section 240-1 for the purpose of overcurrent protection and Sections 210-22 and 220-3 for continuous loads.

210-21 . Outlet Devices. Outlet devices shall have an ampere rating not less than the load to be served and shall comply with (a) and (b) below.

(a) Lampholders. Where connected to a branch circuit having a rating in excess of 20 amperes, lampholders shall be of the heavy-duty type. A heavy-duty lampholder shall have a rating of not less than 660 watts if of the admedium type and not less than 750 watts if of any other type.

The intent is to restrict a fluorescent lighting branch-circuit rating to not more than 20 A, because most lampholders manufactured for use with fluorescent lights are not of the heavy-duty type and are rated at 660 W or 250 W.

Branch-circuit conductors for fluorescent electric-discharge lighting are usually connected to a ballast rather than to lampholders, and, by specifying a wattage rating for these lampholders, a limit of 20 A is applied to ballast circuits.

It is only the admedium-base lampholder that is recognized as heavy duty at the rating of 660 W. Other lampholders are required to have a rating of not less than 750 watts to be recognized as heavy duty. The requirement stated in Section 210-21(a) prohibits the use of medium-base screw-shell lampholders on branch circuits in excess of 20 amperes.

(b) Receptacles.

(1) A single receptacle installed on an individual branch circuit shall have an ampere rating of not less than that of the branch circuit.

See commentary following Section 210-7(a).

Exception: Where installed in accordance with Section 430-81(c).

(FPN):   See definition of "Receptacle" in Article 100.

(2) Where connected to a branch circuit supplying two or more receptacles or outlets, a receptacle shall not supply a total cord- and plug-connected load in excess of the maximum specified in Table 210-21(b)(2).

(3) Where connected to a branch circuit supplying two or more receptacles or outlets, receptacle ratings shall conform to the values listed in Table 210-21(b)(3), or where larger than 50 amperes, the receptacle rating shall not be less than the branch-circuit rating.

A single receptacle installed on an individual branch circuit is required to have an ampere rating of not less than that of the branch circuit. For example, a single receptacle on a 20-A branch circuit must be rated at 20 A; however, two or more 15-A receptacles are permitted on a 20-A general-purpose branch circuit.

(4) It shall be permitted to base the ampere rating of a range receptacle on a single range demand load specified in Table 220-19.

Table 210-21(b)(2).   Maximum Cord- and Plug-Connected Load to Receptacle

Circuit Rating Amperes	Receptacle Rating Amperes	Maximum Load Amperes
15 or 20	15	12
20	20	16
30	30	24

Table 210-21(b)(3).   Receptacle Ratings for Various Size Circuits

Circuit Rating Amperes	Receptacle Rating Amperes
15	Not over 15
20	15 or 20
30	30
40	40 or 50
50	50

210-22. Maximum Loads.

The total load shall not exceed the rating of the branch circuit, and it shall not exceed the maximum loads specified in Sections 210-22(a) through (c) under the conditions specified therein.

(a) Motor-Operated and Combination Loads. Where a circuit supplies only motor-operated loads, Article 430 shall apply. Where a circuit supplies only air-conditioning equipment, refrigerating equipment, or both, Article 440 shall apply. For circuits supplying loads consisting of motor-operated utilization equipment that is fastened in place and that has a motor larger than $1/8$ horsepower in combination with other loads, the total computed load shall be based on 125 percent of the largest motor load plus the sum of the other loads.

(b) Inductive Lighting Loads. For circuits supplying lighting units having ballasts, transformers, or autotransformers, the computed load shall be based on the total ampere ratings of such units and not on the total watts of the lamps.

(c) Other Loads. The rating of the branch-circuit overcurrent device serving continuous loads, such as store lighting and similar loads, shall be not less than the noncontinuous load plus 125 percent of the continuous load.

Exception: Circuits supplied by an assembly together with its overcurrent devices that is listed for continuous operation at 100 percent of its rating.

It shall be acceptable to apply demand factors for range loads in accordance with Table 220-19, including Note 4.

Article 100 defines a "continuous load" as "a load where the maximum current is expected to continue for three hours or more." Continuous loads, such as lighting in mercantile occupancies, restaurants, etc., must not exceed 80 percent of the branch-circuit rating. The exception provides for a 100 percent rating of a circuit if supplied by an overcurrent device and assembly listed by a qualified testing laboratory for continuous operation.

210-23. Permissible Loads.

In no case shall the load exceed the branch-circuit ampere rating. An individual branch circuit shall be permitted to supply any load for which it is rated. A branch circuit supplying two or more outlets shall supply only the loads specified according to its size in (a) through (d) below and summarized in Section 210-24 and Table 210-24.

(a) 15- and 20-Ampere Branch Circuits. A 15- or 20-ampere branch circuit shall be permitted to supply lighting units, other utilization equipment, or a combination of both. The rating of any one cord- and plug-connected utilization equipment shall not exceed 80 percent of the branch-circuit ampere rating. The total rating of utilization equipment fastened in place shall not exceed 50 percent of the branch-circuit ampere rating where lighting units, cord- and plug-connected utilization equipment not fastened in place, or both, are also supplied.

Exception: The small appliance branch circuits required in a dwelling unit(s) by Section 220-4(b) shall supply only the receptacle outlets specified in that section.

This permits a 15- or 20-A branch circuit for lighting to also supply utilization equipment fastened in place, such as an air conditioner rated not to exceed 50 percent of the branch-circuit ampere rating (7.5 A on a 15-A circuit and 10 A on a 20-A circuit). Such equipment, fastened in place, is not permitted to be installed on the small-appliance branch circuits required in the kitchen, dining room, etc., by Section 220-4(b).

(b) 30-Ampere Branch Circuits. A 30-ampere branch circuit shall be permitted to supply fixed lighting units with heavy-duty lampholders in other than dwelling unit(s) or utilization equipment in any occupancy. A rating of any one cord- and plug-connected utilization equipment shall not exceed 80 percent of the branch-circuit ampere rating.

(c) 40- and 50-Ampere Branch Circuits. A 40- or 50-ampere branch circuit shall be permitted to supply cooking appliances that are fastened in place in any occupancy. In other than dwelling units, such circuits shall be permitted to supply fixed lighting units with heavy-duty lampholders, infrared heating units, or other utilization equipment.

A branch circuit supplying two or more outlets is permitted to supply only the loads specified according to its size in accordance with Sections 210-23(a) through (c) and summarized in Section 210-24 and Table 210-24. Other circuits are not permitted to have more than one outlet and are considered individual branch circuits. However, individual branch circuits are not required for portable, mobile, and transportable medical X-ray equipment requiring a capacity of not over 60 A. See Sections 517-71 and 660-4(b).

(d) Branch Circuits Larger than 50 Amperes. Branch circuits larger than 50 amperes shall supply only nonlighting outlet loads.

See commentary following the exception to Section 210-3.

Table 210-24. Summary of Branch-Circuit Requirements

CIRCUIT RATING	15 Amp	20 Amp	30 Amp	40 Amp	50 Amp
CONDUCTORS: (Min. Size)					
Circuit Wires*	14	12	10	8	6
Taps	14	14	14	12	12
Fixture Wires and Cords			Refer to Section 240-4		
OVERCURRENT PROTECTION	**15 Amp**	**20 Amp**	**30 Amp**	**40 Amp**	**50 Amp**
OUTLET DEVICES:					
Lampholders Permitted	Any Type	Any Type	Heavy Duty	Heavy Duty	Heavy Duty
Receptacle Rating**	15 Max. Amp	15 or 20 Amp	30 Amp	40 or 50 Amp	50 Amp
MAXIMUM LOAD	**15 Amp**	**20 Amp**	**30 Amp**	**40 Amp**	**50 Amp**
PERMISSIBLE LOAD	Refer to Section 210-23(a)	Refer to Section 210-23(a)	Refer to Section 210-23(b)	Refer to Section 210-23(c)	Refer to Section 210-23(c)

*These gauges are for copper conductors.
**For receptacle rating of cord-connected electric-discharge lighting fixtures, see Section 410-30(c).

210-24. **Branch-Circuit Requirements — Summary.** The requirements for circuits having two or more outlets, other than the receptacle circuits of Section 220-4(b) as specifically provided for above, are summarized in Table 210-24. Branch circuits in dwelling units shall supply only loads within that dwelling unit or loads associated only with that dwelling unit. Branch circuits required for the purpose of lighting, central alarm, signal, communications, or other needs for public or common areas shall not be supplied from a dwelling unit panelboard.

The second sentence of Section 210-24 is intended to prevent overloading of branch circuits. The last sentence requires the house loads for common areas and common systems to be supplied from a panelboard that is not located in any of the dwelling units. This is intended to permit access to the branch-circuit disconnecting means without the need to enter the space of any tenants. It also is intended to prevent a tenant from turning off important circuits that may affect other tenants.

Table 210-24 summarizes branch-circuit requirements of conductors, overcurrent protection, outlet devices, maximum load, and permissible loads where two or more outlets are supplied.

Where the branch circuit serves a fixture load and supplies two or more fixture outlets, Section 210-23 requires the branch circuit to have a specific ampere rating that is also the rating of the overcurrent device as stated in Section 210-3. Thus, if the circuit breaker protecting the branch circuit is rated 20 A, the conductors supplying this circuit must have an ampacity of 20 amperes. Note that in accordance with the definition of ampacity, the ampacity is determined after applying all derating factors, such as those in Note 8(a) of Notes to Ampacity Tables of 0 to 2,000 Volts. Where 7 to 9 such conductors are in one conduit, a No. 12 THHN copper conductor (30 A per Table 310-16) derated to 70 percent per Note 8(a) would have an ampacity of 21 A and would be suitable for a load of 20 A. It would thus be acceptable for use on the 20-A multioutlet branch circuit.

C. Required Outlets

210-50. **General.** Receptacle outlets shall be installed as specified in Sections 210-52 through 210-63.

(a) **Cord Pendants.** A cord connector that is supported by a permanently installed cord pendant shall be considered a receptacle outlet.

(b) Cord Connections. A receptacle outlet shall be installed wherever flexible cords with attachment plugs are used. Where flexible cords are permitted to be permanently connected, it shall be permitted to omit receptacles for such cords.

Flexible cords are permitted to be permanently connected to boxes or fittings where specifically permitted by the *Code.* However, plugging a cord into a lampholder by inserting a screw-plug adapter is not permissible. See Section 410-47.

(c) Appliance Outlets. Appliance receptacle outlets installed in a dwelling unit for specific appliances, such as laundry equipment, shall be installed within 6 feet (1.83 m) of the intended location of the appliance.

See Sections 210-52(f) and (g) and 220-4(c).

210-52. Dwelling Unit Receptacle Outlets.

(a) General Provisions. In every kitchen, family room, dining room, living room, parlor, library, den, sun room, bedroom, recreation room, or similar room or area of dwelling units, receptacle outlets shall be installed so that no point along the floor line in any wall space is more than 6 feet (1.83 m), measured horizontally, from an outlet in that space, including any wall space 2 feet (610 mm) or more in width and the wall space occupied by fixed panels in exterior walls, but excluding sliding panels in exterior walls. The wall space afforded by fixed room dividers, such as freestanding bar-type counters or railings, shall be included in the 6-foot (1.83-m) measurement.

As used in this section, a "wall space" shall be considered a wall unbroken along the floor line by doorways, fireplaces, and similar openings. Each wall space 2 feet or more (610 mm or more) wide shall be treated individually and separately from other wall spaces within the room. A wall space shall be permitted to include two or more walls of a room (around corners) where unbroken at the floor line.

(FPN): The purpose of this requirement is to minimize the use of cords across doorways, fireplaces, and similar openings.

Receptacles are required to be located so that no "point" in any wall space is more than 6 feet from a receptacle. This rule intends that an appliance or lamp with a flexible cord attached may be placed anywhere in the room and be within 6 feet of a receptacle, thus eliminating the need for extension cords.

A "wallspace" is a wall unbroken along the floor line by doorways, fireplaces, archways, and similar openings and may include two or more walls of a room (around corners, as illustrated in Figure 210-26).

Fixed room dividers, such as bar-type counters and railings, are to be included in the 6-foot measurement. Fixed panels in exterior walls are counted as regular wall space, and a floor-type receptacle close to the wall can be used to meet the required spacing. Isolated, individual wall spaces 2 feet or more in width are considered usable for the location of a lamp or appliance, and a receptacle outlet is required to be provided.

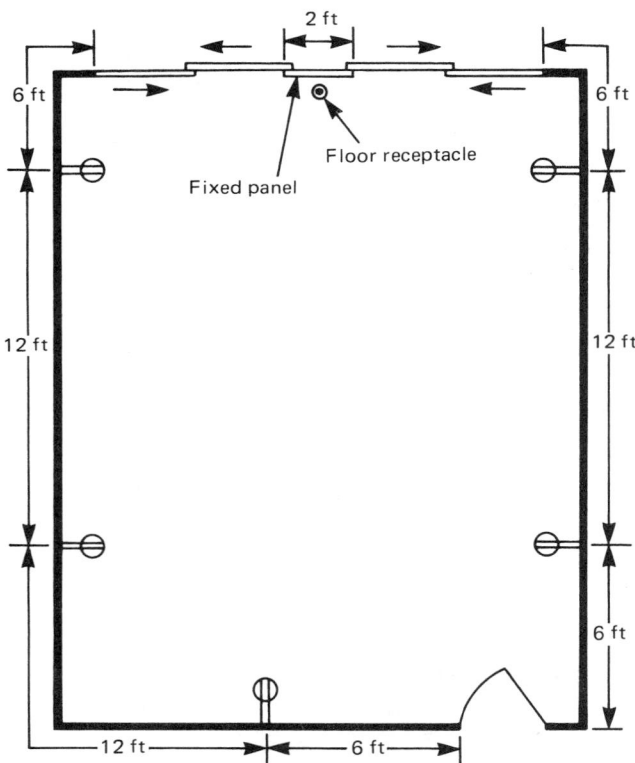

Figure 210-26. *Plan view of the location of receptacles in a typical room.*

Receptacle outlets shall, insofar as practicable, be spaced equal distances apart. Receptacle outlets in floors shall not be counted as part of the required number of receptacle outlets unless located close to the wall.

The receptacle outlets required by this section shall be in addition to any receptacle that is part of any lighting fixture or appliance, located within cabinets or cupboards, or located over 5½ feet (1.68 m) above the floor.

Exception: Permanently installed electric baseboard heaters equipped with factory-installed receptacle outlets or outlets provided as a separate assembly by the manufacturer shall be permitted as the required outlet or outlets for the wall space utilized by such permanently installed heaters. Such receptacle outlets shall not be connected to the heater circuits.

(FPN): Listed baseboard heaters include instructions that may not permit their installation below receptacle outlets.

According to listing instructions [see Section 110-3(b)], permanent electric baseboard heaters are not permitted to be located beneath wall receptacles. Where the receptacle is a part of the heater, cords of appliances or lamps are less apt to be exposed to the heating elements, as might occur should they fall into convector slots. See Figures 210-27 and 210-28.

Figure 210-27. An electric baseboard heater with a receptacle outlet provided as the required receptacle outlet for the wall space. (Square D Co.)

(b) Small Appliances.

(1) The two or more 20-ampere small appliance branch circuits required by Section 220-4(b) shall serve all receptacle outlets, including refrigeration equipment, in the kitchen,

Figure 210-28. Many electrical baseboard heaters are of the low-density type and are designed to be longer than 12 feet. To meet the spacing requirements of Section 210-52(a), it is necessary that the required receptacle be located as a part of the heater unit.

pantry, breakfast room, dining room, or similar area of a dwelling unit. Such circuits, whether two or more are used, shall have no other outlets.

Exception No. 1: A receptacle installed solely for the electrical supply to and support of an electric clock in any of the rooms specified above.

Exception No. 2: Outdoor receptacles.

Exception No. 3: In addition to the required receptacles specified by Section 210-52, switched receptacles supplied from a general-purpose branch circuit as defined in Section 210-70(a), Exception No. 1 shall be permitted.

Exception No. 4: A receptacle served by a circuit supplying only motor loads.

Exception No. 5: Receptacles installed to provide power for electric ignition systems or clock timers for gas-fired ranges, ovens, or counter-mounted cooking units.

This exception is intended to allow the small electrical loads associated with gas-fired appliances to be connected to small-appliance branch circuits.

(2) Receptacles installed in the kitchen to serve counter top surfaces shall be supplied by not less than two small appliance branch circuits, either or both of which shall also be permitted to supply receptacle outlets in the kitchen and other rooms specified in Section 210-52(b)(1). Additional small appliance branch circuits shall be permitted to supply receptacle outlets in the kitchen and other rooms specified in Section 210-52(b)(1).

Section 210-52(b) requires two or more 20-A circuits for all receptacle outlets for the small appliance loads, including refrigeration equipment [see FPN following Section 210-8(a)(5)], in the kitchen, dining room, pantry, and breakfast room of a dwelling unit. Counter top receptacle outlets in kitchens are required to be supplied by no fewer than two small-appliance branch circuits. These circuits may also supply receptacle outlets in the pantry, dining room, and breakfast room as well as an electric clock receptacle, electric loads associated with gas fired appliances, or outdoor receptacles, but are to have no other outlets. See Sections 210-8(a)(3) and (a)(5) for GFCI requirements.

At least one additional 20-A branch circuit is required to be provided for the supply to the laundry receptacle outlet(s). This circuit is to have no other outlets. See Figure 210-29.

Figure 210-29. *This figure illustrates the application of requirements of Section 210-52(b)(1) and (2). Though these small-appliance branch circuits may serve certain outlets in other specified areas, they are not permitted to serve any other outlets such as might be connected to exhaust hoods or fans, disposals or dishwashers. The counter top receptacles are required to be supplied by two circuits [see Section 210-52(b)(2)]; receptacles in other rooms are not. Receptacles within 6 feet of the kitchen sink installed to serve counter top surfaces are required to be GFCI protected in accordance with Section 210-8(a)(5).*

There is no restriction placed on the number of outlets connected to a general lighting or small-appliance branch circuit. The minimum number of receptacle outlets in a room is determined by Section 210-52(a). It is desirable to provide more than the minimum number of receptacle outlets required, thereby further reducing the need for use of extension cords. Section 210-52(b)(1), Exception No. 3 permits switched receptacles supplied from general purpose branch circuits to be located in these areas.

(c) **Counter Tops.** In kitchens and dining areas of dwelling units, a receptacle outlet shall be installed at each wall counter space 12 inches (305 mm) or wider. Receptacle outlets shall be installed so that no point along the wall line is more than 24 inches (610 mm), measured horizontally from a receptacle outlet in that space.

Counter top receptacles in kitchens and dining areas are now required to be located so that no point along the wall line is more than 24 inches from a receptacle. Island and peninsular counter tops 12 inches and wider are required to have at least one receptacle for each 4 feet of counter space.

Receptacles rendered inaccessible by appliances fastened in place or installed for appliances occupying dedicated space, such as dishwashers, garbage disposal units, built-in gas ovens, waste compactors, etc., are not considered as the required receptacles.

A receptacle outlet shall be installed at each island or peninsular counter top with a long dimension of 24 inches (610 mm) or greater and a short dimension of 12 inches (305 mm) or greater. Receptacle outlets to serve island or peninsular counter tops shall be installed above, or within 12 inches (305 mm) below the counter top. Receptacle outlets shall be installed so that no point along the centerline of the long dimension is more than 24 inches (610 mm), measured horizontally from a receptacle outlet in that space. A peninsular counter top is measured from the connecting edge.

Counter top spaces separated by range tops, refrigerators, or sinks shall be considered as separate counter top spaces. Receptacle outlets rendered not readily accessible by appliances fastened in place or appliances occupying dedicated space shall not be considered as these required outlets.

Receptacle outlets shall not be installed in a face-up position in the work surfaces or counter tops in a kitchen or dining area.

Figure 210-30. Section 210-52(c) requires a receptacle outlet at each counter space wider than 12 inches spaced so that no point along the wall line is more than 24 inches from a receptacle. Peninsular type counter tops are required to have one receptacle for each 4 feet of counter top. The measurement of a peninsular type counter top is from the edge connecting to the nonpeninsular counter. A receptacle outlet is required at each island-type counter top with a short dimension of at least 12 inches and a long dimension of at least 24 inches. A receptacle outlet is required for each 4 feet of island counter top space, so located that no point along the center line of the long dimension is more than 24 inches measured horizontally from the receptacle outlet.

Receptacles installed in a face-up position in a counter top could collect crumbs, liquids, and other debris, resulting in a potential fire or shock hazard.

(FPN): The 24-inch (610-mm) dimension is measured along the wall line or centerline, and the intent is that there be a receptacle outlet for every 4 linear feet (1.2 m) or fraction thereof of counter length.

(d) Bathrooms. In dwelling units, at least one wall receptacle outlet shall be installed in the bathroom adjacent to each basin location. See Section 210-8(a)(1).

In bathrooms of a dwelling unit, one wall receptacle is required to be installed adjacent to the wash basin and is required in addition to any receptacle that may be part of any lighting fixture or medicine cabinet. Where there is more than one basin, a receptacle outlet is required adjacent to each basin location. Where the basins are in close proximity, one receptacle outlet installed between the two basins may satisfy this requirement. All 125-V single-phase, 15- and 20-A receptacles installed in bathroom areas are required to have ground-fault circuit-interrupter protection for personnel including the optional receptacle that may be part of a lighting fixture. See Figure 210-9.

(e) Outdoor Outlets. For a one-family dwelling and each unit of a two-family dwelling that is at grade level, at least one receptacle outlet accessible at grade level shall be installed at the front and back of the dwelling. See Section 210-8(a)(3).

The rule for one- and two-family dwellings requires two receptacle outlets for each dwelling unit, as shown in Figure 210-31.

Installation of outdoor receptacles requires that care be taken to ensure that the receptacle faceplate rests securely on the supporting surface to prevent moisture from entering the enclosure. Where uneven surfaces such as brick, stone, or stucco are encountered, it may be necessary to close openings with caulking compound or mastic. See also Section 410-57.

Figure 210-31. An example of "row" housing. A receptacle is required at the front and rear of each one-family dwelling.

(f) Laundry Areas. In dwelling units, at least one receptacle outlet shall be installed for the laundry.

Exception No. 1: In a dwelling unit that is an apartment or living area in a multifamily building where laundry facilities are provided on the premises that are available to all building occupants, a laundry receptacle shall not be required.

Exception No. 2: In other than one-family dwellings where laundry facilities are not to be installed or permitted, a laundry receptacle shall not be required.

(g) Basements and Garages. For a one-family dwelling, at least one receptacle outlet, in addition to any provided for laundry equipment, shall be installed in each basement and in each attached garage, and in each detached garage with electric power. See Sections 210-8(a)(2) and (a)(4).

In a one-family dwelling, it is mandatory to install a receptacle in a basement (in addition to the laundry receptacle), in each attached garage, and in each detached garage with electric power. Section 210-8(a)(4) requires receptacles in unfinished basements to be protected by a GFCI. Section 210-8(a)(2) requires receptacles installed in garages to be protected by a GFCI. If no electric power is provided, it is not mandatory to install a receptacle in detached garages.

(h) Hallways. In dwelling units, hallways of 10 feet (3.05 m) or more in length shall have at least one receptacle outlet.

As used in this subsection, the hall length shall be considered the length along the centerline of the hall without passing through a doorway.

This is intended to minimize strain or damage to cords and receptacles. The requirement is for dwelling unit receptacles and is not applicable to common hallways of hotels, motels, apartment buildings, condominiums, etc.

210-60. **Guest Rooms.** Guest rooms in hotels, motels, and similar occupancies shall have receptacle outlets installed in accordance with Section 210-52. See Section 210-8(b)(1).

Exception: In rooms of hotels and motels, the required number of receptacle outlets determined by Section 210-52(a) shall be permitted to be located convenient for permanent furniture layout.

This exception to Section 210-60 permits receptacles in guest rooms of hotels and motels to be placed in accessible locations compatible with the existence of permanent furniture. However, the minimum number of receptacles required in accordance with Section 210-52 are not permitted to be reduced. The minimum number of receptacle outlets should be determined by assuming there is no furniture in the room. The location of this minimum number of receptacles is then determined based on the permanent furniture layout.

Bathroom areas for guest rooms of hotels and motels are required to be provided with a receptacle outlet adjacent to the basin location in accordance with Section 210-8(b).

See Figure 210-32. There are no receptacle outlets in some spaces 2 feet or more in width because the exception permits the required number of outlets to be located conveniently with respect to the permanent furniture layout.

Figure 210-32. Receptacle outlets in guest rooms of hotels may be located conveniently with respect to the permanent furniture layout. The receptacle outlet adjacent to the permanent dresser is needed because the exception applies only to the location of receptacle outlets, not the minimum number.

210-62. **Show Windows.** At least one receptacle outlet shall be installed directly above a show window for each 12 linear feet (3.66 m) or major fraction thereof of show window area measured horizontally at its maximum width.

Show windows are usually designed from floor to ceiling for maximum display. To discourage floor receptacles and unsightly extension cords likely to cause physical injury, receptacles must be installed "directly above" a show window, and one receptacle is required for every 12 linear feet or "major fraction (6 feet or more)" thereof. See Section 220-3(c)(6), Exception No. 3 and Section 220-12 for information regarding load computations for show windows.

210-63. **Rooftop Heating, Air-Conditioning, and Refrigeration Equipment Outlet.** A 125-volt, single-phase, 15- or 20-ampere-rated receptacle outlet shall be installed at an accessible location for the servicing of heating, air-conditioning, and refrigeration equipment on rooftops and in attics and crawl spaces. The receptacle shall be located on the same level and within 25 feet (7.62 m) of the heating, air-conditioning, and refrigeration equipment. The receptacle outlet shall not be connected to the load side of the equipment disconnecting means.

Exception: Rooftop equipment on one- and two-family dwellings.

This requirement is intended to help prevent makeshift methods of obtaining power for servicing and troubleshooting heating, air-conditioning, and refrigeration equipment in attics, crawl spaces, and on rooftops. This section has been revised for the 1993 *Code* to reduce the distance of the receptacle from 75 feet to 25 feet.

Note the exception for rooftop equipment on one- and two-family dwellings.

210-70. **Lighting Outlets Required.** Lighting outlets shall be installed where specified in Sections 210-70(a), (b), and (c) below.

(a) Dwelling Unit(s). At least one wall switch-controlled lighting outlet shall be installed in every habitable room; in bathrooms, hallways, stairways, attached garages, and detached garages with electric power; and at outdoor entrances or exits.

It is not permitted to switch a receptacle as a lighting outlet on a small-appliance branch circuit. It is permitted to switch a receptacle as a lighting outlet (in the dining room for example) supplied by a branch circuit other than a small-appliance branch circuit. See Figure 210-29.

(FPN): A vehicle door in a garage is not considered as an outdoor entrance.

At least one lighting outlet controlled by a light switch located at the point of entry to the attic, underfloor space, utility room, and basement shall be installed where these spaces are used for storage or contain equipment requiring servicing. The lighting outlet shall be provided at or near the equipment requiring servicing.

Where lighting outlets are installed according to (a) above in interior stairways, there shall be a wall switch at each floor level to control the lighting outlet where the difference between floor levels is six steps or more.

Exception No. 1: In habitable rooms, other than kitchens and bathrooms, one or more receptacles controlled by a wall switch shall be permitted in lieu of lighting outlets.

Exception No. 2: In hallways, stairways, and at outdoor entrances, remote, central, or automatic control of lighting shall be permitted.

(b) Guest Rooms. At least one wall switch-controlled lighting outlet or wall switch-controlled receptacle shall be installed in guest rooms in hotels, motels, or similar occupancies.

(c) Other Locations. At least one wall switch-controlled lighting outlet shall be installed at or near equipment requiring servicing such as heating, air-conditioning, and refrigeration equipment in attics or underfloor spaces. The wall switch shall be located at the point of entry to the attic or underfloor space.

This section points out that adequate lighting and proper control and location of switching is as essential to the safety of occupants of dwelling units(s), hotels, motels, etc., as are proper wiring requirements. Proper illumination ensures safe movement for persons of all ages, thus many accidents are avoided.

Installation of lighting outlets in attics, under floor space or crawl areas, and in utility rooms or basements is required "only" where these spaces are used for storage (e.g., Christmas decorations, luggage, etc.) or where such spaces contain equipment requiring servicing (e.g., air-handling units, cooling and heating equipment, water pumps, sump pumps, etc.).

Remote, central, or automatic control of lighting for hallways, stairways, and outdoor entrances is practical in multifamily dwellings where it is desirable to use time clocks or to locate switches where they may not be intentionally or inadvertently turned to the "off" position.

Although the requirement calls for a switched lighting outlet at outdoor entrances and exits, it does not prohibit a single lighting outlet, if suitably located, from serving more than one door.

A wall switch-controlled lighting outlet is required in the kitchen and bathroom. A receptacle outlet controlled by a wall switch is not permitted to serve as a lighting outlet in these rooms.

ARTICLE 215   Feeders

Contents

215-1. **Scope.** This article covers the installation requirements and minimum size and ampacity of conductors for feeders supplying branch-circuit loads as computed in accordance with Article 220.

Exception: Feeders for electrolytic cells as covered in Section 668-3(c), Exception Nos. 1 and 4.

A thorough calculation of the total connected load to be supplied by the feeder is required to accurately determine feeder conductor ampacity. The sum of the computed and connected loads supplied by a feeder is multiplied by the "demand factor" to determine the load that the feeder conductors must be sized to serve. See Article 100 for definition of "Demand Factor."

When the total connected load is operated simultaneously, the demand factor is 100 percent; that is, the maximum demand is equal to the total connected load. Due to diversity, the maximum operating load carried at any time may be only $\frac{3}{4}$ of the total connected load; the demand factor is thus 75 percent.

On a new installation, a minimum value for the demand factor can be determined by applying the requirements and tables of Article 220, Branch Circuit, Feeder, and Service Calculations.

Feeder conductor sizes are determined by calculating the total volt-amperes of the feeder load at the nominal voltage of the feeder circuit. See Section 220-2.

$$\text{Single Phase} \qquad\qquad \text{Three Phase}$$
$$I = \frac{\text{volt-amperes load}}{E} \qquad I = \frac{\text{volt-amperes load}}{E \times 1.73}$$

$$\text{where } I = \text{current in amperes}$$
$$E = \text{volts}$$

See Section 310-15 for allowable ampacities and sizes of insulated conductors.

Feeder circuits are required to have sufficient ampacity for safety. Overloading of a wiring system that does not provide for increases in the use of electricity often creates hazards. It is good practice to allow for future expansion and convenience increases. See Section 90-8.

215-2. **Minimum Rating and Size.** Feeder conductors shall have an ampacity not less than required to supply the load as computed in Parts B, C, and D of Article 220. The minimum sizes shall be as specified in (a) and (b) below under the conditions stipulated. Feeder conductors for a dwelling unit or a mobile home need not be larger than service-entrance conductors. Article 310, Note 3, Notes to Ampacity Tables of 0 to 2000 Volts shall be permitted to be used for conductor size.

(a) **For Specified Circuits.** The ampacity of feeder conductors shall not be less than 30 amperes where the load supplied consists of any of the following number and types of circuits: (1) two or more 2-wire branch circuits supplied by a 2-wire feeder; (2) more than two 2-wire branch circuits supplied by a 3-wire feeder; (3) two or more 3-wire branch circuits supplied by a 3-wire feeder; or (4) two or more 4-wire branch circuits supplied by a 3-phase 4-wire feeder.

(b) Ampacity Relative to Service-Entrance Conductors.
The feeder conductor ampacity shall not be less than that of the
service-entrance conductors where the feeder conductors carry
the total load supplied by service-entrance conductors with an
ampacity of 55 amperes or less.

This section correlates with Note 3, Notes to Ampacity
Tables of 0 to 2,000 Volts. For example, Table 310-16 allows
200 amperes for a 3/0 THW copper wire. However, for a
3-wire, single-phase dwelling service, Note 3 permits 200
amperes for a 2/0 AWG copper THW conductor or 200
amperes for a 4/0 AWG aluminum THW conductor. It stands
to reason that feeder conductors carrying the total load supplied by the service should not be required to be sized larger
than the service-entrance conductors. See Figure 215-1.

*Figure 215-1. For a 3-wire, single-phase dwelling service, Note
3 permits an ampacity of 200 A for 2/0 copper conductors for use
as service-entrance conductors and for feeder conductors.*

(FPN No. 1):   See Examples 1 through 10 in Chapter 9.

(FPN No. 2):   Conductors for feeders as defined in Article 100, sized
to prevent a voltage drop exceeding 3 percent at the farthest outlet of power, heating, and lighting loads, or combinations of such
loads, and where the maximum total voltage drop on both feeders
and branch circuits to the farthest outlet does not exceed 5 percent,
will provide reasonable efficiency of operation.

(FPN No. 3):   See Section 210-19(a) for voltage drop for branch
circuits.

Reasonable operating efficiency will be achieved if the
voltage drop of a feeder or the voltage drop of a branch
circuit is limited to 3 percent. However, the total voltage
drop of a branch circuit plus a feeder can reach 5 percent
and still allow for reasonable operating efficiency. See Article 100 for definitions of "feeder" and "branch circuit."

The 5 percent voltage drop value is explanatory material,
and, as such, it appears as a Fine Print Note. Fine Print Notes
are not mandatory (see Section 90-5). See Section 250-95,
which requires adjustment according to circular mil area,
for equipment grounding conductors where voltage drop is
considered.

The resistance or impedance of conductors may cause a
substantial difference between voltage values at service equipment and voltage values at the point of utilization equipment. Excessive voltage drop impairs the starting and
operation of electrical equipment. Undervoltage can result
in inefficient operation of lighting and motor loads. An
applied voltage of 10 percent below rating can result in a
decrease in efficiency of substantially more than 10 percent.
For example, fluorescent light output would be reduced by
15 percent, while incandescent light output would be
reduced by 30 percent. Induction motors would run hot-
ter and produce less torque. The running current would
increase 11 percent while the operating temperature rise
increased by 12 percent. At the same time, torque would
be reduced by 19 percent.

In addition to resistance or impedance, the type of raceway or cable enclosure, type of circuit (ac, dc, single-phase,
3-phase), and power factor should be considered to determine voltage drop.

The basic formula for determining voltage drop in a
2-wire dc circuit, a 2-wire ac circuit, or a 3-wire ac single-
phase circuit with a balanced load at 100 percent power
factor and where reactance can be neglected is:

$$VD = \frac{2 \times L \times R \times I}{1000}$$

where VD = voltage drop (based on conductor tempera-
ture of 75°F)
L = One-way length of circuit (feet)
R = Conductor resistance in ohms per thousand
feet (from Chapter 9, Table 8)
I = Load current (amperes)

For 3-phase circuits (at 100 percent power factor) the
voltage drop between any 2-phase conductors is 0.866 times
the voltage drop calculated by this formula.

Example: 240-V 2-wire heating circuit. Load is 50 A. Circuit size is 6 AWG THHN copper, and the one-way circuit length is 100 feet.

$$VD = \frac{2 \times L \times R \times I}{1000} = \frac{2 \times 100 \times 0.491 \times 50}{1000}$$

$$VD = \frac{4910}{1000} = 4.91\text{-V drop}$$

A 12-V drop on a 240-V circuit is a 5 percent drop. A 4.91-V drop falls within this percentage.

Should the total voltage drop exceed 5 percent, larger size conductors should be used, the circuit length shortened, or the circuit load reduced.

Voltage drop tables and calculations are available from various manufacturers.

215-3. Overcurrent Protection. Feeders shall be protected against overcurrent in accordance with the provisions of Part A of Article 240.

215-4. Feeders with Common Neutral.

(a) Feeders with Common Neutral. Feeders containing a common neutral shall be permitted to supply two or three sets of 3-wire feeders, or two sets of 4-wire or 5-wire feeders.

(b) In Metal Raceway or Enclosure. Where installed in a metal raceway or other metal enclosure, all conductors of all feeders using a common neutral shall be enclosed within the same raceway or other enclosure as required in Section 300-20.

Where feeder conductors carrying ac current, including the neutral, are installed in metal raceways, they are required to be grouped together to avoid induction heating of the surrounding metal. Where it is necessary to run parallel conductors through multiple raceways, it is necessary to run conductors from each phase plus the neutral in each raceway. See Sections 300-3, 250-57(b), 250-79(f), 300-5(i), and 300-20(a).

A 3-phase, 4-wire (208 wye/120-V, 480 wye/277-V) system is often used to supply both lighting and motor loads. The 3-phase motor loads will not cause current to flow in the neutral conductor. Therefore, the maximum current on the neutral is due to lighting loads or circuits where the neutral is used. On this type of system (3-phase, 4-wire), a demand factor of 70 percent is permitted for that portion of the neutral load in excess of 200 A. See Section 220-22. Thus, if the maximum possible load is 500 A, the neutral would have to be large enough to carry 200 A plus 70 percent of 300 A, or 410 A. No reduction of the neutral capac-

ity for that portion of the load consisting of electric-discharge lighting is permitted. See Note 10(a), Notes to Ampacity Tables of 0 to 2,000 Volts. See Section 220-22 for other systems to which the 70 percent demand factor may be applied. The maximum unbalanced load for feeders supplying clothes dryers, household ranges, wall-mounted ovens, and counter-mounted cooking units is required to be considered as 70 percent of the load on the ungrounded conductors. See Example Nos. 1 through 5(b) of Chapter 9.

See Examples 5(a) and 5(b) of Chapter 9 for a multifamily dwelling served at 208Y/120 volts, 3-phase.

215-5. Diagrams of Feeders. If required by the authority having jurisdiction, a diagram showing feeder details shall be provided prior to the installation of the feeders. Such a diagram shall show the area in square feet of the building or other structure supplied by each feeder, the total connected load before applying demand factors, the demand factors used, the computed load after applying demand factors, and the size and type of conductors to be used.

215-6. Feeder Conductor Grounding Means. Where a feeder supplies branch circuits in which equipment grounding conductors are required, the feeder shall include or provide a grounding means in accordance with the provisions of Section 250-57 to which the equipment grounding conductors of the branch circuits shall be connected.

215-7. Ungrounded Conductors Tapped from Grounded Systems. Two-wire dc circuits and ac circuits of two or more ungrounded conductors shall be permitted to be tapped from the ungrounded conductors of circuits having a grounded neutral conductor. Switching devices in each tapped circuit shall have a pole in each ungrounded conductor.

It is not intended by Section 215-7 to require a common trip or simultaneous opening of circuit breakers or fuses but to provide a switching device to disconnect "manually" the ungrounded conductors of the feeder. See Section 210-10.

215-8. Means of Identifying Conductor with the Higher Voltage to Ground. On a 4-wire, delta-connected secondary where the midpoint of one phase is grounded to supply lighting and similar loads, the phase conductor having the higher voltage to ground shall be identified by an outer finish that is orange in color or by tagging or other effective means. Such identification shall be placed at each point where a connection is made if the grounded conductor is also present.

Where it is required to ground the midpoint of one phase winding to supply 120-V lighting and similar loads from a delta-connected secondary. This results in one phase conductor having a higher voltage to ground, and it is identified by an orange finish or other effective means at any point, such as junction or pull boxes or panelboards, where connections may be made and the grounded conductor is also present. The orange high-leg of a 3-phase, 4-wire (120/240-V) delta system is 208 V to ground (120 V × 1.73 = 208V) and should obviously not be used for 120-V circuits. See Sections 230-56 and 384-3(e) and (f). See Figure 215-2.

215-9. **Ground-Fault Protection for Personnel.** Feeders supplying 15- and 20-ampere receptacle branch circuits shall be permitted to be protected by a ground-fault circuit-interrupter in lieu of the provisions for such interrupters as specified in Section 210-8 and Article 305.

Several manufacturers offer double-pole 120/240-V circuit breaker-type ground-fault circuit-interrupters for application to a feeder, thereby protecting all branch circuits supplied by that feeder. This installation is in lieu of provisions of Section 210-8 for outdoor, bathroom, garage, kitchen, basement, and boathouse receptacles. They can also be used to protect construction-site receptacles as covered in Section 305-6(a), provided that the feeder supplies no lighting branch circuits.

It may be more economical or convenient to install ground-fault circuit-interrupters for feeders. However, consideration should be given to the fact that a ground-fault circuit-interrupter will be monitoring several branch circuits and will deenergize all branch circuits in response to a line-to-ground fault from one branch circuit.

215-10. **Ground-Fault Protection of Equipment.** Ground-fault protection of equipment as specified by Section 230-95 shall be provided for a feeder disconnect rated 1000 amperes or more in a solidly grounded wye system with greater than 150 volts to ground, but not exceeding 600 volts phase-to-phase.

Exception: Feeder ground-fault protection of equipment shall not be required where ground-fault protection of equipment is provided on the supply side of the feeder.

Figure 215-2. *With a 4-wire, delta-connected secondary in which the midpoint of one phase is grounded, one phase conductor has a higher voltage to ground than the other two. It is identified in this illustration as having an "orange" finish. The identification must be visible at every point where a connection is made, if the grounded conductor (neutral) is present.*

This section was new in the 1990 *Code*. The intent is to require ground-fault protection of equipment for feeder disconnects rated 1,000 amps or more at 480/277 volts. A similar requirement for services may be found in Section 230-95. The reason for the requirement is the unusually high number of burndowns that have been reported on feeders and services in this voltage range.

It should be noted that ground-fault protection of feeder equipment is not required if protection is provided on an upstream feeder or at the service. See also commentary following Section 230-95.

ARTICLE 220   Branch-Circuit, Feeder, and Service Calculations

Contents

A. General

B. Feeders

C. Optional Calculations for Computing Feeder and Service Loads

D. Method for Computing Farm Loads

A. General

220-1. **Scope.** This article provides requirements for determining the number of branch circuits required and for computing branch-circuit, feeder, and service loads.

The scope of Article 220 is clarified in the 1993 *Code* to verify that it includes services. See Section 230-42(a).

Exception: Branch-circuit and feeder calculations for electrolytic cells as covered in Section 668-3(c), Exception Nos. 1 and 4.

A similar exception also appears after Sections 210-1, 215-1, and 225-1.

220-2. **Voltages.** Unless other voltages are specified, for purposes of computing branch-circuit and feeder loads, nominal system voltages of 120, 120/240, 208Y/120, 240, 480Y/277, 480, and 600 volts shall be used.

For uniform application of the provisions of Articles 210, 215, and 220, nominal voltages as listed in Section 220-2 are required to be used in computing the ampere load on the conductors.

See Chapter 9, Examples 1 through 5(b). The results of these examples are generally expressed in amperes. Except where the computations result in a major fraction of an ampere (0.5 or larger), such fractions may be dropped.

To select conductor sizes, refer to Section 310-15 and, where applicable, the Notes to Ampacity Tables of 0 to 2,000 Volts.

Loads are computed on the basis of volt-amperes (VA) or kVA rather than watts or kW. However, the rating of equipment is given in watts or kW. Such ratings are considered the equivalent of the same rating in volt-amperes or kVA. See, for example, Section 220-19. This recognizes that load calculations are to determine conductor and circuit sizes, that the power-factor of the load is often unknown, and that the conductor "sees" the circuit volt-amperes only, not the circuit power (watts).

220-3. **Computation of Branch Circuits.** Branch-circuit loads shall be computed as shown in (a) through (d) below.

(FPN): See Section 600-6(c) for exterior signs and outline lighting.

(a) Continuous and Noncontinuous Loads. The branch-circuit rating shall not be less than the noncontinuous load plus 125 percent of the continuous load.

See Figure 220-1.

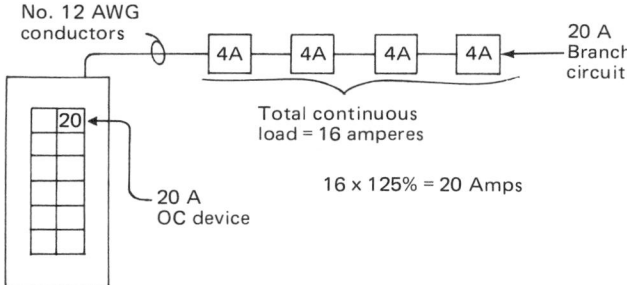

Figure 220-1. Continuous loads, such as store lighting, must be calculated at 125 percent to determine the ampacity of the conductor and the branch circuit size.

Exception: Where the assembly, including overcurrent devices, is listed for continuous operation of 100 percent of its rating.

The computed load is used to determine the ampacity required for the branch-circuit conductors. Continuous computed loads or the continuous portions of combined continuous and noncontinuous computed loads are to be calculated at 125 percent. See Section 220-3(a).

The rating of the overcurrent device must not exceed the final ampacity of the conductors after any applicable derating factors (such as a high ambient location) have been calculated. See Section 240-3 (a) through (m) for information permitting exceptions to this basic rule.

The rating of the overcurrent device is then used to rate the branch circuit. For example, it may be a 15-, 20-, 30-, 40-, or 50-amp branch circuit. See Section 210-3.

(b) Lighting Load for Listed Occupancies. A unit load of not less than that specified in Table 220-3(b) for occupancies listed therein shall constitute the minimum lighting load for each square foot (0.093 sq m) of floor area. The floor area for each floor shall be computed from the outside dimensions of the building, apartment, or other area involved. For dwelling unit(s), the computed floor area shall not include open porches, garages, or unused or unfinished spaces not adaptable for future use.

Examples of "unused or unfinished" spaces are some attics and some crawl spaces.

(FPN): The unit values herein are based on minimum load conditions and 100 percent power factor, and may not provide sufficient capacity for the installation contemplated.

(c) Other Loads — All Occupancies. In all occupancies, the minimum load for each outlet for general-use receptacles and outlets not used for general illumination shall be not less than the following, the loads shown being based on nominal branch-circuit voltages.

(1) Outlet for a specific appliance or other load except for a motor load ....ampere rating of appliance or load served.

(2) Outlet for motor load. See Sections 430-22 and 430-24 and Article 440.

(3) An outlet supplying recessed lighting fixture(s) shall be the maximum volt-ampere rating of the equipment and lamps for which the fixture(s) is rated.

Recessed lighting is included in the 3 volt-amperes per square foot for dwellings where used for general lighting.

(4) Outlet for heavy-duty lampholder ....600 volt-amperes.

(5) Track Lighting. See Section 410-102.

(6) Other outlets* ....180 volt-amperes per outlet.

For receptacle outlets, each single or each multiple receptacle on one strap shall be considered at not less than 180 volt-amperes.

*This provision shall not be applicable to receptacle outlets connected to the circuit specified in Section 220-4(b).

Table 220-3(b). General Lighting Loads By Occupancies

Type of Occupancy	Unit Load per Square Foot (Volt-Amperes)
Armories and Auditoriums	1
Banks	$3\frac{1}{2}$**
Barber Shops and Beauty Parlors	3
Churches	1
Clubs	2
Court Rooms	2
Dwelling Units*	3
Garages — Commercial (storage)	$\frac{1}{2}$
Hospitals	2
Hotels and Motels, including apartment houses without provision for cooking by tenants*	2
Industrial Commercial (Loft) Buildings	2
Lodge Rooms	$1\frac{1}{2}$
Office Buildings	$3\frac{1}{2}$**
Restaurants	2
Schools	3
Stores	3
Warehouses (storage)	$\frac{1}{4}$
In any of the above occupancies except one-family dwellings and individual dwelling units of two-family and multifamily dwellings:	
Assembly Halls and Auditoriums	1
Halls, Corridors, Closets, Stairways	$\frac{1}{2}$
Storage Spaces	$\frac{1}{4}$

For SI units: one square foot = 0.093 square meter.
*All general-use receptacle outlets of 20-ampere or less rating in one-family, two-family, and multifamily dwellings and in guest rooms of hotels and motels [except those connected to the receptacle circuits specified in Sections 220-4(b) and (c)] shall be considered as outlets for general illumination, and no additional load calculations shall be required for such outlets.
**In addition, a unit load of 1 volt-ampere per square foot shall be included for general-purpose receptacle outlets where the actual number of general-purpose receptacle outlets is unknown.

The 180-VA load is applied to single and multiple receptacles mounted on a single yoke or strap and is considered as "other outlets" in accordance with Section 220-3(c)(6). The "other outlets" mentioned above are not the outlets installed for general illumination or the small-appliance branch circuits.

The receptacle load for outlets for general illumination in one- and two-family and multifamily dwellings and in guest rooms of hotels and motels is included in Table 220-3(b). (See asterisk note to table.) The load requirement for the small-appliance branch circuits is 1,500 VA per circuit. See Section 220-16(a).

180 VA outlet   180 VA outlet   180 VA outlet   360 VA outlet

Figure 220-2. *The 180-VA rating is applied to single- and multiple- receptacle outlets on a single strap. Note that the last outlet consists of two duplex outlets on separate straps. Therefore, it would be calculated at 360 VA.*

A load of 180 volt-amperes is not required to be considered for outlets supplying recessed lighting fixtures, outlets for general illumination, and small-appliance branch circuits. To apply the 180-VA requirement in this case would be unrealistic, as it would unnecessarily restrict the number of lighting or receptacle outlets on a branch circuit. See the single asterisk note below Table 220-3(b) and the asterisk note below Section 220-3(c)(5). These indicate the 180-VA requirement is not applicable to most receptacle outlets in dwellings.

10 Outlets on a 15 A receptacle circuit

13 Outlets on a 20 A receptacle circuit

Figure 220-3. *Computation of the maximum number of outlets permitted on 15- and 20-A branch circuits. This is not applicable to outlets connected to a general lighting or small appliance branch circuit.*

Exception No. 1: Where fixed multioutlet assemblies are employed, each 5 feet (1.52 m) or fraction thereof of each separate and continuous length shall be considered as one outlet of not less than 180 volt-amperes capacity; except in locations where a number of appliances are likely to be used simultaneously, each 1 foot (305 mm) or fraction thereof shall be considered as an outlet of not less than 180 volt-amperes. The requirements of this exception shall not apply to dwelling unit(s) or the guest rooms of hotels or motels.

Figure 220-4. *Fixed multioutlet assemblies are commonly used in commercial or industrial locations and may have been selected for a number of receptacles along a given work area (light use) or for the simultaneous connection and use of a number of appliances (heavy use).*

Exception No. 2: Table 220-19 shall be permitted for computing the load of household electric ranges.

Exception No. 3: A load of not less than 200 volt-amperes per linear foot (305 mm) of show window, measured horizontally along its base, shall be permitted instead of the specified unit load per outlet.

There are two options permitted for the load calculations for branch circuits serving show windows.
Option No. 1: 180 VA per receptacle (Note Section 210-62 requires 1 receptacle per 12 linear feet.)
Option No. 2: 200 VA per linear feet per Exception No. 3 to Section 220-3(c) above.
See Figure 220-5.

200 volt-amperes per linear foot
200 VA × 10 ft = 2000 volt-amperes

Figure 220-5. *For branch-circuit loads, the linear foot calculation method is permitted in lieu of the specified unit load per outlet.*

Exception No. 4: The loads of outlets serving switchboards and switching frames in telephone exchanges shall be waived from the computations.

Exception No. 5: Section 220-18 shall be considered as a permitted method of computing the load for a household electric clothes dryer.

(d) Loads for Additions to Existing Installations.
(1) Dwelling Units. Loads for structural additions to an existing dwelling unit or to a previously unwired portion of an existing dwelling unit, either of which exceeds 500 square feet (46.5 sq m), shall be computed in accordance with (b) above. Loads for new circuits or extended circuits in previously wired dwelling units shall be computed in accordance with either (b) or (c) above.
(2) Other than Dwelling Units. Loads for new circuits or extended circuits in other than dwelling units shall be computed in accordance with either (b) or (c) above.

220-4. **Branch Circuits Required.** Branch circuits for lighting and for appliances, including motor-operated appliances, shall be provided to supply the loads computed in accordance with Section 220-3. In addition, branch circuits shall be provided for specific loads not covered by Section 220-3 where required elsewhere in this Code; for small appliance loads as specified in (b) below; and for laundry loads as specified in (c) below.

(a) Number of Branch Circuits. The minimum number of branch circuits shall be determined from the total computed load and the size or rating of the circuits used. In all installations, the number of circuits shall be sufficient to supply the load served.

In no case shall the load on any circuit exceed the maximum specified by Section 210-22.

(b) Small Appliance Branch Circuits — Dwelling Unit. In addition to the number of branch circuits determined in accordance with (a) above, two or more 20-ampere small appliance branch circuits shall be provided for all receptacle outlets specified by Section 210-52 for the small appliance loads.

See Section 210-52(c) for requirements for the spacing of counter top receptacle outlets.

(c) Laundry Branch Circuits — Dwelling Unit. In addition to the number of branch circuits determined in accordance with (a) and (b) above, at least one additional 20-ampere branch circuit shall be provided to supply the laundry receptacle outlet(s) required by Section 210-52(f). This circuit shall have no other outlets.

At least one additional 20-A branch circuit is required to be provided for the supply to the laundry receptacle outlet(s) required by Section 210-52(f). This circuit is to have no other outlets. Laundry receptacle outlets are not required in apartments or similar occupancies where there are common laundry facilities available to all occupants. In addition, a laundry outlet is not required if laundry facilities are not to be installed or permitted. See Figure 220-6.

Figure 220-6. *At least one 20-A branch circuit is required to supply the laundry receptacle outlet(s). Lighting outlets in laundry areas are not permitted to be connected to the laundry branch circuit. If the laundry area is in a basement or garage, this receptacle outlet is not considered as that required by Section 210-52(g).*

(d) Load Evenly Proportioned Among Branch Circuits. Where the load is computed on a volt-amperes-per-square-foot (0.093-sq m) basis, the wiring system up to and including the branch-circuit panelboard(s) shall be provided to serve not less than the calculated load. This load shall be evenly proportioned among multioutlet branch circuits within the panelboard(s). Branch-circuit overcurrent devices and circuits need only be installed to serve the connected load.

(FPN): See Examples 1(a), 1(b), 2(b), and 4(a), Chapter 9.

There is no restriction placed on the number of outlets connected to a general lighting or small-appliance branch-circuit. The number of general receptacle outlets in a room is determined by Section 210-52(a). See Section 210-52(c) for number of receptacle outlets at counter tops. It is desirable to provide more than the minimum number of receptacle outlets required, thereby further reducing the need for use of extension cords.

Consideration must be given to balancing the loads when terminating circuits in panelboards.

B. Feeders

220-10. General.

(a) Ampacity and Computed Loads. Feeder conductors shall have sufficient ampacity to supply the load served. In no case shall the computed load of a feeder be less than the sum of the loads on the branch circuits supplied as determined by Part A of this article after any applicable demand factors permitted by Parts B, C, or D have been applied.

See Figure 220-7.

(FPN): See Examples 1 through 10, Chapter 9. See Section 210-22(b) for maximum load in amperes permitted for lighting units operating at less than 100 percent power factor.

(b) Continuous and Noncontinuous Loads. Where a feeder supplies continuous loads or any combination of continuous and noncontinuous loads, the rating of the overcurrent device shall not be less than the noncontinuous load plus 125 percent of the continuous load.

This section was revised for the 1990 *Code.* It requires the overcurrent device for a feeder to be sized at not less than the sum of the combination of the noncontinuous loads plus 125 percent of the continuous loads.

Figure 220-7. Each panel serves a computed load of 80 amps. The main feeder is sized to carry a minimum of 240 amps (3 × 80). The feeders from the meter enclosure to the panelboards are sized to provide a minimum of 80 amps. It is not intended that the main feeder be sized to carry 300 amps. See Figure 230-16 for a similar example for service conductors.

The ungrounded service conductors are no longer required to be sized at this value. Service conductors are required to have sufficient ampacity to carry the loads computed in accordance with Article 220, with appropriate demand factors applied.

See Sections 230-23, 230-31, and 230-42.

Exception: Where the assembly including the overcurrent devices protecting the feeder(s) are listed for operation at 100 percent of their rating, neither the ampere rating of the overcurrent device nor the ampacity of the feeder conductors shall be less than the sum of the continuous load plus the noncontinuous load.

Sections 220-10 through 220-22, which are included in Part B, contain the requirements for calculating feeder and service loads. Sections 220-30 and 220-32 contain optional methods for calculating feeder and service loads in dwelling units and multifamily dwellings.

220-11. **General Lighting.** The demand factors listed in Table 220-11 shall apply to that portion of the total branch-circuit load computed for general illumination. They shall not be applied in determining the number of branch circuits for general illumination.

(FPN): See Section 220-16 for application of demand factors to small appliance and laundry loads in dwellings.

Table 220-11.   Lighting Load Feeder Demand Factors

Type of Occupancy	Portion of Lighting Load to which Demand Factor Applies (volt-amperes)	Demand Factor Percent
Dwelling Units	First 3000 or less at	100
	From 3001 to 120,000 at	35
	Remainder over 120,000 at	25
Hospitals*	First 50,000 or less at	40
	Remainder over 50,000 at	20
Hotels and Motels — Including Apartment Houses without Provision for Cooking by Tenants*	First 20,000 or less at	50
	From 20,001 to 100,000 at	40
	Remainder over 100,000 at	30
Warehouses (Storage)	First 12,500 or less at	100
	Remainder over 12,500 at	50
All Others	Total volt-amperes	100

*The demand factors of this table shall not apply to the computed load of feeders to areas in hospitals, hotels, and motels where the entire lighting is likely to be used at one time, as in operating rooms, ballrooms, or dining rooms.

See Figure 220-6 for an example of a 20-A laundry branch circuit.

220-12. **Show-Window Lighting.** For show-window lighting, a load of not less than 200 volt-amperes shall be included for each linear foot (305 mm) of show window, measured horizontally along its base.

The 200-VA calculation for each linear foot of a show window is required to calculate the FEEDER load. See commentary following Section 220-3(c)(6) Exception No. 3 for load calculations for branch circuits.

(FPN): See Section 220-3(c), Exception No. 3, for branch circuits supplying show windows.

220-13. **Receptacle Loads — Nondwelling Units.** In other than dwelling units, receptacle loads computed at not more than 180 volt-amperes per outlet in accordance with Section 220-3(c)(6) shall be permitted to be added to the lighting loads and made subject to the demand factors given in Table 220-11, or they shall be permitted to be made subject to the demand factors given in Table 220-13.

Table 220-13. Demand Factors for Nondwelling Receptacle Loads

Portion of Receptacle Load to which Demand Factor Applies (volt-amperes)	Demand Factor Percent
First 10 kVA or less	100
Remainder over 10 kVA at	50

This section permits receptacle loads, calculated at not more than 180 volt-amperes per strap, to be computed by either of two methods. The first method permits the receptacle loads to be added to the lighting load. The demand factors in Table 220-11 are then applied to the combined load. The second method permits the receptacle load to be calculated (without the lighting load) with demand factors from Table 220-13 applied. The computation resulting in the lowest value is allowed to be used.

220-14. **Motors.** Motor loads shall be computed in accordance with Sections 430-24, 430-25, and 430-26.

220-15. **Fixed Electric Space Heating.** Fixed electric space heating loads shall be computed at 100 percent of the total connected load; however, in no case shall a feeder load current rating be less than the rating of the largest branch circuit supplied.

Exception No. 1: Where reduced loading of the conductors results from units operating on duty-cycle, intermittently, or from all units not operating at one time, the authority having jurisdiction may grant permission for feeder conductors to have an ampacity less than 100 percent, provided the conductors have an ampacity for the load so determined.

Exception No. 2: The use of the optional calculations in Sections 220-30 and 220-31 shall be permitted for fixed electric space heating loads in a dwelling unit. In a multifamily dwelling, the use of the optional calculation in Section 220-32 shall be permitted.

220-16. **Small Appliance and Laundry Loads — Dwelling Unit.**

(a) **Small Appliance Circuit Load.** In each dwelling unit, the feeder load shall be computed at 1500 volt-amperes for each 2-wire small appliance branch circuit required by Section 220-4(b) for small appliances supplied by 15- or 20-ampere

receptacles on 20-ampere branch circuits in the kitchen, pantry, dining room, and breakfast room. Where the load is subdivided through two or more feeders, the computed load for each shall include not less than 1500 volt-amperes for each 2-wire branch circuit for small appliances. These loads shall be permitted to be included with the general lighting load and subjected to the demand factors permitted in Table 220-11 for the general lighting load.

See commentary following Section 210-52(b).

(b) **Laundry Circuit Load.** A feeder load of not less than 1500 volt-amperes shall be included for each 2-wire laundry branch circuit installed as required by Section 220-4(c). It shall be permissible to include this load with the general lighting load and subject it to the demand factors provided in Section 220-11.

In each dwelling unit, the feeder load is required to be calculated at 1500 VA for each of the two or more (2-wire) small-appliance branch-circuits and 1500 VA for each (2-wire) laundry branch circuit. It is permissible to total these loads and add them to the general lighting load and subject the total load (small appliance, laundry, plus general lighting) to the demand factors provided in Table 220-11.

220-17. **Appliance Load — Dwelling Unit(s).** It shall be permissible to apply a demand factor of 75 percent to the nameplate-rating load of four or more appliances fastened in place that are served by the same feeder in a one-family, two-family, or multifamily dwelling.

Exception: This demand factor shall not be applied to electric ranges, clothes dryers, space heating equipment, or air-conditioning equipment.

Example: 120/240 V fastened in place appliance load — dwelling unit(s)

water heater	4,000 W	240 V	4,000 VA
kitchen disposal	½ hp	120 V	1,176 VA
dishwater	1,200 W	120 V	1,200 VA
furnace motor	¼ hp	120 V	696 VA
attic fan	¼ hp	120 V	696 VA
water pump	½ hp	240 V	1,176 VA
		Total	8,944 VA

For appliances fastened in place (other than ranges, clothes dryers, space heating equipment, and air-conditioning equipment), feeder capacity must be provided for the sum of these loads, and the total load of four or more such appliances may be reduced by a demand factor of 75 percent.

Seventy-five percent of 8,944 VA = 6,708 VA, which is the load to be added to the other determined loads where calculating the size of service and/or feeder conductors.

See Table 430-148 for the full-load current in amperes for single-phase ac motors in accordance with Section 220-14.

220-18. Electric Clothes Dryers — Dwelling Unit(s). The load for household electric clothes dryers in a dwelling unit(s) shall be 5000 watts (volt-amperes) or the nameplate rating, whichever is larger, for each dryer served. The use of the demand factors in Table 220-18 shall be permitted.

Table 220-18. Demand Factors for Household Electric Clothes Dryers

Number of Dryers	Demand Factor Percent
1	100
2	100
3	100
4	100
5	80
6	70
7	65
8	60
9	55
10	50
11-13	45
14-19	40
20-24	35
25-29	32.5
30-34	30
35-39	27.5
40 and over	25

To compute the load of household electric dryers, this requirement specifies a minimum demand of 5 kVA for the calculation of feeder conductors. Where the nameplate rating is known and exceeds 5 kW, the larger rating is to be applied.

220-19. Electric Ranges and Other Cooking Appliances — Dwelling Unit(s). The feeder demand load for household electric ranges, wall-mounted ovens, counter-mounted cooking units, and other household cooking appliances individually rated in excess of 1¾ kW shall be permitted to be computed in accordance with Table 220-19. Where two or more single-phase ranges are supplied by a 3-phase, 4-wire feeder, the total load shall be computed on the basis of twice the maximum number connected between any two phases. kVA shall be considered equivalent to kW for loads computed under this section.

(FPN): See Example 5(a), Chapter 9.

It is permissible to add the nameplate ratings of all household cooking appliances rated more than 1¾ kW, but not more than 8¾ kW, and multiply the sum by the demand factors specified in Column B or C of Table 220-19 for the given number of appliances.

For feeder demand factors other than for dwelling unit(s), that is, commercial electric cooking equipment, dishwasher booster heaters, water heaters, etc., see Table 220-20.

Demand factors of this *Code* are based on the diversified use of appliances, since it is unlikely that all appliances will be utilized simultaneously or that all cooking units and the oven of a range will be at maximum heat for any length of time.

Table 220-19. Demand Loads for Household Electric Ranges, Wall-Mounted Ovens, Counter-Mounted Cooking Units, and Other Household Cooking Appliances over 1¾ kW Rating. Column A to be used in all cases except as otherwise permitted in Note 3 below

| Number of Appliances | Maximum Demand (See Notes) | Demand Factors Percent (See Note 3) | |
	Column A (Not over 12 kW Rating)	Column B (Less than 3½ kW Rating)	Column C (3½ kW to 8¾ kW Rating)
1	8 kW	80%	80%
2	11 kW	75%	65%
3	14 kW	70%	55%
4	17 kW	66%	50%
5	20 kW	62%	45%

Table 220-19, continued

Number of Appliances	Maximum Demand (See Notes) Column A (Not over 12 kW Rating)	Demand Factors Percent (See Note 3) Column B (Less than 3½ kW Rating)	Demand Factors Percent (See Note 3) Column C (3½ kW to 8¾ kW Rating)
6	21 kW	59%	43%
7	22 kW	56%	40%
8	23 kW	53%	36%
9	24 kW	51%	35%
10	25 kW	49%	34%
11	26 kW	47%	32%
12	27 kW	45%	32%
13	28 kW	43%	32%
14	29 kW	41%	32%
15	30 kW	40%	32%
16	31 kW	39%	28%
17	32 kW	38%	28%
18	33 kW	37%	28%
19	34 kW	36%	28%
20	35 kW	35%	28%
21	36 kW	34%	26%
22	37 kW	33%	26%
23	38 kW	32%	26%
24	38 kW	31%	26%
25	40 kW	30%	26%
26-30	15 kW plus 1 kW	30%	24%
31-40	for each range	30%	22%
41-50	25 kW plus ¾	30%	20%
51-60	kW for each	30%	18%
61 and over	range	30%	16%

Note 1.   Over 12 kW through 27 kW ranges all of same rating. For ranges individually rated more than 12 kW but not more than 27 kW, the maximum demand in Column A shall be increased 5 percent for each additional kW of rating or major fraction thereof by which the rating of individual ranges exceeds 12 kW.

The size of the conductors is required to be determined by the rating of the range. By referring to Table 220-19, it can be seen that for a range rated not over 12 kW the demand load is 8 kW (8 kVA per Section 220-19), and No. 8 copper conductors, with 60°C insulation, would suffice. Note: Section 210-19(b) does not permit the branch-circuit rating of a circuit supplying household ranges of 8¾ kW nameplate rating to be less than 40 amperes.

Note 2.   Over 8¾ kW through 27 kW ranges of unequal ratings. For ranges individually rated more than 8¾ kW and of different ratings, but none exceeding 27 kW, an average value of rating shall be computed by adding together the ratings of all ranges to obtain the total connected load (using 12 kW for any range rated less than 12 kW) and dividing by the total number of ranges; and then the maximum demand in Column A shall be increased 5 percent for each kW or major fraction thereof by which this average value exceeds 12 kW.

Note 2 provides for ranges larger than 8¾ kW, and Note 4 covers installations where the circuit supplies multiple cooking components, which are combined and treated as a single range.

Note 3.   Over 1¾ kW through 8¾ kW. In lieu of the method provided in Column A, it shall be permissible to add the nameplate ratings of all ranges rated more than 1¾ kW but not more than 8¾ kW and multiply the sum by the demand factors specified in Column B or C for the given number of appliances.

Note 4.   Branch-Circuit Load. It shall be permissible to compute the branch-circuit load for one range in accordance with Table 220-19. The branch-circuit load for one wall-mounted oven or one counter-mounted cooking unit shall be the nameplate rating of the appliance. The branch-circuit load for a counter-mounted cooking unit and not more than two wall-mounted ovens, all supplied from a single branch circuit and located in the same room, shall be computed by adding the nameplate rating of the individual appliances and treating this total as equivalent to one range.

It is permissible to compute the branch-circuit load for one range by using the nameplate rating of the appliance or Table 220-19. Where a single branch circuit supplies a counter-mounted cooking unit and not more than two wall-mounted ovens, all of which are located in the same room, it is permissible to add the nameplate ratings of these appliances and treat this total as equivalent to one range.

Example: a single branch circuit for

one counter-mounted cooking unit	8 kW
one wall-mounted oven	7 kW
one wall-mounted	6 kW
Total	21 kW

The maximum demand from Column A of Table 220-19 for one range not over 12 kW is 8 kW.

21 kW is less than 27 kW and exceeds 12 kW by 9 kW (see Note 1). The maximum demand in Column A (8 kW) is to be increased 5 percent for each additional kW exceeding 12 kW (9 kW).

$$\frac{5\%}{\text{kW}} \times 9 \text{ kW} = 45 \text{ \% Increase}$$

$$45\% \times 8 \text{ kW} = 3.6 \text{ kW Increase}$$
$$8 \text{ kW} + 3.6 \text{ kW} = 11.6 \text{ kW}$$
$$11,600 \text{ Watts} = 11,600 \text{ Volt-Amperes} \div 240 \text{ Volts} = 48.3\text{A}$$

Note 5. This table also applies to household cooking appliances rated over $1\frac{3}{4}$ kW and used in instructional programs.

(FPN No. 1): See Table 220-20 for commercial cooking equipment.

(FPN No. 2): See Examples, Chapter 9.

220-20. Kitchen Equipment — Other than Dwelling Unit(s). It shall be permissible to compute the load for commercial electric cooking equipment, dishwasher booster heaters, water heaters, and other kitchen equipment in accordance with Table 220-20. These demand factors shall be applied to all equipment that has either thermostatic control or intermittent use as kitchen equipment. They shall not apply to space heating, ventilating, or air-conditioning equipment.

However, in no case shall the feeder demand be less than the sum of the largest two kitchen equipment loads.

Table 220-20. Feeder Demand Factors for Kitchen Equipment—Other than Dwelling Unit(s)

Number of Units of Equipment	Demand Factors Percent
1	100
2	100
3	90
4	80
5	70
6 and over	65

220-21. Noncoincident Loads. Where it is unlikely that two dissimilar loads will be in use simultaneously, it shall be permissible to omit the smaller of the two in computing the total load of a feeder.

220-22. Feeder Neutral Load. The feeder neutral load shall be the maximum unbalance of the load determined by this article. The maximum unbalanced load shall be the maximum net computed load between the neutral and any one ungrounded conductor, except that the load thus obtained shall be multiplied by 140 percent for 3-wire, 2-phase or 5-wire, 2-phase systems. For a feeder supplying household electric ranges, wall-mounted ovens, counter-mounted cooking units, and electric dryers, the maximum unbalanced load shall be considered as 70 percent of the load on the ungrounded conductors, as determined in accordance with Table 220-19 for ranges and Table 220-18 for dryers. For 3-wire dc or single-phase ac, 4-wire, 3-phase, 3-wire, 2-phase, or 5-wire, 2-phase systems, a further demand factor of 70 percent shall be permitted for that portion of the unbalanced load in excess of 200 amperes. There shall be no reduction of the neutral capacity for that portion of the load that consists of electric-discharge lighting, electronic computer/data processing, or similar equipment, and supplied from a 4-wire, wye-connected, 3-phase system nor the grounded conductor of a 3-wire circuit consisting of two phase wires and the neutral of a 4-wire, 3-phase wye-connected system.

(FPN No. 1): See Examples 1(a), 1(b), 2(b), 4(a), and 5(a), Chapter 9.

(FPN No. 2): A 3-phase, 4-wire power system used to supply power to computer systems or other similar electronic loads may necessitate that the power system design allow for the possibility of high harmonic neutral currents.

Section 220-22 of the *Code* describes the basis for calculating the neutral load as the maximum unbalanced load that can occur between the neutral and any other ungrounded conductor.

For a household electric range or clothes dryer, the maximum unbalanced load may be assumed at 70 percent, so the neutral may be sized on this basis. Section 250-60 of the *Code* permits use of the grounded circuit conductor, where sized at not less than No. 10 AWG, to ground the frame of a range, except for ranges in mobile homes and travel trailers. The supply cable to the range or electric clothes dryer may be service-entrance cable with an uninsulated grounded conductor if the branch circuit originates at the service equipment. If the range or dryer is supplied with a three-conductor branch circuit, a receptacle and attachment plug, if used, may be of the three-pole type without an equipment ground. If nonmetallic-sheathed cable is used to supply the range, the conductor provided for equipment grounding purposes cannot be used for the grounded circuit conductor, as stated in Section 336-25.

Where the system supplies electric discharge lighting, such as fluorescent or HID, or data processing or similar equipment, the neutral is considered to be a current-carrying conductor if the electric discharge lighting, data processing, etc., load on the feeder neutral consists of more than half of the total load. Electric discharge lighting and data processing equipment may have harmonic currents in the neutral that may exceed the load current in the ungrounded conductors, and it would be appropriate to require a full-size or larger feeder neutral conductor depending on the total harmonic distortion contributed by the equipment to be supplied. See Section 220-22, FPN No. 2 in the 1993 *Code*.

In some instances, the neutral current may exceed the current in the phase conductors. See commentary following Article 310 Note 10 to the Ampacity Tables of 0 through 2,000 Volts.

C. Optional Calculations for Computing Feeder and Service Loads

220-30. Optional Calculation — Dwelling Unit.

(a) Feeder and Service Load. For a dwelling unit having the total connected load served by a single 3-wire, 120/240-volt or 208Y/120-volt set of service-entrance or feeder conductors with an ampacity of 100 or greater, it shall be permissible to compute the feeder and service loads in accordance with Table 220-30 instead of the method specified in Part B of this article. Feeder and service-entrance conductors whose demand load is determined by this optional calculation shall be permitted to have the neutral load determined by Section 220-22.

The optional method given in Section 220-30 is applicable to a single-dwelling unit, whether it is a separate building or located in a multifamily dwelling. The optional calculation permitted by Section 220-30 may be used only where the service-entrance or feeder conductors have an ampacity of at least 100 amperes.

Examples of the optional calculation for a dwelling unit are given in Chapter 9, Example Nos. 2(a), 2(b), 2(c), and 4(b). See Article 100 for definition of "Dwelling Unit."

(b) Loads. The loads identified in Table 220-30 as "other load" and as "remainder of other load" shall include the following:

(1) 1500 volt-amperes for each 2-wire, 20-ampere small appliance branch circuit and each laundry branch circuit specified in Section 220-16.

(2) 3 volt-amperes per square foot (0.093 sq m) for general lighting and general-use receptacles.

(3) The nameplate rating of all appliances that are fastened in place, permanently connected, or located to be on a specific circuit, ranges, wall-mounted ovens, counter-mounted cooking units, clothes dryers, and water heaters.

For the 1990 *Code*, this section was revised to include appliances that may not be "fastened in place," but may be permanently connected or on a specific circuit. It now includes appliances such as clothes dryers, dishwashers, freezers, etc.

(4) The nameplate ampere or kVA rating of all motors and of all low-power-factor loads.

Section 220-21 states that when considering loads that do not operate simultaneously, the largest of those being considered is to be used. The air-conditioning load including heat pump compressors is considered at 100 percent of the nameplate rating. The sum of electric space heating loads consisting of heat pumps and supplementary heaters is considered at 65 percent of the nameplate rating.

Table 220-30. Optional Calculation for Dwelling Unit Load in kVA

Largest of the following five selections.
(1) 100 percent of the nameplate rating(s) of the air conditioning and cooling, including heat pump compressors.
(2) 100 percent of the nameplate ratings of electric thermal storage and other heating systems where the usual load is expected to be continuous at the full nameplate value. Systems qualifying under this selection shall not be figured under any other selection in this table.
(3) 65 percent of the nameplate rating(s) of the central electric space heating, including integral supplemental heating in heat pumps.
(4) 65 percent of the nameplate rating(s) of electric space heating if less than four separately controlled units.
(5) 40 percent of the nameplate rating(s) of electric space heating of four or more separately controlled units.
Plus: 100 percent of the first 10 kVA of all other load.
40 percent of the remainder of all other load.

220-31. Optional Calculation for Additional Loads in Existing Dwelling Unit. For an existing dwelling unit presently being served by an existing 120/240-volt or 208Y/120, 3-wire service, it shall be permissible to compute load calculations as follows:

Load (in kVa)	Percent of Load
First 8 kVA of load at	100%
Remainder of load at	40%

Load calculation shall include lighting at 3 volt-amperes per square foot (0.093 sq m); 1500 volt-amperes for each 20-ampere appliance circuit; range or wall-mounted oven and counter-mounted cooking unit; and other appliances that are permanently connected or fastened in place, at nameplate rating.

If air-conditioning equipment or electric space heating equipment is to be installed, the following formula shall be applied to determine if the existing service is of sufficient size.

Air-conditioning equipment*	100%
Central electric space heating*	100%
Less than four separately controlled space heating units*	100%
First 8 kVA of all other load	100%
Remainder of all other load	40%

Other loads shall include:

1500 volt-amperes for each 20-ampere appliance circuit.

Lighting and portable appliances at 3 volt-amperes per square foot (0.093 sq m).

Household range or wall-mounted oven and counter-mounted cooking unit.

All other appliances fastened in place, including four or more separately controlled space heating units, at nameplate rating.

*Use larger connected load of air conditioning and space heating, but not both.

This optional method allows an additional load to be supplied by an existing service.

Example: An existing dwelling unit is served by a 100-A service. An additional load of 5 kVA, 240-V air conditioning is to be installed. The existing load consists of the following:

general lighting 24 ft × 40 ft = 960 sq ft × 3 VA/sq ft	=	2880 VA
small appliance circuits 3 × 1500 VA	=	4500 VA
laundry circuit at 1500 VA	=	1500 VA
electric range rated 10.5 kW	=	10,500 VA
electric water heater rated 3.0 kW	=	3000 VA
existing other load Total		23,380 VA

Computation of existing load plus additional load air conditioning 5 kVA at 100%	=	5000 VA
first 8 kVA of all other load at 100%	=	8000 VA
remainder of other load at 40% 22,380 − 8000 = 14,380 × 0.40	=	5752 VA
Total		18,752 VA

18,752 ÷ 240 = 78.1 amperes

The additional load contributed by the 5 kVA air conditioning does not exceed the allowable load permitted on a 100-A service.

220-32. Optional Calculation — Multifamily Dwelling.

(a) Feeder or Service Load. It shall be permissible to compute the feeder or service load of a multifamily dwelling in accordance with Table 220-32 instead of Part B of this article where all the following conditions are met:

(1) No dwelling unit is supplied by more than one feeder.

(2) Each dwelling unit is equipped with electric cooking equipment.

It should be recognized that the method of calculation of load under Section 220-32 is optional and only applies where one service or feeder supplies the entire load of a dwelling unit and that it has other limitations that are intended to provide appropriate diversity. It should also be understood that where all of the stated conditions prevail, it is intended that the optional calculations in Section 220-32 may be used instead of those in Part B of Article 220; this is stated in paragraph (a).

Exception: When the computed load for multifamily dwellings without electric cooking in Part B of this article exceeds that computed under Part C for the identical load plus electric cooking (based on 8 kW per unit), the lesser of the two loads shall be permitted to be used.

Section 220-32(a)(2) requires each dwelling unit to be equipped with electric cooking in order to use this method of calculation. This exception permits calculation under this section for dwelling units that do not have electric cooking by calculating a SIMULATED electric cooking load of 8 kW per unit and selecting the lesser of the two loads.

(3) Each dwelling unit is equipped with either electric space heating or air conditioning or both.

Feeders and service-entrance conductors whose demand load is determined by this optional calculation shall be permitted to have the neutral load determined by Section 220-22.

(b) House Loads. House loads shall be computed in accordance with Part B of this article and shall be in addition to the dwelling unit loads computed in accordance with Table 220-32.

(c) Connected Loads. The connected load to which the demand factors of Table 220-32 apply shall include the following:

(1) 1500 volt-amperes for each 2-wire, 20-ampere small appliance branch circuit and each laundry branch circuit specified in Section 220-16.

(2) 3 volt-amperes per square foot (0.093 sq m) for general lighting and general-use receptacles.

(3) The nameplate rating of all appliances that are fastened in place, permanently connected or located to be on a specific circuit, ranges, wall-mounted ovens, counter-mounted cooking units, clothes dryers, water heaters, and space heaters.

If water heater elements are so interlocked that all elements cannot be used at the same time, the maximum possible load shall be considered the nameplate load.

(4) The nameplate ampere or kVA rating of all motors and of all low-power-factor loads.

(5) The larger of the air-conditioning load or the space heating load.

220-33. Optional Calculation — Two Dwelling Units. Where two dwelling units are supplied by a single feeder and the computed load under Part B of this article exceeds that for three identical units computed under Section 220-32, the lesser of the two loads shall be permitted to be used.

220-34. Optional Method — Schools. The calculation of a feeder or service load for schools shall be permitted in accordance with Table 220-34 in lieu of Part B of this article where equipped with electric space heating or air conditioning, or both. The connected load to which the demand factors of Table 220-34 apply shall include all of the interior and exterior lighting, power, water heating, cooking, other loads, and the larger of the air-conditioning load or space heating load within the building or structure.

Feeders and service-entrance conductors whose demand load is determined by this optional calculation shall be permitted to have the neutral load determined by Section 220-22. Where the building or structure load is calculated by this optional method, feeders within the building or structure shall have ampacity as permitted in Part B of this article; however, the ampacity of an individual feeder need not be larger than the ampacity for the entire building.

This section shall not apply to portable classroom buildings.

Many schools add small portable classroom buildings. The air-conditioning load must comply with Article 440, and the lighting load is to be considered as continuous. The demand factors of Table 220-34 are not to be applied to a portable classroom, since it would decrease the feeder or service size to below that required for the connected continuous load.

Table 220-32. Optional Calculation — Demand Factors for Three or More Multifamily Dwelling Units

Number of Dwelling Units	Demand Factor Percent
3–5	45
6–7	44
8–10	43
11	42
12–13	41
14–15	40
16–17	39
18–20	38
21	37
22–23	36
24–25	35
26–27	34
28–30	33
31	32
32–33	31
34–36	30
37–38	29
39–42	28
43–45	27
46–50	26
51–55	25
56–61	24
62 and over	23

Table 220-34. Optional Method — Demand Factors for Feeders and Service-Entrance Conductors for Schools

Connected Load Volt-Amperes per Square Foot	Demand Factors Percent
Connected load up to and including 3, plus	100
Conected load over 3 and including 20, plus	75
Connected load over 20 at	25

For SI units: one square foot = 0.093 square meter.

220-35. **Optional Calculations for Additional Loads to Existing Installations.** For the purpose of allowing additional loads to be connected to existing feeders and services, it shall be permitted to use actual maximum kVA demand figures to determine the existing load on a service or feeder when all the following conditions are met:

(1) The maximum demand data is available in kVA for a minimum of a one-year period.

(2) The existing demand at 125 percent plus the new load does not exceed the ampacity of the feeder or rating of the service.

(3) The feeder has overcurrent protection in accordance with Sections 240-3, and the service has overload protection in accordance with Section 230-90.

Where existing installations have been checked, and the maximum demand kVA data for a minimum of a one-year period is available, and the installation complies with (2) and (3), connection of additional loads to existing services and feeders is permitted.

220-36. **Optional Calculation — New Restaurants.** Calculation of a service load or feeder, where the feeder serves the total load, for a new restaurant shall be permitted in accordance with Table 220-36 in lieu of Part B of this article.

The overload protection of the service-entrance conductors shall be in accordance with Sections 230-90 and 240-3.

Feeder conductors shall not be required to be of greater ampacity than the service-entrance conductors.

Service-entrance or feeder conductors whose demand load is determined by this optional calculation shall be permitted to have the neutral load determined by Section 220-22.

Table 220-36. Optional Method — Demand Factors for Service-Entrance and Feeder Conductors for New Restaurants

Connected Load (kVA)	All Electric Demand Factor (Percent)	Not All Electric Demand Factor (Percent)
0-325	80	100
Remainder over 325	50	70

This section was introduced in the 1990 *National Electrical Code*. It recognizes the effects of diversity on many pieces of cooking equipment. The data for this change was based on load studies of 262 restaurants by the National Restaurant Association, the Edison Electric Institute, and the Electric Power Research Institute. These studies have shown that the demand factors decline as the connected loads increase. Based on this information, it was determined that demand factors would be appropriate.

Example No. 1
An all-electric restaurant with a total connected load of 300 kVA at 208Y/120 volts would have a demand factor of 80 percent. Therefore the service would be sized at:
300 kVA × 80 percent/(208 volts)(1.73) = 666 amperes
The next standard size overcurrent device is 700 amperes. The minimum size of the conductors must be adequate to handle the load, but Section 240-3(b), would permit the next standard rated overcurrent device to be used.

Example No. 2
A restaurant with gas cooking appliances and a total connected load of 300 kVA at 208Y/120 volts would have a demand factor of 100 percent. Therefore the service would be sized at:
300 kVA × 100 percent/(208 volts)(1.73) = 832 amperes
Section 230-79 requires that the service disconnecting means have a rating not less than the computed load (832 amps). The next higher standard rating for an overcurrent device, according to Section 240-6, is 1,000 amperes.

Since the overcurrent device in this example is rated at 1,000 amps, the ampacity of the conductors must be 1,000 amps, in accordance with Section 240-3(c).

Where circuit breakers of the adjustable type are used, the maximum setting of the long-time pickup is considered the rating of the circuit breaker. See Section 240-6(b).

Example No. 3
An all-electric restaurant with a total connected load of 400 kVA at 208Y/120 volts will have the demand factors applied in steps as follows:
First 325 kVA at 80 percent, 325 kVA × .80 = 260 kVA
Remainder over 325 kVA at 50 percent, 400 kVA − 325 kVA = 75 kVA, 75 kVA × .50 = 37.5 kVA
Total load 297.5 kVA

The next standard size overcurrent protective device according to Section 240-6, is 300 amperes. The minimum size of the conductors must have an ampacity sufficient to carry the load.

D. Method for Computing Farm Loads

220-40. **Farm Loads — Buildings and Other Loads.**

(a) Dwelling Unit. The feeder or service load of a farm dwelling unit shall be computed in accordance with the provisions for dwellings in Part B or C of this article. Where the dwelling has electric heat and the farm has electric grain drying systems, Part C of this article shall not be used to compute the dwelling load.

(b) Other than Dwelling Unit. For each farm building or load supplied by two or more branch circuits, the load for feeders, service-entrance conductors, and service equipment shall be computed in accordance with demand factors not less than indicated in Table 220-40.

(FPN): See Section 230-21 for overhead conductors from a pole to a building or other structure.

Section 230-21 requires such overhead conductors to be considered as a service drop and installed accordingly.

Table 220-40. Method for Computing Farm Loads for Other than Dwelling Unit

Ampere Load at 240 Volts	Demand Factor Percent
Loads expected to operate without diversity, but not less than 125 percent full-load current of the largest motor and not less than the first 60 amperes of load	100
Next 60 amperes of all other loads	50
Remainder of other load	25

220-41. **Farm Loads — Total.** The total load of the farm for service-entrance conductors and service equipment shall be computed in accordance with the farm dwelling unit load and demand factors specified in Table 220-41. Where there is equipment in two or more farm equipment buildings or for loads having the same function, such loads shall be computed in accordance with Table 220-40 and shall be permitted to be combined as a single load in Table 220-41 for computing the total load.

(FPN): See Section 230-21 for overhead conductors from a pole to a building or other structure.

Table 220-41. Method for Computing Total Farm Load

Individual Loads Computed in Accordance with Table 220-40	Demand Factor Percent
Largest load	100
Second largest load	75
Third largest load	65
Remaining loads	50

To this total load, add the load of the farm dwelling unit computed in accordance with Part B or C of this article. Where the dwelling has electric heat and the farm has electric grain drying systems, Part C of this article shall not be used to compute the dwelling load.

ARTICLE 225 Outside Branch Circuits and Feeders

Contents

225-14. Open-Conductor Spacings.

  (a) 600 Volts, Nominal, or Less.

  (b) Over 600 Volts, Nominal.

  (c) Separation from Other Circuits.

  (d) Conductors on Poles.

225-15. Supports Over Buildings.

225-16. Point of Attachment to Buildings.

225-17. Means of Attachment to Buildings.

225-18. Clearance from Ground.

225-19. Clearances from Buildings for Conductors of Not Over 600 Volts, Nominal.

  (a) Above Roofs.

  (b) From Nonbuilding or Nonbridge Structures.

  (c) Horizontal Clearances.

  (d) Final Spans.

  (e) Zone for Fire Ladders.

225-20. Mechanical Protection of Conductors.

225-21. Multiconductor Cables on Exterior Surfaces of Buildings.

225-22. Raceways on Exterior Surfaces of Buildings.

225-23. Underground Circuits.

225-24. Outdoor Lampholders.

225-25. Location of Outdoor Lamps.

225-26. Vegetation.

225-1. **Scope.** This article covers requirements for outside branch circuits and feeders run between buildings, structures, or poles on the premises; and electric equipment and wiring for the supply of utilization equipment that is located on or attached to the outside of buildings, structures, or poles.

Exception: Outside branch circuits and feeders for electrolytic cells as covered in Section 668-3(c), Exception Nos. 1 and 4.

(FPN): For additional information on wiring over 600 volts, see National Electrical Safety Code, ANSI C2-1990.

225-2. **Other Articles.** Application of other articles, including additional requirements to specific cases of equipment and conductors, is as follows:

	Article
Branch Circuits	210
Class 1, Class 2, and Class 3 Remote-Control, Signaling, and Power-Limited Circuits	725
Communications Circuits	800
Community Antenna Television and Radio Distribution Systems	820
Conductors for General Wiring	310
Electrically Driven or Controlled Irrigation Machines	675
Electric Signs and Outline Lighting	600
Feeders	215
Fire Protective Signaling Systems	760
Fixed Outdoor Electric Deicing and Snow-Melting Equipment	426
Floating Buildings	553
Grounding	250
Hazardous (Classified) Locations	500
Hazardous (Classified) Locations — Specific	510
Marinas and Boatyards	555
Messenger Supported Wiring	321
Open Wiring on Insulators	320
Overcurrent Protection	240
Radio and Television Equipment	810
Services	230
Solar Photovoltaic Systems	690
Swimming Pools, Fountains, and Similar Installations	680
Use and Identification of Grounded Conductors	200

225-3. **Calculation of Load.**

  (a) Branch Circuits. The load on outdoor branch circuits shall be as determined by Section 220-3.

  (b) Feeders. The load on outdoor feeders shall be as determined by Part B of Article 220.

225-4. **Conductor Covering.** Where within 10 feet (3.05 m) of any building or other structure, open wiring on insulators shall be insulated or covered. Conductors in cables or raceways, except Type MI cable, shall be of the rubber-covered type or thermoplastic type and in wet locations shall comply with Section 310-8. Conductors for festoon lighting shall be of the rubber-covered or thermoplastic type.

Exception: Equipment grounding conductors and grounded circuit conductors where permitted to be bare or covered elsewhere in this Code.

This exception and Section 250-152(a), Exception No. 2, clarify that bare neutral messenger wire cable assemblies that are regrounded at additional buildings are permitted.

225-5. **Size of Conductors.** The ampacity of outdoor branch-circuit and feeder conductors shall be in accordance with Section 310-15 based on loads as determined under Section 220-3 and Part B of Article 220.

225-6. **Minimum Size of Conductor.**

(a) Overhead Spans. Open individual conductors shall not be smaller than the following:

(1) For 600 volts, nominal, or less, No. 10 copper or No. 8 aluminum for spans up to 50 feet (15.2 m) in length and No. 8 copper or No. 6 aluminum for a longer span.

Exception: Where supported by a messenger wire.

(2) For over 600 volts, nominal, No. 6 copper or No. 4 aluminum where open individual conductors and No. 8 copper or No. 6 aluminum where in cable.

The size limitation of copper and aluminum conductors is based on the need for adequate mechanical strength to support the weight of the conductors and withstand wind, icing conditions, etc. See Figure 225-1. Where the conductors are supported on a messenger, the messenger cable provides the mechanical strength. See Section 321-3 for wiring methods permitted to be messenger supported.

(b) Festoon Lighting. Overhead conductors for festoon lighting shall not be smaller than No. 12.

Exception: Where supported by messenger wires.

(FPN): See Section 225-24 for outdoor lampholders.

Figure 225-1. *Overhead spans that are not messenger supported, run between buildings, structures, or poles for 600 V or less.*

Definition. Festoon lighting is a string of outdoor lights suspended between two points more than 15 feet (4.57 m) apart.

See Figure 225-7.

225-7. **Lighting Equipment Installed Outdoors.**

(a) General. For the supply of lighting equipment installed outdoors, the branch circuits shall comply with Article 210 and (b) through (d) below.

(b) Common Neutral. The ampacity of the neutral conductor shall not be less than the maximum net computed load current between the neutral and all ungrounded conductors connected to any one phase of the circuit.

See Figures 225-2 and 225-3.

Multiwire branch circuits consisting of a neutral and two or more ungrounded conductors are permissible, provided the neutral capacity is not less than the total load of all ungrounded conductors connected to any one phase of the circuit.

Branch circuits for outdoor illumination of industrial establishments, office buildings, schools, stores, and other commercial or public buildings are permitted to operate with a voltage to ground of 277 volts. See Section 210-6(d)(1) for voltages greater than 277 volts to ground.

Many designers of outdoor lighting installations on poles prefer a nominal 10 percent under voltage (130-V rated lamps on nominal 120-V circuits). Although this decreases the light intensity somewhat, it prolongs the life of the lamps, minimizing pole lamp maintenance, which can be difficult.

The restrictions in Section 225-7(c) are in addition to those in Section 210-6.

Figure 225-2. *Single-phase system 3-wire, 240/120 volts. All branch circuits are rated at 20 amperes. The maximum unbalanced current that can occur will be four times 20 A, which is 80 A.*

Figure 225-3. *Three-phase, 4-wire system, 208Y/120 volts. All branch circuits are rated at 20 amperes. The maximum unbalanced current that can occur on a 3-phase system with the load connected as shown will be 80 A due to the load on phase C.*

(c) 277 Volts to Ground. Circuits exceeding 120 volts, nominal, between conductors and not exceeding 277 volts, nominal, to ground shall be permitted to supply lighting fixtures for illumination of outdoor areas of industrial establishments, office buildings, schools, stores, and other commercial or public buildings where the fixtures are not less than 3 feet (914 mm) from windows, platforms, fire escapes, and the like.

(d) 600 Volts Between Conductors. Circuits exceeding 277 volts, nominal, to ground and not exceeding 600 volts, nominal, between conductors shall be permitted to supply the auxiliary equipment of electric-discharge lamps in accordance with Section 210-6(d)(1).

Section 210-6(d)(1)a. and b. lists the height requirements for circuits exceeding 277 volts, nominal, to ground but not exceeding 600 volts, nominal, between conductors and that supply the auxiliary equipment of electric-discharge lamps.

225-8. Disconnection.

(a) Disconnecting Means. The disconnecting means for branch-circuit and feeder fuses shall be in accordance with Section 240-40.

The intent of this reference to Section 240-40 is to assure that fuses accessible to other than qualified persons can be disconnected from their source of supply.

(b) Disconnect Required for Each. Where more than one building or other structure is on the same property and under single management, each building or other structure served shall be provided with means for disconnecting all ungrounded conductors.

The disconnecting means shall be installed either inside or outside of a building or structure at a readily accessible location nearest the point of entrance of the supply conductors.

Disconnects shall be installed in accordance with the requirements of Sections 230-71 and 230-72.

Exception No. 1: For large capacity multibuilding industrial installations under single management, where it is assured that the disconnecting can be accomplished by establishing and maintaining safe switching procedures, the disconnecting means shall be permitted to be located elsewhere on the premises.

Exception No. 2: Buildings or other structures qualifying under the provisions of Article 685.

The requirements in Section 230-84 for the disconnecting means for one or more buildings on the same property and supplied from the same service has been revised for the 1993 *Code* and relocated as a new Section 225-8 "Disconnection."

The requirements for applying the rule for two or more buildings under single management, are shown in Figures 225-4 and 225-5.

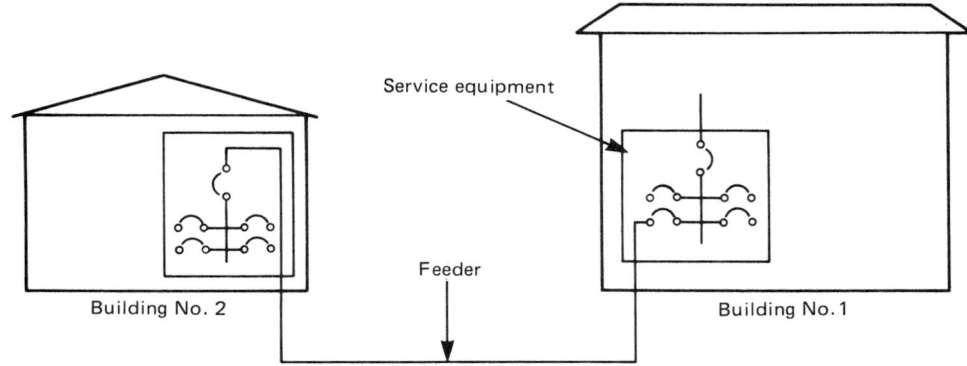

Figure 225-4. *Disconnecting means required in Building No. 2. It must be readily accessible and located NEAREST THE POINT OF ENTRANCE of the feeder conductors. The number of disconnects in Building No. 2 is limited to six. See Section 225-8(b).*

Figure 225-5. *Disconnecting means required in Buildings No. 2 and 3. The number of disconnects in buildings 2 and 3 is limited to six. See Section 225-8(b).*

(c) Suitable for Service Equipment. The disconnecting means specified in (b) above shall be suitable for use as service equipment.

Exception: For garages and outbuildings on residential property, a snap switch or a set of 3-way or 4-way snap switches suitable for use on branch circuits shall be permitted as the disconnecting means.

225-9. **Overcurrent Protection.** Overcurrent protection shall be in accordance with Section 210-20 for branch circuits and Article 240 for feeders.

(FPN): See Section 240-24 for requirements for access to overcurrent devices.

225-10. **Wiring on Buildings.** The installation of outside wiring on surfaces of buildings shall be permitted for circuits of not over 600 volts, nominal, as open wiring on insulators, as multiconductor cable, as Type MC cable, as Type MI cable, as messenger supported wiring, in rigid metal conduit, in intermediate metal conduit, in rigid nonmetallic conduit, in cable trays, as cablebus, in wireways, in auxiliary gutters, in electrical metallic tubing, in flexible metal conduit, in liquidtight flexible metal conduit, liquidtight flexible nonmetallic conduit, and in busways. Circuits of over 600 volts, nominal, shall be installed as provided in Section 710-4. Circuits for signs and outline lighting shall be installed in accordance with Article 600.

225-11. **Circuit Exits and Entrances.** Where outside branch and feeder circuits leave or enter a building, the requirements of Sections 230-52 and 230-54 shall apply.

See Figure 225-6.

225-12. **Open-Conductor Supports.** Open conductors shall be supported on glass or porcelain knobs, racks, brackets, or strain insulators.

225-13. **Festoon Supports.** In spans exceeding 40 feet (12.2 m), the conductors shall be supported by a messenger wire; and the messenger wire shall be supported by strain insulators. Conductors or messenger wires shall not be attached to any fire escape, downspout, or plumbing equipment.

Section 225-6 defines "festoon lighting" as "a string of outdoor lights suspended between two points more than 15 feet apart." The conductors are not permitted to be smaller than No. 12, unless they are supported by a messenger wire. On all spans of festoon lighting exceeding 40 feet, messenger wire is required and is to be supported by strain insulators. Where no messenger wire is required, the No. 12 or larger conductors are required to be supported by strain insulators. See Figure 225-7.

Attachment to fire escapes, plumbing equipment, or drain spouts is prohibited since it could provide a path to ground. Moreover, such methods of attachment could not be relied on for a permanent or secure means of support.

225-14. **Open-Conductor Spacings.**

(a) 600 Volts, Nominal, or Less. Conductors of 600 volts, nominal, or less, shall comply with the spacings provided in Table 230-51(c).

(b) Over 600 Volts, Nominal. Conductors of over 600 volts, nominal, shall comply with the spacings provided in Part D of Article 710.

(c) Separation from Other Circuits. Open conductors shall be separated from open conductors of other circuits or systems by not less than 4 inches (102 mm).

(d) Conductors on Poles. Conductors on poles shall have a separation of not less than 1 foot (305 mm) where not placed on racks or brackets. Conductors supported on poles shall provide a horizontal climbing space not less than the following:

Power conductors, below communication conductors	30 inches (762 mm)
Power conductors alone or above communication conductors:	
300 volts or less	24 inches (610 mm)
Over 300 volts	30 inches (762 mm)
Communication conductors below power conductors	same as power conductors
Communication conductors alone	no requirement

Ample space is required to enable linemen to climb over or through conductors to safely service conductors on the pole.

Figure 225-6. *Section 225-11 references Sections 230-52 (Individual Conductors Entering Buildings or Other Structures) and 230-54 (Connections at Service Head). Section 225-18 covers the requirements for clearances from ground (not over 600 V) and Section 225-19 covers the requirements for clearances from buildings (not over 600 V). See Section 225-19(d) for clearances from windows, doors, fire escapes, etc.*

Figure 225-7. *Messenger wires are required for festoon lighting conductors smaller than No. 12 or for spans exceeding 40 feet.*

225-15. **Supports Over Buildings.** Supports over a building shall be in accordance with Section 230-29.

225-16. **Point of Attachment to Buildings.** The point of attachment to a building shall be in accordance with Section 230-26.

225-17. **Means of Attachment to Buildings.** The means of attachment to a building shall be in accordance with Section 230-27.

225-18. **Clearance from Ground.** Overhead spans of open conductors and open multiconductor cables of not over 600 volts, nominal, shall conform to the following:

10 feet (3.05 m) — above finished grade, sidewalks, or from any platform or projection from which they might be reached where the supply conductors are limited to 150 volts to ground and accessible to pedestrians only.

12 feet (3.66 m) — over residential property and driveways, and those commercial areas not subject to truck traffic where the voltage is limited to 300 volts to ground.

15 feet (4.57 m) — for those areas listed in the 12-foot (3.66-m) classification where the voltage exceeds 300 volts to ground.

18 feet (5.49 m) — over public streets, alleys, roads, parking areas subject to truck traffic, driveways on other than residential property, and other land traversed by vehicles such as cultivated, grazing, forest, and orchard.

(FPN): Note: For clearances of conductors of over 600 volts, see National Electrical Safety Code, ANSI C2-1990.

225-19. **Clearances from Buildings for Conductors of Not Over 600 Volts, Nominal.**

(a) **Above Roofs.** Overhead spans of open conductors and open multiconductor cables shall have a vertical clearance of not less than 8 feet (2.44 m) above the roof surface. The vertical clearance above the roof level shall be maintained for a distance not less than 3 feet (914 mm) in all directions from the edge of the roof.

Exception No. 1: The area above a roof surface subject to pedestrian or vehicular traffic shall have a vertical clearance from the roof surface in accordance with the clearance requirements of Section 225-18.

Exception No. 2: Where the voltage between conductors does not exceed 300 and the roof has a slope of not less than 4 inches (102 mm) in 12 inches (305 mm), a reduction in clearance to 3 feet (914 mm) shall be permitted.

Exception No. 3: Where the voltage between conductors does not exceed 300, a reduction in clearance above only the overhanging portion of the roof to not less than 18 inches (457 mm) shall be permitted if (1) not more than 4 feet (1.22 m) of the conductors pass above the roof overhang, and (2) they are terminated at a through-the-roof raceway or approved support.

Exception No. 4: The requirement for maintaining the vertical clearance 3 feet (914 mm) from the edge of the roof shall not apply to the final conductor span where the conductors are attached to the side of a building.

(b) **From Nonbuilding or Nonbridge Structures.** From signs, chimneys, radio and television antennas, tanks, other nonbuilding or nonbridge structures, clearances, vertical, diagonal and horizontal, shall not be less than 3 feet (914 mm).

(c) **Horizontal Clearances.** Clearances shall not be less than 3 feet (914 mm).

(d) **Final Spans.** Final spans of feeders or branch circuits to a building they supply or from which they are fed shall be permitted to be attached to the building, but they shall be kept 3 feet (914 mm) from windows, doors, porches, fire escapes, or similar locations.

Exception: Conductors run above the top level of a window shall be permitted to be less than the 3 feet (914 mm) requirement above.

Overhead branch-circuit and feeder conductors shall not be installed beneath openings through which materials may be moved, such as openings in farm and commercial buildings, and shall not be installed where they will obstruct entrance to these building openings.

See Figure 225-6.

(e) **Zone for Fire Ladders.** Where buildings exceed three stories or 50 feet (15.2 m) in height, overhead lines shall be arranged, where practicable, so that a clear space (or zone) at least 6 feet (1.83 m) wide will be left either adjacent to the buildings or beginning not over 8 feet (2.44 m) from them to facilitate the raising of ladders when necessary for fire fighting.

(FPN): Note: For clearance of conductors over 600 volts, see National Electrical Safety Code, ANSI C2-1990.

225-20. **Mechanical Protection of Conductors.** Mechanical protection of conductors on buildings, structures, or poles shall be as provided for services in Section 230-50.

225-21. **Multiconductor Cables on Exterior Surfaces of Buildings.** Supports for multiconductor cables on exterior surfaces of buildings shall be as provided in Section 230-51.

225-22. **Raceways on Exterior Surfaces of Buildings.** Raceways on exterior surfaces of buildings shall be raintight and arranged to drain.

Exception: As permitted in Section 350-2.

"Raintight" is defined as "so constructed or protected that exposure to a beating rain will not result in the entrance of water under specified test conditions." To assure this, all conduit bodies, fittings, and boxes used in wet locations are required to be provided with threaded hubs or other approved means. Threadless couplings and connectors used with metal conduit or electrical metallic tubing are required to be of the raintight type (see Sections 345-9, 346-9, and 348-8).

Where exposed to weather or rain through weatherhead openings, condensation is likely to occur, causing moisture to accumulate within raceways at low points of the installation and in junction boxes. Raceways should thus be installed to permit drainage through drain holes at appropriate locations.

225-23. **Underground Circuits.** Underground circuits shall meet the requirements of Section 300-5.

225-24. **Outdoor Lampholders.** Where outdoor lampholders are attached as pendants, the connections to the circuit wires shall be staggered. Where such lampholders have terminals of a type that puncture the insulation and make contact with the conductors, they shall be attached only to conductors of the stranded type.

Splices to branch-circuit conductors for outdoor lampholders of the Edison-base type or "pig-tail sockets" are required to be staggered so as not to place splices in close proximity to each other.

"Pin-type" terminal sockets are required to be attached to STRANDED conductors only and are intended for installations for temporary lighting or decorations, signs, or specifically approved applications.

225-25. **Location of Outdoor Lamps.** Locations of lamps for outdoor lighting shall be below all energized conductors, transformers, or other electric utilization equipment.

Exception No. 1: Where clearances or other safeguards are provided for relamping operations.

Exception No. 2: Where equipment is controlled by a disconnecting means that can be locked in the open position.

Since Section 225-18 requires a minimum clearance for open conductors of 10 feet above grade or platforms, it would be difficult to keep all electrical equipment above the lamps. Section 225-5, Exception No. 1, allows other clearances or safeguards to permit safe relamping, and Exception No. 2 permits the use of a disconnecting means to deenergize the circuit.

225-26. **Vegetation.** Vegetation such as trees shall not be used for support of overhead conductor spans.

Exception: For temporary wiring in accordance with Article 305.

Where overhead conductor spans are attached to a tree, normal tree growth around the attachment device causes the mounting insulators to break and conductor insulation is degraded. This requirement also reduces the likelihood of chafing of the conductor insulation and the danger of shock to tree trimmers and tree climbers. Trees are permitted as support of overhead conductor spans on a temporary basis only. Outdoor lighting fixtures and associated equipment are permitted to be supported by trees. In order to prevent the chafing damage, conductors are run up the tree from an underground wiring method. See Section 410-16(h).

ARTICLE 230   Services

Contents

F. Service Equipment — Disconnecting Means

G. Service Equipment — Overcurrent Protection

H. Services Exceeding 600 Volts, Nominal

230-1. **Scope.** This article covers service conductors and equipment for control and protection of services and their installation requirements.

(FPN): See Diagram 230-1.

The part numbers include the following sections:

Subject	Part	Section
General	A	230-2 — 230-9
Overhead Service-Drop Conductors	B	230-21 — 230-29
Underground Service-Lateral Conductors	C	230-30 — 230-32
Service-Entrance Conductors	D	230-40 — 230-56
Service-Equipment — General	E	230-62 — 230-65
Service-Equipment — Disconnecting Means	F	230-70 — 230-84
Service-Equipment — Overcurrent Protection	G	230-90 — 230-95
Services Exceeding 600 Volts, Nominal	H	230-200 — 230-211

Diagram 230-1.

A. General

230-2. **Number of Services.** A building or other structure served shall be supplied by only one service.

Where more than one service is permitted by any of the following exceptions, a permanent plaque or directory shall be installed at each service drop or lateral or at each service-equipment location denoting all other services on or in that building or structure and the area served by each.

The basic requirement of this section is that a building or other structure can be supplied by only one service. Where more than one service is installed as permitted by the exceptions, a permanent plaque or directory is required to be installed at each service drop or lateral or at each service-equipment location denoting all of the other services on or in that building or structure and the area served by each. This plaque or directory should be constructed of sufficient durability to withstand the ambient environment. See Figure 230-1.

Exception No. 1: For fire pumps where a separate service is required.

Exception No. 2: For emergency, legally required standby, optional standby, or parallel power production systems where a separate service is required.

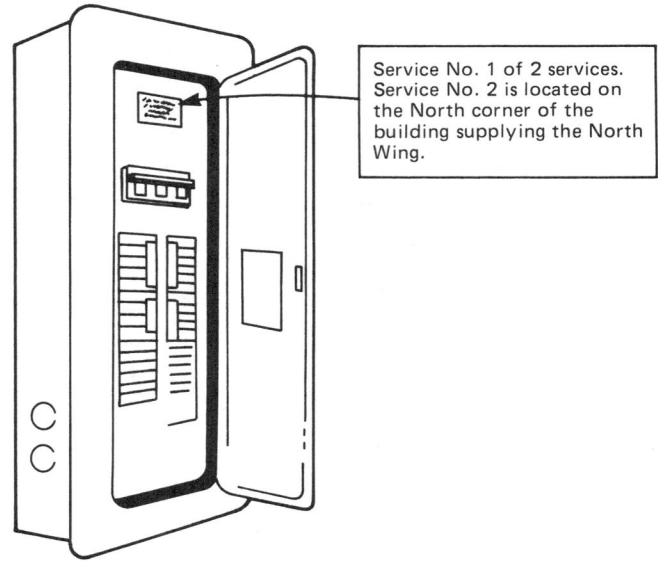

Service No. 1 of 2 services. Service No. 2 is located on the North corner of the building supplying the North Wing.

Figure 230-1. Where more than one service is installed, a permanent plaque or directory is required, denoting all other services and the area served by each.

The basic rule is that a building or other structure is to be supplied by only one service. There are, however, several exceptions.

Exception Nos. 1 and 2 permit separate services where necessary for fire pumps (with one to six switches or circuit breakers) or emergency, legally required standby, optional standby electrical systems, or parallel power production systems in accordance with Article 705 (with one to six switches or circuit breakers) in addition to the regular building service (with one to six switches or circuit breakers). The intent here is that a disruption of the main building service should not disconnect fire pump equipment or emergency, legally required standby, optional standby, or parallel power production systems.

Exception No. 2 permits a solar photovoltaic system as covered in Article 690. See Section 230-72(b).

Exception No. 3: Multiple-Occupancy Buildings. By special permission, in multiple-occupancy buildings where there is no available space for service equipment accessible to all the occupants.

Exception No. 3 permits a separate service in multiple-occupancy buildings by special permission (the written consent of the authority having jurisdiction; see Definitions, Article 100), where there is no space available for service equipment accessible to all occupants.

Exception No. 4: Capacity Requirements. Two or more services shall be permitted:

a. Where the capacity requirements are in excess of 2000 amperes at a supply voltage of 600 volts or less; or

b. Where the load requirements of a single-phase installation are greater than the serving agency normally supplies through one service; or

c. By special permission.

Exception No. 4 permits two or more services where capacity requirements are in excess of 2,000 A, where supplied by 600 V or less, or for lesser loads by special permission.

Many electric power companies have specifications and have adopted special regulations covering certain types of electrical loads and service equipment that may be energized from their lines. It is advisable to consult with the serving utility to determine line capacities before designing electrical services for large buildings.

Exception No. 5: Buildings of Large Area. By special permission, for a single building or other structure sufficiently large to make two or more services necessary.

Exception No. 5 requires special permission for the installation of more than one service to a sufficiently large building. Expansion of buildings, shopping centers, or industrial plants often necessitates the addition of one or more services. It may, for example, be impractical or impossible to install one service for an industrial plant with capacity requirements to compensate for any and all future load requirements. It is also impractical to run feeders for extremely long distances, due to high costs and voltage drop problems. Again, it is advisable to consult with the serving utility and the authority having jurisdiction before contemplating use of this exception.

Exception No. 6: For different characteristics, such as for different voltages, frequencies, or phases, or for different uses, such as for different rate schedules.

Exception No. 7: For the purpose of Section 230-40, Exception No. 2 only, underground sets of conductors, size 1/0 and larger, running to the same location and connected together at their supply end but not connected together at their load end shall be considered to be one service lateral.

Exception No. 6 permits the installation of more than one service for different characteristics, such as different voltages, frequencies, single-phase or 3-phase services, or different utility rate schedules. For example, different service characteristics exist between a 3-wire, 120/240-V single-phase service and a 3-phase, 4-wire, 480Y/277-V service. For different applications, such as different rate schedules, it is intended to allow a second service for supplying a second meter on a different rate for equipment such as an electric water heater.

Exception No. 7 permits two to six sets of service lateral conductors, size 1/0 or larger and connected together at their supply end, to be considered as ONE service lateral. These conductors are permitted to supply up to six service disconnecting means installed at one location in a group as required by Section 230-72(a). This exception is included in the *Code* to increase the cable impedance by not paralleling the conductors, thereby lowering the available short-circuit current at the building. See Sections 110-9 and 110-10. Also, Exception No. 7 does not require that each set of service lateral conductors be of the same size, provided that each set of service lateral conductors is 1/0 AWG or larger. Note that this lateral arrangement is considered to be ONE service lateral. Therefore, the total number of disconnects cannot exceed six in accordance with Section 230-71(a). See Figures 230-2 a through m.

DIAGRAMS A THROUGH M

The following diagrams, 230-2 a through m, illustrate some examples of permitted service configurations. The intent is to clarify some of the *Code* rules affecting services that are often misunderstood. No attempt has been made to include every type of service arrangement. It should be understood that the term "one location" as applied to services is to be determined by the authority having jurisdiction. Circuit breakers are shown in all diagrams for consistency. However, the service overcurrent device may consist of fuses.

Figure 230-2b. More than one service.

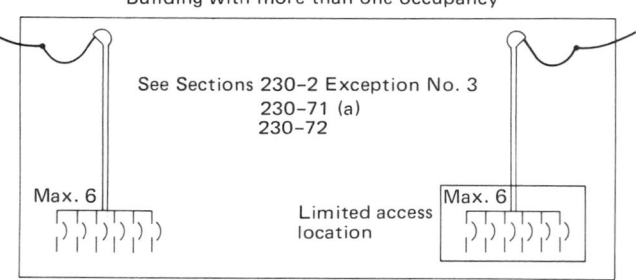

Figure 230-2a. More than one service. No available space accessible to all occupants.

Figure 230-2c. One service. Two sets of service-entrance conductors in different locations.

Figure 230-2d. One service. Seven sets of service-entrance conductors in different locations.

Figure 230-2e. One service. Six sets of service-entrance conductors connected to separate enclosures supplying separate loads in a group at one location.

Figure 230-2f. Same as Figure 230-2e. Optional arrangement.

Figure 230-2g. One service lateral. One location.

Figure 230-2h. One service lateral. One location.

Figure 230-2i. Two sets of service-entrance conductors, each supplying three disconnects. One location.

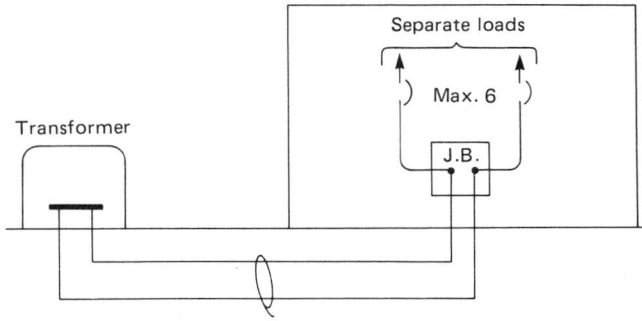

Figure 230-2j. One service lateral. One set of service-entrance conductors tapped from each service lateral set supplying one disconnect. One location.

Four separate buildings

See Sections
230-2
230-71 (a)

Fire walls (see definition of Building)

Transformer

Max. 6   Max. 6   Max. 6   Max. 6

Four service laterals

Figure 230-2k. Four service laterals. Four different locations.

Building with more than one occupancy or single occupancy

See Sections
230-2 Exceptions 1–5

Separate loads   Separate loads

Transformer

Max. 6   Max. 6

Figure 230-2l. Two service laterals. Two different locations.

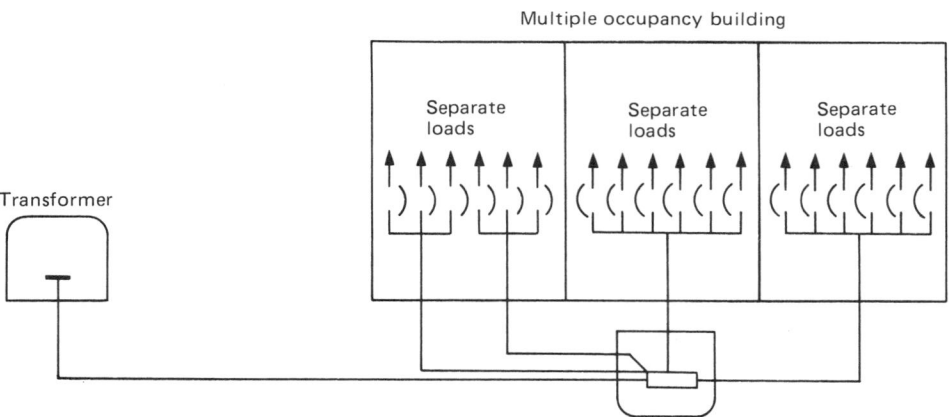

Multiple occupancy building

Separate loads   Separate loads   Separate loads

Transformer

Figure 230-2m. One service lateral with four sets of service-entrance conductors.

230-3. One Building or Other Structure Not to Be Supplied Through Another.
Service conductors supplying a building or other structure shall not pass through the interior of another building or other structure.

(FPN): See Section 230-6 for concrete or masonry-encased conductors considered outside of a building.

It is permissible for service conductors to be installed along the "exterior" of one building to supply another building. However, service conductors supplying a building are not permitted to pass through the "interior" of a building. Each building served in this manner is required to be provided with a disconnecting means for all ungrounded conductors in accordance with Part "F," Service Equipment — Disconnecting Means. See Figure 230-3.

Service-entrance conductors are considered to be outside of a building where they are installed beneath the building under not less than 2 inches of concrete, concealed in a raceway within the building and encased by not less than 2 inches of concrete or brick, or installed in a transformer vault. See Section 230-6 and Figure 230-4.

Figure 230-3. Service conductors are not permitted to pass through the interior of Building No. 1 to supply Building No. 2. The disconnecting means shown for Buildings No. 1 and No. 2 are located on the exterior walls. A disconnecting means suitable for use as service equipment is required to be provided for each building.

230-6. Conductors Considered Outside of Building.
Conductors shall be considered outside of a building or other structure under any of the following conditions: (1) where installed under not less than 2 inches (50.8 mm) of concrete beneath a building or other structure; (2) where installed within a building or other structure in a raceway that is encased in concrete or brick not less than 2 inches (50.8 mm) thick; or (3) where installed in a transformer vault conforming to the requirements of Article 450, Part C.

Figure 230-4. Conductors are considered outside of a building where installed under not less than 2 inches of concrete beneath a building or in a raceway encased by 2 inches of concrete or brick within a building. They are also considered outside the building where installed in a transformer vault. See Sections 450-41 through 450-48.

230-7. Other Conductors in Raceway or Cable.
Conductors other than service conductors shall not be installed in the same service raceway or service cable.

Exception No. 1: Grounding conductors.

Exception No. 2: Load management control conductors having overcurrent protection.

Load management control conductors are control circuit or switch leg conductors for use with special rate meters, usually for water heater circuits. Electric utility companies usually refer to these special-rate meters as "off peak." See Figure 230-11.

230-8. Raceway Seal.
Where a service raceway enters from an underground distribution system, it shall be sealed in accordance with Section 300-5. Spare or unused raceways shall also be sealed. Sealants shall be identified for use with the cable insulation, shield, or other components.

Sealing, such as duct seal or a bushing incorporating the physical characteristics of a seal, is required to be used to seal the ends of service raceways. The intent of this requirement is to prevent water, usually the result of condensation, from entering the service equipment via the raceway. See Figure 300-7. Some sealants are known to have deleterious effects on insulations, extruded semiconducting layers, etc.

230-9. **Clearance from Building Openings.** Service conductors installed as open conductors or multiconductor cable without an overall outer jacket shall have a clearance of not less than 3 feet (914 mm) from windows that are designed to be opened, doors, porches, fire escapes, or similar locations.

Exception: Conductors run above the top level of a window shall be permitted to be less than the 3 feet (914 mm) requirement above.

The clearance of 3 feet is applicable to open conductors, not to a raceway or cable assembly with an overall outer jacket approved for use as service conductors. The intent is to protect the conductors from physical damage and/or accidental contact. The exception permits service conductors, including drip loops and service-drop conductors, to be located just above window openings, because they are considered to be "out of reach." See Figure 230-5.

Figure 230-5. Required dimensions for service conductors located alongside a window and service conductors above the top level of a window designed to be opened.

Overhead service conductors shall not be installed beneath openings through which materials may be moved, such as openings in farm and commercial buildings, and shall not be installed where they will obstruct entrance to these building openings.

Elevated building openings through which materials may be moved are often high enough for the service conductors

to be installed below the opening. This is prohibited by this requirement so as to reduce the likelihood of damage to the service conductors and the potential for electric shock to persons using these high building openings.

230-10. **Service Conductors.** The conductors from the service point to the service disconnecting means shall be considered service conductors.

Section 230-10 is new in the 1993 *Code.* It consists of former Section 230-201 and clarifies the code-making panel's intent that the terms "Service Conductors" and "Service Point" apply to all services both above and below 600 volts. The definition of "Service Point" is now included in Article 100.

B. Overhead Service-Drop Conductors

230-21. **Overhead Supply.** Overhead conductors to a building or other structure (such as a pole) on which a meter or disconnecting means is installed shall be considered as a service drop and installed accordingly.

(FPN): Example: Farm loads in Part D of Article 220.

230-22. **Insulation or Covering.** Service conductors shall normally withstand exposure to atmospheric and other conditions of use without detrimental leakage of current. Individual conductors shall be insulated or covered with an extruded thermoplastic or thermosetting insulating material.

The intent of this section is to prevent problems that are created by weather, abrasion, and other deleterious effects that reduce the insulating quality of the covering or insulation.

Exception: The grounded conductor of a multiconductor cable shall be permitted to be bare.

230-23. **Size and Rating.**

(a) General. Conductors shall have sufficient ampacity to carry the load without a temperature rise detrimental to the covering or insulation of the conductors and shall have adequate mechanical strength.

Where adding load to any service it is the installer's responsibility to be aware of all existing loads. The potential for overloading the service conductors must be governed by installer responsibility and inspector awareness, not by the usual method of overcurrent protection. Load diversity makes this a reasonable approach.

(b) Minimum Size. The conductors shall not be smaller than No. 8 copper or No. 6 aluminum or copper-clad aluminum.

Exception: For installations to supply only limited loads of a single branch circuit such as small polyphase power, controlled water heaters and the like, they shall not be smaller than No. 12 hard-drawn copper or equivalent.

(c) Grounded Conductors. The grounded conductor shall not be less than the minimum size as required by Section 250-23(b).

230-24. **Clearances.** The vertical clearances of all service-drop conductors shall be based on conductor temperature of 60°F (15°C), no wind, with final unloaded sag in the wire, conductor, or cable.

Service-drop conductors shall not be readily accessible and shall comply with (a) through (d) below for services not over 600 volts, nominal.

(a) Above Roofs. Conductors shall have a vertical clearance of not less than 8 feet (2.44 m) above the roof surface. The vertical clearance above the roof level shall be maintained for a distance not less than 3 feet (914 mm) in all directions from the edge of the roof.

Service-drop conductors are not permitted to be readily accessible. The main rule applies to voltages up to 600. An 8-foot vertical clearance is required over the roof surface and extending 3 feet in all directions from the edge with an Exception No. 4 that applies to the final span. See Figure 230-6(a).

Exception No. 1: The area above a roof surface subject to pedestrian or vehicular traffic shall have a vertical clearance from the roof surface in accordance with the clearance requirements of Section 230-24(b).

Exception No. 2: Where the voltage between conductors does not exceed 300 and the roof has a slope of not less than 4 inches

(102 mm) in 12 inches (305 mm), a reduction in clearance to 3 feet (914 mm) shall be permitted.

Exception No. 2 permits a clearance of 3 feet where the voltage between conductors does not exceed 300 and the

Clearance for service conductors   230-24(a), Exception No. 4
supplied at 600 volts or less.   225-19(a), Exception No. 4

Figure 230-6(a). *Exception No. 4 to Section 230-24(a) permits the final span clearance to be less than 8 feet. See Exceptions 2 and 3 for other reductions.*

Figure 230-6(b). *Exception No. 2 applies to steep sloped roofs that are not easily walked on. These roofs have a slope of not less than 4 inches in 12 inches. On such roofs, the vertical clearance of overhead conductors may be reduced from 8 feet to 3 feet. There are no restrictions on the length of the conductors over the roof or the horizontal distance over the roof.*

300 Volts or less (between conductors)

6 ft Maximum

18 in. Minimum

4 ft

Figure 230-6(c). *Exception No. 3 permits service conductor clearances to be reduced to 18 inches for through-the-roof raceways passing through the overhanging portion, provided not more than 6 feet of conductors pass over 4 feet of roof surface measured horizontally. This applies to flat or sloped roofs that are easily walked on (less than 4 inches in 12 inches).*

roof is sloped at not less than 4 inches in 12 inches. It is difficult to walk on a sloped roof of this angle or pitch. See Figure 230-6(b).

Exception No. 3: Where the voltage between conductors does not exceed 300, a reduction in clearance above only the overhanging portion of the roof to not less than 18 inches (457 mm) shall be permitted if (1) not more than 6 feet (1.83 m) of service-drop conductors, 4 feet (1.22 m) horizontally, pass above the roof overhang, and (2) they are terminated at a through-the-roof raceway or approved support.

(FPN): See Section 230-28 for mast supports.

A further reduction of service-drop conductor clearances to 18 inches is permitted by Exception No. 3 for service-mast (through-the-roof) installations where the voltage between conductors does not exceed 300 and the mast is located within 4 feet of the edge of the roof. See Figure 230-6(c). This exception applies to either sloped or flat roofs. Many electric utility companies will not permit a coupling between the weather head and the point where a service raceway extends through the roof.

Clearance per Section 230-24(b)

Service drop

Figure 230-7. *Section 230-24(a), Exception No. 1 requires clearance above a roof surface subject to vehicular or pedestrian traffic, such as rooftop parking areas, to meet the clearance requirements of Section 230-24(b). See Figure 230-8.*

Exception No. 4: The requirement for maintaining the vertical clearance 3 feet (914 mm) from the edge of the roof shall not apply to the final conductor span where the service drop is attached to the side of a building.

Section 230-24(a) applies to the vertical clearance above roofs for service conductors up to 600 volts. The MAIN rule requires a vertical clearance of 8 feet above the roof including those areas 3 feet in all directions beyond the edge of the roof.

Exception No. 4 new in the 1993 *Code*, exempts the final span of a service drop attached to the side of a building from the 8-foot requirement.

See Figure 230-6(a). Exception Nos. 2 and 3 permit lesser clearances for service drops of 300 volts or less. See Figures 230-6(b) and (c).

If the roof is subject to pedestrian or vehicular traffic, the vertical clearance of the service drop must be the same as the vertical clearances from the ground, in accordance with Section 230-24(b). See Figures 230-7 and 8.

(b) Vertical Clearance from Ground. Service-drop conductors where not in excess of 600 volts, nominal, shall have the following minimum clearance from final grade.

10 feet (3.05 m) — at the electric service entrance to buildings, or at the drip loop of the building electric entrance, or above areas or sidewalks accessible only to pedestrians, measured from final grade or other accessible surface only for service-drop cables

supported on and cabled together with a grounded bare messenger and limited to 150 volts to ground.

12 feet (3.66 m) — over residential property and driveways, and those commercial areas not subject to truck traffic where the voltage is limited to 300 volts to ground.

15 feet (4.57 m) — for those areas listed in the 12-foot (3.66-m) classification where the voltage exceeds 300 volts to ground.

18 feet (5.49 m) — over public streets, alleys, roads, parking areas subject to truck traffic, driveways on other than residential property, and other land traversed by vehicles such as cultivated, grazing, forest, and orchard.

See Figure 230-8.

Figure 230-8. Clearances in accordance with Section 230-24(b).

(c) **Clearance from Building Openings.** See Section 230-9.
(d) **Clearance from Swimming Pools.** See Section 680-8.

230-26. **Point of Attachment.** The point of attachment of the service-drop conductors to a building or other structure shall provide the minimum clearances as specified in Section 230-24. In no case shall this point of attachment be less than 10 feet (3.05 m) above finished grade.

230-27. **Means of Attachment.** Multiconductor cables used for service drops shall be attached to buildings or other structures by fittings identified for use with service conductors. Open conductors shall be attached to fittings identified for use with service conductors or to noncombustible, nonabsorbent insulators securely attached to the building or other structure.

See Section 230-51 for mounting and supporting of service cables or individual open service conductors and Section 230-54 for connections at service heads.

230-28. **Service Masts as Supports.** Where a service mast is used for the support of service-drop conductors, it shall be of adequate strength or be supported by braces or guys to withstand safely the strain imposed by the service drop. Where raceway-type service masts are used, all raceway fittings shall be identified for use with service masts.

See Figure 230-6(b) and (c).

(FPN): It is the intent of this section to allow only power service-drop conductors to be attached to a service mast.

230-29. **Supports Over Buildings.** Service-drop conductors passing over a roof shall be securely supported by substantial structures. Where practicable, such supports shall be independent of the building.

C. Underground Service-Lateral Conductors

230-30. **Insulation.** Service-lateral conductors shall withstand exposure to atmospheric and other conditions of use without detrimental leakage of current. Service-lateral conductors shall be insulated for the applied voltage.

Exception: A grounded conductor shall be permitted to be uninsulated as follows:

a. Bare copper used in a raceway.

b. Bare copper for direct burial where bare copper is judged to be suitable for the soil conditions.

c. Bare copper for direct burial without regard to soil conditions where part of a cable assembly identified for underground use.

d. Aluminum or copper-clad aluminum without individual insulation or covering where part of a cable assembly identified for underground use in a raceway or for direct burial.

See Figure 230-9.

Bare copper, in raceway

Bare copper direct buried, suitable for soil conditions.

Bare copper or aluminum, part of an identified cable assembly.

Figure 230-9. Various applications of bare grounded service-lateral and service-entrance conductors for underground locations. Aluminum or copper-clad aluminum conductors must be insulated where run in a raceway or direct-buried, unless they are part of a cable assembly identified for the use.

230-31. **Size and Rating.**

(a) General. Service-lateral conductors shall have sufficient ampacity to carry the current for the load as computed in accordance with Article 220 and shall have adequate mechanical strength.

(b) Minimum Size. The conductors shall not be smaller than No. 8 copper or No. 6 aluminum or copper-clad aluminum.

Exception: For installations to supply only limited loads of a single branch circuit such as small polyphase power, controlled water heaters and the like, they shall not be smaller than No. 12 copper or No. 10 aluminum or copper-clad aluminum.

(c) Grounded Conductors. The grounded conductor shall not be less than the minimum size required by Section 250-23(b).

See Notes 3 and 5 to Ampacity Tables of 0 to 2,000 Volts.

(FPN): Reasonable efficiency of operation can be provided when voltage drop is taken into consideration in sizing the service-lateral conductors.

See Section 215-2(b) and commentary to FPN No. 2.

230-32. **Protection Against Damage.** Underground service-lateral conductors shall be protected against damage in accordance with Section 300-5. Service-lateral conductors entering a building shall be installed in accordance with Section 230-6 or protected by a raceway wiring method identified in Section 230-43.

D. Service-Entrance Conductors

230-40. **Number of Service-Entrance Conductor Sets.** Each service drop or lateral shall supply only one set of service-entrance conductors.

Exception No. 1: Buildings with more than one occupancy shall be permitted to have one set of service-entrance conductors run to each occupancy or to a group of occupancies.

Exception No. 2: Where two to six service disconnecting means in separate enclosures are grouped at one location and supply separate loads from one service drop or lateral, one set of service-entrance conductors shall be permitted to supply each or several such service equipment enclosures.

See Figures 230-2a through 230-2m. Note in such cases the lateral conductors are considered as ONE service lateral. See Section 230-7, Exception No. 7.

230-41. **Insulation of Service-Entrance Conductors.** Service-entrance conductors shall normally withstand exposure to atmospheric and other conditions of use without detrimental leakage of current. Service-entrance conductors entering or on the exterior of buildings or other structures shall be insulated.

Exception: A grounded conductor shall be permitted to be uninsulated as follows:

a. Bare copper used in a raceway or part of a service cable assembly.

b. Bare copper for direct burial where bare copper is judged to be suitable for the soil conditions.

c. Bare copper for direct burial without regard to soil conditions where part of a cable assembly identified for underground use.

d. Aluminum or copper-clad aluminum without individual insulation or covering where part of a cable assembly or identified for underground use in a raceway or for direct burial.

Service entrance conductors are required to be insulated; however, bare grounded conductors are permitted under the same conditions as underground service laterals. See Figure 230-9.

230-42. **Size and Rating.**

(a) General. Service-entrance conductors shall be of sufficient size to carry the loads as computed in Article 220. Ampacity shall be determined from Section 310-15.

Exception: The maximum allowable current of approved busways shall be that value for which the busway has been listed or labeled.

(b) Ungrounded Conductors. Ungrounded conductors shall have an ampacity of not less than:

(1) 100 amperes, 3-wire for a service to a one-family dwelling with six or more 2-wire branch circuits.

(2) 100 amperes, 3-wire for a service to a one-family dwelling with an initial net computed load of 10 kVA or more.

The basic rule in this section requires the UNGROUNDED SERVICE conductors to be sized large enough to carry the load.

Three-wire services supplying one-family dwellings are required to be installed using 100-amp wire if the service consists of 6 or more 2-wire branch circuits, which is typically the case since Section 220-4 requires at least 3 branch circuits for kitchen and laundry loads. Section 422-7 requires an individual branch circuit for a central heating system and 2 more branch circuits are usually required to handle the lighting load or if it has an initial load of 10 kVa or more.

A conductor size of 60 amps is permitted for other loads, with several exceptions allowing smaller sizes down to No. 12 copper (No. 10 aluminum) for limited loads.

(3) 60 amperes for other loads.

See Figure 230-10.

Exception No. 1: For loads consisting of not more than two 2-wire branch circuits, No. 8 copper or No. 6 aluminum or copper-clad aluminum.

Exception No. 2: By special permission, for loads limited by demand or by the source of supply, No. 8 copper or No. 6 aluminum or copper-clad aluminum.

Exception No. 3: For limited loads of a single branch circuit, No. 12 copper or No. 10 aluminum or copper-clad aluminum, but in no case smaller than the branch-circuit conductors.

(c) Grounded Conductors. The grounded conductor shall not be less than the minimum size as required by Section 250-23(b).

The size of the GROUNDED service conductor is determined by Section 220-22 and is based on the maximum

Figure 230-10. Ungrounded service-entrance conductors are required to have an ampacity of at least 100 A for a 3-wire service to a one-family dwelling if it has six or more 2-wire branch circuits or a computed load of 10 kVA or more. Conductors with an ampacity of 60 amperes would be permissible for a one-family dwelling or other occupancy with less than 6 branch circuits or a computed load of less than 10 kVA.

unbalanced load. This usually results in a smaller conductor. However, the minimum size of the grounded service conductor is limited by Section 250-23(b). See also Section 230-42(c). A new FPN was added to the 1993 *Code* alerting users that they should consider the additional heating effect of harmonic currents in the neutral conductor of a 3-phase, 4-wire, wye system when sizing the neutral conductor. If the service to a building is a single-phase, 3-wire, 120/240-volt system with no 240-volt loads, the maximum current in the neutral would be the same as the maximum current in the ungrounded conductor when all loads connected to one leg are "on" and all on the other are "off." In such cases the service neutral size could not be reduced, but would be sized the same as the ungrounded conductors. See Note 3 of Notes to Ampacity Tables of 0 to 2,000 Volts for more information on sizing the ungrounded conductor.

230-43 . **Wiring Methods for 600 Volts, Nominal, or Less.** Service-entrance conductors shall be installed in accordance with the applicable requirements of this Code covering the type of wiring method used and limited to the following methods: (1) open wiring on insulators; (2) rigid metal conduit; (3) intermediate metal conduit; (4) electrical metallic tubing; (5) service-entrance cables; (6) wireways; (7) busways; (8) auxiliary gutters; (9) rigid nonmetallic conduit; (10) cablebus; (11) Type MC cable; (12) mineral-insulated, metal-sheathed cable; (13) flexible metal conduit or liquidtight flexible metal conduit not over 6 feet (1.83 m) long between raceways, or between raceway and service equipment, with equipment bonding jumper routed with the flexible metal conduit according to provisions of Section 250-79(a), (c), (d), and (f); or (14) liquidtight flexible nonmetallic conduit.

Approved cable tray systems shall be permitted to support cables approved for use as service-entrance conductors.

The required bonding jumper is not permitted to be wrapped or spiraled around the flexible metal conduit. Item (14) was new in the 1990 *Code* and liquidtight flexible metal conduit, item(13), is new in the 1993 *Code*.

230-46 . **Unspliced Conductors.** Service-entrance conductors shall not be spliced.

Exception No. 1: Clamped or bolted connections in metering equipment enclosures shall be permitted.

Exception No. 2: Where service-entrance conductors are tapped to supply two to six disconnecting means grouped at a common location.

Exception No. 3: At a properly enclosed junction point where an underground wiring method is changed to another type of wiring method.

Where a building has a basement, an underground service lateral usually terminates at a terminal box. At this point, service conductors may be spliced or run directly to the service equipment. Splices are permitted where, for example, conduit enters a terminal box and a different wiring method, such as service cable, continues to the service equipment. See Section 230-43 for wiring methods for service conductors for 600 V, nominal, or less.

Exception No. 4: A connection shall be permitted where service conductors are extended from a service drop to an outside meter location and returned to connect to the service-entrance conductors of an existing installation.

Splices may be necessary where metering equipment is located on the line side of service equipment. See Figure 230-11.

Figure 230-11. Time clock and control switch integral to a meter for use, generally, with water heaters.

Exception No. 5: Where the service-entrance conductors consist of busway, connections shall be permitted as required to assemble the various sections and fittings.

Exception No. 5 permits splicing (connecting) busway to facilitate the necessary splices required to connect the various components of a busway service-entrance system.

230-49. Protection Against Physical Damage — Underground. Underground service-entrance conductors shall be protected against physical damage in accordance with Section 300-5.

230-50. Protection of Open Conductors and Cables Against Damage — Aboveground. Service-entrance conductors installed aboveground shall be protected against physical damage as specified in (a) or (b) below.

(a) **Service-Entrance Cables.** Service-entrance cables, where subject to physical damage, such as where installed in exposed places near sidewalks, walkways, driveways, or coal chutes, or where subject to contact with awnings, shutters, swinging signs, or similar objects, shall be protected in any of the following ways: (1) by rigid metal conduit; (2) by intermediate metal conduit; (3) by rigid nonmetallic conduit suitable for the location; (4) by electrical metallic tubing; or (5) by other approved means.

(b) **Other than Service-Entrance Cable.** Individual open conductors and cables other than service-entrance cables shall not be installed within 10 feet (3.05 m) of grade level or where exposed to physical damage.

Exception: Type MI and Type MC cable shall be permitted within 10 feet (3.05 m) of grade level where not exposed to physical damage or where protected in accordance with Section 300-5(d).

230-51. Mounting Supports. Cables or individual open service conductors shall be supported as specified in (a), (b), or (c) below.

(a) **Service-Entrance Cables.** Service-entrance cables shall be supported by straps or other approved means within 12 inches (305 mm) of every service head, gooseneck, or connection to a raceway or enclosure and at intervals not exceeding 30 inches (762 mm).

(b) **Other Cables.** Cables that are not approved for mounting in contact with a building or other structure shall be mounted on insulating supports installed at intervals not exceeding 15 feet (4.57 m) and in a manner that will maintain a clearance of not less than 2 inches (50.8 mm) from the surface over which they pass.

(c) **Individual Open Conductors.** Individual open conductors shall be installed in accordance with Table 230-51(c). Where exposed to the weather, the conductors shall be mounted on insulators or on insulating supports attached to racks, brackets, or other approved means. Where not exposed to the weather, the conductors shall be mounted on glass or porcelain knobs.

Table 230-51(c). Supports and Clearances for Individual Open Service Conductors

Maximum Volts	Maximum Distance in Feet Between Supports	Minimum Clearances In Inches	
		Between Conductors	From Surface
600	9	6	2
600	15	12	2
300	4 1/2	3	2
600*	4 1/2*	2 1/2*	1*

For SI units: one inch = 25.4 millimeters; one foot = 0.3048 meter.
*Where not exposed to weather.

230-52. Individual Conductors Entering Buildings or Other Structures. Where individual open conductors enter a building or other structure, they shall enter through roof bushings or through the wall in an upward slant through individual, noncombustible, nonabsorbent insulating tubes. Drip loops shall be formed on the conductors before they enter the tubes.

230-53. Raceways to Drain. Where exposed to the weather, raceways enclosing service-entrance conductors shall be raintight and arranged to drain. Where embedded in masonry, raceways shall be arranged to drain.

Service raceways exposed to the weather are required to have raintight fittings and drain holes. During installation of raceways in masonry, it is nearly impossible to prevent the entrance of surface water, rain, or water from poured concrete.

Exception: As permitted in Section 350-2.

230-54. Connections at Service Head.

(a) **Raintight Service Head.** Service raceways shall be equipped with a raintight service head at the point of connection to service-drop conductors.

(b) **Service Cable Equipped with Raintight Service Head or Gooseneck.** Service cables, either (1) unless continuous from pole to service equipment or meter, shall be equipped with a raintight service head, or (2) shall be formed in a gooseneck and taped and painted or taped with a self-sealing, weather-resistant thermoplastic.

(c) Service Heads Above Service-Drop Attachment. Service heads, and goosenecks in service-entrance cables, shall be located above the point of attachment of the service-drop conductors to the building or other structure.

Exception: Where it is impracticable to locate the service head above the point of attachment, the service head location shall be permitted not farther than 24 inches (610 mm) from the point of attachment.

(d) Secured. Service cables shall be held securely in place.

(e) Separately Bushed Openings. Service heads shall have conductors of different potential brought out through separately bushed openings.

(f) Drip Loops. Drip loops shall be formed on individual conductors. To prevent the entrance of moisture, service-entrance conductors shall be connected to the service-drop conductors either (1) below the level of the service head, or (2) below the level of the termination of the service-entrance cable sheath.

(g) Arranged that Water Will Not Enter Service Raceway or Equipment. Service-drop conductors and service-entrance conductors shall be arranged so that water will not enter service raceway or equipment.

Many areas throughout the country require that service raceways and service cables be equipped with a raintight service (weather) head. Type SE service-entrance cables, however, may be run continuously from a utility pole to metering or service equipment or, where shaped in a downward direction or "gooseneck" and sealed by taping and painting, may be installed without a service head. See Figure 230-12.

Service heads and goosenecks are required to be located above the service-drop attachment. Individual conductors should extend in a downward direction, as shown in Figure 230-12, or drip loops are required to be formed.

230-55. **Termination at Service Equipment.** Any service raceway or cable shall terminate at the inner end in a box, cabinet, or equivalent fitting that effectively encloses all energized metal parts.

Exception: Where the service disconnecting means is mounted on a switchboard having exposed busbars on the back, a raceway shall be permitted to terminate at a bushing.

Figure 230-12. A service-entrance cable that terminates in a "gooseneck" without a raintight service weather head.

230-56. **Service-Entrance Conductor with the Higher Voltage-to-Ground.** On a 4-wire delta-connected service where the midpoint of one phase is grounded, the service-entrance conductor having the higher phase voltage to ground shall be durably and permanently marked by an outer finish that is orange in color or by other effective means.

Proper service connections require the service conductor having the higher voltage-to-ground to be durably marked by an outer finish of orange, by tagging, etc. Marking should be both at the point of connection to the service-entrance conductors and the point of connection to the service disconnect. See Figure 215-2. See Sections 215-8 and 384-3(e) and (f).

E. Service Equipment — General

230-62. **Service Equipment — Enclosed or Guarded.** Energized parts of service equipment shall be enclosed as specified in (a) below, or guarded as specified in (b) below.

(a) Enclosed. Energized parts shall be enclosed so that they will not be exposed to accidental contact or guarded as in (b) below.

(b) Guarded. Energized parts that are not enclosed shall be installed on a switchboard, panelboard, or control board and guarded in accordance with Sections 110-17 and 110-18. Such an enclosure shall be provided with means for locking or sealing doors providing access to energized parts.

230-63. **Grounding and Bonding.** Service equipment, raceways, cable armor, cable sheaths, etc., and any service conductor that is to be grounded shall be grounded in accordance with the following parts of Article 250.

  Part B. Circuit and System Grounding.
  Part C. Location of System Grounding Connections.
  Part D. Enclosure Grounding.
  Part F. Methods of Grounding.
  Part G. Bonding.
  Part H. Grounding Electrode System.
  Part J. Grounding Conductors.

230-64. **Working Space.** Sufficient working space shall be provided in the vicinity of the service equipment to permit safe operation, inspection, and repairs. In no case shall this be less than that specified by Section 110-16.

230-65. **Available Short-Circuit Current.** Service equipment shall be suitable for the short-circuit current available at its supply terminals.

See commentary for Sections 110-9 and 110-10.

230-66. **Marking.** Service equipment shall be marked to identify it as being suitable for use as service equipment.

According to the listing information, a panelboard with the neutral "factory-bonded" to the enclosure will be marked "Suitable Only for Use as Service Equipment." Other types of equipment intended for optional use, either as service equipment or feeder equipment, are required by Section 230-66 to be marked to identify it as being suitable for use as service equipment. Section 225-8 requires the feeder disconnecting means to be suitable for use as service equipment.

F. Service Equipment — Disconnecting Means

230-70. **General.** Means shall be provided to disconnect all conductors in a building or other structure from the service-entrance conductors.

(a) **Location.** The service disconnecting means shall be installed at a readily accessible location either outside of a building or structure, or inside nearest the point of entrance of the service conductors.

No maximum distance is specified from the point of entrance of service conductors to a readily accessible location for the installation of a service disconnecting means. The authority enforcing this *Code* has the responsibility for and is charged with making interpretations related to specific individual installations. The length of service-entrance conductors should be kept to a minimum inside buildings since power utilities provide limited overcurrent protection and, in the event of a "fault," the service conductors could ignite nearby combustible materials.

Some local jurisdictions have written rules on the allowable length of service-entrance conductors run within buildings. The authority having jurisdiction may permit service conductors to bypass fuel storage tanks or gas meters, etc., permitting the service disconnecting means to be located in a readily accessible location. However, if the authority judges the distance as being excessive, the disconnecting means may be required to be located outside at a readily accessible location that is not necessarily nearest the point of entry. See also Section 230-6 and Figure 230-4 for conductors considered to be outside of a building.

See Section 380-8(a) for mounting height restrictions for switches and circuit breakers used as switches.

(b) **Marking.** Each service disconnecting means shall be permanently marked to identify it as a service disconnecting means.

(c) **Suitable For Use.** Each service disconnecting means shall be suitable for the prevailing conditions. Service equipment installed in hazardous (classified) locations shall comply with the requirements of Articles 500 through 517.

230-71. **Maximum Number of Disconnects.**

(a) **General.** The service disconnecting means for each service permitted by Section 230-2, or for each set of service-entrance conductors permitted by Section 230-40, Exception No. 1, shall consist of not more than six switches or six circuit breakers mounted in a single enclosure, in a group of separate enclosures, or in or on a switchboard. There shall be no more than six disconnects per service grouped in any one location.

One set of service-entrance conductors, either overhead or underground, is permitted to supply two to six service disconnecting means in lieu of a single main disconnect. A single-occupancy or multiple-occupancy building (residential or other than residential) may have one main service disconnect or up to six main disconnects supplying separate loads.

Multiple-occupancy buildings may have service-entrance conductors run to each occupancy, and each such set of service-entrance conductors may have from one to six disconnects. See Section 230-40, Exception No. 1 and Section 230-71(a).

Where service-entrance conductors are routed outside the building (see Section 230-6 and Figure 230-4), each set of service-entrance conductors is permitted to supply not more than six disconnecting means at each occupancy of a multiple-occupancy building.

See Figures 230-2a through m.

Figure 230-13. *An enclosure for grouping service equipment consisting of six circuit breakers or six fused switches. This arrangement does not require a main switch. Six separate enclosures would also be permitted as the service equipment. (Anchor Electric)*

Exception: For the purpose of this section, disconnecting means used solely for the control circuit of the ground-fault protection system, installed as part of the listed equipment, shall not be considered a service disconnecting means.

This exception makes it clear that the disconnect for the control circuit of a ground-fault protector is a seventh disconnect switch, it is not considered as one of the one to six service disconnects.

(b) Single-Pole Units. Two or three single-pole switches or breakers, capable of individual operation, shall be permitted on multiwire circuits, one pole for each ungrounded conductor, as one multipole disconnect, provided they are equipped with "handle ties" or a "master handle" to disconnect all conductors of the service with no more than six operations of the hand.

(FPN): See Section 384-16(a) for service equipment in panelboards.

230-72 . **Grouping of Disconnects.**

(a) General. The two to six disconnects as permitted in Section 230-71 shall be grouped. Each disconnect shall be marked to indicate the load served.

See Figures 230-2a through m.

Exception: One of the two to six service disconnecting means permitted in Section 230-71, where used only for a water pump also intended to provide fire protection, shall be permitted to be located remote from the other disconnecting means.

(b) Additional Service Disconnecting Means. The one or more additional service disconnecting means for fire pumps or for emergency, legally required standby, or optional standby services permitted by Section 230-2 shall be installed sufficiently remote from the one to six service disconnecting means for normal service to minimize the possibility of simultaneous interruption of supply.

The intent of Section 230-2, Exception Nos. 1 and 2 is to permit separate services where necessary for fire pumps (with one to six disconnects) or emergency, legally required standby, or optional standby systems (with one to six disconnects) in addition to the one to six disconnects for the normal building service. Article 230 recognizes that a disruption of the normal building service should not disconnect the fire pump, emergency, or other exempted systems. Since the above services are in addition to the normal services, the one to six disconnects allowed for them are not included as one of the six disconnects for the normal supply.

(FPN): See Sections 700-12(d) and (e) for emergency system services.

(c) **Access to Occupants.** In a multiple-occupancy building, each occupant shall have access to the occupant's service disconnecting means.

Exception: In a multiple-occupancy building where electric service and electrical maintenance are provided by the building management and where these are under continuous building management supervision, the service disconnecting means supplying more than one occupancy shall be permitted to be accessible to authorized management personnel only.

A multiple-occupancy building is a building that may have any number of dwelling units, offices, and the like that are independent of each other. Unless electric service and maintenance are provided by and under continuous supervision of the building management, each occupant is to have ready access to his or her disconnecting means. See Section 240-24(b).

230-74. **Simultaneous Opening of Poles.** Each service disconnecting means shall simultaneously disconnect all ungrounded service conductors from the premises wiring system.

230-75. **Disconnection of Grounded Conductor.** Where the service disconnecting means does not disconnect the grounded conductor from the premises wiring, other means shall be provided for this purpose in the service equipment. A terminal or bus to which all grounded conductors can be attached by means of pressure connectors shall be permitted for this purpose.

Provisions are required at the service equipment for disconnecting the grounded conductor from the premises wiring. This disconnection need not be by operation of the service disconnecting means. Disconnection can be, and most commonly is, accomplished by manually removing the grounded conductor from the bus or terminal bar to which it is lugged or bolted. This is often referred to as the "neutral disconnect link."

Manufacturers design neutral terminal bars for service equipment so that grounded conductors must be cut to be attached; that is, the grounded conductor cannot be run straight through the service equipment without means of disconnection from the premises wiring.

In a multisection switchboard, disconnects for the grounded conductor shall be permitted to be in any section of the switchboard, provided any such switchboard section is marked.

230-76. **Manually or Power Operable.** The service disconnecting means for ungrounded service conductors shall consist of either (1) a manually operable switch or circuit breaker equipped with a handle or other suitable operating means, or (2) a power-operated switch or circuit breaker provided the switch or circuit breaker can be opened by hand in the event of a power supply failure.

230-77. **Indicating.** The service disconnecting means shall plainly indicate whether it is in the open or closed position.

230-78. **Externally Operable.** An enclosed service disconnecting means shall be externally operable without exposing the operator to contact with energized parts.

Exception: A power-operated switch or circuit breaker shall not be required to be externally operable by hand to a closed position.

A service disconnecting means must be capable of being operated to the "on" or "off" position without exposing unqualified persons to live parts. See Article 100 for definition of "dead front."

230-79. **Rating of Disconnect.** The service disconnecting means shall have a rating not less than the load to be carried, determined in accordance with Article 220. In no case shall the rating be lower than specified in (a), (b), (c), or (d) below.

(a) **One-Circuit Installation.** For installations to supply only limited loads of a single branch circuit, the service disconnecting means shall have a rating of not less than 15 amperes.

(b) **Two-Circuit Installations.** For installations consisting of not more than two 2-wire branch circuits, the service disconnecting means shall have a rating of not less than 30 amperes.

(c) **One-Family Dwelling.** For a one-family dwelling, the service disconnecting means shall have a rating of not less than 100 amperes, 3-wire under either of the following conditions: (1) where the initial computed load is 10 kVA or more, or (2) where the initial installation consists of six or more 2-wire branch circuits.

A service disconnecting means is required to have a rating of not less than the load to be carried. See Example 2(a) in Chapter 9 and Figure 230-10.

(d) All Others. For all other installations, the service disconnecting means shall have a rating of not less than 60 amperes.

230-80. Combined Rating of Disconnects.
Where the service disconnecting means consists of more than one switch or circuit breaker, as permitted by Section 230-71, the combined ratings of all the switches or circuit breakers used shall not be less than the rating required for a single switch or circuit breaker.

Section 230-71(a) permits up to six individual switches or circuit breakers, mounted in a single enclosure, in a group of separate enclosures, or in or on a switchboard or several switchboards, to serve as the required service disconnecting means at any one location. Section 230-80 refers to situations where more than one switch or circuit breaker is used and indicates that the combined rating of all the switches or circuit breakers used shall not be less than the rating required for a single switch or circuit breaker. Section 230-90 requires that overcurrent protection be provided in each ungrounded service conductor. This overcurrent protection must have a rating or setting not higher than the allowable ampacity of the service conductors. Exception No. 3 to Section 230-90(a) allows not more than six circuit breakers or six sets of fuses to be considered as the overcurrent device. None of these individual overcurrent devices can have a rating or setting higher than the ampacity of the service conductors.

In complying with these rules, it is possible for the total of the six overcurrent devices to be greater than the rating of the service-entrance conductors. However, the size of the service-entrance conductors is required to be adequate for the connected load only, and each individual service disconnecting means is required to be large enough for the individual loads supplied. See Figure 230-14 and commentary following Section 230-90(a), Exception No. 3.

230-81. Connection to Terminals.
The service conductors shall be connected to the service disconnecting means by pressure connectors, clamps, or other approved means. Connections that depend upon solder shall not be used.

230-82. Equipment Connected to the Supply Side of Service Disconnect.
Equipment shall not be connected to the supply side of the service disconnecting means.

(FPN): It is not the intent of this section to require individual meter socket enclosures to be suitable for use as service equipment.

Exception No. 1: Cable limiters or other current-limiting devices.

Section 230-91 does not permit service overcurrent devices to be located at the point of connection to the service drop where joined to the service-entrance conductors. The requirement is that the overcurrent device be an integral part of the service disconnecting means. The safest practice is to turn off the disconnect before replacing an overcurrent device.

Exception No. 2: Fuses and disconnecting means or circuit breakers suitable for use as service equipment, in meter pedestals or otherwise provided and connected in series with the ungrounded service conductors and located away from the building supplied.

Exception No. 3: Meters nominally rated not in excess of 600 volts, provided all metal housings and service enclosures are grounded in accordance with Article 250.

Exception No. 4: Instrument transformers (current and voltage), high-impedance shunts, surge-protective devices identified for use on the supply side of the service disconnect, load management devices, and surge arresters.

Exception No. 5: Taps used only to supply load management devices, circuits for emergency systems, stand-by power systems, fire pump equipment, and fire and sprinkler alarms if provided with service equipment and installed in accordance with requirements for service-entrance conductors.

Systems such as emergency lighting, fire alarms, fire pumps, stand-by power, and sprinkler alarms are permitted to be connected ahead of the normal service disconnecting means only where such systems are provided with a separate disconnecting means and overcurrent protection. See Section 700-12(e).

Exception No. 6: Solar photovoltaic systems or interconnected electric power production sources. See Articles 690 or 705 as applicable.

Exception No. 7: Where the service disconnecting means is power operable, the control circuit shall be permitted to be connected ahead of the service disconnecting means if suitable overcurrent protection and disconnecting means are provided.

Exception No. 8: Ground-fault protection systems where installed as part of listed equipment, if suitable overcurrent protection and disconnecting means are provided.

230-83. **Transfer Equipment.** Transfer equipment, including transfer switches, shall operate such that all ungrounded conductors of one source of supply are disconnected before any ungrounded conductors of the second source are connected.

Exception No. 1: Where manual equipment identified for the purpose or suitable automatic equipment is utilized, two or more sources shall be permitted to be connected in parallel through transfer equipment.

Suitable transfer equipment, including transfer switches, is required to ensure that successful shifting of loads from normal power to emergency power will occur without backfeeding into utility power lines.

Exception No. 2: Where parallel operation is used and suitable automatic or manual control equipment is provided.

See Article 705.

G. Service Equipment — Overcurrent Protection

230-90. **Where Required.** Each ungrounded service conductor shall have overload protection.

Service-entrance conductors, overhead or underground, are the supply conductors from the point of connection of service drop or service lateral conductors to the service equipment. Service equipment is intended to constitute the main control and means of cutoff of the supply to the premises wiring system. At this point, an overcurrent device, which usually consists of circuit breakers or a set of fuses, is required to be installed in series with each ungrounded service conductor.

The service overcurrent device will not protect the service conductors under conditions of short circuit or ground fault on the line side of the disconnect. A degree of protection under these overcurrent conditions is provided by the special requirements for service conductor physical protection and location.

(a) **Ungrounded Conductor.** Such protection shall be provided by an overcurrent device in series with each ungrounded service conductor having a rating or setting not higher than the allowable ampacity of the conductor.

Exception No. 1: For motor-starting currents, ratings in conformity with Sections 430-52, 430-62, and 430-63 shall be permitted.

Where a service supplies a motor load as well as lighting or a lighting and appliance load, the overcurrent protective device is required to have a rating sufficient for the lighting and/or appliance load as determined in accordance with Articles 210 and 220, plus, for an individual motor, the rating permitted by Section 430-52 and, for two or more motors, the rating permitted by Section 430-62.

Example: A service consisting of a 100-A lighting and appliance load, one 25-hp squirrel cage induction motor (full-voltage starting, service factor 1.15, Code letter F), and two 30-hp wound rotor induction motors (40°C rise) on a 240-V, 3-phase system is to have the service conductors and service disconnecting means calculated as follows:

CONDUCTOR LOADS

The full-load current of the 25-hp motor is 68 A (Table 430-150). The full-load current of the 30-hp motor is 80 A (Table 430-150). The service-entrance conductors are calculated at 125 percent of 80 A (100 A), plus 80 A, plus 68 A, for a total of 248 A (Section 430-24).

	248-A motors
	100-A lighting and appliance
Total	348 A

Therefore, the service-entrance conductors would have to be, for example, 500 kcmil Type THW copper or 700 kcmil Type THW aluminum or copper-clad aluminum conductors (Table 310-16).

OVERCURRENT PROTECTION

The maximum rating of the service overcurrent protective device is based on the sum of the largest branch-circuit overcurrent device [300 percent for the 25-hp motor using a nontime delay fuse (Table 430-152) = 68 × 3 = 204 A; therefore the next lower size is 200 A] plus the sum of the full-load currents of the other motors, plus the lighting and appliance loads. See Section 430-63.

        200-A 25-hp motor
         80-A 30-hp motor
         80-A 30-hp motor
        100-A lighting and appliance load
Total   460 A

The nearest standard fuse that does not exceed this total value is 450 A. See Section 240-6.

Exception No. 2: Fuses and circuit breakers with a rating or setting in conformity with Section 240-3(b) or (c) and Section 240-6.

Exception No. 3: Not more than six circuit breakers or six sets of fuses shall be permitted as the overcurrent device to provide the overload protection. The sum of the ratings of the circuit breakers or fuses shall be permitted to exceed the ampacity of the service conductors, provided the calculated load in accordance with Article 220 does not exceed the ampacity of the service conductors.

Circuit-breaker or fuse-ampere ratings are not permitted to be greater than the ampacity of the service conductor (except for motor-starting currents), unless such conductor rating does not correspond to the standard ampere rating of a circuit breaker or fuse, whereupon the next larger size circuit breaker or fuse may be used, provided its rating does not exceed 800 A as permitted in Section 240-3, Exception No. 4. See Section 240-6 for standard ampere ratings of fuses and circuit breakers.

Example: The ampacity of a 500 kcmil THW copper conductor is 380 A (Table 310-16) and may be protected by a 400-A fuse or circuit breaker. The rating of the fuse or circuit breaker is based on the ampacity of the service conductor and not the rating of the service disconnect switch.

As shown in the example, a 400-A fuse or circuit breaker may be considered as properly sized for the protection of 500 kcmil THW copper service conductors. If the service disconnecting means (see Exception No. 3) consists of six circuit breakers or six sets of fuses, the combined ratings must not be less than the rating required for a single switch or circuit breaker in accordance with Section 230-80. See commentary following Section 230-80. Also see Figure 230-14.

In the example shown in Figure 230-14, the combined ratings of the overcurrent devices equals the size of the overcurrent device required by Section 240-3 and Exception No. 4 to this section. However, the combined ratings of the overcurrent devices is not required to be equal to

or less than this value. For example, all disconnects could have been rated 100 amperes. See commentary following Section 230-23(a).

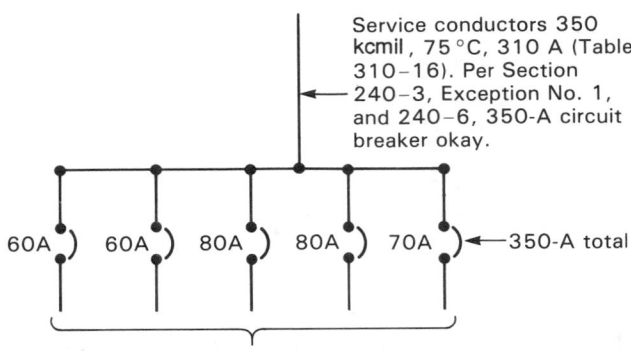

Figure 230-14. *The combined ratings of the overcurrent devices is permitted to exceed the ampacity of the service conductors.*

Exception No. 4: Fire Pumps. Where the service to the fire pump room is judged to be outside of buildings, these provisions shall not apply. Overcurrent protection for fire pump services shall be selected or set to carry locked-rotor current of the motor(s) indefinitely.

(FPN): See Centrifugal Fire Pumps, NFPA 20-1990 (ANSI).

Section 230-90(a), Exception No. 4 permits service-entrance conductors connected ahead of the main service disconnect for a service to a fire pump to be installed without overload protection for the conductors. Two methods of installation are considered as meeting the intent of this section. They are: (1) where the service conductors to the pump room are installed physically outside the building; or (2) where the conductors are installed under not less than 2 inches of concrete or concealed in a raceway encased by concrete or brick not less than 2 inches thick that terminates in a pump room (see Section 230-6 and Figure 230-4).

Section 430-31 of the *Code* indicates that provisions for motor- and branch-circuit running overload protection are not to be interpreted as requiring overload protection in cases where it might introduce additional or increased hazards. Fire pump motors are a case in point; they are permitted much larger overcurrent protection than other motors, recognizing that fire pumps should be allowed to operate to failure rather than be removed from the line in order to prolong their usefulness under adverse fire conditions. See Section 230-95, Exception No. 2.

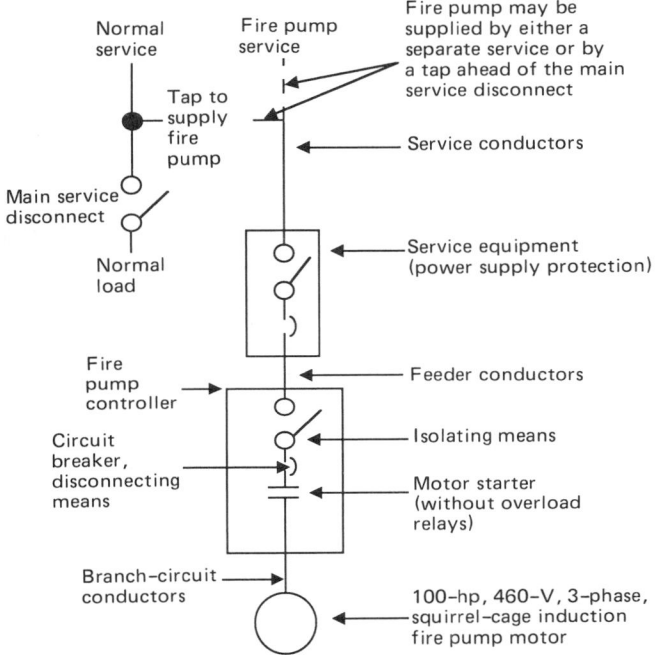

Figure 230-15. A typical fire pump installation.

Figure 230-15 is a diagram of the wiring and components of a fire pump circuit designed to comply with requirements of the *NEC* and NFPA 20, *Standard for the Installation of Centrifugal Fire Pumps*. The pump motor represented is a 100-hp, 460-V, 3-phase, squirrel-cage induction type, and its full-load current, taken from Table 430-150, is 124 A.

The service conductors, feeder conductors, and branch-circuit conductors are sized at 125 percent of the motor full-load current rating (124 A × 125 percent = 155 A). According to Table 310-16, the next closest copper wire size for 155 A is a No. 2/0 THW conductor with an allowable ampacity of 175 A; therefore, all of the conductors would be sized at No. 2/0 THW copper. See Sections 430-22 and 430-23 for sizing of conductors. Other conductors with an ampacity of 155 A or more would also be permitted in this instance.

The locked-rotor current of the motor in the installation illustrated is 744 A, as derived from Table 430-151, and the power supply protection may consist of either fuses or circuit breakers sized so that they will not open at locked-rotor current. In either case, the next standard ampere rating for fuses or circuit breakers is 800 A. See Section 240-6. This protection complies with the intent of the requirements of Section 6-3.4.1 and 6-3.4.2 of NFPA 20 and also of Section 430-31 of the *NEC*.

The isolating means in the illustrated pump's controller could be a motor circuit switch rated in horsepower (see Section 430-109) or a suitable nonautomatic circuit interrupter (molded case switch), as required by Section 7-4.2 of NFPA 20.

If a motor circuit switch were used for the isolating means, it would be horsepower rated at 100 hp and have an ampere rating of at least 115 percent of the full-load current rating of the motor in order to meet the requirements of Section 430-110(a) of the *NEC* and Section 7-4.2.2 of NFPA 20; that is, 124 A × 115 percent = 142.6 A.

The circuit breaker used to protect the branch circuit to the squirrel-cage induction motor would be a magnetic trip type having a time delay of not over 20 seconds at locked-rotor current, and it would be calibrated up to and set at 300 percent of the motor's full-load current. See Section 7-4.4 of NFPA 20. In this particular instance it would be calibrated at 372 A (124 A × 300 percent).

Circuit breakers for dc and wound-rotor ac motors for fire pumps are of the instantaneous type, calibrated up to and set at 400 percent of the motor's full-load current. See Section 7-4.4 of NFPA 20.

Listed pump controllers are investigated to verify their ability to meet the requirements of the *NEC* and NFPA 20 for time-current characteristics of magnetic circuit breakers in order to assure the 20-second delay at locked-rotor current and 300 percent or 400 percent trip setting, depending on the type of motor used.

The motor starter (without overload relays) is of a magnetic type with a contact in each ungrounded conductor in accordance with Section 7-4.5.1 of NFPA 20.

A set of fuses shall be considered all the fuses required to protect all the ungrounded conductors of a circuit. Single-pole circuit breakers, grouped in accordance with Section 230-71(b), shall be considered as one protective device.

Two or three single-pole switches or circuit breakers on multiwire circuits that are capable of individual operation are permitted as one protective device, provided they are equipped with handle ties or a master handle so that all ungrounded conductors of a service can be disconnected with not more than six operations of the hand. See Section 230-71(b).

(b) Not in Grounded Conductor. No overcurrent device shall be inserted in a grounded service conductor except a circuit breaker that simultaneously opens all conductors of the circuit.

230-91. Location of Overcurrent Protection.

(a) General. The service overcurrent device shall be an integral part of the service disconnecting means or shall be located immediately adjacent thereto.

Service overcurrent protective devices (fuses or circuit breakers) within a building are required to be located at a readily accessible location nearest to the point of entrance of the service conductors. If there is no readily accessible area or if the available readily accessible area is not near the point of entrance of the service conductors, and the distance is judged by the authority having jurisdiction to be a potential hazard, the overcurrent devices are permitted to be located outside of the building. See Section 230-70(a) and its following commentary.

(b) Access to Occupants. In a multiple-occupancy building, each occupant shall have access to the overcurrent protective devices.

See Section 225-8(b) also.

Exception: As permitted in Section 240-24(b), Exception.

230-92. Locked Service Overcurrent Devices. Where the service overcurrent devices are locked or sealed, or otherwise not readily accessible, branch-circuit overcurrent devices shall be installed on the load side, shall be mounted in a readily accessible location, and shall be of lower ampere rating than the service overcurrent device.

230-93. Protection of Specific Circuits. Where necessary to prevent tampering, an automatic overcurrent device protecting service conductors supplying only a specific load, such as

a water heater, shall be permitted to be locked or sealed where located so as to be accessible.

230-94. Relative Location of Overcurrent Device and Other Service Equipment. The overcurrent device shall protect all circuits and devices.

Exception No. 1: The service switch shall be permitted on the supply side.

Exception No. 2: High-impedance shunt circuits, lightning arresters, surge protective capacitors, and instrument transformers (current and voltage) shall be permitted to be connected and installed on the supply side of the service disconnecting means as permitted in Section 230-82.

Exception No. 3: Circuits for emergency supply and load management devices shall be permitted to be connected on the supply side of the service overcurrent device where separately provided with overcurrent protection.

Exception No. 4: Circuits used only for the operation of fire alarm, other protective signaling systems, or the supply to fire pump equipment shall be permitted to be connected on the supply side of the service overcurrent device where separately provided with overcurrent protection.

Exception No. 5: Meters nominally rated not in excess of 600 volts, provided all metal housings and service enclosures are grounded in accordance with Article 250.

Exception No. 6: Where service equipment is power operable, the control circuit shall be permitted to be connected ahead of the service equipment if suitable overcurrent protection and disconnecting means are provided.

230-95. Ground-Fault Protection of Equipment. Ground-fault protection of equipment shall be provided for solidly grounded wye electrical services of more than 150 volts to ground, but not exceeding 600 volts phase-to-phase for each service disconnecting means rated 1000 amperes or more.

See definition of "ground-fault protection of equipment" in Article 100. Ground-fault protection of equipment on services rated 1,000 amps or more operating at 480Y/277 V was first required in the 1971 *Code* because of the unusually high number of burndowns that were reported on this type of service. Ground-fault protection of services will not protect the conductors on the supply side of the service disconnecting means, but is designed to provide protection from line-to-ground faults that occur on the load side of the service disconnecting means rated 1,000 A or more. An alternative to installing ground-fault protection may be to provide multiple disconnects rated less than 1,000 A. For instance, six 800-A disconnecting means may be used and, in this case, ground-fault protection would not be necessary. The second Fine Print Note in Section 230-95(b) recognizes that ground-fault protection may be desirable at lesser amperages on solidly grounded systems for voltages exceeding 150 V to ground, but not exceeding 600 V phase-to-phase.

In addition to providing ground-fault protection, engineering studies should be made to determine the circuit impedance and the short-circuit currents that would be available at the supply terminals so that equipment and overcurrent protection of the proper interrupting rating is used. See Sections 110-9 and 110-10.

Figure 230-16. Ground-fault sensor encircling all circuit conductors, including the neutral.

There are two basic types of ground-fault equipment protectors. They are illustrated in Figures 230-16 and 230-17. In Figure 230-16, the ground-fault sensor is installed around all the circuit conductors, and a stray current on a line-to-ground fault will set up an unbalance of the currents flowing in individual conductors installed through the ground-fault sensor. When this current exceeds the setting of the ground-fault sensor, the shunt trip will operate and open the circuit breakers.

The ground-fault sensor illustrated in Figure 230-17 is installed around the bonding jumper only, and when an unbalanced current from a line-to-ground fault occurs, the current will flow through the bonding jumper and the shunt trip will cause the circuit breaker to operate and remove the load from the line. See also Section 250-23(a), Exception No. 5.

Figure 230-17. Ground-fault sensor encircling the bonding jumper conductor only.

The maximum setting for ground-fault sensors is 1,200 A; however, there is no minimum, and it should be noted that setting at lower levels increases the likelihood of unwanted shutdowns. The requirements provide a maximum time delay of 1 second for ground-fault currents equal to or greater than 3,000 A in order to minimize the amount of damage done by an arcing fault, which is directly proportional to the time it is allowed to burn.

Where interconnection is made between multiple supply systems, care should be taken to ensure proper ground-fault sensing by the ground-fault protection equipment and, in most cases, a careful engineering study must be made to ensure that fault currents do not take parallel paths to ground, causing no trip or unwanted trips on the ground-fault protected system. See Section 705-32. See Sections 215-10 and 240-13 for ground-fault protection of feeder disconnects.

Exception No. 1: The provisions of this section shall not apply to a service disconnecting means for a continuous industrial process where a nonorderly shutdown will introduce additional or increased hazards.

Exception No. 2: The provisions of this section shall not apply to fire pumps.

Most fire pumps rated 100 horsepower and over would require a disconnecting means rated at 1,000 A or more. However, due to the emergency nature of their use, fire pumps are exempt from the provisions of Section 230-95.

(a) Setting. The ground-fault protection system shall operate to cause the service disconnecting means to open all ungrounded conductors of the faulted circuit. The maximum setting of the ground-fault protection shall be 1200 amperes, and the maximum time delay shall be one second for ground-fault currents equal to or greater than 3000 amperes.

(b) Fuses. If a switch and fuse combination is used, the fuses employed shall be capable of interrupting any current higher than the interrupting capacity of the switch during a time when the ground-fault protective system will not cause the switch to open.

(FPN No. 1): As used in this section, the rating of the service disconnecting means is considered to be the rating of the largest fuse that can be installed or the highest continuous current trip setting for which the actual overcurrent device installed in a circuit breaker is rated or can be adjusted.

(FPN No. 2): It is recognized that ground-fault protection may be desirable for service disconnecting means rated less than 1000 amperes on solidly grounded wye systems having more than 150 volts to ground, not exceeding 600 volts phase-to-phase.

(FPN No. 3): As used in this section, solidly grounded means that the grounded conductor (neutral) is grounded without inserting any resistor or impedance device.

(FPN No. 4): Ground-fault protection that functions to open the service disconnecting means will afford no protection from faults on the line side of the protective element. It serves only to limit damage to conductors and equipment on the load side in the event of an arcing ground fault on the load side of the protective element.

(FPN No. 5): This added protective equipment at the service equipment will make it necessary to review the overall wiring system for proper selective overcurrent protection coordination. Additional installations of ground-fault protective equipment will be needed on feeders and branch circuits where maximum continuity of electrical service is necessary.

(FPN No. 6): Where ground-fault protection is provided for the service disconnecting means and interconnection is made with another supply system by a transfer device, means or devices may be needed to assure proper ground-fault sensing by the ground-fault protection equipment.

(c) Performance Testing. The ground-fault protection system shall be performance tested when first installed on site. The test shall be conducted in accordance with instructions

Figure 230-18. Ground-fault protection system. (Square D Co.)

Ground-fault sensor

Ground trip of circuit interrupter

N

φ
φ
φ

Ground-fault relay

which shall be provided with the equipment. A written record of this test shall be made and shall be available to the authority having jurisdiction.

The requirement for ground-fault protection system performance testing is a result of numerous reports of ground-fault protection systems that were improperly wired and that could not or did not perform the function for which they were intended. The *Code* and qualified testing laboratories require a set of performance testing instructions to be supplied with the equipment. Evaluation and listing of the instructions falls under the jurisdiction of those best qualified to make such judgments: the Qualified Electrical Testing Laboratory. See Section 90-6. If listed equipment is not installed in accordance with the instructions provided, the installation does not comply with Section 110-3(b).

H. Services Exceeding 600 Volts, Nominal

230-200. **General.** Service conductors and equipment used on circuits exceeding 600 volts, nominal, shall comply with all applicable provisions of the preceding sections of this article and with the following sections, which supplement or modify the preceding sections. In no case shall the provisions of this article apply to equipment on the supply side of the service point.

Where services rated over 600 volts supply utility owned and maintained transformers, the conductors on the line side of the service point are service lateral conductors and the conductors on the load side of the service point are service-entrance conductors as shown in Figure 230-19(a).

In this case, the main service disconnecting means is located as shown at the building location in accordance with Sections 230-70 or 230-208(b).

Where the transformer is owned and maintained by the customer, the conductors on the load side of the service point are service-lateral conductors up to the transformers primary overcurrent protective device.

The conductors extending from the load side of the transformer primary overcurrent protection to the building disconnecting means are feeders. The main service disconnecting means is the disconnect on the transformer primary as shown in Figure 230-19(b).

Each building or structure is required to have a disconnecting means in accordance with Section 225-8(b).

(FPN): For clearances of conductors of over 600 volts, nominal, see National Electrical Safety Code, ANSI C2-1990.

230-202. **Service-Entrance Conductors.** Service-entrance conductors to buildings or enclosures shall be installed to conform to the following:

(a) **Conductor Size.** Service-entrance conductors shall not be smaller than No. 6 unless in cable. Conductors in cable shall not be smaller than No. 8.

(b) **Wiring Methods.** Service-entrance conductors shall be installed by means of one of the following wiring methods: (1) in rigid metal conduit; (2) in intermediate metal conduit; (3) in rigid nonmetallic conduit; (4) as multiconductor cable identified as service cable; (5) as open conductors where supported on insulators and where either accessible only to qualified persons or where effectively guarded against accidental contact; (6) in cablebus; or (7) in busways.

Underground service-entrance conductors shall conform to Section 710-4(b).

Cable tray systems shall be permitted to support cables identified as service-entrance conductors. See Article 318.

(FPN): See Section 310-6 for shielding of solid dielectric insulated conductors.

(c) **Open Work.** Open wire services shall be installed in accordance with the provisions of Article 710, Part D.

(d) **Supports.** Service-entrance conductors and their supports, including insulators, shall have strength and stability sufficient to ensure maintenance of adequate clearance with abnormal currents in case of short circuits.

(e) **Guarding.** Open wires shall be guarded to make them accessible only to qualified persons.

(f) **Service Cable.** Where cable conductors emerge from a metal sheath or raceway, the insulation of the conductors shall be protected from moisture and physical damage by a pothead or other approved means.

(g) **Draining Raceways.** Unless conductors identified for use in wet locations are used, raceways embedded in masonry or exposed to the weather shall be arranged to drain.

(h) **Over 15,000 Volts.** Where the voltage exceeds 15,000 volts between conductors, they shall enter either metal-enclosed switchgear or a transformer vault conforming to the requirements of Sections 450-41 through 450-48.

Figure 230-19(a) and (b).   *Figure 230-19(a): Service rated over 600 volts supplying utility-owned transformer. Conductors on line side of the service point are service lateral conductors. Conductors on the load side of the service point are service entrance conductors. Figure 230-19(b): Service rated over 600 volts supplying customer-owned transformer. Conductors on the load side of the transformer primary overcurrent protection are feeders.*

230-203 .   **Warning Signs.** Signs with the words "Danger High Voltage—Keep Out" shall be posted in plain view where unauthorized persons might come in contact with energized parts.

230-204 .   **Isolating Switches.**

(a) **Where Required.** Where oil switches or air, oil, vacuum, or sulfur hexafluoride circuit breakers constitute the service disconnecting means, an air-break isolating switch shall be installed on the supply side of the disconnecting means and all associated service equipment.

Exception: Where such equipment is mounted on removable truck panels or metal-enclosed switchgear units, which cannot be opened unless the circuit is disconnected, and which, when removed from the normal operating position, automatically disconnect the circuit breaker or switch from all energized parts.

(b) **Fuses as Isolating Switch.** Where fuses are of the type that can be operated as a disconnecting switch, a set of such fuses shall be permitted as the isolating switch where: (1) the oil disconnecting means is a nonautomatic switch, and (2) the set of fuses disconnect the oil switch and all associated service equipment from the service conductors.

(c) **Accessible to Qualified Persons Only.** The isolating switch shall be accessible to qualified persons only.

(d) **Grounding Connection.** Isolating switches shall be provided with a means for readily connecting the load side conductors to ground when disconnected from the source of supply.

A means for grounding the load side conductors shall not be required for any duplicate isolating switch installed and maintained by the electric supply company.

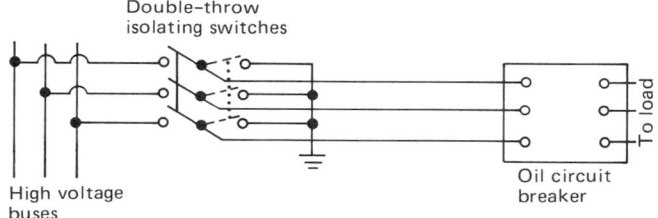

Figure 230-20.   *A two-position switch grounds load-side conductors when disconnected from high-voltage line buses.*

230-205 .   **Disconnecting Means.**

(a) **Location.** The service disconnecting means shall be located in accordance with Section 230-70 or Section 230-208(b).

Exception: Where under single management, the service disconnecting means shall be permitted to be located in a separate building or structure on the same premises. In such case, the service disconnecting means shall be capable of being electrically opened by a readily accessible control device located as near as practicable to where the feeder conductors enter the building served. The control device shall be permanently marked to identify its function and shall provide visual indication of the "on" or "off" status of the remote service disconnect.

(b) Type. The service disconnecting means shall simultaneously disconnect all ungrounded conductors and shall have a fault-closing rating not less than the maximum short-circuit current available at its supply terminals.

Where fused switches or separately mounted fuses are installed, the fuse characteristics shall be permitted to contribute to the fault-closing rating of the disconnecting means.

230-206. **Overcurrent Devices as Disconnecting Means.** Where the circuit breaker or alternative for it specified in Section 230-208 for service overcurrent devices meets the requirements specified in Section 230-205, they shall constitute the service disconnecting means.

230-207. **Equipment in Secondaries.** Where the primary service equipment supplies one or more transformers whose secondary windings connect to a common bus of bars or wires, and the primary load-interrupter switch or circuit breaker is capable of being opened and closed from a point outside the transformer vault, the disconnecting means and overcurrent protection shall not be required in the secondary circuit if the primary fuse or circuit breaker is rated or set to protect the secondary circuit.

230-208. **Overcurrent Protection Requirements.** Service-entrance conductors shall have a short-circuit protective device in each ungrounded conductor on the load side of, or as an integral part of, the service-entrance switch. The protective device shall be capable of detecting and interrupting all values of current in excess of its trip setting or melting point, that can occur at its location. A fuse rated in continuous amperes not to exceed three times the ampacity of the conductor, or a circuit breaker with a trip setting of not more than six times the ampacity of the conductors, shall be considered as providing the required short-circuit protection.

(FPN): See Tables 310-69 through 310-84 for ampacities of conductors rated 2001 volts and above.

Overcurrent devices shall conform to the following:

(a) In Vault or Consisting of Metal-Enclosed Switchgear. Where the service equipment is installed in a transformer vault meeting the provisions of Sections 450-41 through 450-48, or consists of metal-enclosed switchgear, the overcurrent protection and disconnecting means shall be one of the following:

Figure 230-21. *In installations where a transformer supplies a single set of secondary mains, the mains may be connected directly to the buses at the distribution center without a switch or overload protection; however, the primary breaker must be set to protect the secondary circuit.*

(1) A nonautomatic oil switch, oil fuse cutout, or air load-interrupter switch shall be permitted with fuses. The interrupting rating of this switch shall equal or exceed the continuous current rating of the fuse.

(2) An automatic trip circuit breaker of suitable current-carrying and interrupting capacity.

(3) A switch capable of interrupting the no-load current of the transformer supplied through the switch and suitable fuses shall be permitted provided the switch is interlocked with a single switch or circuit breaker on the secondary circuit of the transformer so that the primary switch cannot be opened when the secondary circuit is closed.

(b) Not in Vault or Not Consisting of Metal-Enclosed Switchgear. Where the service equipment is not in a vault or metal-enclosed switchgear, the overcurrent protection and disconnecting means shall be either of the following:

(1) An air load-interrupter switch or other switch capable of interrupting the rated circuit load shall be permitted with fuses on a pole or elevated structure outside the building, provided the switch is operable by persons using the building.

(2) An automatic-trip circuit breaker of suitable ampacity and interrupting capacity. The circuit breaker shall be located outside the building as near as practicable to where the feeder conductors enter the building. The location shall be permitted on a pole, roof, foundation, or other structure.

(c) Fuses. Fuses shall have an interrupting rating no less than the maximum available short-circuit current in the circuit at their supply terminals.

Figure 230-22. An assembly of metal-enclosed switchgear. (Square D Co.)

(d) Circuit Breakers. Circuit breakers shall be free to open in case the circuit is closed on an overload. This can be accomplished by means such as trip-free circuit breakers. A service circuit breaker shall indicate clearly whether it is open or closed, and shall have an interrupting rating no less than the maximum available short-circuit current at its supply terminals.

Overcurrent relays shall be furnished in connection with current transformers in one of the following combinations:

(1) Three overcurrent relays operated from current transformers in each phase.

(2) Two overcurrent relays operated by current from current transformers in any two phases and one overcurrent relay sensitive to ground-fault current that is operated by the sum of the currents from current transformers in each phase.

(3) Two overcurrent relays operated by current from current transformers in any two phases and one overcurrent relay sensitive to ground-fault current that is operated from a current transformer that links all three phase conductors and the grounded circuit conductor (neutral), if provided.

(e) Enclosed Overcurrent Devices. The restriction to 80 percent of rating for an enclosed overcurrent device on continuous loads shall not apply to overcurrent devices installed in services operating at over 600 volts.

230-209. **Surge Arresters (Lightning Arresters).** Surge arresters installed in accordance with the requirements of Article 280 shall be permitted on each ungrounded overhead service conductor.

230-210. **Service Equipment—General Provisions.** Service equipment including instrument transformers shall conform to Article 710, Part B.

230-211. **Metal-Enclosed Switchgear.** Metal-enclosed switchgear shall consist of a substantial metal structure and a sheet metal enclosure. Where installed over a combustible floor, suitable protection thereto shall be provided.

ARTICLE 240   Overcurrent Protection

Contents

240-1. Scope.

A. General

240-2. Protection of Equipment.
240-3. Protection of Conductors.
  (a) Power Loss Hazard.
  (b) Devices Rated 800 Amperes or Less.
  (c) Devices Rated Over 800 Amperes.
  (d) Tap Conductors.
  (e) Motor-Operated Appliance Circuit Conductors.
  (f) Motor and Motor-Control Circuit Conductors.
  (g) Phase Converter Supply Conductors.
  (h) Air-Conditioning and Refrigeration Equipment Circuit Conductors.
  (i) Transformer Secondary Conductors.
  (j) Capacitor Circuit Conductors.

G. Circuit Breakers

240-80. Method of Operation.
240-81. Indicating.
240-82. Nontamperable.
240-83. Marking.
   (a) Durable and Visible.
   (b) Location.
   (c) Interrupting Rating.
   (d) Circuit Breakers Used as Switches.
   (e) Voltage Marking.

H. Overcurrent Protection Over 600 Volts, Nominal

240-100. Feeders.
240-101. Branch Circuits.

240-1. **Scope.** Parts A through G of this article provide the general requirements for overcurrent protection and overcurrent protective devices not more than 600 volts, nominal. Part H covers overcurrent protection over 600 volts, nominal.

(FPN): Overcurrent protection for conductors and equipment is provided to open the circuit if the current reaches a value that will cause an excessive or dangerous temperature in conductors or conductor insulation. See also Sections 110-9 and 110-10 for requirements for interrupting capacity and protection against fault currents.

A. General

240-2. **Protection of Equipment.** Equipment shall be protected against overcurrent in accordance with the article in this Code covering the type of equipment as specified in the following list.

	Article
Air-Conditioning and Refrigerating Equipment	440
Appliances	422
Branch Circuits	210
Busways	364
Capacitors	460
Class 1, Class 2, and Class 3 Remote-Control, Signaling, and Power-Limited Circuits	725

	Article
Closed-Loop and Programmed Power Distribution	780
Cranes and Hoists	610
Electric Signs and Outline Lighting	600
Electric Welders	630
Electrolytic Cells	668
Elevators, Dumbwaiters, Escalators, Moving Walks, Wheelchair Lifts, and Stairway Chair Lifts	620
Emergency Systems	700
Fire Protective Signaling Systems	760
Fixed Electric Heating Equipment for Pipelines and Vessels	427
Fixed Electric Space Heating Equipment	424
Fixed Outdoor Electric Deicing and Snow-Melting Equipment	426
Generators	445
Health Care Facilities	517
Induction and Dielectric Heating Equipment	665
Industrial Machinery	670
Lighting Fixtures, Lampholders, Lamps, and Receptacles	410
Motion Picture and Television Studios and Similar Locations	530
Motors, Motor Circuits, and Controllers	430
Phase Converters	455
Pipe Organs	650
Places of Assembly	518
Services	230
Solar Photovoltaic Systems	690
Sound-Recording and Similar Equipment	640
Switchboards and Panelboards	384
Theaters, Audience Areas of Motion Picture and Television Studios, and Similar Locations	520
Transformers and Transformer Vaults	450
X-Ray Equipment	660

240-3. **Protection of Conductors.** Conductors, other than flexible cords and fixture wires, shall be protected against overcurrent in accordance with their ampacities as specified in Section 310-15, unless otherwise permitted in (a) through (m) below.

(a) Power Loss Hazard. Conductor overload protection shall not be required where the interruption of the circuit would create a hazard, such as in a material handling magnet circuit or fire pump circuit. Short-circuit protection shall be provided.

(FPN): See Installation of Centrifugal Fire Pumps, NFPA 20 - 1990 (ANSI).

(b) Devices Rated 800 Amperes or Less. Conductors not part of a multioutlet branch circuit supplying receptacles for cord- and plug-connected portable loads and where the ampacity of the conductors does not correspond with the standard ampere rating of a fuse or a circuit breaker without overload trip adjustments above its rating (but that may have other trip or rating adjustments), the next higher standard device rating shall be permitted only if this rating does not exceed 800 amperes.

Table 210-24 summarizes the requirements for the size of conductors where two or more outlets are required. The first footnote also indicates that the wire sizes are for copper conductors. Section 210-3 indicates that branch-circuit conductors rated 15, 20, 30, 40, and 50 A, with two or more outlets, must be protected at their ratings. Section 210-19(a) requires that branch-circuit conductors have an ampacity of not less than the rating of the branch circuit and not less than the maximum load to be served.

These are specific requirements and take precedence over Section 240-3(b), which applies generally. Where the conductor is not part of a multioutlet branch circuit supplying receptacles for cord- and plug-connected portable loads and the conductor ampacities do not correspond to standard ampere ratings of fuses or circuit breakers, the next standard device rating is permitted if this rating does not exceed 800 A.

(c) Devices Rated Over 800 Amperes. Where the overcurrent device is rated over 800 amperes, the ampacity of the conductors it protects shall be equal to or greater than the rating of the overcurrent device as defined in Section 240-6.

(d) Tap Conductors. Tap conductors shall be permitted to be protected against overcurrent in accordance with Sections 210-19(c), 240-21, 364-11, 364-12, and 430-53(d).

(e) Motor-Operated Appliance Circuit Conductors. Motor-operated appliance circuit conductors shall be permitted to be protected against overcurrent in accordance with Parts B and D of Article 422.

(f) Motor and Motor-Control Circuit Conductors. Motor and motor-control circuit conductors shall be permitted to be protected against overcurrent in accordance with Parts C, D, E, and F of Article 430.

(g) Phase Converter Supply Conductors. Phase converter supply conductors for motor loads and nonmotor loads shall be permitted to be protected against overcurrent in accordance with Section 455-7.

(h) Air-Conditioning and Refrigeration Equipment Circuit Conductors. Air-conditioning and refrigeration equipment circuit conductors shall be permitted to be protected against overcurrent in accordance with Parts C and F of Article 440.

(i) Transformer Secondary Conductors. Single-phase (other than 2-wire) and multiphase transformer secondary conductors are not considered to be protected by the primary overcurrent protection. Conductors supplied by the secondary side of a single-phase transformer having a 2-wire (single-voltage) secondary shall be permitted to be protected by overcurrent protection provided on the primary (supply) side of the transformer, provided this protection is in accordance with Section 450-3 and does not exceed the value determined by multiplying the secondary conductor ampacity by the secondary to primary transformer voltage ratio.

The first paragraph of Section 240-3 requires that conductors be protected against overcurrent in accordance with their ampacity. Section 240-3(i) permits the secondary circuit conductors from a transformer to be protected by overcurrent devices in the primary circuit conductors of the transformer, provided the transformer consists of a 2-wire primary and a 2-wire secondary and the transformer is protected in accordance with Section 450-3.

For example, a transformer that has a 2-wire, 480-V primary and a 2-wire, 240-V secondary with overcurrent protection in the primary rated at 50 A is considered to be protection for the secondary circuit conductors whose ampacity is not less than 100 A.

The secondary to primary voltage ratio of the above transformer is 1:2 or 0.5. Multiplying the secondary conductor ampacity by the secondary to primary ratio results in the maximum rating of the overcurrent device permitted in the primary conductors required for protection of the secondary conductors. Therefore, the length of the secondary conductors is not limited, and no overcurrent protection is required on the secondary side.

If the secondary consists of a 3-wire, 240/120-V system, a 120-volt line-to-neutral load could draw up to 200 A before the overcurrent device in the primary actuates. This is the result of the 1:4 secondary to primary voltage ratio of the 120-V winding of the transformer secondary, which can cause dangerous overloading of the secondary conductors.

Where 3-phase transformers are involved, secondary circuit conductors are not protected by overcurrent protective devices on the transformer primary. Where a single-phase overload occurs in the secondary circuit, the three transformer primary windings share the load between them and may not actuate the overcurrent device on the primary.

(j) Capacitor Circuit Conductors. Capacitor circuit conductors shall be permitted to be protected against overcurrent in accordance with Sections 460-8(b) and 460-25(a) through (d).

(k) Electric Welder Circuit Conductors. Welder circuit conductors shall be permitted to be protected against overcurrent in accordance with Sections 630-12, 630-22, and 630-32.

(l) Remote-Control, Signaling, and Power-Limited Circuit Conductors. Remote-control, signaling, and power-limited circuit conductors shall be permitted to be protected against overcurrent in accordance with Sections 725-12, 725-13, 725-31, 725-35, and 725-36.

(m) Fire Protective Signaling System Circuit Conductors. Fire protective signaling system circuit conductors shall be permitted to be protected against overcurrent in accordance with Sections 760-12, 760-13, 760-21, 760-23, and 760-24.

240-4. **Protection of Flexible Cords and Fixture Wires.** Flexible cord, including tinsel cord and extension cords, shall be protected against overcurrent in accordance with their ampacities as specified in Tables 400-5(A) and 400-5(B). Fixture wire shall be protected against overcurrent in accordance with its ampacity as specified in Table 402-5. Supplementary overcurrent protection as in Section 240-10 shall be permitted to be an acceptable means for providing this protection.

Exception No. 1: Where a flexible cord or a tinsel cord approved for and used with a specific listed appliance or portable lamps is connected to a branch circuit of Article 210 in accordance with the following:

20-ampere circuits, tinsel cord or No. 18 cord and larger.
30-ampere circuits, No. 16 cord and larger.
40-ampere circuits, cord of 20-ampere capacity and over.
50-ampere circuits, cord of 20-ampere capacity and over.

Exception No. 2: Where fixture wire is connected to 120-volt or higher branch circuit of Article 210 in accordance with the following:

20-ampere circuits, No. 18 up to 50 feet (15.2 m) of run length.
20-ampere circuits, No. 16 up to 100 feet (30.5 m) of run length.
20-ampere circuits, No. 14 and larger.
30-ampere circuits, No. 14 and larger.
40-ampere circuits, No. 12 and larger.
50-ampere circuits, No. 12 and larger.

Exception No. 3: Flexible cord used in listed extension cord sets having No. 16 or larger conductors shall be considered to be protected by 20-ampere branch-circuit overcurrent protection.

Section 240-4 clarifies the requirements for overcurrent protection of flexible cords and fixture wire by referencing Tables 400-5(A) and 400-5(B) for flexible cords and Table 402-5 for fixture wire ampacity.

Exceptions No. 1 and No. 2 permit smaller conductors to be connected to branch circuits of a greater rating where the smaller conductors are approved for and used with a specific listed appliance, portable lamp, or extension cord, or where fixture wire is protected as listed in the exceptions. Exception No. 3 permits listed cord sets No. 16 AWG or larger to be protected by 20-ampere or less branch-circuit overcurrent devices.

240-6. **Standard Ampere Ratings.**

(a) Fuses and Fixed Trip Circuit Breakers. The standard ampere ratings for fuses and inverse time circuit breakers shall be considered 15, 20, 25, 30, 35, 40, 45, 50, 60, 70, 80, 90, 100, 110, 125, 150, 175, 200, 225, 250, 300, 350, 400, 450, 500, 600, 700, 800, 1000, 1200, 1600, 2000, 2500, 3000, 4000, 5000, and 6000 amperes.

Exception: Additional standard ratings for fuses shall be considered 1, 3, 6, 10, and 601.

(b) Adjustable Trip Circuit Breakers. The rating of an adjustable trip circuit breaker having external means for adjusting the long-time pickup (ampere rating or overload) setting shall be the maximum setting possible.

Exception: Circuit breakers that have removable and sealable covers over the adjusting means, or are located behind bolted equipment enclosure doors, or are located behind locked doors accessible only to qualified personnel, shall be permitted to have ampere ratings equal to the adjusted (set) long-time pickup settings.

This exception was new in the 1990 *NEC*. The exception was added, and the paragraph preceding the exception modified, to make it clear that the set long-time pickup rating (as opposed to the instantaneous trip rating) of an adjustable trip circuit breaker can be considered the circuit breaker rating if access to the adjustment means is limited due to location of the adjustment means behind sealable covers or locked doors accessible only to qualified personnel.

(FPN): It is not the intent to prohibit the use of nonstandard ampere ratings for fuses and inverse time circuit breakers.

Manufacturers of both fuses and inverse time circuit breakers have or can make available products with ampere ratings other than those listed in Section 240-6 or the exception. Selection of such nonstandard ratings is not required by the *Code*, but will permit better protection for conductors.

240-8. **Fuses or Circuit Breakers in Parallel.** Fuses, circuit breakers, or combinations thereof shall not be connected in parallel.

Exception: Circuit breakers or fuses, factory-assembled in parallel, and listed as a unit.

Section 240-8 prohibits the use of fuses or circuit breakers in parallel, and Section 380-17 prohibits the use of fuses in parallel in fused switches.

It is not the intent of this exception to restore the use of standard fuses in parallel in disconnect switches. However, this exception gives recognition to parallel low-voltage circuit breakers or fuses and parallel high-voltage circuit breakers or fuses where tested and factory-assembled in parallel and listed as a unit.

High-voltage fuses have long been recognized in parallel where assembled in an identified common mounting as per Section 710-21(b)(1).

240-9. **Thermal Devices.** Thermal relays and other devices not designed to open short circuits shall not be used for the protection of conductors against overcurrent due to short circuits or grounds, but the use of such devices shall be permitted to protect motor-branch-circuit conductors from overload if protected in accordance with Section 430-40.

240-10. **Supplementary Overcurrent Protection.** Where supplementary overcurrent protection is used for lighting fixtures, appliances, and other equipment or for internal circuits and components of equipment, it shall not be used as a substitute for branch-circuit overcurrent devices or in place of the branch-circuit protection specified in Article 210. Supplementary overcurrent devices shall not be required to be readily accessible.

240-11. **Definition of Current-Limiting Overcurrent Protective Device.** A current-limiting overcurrent protective device is a device that, when interrupting currents in its current-limiting range, will reduce the current flowing in the faulted circuit to a magnitude substantially less than that obtainable in the same circuit if the device were replaced with a solid conductor having comparable impedance.

Most electrical distribution systems can deliver large short-circuit currents to components, such as conductors, service equipment, etc. These components may not be able to handle short-circuit currents; they may be damaged or destroyed and serious "burndowns" and fires could result. Properly selected current-limiting overcurrent protective devices will limit the let-through energy to within the rating of the

Figure 240-1. Adjustable trip circuit breaker with (transparent) removable and sealable cover. (Square D Co.)

components in spite of high available short-circuit currents. See Figures 240-2 and 240-3 and commentary immediately preceding Section 240-83(d).

See Sections 110-9 and 110-10 for interrupting ratings, circuit impedance, and other characteristics requirements.

240-12. **Electrical System Coordination.** Where an orderly shutdown is required to minimize hazard(s) to personnel and equipment, a system of coordination based on the following two conditions shall be permitted:

Figure 240-2. Class R current-limiting fuse with rejection feature to prohibit the installation of noncurrent-limiting fuses. (Bussman Division Cooper Industries)

(1) Coordinated short-circuit protection.

(2) Overload indication based on monitoring systems or devices.

(FPN): Coordination is defined as properly localizing a fault condition to restrict outages to the equipment affected, accomplished by choice of selective fault-protective devices. The monitoring system may cause the condition to go to alarm, allowing corrective action or an orderly shutdown, thereby minimizing personnel hazard and equipment damage.

240-13. **Ground-Fault Protection of Equipment.** Ground-fault protection of equipment shall be provided in accordance with the provisions of Section 230-95 for solidly grounded wye electrical systems of more than 150 volts to ground, but not exceeding 600 volts phase-to-phase for each building or structure main disconnecting means rated 1000 amperes or more.

Exception No. 1: The provisions of this section shall not apply to a disconnecting means for a continuous industrial process

Figure 240-3. Current-limiting circuit breaker within requirements of UL 489-91 Section 32A. (Square D Co.)

where a nonorderly shutdown will introduce additional or increased hazards.

Exception No. 2: The provisions of this section shall not apply to fire pumps.

Exception No. 3: The provisions of this section shall not apply if the disconnect is protected by the service ground-fault protection, and this protection is not nullified by subsequent grounded circuit conductor connections to additional grounding electrodes, as may be permitted in Section 250-24.

Section 240-13 was added in the 1990 *NEC*. It extends the requirement of Section 230-95 to building disconnects, regardless of how the disconnects are classified (service disconnects or building disconnects for feeders or even branch circuits). See Sections 215-10 and 225-8(a) for the requirement for building disconnects not on the utility service.

Section 240-13 requires each building or structure disconnect rated 1,000 amperes or more, on a solidly grounded system of more than 150 volts to ground (e.g., a 480-volt, 3-phase, 4-wire, Y-connected system), to be provided with ground-fault protection of equipment. Exceptions are included for systems over 600 volts phase-to-phase, continuous industrial processes (see Article 685) where a nonorderly shutdown will introduce additional hazards, and fire pumps. These are the same exceptions applicable to Section 230-95.

If ground-fault protection is provided upstream at the service, and this protection is not nullified by regrounding of the neutral conductor at the disconnect, Exception No. 3 permits deletion of this disconnect ground-fault protection. Note that Section 250-24 requires regrounding of the feeder neutral conductor at a second building if an equipment grounding conductor is not installed from the building with the main service disconnect to the disconnect at the second building. Regrounding of the neutral at the second building may nullify the ground-fault protection of the second building that would otherwise be provided by ground-fault protection at the main service.

B. Location

240-20. **Ungrounded Conductors.**

(a) **Overcurrent Device Required.** A fuse or an overcurrent trip unit of a circuit breaker shall be connected in series with each ungrounded conductor. A combination of a current transformer and overcurrent relay shall be considered equivalent to an overcurrent trip unit.

(FPN): For motor circuits, see Parts C, D, F, and J of Article 430.

(b) **Circuit Breaker as Overcurrent Device.** Circuit breakers shall open all ungrounded conductors of the circuit.

Exception: In grounded systems, individual single-pole circuit breakers with handle ties shall be permitted as the protection for each ungrounded conductor for line-to-line connected loads of the following:
   a. Single-phase circuits,
   b. 3- wire direct-current circuits, or
   c. Lighting or appliance branch circuits connected to 4-wire, 3-phase systems or 5-wire, 2-phase systems, provided such lighting or appliance circuits are supplied from a system having a grounded neutral and no conductor operates at a voltage greater than permitted in Section 210-6.

It is not the intent to require handle ties on multiwire branch circuits.

Note: Multiwire branch circuits are permitted to serve *line-to-line* loads consisting of one utilization equipment or where all ungrounded conductors are opened simultaneously by the branch circuit overcurrent device. See Section 210-4(c) and Figure 210-2.

(c) **Closed-Loop Power Distribution Systems.** Listed devices providing equivalent overcurrent protection in closed-loop power distribution systems shall be permitted as a substitute for fuses or circuit breakers.

240-21. **Location in Circuit.** An overcurrent device shall be connected in each ungrounded circuit conductor as follows:

Section 240-21, which contained 11 exceptions, was revised by rewriting the exceptions as positive statements. Exception No. 1 was deleted, since it was covered by Section 240-3.

(a) **Feeder and Branch-Circuit Conductors.** Feeder and branch-circuit conductors shall be protected by overcurrent-protective devices connected at the point the conductors receive their supply, unless otherwise permitted in (b) through (m) below.

Figure 240-9 illustrates how a smaller 1/0 THW conductor (150 A) is tapped from a larger 3/0 THW feeder conductor (200 A) that is in turn protected by a 150-A circuit breaker that is equal to the ampacity of the 1/0 tap conductor. The circuit breaker protecting the feeder conductors is rated to protect the tap conductors.

1φ Ungrounded system   1φ 2 Wire ungrounded circuit

3φ Ungrounded system   3φ 3 Wire ungrounded circuit

3φ Grounded system   3φ 3 Wire circuit supplied from a grounded system

Not a lighting or appliance branch circuit

Figure 240-4. *Circuits requiring multipole common trip-type circuit breakers in accordance with the main rule in Section 240-20(b).*

(b) Feeder Taps Not Over 10 Feet (3.05 m) Long. Conductors shall be permitted to be tapped, without overcurrent protection at the tap, to a feeder or transformer secondary where all the following conditions are met:

(1) The length of the tap conductors does not exceed 10 feet (3.05 m).

(2) The ampacity of the tap conductors is:

3φ Grounded system   1φ 3 Wire multiwire branch circuit

Lighting or appliance branch circuits

3φ Grounded system   3φ 4 Wire multiwire branch circuit

Lighting or appliance branch circuits

Figure 240-5. *Examples where single pole circuit breakers are permitted. These circuits satisfy the main rule because the single pole circuit breakers open the ungrounded conductor of the circuit. Handle ties are not required since there are no line-to-line loads.*

a. Not less than the combined computed loads on the circuits supplied by the tap conductors, and

b. Not less than the rating of the device supplied by the tap conductors, or not less than the rating of the overcurrent-protective device at the termination of the tap conductors.

(3) The tap conductors do not extend beyond the switchboard, panelboard, or control devices they supply.

(4) Except at the point of connection to the feeder, the tap conductors are enclosed in a raceway, which shall extend from the tap to the enclosure of an enclosed switchboard, panelboard, or control devices, or to the back of an open switchboard.

Figure 240-6. Where line-to-line loads are supplied from a grounded system, handle ties are permitted in accordance with the exception to the main rule of Section 240-20(b).

Figure 240-7. Section 240-3 permits the circuit breaker protecting the feeder conductors to protect the tap conductors to the cabinet.

(5) For field installations where the tap conductors leave the enclosure or vault in which the tap is made, the rating of the overcurrent device on the line side of the tap conductors shall not exceed 1000 percent of the tap conductor's ampacity.

Section 240-21(b)(5) permits a tap from a feeder or from a transformer secondary without requiring overcurrent protection at the point where the tap conductor receives its supply, provided the tap conductor: (1) is not more than 10 feet long; (2) is enclosed in a raceway; (3) does not extend beyond the switchboard, panelboard, or control devices that it supplies; and (4) has an ampacity not less than the combined computed loads supplied and not less than the ampere rating of the switchboard, panelboard, or control devices supplied, except where the tap conductor terminates in an overcurrent protective device that does not exceed the ampacity of the tap conductor.

In addition, if the tap conductors are field installed, the overcurrent protection on the line side of the tap conductors is not permitted to exceed 10 times the tap conductor's ampacity. A factory-installed conductor in a switchboard, panelboard, or unit substation, for example, is not a field-installed conductor.

(FPN): See Sections 384-16(a) and (d) for lighting and appliance branch-circuit panelboards.

(c) Feeder Taps Not Over 25 Feet (7.62 m) Long. Conductors shall be permitted to be tapped, without overcurrent protection at the tap, to a feeder where all the following conditions are met:

(1) The length of the tap conductors does not exceed 25 feet (7.62 m).

(2) The ampacity of the tap conductors is not less than 1/3 of the rating of the overcurrent device protecting the feeder conductors.

(3) The tap conductors terminate in a single circuit breaker or a single set of fuses that will limit the load to the ampacity of the tap conductors. This device shall be permitted to supply any number of additional overcurrent devices on its load side.

(4) The tap conductors are suitably protected from physical damage or are enclosed in a raceway.

Section 240-21(c)(4) is illustrated in Figure 240-8. Three No. 3/0 THW copper tap conductors are protected from physical damage in a raceway. The lengths of the tap conductors are not more than 25 feet between terminations. They are tapped from a 500 kcmil feeder and terminate in a circuit breaker.

Note: A No. 3/0 THW copper conductor (200 A) is more than ⅓ the ampacity of a 500 kcmil THW (380 A) copper conductor. See Table 310-16 for ampacity of copper conductors in conduit.

Figure 240-8. *Feeder taps terminating in a single circuit breaker. See Section 240-21(c)(4).*

(d) Transformer Feeder Taps With Primary Plus Secondary Not Over 25 Feet (7.62 m) Long. Conductors supplying a transformer shall be permitted to be tapped, without overcurrent protection at the tap, from a feeder where all the following conditions are met:

(1) The conductors supplying the primary of a transformer have an ampacity at least ⅓ of the rating of the overcurrent device protecting the feeder conductors.

(2) The conductors supplied by the secondary of the transformer shall have an ampacity that, when multiplied by the ratio of the secondary-to-primary voltage, is at least ⅓ of the rating of the overcurrent device protecting the feeder conductors.

(3) The total length of one primary plus one secondary conductor, excluding any portion of the primary conductor that is protected at its ampacity, is not over 25 feet (7.62 m).

(4) The primary and secondary conductors are suitably protected from physical damage.

(5) The secondary conductors terminate in a single circuit breaker or set of fuses that will limit the load to that allowed in Section 310-15.

See Figure 240-9.

Taps protected from physical damage
Secondary-to-primary voltage ratio = 208/480 = 1:2.3 or 0.43

Figure 240-9. *Transformer feeder taps (primary plus secondary) not over 25 feet long, as per Section 240-21(d)(5). Also applies to overcurrent protection requirements of Sections 384-16(a) and 450-3(b).*

(e) Feeder Taps Over 25 Feet (7.62 m) Long. Conductors over 25 feet (7.62 m) long shall be permitted to be tapped from feeders in high bay manufacturing buildings over 35 feet (10.67 m) high at walls, where conditions of maintenance and supervision ensure that only qualified persons will service the systems. Conductors tapped, without overcurrent protection at the tap, to a feeder shall be permitted to be not over 25 feet (7.62 m) long horizontally and not over 100 feet (30.5 m) total length where all the following conditions are met:

(1) The ampacity of the tap conductors is not less than ⅓ of the rating of the overcurrent device protecting the feeder conductors.

(2) The tap conductors terminate at a single circuit breaker or a single set of fuses that will limit the load to the ampacity of the tap conductors. This single overcurrent device shall be permitted to supply any number of additional overcurrent devices on its load side.

(3) The tap conductors are suitably protected from physical damage or are enclosed in a raceway.

(4) The tap conductors are continuous from end-to-end and contain no splices.

(5) The tap conductors are sized No. 6 copper or No. 4 aluminum or larger.

(6) The tap conductors do not penetrate walls, floors, or ceilings.

(7) The tap is made no less than 30 feet (9.14 m) from the floor.

See Figure 240-10.

10 ft

15 ft

Conductor length not to exceed 100 ft

Wall over 35 ft

Not less than 30 ft

Figure 240-10. Section 240-21(e)(7) permits a tap of 100 feet for manufacturing buildings with walls over 35 feet high. The tap connection is not less than 30 feet from the floor, and conditions of maintenance and supervision must ensure that only qualified persons will service these systems.

(f) Branch-Circuit Taps. Taps to individual outlets and circuit conductors supplying a single electric household range shall be permitted to be protected by the branch-circuit overcurrent devices where in accordance with the requirements of Sections 210-19, 210-20, and 210-24.

(g) Busway Taps. Busways and busway taps shall be permitted to be protected against overcurrent in accordance with Sections 364-10 through 364-14.

(h) Motor Circuit Taps. Motor-branch-circuit conductors shall be permitted to be protected against overcurrent in accordance with Sections 430-28 and 430-53.

(i) Conductors From Generator Terminals. Conductors from generator terminals shall be permitted to be protected against overcurrent in accordance with Section 445-5.

(j) Transformer Secondary Conductors of Separately Derived Systems for Industrial Installations. Conductors connected to a transformer secondary of a separately derived system for industrial installations shall be considered to be protected against overcurrent where all the following conditions are met:

(1) The length of the secondary conductors does not exceed 25 feet (7.62 m).

(2) The ampacity of the secondary conductors is not less than the secondary current rating of the transformer, and the sum of the ratings of the overcurrent devices does not exceed the ampacity of the secondary conductors.

(3) All overcurrent devices are grouped.

(4) The tap conductors are suitably protected from physical damage.

(m) Outside Feeder Taps. Outside conductors tapped to a feeder or connected to a transformer secondary shall be permitted to be protected by complying with all of the following conditions:

(1) The conductors are suitably protected from physical damage.

(2) The conductors terminate at a single circuit breaker or a single set of fuses that will limit the load to the ampacity of the conductors. This single overcurrent device shall be permitted to supply any number of additional overcurrent devices on its load side.

(3) The overcurrent device for the conductors is an integral part of a disconnecting means or shall be located immediately adjacent thereto.

(4) The disconnecting means for the conductors are installed at a readily accessible location either outside of a building or structure, or inside nearest the point of entrance of the conductors.

A new Section 240-21(m) was added to the 1993 *Code* permitting outside conductors that are tapped to a feeder or transformer secondary without any limitations on the length of the tap conductors. The tap conductors must terminate in a fused disconnect or circuit breaker rated not at more than the ampacity of the tap conductors and installed at a readily accessible location either outside a building or structure, or where installed inside a building or structure, located nearest the point of entrance of the tap conductors.

(n) Service Conductors. Service-entrance conductors shall be permitted to be protected by overcurrent devices in accordance with Section 230-91.

240-22. **Grounded Conductors.** No overcurrent device shall be connected in series with any conductor that is intentionally grounded.

Exception No. 1: Where the overcurrent device opens all conductors of the circuit, including the grounded conductor, and is so designed that no pole can operate independently.

Exception No. 2: Where required by Sections 430-36 and 430-37 for motor overload protection.

240-23. **Change in Size of Grounded Conductor.** Where a change occurs in the size of the ungrounded conductor, a similar change shall be permitted to be made in the size of the grounded conductor.

This section acknowledges that the size of a grounded conductor may be increased (because of voltage drop problems, for example) or reduced to correspond to a change made in the size of an ungrounded conductor, as in the case of tap conductors, where all are of the same circuit.

240-24. **Location in or on Premises.**

(a) **Readily Accessible.** Overcurrent devices shall be readily accessible.

This section is intended to correlate with Section 230-91, i.e., the service overcurrent device shall be an integral part of the service disconnecting means or shall be located immediately adjacent thereto. See commentary following Section 230-91(a).

Exception No. 1: For busways as provided in Section 364-12.

Exception No. 2: For supplementary overcurrent protection as described in Section 240-10.

Exception No. 3: For service overcurrent devices as described in Section 230-92.

(b) **Occupant to Have Ready Access.** Each occupant shall have ready access to all overcurrent devices protecting the conductors supplying that occupancy.

Exception: In a multiple-occupancy building where electric service and electrical maintenance are provided by the building management and where these are under continuous building management supervision, the service overcurrent devices and feeder overcurrent devices supplying more than one occupancy shall be permitted to be accessible to authorized management personnel only.

(c) **Not Exposed to Physical Damage.** Overcurrent devices shall be located where they will not be exposed to physical damage.

(FPN): See Section 110-11, Deteriorating Agents.

(d) **Not in Vicinity of Easily Ignitible Material.** Overcurrent devices shall not be located in the vicinity of easily ignitible material such as in clothes closets.

Examples of locations where combustibles may be stored are linen closets, paper storage closets, and clothes closets. Section 550-6(a) no longer permits a distribution panelboard to be located in a closet entry of a mobile home.

(e) **Not Located in Bathrooms.** In dwelling units and guest rooms of hotels and motels, branch-circuit overcurrent devices shall not be located in bathrooms as defined in Section 210-8.

C. Enclosures

240-30. **General.** Overcurrent devices shall be enclosed in cabinets or cutout boxes.

Exception No. 1: Where a part of an assembly that provides equivalent protection.

Exception No. 2: Where mounted on open-type switchboards, panelboards, or control boards that are in rooms or enclosures free from dampness and easily ignitible material and accessible only to qualified personnel.

Exception No. 3: The operating handle of a circuit breaker shall be permitted to be accessible without opening a door or cover.

Properly selected overcurrent protective devices are designed to open a circuit before an overcurrent condition can seriously damage conductor insulation, and requirements that overcurrent devices be enclosed in cabinets or cutout boxes are to ensure that hot metal particles will not be ejected in the vicinity of combustibles and to prevent contact with live parts by personnel.

Overcurrent devices mounted on open-type switchboards, panelboards, or controlboards and having exposed energized parts are to be located where accessible only to qualified persons.

240-32. **Damp or Wet Locations.** Enclosures for overcurrent devices in damp or wet locations shall comply with Section 373-2(a).

240-33. **Vertical Position.** Enclosures for overcurrent devices shall be mounted in a vertical position.

Exception: Where this is shown to be impracticable and complies with Section 240-81.

This section indicates that a wall-mounted, vertical position is desirable to achieve easier access, natural hand operation, normal swing or closing of doors or covers, and legibility of manufacturer's markings.

D. Disconnecting and Guarding

240-40. **Disconnecting Means for Fuses.** Disconnecting means shall be provided on the supply side of all fuses in circuits of over 150 volts to ground and cartridge fuses in circuits of any voltage, where accessible to other than qualified persons, so that each individual circuit containing fuses can be independently disconnected from the source of electric energy.

Exception No. 1: A device provided for current-limiting on the supply side of the service disconnecting means as permitted by Section 230-82.

Exception No. 2: A single disconnecting means shall be permitted on the supply side of more than one set of fuses as provided by Section 430-112 for group operation of motors and in Section 424-22 for fixed electric space heating equipment.

A single disconnect switch is allowed to serve more than one set of fuses, such as in multimotor installations or for electric space heating equipment where the heating element load is required to be subdivided, each with its own set of fuses.

240-41. **Arcing or Suddenly Moving Parts.** Arcing or suddenly moving parts shall comply with (a) and (b) below.

(a) **Location.** Fuses and circuit breakers shall be so located or shielded that persons will not be burned or otherwise injured by their operation.

(b) **Suddenly Moving Parts.** Handles or levers of circuit breakers, and similar parts that may move suddenly in such a way that persons in the vicinity are likely to be injured by being struck by them, shall be guarded or isolated.

Arcing or suddenly moving parts are usually associated with switchboards or control boards that may be of the open type and should be under competent supervision and accessible only to qualified persons. Fuses or circuit breakers are required to be so located or shielded that under an abnormal condition the subsequent arc across the opening device will not injure persons in the vicinity.

Guardrails may be provided in the vicinity of disconnecting means. Modern switchboards, etc., are equipped with removable handles, but sudden-moving handles may be capable of causing injury.

See Article 100 for definition of "Guarded." See also Section 110-17.

E. Plug Fuses, Fuseholders, and Adapters

240-50. **General.**

(a) **Maximum Voltage.** Plug fuses and fuseholders shall not be used in circuits exceeding 125 volts between conductors.

Exception: In circuits supplied by a system having a grounded neutral and having no conductor at over 150 volts to ground.

This permits plug fuses to be installed in circuits supplied by 120/240-V, single-phase, 3-wire systems and 208Y/120-V, 3-phase, 4-wire systems.

(b) **Marking.** Each fuse, fuseholder, and adapter shall be marked with its ampere rating.

(c) **Hexagonal Configuration.** Plug fuses of 15-ampere and lower rating shall be identified by a hexagonal configuration of the window, cap, or other prominent part to distinguish them from fuses of higher ampere ratings.

(d) **No Energized Parts.** Plug fuses, fuseholders, and adapters shall have no exposed energized parts after fuses or fuses and adapters have been installed.

(e) **Screw Shell.** The screw shell of a plug-type fuseholder shall be connected to the load side of the circuit.

240-51. Edison-Base Fuses.

(a) Classification. Plug fuses of the Edison-base type shall be classified at not over 125 volts and 30 amperes and below.

(b) Replacement Only. Plug fuses of the Edison-base type shall be used only for replacements in existing installations where there is no evidence of overfusing or tampering.

240-52. Edison-Base Fuseholders.
Fuseholders of the Edison-base type shall be installed only where they are made to accept Type S fuses by the use of adapters.

240-53. Type S Fuses.
Type S fuses shall be of the plug type and shall comply with (a) and (b) below.

(a) Classification. Type S fuses shall be classified at not over 125 volts and 0 to 15 amperes, 16 to 20 amperes, and 21 to 30 amperes.

(b) Noninterchangeable. Type S fuses of an ampere classification as specified in (a) above shall not be interchangeable with a lower ampere classification. They shall be so designed that they cannot be used in any fuseholder other than a Type S fuseholder or a fuseholder with a Type S adapter inserted.

240-54. Type S Fuses, Adapters, and Fuseholders.

(a) To Fit Edison-Base Fuseholders. Type S adapters shall fit Edison-base fuseholders.

(b) To Fit Type S Fuses Only. Type S fuseholders and adapters shall be so designed that either the fuseholder itself or the fuseholder with a Type S adapter inserted cannot be used for any fuse other than a Type S fuse.

(c) Nonremovable. Type S adapters shall be so designed that once inserted in a fuseholder, they cannot be removed.

(d) Nontamperable. Type S fuses, fuseholders, and adapters shall be so designed that tampering or shunting (bridging) would be difficult.

(e) Interchangeability. Dimensions of Type S fuses, fuseholders, and adapters shall be standardized to permit interchangeability regardless of the manufacturer.

F. Cartridge Fuses and Fuseholders

240-60. General.

(a) Maximum Voltage—300-Volt Type. Cartridge fuses and fuseholders of the 300-volt type shall not be used in circuits of over 300 volts between conductors.

Exception: In single-phase line-to-neutral circuits supplied from 3-phase, 4-wire, solidly grounded neutral systems where the line-to-neutral voltage does not exceed 300V.

(b) Noninterchangeable—0-6000 Ampere Cartridge Fuseholders. Fuseholders shall be so designed that it will be difficult to put a fuse of any given class into a fuseholder that is designed for a current lower, or voltage higher, than that of the class to which the fuse belongs. Fuseholders for current-limiting fuses shall not permit insertion of fuses that are not current-limiting.

(c) Marking. Fuses shall be plainly marked, either by printing on the fuse barrel or by a label attached to the barrel, showing the following: (1) ampere rating; (2) voltage rating; (3) interrupting rating where other than 10,000 amperes; (4) "current-limiting" where applicable; and (5) the name or trademark of the manufacturer.

Class H-type cartridge fuses have an interrupting capacity (IC) rating of 10,000 A, and this rating need not be marked on the fuse. However, Class CC, G, J, K, L, R, and T cartridge fuses have over a 10,000-A IC rating and must be marked with the IC rating.

Section 240-83(c) requires that the IC rating for circuit breakers for other than 5,000 A be indicated on the circuit breaker.

Fuses or circuit breakers used for supplementary protection of fluorescent fixtures, semiconductor rectifiers, motor-operated appliances, etc., need not be marked for IC. See also commentary on circuit breakers following Section 110-10.

Exception: Interrupting rating marking shall not be required on fuses used for supplementary protection.

240-61. Classification.
Cartridge fuses and fuseholders shall be classified according to voltage and amperage ranges. Fuses rated 600 volts, nominal, or less, shall be permitted to be used for voltages at or below their ratings.

See Section 710-21(b) for application of high-voltage fuses.

G. Circuit Breakers

240-80. Method of Operation.
Circuit breakers shall be trip free and capable of being closed and opened by manual operation. Their normal method of operation by other than manual means, such as electrical or pneumatic, shall be permitted if means for manual operation is also provided.

Exception: As provided in Section 230-76(2) for circuit breakers used as service disconnecting means.

240-81. **Indicating.** Circuit breakers shall clearly indicate whether they are in the open "off" or closed "on" position.

See Sections 240-83(d), 380-11, and 410-81(a) for requirements on circuit breakers used as switches.

Where circuit breaker handles are operated vertically rather than rotationally or horizontally, the "up" position of the handle shall be the "on" position.

240-82. **Nontamperable.** A circuit breaker shall be of such design that any alteration of its trip point (calibration) or the time required for its operation will require dismantling of the device or breaking of a seal for other than intended adjustments.

240-83. **Marking.**

(a) Durable and Visible. Circuit breakers shall be marked with their ampere rating in a manner that will be durable and visible after installation. Such marking shall be permitted to be made visible by removal of a trim or cover.

(b) Location. Circuit breakers rated at 100 amperes or less and 600 volts or less shall have the ampere rating molded, stamped, etched, or similarly marked into their handles or escutcheon areas.

(c) Interrupting Rating. Every circuit breaker having an interrupting rating other than 5000 amperes shall have its interrupting rating shown on the circuit breaker.

Exception: Interrupting rating marking shall not be required on circuit breakers used for supplementary protection.

If a circuit breaker is used on a circuit having an available fault current higher than its marked interrupting rating by being connected on the load side of an acceptable overcurrent-protective device having the higher rating, this additional series combination interrupting rating shall be marked on the end use equipment, such as switchboards and panelboards.

This requirement was new in the 1990 *NEC*. It recognizes series-rated circuit breakers, and requires that the end-use equipment be marked with the series combination rating. For example, a circuit breaker with an interrupting rating of 10,000 amperes may perform safely on a circuit with an available fault current greater than

10,000 amperes if it is protected on its line side by a circuit breaker with a suitable interrupting rating, and the series combination has been tested and demonstrated to safely open a short-circuit current higher than the 10,000 A on the load-side of the breaker.

In the information preceding the listings of dead-front type switchboards, UL provides the following:

"Dead-front switchboard sections or interiors are marked with their DC or RMS symmetrical short-circuit current rating in amperes. The marking states that short-circuit ratings are limited to the lowest short-circuit rating of (1) any switchboard section connected in series or (2) the lowest short-circuit rating of any device installed or intended to be installed therein. However, for combination series-connected devices, the short-circuit current rating marked on the switchboard may be higher than the short-circuit current rating of a specific circuit breaker installed or to be installed in the switchboard. In many cases, the short-circuit ratings are associated with instructions for securing supply wiring within the switchboard."

Since the line-side (protecting) circuit breaker may be field-installed, and the series rating may or may not be needed depending on the equipment installed and the available fault current, only the system installer or designer can determine the need for this newly required marking in any particular installation.

(d) Circuit Breakers Used as Switches. Where used as switches in 120-volt and 277-volt fluorescent lighting circuits, circuit breakers shall be listed and shall be marked "SWD."

(e) Voltage Marking. Circuit breakers shall be marked with a voltage rating no less than the nominal system voltage that is indicative of their capability to interrupt fault currents between phases or phase to ground.

(FPN): A circuit breaker with a straight voltage rating, e.g., 240V or 480V, may be applied in a circuit in which the nominal voltage between any two conductors does not exceed the circuit breaker's voltage rating; except that a two-pole circuit breaker is not suitable for protecting a 3-phase corner-grounded delta circuit unless it is marked 1-phase/3-phase to indicate such suitability.

A circuit breaker with a slash rating, e.g., 120/240V or 480Y/277V, may only be applied in a circuit in which the nominal voltage to ground from any conductor does not exceed the lower of the two values of the circuit breaker's voltage rating and the nominal voltage between any two conductors does not exceed the higher value of the circuit breaker's voltage rating.

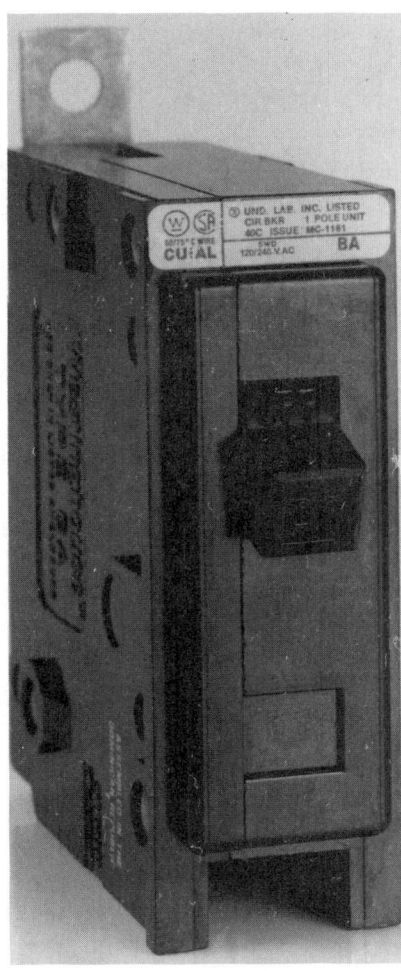

Figure 240-11. Switching duty circuit breakers (SWD) are required where the breakers are used as switches for 120-V and 277-V fluorescent lighting. Switching duty circuit breakers generally have heavier-duty contacts.

This requirement and the Fine Print Note were new in the 1990 *NEC*. If a circuit breaker is marked "480Y/277V," it is not intended for use on a 480-volt system with up to

480 volts to ground, such as a 480-volt circuit derived from a delta-connected system.

A circuit breaker marked "480 V" or "600 V" should be used on such a system. In a like manner, a circuit breaker marked "120/240 V" is not intended for use on a delta-connected 240-volt circuit. A 240-volt, 480-volt, or 600-volt circuit breaker should be used on such a circuit. The slash (/) between the lower and higher voltage rating in the marking means the circuit breaker has been tested on a circuit with the higher voltage between phases but with the lower voltage to ground.

H. Overcurrent Protection Over 600 Volts, Nominal

240-100. **Feeders.** Feeders shall have a short-circuit protective device in each ungrounded conductor or comply with Section 230-208(d)(2) or (d)(3). The protective device(s) shall be capable of detecting and interrupting all values of current that can occur at their location in excess of their trip setting or melting point. In no case shall the fuse rating in continuous amperes exceed three times, or the long-time trip element setting of a breaker, six times, the ampacity of the conductor.

Conductors tapped to a feeder shall be permitted to be protected by the feeder overcurrent device where that overcurrent device also protects the tap conductors.

(FPN): The operating time of the protective device, the available short-circuit current, and the conductor used will need to be coordinated to prevent damaging or dangerous temperatures in conductors or conductor insulation under short-circuit conditions.

240-101. **Branch Circuits.** Branch circuits shall have a short-circuit protective device in each ungrounded conductor or comply with Section 230-208(d)(2) or (d)(3). The protective device(s) shall be capable of detecting and interrupting all values of current that can occur at their location in excess of their trip setting or melting point.

ARTICLE 250   Grounding

Contents

A. General

B. Circuit and System Grounding

C. Location of System Grounding Connections

D. Enclosure Grounding

E. Equipment Grounding

A. General

250-1. **Scope.** This article covers general requirements for grounding and bonding of electrical installations, and specific requirements in (a) through (f) below.

(a) Systems, circuits, and equipment required, permitted, or not permitted to be grounded.

(b) Circuit conductor to be grounded on grounded systems.

(c) Location of grounding connections.

(d) Types and sizes of grounding and bonding conductors and electrodes.

(e) Methods of grounding and bonding.

(f) Conditions under which guards, isolation, or insulation may be substituted for grounding.

(FPN No. 1): Systems and circuit conductors are grounded to limit voltages due to lightning, line surges, or unintentional contact with higher voltage lines, and to stabilize the voltage to ground during normal operation. Equipment grounding conductors are bonded to the system grounded conductor to provide a low impedance path for fault current that will facilitate the operation of overcurrent devices under ground-fault conditions.

See Figure 250-1.

(FPN No. 2): Conductive materials enclosing electrical conductors or equipment, or forming part of such equipment, are grounded to limit the voltage to ground on these materials and bonded to facilitate the operation of overcurrent devices under ground-fault conditions. See Section 110-10.

250-2. **Application of Other Articles.** In other articles applying to particular cases of installation of conductors and equipment, there are requirements that are in addition to those of this article or are modifications of them:

	Article	Section
Agricultural Buildings		547-8
Appliances		422-16
Branch Circuits		210-5
		210-6
		210-7
Cablebus		365-9

	Article	Section
Circuits and Equipment Operating at Less Than 50 Volts	720	
Class 1, Class 2, and Class 3 Remote-Control, Signaling, and Power-Limited Circuits		725-20
		725-43
Closed-Loop and Programmed Power Distribution		780-3
Communications Circuits	800	
Community Antenna Television and Radio Distribution Systems		820-33
		820-40
		820-41
Conductors for General Wiring	310	
Cranes and Hoists	610	
Electronic Computer/Data Processing Equipment		645-15
Electrically Driven or Controlled Irrigation Machines		675-11(c)
		675-12
		675-13
		675-14
		675-15
Electric Signs and Outline Lighting	600	
Electrolytic Cells	668	
Elevators, Dumbwaiters, Escalators, Moving Walks, Wheelchair Lifts, and Stairway Chair Lifts	620	
Fire Protective Signaling Systems		760-6
Fixed Electric Heating Equipment for Pipelines and Vessels		427-21
		427-29
		427-48
Fixed Electric Space Heating Equipment		424-14
Fixed Outdoor Electric Deicing and Snow-Melting Equipment		426-27
Fixtures and Lighting Equipment		410-17
		410-18
		410-19
		410-21
		410-105(b)
Flexible Cords and Cables		400-22
		400-23

Figure 250-1. *Typical grounding system for single-phase, 3-wire service.*

B. Circuit and System Grounding

250-3. Direct-Current Systems.

(a) **Two-Wire Direct-Current Systems.** Two-wire dc systems supplying premises wiring shall be grounded.

Exception No. 1: A system equipped with a ground detector and supplying only industrial equipment in limited areas.

Exception No. 2: A system operating at 50 volts or less between conductors.

Exception No. 3: A system operating at over 300 volts between conductors.

Exception No. 4: A rectifier-derived dc system supplied from an ac system complying with Section 250-5.

Exception No. 5: DC fire protective signaling circuits having a maximum current of 0.030 amperes as specified in Article 760, Part C.

(b) Three-Wire Direct-Current Systems. The neutral conductor of all 3-wire dc systems supplying premises wiring shall be grounded.

250-5. **Alternating-Current Circuits and Systems to Be Grounded.** AC circuits and systems shall be grounded as provided for in (a), (b), (c), or (d) below. Other circuits and systems shall be permitted to be grounded.

(FPN): An example of a system permitted to be grounded is a corner-grounded delta transformer connection. See Section 250-25(4) for conductor to be grounded.

(a) Alternating-Current Circuits of Less than 50 Volts. AC circuits of less than 50 volts shall be grounded under any of the following conditions:

(1) Where supplied by transformers if the transformer supply system exceeds 150 volts to ground.

(2) Where supplied by transformers if the transformer supply system is ungrounded.

(3) Where installed as overhead conductors outside of buildings.

(b) Alternating-Current Systems of 50 Volts to 1000 Volts. AC systems of 50 volts to 1000 volts supplying premises wiring and premises wiring systems shall be grounded under any of the following conditions:

(1) Where the system can be so grounded that the maximum voltage to ground on the ungrounded conductors does not exceed 150 volts.

See Figure 250-2.

(2) Where the system is 3-phase, 4-wire wye connected in which the neutral is used as a circuit conductor.

(3) Where the system is 3-phase, 4-wire delta connected in which the midpoint of one phase winding is used as a circuit conductor.

See Figure 250-3.

120 V, 1Φ, 2 wire

240/120 V, 1Φ, 3 wire

Figure 250-2. Typical systems required to be grounded by Section 250-5(b)(1).

(4) Where a grounded service conductor is uninsulated in accordance with the exceptions to Sections 230-22, 230-30, and 230-41.

Exception No. 1: Electric systems used exclusively to supply industrial electric furnaces for melting, refining, tempering, and the like.

Exception No. 2: Separately derived systems used exclusively for rectifiers supplying only adjustable speed industrial drives.

Exception No. 3: Separately derived systems supplied by transformers that have a primary voltage rating less than 1000 volts, provided that all of the following conditions are met:

a. The system is used exclusively for control circuits.

b. The conditions of maintenance and supervision assure that only qualified persons will service the installation.

c. Continuity of control power is required.

d. Ground detectors are installed on the control system.

208/120 V, 3Φ, 4 wire

240/120 V, 3Φ, 4 wire

Figure 250-3. *Grounding is required for all wye systems in which the neutral is used as a grounded circuit conductor and all 3-phase, 4-wire delta systems in which the midpoint of one phase is used as a grounded circuit conductor. See Sections 215-8, 230-56, and 384-3(e) for identification of the "high leg."*

Exception No. 4: Isolated systems as permitted or required in Articles 517 and 668.

(FPN): The proper use of suitable ground detectors on ungrounded systems can provide additional protection.

Exception No. 5: High-impedance grounded neutral systems in which a grounding impedance, usually a resistor, limits the ground-fault current to a low value. High-impedance grounded neutral systems shall be permitted for 3-phase ac systems of 480 volts to 1000 volts where all of the following conditions are met:

a. The conditions of maintenance and supervision assure that only qualified persons will service the installation.

b. Continuity of power is required.

c. Ground detectors are installed on the system.

d. Line-to-neutral loads are not served.

See Section 250-27 for the requirements for high-impedance grounded neutral systems.

(c) Alternating-Current Systems of 1 kV and Over. AC systems supplying mobile or portable equipment shall be grounded as specified in Section 250-154. Where supplying other than portable equipment, such systems shall be permitted to be grounded. Where such systems are grounded, they shall comply with the applicable provisions of this article.

(d) Separately Derived Systems. A premises wiring system whose power is derived from generator, transformer, or converter windings and has no direct electrical connection, including a solidly connected grounded circuit conductor, to supply conductors originating in another system, if required to be grounded as in (a) or (b) above, shall be grounded as specified in Section 250-26.

Transformers are the most common source for a separately derived system. However, not all transformers become the source of such a system, even though they have the secondary winding isolated electrically from the primary winding. The secondary must supply a premises wiring system before the transformer becomes the source of a separately derived system. A step-down transformer that is part of electrical equipment and does not supply premises wiring is not the source of a separately derived system. See definition of "Premises Wiring" in Article 100.

(FPN No. 1): An alternate alternating-current power source such as an on-site generator is not a separately derived system if the neutral is solidly interconnected to a service-supplied system neutral.

Figures 250-4 and 250-5 depict a 120Y/208-V electrical service supplying a service disconnecting means to a building. The system is fed through a transfer switch that is connected to a generator intended to provide power for an emergency or standby system.

Figure 250-4 does not have the neutral conductor connected to the switching contacts of the 3-pole transfer switch; thus there is a direct electrical connection of the grounded circuit conductor (neutral) through the neutral bus to the generator. Therefore, the system supplied by the generator is not a separately derived system, and there are no requirements for grounding the neutral at the generator. Under these conditions it is necessary to run an equipment grounding conductor from the service equipment to the 3-pole transfer switch and from the 3-pole transfer switch to the generator.

Figure 250-5 shows the grounded conductor (neutral) connected to the switching contacts of a 4-pole transfer switch. Therefore, the generator system does not have a direct electrical connection to the grounded circuit conductor (neutral), and the generator is a separately derived system required to be grounded in accordance with Section 250-26.

Section 250-26 requires that a bonding jumper be installed and connected from the generator frame to the grounded circuit conductor (neutral). The grounding electrode conductor from the generator is required to be connected to a grounding electrode. This conductor should be located as close to the generator as practical. The preferred grounding electrode is the nearest effectively grounded structural metal member or the nearest available effectively grounded metal water pipe, if they are available. If neither of these preferred grounding electrodes is available, then other electrodes specified in Sections 250-81 and 250-83 are permitted to be used.

Figure 250-5. *Installation does not have a direct electrical connection of the grounded circuit conductor (neutral); therefore, the generator is a separately derived system and is grounded in accordance with Section 250-26.*

Figure 250-4. *Where a 208Y/120V 3-phase, 4-wire system has a direct electrical connection of the grounded circuit conductor (neutral) to the generator, the generator is not a separately derived system and there are no requirements for grounding the neutral.*

(FPN No. 2): For systems that are not separately derived and are not required to be grounded as specified in Section 250-26, see Section 445-5 for minimum size of conductors that must carry fault current.

250-6. **Portable and Vehicle-Mounted Generators.**

(a) **Portable Generators.** Under the following conditions, the frame of a portable generator shall not be required to be grounded and shall be permitted to serve as the grounding electrode for a system supplied by the generator:

(1) The generator supplies only equipment mounted on the generator or cord- and plug-connected equipment through receptacles mounted on the generator, or both, and

(2) The noncurrent-carrying metal parts of equipment and the equipment grounding conductor terminals of the receptacles are bonded to the generator frame.

(b) **Vehicle-Mounted Generators.** Under the following conditions, the frame of a vehicle shall be permitted to serve as the grounding electrode for a system supplied by a generator located on the vehicle:

(1) The frame of the generator is bonded to the vehicle frame, and

(2) The generator supplies only equipment located on the vehicle or cord- and plug-connected equipment through receptacles mounted on the vehicle or both equipment located on the vehicle and cord- and plug-connected equipment through receptacles mounted on the vehicle or on the generator, and

(3) The noncurrent-carrying metal parts of equipment and the equipment grounding conductor terminals of the receptacles are bonded to the generator frame, and

(4) The system complies with all other provisions of this article.

"Portable" describes equipment that is easily carried from one location to another. "Mobile" describes equipment that is capable of being moved, as on wheels or rollers, such as on a trailer or vehicle mounted.

(c) **Neutral Conductor Bonding.** A neutral conductor shall be bonded to the generator frame where the generator is a component of a separately derived system. The bonding of any conductor other than a neutral within the generator to its frame shall not be required.

(FPN): For grounding of portable generators supplying fixed wiring systems, see Section 250-5(d).

250-7. Circuits Not to Be Grounded. The following circuits shall not be grounded:

(a) **Cranes.** Circuits for electric cranes operating over combustible fibers in Class III locations, as provided in Section 503-13.

(b) **Health Care Facilities.** Circuits as provided in Article 517.

(c) **Electrolytic Cells.** Circuits as provided in Article 668.

C. Location of System Grounding Connections

250-21. Objectionable Current over Grounding Conductors.

(a) **Arrangement to Prevent Objectionable Current.** The grounding of electric systems, circuit conductors, surge arresters, and conductive noncurrent-carrying materials and equipment shall be installed and arranged in a manner that will prevent an objectionable flow of current over the grounding conductors or grounding paths.

(b) **Alterations to Stop Objectionable Current.** If the use of multiple grounding connections results in an objectionable flow of current, one or more of the following alterations shall be permitted to be made, provided that the requirements of Section 250-51 are met:

(1) Discontinue one or more but not all of such grounding connections.

(2) Change the locations of the grounding connections.

(3) Interrupt the continuity of the conductor or conductive path interconnecting the grounding connections.

(4) Take other suitable remedial action satisfactory to the authority having jurisdiction.

Section 250-21(b) is not intended to permit deletion of all grounding connections. See commentary following Section 250-21(d).

(c) **Temporary Currents Not Classified as Objectionable Currents.** Temporary currents resulting from accidental conditions, such as ground-fault currents, that occur only while the grounding conductors are performing their intended protective functions shall not be classified as objectionable current for the purposes specified in (a) and (b) above.

(d) **Limitations to Permissible Alterations.** The provisions of this section shall not be considered as permitting electronic equipment being operated on ac systems or branch circuits that are not grounded as required by this article. Currents that introduce noise or data errors in electronic equipment shall not be considered the objectionable currents addressed in this section.

This section was introduced in the 1990 *Code*. It indicates that currents that result in noise or data errors in electronic equipment are not considered the "objectionable currents" referred to in Section 250-21. This limits the alterations permitted by Section 250-21(b).

Section 250-75, Exception provides methods to eliminate noise and data errors.

250-22. Point of Connection for Direct-Current Systems. DC systems to be grounded shall have the grounding connection made at one or more supply stations. A grounding connection shall not be made at individual services nor at any point on premises wiring.

Exception: Where the dc system source is located on the premises, a grounding connection shall be made either (1) at the source or the first system disconnecting means or overcurrent device, or (2) by another means that accomplishes equivalent system protection and that utilizes equipment listed and identified for the use.

3-wire 120/240-V DC distribution system

Figure 250-6. The neutral is shown grounded at the off-premises generator site in this 3-wire dc distribution system. Grounding of a 2-wire dc system would be accomplished in the same manner. For an on-premises generator, a grounding connection is required and is to be located at the source of the first system disconnecting means or overcurrent device. Other equivalent means that utilize equipment listed and identified for such use is permitted.

3-wire 120/240-V AC single-phase secondary distribution system

Figure 250-7. On a 2-wire or 3-wire, single-phase ac secondary distribution system, grounding connections are made on the secondary side of the transformer and on the supply side of the service disconnecting means.

250-23. Grounding Service-Supplied Alternating-Current Systems.

(a) **System Grounding Connections.** A premises wiring system that is supplied by an ac service and is required to be grounded by Section 250-5 shall have at each service a grounding electrode conductor connected to a grounding electrode that complies with Part H of Article 250. The grounding electrode conductor shall be connected to the grounded service conductor at any accessible point from the load end of the service drop or

service lateral to and including the terminal or bus to which the grounded service conductor is connected at the service disconnecting means. Where the transformer supplying the service is located outside the building, at least one additional grounding connection shall be made from the grounded service conductor to a grounding electrode, either at the transformer or elsewhere outside the building. A grounding connection shall not be made to any grounded circuit conductor on the load side of the service disconnecting means.

Figure 250-8. An example of a grounded AC system. The grounded conductor is brought in to each 3-phase, 4-wire service and also to the 3-phase, 3-wire power service where it is connected to the equipment enclosure.

The power for ac premises wiring systems is either separately derived in accordance with Section 250-5(d) or supplied by the service. See definition of "service" in Article 100. Section 250-26 covers grounding requirements for separately derived ac systems. Section 250-23(a) covers system grounding requirements for service-supplied ac systems.

Section 250-23(a) covers a premises wiring system that is supplied by an ac service, and the system is required to be grounded according to Section 250-5. See Section 250-26 for similar requirements.

This type of system is required to have a grounding electrode conductor at each service connected to a grounding electrode that meets the requirements in Part H. Note the grounding electrode requirements for a separately derived system are specified in Section 250-26(c).

The grounding electrode conductor connection to the grounded conductor is accurately specified. First, the connection is required to be made to the grounded service conductor. Second, the *Code* describes where this connection is permitted to be made to the grounded service conductor.

Where the transformer supplying the service is located outside the building, the additional grounding connection to the grounded service conductor is required to be made outside the building. It is unnecessary to specify that this connection is to be made on the secondary side of the transformer because of the definition of "service conductors" in Article 100.

The main rule is that a grounding connection shall not be made to any grounded circuit conductor on the load side of the service disconnecting means. See Exception Nos. 1 through 6 below.

(FPN): See definition of "Service Drop" and "Service Lateral"; also Section 230-21.

Exception No. 1: A grounding electrode conductor shall be connected to the grounded conductor of a separately derived system in accordance with the provisions of Section 250-26(b).

Where a separately derived system is required to be grounded, a grounding electrode conductor is required to be connected to the grounded conductor of the derived system as specified in Section 250-26(b).

Exception No. 2: A grounding conductor connection shall be made at each separate building where required by Section 250-24.

Exception No. 3: For ranges, counter-mounted cooking units, wall-mounted ovens, clothes dryers, and meter enclosures as permitted by Section 250-61.

Exception No. 4: For services that are dual fed (double ended) in a common enclosure or grouped together in separate enclosures and employing a secondary tie, a single grounding electrode connection to the tie point of the grounded circuit conductors from each power source shall be permitted.

Exception No. 5: Where the main bonding jumper specified in Sections 250-53(b) and 250-79 is a wire or busbar, and is installed from the neutral bar or bus to the equipment grounding terminal bar or bus in the service equipment, the grounding electrode conductor shall be permitted to be connected to the equipment grounding terminal bar or bus to which the main bonding jumper is connected.

Where a ground-return-type sensor is used for ground-fault protection of equipment (see Article 100 for definition of "Ground-Fault Protection of Equipment"), the sensor is required to be installed on the main bonding jumper, and the grounding electrode conductor is required to be connected to the equipment grounding bus or terminal bar so that ground-fault current can be accurately sensed. Where the service equipment is power switchgear, it is often more practical to connect the grounding electrode conductor to the grounding bus inside the switchgear. See Figures 230-18 and 230-19.

Exception No. 6: As covered in Section 250-27 for high-impedance grounded neutral systems grounding connection requirements.

(b) Grounded Conductor Brought to Service Equipment. Where an ac system operating at less than 1000 volts is grounded at any point, the grounded conductor shall be run to each service disconnecting means and shall be bonded to each disconnecting means enclosure. This conductor shall be routed with the phase conductors and shall not be smaller than the required grounding electrode conductor specified in Table 250-94, and, in addition, for service-entrance phase conductors larger than 1100 kcmil copper or 1750 kcmil aluminum, the grounded conductor shall not be smaller than $12\frac{1}{2}$ percent of the area of the largest service-entrance phase conductor. Where the service-entrance phase conductors are paralleled, the size of the grounded conductor shall be based on the equivalent area for parallel conductors as indicated in this section.

(FPN): See Section 310-4 for grounded conductors connected in parallel.

Exception No. 1: The grounded conductor shall not be required to be larger than the largest ungrounded service-entrance phase conductor.

Exception No. 2: As covered in Section 250-27 for high-impedance grounded neutral systems grounding connection requirements.

Exception No. 3: Where more than one service disconnecting means are located in an assembly listed for use as service equipment, one grounded conductor shall be required to be run to the assembly, and it shall be bonded to the assembly enclosure.

Figure 250-9. *The main rule in Section 250-23(b) requires the grounded conductor to be brought in and bonded to EACH service disconnecting means enclosure (see Figure 250-8.) Exception No. 3 permits one bonding connection to a LISTED service assembly containing several service disconnects.*

250-24. Two or More Buildings or Structures Supplied from a Common Service.

(a) **Grounded Systems.** Where two or more buildings or structures are supplied from a common service, the grounded system in each building or structure shall have a grounding electrode as described in Part H connected to the metal enclosure of the building disconnecting means and to the ac system grounded circuit conductor on the supply side of the building or structure disconnecting means.

Exception No. 1: A grounding electrode at separate buildings or structures shall not be required where only one branch circuit is supplied and there is no equipment in the building or structure that requires grounding.

Exception No. 2: A grounded circuit conductor connection to the grounding electrode shall not be required at a separate building or structure if an equipment grounding conductor is run with the circuit conductors for grounding any noncurrent-carrying equipment, interior metal piping systems, and building or structural metal frames, and the equipment grounding conductor is bonded

Figure 250-10. *Where a single service (grounded system) supplies three buildings, each building is required to have a grounding electrode installed, unless conditions prevail as described in the exceptions to Section 250-24(a). See Figure 250-11.*

at a separate building or structure disconnecting means to existing grounding electrodes described in Part H. Where there are no existing electrodes, a grounding electrode meeting the requirements of Part H shall be installed where the building or structure supplies more than one branch circuit. Where livestock is housed, that portion of the equipment grounding conductor run underground to the disconnecting means shall be insulated or covered copper.

(FPN): See Section 547-8(a), Exception for special grounding requirements for agricultural buildings.

(b) **Ungrounded Systems.** Where two or more buildings or structures are supplied by a common service from an ungrounded system, each building or structure shall have a grounding electrode as described in Part H connected to the metal enclosure of the building or structure disconnecting means.

Exception No. 1: A grounding electrode at separate buildings or structures shall not be required where only one branch circuit is supplied and there is no equipment in the building or structure that requires grounding.

Exception No. 2: A grounding electrode and grounding electrode conductor connection to the metal enclosure of the building or structure disconnecting means shall not be required, provided all of the following conditions are met:

a. An equipment grounding conductor is run with the circuit conductors to the building or structure disconnecting means for grounding any noncurrent-carrying equipment, interior metal piping systems, and building or structural metal frames.

b. There are no existing grounding electrodes as described in Part H.

c. The building or structure supplies only one branch circuit.

d. Where livestock is housed, that portion of the equipment grounding conductor run underground to the disconnecting means shall be insulated or covered copper.

(FPN): See Section 547-8(a), Exception for special grounding requirements for agricultural buildings.

(c) Disconnecting Means Located in Separate Building or Structure on the Same Premises. Where one or more disconnecting means supply one or more additional buildings or structures under single management, and where these disconnecting means are located remote from those buildings or structures in accordance with the provisions of Section 225-8(b), Exception Nos. 1 and 2 or Section 230-205(a), Exception, all of the following conditions shall be met:

See Figures 250-11(a) through (d).

A grounding electrode is not required for installations with only one branch circuit that supplies equipment not requiring grounding as permitted by Exception No. 1 and shown in Figure 250-11(a). A grounding electrode is not required (unless it exists) where an equipment grounding conductor is installed with the circuit conductors. [See Figure 250-11(b)]. In such cases, the main bonding jumper is not required at the second building. If the second building has more than one branch circuit, an electrode is required and the main bonding jumper is not required. [See Figure 250-11(c).]

Figure 250-11(d) illustrates a requirement that was new in the 1990 *Code*. See Section 250-24(c). The rules are applicable to separate buildings or structures that do not have a disconnect as permitted by the exceptions to Sections 225-8(b) and 230-205(a). Note the junction box for the connection of the equipment grounding conductor to the grounding electrode.

See Section 547-8 for additional requirements in buildings housing livestock.

(1) The connection of the grounded circuit conductor to the grounding electrode at a separate building or structure shall not be made;

Figure 250-11(a). *A grounding electrode is not required where only one branch circuit is supplied and there are no receptacles or other equipment requiring grounding.*

Figure 250-11(b). *The connection from the enclosure of the building disconnecting means to the electrode is not required where an equipment grounding conductor is run with the circuit conductors for grounding noncurrent carrying equipment, interior metal piping systems, and structural metal frames. An electrode is not required unless one already exists.*

Figure 250-11(c). *The connection from the enclosure of the building disconnecting means to the electrode is not required where an equipment grounding conductor is run with the circuit conductors. The equipment grounding conductor may be one of the types listed in Section 250-91. An electrode is required where there is more than one branch circuit.*

Section 250–24 (c)
(remote disconnect)

Equipment grounding conductor

Building 1

Building 2

Figure 250-11(d). *The grounding and bonding requirements for a separate building under single management with the disconnect remotely located from the building.*

(2) An equipment grounding conductor for grounding any noncurrent-carrying equipment, interior metal piping systems, and building or structural metal frames is run with the circuit conductors to a separate building or structure and bonded to existing grounding electrodes described in Part H, or, where there are no existing electrodes, a grounding electrode meeting the requirements of Part H shall be installed where a separate building or structure supplies more than one branch circuit;

(3) Bonding the equipment grounding conductor to the grounding electrode at a separate building or structure shall be made in a junction box, panelboard, or similar enclosure located immediately inside or outside the separate building or structure.

Exception No. 1: A grounding electrode at a separate building or structure shall not be required where only one branch circuit is supplied and there is no equipment in the building or structure that requires grounding.

Exception No. 2: Where livestock is housed, that portion of the equipment grounding conductor run underground to the disconnecting means shall be insulated or covered copper.

(d) Grounding Conductor. The size of the grounding conductor to the grounding electrode(s) shall not be less than given in Table 250-95, and the installation shall be in accordance with Sections 250-92(a) and (b).

Exception No. 1: The grounding conductor shall not be required to be larger than the largest ungrounded supply conductor.

Exception No. 2: Where connected to made electrodes as in Section 250-83(c) or (d), that portion of the grounding conductor that is the sole connection between the electrode(s) and the grounded or grounding conductor or the metal enclosure of the building disconnecting means shall not be required to be larger than No. 6 copper or No. 4 aluminum.

Section 250-24(d) was new in the 1990 *Code.* It recognizes the difference between a grounding electrode conductor sized in accordance with Table 250-94 and an equipment grounding conductor connected to a grounding electrode to be sized in accordance with Table 250-95.

250-25. **Conductor to Be Grounded — Alternating-Current Systems.** For ac premises wiring systems, the conductor to be grounded shall be as specified in (1) through (5) below.

(1) Single-phase, 2-wire: one conductor.
(2) Single-phase, 3-wire: the neutral conductor.
(3) Multiphase systems having one wire common to all phases: the common conductor.
(4) Multiphase systems requiring one grounded phase: one phase conductor.
(5) Multiphase systems in which one phase is used as in (2) above: the neutral conductor.

Grounded conductors shall be identified by the means specified in Article 200.

250-26. **Grounding Separately Derived Alternating-Current Systems.** A separately derived ac system that is required to be grounded by Section 250-5 shall be grounded as specified in (a) through (d) below.

(a) Bonding Jumper. A bonding jumper, sized in accordance with Section 250-79(d) for the derived phase conductors, shall be used to connect the equipment grounding conductors of the derived system to the grounded conductor. Except as permitted by Exception No. 4 or No. 5 of Section 250-23(a), this connection shall be made at any point on the separately derived system from the source to the first system disconnecting means or overcurrent device; or it shall be made at the source of a separately derived system that has no disconnecting means or overcurrent devices.

The intent of this section is to permit this connection at the transformer or at the first disconnecting means or overcurrent device where there are likely to be more standard arrangements incorporated (as in a panelboard suitable for service equipment).

Exception No. 1: The size of the bonding jumper for a system that supplies a Class 1, Class 2, or Class 3 circuit, and is derived from a transformer rated not more than 1000 volt-amperes, shall not be smaller than the derived phase conductors and shall not be smaller than No. 14 copper or No. 12 aluminum.

Section 250-79(c) requires the bonding jumper to be not smaller than the sizes given in Table 250-94, e.g., not smaller than No. 8 AWG copper. This exception permits a bonding jumper for a Class 1, Class 2, or Class 3 circuit to be not smaller than No. 14 copper or No. 12 aluminum. The expansion of this exception to include Class 2 and 3 circuits is new for the 1993 *Code*.

Exception No. 2: As covered in Section 250-27 and Exception No. 5 for Section 250-5(b) for high-impedance grounded neutral systems grounding connection requirements.

(b) Grounding Electrode Conductor. A grounding electrode conductor, sized in accordance with Section 250-94 for the derived phase conductors, shall be used to connect the grounded conductor of the derived system to the grounding electrode as specified in (c) below. Except as permitted by Exception No. 4 of Section 250-23(a), this connection shall be made at any point

Grounded service conductor

Bonding jumper

Main bonding jumper (screw) to enclosure

——————— Bonding jumper (Section 250-79)

– – – – Grounded service conductor (neutral)

– – – – – Grounding electrode conductor

Figure 250-12. Grounding and bonding at an individual service.

on the separately derived system from the source to the first system disconnecting means or overcurrent device; or it shall be made at the source of a separately derived system that has no disconnecting means or overcurrent devices.

Exception No. 1: A grounding electrode conductor shall not be required for a system that supplies a Class 1, Class 2, or Class 3 circuit, and is derived from a transformer rated not more than 1000 volt-amperes, provided the system grounded conductor is bonded to the transformer frame or enclosure by a jumper sized

1φ 120/240v
Service
entrance

*See section
250-72(d)

Figure 250-13. A grounding and bonding arrangement for six switches that serve as the service disconnecting means for an individual service. Section 250-23(b) clarifies that the grounded service conductor is required to be run to each service disconnect and bonded to the enclosure. Section 250-72(a) permits the bonding of service equipment to be accomplished by bonding to the grounded service conductor.

in accordance with Section 250-26, Exception No. 1 for (a) above, and the transformer frame or enclosure is grounded by one of the means specified in Section 250-57.

Exception No. 2: As covered in Section 250-27 and Exception No. 5 for Section 250-5(b) for high-impedance grounded neutral systems grounding connection requirements.

(c) Grounding Electrode. The grounding electrode shall be as near as practicable to and preferably in the same area as the grounding conductor connection to the system. The grounding electrode shall be (1) the nearest available effectively grounded structural metal member of the structure; or (2) the nearest available effectively grounded metal water pipe; or (3) other electrodes as specified in Sections 250-81 and 250-83 where electrodes specified by (1) or (2) above are not available.

(d) Grounding Methods. In all other respects, grounding methods shall comply with requirements prescribed in other parts of this Code.

A separately derived system is a premises wiring system where power is derived from a generator, a transformer, or converter windings and there is no direct electrical connection, including a solidly grounded circuit conductor, to supply conductors originating in another system. See comments following Section 250-5(d).

The requirements of Section 250-26 are most commonly applied to 480Y/277-V transformers that are used to transform a 480-V supply to a 208Y/120-V system to supply lighting and appliance loads.

These requirements provide for a low-impedance path to ground so that line-to-ground faults on circuits supplied by the transformer will result in sufficient current flow to operate the overcurrent devices. These requirements also apply to generators or systems derived from converter windings, but do not have the same wide use as separately derived systems that are derived from transformers.

Figure 250-14 shows a typical diagram of a dry-type transformer supplied from a 480-V, 3-phase feeder to derive a 208Y/120-V secondary. As indicated in Section 250-26(a), the bonding jumper connection is required to be sized according to Section 250-79(d) and is to be made at the source of the separately derived system such as the transformer enclosure, as illustrated. With the grounding electrode conductor, the bonding jumper, and the bonding of the grounded circuit conductor (neutral) at the transformer

Figure 250-14. *A grounding arrangement for a separately derived system. The bonding jumper connection is permitted at the transformer.*

enclosure, line-to-ground fault currents are able to return to the supply source rather than traveling through the earth. In this way, a path of low impedance is provided that facilitates the operation of overcurrent devices in accordance with Section 250-51(3).

The grounding electrode conductor from the secondary grounded circuit conductor is sized according to Section 250-94.

Section 250-26(c) requires that the grounding electrode be as near as practicable to the grounding conductor connection to the system in order to minimize the impedance to ground. If there is an effectively grounded structural metal member of the (building) structure, or an effectively grounded metal water pipe available, Section 250-26(c) requires that this grounding electrode be used rather than a concrete-encased electrode, ground ring, or made electrode such as a ground rod. The practice of grounding the secondary of an isolating transformer to a ground rod, or running the grounding electrode conductor back to the service ground (usually to reduce electrical noise on data processing systems), is prohibited if Items (1) or (2) of Section 250-26(c) are available.

250-27. **High-Impedance Grounded Neutral System Connections.** High-impedance grounded neutral systems as permitted in Exception No. 5 of Section 250-5(b) shall comply with the provisions of (a) through (f) below.

Section 250-27 covers high-impedance grounded neutral systems of 50 to 1,000 volts. Such systems rated over 1,000 volts are covered in Section 250-153. For information on the differences between solidly grounded systems and high-impedance grounded neutral systems, see *Grounding for Emergency and Standby Power Systems* by Robert B. West, IEEE Transactions on Industry Applications, Vol. IA-15, No. 2, March/April 1979. See Figure 250-15.

High impedance grounded neutral systems are designed to minimize the amount of fault current that can flow during a ground fault. The grounding impedance is usually selected to limit fault current to a value slightly greater than or equal to the capacitive discharge current. These systems are used where continuity of power is required. Therefore, a ground fault results in an alarm condition rather than in the tripping of a circuit breaker. This allows a safe and orderly shutdown. See Figure 250-15.

(a) Grounding Impedance Location. The grounding impedance shall be installed between the grounding electrode conductor and the system neutral. Where a neutral is not available, the grounding impedance shall be installed between the grounding electrode conductor and the neutral derived from a grounding transformer.

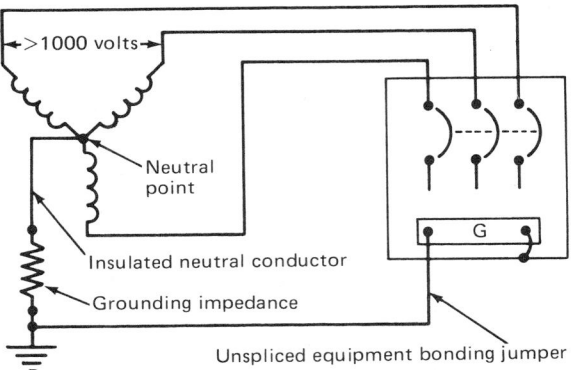

High-impedance grounded neutral system
Section 250-27 and (FPN)

Figure 250-15. *Schematic diagram of a high-impedance grounded neutral system.*

(b) Neutral Conductor. The neutral conductor from the neutral point of the transformer or generator to its connection point to the grounding impedance shall be fully insulated.

The neutral conductor shall have an ampacity of not less than the maximum current rating of the grounding impedance. In no case shall the neutral conductor be smaller than No. 8 copper or No. 6 aluminum, or copper-clad aluminum.

This section was revised for the 1993 *Code* to add requirements for sizing of the neutral conductor for high impedance grounded neutral systems. The current that can flow through the neutral conductor is limited by the grounding impedance; therefore, the size of the neutral conductor must be of sufficient ampacity to carry the fault current, but not smaller than No. 6 copper or No. 8 aluminum.

(c) System Neutral Connection. The system neutral conductor shall not be connected to ground except through the grounding impedance.

(FPN): The impedance is normally selected to limit the ground-fault current to a value slightly greater than or equal to the capacitive charging current of the system. This value of impedance will also limit transient overvoltages to safe values. For guidance, refer to criteria for limiting transient overvoltages in Recommended Practice for Grounding of Industrial and Commercial Power Systems, ANSI/IEEE 142-1982.

Additional information may be found in the following publications:

(1) "Charging Current Data for Guesswork-Free Design of High-Resistance Grounded Systems" by D.S. Baker, IEEE Transactions on Industry Applications, Vol. IA-15, No. 2, March/April, 1979;

(2) "High-Resistance Grounding" by Baldwin Bridger, Jr., IEEE Transactions on Industry Applications, Vol. IA-19, No. 1, January/February, 1983.

(d) Neutral Conductor Routing. The conductor connecting the neutral point of the transformer or generator to the grounding impedance shall be permitted to be installed in a separate raceway. It shall not be required to run this conductor with the phase conductors to the first system disconnecting means or overcurrent device.

(e) Equipment Bonding Jumper. The equipment bonding jumper (the connection between the equipment grounding conductors and the grounding impedance) shall be an unspliced conductor run from the first system disconnecting means or overcurrent device to the grounded side of the grounding impedance.

(f) Grounding Electrode Conductor Location. The grounding electrode conductor shall be attached at any point from the grounded side of the grounding impedance to the equipment grounding connection at the service equipment or first system disconnecting means.

D. Enclosure Grounding

250-32. Service Raceways and Enclosures. Metal enclosures for service conductors and equipment shall be grounded.

Exception: A metal elbow that is installed in an underground installation of rigid nonmetallic conduit and is isolated from possible contact by a minimum cover of 18 inches (457 mm) to any part of the elbow.

This exception is new in the 1993 *Code.* It recognizes that metal sweep elbows are often installed in underground installations of rigid nonmetallic conduit. The metal elbows are installed because nonmetallic elbows can be damaged by pulling ropes during conductor installation. The elbows are isolated from physical contact by burial so that no part of the elbow is less than 18 inches below grade.

250-33. Other Conductor Enclosures. Metal enclosures for other than service conductors shall be grounded.

This section requires bonding, grounding, and electrical continuity of metal raceways and thus requires connectors, couplings, or other such fittings that assure bonding and grounding continuity between the fitting and the raceway metal (such as would be required for liquidtight flexible metal conduit). Metal enclosures are required to be grounded so that any fault between an ungrounded (hot) conductor and a metal enclosure will not allow the enclosure to become and remain energized, thereby presenting a shock hazard to persons.

Exception No. 1: Metal enclosures for conductors added to existing installations of open wire, knob-and-tube wiring, and nonmetallic-sheathed cable, that do not provide an equipment ground, if in runs of less than 25 feet (7.62 m), if free from probable contact with ground, grounded metal, metal lath, or other conductive material, and if guarded against contact by persons, shall not be required to be grounded.

Exception No. 2: Short sections of metal enclosures used to provide support or protection of cable assemblies from physical damage shall not be required to be grounded.

Exception No. 3: Enclosures not required to be grounded by Section 250-43(i) shall not be required to be grounded.

Exception No. 4: A metal elbow that is installed in an underground installation of rigid nonmetallic conduit and is isolated from possible contact by a minimum cover of 18 inches (457 mm) to any part of the elbow.

See commentary following Section 250-32, Exception.

E. Equipment Grounding

250-42. Equipment Fastened in Place or Connected by Permanent Wiring Methods (Fixed). Exposed noncurrent-carrying metal parts of fixed equipment likely to become energized shall be grounded under any of the conditions in (a) through (f) below.

(a) Vertical and Horizontal Distances. Where within 8 feet (2.44 m) vertically or 5 feet (1.52 m) horizontally of ground or grounded metal objects and subject to contact by persons.

Exposed noncurrent-carrying metal parts of fixed equipment unlikely to become energized are not required to be grounded. These include some metal nameplates on non-metallic enclosures and small parts such as bolts and screws so located that they are not likely to become energized.

(b) Wet or Damp Locations. Where located in a wet or damp location and not isolated.

(c) Electrical Contact. Where in electrical contact with metal.

(d) Hazardous (Classified) Locations. Where in a hazardous (classified) location as covered by Articles 500 through 517.

(e) Wiring Methods. Where supplied by a metal-clad, metal-sheathed, metal-raceway, or other wiring method that provides an equipment ground, except as permitted by Section 250-33 for short sections of metal enclosures.

(f) Over 150 Volts to Ground. Where equipment operates with any terminal at over 150 volts to ground.

Exception No. 1: Enclosures for switches or circuit breakers used for other than service equipment and accessible to qualified persons only.

Exception No. 2: Metal frames of electrically heated appliances, exempted by special permission, in which case the frames shall be permanently and effectively insulated from ground.

Exception No. 3: Distribution apparatus, such as transformer and capacitor cases, mounted on wooden poles, at a height exceeding 8 feet (2.44 m) above ground or grade level.

Exception No. 4: Listed equipment protected by a system of double insulation, or its equivalent, shall not be required to be grounded. Where such a system is employed, the equipment shall be distinctively marked.

250-43 . **Fastened in Place or Connected by Permanent Wiring Methods (Fixed) — Specific.** Exposed, noncurrent-carrying metal parts of the kinds of equipment described in (a) through (j) below, and noncurrent-carrying metal parts of equipment and enclosures described in (k) and (l) below, shall be grounded regardless of voltage.

(a) Switchboard Frames and Structures. Switchboard frames and structures supporting switching equipment.

Exception: Frames of 2-wire dc switchboards where effectively insulated from ground.

This exception was revised for the 1993 *Code* to clarify that dc switchboards that are insulated from ground are not required to be grounded.

(b) Pipe Organs. Generator and motor frames in an electrically operated pipe organ.

Exception: Where the generator is effectively insulated from ground and from the motor driving it.

(c) Motor Frames. Motor frames, as provided by Section 430-142.

(d) Enclosures for Motor Controllers. Enclosures for motor controllers.

Exception No. 1: Enclosures attached to ungrounded portable equipment.

Exception No. 2: Lined covers of snap switches.

(e) Elevators and Cranes. Electric equipment for elevators and cranes.

(f) Garages, Theaters, and Motion Picture Studios. Electric equipment in commercial garages, theaters, and motion picture studios.

Exception: Pendant lampholders supplied by circuits not over 150 volts to ground.

(g) Electric Signs. Electric signs and associated equipment.

(h) Motion Picture Projection Equipment. Motion picture projection equipment.

(i) Remote-Control, Signaling, and Fire Protective Signaling Circuits. Equipment supplied by Class 1, Class 2, and Class 3 remote-control and signaling circuits, and by fire protective signaling circuits, shall be grounded where system grounding is required by Part B of this article.

If the *system* is required to be grounded by Article 250 Part B, then the *equipment* is required to be grounded.

(j) Lighting Fixtures. Lighting fixtures as provided in Part E of Article 410.

(k) Motor-Operated Water Pumps. Motor-operated water pumps including the submersible type.

This requirement is intended to reduce stray voltages and minimize shock hazard during maintenance.

(l) Metal Well Casings. Where a submersible pump is used in a metal well casing, the well casing shall be bonded to the pump circuit equipment grounding conductor.

This requirement is new in the 1993 *Code*. It is intended to prevent a shock hazard that could exist due to a grounding potential difference between the pump, which is grounded to the system ground, and the metal well casing.

250-44. **Nonelectric Equipment.** The metal parts of nonelectric equipment described in (a) through (e) below shall be grounded.

(a) **Cranes.** Frames and tracks of electrically operated cranes.

(b) **Elevator Cars.** Frames of nonelectrically driven elevator cars to which electric conductors are attached.

(c) **Electric Elevators.** Hand-operated metal shifting ropes or cables of electric elevators.

(d) **Metal Partitions.** Metal partitions, grill work, and similar metal enclosures around equipment of 1 kV and over between conductors except substations or vaults under the sole control of the supply company.

(e) **Mobile Homes and Recreational Vehicles.** Mobile homes and recreational vehicles as required in Articles 550 and 551.

(FPN):   Where extensive metal in or on buildings may become energized and is subject to personal contact, adequate bonding and grounding will provide additional safety.

Because construction such as metal siding on buildings is not electric equipment, it is outside the scope of the *National Electrical Code* [see Section 90-2(a)] and the *Code* cannot require that it be grounded. Grounding of metal siding that is likely to become energized and is subject to contact by persons is, however, an excellent safety precaution.

See Section 547-8 for grounding and bonding of agricultural buildings.

250-45. **Equipment Connected by Cord and Plug.** Under any of the conditions described in (a) through (d) below, exposed noncurrent-carrying metal parts of cord- and plug-connected equipment likely to become energized shall be grounded.

(a) **In Hazardous (Classified) Locations.** In hazardous (classified) locations (see Articles 500 through 517).

(b) **Over 150 Volts to Ground.** Where operated at over 150 volts to ground.

Exception No. 1: Motors, where guarded.

Exception No. 2: Metal frames of electrically heated appliances, exempted by special permission, in which case the frames shall be permanently and effectively insulated from ground.

Exception No. 3: Listed equipment protected by a system of double insulation, or its equivalent, shall not be required to be grounded. Where such a system is employed, the equipment shall be distinctively marked.

(c) **In Residential Occupancies.** In residential occupancies: (1) refrigerators, freezers, and air conditioners; (2) clothes-washing, clothes-drying, dish-washing machines, kitchen waste disposers, sump pumps, electrical aquarium equipment; (3) hand-held motor-operated tools, stationary and fixed motor-operated tools, light industrial motor-operated tools; (4) motor-operated appliances of the following types: hedge clippers, lawn mowers, snow blowers, and wet scrubbers; (5) portable handlamps.

Exception: Listed tools and listed appliances protected by a system of double insulation, or its equivalent, shall not be required to be grounded. Where such a system is employed, the equipment shall be distinctively marked.

(d) **In Other than Residential Occupancies.** In other than residential occupancies: (1) refrigerators, freezers, and air conditioners; (2) clothes-washing, clothes-drying, dish-washing machines, electronic computer/data processing equipment, sump pumps, electrical aquarium equipment; (3) hand-held motor-operated tools, stationary and fixed motor-operated tools, light industrial motor-operated tools; (4) motor-operated appliances of the following types: hedge clippers, lawn mowers, snow blowers, and wet scrubbers; (5) cord- and plug-connected appliances used in damp or wet locations or by persons standing on the ground or on metal floors or working inside of metal tanks or boilers; (6) tools likely to be used in wet or conductive locations; and (7) portable handlamps.

Exception No. 1: Tools and portable handlamps likely to be used in wet or conductive locations shall not be required to be grounded where supplied through an isolating transformer with an ungrounded secondary of not over 50 volts.

Figure 250-16. Lighting equipment supplied through an isolating transformer operating at 6 or 12 volts provides safe illumination for work inside of boilers, tanks, and similar locations that may be metal and/or wet. (Daniel Woodhead Co.)

Exception No. 2: Listed, hand-held, motor-operated tools, listed stationary and fixed motor-operated tools, listed, light industrial, motor-operated tools, and listed appliances protected by an approved system of double insulation or its equivalent shall not be required to be grounded. Where such a system is employed, the equipment shall be distinctively marked.

(FPN): With reference to (c) and (d), portable tools or appliances are not intended to be used in damp, wet, or conductive locations unless they are grounded, double insulated, or supplied through an isolating transformer.

Tools are required to be grounded by an equipment grounding conductor in a cord or cable supplying the tool, except where supplied by an isolating transformer as permitted by Exception No. 1. Portable tools and appliances protected by an approved system of double insulation are required to be listed by a qualified electrical testing laboratory as being suitable for the purpose, and the equipment is required to be distinctively marked as double insulated.

Cord-connected portable tools or appliances are not intended to be used in damp, wet, or conductive locations, unless they are grounded, supplied by an isolation transformer, or protected by an approved system of double insulation.

Exception No. 2 was expanded for the 1993 *Code* to recognize listed, double-insulated stationary and fixed motor-operated tools and light industrial motor operated tools.

250-46. **Spacing from Lightning Rods.** Metal raceways, enclosures, frames, and other noncurrent-carrying metal parts of electric equipment shall be kept at least 6 feet (1.83 m) away from lightning rod conductors, or they shall be bonded to the lightning rod conductors.

(FPN): See Sections 250-86 and 800-40(b)(3)(3). For further information, see Lightning Protection Code, NFPA 780-1992 (ANSI), which contains detailed information on grounding lightning protection systems.

F. Methods of Grounding

250-50. **Equipment Grounding Conductor Connections.** Equipment grounding conductor connections at the source of separately derived systems shall be made in accordance with Section 250-26(a). Equipment grounding conductor connections at service equipment shall be made as indicated in (a) or (b) below.

(a) For Grounded System. The connection shall be made by bonding the equipment grounding conductor to the grounded service conductor and the grounding electrode conductor.

See Figure 250-17.

Figure 250-17. Grounding for grounded systems, illustrating connection of equipment grounding bus to the enclosures and the grounded service conductor.

(b) For Ungrounded System. The connection shall be made by bonding the equipment grounding conductor to the grounding electrode conductor.

Exception for (a) and (b) above: For replacement of nongrounding-type receptacles with grounding-type receptacles and for branch-circuit extensions only in existing installations that do not have an equipment grounding conductor in the branch circuit, the grounding conductor of a grounding-type receptacle outlet shall be permitted to be grounded to any accessible point on the grounding electrode system as described in Section 250-81.

This exception permits a nongrounding-type receptacle outlet to be replaced with a grounding-type receptacle outlet where an equipment grounding conductor is connected to an accessible point on the grounding electrode system. Due to changes in Section 250-81 of the 1993 *Code*, this will no longer include an interior metal water pipe that is more than 5 feet from the point of entrance of the water pipe into the building. This revision is due to the increasing use of nonmetallic piping and fittings.

See Figure 250-18.

(FPN): See Section 210-7(d), Exception for the use of a ground-fault circuit-interrupter-type of receptacle.

250-51. **Effective Grounding Path.** The path to ground from circuits, equipment, and metal enclosures for conductors shall (1) be permanent and continuous; (2) have capacity to conduct safely any fault current likely to be imposed on it; and (3) have sufficiently low impedance to limit the voltage to ground and to facilitate the operation of the circuit protective devices.

The earth shall not be used as the sole equipment grounding conductor.

250-53. **Grounding Path to Grounding Electrode at Services.**

(a) **Grounding Electrode Conductor.** A grounding electrode conductor shall be used to connect the equipment grounding conductors, the service-equipment enclosures, and, where the system is grounded, the grounded service conductor to the grounding electrode.

Exception: As covered in Section 250-27 for high-impedance grounded neutral system connections.

(FPN): See Section 250-23(a) for alternating-current system grounding connections.

Type NM cable without equipment grounding conductor

Existing installation

Metal box

Grounding screw

Grounding conductor

Grounding electrode system complying with 250-81

Figure 250-18. Branch-circuit extension to existing installation per Section 250-50, Exception for (a) and (b) illustrating a separate grounding conductor connected to the main grounding electrode. This method is also permitted to ground a replacement 3-wire receptacle in the existing ungrounded box on the left where no grounding conductor is available.

Reference to Section 250-23(a) directs the reader to more detailed specifications for connecting the grounding electrode conductor.

(b) Main Bonding Jumper. For a grounded system, an unspliced main bonding jumper shall be used to connect the equipment grounding conductor and the service-disconnect enclosure to the grounded conductor of the system at each service disconnect.

This section was revised for the 1993 *Code* to clarify that where the service equipment of a grounded system consists of multiple disconnects, a main bonding jumper is required to connect the grounded service conductor, the equipment grounding conductor, and the service equipment enclosure.

Exception No. 1: Where more than one service disconnecting means are located in an assembly listed for use as service equipment, one grounded conductor shall be required to be run to the assembly, and it shall be bonded to the assembly enclosure.

Exception No. 2: As covered in Section 250-27 for high-impedance grounded neutral system connections.

Where multiple service disconnects are part of an assembly that is listed as service equipment, only one grounded service conductor is required to be run to and bonded to the assembly.

250-54. **Common Grounding Electrode.** Where an ac system is connected to a grounding electrode in or at a building as specified in Sections 250-23 and 250-24, the same electrode shall be used to ground conductor enclosures and equipment in or on that building. Where separate services supply a building and are required to be connected to a grounding electrode, the same grounding electrode shall be used.

Two or more grounding electrodes that are effectively bonded together shall be considered as a single grounding electrode system in this sense.

250-55. **Underground Service Cable.** Where served from a continuous underground metal-sheathed cable system, the sheath or armor of underground service cable metallically connected to the underground system, or underground service conduit containing a metal-sheathed cable bonded to the underground system, shall not be required to be grounded at the building and shall be permitted to be insulated from the interior conduit or piping.

250-56. **Short Sections of Raceway.** Isolated sections of metal raceway or cable armor, where required to be grounded, shall be grounded in accordance with Section 250-57.

See Part D for enclosure grounding requirements.

250-57. **Equipment Fastened in Place or Connected by Permanent Wiring Methods (Fixed) — Grounding.** Noncurrent-carrying metal parts of equipment, raceways, and other enclosures, where required to be grounded, shall be grounded by one of the methods indicated in (a) or (b) below.

Exception: Where equipment, raceways, and enclosures are grounded by connection to the grounded circuit conductor as permitted by Sections 250-24, 250-60, and 250-61.

This exception eliminates any possible conflict between Section 250-57, which requires an equipment grounding conductor to be used for equipment grounding, and Sections 250-24, 250-60, and 250-61, which permit the grounded circuit conductor to be used for equipment grounding if certain specified conditions are met.

(a) Equipment Grounding Conductor Types. By any of the equipment grounding conductors permitted by Section 250-91(b).

(b) With Circuit Conductors. By an equipment grounding conductor contained within the same raceway, cable, or cord or otherwise run with the circuit conductors. Bare, covered, or insulated equipment grounding conductors shall be permitted. Individually covered or insulated equipment grounding conductors shall have a continuous outer finish that is either green or green with one or more yellow stripes.

It is necessary to run the equipment grounding conductor with the circuit conductors on alternating current circuits to keep the ac impedance of the equipment grounding conductor as low as possible.

Exception No. 1: An insulated or covered conductor larger than No. 6 copper or aluminum shall, at the time of installation, be permitted to be permanently identified as an equipment grounding conductor at each end and at every point where the conductor is accessible. Identification shall be accomplished by one of the following:

a. Stripping the insulation or covering from the entire exposed length,

b. Coloring the exposed insulation or covering green, or

c. Marking the exposed insulation or covering with green colored tape or green colored adhesive labels.

Exception No. 2: For direct-current circuits only, the equipment grounding conductor shall be permitted to be run separately from the circuit conductors.

Exception No. 3: As provided in the exception to Sections 250-50(a) and (b), the equipment grounding conductor shall be permitted to be run separately from the circuit conductors.

This exception is new in the 1993 *Code*. It permits an equipment grounding conductor to be run separately from the other conductors of the circuit to the grounding electrode. This exception applies where a grounding-type receptacle is used on a circuit that does not include an equipment grounding conductor. See commentary following Section 250-50(b), Exception.

Exception No. 4: Where the conditions of maintenance and supervision assure that only qualified persons will service the installation, one or more insulated conductors in a multiconductor cable shall, at the time of installation, be permitted to be permanently identified as equipment grounding conductors at each end and at every point where the conductors are accessible by one of the following means:

a. Stripping the insulation from the entire exposed length,

b. Coloring the exposed insulation green, or

c. Marking the exposed insulation with green tape or green colored adhesive labels.

(FPN No. 1): See Section 250-79 for equipment bonding jumper requirements.

(FPN No. 2): See Section 400-7 for use of cords for fixed equipment.

250-58 . **Equipment Considered Effectively Grounded.** Under the conditions specified in (a) and (b) below, the noncurrent-carrying metal parts of the equipment shall be considered effectively grounded.

(a) Equipment Secured to Grounded Metal Supports. Electric equipment secured to and in electrical contact with a metal rack or structure provided for its support and grounded by one of the means indicated in Section 250-57. The structural metal frame of a building shall not be used as the required equipment grounding conductor for ac equipment.

See Figure 250-19.

Figure 250-19.   Example of equipment grounding on metal rack.

(b) Metal Car Frames. Metal car frames supported by metal hoisting cables attached to or running over metal sheaves or drums of elevator machines that are grounded by one of the methods indicated in Section 250-57.

250-59 . **Cord- and Plug-Connected Equipment.** Noncurrent-carrying metal parts of cord- and plug-connected equipment, where required to be grounded, shall be grounded by one of the methods indicated in (a), (b), or (c) below.

(a) By Means of the Metal Enclosure. By means of the metal enclosure of the conductors supplying such equipment if a grounding-type attachment plug with one fixed grounding contact is used for grounding the metal enclosure, and if the metal enclosure of the conductors is secured to the attachment plug and to equipment by approved connectors.

Exception: A self-restoring grounding contact shall be permitted on grounding-type attachment plugs used on the power supply cord of portable hand-held, hand-guided, or hand-supported tools or appliances.

(b) By Means of a Grounding Conductor. By means of an equipment grounding conductor run with the power supply conductors in a cable assembly or flexible cord properly terminated in grounding-type attachment plug with one fixed grounding contact. An uninsulated equipment grounding conductor shall be permitted, but, if individually covered, the covering shall have a continuous outer finish that is either green or green with one or more yellow stripes.

Exception: A self-restoring grounding contact shall be permitted on grounding-type attachment plugs used on the power supply cord of portable hand-held, hand-guided, or hand-supported tools or appliances.

(c) Separate Flexible Wire or Strap. By means of a separate flexible wire or strap, insulated or bare, protected as well as practicable against physical damage, where part of equipment.

250-60. **Frames of Ranges and Clothes Dryers.** Frames of electric ranges, wall-mounted ovens, counter-mounted cooking units, clothes dryers, and outlet or junction boxes that are part of the circuit for these appliances shall be grounded in the manner specified by Section 250-57 or 250-59; or, except for mobile homes and recreational vehicles, shall be permitted to be grounded to the grounded circuit conductor if all of the conditions indicated in (a) through (d) below are met.

(a) The supply circuit is 120/240-volt, single-phase, 3-wire; or 208Y/120-volt derived from a 3-phase, 4-wire wye-connected system.

(b) The grounded conductor is not smaller than No. 10 copper or No. 8 aluminum.

(c) The grounded conductor is insulated; or the grounded conductor is uninsulated and part of a Type SE service-entrance cable and the branch circuit originates at the service equipment.

(d) Grounding contacts of receptacles furnished as part of the equipment are bonded to the equipment.

The grounded circuit conductor is permitted to be used to ground the frame of an electric range, wall-mounted oven, or counter-mounted cooking unit, provided all the conditions of (a) through (d) are met. The grounded circuit conductor is also permitted to be used to ground any junction boxes in the circuit supplying the appliance, and a 3-wire pigtail and range receptacle are permitted to be used regardless of whether or not the circuit to the receptacle contains a separate equipment grounding conductor.

The use of the grounded circuit conductor for grounding purposes is contrary to other requirements of the *Code*. See commentary following Section 250-61(b). However, it has been allowed for many years because of the good safety record of these particular appliances that are grounded through the grounded circuit conductor and because an open splice or break in the grounded circuit conductor would normally render the appliance inoperable. A subcommittee

reevaluated this requirement for the 1984 *NEC* and verified the continued good safety record.

Where service-entrance cable with an uninsulated neutral is used, it is required that the circuit originate from the service equipment in order to avoid multiple grounding from downstream panelboards. See Figure 250-20. Multiple grounding downstream would raise the potential of all exposed dead metal parts of equipment using this downstream grounding point for equipment grounding by an amount equal to the voltage drop along the grounded circuit conductor, a current-carrying conductor. Thus, under normal conditions, adjacent exposed dead metal parts could be raised to a potential difference of several volts.

Type SE service entrance cable with <u>insulated</u> or <u>uninsulated</u> grounded neutral conductor

Figure 250-20. Use of Type SE service-entrance cable for ranges, dryers, wall-mounted ovens, and counter-mounted cooking units. Junction boxes in the supply circuit are also permitted to be grounded from the grounded neutral conductor.

250-61. **Use of Grounded Circuit Conductor for Grounding Equipment.**

(a) Supply-Side Equipment. A grounded circuit conductor shall be permitted to ground noncurrent-carrying metal parts of equipment, raceways, and other enclosures at any of the following locations:

(1) On the supply side of the service disconnecting means.

(2) On the supply side of the main disconnecting means for separate buildings as provided in Section 250-24.

(3) On the supply side of the disconnecting means or overcurrent devices of a separately derived system.

In separately derived systems, the grounded circuit conductor is permitted to ground noncurrent-carrying metal parts of equipment, raceways, and other enclosures.

(b) Load-Side Equipment. A grounded circuit conductor shall not be used for grounding noncurrent-carrying metal parts of equipment on the load side of the service disconnecting means or on the load side of a separately derived system disconnecting means or the overcurrent devices for a separately derived system not having a main disconnecting means.

One major reason that the grounded circuit conductor is not permitted (except as noted in Section 250-60) to be grounded on the load side of the service is that, should the grounded service conductor become disconnected at any point on the line side of the ground, the equipment grounding conductor and all conductive parts connected to this equipment grounding conductor will carry the neutral current, raising the potential to ground of exposed metal parts not normally intended to carry current. This could result in arcing in concealed spaces, and it could pose a severe shock hazard, particularly if a single point in the path should be opened inadvertently by a workman. However, even without an open grounded conductor (usually referred to as an open neutral), the equipment grounding conductor path will become a parallel path with the grounded conductor, and there will be some potential drop on exposed and concealed dead metal parts. The size of this potential drop will be determined by the relative impedances of the equipment grounding path and grounded conductor circuits. Not only the equipment grounding conductor path, but all parallel paths not depended on as an equipment grounding conductor would be affected. This could involve current flowing through metal building structures, piping, and ducts.

Exception No. 1: The frames of ranges, wall-mounted ovens, counter-mounted cooking units, and clothes dryers under the conditions specified by Section 250-60.

Exception No. 2: As permitted in Section 250-24 for separate buildings.

Exception No. 3: It shall be permissible to ground meter enclosures by connection to the grounded circuit conductor on the load-side of the service disconnect if:

a. No service ground-fault protection is installed; and

b. All meter enclosures are located near the service disconnecting means.

Exception No. 4: As required in Sections 710-72(e)(1) and 710-74.

Exception No. 5: DC systems shall be permitted to be grounded on the load side of the disconnecting means or overcurrent device in accordance with Section 250-22, Exception.

250-62. **Multiple Circuit Connections.** Where equipment is required to be grounded, and is supplied by separate connection to more than one circuit or grounded premises wiring system, a means for grounding shall be provided for each such connection as specified in Sections 250-57 and 250-59.

G. Bonding

250-70. **General.** Bonding shall be provided where necessary to assure electrical continuity and the capacity to conduct safely any fault current likely to be imposed.

250-71. **Service Equipment.**

(a) Bonding of Service Equipment. The noncurrent-carrying metal parts of equipment indicated in (1), (2), and (3) below shall be effectively bonded together.

(1) Except as permitted in Section 250-55, the service raceways, cable trays, cablebus framework, or service cable armor or sheath.

(2) All service equipment enclosures containing service conductors, including meter fittings, boxes, or the like, interposed in the service raceway or armor.

(3) Any metallic raceway or armor enclosing a grounding electrode conductor as permitted in Section 250-92(a). Bonding shall apply at each end and to all intervening raceways, boxes, and enclosures between the service equipment and the grounding electrode.

This section was revised for the 1993 *Code* to clarify that where metal raceways, boxes, or enclosures contain a grounding electrode conductor, both ends of the raceway,

Figure 250-21. *Two different types of grounding and bonding arrangements. On the left is a grounding electrode conductor at the meter housing with the service equipment enclosure bonded to the grounded service conductor. On the right is the grounding electrode conductor at the service equipment with the service equipment enclosure and the meter housing bonded to the grounded service conductor.*

box, or enclosure must be bonded to the grounding electrode conductor.

(b) Bonding to Other Systems. An accessible means external to enclosures for connecting intersystem bonding and grounding conductors shall be provided at the service by at least one of the following means:

(1) Exposed metallic service raceways.

(2) Exposed grounding electrode conductor.

(3) Approved means for the external connection of a copper or other corrosion-resistant bonding or grounding conductor to the service raceway or equipment.

For the purposes of providing an accessible means for intersystem bonding, the disconnecting means at a separate building or structure as permitted in Section 250-24 and the disconnecting means at a mobile home as permitted in Section 550-23(a), Exception No. 1 shall be considered the service equipment.

This section was revised for the 1993 *Code.* It clarifies that the approved means for an external connection for bonding other systems must be copper or another approved corrosion resistant material. For example, aluminum would not be suitable for connection to electrodes near earth or in concrete.

A new second paragraph was added for separate buildings and mobile homes where the service equipment is

external or in another building. The need for an accessible bonding means is equally important in these occupancies, therefore the disconnecting means enclosure can be considered as the equivalent of the service equipment for the purpose of intrasystem bonding.

(FPN No. 1): A No. 6 copper conductor with one end bonded to the service raceway or equipment and with 6 inches (152 mm) or more of the other end made accessible on the outside wall is an example of the approved means covered in (b)(3).

See Figure 250-22 for another means.

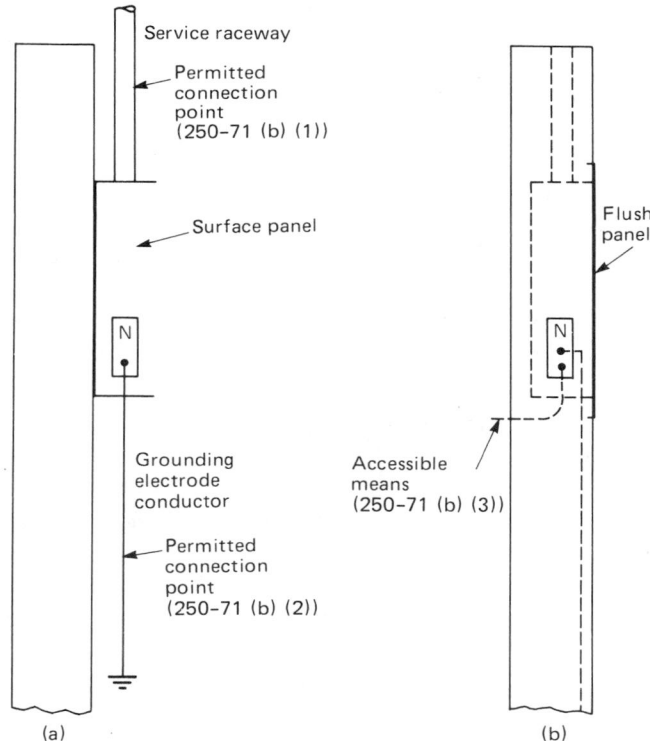

Figure 250-22. *An accessible external means is required to be provided for intersystem bonding. Figure 250-22(a) illustrates accessible means for the connection. Figure 250-22(b) illustrates a method of providing the required bonding means when the panelboard is a flush type (see FPN).*

(FPN No. 2): See Sections 800-40 and 820-40 for bonding and grounding requirements for communications and CATV circuits.

The *Code* requires that separate systems be bonded together to reduce their differences of potential, which can result from lightning or power contacts. Interconnection is required for lightning rod systems (Section 250-46), communications systems [Section 800-40(b)], radio and TV (Section 810-21), and CATV systems [Section 820-40(b)]. Lack of interconnection can result in a severe shock and fire hazard.

The reason for this potential hazard is as follows. See Figure 250-23, which shows a CATV cable with the jacket grounded to a separate ground rod and not bonded to the power ground. This cable is connected to the tuner of a television set inside a home. Also connected to the tuner is the 120-volt supply with one conductor grounded at the service (the power ground). In each case there will be a dc resistance to ground at the grounding electrode, as shown in the equivalent circuit. This resistance to ground will vary widely, depending on soil conditions and the type of grounding electrode. The resistance at the CATV ground is likely to be higher than the power ground resistance because the power ground is often an underground metal water piping system or concrete-encased electrode; whereas the CATV ground is commonly a ground rod.

Assume that there is a current induced in the power line by a switching surge or a nearby lightning strike so that a momentary current of 1,000 amperes flows over the power line to the power line ground. This amount of current is not unusual under such circumstances. It could be, and often is, considerably greater. Also assume that the power ground has a resistance (Rp) of 10 ohms, a *very* low value in most circumstances. A single ground rod in average soil has a resistance to ground in the neighborhood of 40 ohms. According to Ohm's law, point B will be raised momentarily to a potential of 1,000 × 10 = 10,000 volts, resulting in a potential of 10,000 volts between points A and B and anything connected to them; in this case, parts within the tuner. This voltage would also exist between the grounded conductor within the CATV cable and grounded surfaces in the walls of the home, such as water pipes (which are connected to the power ground), over which the cable runs. This potential could also appear across a person with one hand on the CATV cable and the other on a metal surface connected to the power ground (a radiator or refrigerator, for example). Actual voltage is more than likely to be many times the 10,000 volts calculated above, as extremely low

(below normal) values were assumed for both the resistance to ground and the current. However, most insulation systems are not designed to withstand even 10,000 V. Even if the insulation system does withstand this voltage surge, it is likely to be damaged.

Breakdown of the insulation system will result in sparking.

The same situation would exist if the current surge was on the CATV cable or on a telephone line. The only difference would be the voltage involved, depending on the individual resistance to ground of the grounding electrodes.

The solution is to bond between points A and B or to connect the CATV cable jacket to the power ground, and this is exactly what the *Code* requires. Thus, even though point A is raised to some very high voltage above ground, so is point B, and no voltage exists between the two grounding systems.

Figure 250-23. *This installation does not comply with the Code and illustrates why bonding between different systems is necessary. See preceding commentary.*

These rules are provided because of the difficulties encountered by communications and CATV installers in complying with *Code* grounding and bonding requirements, because of the increasing use of plastic for water pipe, fittings, water meters, and service conduit. In the past, bonding between communications, CATV, and power systems was usually achieved by connecting the communications protector grounds or cable shield to an interior metallic water pipe, because the pipe was often used as the power grounding electrode. Thus, the requirement that the power, communications, CATV cable shield, and metallic water piping systems be bonded together was easily satisfied. In the event that the power was grounded to one of the other electrodes permitted by the *Code*, usually by use of a made electrode such as a ground rod, the bond was connected to the power grounding electrode conductor or to a metallic service raceway, since at least one of these was usually accessible. With the growing proliferation of plastic water pipe, the increasing tendency for the service equipment to be installed in finished areas where the grounding electrode conductor is often concealed (and flush-mounted service equipment installed), as well as the use of plastic service-entrance conduit, communications and CATV installers no longer have access to a point for connecting bonding jumpers or grounding conductors. See Figure 250-22, Points A or B. Also see the commentary to Section 820-22(h).

250-72 . Method of Bonding Service Equipment. Electrical continuity at service equipment shall be assured by one of the methods specified in (a) through (e) below.

(a) Grounded Service Conductor. Bonding equipment to the grounded service conductor in a manner provided in Section 250-113.

(b) Threaded Connections. Connections utilizing threaded couplings or threaded bosses on enclosures shall be made up wrenchtight where rigid metal conduit or intermediate metal conduit is involved.

(c) Threadless Couplings and Connectors. Threadless couplings and connectors made up tight for rigid metal conduit, intermediate metal conduit and electrical metallic tubing. Standard locknuts or bushings shall not be used for the bonding required by this section.

(d) Bonding Jumpers. Bonding jumpers meeting the other requirements of this article shall be used around concentric or eccentric knockouts that are punched or otherwise formed so as to impair the electrical connection to ground.

(e) Other Devices. Other approved devices, such as bonding-type locknuts and bushings.

Note that paragraph (e) requires bonding-type locknuts. Standard locknuts or sealing locknuts are not acceptable for bonding at service equipment.

Bonding bushings for use with rigid or intermediate metal conduit are provided with means (usually one or more set-screws) for reliably bonding the bushing and the conduit on which it is threaded to the metal equipment enclosure or box. Where means for connecting a grounding conductor or bonding jumper are not provided, and there is need for such a conductor, a grounding-type bushing is required to be used.

Grounding-type bushings used with rigid or intermediate metal conduit have provisions for the connection of a bonding jumper or have means available from the manufacturer for use in mounting a wire connector. This type of bushing may also have means (usually one or more set-screws) that are used for reliably bonding the bushing to the metal equipment enclosure or box in the same manner that is accomplished by using a bonding jumper.

Figure 250-24. A grounding bushing used to connect a copper bonding or grounding wire to a conduit. (The Thomas & Betts Co., Inc.)

250-73 . Metal Armor or Tape of Service Cable. The metal covering of service cable having an uninsulated grounded service conductor in continuous electrical contact with its metallic armor or tape shall be considered to be grounded.

Figures 250-25 and 250-26. *Figure 250-25 (left) shows a grounding wedge lug for providing an electrical connection between a conduit and a box. Figure 250-26 (right) shows the manner in which the lug is installed. (The Thomas & Betts Co., Inc.)*

Figure 250-27. *A threaded grounding bushing showing openings for setscrews to assure electrical and mechanical connection. (General Electric Co.)*

250-74. **Connecting Receptacle Grounding Terminal to Box.**
An equipment bonding jumper shall be used to connect the grounding terminal of a grounding-type receptacle to a grounded box.

Exception No. 1: Where the box is surface mounted, direct metal-to-metal contact between the device yoke and the box shall be permitted to ground the receptacle to the box. This exception shall not apply to cover-mounted receptacles unless the box and cover combination are listed as providing satisfactory ground continuity between the box and the receptacle.

Exception No. 1, which permits the equipment bonding jumper to be omitted, is not applicable to cover-mounted receptacles as illustrated in Figure 250-28A. Listed box-cover combinations are permitted.

Figure 250-28A. *An example of a cover-mounted receptacle attached to a surface box. A bonding jumper is required.*

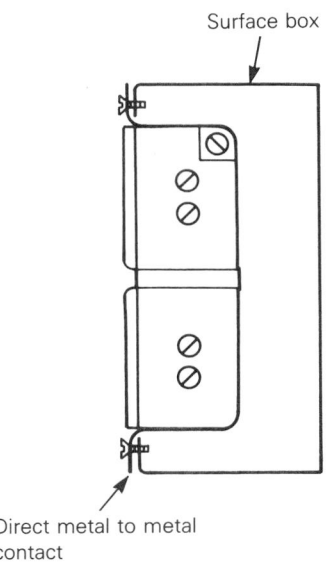

Figure 250-28B. *An example of a box-mounted receptacle attached to a surface box. A bonding jumper is not required.*

Exception No. 2: Contact devices or yokes designed and listed for the purpose shall be permitted in conjunction with the supporting screws to establish the grounding circuit between the device yoke and flush-type boxes.

See Figure 250-29.

Figure 250-29. *Receptacle designed with spring-type grounding strap that holds mounting screw captive and eliminates a bonding jumper to box in accordance with Exception No. 2 of Section 250-74.*

Exception No. 3: Floor boxes designed for and listed as providing satisfactory ground continuity between the box and the device.

Exception No. 4: Where required for the reduction of electrical noise (electromagnetic interference) on the grounding circuit, a receptacle in which the grounding terminal is purposely insulated from the receptacle mounting means shall be permitted. The receptacle grounding terminal shall be grounded by an insulated equipment grounding conductor run with the circuit conductors. This grounding conductor shall be permitted to pass through one or more panelboards without connection to the panelboard grounding

terminal as permitted in Section 384-20, Exception so as to terminate within the same building or structure directly at an equipment grounding conductor terminal of the applicable derived system or service.

It is essential to run the equipment grounding conductor with the circuit conductors to maintain low alternating current impedance in the grounding path.

This exception was revised for the 1993 *Code.* Where isolated ground-type receptacles are used, the isolated equipment grounding conductor must terminate at an equipment grounding terminal of the applicable service or derived system within the same building as the receptacle. During lightning transients, a large voltage difference may exist between buildings where the isolated equipment grounding conductor terminates at a separate building. These transients could cause damage to equipment that is connected to an isolated ground-type receptacle and could present a shock hazard between the isolated equipment frame and other grounded surfaces.

(FPN): Use of an isolated equipment grounding conductor does not relieve the requirement for grounding the raceway system and outlet box.

This fine print note is a reminder that metallic raceways and boxes are still required to be grounded by one of the usual required methods. This could require a separate grounding conductor, for example, to ground a metal box in a nonmetallic raceway system, or to ground flexible metal conduit. Where replacing an ordinary grounding-type receptacle with an isolated ground receptacle, use of an existing equipment grounding conductor as the isolated receptacle grounding conductor could effectively defeat or seriously compromise the required box or raceway equipment ground.

250-75. **Bonding Other Enclosures.** Metal raceways, cable trays, cable armor, cable sheath, enclosures, frames, fittings, and other metal noncurrent-carrying parts that are to serve as grounding conductors with or without the use of supplementary equipment grounding conductors shall be effectively bonded where necessary to assure electrical continuity and the capacity to conduct safely any fault current likely to be imposed on them. Any nonconductive paint, enamel, or similar coating shall be removed at threads, contact points, and contact surfaces or be connected by means of fittings so designed as to make such removal unnecessary.

Exception: Where required for the reduction of electrical noise (electromagnetic interference) on the grounding circuit, an equipment enclosure supplied by a branch circuit shall be permitted to be isolated from a raceway containing circuits supplying only that equipment by one or more listed nonmetallic raceway fittings located at the point of attachment of the raceway to the equipment enclosure. The metal raceway shall comply with provisions of this article and shall be supplemented by an internal insulated equipment grounding conductor installed in accordance with Section 250-74, Exception No. 4 to ground the equipment enclosure.

This exception was new in the 1990 *Code*. It permits electronic equipment to be isolated from the raceway in a manner similar to that for cord-connected equipment to reduce EMI. It was further revised for the 1993 *Code* to clarify that an equipment enclosure supplied by a branch circuit is the subject of the exception and that subsequent wiring, raceways, or other equipment beyond the insulating fitting is not permitted.

Section 384-20, Exception permits the isolated grounding conductor to pass through the panelboard.

(FPN): Use of an isolated equipment grounding conductor does not relieve the requirement for grounding the raceway system.

250-76. **Bonding for Over 250 Volts.** For circuits of over 250 volts to ground, the electrical continuity of metal raceways and cables with metal sheaths that contain any conductor other than service conductors shall be assured by one or more of the methods specified for services in Sections 250-72(b) through (e).

Exception: Where oversized, concentric, or eccentric knockouts are not encountered, the following methods shall be permitted:

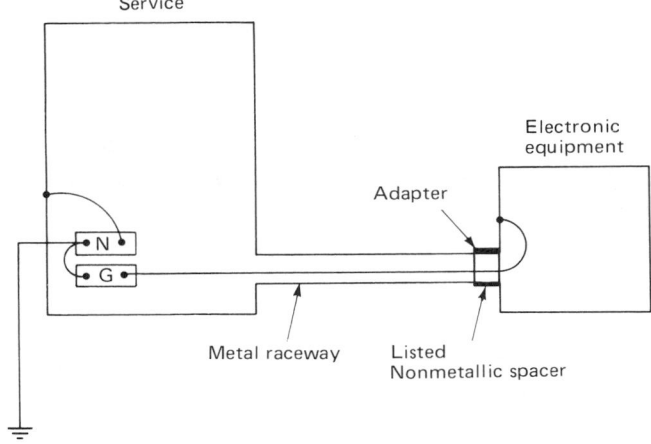

Figure 250-30(a). *The electronic equipment is grounded through the isolated grounding conductor. The metal raceway is grounded in the usual manner by attachment to the grounded service enclosure satisfying the concern mentioned in the FPN.*

a. Threadless couplings and connectors for cables with metal sheaths.

b. Two locknuts, on rigid metal conduit, or intermediate metal conduit, one inside and one outside of boxes and cabinets.

c. Fittings with shoulders that seat firmly against the box or cabinet, such as electrical metallic tubing connectors, flexible metal conduit connectors, and cable connectors, with one locknut on the inside of boxes and cabinets.

The methods in a, b, and c are permitted for circuits over 250 volts to ground *only* where there are no oversize, concentric, or eccentric knockouts. Note that condition c

Figure 250-30(b). *An example of isolated ground connections from a sub panel.*

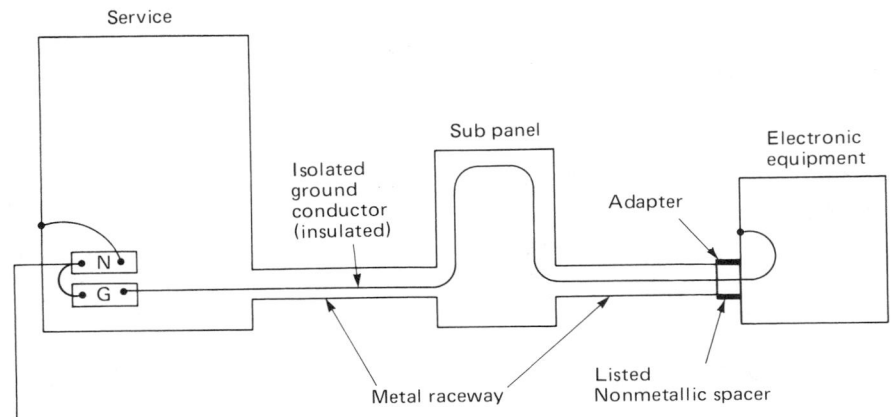

permits fittings, such as EMT connectors, cable connectors, etc., that have their shoulders firmly seated against the full metal of a box or cabinet to be installed with only one locknut located on the inside of the box.

250-77. **Bonding Loosely Jointed Metal Raceways.** Expansion joints and telescoping sections of raceways shall be made electrically continuous by equipment bonding jumpers or other means.

250-78. **Bonding in Hazardous (Classified) Locations.** Regardless of the voltage of the electrical system, the electrical continuity of noncurrent-carrying metal parts of equipment, raceways, and other enclosures in any hazardous (classified) location as defined in Article 500 shall be assured by any of the methods specified for services in Sections 250-72(b) through (e) that are approved for the wiring method used.

250-79. **Main and Equipment Bonding Jumpers.**

(a) Material. Main and equipment bonding jumpers shall be of copper or other corrosion-resistant material. A main bonding jumper shall be a wire, bus, screw, or similar suitable conductor.

(b) Construction. Where a main bonding jumper is a screw only, the screw shall be identified with a green finish that shall be visible with the screw installed.

This requirement makes it possible to readily distinguish the main bonding jumper screw for inspection purposes.

(c) Attachment. Main and equipment bonding jumpers shall be attached in the manner specified by the applicable provisions of Section 250-113 for circuits and equipment and by Section 250-115 for grounding electrodes.

(d) Size — Equipment Bonding Jumper on Supply Side of Service and Main Bonding Jumper. The bonding jumper shall not be smaller than the sizes shown in Table 250-94 for grounding electrode conductors. Where the service-entrance phase conductors are larger than 1100 kcmil copper or 1750 kcmil aluminum, the bonding jumper shall have an area not less than 12½ percent of the area of the largest phase conductor except that, where the phase conductors and the bonding jumper are of different materials (copper or aluminum), the minimum size of the bonding jumper shall be based on the assumed use of phase conductors of the same material as the

bonding jumper and with an ampacity equivalent to that of the installed phase conductors. Where the service-entrance conductors are paralleled in two or more raceways or cables, the equipment bonding jumper, where routed with the raceways or cables, shall be run in parallel. The size of the bonding jumper for each raceway or cable shall be based on the size of the service-entrance conductors in each raceway or cable.

The bonding jumper for a grounding electrode conductor raceway or cable armor as covered in Section 250-92(b) shall be the same size or larger than the required enclosed grounding electrode conductor.

Types MI and MC cable are also permitted to be used for services. See Section 230-43.

The size required for the equipment bonding jumper and the main bonding jumper on the *supply* side of a service is the same as for the grounding electrode conductor raceway jumpers required by Section 250-92(b) and the grounding electrode conductor taken from Table 250-94 (including the 12½ percent requirement for phase conductors larger than 1,100 kcmil copper or 1,750 kcmil aluminum).

Example: In applying the bonding requirements of Figure 250-13, if one of the switches is rated 100 A and the supply conductors are No. 2 Type THW copper conductors, Table 250-94 requires a grounding electrode conductor sized at No. 8 copper or No. 6 aluminum or copper-clad aluminum. The bonding jumper would also be sized at No. 8 copper or No. 6 aluminum or copper-clad aluminum.

If another switch is rated at 200 A and the conductors supplying it are No. 3/0 Type THW copper, the grounding electrode conductor and the bonding jumper are required to be sized at a minimum of No. 4 copper or No. 2 aluminum or copper-clad aluminum.

To apply the bonding jumper requirements, each switch should be treated as separate service equipment, and Table 250-94 should be used to determine the size of the bonding jumper.

In some instances, the bonding jumper may be required to be larger than the grounding electrode conductor. Section 250-79(d) indicates that, where the service-entrance conductors are larger than 1,100 kcmil copper or 1,750 kcmil aluminum, the bonding jumper is required to have a cross-sectional area of not less than 12½ percent of the cross-sectional area of the largest phase conductor. For example, if a service is supplied by four 500 kcmil conductors in parallel for each phase, the minimum cross-sectional area of the bonding jumper is required to be 250 kcmil (4 × 500 kcmil = 2,000 kcmil × .125). See Table 8, Conductor Properties, in Chapter 9 for area in circular mils or AWG.

(e) Size — Equipment Bonding Jumper on Load Side of Service. The equipment bonding jumper on the load side of the service overcurrent devices shall not be smaller than the sizes listed in Table 250-95. A single common continuous equipment bonding jumper shall be permitted to bond two or more raceways or cables where the bonding jumper is sized in accordance with Table 250-95 for the largest overcurrent device supplying circuits therein.

Exception: The equipment bonding jumper shall not be required to be larger than the circuit conductors supplying the equipment, but shall not be smaller than No. 14.

(f) Installation — Equipment Bonding Jumper. The equipment bonding jumper shall be permitted to be installed inside or outside of a raceway or enclosure. Where installed on the outside, the length of the equipment bonding jumper shall not exceed 6 feet (1.83 m) and shall be routed with the raceway or enclosure. Where installed inside of a raceway, the equipment bonding jumper shall comply with the requirements of Sections 250-114 and 310-12(b).

In many applications it is necessary to install equipment bonding jumpers on the outside of metal raceways and enclosures. For example, it would be impractical to install the bonding jumper for a conduit expansion joint on the inside of the conduit. For some metal raceway and rigid conduit systems and conduit systems in hazardous (classified) locations, it is desirable to install the bonding jumper where it is visible and accessible for inspection and maintenance. An external bonding jumper will have a higher impedance than an internal bonding jumper. However, by limiting the length to 6 feet and routing it with the raceway, there will not be a significant increase in the total impedance of the equipment grounding circuit. For example, this rule permits an exterior bonding jumper where run around a section of flexible metal conduit. See Figure 250-31. Since the function of a bonding jumper is readily apparent, color identification is not necessary.

Figure 250-31. *Bonding around outside of flexible metal conduit.*

250-80. Bonding of Piping Systems.

(a) Metal Water Piping. The interior metal water piping system shall be bonded to the service equipment enclosure, the grounded conductor at the service, the grounding electrode conductor where of sufficient size, or to the one or more grounding electrodes used. The bonding jumper shall be sized in accordance with Table 250-94 and installed in accordance with Sections 250-92(a) and (b). The points of attachment of the bonding jumper shall be accessible.

This section requires a single connection to the interior metal water piping system. However, some judgment must be exercised in each specific case. Where it cannot reasonably be concluded that the hot and cold water pipes are reliably interconnected, an electrical bonding jumper is required to assure that this connection is made. The special installation requirements provided in Section 250-92(a) and (b) are also required for the water piping bonding jumper.

Exception: In buildings of multiple occupancy, where the interior metal water piping system for the individual occupancies is metallically isolated from all other occupancies by use of nonmetallic water piping, the interior metal water piping system for each occupancy shall be permitted to be bonded to the panelboard or switchboard enclosure (other than service equipment) supplying that occupancy. The bonding jumper shall be sized in accordance with Table 250-95.

The intent of the exception is to recognize the fact that increased use of nonmetallic water piping systems underground makes it virtually impossible to assure compliance with the main rule of Section 250-80 in the circumstances described.

(b) Other Metal Piping. Interior metal piping that may become energized shall be bonded to the service equipment enclosure, the grounded conductor at the service, the grounding electrode conductor where of sufficient size, or to the one or more grounding electrodes used. The bonding jumper shall be sized in accordance with Table 250-95 using the rating of the circuit that may energize the piping.

The equipment grounding conductor for the circuit that may energize the piping shall be permitted to serve as the bonding means.

(FPN): Bonding all piping and metal air ducts within the premises will provide additional safety.

Paragraph 3.14a. of the *National Fuel Gas Code*, NFPA 54-1992, ANSI Z223.1-1992, requires that each ABOVE-GROUND portion of a gas piping system upstream from the equipment shutoff valve shall be electrically continuous and bonded to any grounding electrode, as defined by the *National Electrical Code*, ANSI/NFPA 70. The UNDERGROUND portions of gas piping systems are not permitted to serve as a grounding electrode. See Section 250-83(a).

H. Grounding Electrode System

250-81. **Grounding Electrode System.** If available on the premises at each building or structure served, each item (a) through (d) below, and any made electrodes in accordance with Sections 250-83(c) and (d), shall be bonded together to form the grounding electrode system. Interior metal water piping located more than 5 feet (152 cm) from the point of entrance to the building shall not be used as a conductor to interconnect the electrodes and the grounding electrode conductor. The bonding jumper shall be installed in accordance with Sections 250-92(a) and (b), shall be sized in accordance with Section 250-94, and shall be connected in the manner specified in Section 250-115. The unspliced grounding electrode conductor shall be permitted to run to any convenient grounding electrode available in the grounding electrode system. It shall be sized for the largest grounding electrode conductor required among all the available electrodes.

This section has been revised for the 1993 *Code*. It now prohibits the use of that portion of the interior metal water piping system that extends more than 5 feet beyond the point of entrance into the building to interconnect grounding electrodes and the grounding electrode con-

ductor. However, Exception No. 2 permits this practice provided there is qualified maintenance and the entire length of the pipe is exposed. See also commentary following Section 250-50(b), Exception.

Exception No. 1: It shall be permitted to splice the grounding electrode conductor by means of irreversible compression-type connectors listed for the purpose or the exothermic welding process.

This exception has been revised for the 1993 *Code* to recognize the use of listed irreversible compression-type connectors. In addition, the permission to splice has been expanded to all locations.

Exception No. 2: In industrial and commercial buildings where conditions of maintenance and supervision ensure that only qualified persons will service the installation and the entire length of the interior metal water pipe that is being used for the conductor is exposed.

(FPN): See Section 547-8 for special grounding and bonding requirements for agricultural buildings.

(a) Metal Underground Water Pipe. A metal underground water pipe in direct contact with the earth for 10 feet (3.05 m) or more (including any metal well casing effectively bonded to the pipe) and electrically continuous (or made electrically continuous by bonding around insulating joints or sections or insulating pipe) to the points of connection of the grounding electrode conductor and the bonding conductors. Continuity of the grounding path or the bonding connection to interior piping shall not rely on water meters. A metal underground water pipe shall be supplemented by an additional electrode of a type specified in Section 250-81 or in Section 250-83. The supplemental electrode shall be permitted to be bonded to the grounding electrode conductor, the grounded service-entrance conductor, the grounded service raceway, or any grounded service enclosure.

One of the permitted methods of bonding a supplemental grounding electrode conductor to the primary electrode system is to connect it to a service enclosure.

Where the supplemental electrode is a made electrode as in Section 250-83(c) or (d), that portion of the bonding jumper that is the sole connection to the supplemental grounding electrode shall not be required to be larger than No. 6 copper wire or No. 4 aluminum wire.

This paragraph correlates with Section 250-83(c) or (d) and Section 250-94. If a "made electrode" is utilized, the size of the "sole" bonding jumper between the service equipment grounded conductor and, for example, a ground rod is not required to be larger than No. 6 copper or No. 4 aluminum.

The requirement to supplement the metal water pipe is based on the practice of using a plastic pipe for replacement when the original metal water pipe fails from corrosion, which leaves the system without a grounding electrode where the supplementary electrode is not provided.

Exception: The supplemental electrode shall be permitted to be bonded to the interior metal water piping at any convenient point as covered in Section 250-81, Exception No. 2.

(b) Metal Frame of the Building. The metal frame of the building, where effectively grounded.

(FPN): Effectively grounded means intentionally connected to earth through a ground connection or connections of sufficiently low impedance and having sufficient current-carrying capacity to prevent the buildup of voltages that may result in undue hazard to connected equipment or to persons.

(c) Concrete-Encased Electrode. An electrode encased by at least 2 inches (50.8 mm) of concrete, located within and near the bottom of a concrete foundation or footing that is in direct contact with the earth, consisting of at least 20 feet (6.1 m) of one or more bare or zinc galvanized or other electrically conductive coated steel reinforcing bars or rods of not less than ¹/₂ inch (12.7 mm) diameter, or consisting of at least 20 feet (6.1 m) of bare copper conductor not smaller than No. 4.

(d) Ground Ring. A ground ring encircling the building or structure, in direct contact with the earth at a depth below earth surface not less than 2¹/₂ feet (762 mm), consisting of at least 20 feet (6.1 m) of bare copper conductor not smaller than No. 2.

Section 250-81 requires the metal underground water pipe, the metal frame of the building, a concrete-encased electrode, and a ground-ring type of electrode, only where they are available, to be bonded together to form the grounding electrode system. See Figure 250-33. Where a metal underground water pipe is the only grounding electrode available, it must be supplemented by one of the grounding electrodes specified in Section 250-81 or Section 250-83.

There has always been a degree of misunderstanding as to whether metal water piping systems should be used as a grounding electrode, and a number of years ago the electrical industry and the water works industry formed a committee of all the affected interests to evaluate the use of metal underground water piping systems as the grounding electrode. Based on their findings, the committee issued an authoritative report on this subject. The International

Figure 250-32. A concrete-encased electrode.

Association of Electrical Inspectors published the "Interim Report of the American Research Committee on Grounding" in January 1944 and had reprints made in March 1949.

The National Institute of Standards and Technology has monitored the electrolysis of metal systems because a flow of current at a grounding electrode on dc systems can cause displacement of metal. The results of this monitoring have shown that problems are minimal.

250-83. **Made and Other Electrodes.** Where none of the electrodes specified in Section 250-81 is available, one or more of the electrodes specified in (b) through (d) below shall be used. Where practicable, made electrodes shall be embedded below permanent moisture level. Made electrodes shall be free from nonconductive coatings, such as paint or enamel. Where more than one electrode is used, each electrode of one grounding system (including that used for lightning rods) shall not be less than 6 feet (1.83 m) from any other electrode of another grounding system.

(FPN): Two or more electrodes that are effectively bonded together are to be treated as a single electrode system in this sense.

(a) Metal Underground Gas Piping System. A metal underground gas piping system shall not be used as a grounding electrode.

Figure 250-33. A grounding electrode system.

Figure 250-34. Section 250-83 requires a spacing of 6 feet between electrodes of different systems. Section 250-84 requires a 6-foot spacing between electrodes of the same system.

Paragraph 3.14b. of the *National Fuel Gas Code*, NFPA 54-1992, ANSI Z223.1-1992, indicates that gas piping shall not be used as a grounding electrode. This correlates with Section 250-83(a) new in the *Code*.

(b) Other Local Metal Underground Systems or Structures. Other local metal underground systems or structures, such as piping systems and underground tanks.

(c) Rod and Pipe Electrodes. Rod and pipe electrodes shall not be less than 8 feet (2.44 m) in length and shall consist of the following materials, and shall be installed in the following manner:

(1) Electrodes of pipe or conduit shall not be smaller than ³/₄-inch trade size and, where of iron or steel, shall have the outer surface galvanized or otherwise metal-coated for corrosion protection.

(2) Electrodes of rods of iron or steel shall be at least ⅝ inch (15.87 mm) in diameter. Stainless steel rods less than ⅝ inch (15.87 mm) in diameter, nonferrous rods, or their equivalent shall be listed and shall be not less than ½ inch (12.7 mm) in diameter.

(3) The electrode shall be installed such that at least 8 feet (2.44 m) of length is in contact with the soil. It shall be driven to a depth of not less than 8 feet (2.44 m) except that, where rock bottom is encountered, the electrode shall be driven at an oblique angle not to exceed 45 degrees from the vertical or shall be buried in a trench that is at least 2½ feet (762 mm) deep. The upper end of the electrode shall be flush with or below ground level unless the aboveground end and the grounding electrode conductor attachment are protected against physical damage as specified in Section 250-117.

Figure 250-35. *All pipe and rod electrodes must have 8 feet of length in contact with soil regardless of rock bottom in order to ensure that the upper end of the electrode is flush with or below ground level unless the aboveground portion is protected against physical damage.*

(d) Plate Electrodes. Each plate electrode shall expose not less than 2 square feet (0.186 sq m) of surface to exterior soil. Electrodes of iron or steel plates shall be at least ¼ inch (6.35 mm) in thickness. Electrodes of nonferrous metal shall be at least 0.06 inch (1.52 mm) in thickness.

(e) Aluminum Electrodes. Aluminum electrodes shall not be permitted.

250-84. **Resistance of Made Electrodes.** A single electrode consisting of a rod, pipe, or plate that does not have a resistance to ground of 25 ohms or less shall be augmented by one additional electrode of any of the types specified in Section 250-81 or 250-83. Where multiple rod, pipe, or plate electrodes are installed to meet the requirements of this section, they shall be not less than 6 feet (1.83 m) apart.

(FPN): The paralleling efficiency of rods longer than 8 feet (2.44 m) is improved by spacing greater than 6 feet (1.83 m).

250-86. **Use of Lightning Rods.** Lightning rod conductors and driven pipes, rods, or other made electrodes used for grounding lightning rods shall not be used in lieu of the made grounding electrodes required by Section 250-83 for grounding wiring systems and equipment. This provision shall not prohibit the required bonding together of grounding electrodes of different systems.

(FPN No. 1): See Sections 250-46, 800-40(d), 810-21(j), and 820-40(d) for bonding of electrodes.

(FPN No. 2): Bonding together of all separate grounding electrodes will limit potential differences between them and between their associated wiring systems.

J. Grounding Conductors

250-91. **Material.** The material for grounding conductors shall be as specified in (a), (b), and (c) below.

Figure 250-36. *The resistance to ground of a driven grounding electrode can be measured by a ground tester used in this manner.*

(a) Grounding Electrode Conductor. The grounding electrode conductor shall be of copper, aluminum, or copper-clad aluminum. The material selected shall be resistant to any corrosive condition existing at the installation or shall be suitably protected against corrosion. The conductor shall be solid or stranded, insulated, covered, or bare and shall be installed in one continuous length without a splice or joint.

Exception No. 1: Splices in busbars shall be permitted.

Exception No. 2: Where a service consists of more than a single enclosure as permitted in Section 230-40, Exception No. 2, it shall be permissible to connect taps to the grounding electrode conductor. Each such tap conductor shall extend to the inside of each such enclosure. The grounding electrode conductor shall be sized in accordance with Section 250-94, but the tap conductors shall be permitted to be sized in accordance with the grounding electrode conductors specified in Section 250-94 for the largest conductor serving the respective enclosures. The tap conductors shall be connected to the grounding electrode conductor in such a manner that the grounding electrode conductor remains without a splice or joint.

The grounding electrode (tap) conductors are required to be sized using Table 250-94 and are based on the size of the largest phase conductors serving each enclosure. The grounding electrode conductor is determined by the size of the largest service-entrance conductor or equivalent cross-sectional area for parallel conductors as per Table 250-94. See Figure 250-37(a).

Exception No. 3: It shall be permitted to splice the grounding electrode conductor by means of irreversible compression-type connectors listed for the purpose or the exothermic welding process.

Section 250-91(a), Exception No. 3 was revised for the 1993 *Code.* It is frequently necessary to splice the grounding electrode conductor to add additional equipment. This exception now permits splicing the grounding electrode conductor by irreversible compression type fittings or the exothermal welding process. The intent of these requirements is that the fitting that is used is a permanent fitting that will not become loose after installation. The application of this permission is no longer limited to commercial and industrial locations.

Figure 250-37(a). *The tap method eliminates the difficulties found in looping grounding electrode conductors from one enclosure to another. The No. 2 grounding electrode conductor is required to be installed without a splice or joint except as permitted in Section 250-81(a), Exception No. 3.*

(b) Types of Equipment Grounding Conductors. The equipment grounding conductor run with or enclosing the circuit conductors shall be one or more or a combination of the following: (1) a copper or other corrosion-resistant conductor. This conductor shall be solid or stranded; insulated, covered, or bare; and in the form of a wire or a busbar of any shape; (2) rigid metal conduit; (3) intermediate metal conduit; (4) electrical metallic tubing; (5) flexible metal conduit where both the conduit and fittings are listed for grounding; (6) armor of Type AC cable; (7) the copper sheath of mineral-insulated, metal-sheathed cable; (8) the metallic sheath or the combined metallic sheath and grounding conductors of Type MC cable; (9) cable trays as permitted in Sections 318-3(c) and 318-7; (10) cablebus framework as permitted in Section 365-2(a); (11) other electrically continuous metal raceways listed for grounding.

Exception No. 1: Listed flexible metal conduit and listed flexible metallic tubing shall be permitted for grounding if all the following conditions are met:

a. The total combined length of flexible metal conduit and flexible metallic tubing and liquidtight flexible metal conduit in the same ground return path does not exceed 6 ft (1.83 m).

b. The circuit conductors contained therein are protected by overcurrent devices rated at 20 amperes or less.

c. The conduit or tubing is terminated in fittings listed for grounding.

No. 3

No. 3/0

8 AWG Cu tap

2 AWG Cu GEC

Example: Sizing the grounding electrode conductor

No. 3 AWG   = 52,620 CMA Table 8
No. 3/0 AWG = 167,800 CMA Table 8
                        220,420 Sum of areas

From Table 8 nearest size = 250 kcmil.
From Table 250-94 = No. 2 AWG GEC.

Figure 250-37(b). Sizing of the grounding electrode conductor where there are multiple sets of service entrance conductors. See Notes to Table 250-94. The size of the tap to the grounding electrode conductor from the disconnect on the left is based on the size of the service entrance conductors supplying the enclosure.

Exception No. 2: Listed liquidtight flexible metal conduit shall be permitted as a grounding means in the 1¼-inch and smaller trade sizes if the total combined length of liquidtight flexible metal conduit and flexible metal conduit and flexible metallic tubing in the same ground return path does not exceed 6 ft (1.83 m), the conduit is terminated in fittings listed for grounding, and the circuit conductors contained therein are protected by overcurrent devices rated at 20 amperes or less for ⅜-inch and ½-inch trade sizes and 60 amperes or less for ¾-inch through 1¼-inch trade sizes.

Exception No. 3: For direct-current circuits only, the equipment grounding conductor shall be permitted to be run separately from the circuit conductors.

The various types of conductors, armored or metal-sheathed cables, or metal raceways that are considered as suitable for use as equipment grounding conductors are described in Section 250-91(b).

Where termination fittings approved for grounding are used, listed flexible metal conduit and listed flexible metallic tubing are recognized in Exception No. 1 as equipment grounding conductors if the total length is not over 6 feet in any ground return path (the sum of all lengths of flexible metal conduit and flexible metallic tubing in the ground return path from the part to be grounded to the branch-circuit overcurrent protection), and the contained circuit conductors are protected by overcurrent devices rated at 20 A or less.

Listed liquidtight flexible metal conduit is recognized as an equipment grounding conductor by Exception No. 2 where used with termination fittings approved for grounding in sizes not over 1¼ inches and in lengths not over 6 feet in any ground return path.

Exception No. 2 places limitations on the overcurrent protection provided for the circuit conductors, thus providing overcurrent protection for the conduit when used as an equipment grounding conductor. Field experience and laboratory tests indicated that it was possible to overload the grounding path provided in the ⅜ inch through 1¼-inch trade sizes of UL-listed liquidtight flexible metal conduit under certain fault conditions, causing the liquidtight outer jacket to melt and emit smoke. This led to a study by UL and the electrical industry to determine the practical limits for the use of this type of conduit as a grounding conductor. Ground-fault current tests were conducted, and it was determined that overcurrent protection as now specified would maintain the integrity of the outer jacket and the equipment grounding circuit.

The overcurrent protection limitations for the circuit conductors are not required if the conduit is not used as an equipment grounding conductor.

Termination fittings that are approved for grounding may be determined by a qualified electrical testing laboratory, inspection agency, or other organization concerned with product evaluation as part of its listing and labeling program. See the definitions for "Approved,"

"Identified," "Listed," and "Labeled" in Article 100. For grounding requirements, also see Sections 349-16, 350-5, and 351-9.

(c) Supplementary Grounding. Supplementary grounding electrodes shall be permitted to augment the equipment grounding conductors specified in Section 250-91(b), but the earth shall not be used as the sole equipment grounding conductor.

Grounding electrodes (ground rods, etc.) connected to equipment are not permitted to be used in lieu of the equipment grounding conductor but may be used for supplementary protection. For example, they may be used for lightning protection or to equalize potentials in the area of the equipment. See Section 250-51, second paragraph.

250-92. **Installation.** Grounding conductors shall be installed as specified in (a), (b), and (c) below.

(a) Grounding Electrode Conductor. A grounding electrode conductor or its enclosure shall be securely fastened to the surface on which it is carried. A No. 4, copper or aluminum, or larger conductor shall be protected if exposed to severe physical damage. A No. 6 grounding conductor that is free from exposure to physical damage shall be permitted to be run along the surface of the building construction without metal covering or protection where it is securely fastened to the construction; otherwise, it shall be in rigid metal conduit, intermediate metal conduit, rigid nonmetallic conduit, electrical metallic tubing, or cable armor. Grounding conductors smaller than No. 6 shall be in rigid metal conduit, intermediate metal conduit, rigid nonmetallic conduit, electrical metallic tubing, or cable armor.

Insulated or bare aluminum or copper-clad aluminum grounding conductors shall not be used where in direct contact with masonry or the earth or where subject to corrosive conditions. Where used outside, aluminum or copper-clad aluminum grounding conductors shall not be installed within 18 inches (457 mm) of the earth.

(b) Enclosures for Grounding Electrode Conductors. Metal enclosures for grounding electrode conductors shall be electrically continuous from the point of attachment to cabinets or equipment to the grounding electrode, and shall be securely fastened to the ground clamp or fitting. Metal enclosures that are not physically continuous from cabinet or equipment to the grounding electrode shall be made electrically continuous by bonding each end to the grounding conductor. Where a raceway is used as protection for a grounding conductor, the installation shall comply with the requirements of the appropriate raceway article.

Bonding jumpers installed to ensure the electrical continuity of metal enclosures are required to be sized in accordance with Section 250-79(d). This last sentence was added in the 1990 *Code.*

(c) Equipment Grounding Conductor. An equipment grounding conductor shall be installed as follows.

(1) Where it consists of a raceway, cable tray, cable armor, or cable sheath or where it is a wire within a raceway or cable, it shall be installed in accordance with the applicable provisions in this Code using fittings for joints and terminations approved for use with the type raceway or cable used. All connections, joints, and fittings shall be made tight using suitable tools.

(2) Where it is a separate equipment grounding conductor as provided in the exception for Sections 250-50(a) and (b), it shall be installed in accordance with (a) above in regard to restrictions for aluminum and also in regard to protection from physical damage.

Exception: Sizes smaller than No. 6 shall not be required to be enclosed in a raceway or armor where run in the hollow spaces of a wall or partition or where otherwise installed so as not to be subject to physical damage.

250-93. **Size of Direct-Current System Grounding Conductor.** The size of the grounding conductor for a dc system shall be as specified in (a) through (c) below.

(a) Not Be Smaller than the Neutral Conductor. Where the dc system consists of a 3-wire balancer set or a balancer winding with overcurrent protection as provided in Section 445-4(d), the grounding conductor shall not be smaller than the neutral conductor.

(b) Not Be Smaller than the Largest Conductor. Where the dc system is other than as in (a) above, the grounding conductor shall not be smaller than the largest conductor supplied by the system.

(c) Not Be Smaller than No. 8. In no case shall the grounding conductor be smaller than No. 8 copper or No. 6 aluminum.

250-94. Size of Alternating-Current Grounding Electrode Conductor. The size of the grounding electrode conductor of a grounded or ungrounded ac system shall not be less than given in Table 250-94.

Exception No. 1: Grounded Systems.

a. Where connected to made electrodes as in Section 250-83 (c) or (d), that portion of the grounding electrode conductor that is the sole connection to the grounding electrode shall not be required to be larger than No. 6 copper wire or No. 4 aluminum wire.

b. Where connected to a concrete-encased electrode as in Section 250-81(c), that portion of the grounding electrode conductor that is the sole connection to the grounding electrode shall not be required to be larger than No. 4 copper wire.

c. Where connected to a ground ring as in Section 250-81(d), that portion of the grounding electrode conductor that is the sole connection to the grounding electrode shall not be required to be larger than the conductor used for the ground ring.

Exception No. 2: Ungrounded Systems.

a. Where connected to made electrodes as in Section 250-83 (c) or (d), that portion of the grounding electrode conductor that is the sole connection to the grounding electrode shall not be required to be larger than No. 6 copper wire or No. 4 aluminum wire.

b. Where connected to a concrete-encased electrode as in Section 250-81(c), that portion of the grounding electrode conductor that is the sole connection to the grounding electrode shall not be required to be larger than No. 4 copper wire.

c. Where connected to a ground ring as in Section 250-81(d), that portion of the grounding electrode conductor that is the sole connection to the grounding electrode shall not be required to be larger than the conductor used for the ground ring.

If a grounding electrode conductor is run from the service equipment or separately derived system to a water pipe or structural metal building member, and from that point to one of the electrodes mentioned in Section 250-94, Exception No. 1, that portion of the grounding electrode between the service equipment or separately derived system to the water pipe or structural metal building member must be a full-sized conductor sized per Table 250-94. See Figure 250-38.

The first footnote in Table 250-94 was new in the 1990 *Code* and clarifies the sizing of the grounding electrode

Figure 250-38. Illustration of Section 250-94, Exception No. 1. If the grounding electrode conductor from the service equipment were run (for example) to the ground rod first, and then to the water pipe, the conductor to the ground rod would also have to be full-sized per Table 250-94.

conductor where there are multiple sets of service-entrance conductors.

The second footnote refers to lateral-type services where service-entrance conductors extend from the point of connection to the service equipment. The point of connection is considered to be the point of entrance of the service conductors to the building.

250-95. Size of Equipment Grounding Conductors. Copper, aluminum, or copper-clad aluminum equipment grounding conductors shall not be less than shown in Table 250-95.

Where conductors are run in parallel in multiple raceways or cables, as permitted in Section 310-4, the equipment grounding conductor, where used, shall be run in parallel. Each parallel equipment grounding conductor shall be sized on the basis of the ampere rating of the overcurrent device protecting the circuit conductors in the raceway in accordance with Table 250-95.

Figure 250-39. This illustration is an example of service-entrance conductors that are part of a service lateral as defined in Article 100.

Table 250-94. Grounding Electrode Conductor for AC Systems

Size of Largest Service-Entrance Conductor or Equivalent Area for Parallel Conductors		Size of Grounding Electrode Conductor	
Copper	Aluminum or Copper-Clad Aluminum	Copper	Aluminum or Copper-Clad Aluminum*
2 or smaller	1/0 or smaller	8	6
1 or 1/0	2/0 or 3/0	6	4
2/0 or 3/0	4/0 or 250 kcmil	4	2
Over 3/0 thru 350 kcmil	Over 250 kcmil thru 500 kcmil	2	1/0
Over 350 kcmil thru 600 kcmil	Over 500 kcmil thru 900 kcmil	1/0	3/0
Over 600 kcmil thru 1100 kcmil	Over 900 kcmil thru 1750 kcmil	2/0	4/0
Over 1100 kcmil	Over 1750 kcmil	3/0	250 kcmil

Where multiple sets of service-entrance conductors are used as permitted in Section 230-40, Exception No. 2, the equivalent size of the largest service-entrance conductor shall be determined by the largest sum of the areas of the corresponding conductors of each set.

Where there are no service-entrance conductors, the grounding electrode conductor size shall be determined by the equivalent size of the largest service-entrance conductor required for the load to be served.

*See installation restrictions in Section 250-92(a).

(FPN): See Section 250-23(b) for size of alternating-current system grounded conductor brought to service equipment.

A full-sized equipment grounding conductor is needed in each raceway of an array of raceways enclosing paralleled phase conductors to prevent overloading and possible burn-out of the grounding conductor should there be a ground fault condition along one of the parallel branches. The installation conditions for paralleled conductors prescribed in Section 310-4 result in proportional distribution of the current-time duty among the several paralleled grounding conductors only for overcurrent conditions downstream of the paralleled array.

Figure 250-40 shows a parallel array of three nonmetallic conduits installed underground. For clarity, only phase "A" and the grounding conductors are shown. A short-circuit at point "X" due to a dig-in, for example, will cause the equipment grounding conductor in conduit no. 1 to carry more than its proportionate share of current. Note that point "X" is fed by three different conductors of phase "A", one from the left and two from the right. The lowest impedance path to ground is the equipment grounding conductor in conduit no. 1 from the supply panelboard to point "X." The grounding path from point "X" through conduit no. 2 and no. 3 is three times as long as the grounding path from point "X" to the supply panelboard.

Figure 250-40. Grounding paths for ground fault at point "X" in parallel array of nonmetallic raceways. This illustrates the reason for the requirement in the second paragraph of Section 250-95.

When conductors are adjusted in size to compensate for voltage drop, equipment grounding conductors, where required, shall be adjusted proportionately according to circular mil area.

Where a single equipment grounding conductor is run with multiple circuits in the same raceway, it shall be sized for the largest overcurrent device protecting conductors in the raceway or cable.

Where the overcurrent device consists of an instantaneous trip circuit breaker or a motor short-circuit protector, as allowed in Section 430-52, the equipment grounding conductor size shall be permitted to be based on the rating of the motor overload protective device but not less than the size shown in Table 250-95.

A single equipment grounding conductor is required to be sized for the largest overcurrent device and is not required to be sized for the composite of all the circuits in the raceway. For example, three 3-phase circuits protected by overcurrent devices at 30, 60, and 100 A installed in the same raceway would require only one equipment grounding conductor sized according to the largest (100 A in this case) overcurrent device. Therefore, a No. 8 AWG copper or No. 6 AWG aluminum or copper-clad aluminum is required by Table 250-95.

Exception No. 1: An equipment grounding conductor not smaller than No. 18 copper and not smaller than the circuit conductors and part of fixture wires or cords in accordance with Section 240-4.

Exception No. 2: The equipment grounding conductor shall not be required to be larger than the circuit conductors supplying the equipment.

Exception No. 3: Where a raceway or a cable armor or sheath is used as the equipment grounding conductor, as provided in Sections 250-51, 250-57(a), 250-73, and 250-91(b).

250-97. **Outline Lighting.** Isolated noncurrent-carrying metal parts of outline lighting systems shall be permitted to be bonded together by a No. 14 copper or No. 12 aluminum conductor protected from physical damage, where a conductor complying with Section 250-95 is used to ground the group.

250-99. **Equipment Grounding Conductor Continuity.**

(a) Separable Connections. Separable connections such as those provided in draw-out equipment or attachment plugs and mating connectors and receptacles shall provide for first-make, last-break of the equipment grounding conductor.

Table 250-95. Minimum Size Equipment Grounding Conductors for Grounding Raceway and Equipment

Rating or Setting of Automatic Overcurrent Device in Circuit Ahead of Equipment, Conduit, etc., Not Exceeding (Amperes)	Size	
	Copper Wire No.	Aluminum or Copper-Clad Aluminum Wire No.*
15	14	12
20	12	10
30	10	8
40	10	8
60	10	8
100	8	6
200	6	4
300	4	2
400	3	1
500	2	1/0
600	1	2/0
800	1/0	3/0
1000	2/0	4/0
1200	3/0	250 kcmil
1600	4/0	350 "
2000	250 kcmil	400 "
2500	350 "	600 "
3000	400 "	600 "
4000	500 "	800 "
5000	700 "	1200 "
6000	800 "	1200 "

* See installation restrictions in Section 250-92(a).

Exception: Interlocked equipment, plugs, receptacles, and connectors that preclude energization without grounding continuity.

(b) Switches. No automatic cutout or switch shall be placed in the equipment grounding conductor of a premises wiring system.

Exception: Where the opening of the cutout or switch disconnects all sources of energy.

Figure 250-41. *Shown is one example of the various sizes of enclosing metal conduits used as equipment grounding conductors as they apply to a service and feeder system.*

Enclosing conduits are suitable for equipment grounding purposes, see Sections 250-57(a), 250-91(b) and 250-95

Feeders

3 No. 1, 1¼ in.
3 No. 1, 1¼ in.
3 No. 2/0, 1½ in.

3 No. 6, 1 in.
3 No. 3, 1¼ in.

120/240-V service conductors 500 kcmil

400 A Fused/service disconnecting means

175A 125A 125A
Feeder distribution panelboard No. 1

100A   60A
Feeder distribution panelboard No. 2

2½-in. conduit

2-in. conduit

Grounding electrode conductor, No. 1/0 copper based on 500 kcmil service conductors, see Table 250-94

Main feeder 3 500 kcmil 3-in. conduit

Auxiliary gutter

K. Grounding Conductor Connections

250-112. To Grounding Electrode. The connection of a grounding electrode conductor to a grounding electrode shall be accessible and made in a manner that will assure a permanent and effective ground. Where necessary to assure this for a metal piping system used as a grounding electrode, effective bonding shall be provided around insulated joints and sections and around any equipment that is likely to be disconnected for repairs or replacement. Bonding conductors shall be of sufficient length to permit removal of such equipment while retaining the integrity of the bond.

A water meter is typical of equipment likely to be disconnected for repairs or replacement.

Exception: An encased or buried connection to a concrete-encased, driven, or buried grounding electrode shall not be required to be accessible.

Where the exposed portion of an encased, driven, or buried electrode is used for the termination of a grounding electrode conductor, the connection between them is required to be accessible. However, if the connection is buried or encased, it is not required to be accessible. Note that ground clamps and other connectors that are suitable for use where buried in earth or embedded in concrete are identified for such use, either by a marking on the connector or by a tag attached to the connector.

See Figures 250-32 and 250-34.

250-113. To Conductors and Equipment. Grounding conductors and bonding jumpers shall be connected by exothermic welding, listed pressure connectors, listed clamps, or other listed means. Connection devices or fittings that depend solely on solder shall not be used.

See Figures 250-24 through 250-27.

250-114. Continuity and Attachment of Branch-Circuit Equipment Grounding Conductors to Boxes. Where more than one equipment grounding conductor enters a box, all such conductors shall be spliced or joined within the box or to the box with devices suitable for the use. Connections depending solely on solder shall not be used. Splices shall be made in accordance with Section 110-14(b) except that insulation shall not be required. The arrangement of grounding connections shall be such that the disconnection or the removal of a receptacle, fixture, or other device fed from the box will not interfere with or interrupt the grounding continuity.

This section permits either of two arrangements for the termination of equipment grounding conductors. The first is shown in Figure 250-43. The second arrangement is for each equipment grounding conductor to terminate under separate ground clips such as the one shown in Figure 250-42 or under a separate grounding screw such as shown in Figure 250-44. Metal outlet or device boxes provided with only one 10-32 tapped hole marked GR are intended for the connection of only one equipment grounding conductor.

Figure 250-42. A clip used to connect a copper grounding conductor to a box.

Exception: The equipment grounding conductor permitted in Section 250-74, Exception No. 4 shall not be required to be connected to the other equipment grounding conductors or to the box.

(a) **Metal Boxes.** A connection shall be made between the one or more equipment grounding conductors and a metal box by means of a grounding screw that shall be used for no other purpose, or a listed grounding device.

(b) **Nonmetallic Boxes.** One or more equipment grounding conductors brought into a nonmetallic outlet box shall be so arranged that a connection can be made to any fitting or device in that box requiring grounding.

250-115. **Connection to Electrodes.** The grounding conductor shall be connected to the grounding electrode by exothermic welding, listed lugs, listed pressure connectors, listed clamps, or other listed means. Connections depending on solder shall not be used. Ground clamps shall be listed for the materials of the grounding electrode and the grounding electrode conductor and, where used on pipe, rod, or other buried electrodes, shall also be listed for direct soil burial. Not more than one conductor shall be connected to the grounding electrode by a single clamp or fitting unless the clamp or fitting is listed for multiple conductors. One of the methods indicated in (a), (b), (c), or (d) below shall be used.

Figure 250-43. An application of a grounding clip.

Figure 250-44. Grounding conductors may be attached to a box by a variety of methods, such as with a screw, as shown here, or with a grounding clip as shown in Figure 250-42.

Consideration should be given to the suitability of ground clamps for direct soil burial when used on ground rod or pipe electrodes or other buried electrodes. See commentary following Section 250-112, Exception.

Where a ground clamp is used and terminates on a galvanized water pipe, for example, it is required to be of material that is compatible with steel so as to prevent corrosion. The same type of compatability requirement applies to ground clamps on copper water pipe.

See Section 250-83(c)(3) for rod and pipe electrode installation requirements.

Figure 250-45. A listed ground clamp generally used with No. 8 through No. 4 grounding electrode conductors. Exothermic welds are also acceptable. Kits are commercially available for this purpose.

Figure 250-46. Listed U-bolt ground clamps are available for all pipe sizes and all grounding electrode conductor sizes. Where grounding electrode conductors are run in conduits, conduit hubs may be bolted to the threaded portion of the U-bolt.

(a) **Bolted Clamp.** A listed bolted clamp of cast bronze or brass, or plain or malleable iron.

(b) **Pipe Fitting, Pipe Plug, etc.** A pipe fitting, pipe plug, or other approved device screwed into a pipe or pipe fitting.

(c) **Sheet-Metal-Strap Type Ground Clamp.** A listed sheet-metal-strap type ground clamp having a rigid metal base that seats on the electrode and having a strap of such material and dimensions that it is not likely to stretch during or after installation.

(d) **Other Means.** An equally substantial approved means.

250-117. **Protection of Attachment.** Ground clamps or other fittings shall be approved for general use without protection or shall be protected from ordinary physical damage as indicated in (a) or (b) below.

(a) **Not Likely to Be Damaged.** Installations where they are not likely to be damaged.

(b) **Protective Covering.** Enclosing in metal, wood, or equivalent protective covering.

250-118. **Clean Surfaces.** Nonconductive coatings (such as paint, lacquer, and enamel) on equipment to be grounded shall be removed from threads and other contact surfaces to assure good electrical continuity or be connected by means of fittings so designed as to make such removal unnecessary.

250-119. **Identification of Wiring Device Terminals.** The terminal for the connection of the equipment grounding conductor shall be identified by (1) a green-colored, not readily removable terminal screw with a hexagonal head; (2) a green-colored, hexagonal, not readily removable terminal nut; or (3) a green-colored pressure wire connector. If the terminal for the grounding conductor is not visible, the conductor entrance hole shall be marked with the word "green" or otherwise identified by a distinctive green color.

L. Instrument Transformers, Relays, Etc.

250-121. **Instrument Transformer Circuits.** Secondary circuits of current and potential instrument transformers shall be grounded where the primary windings are connected to circuits of 300 volts or more to ground and, where on switchboards, shall be grounded irrespective of voltage.

Exception: Circuits where the primary windings are connected to circuits of less than 1000 volts with no live parts or wiring exposed or accessible to other than qualified persons.

250-122. **Instrument Transformer Cases.** Cases or frames of instrument transformers shall be grounded where accessible to other than qualified persons.

Exception: Cases or frames of current transformers, the primaries of which are not over 150 volts to ground and that are used exclusively to supply current to meters.

250-123. Cases of Instruments, Meters, and Relays — Operating at Less than 1000 Volts. Instruments, meters, and relays operating with windings or working parts at less than 1000 volts shall be grounded as specified in (a), (b), or (c) below.

(a) Not on Switchboards. Instruments, meters, and relays not located on switchboards, operating with windings or working parts at 300 volts or more to ground, and accessible to other than qualified persons, shall have the cases and other exposed metal parts grounded.

(b) On Dead-Front Switchboards. Instruments, meters, and relays (whether operated from current and potential transformers or connected directly in the circuit) on switchboards having no live parts on the front of the panels shall have the cases grounded.

(c) On Live-Front Switchboards. Instruments, meters, and relays (whether operated from current and potential transformers or connected directly in the circuit) on switchboards having exposed live parts on the front of panels shall not have their cases grounded. Mats of insulating rubber or other suitable floor insulation shall be provided for the operator where the voltage to ground exceeds 150.

250-124. Cases of Instruments, Meters, and Relays — Operating Voltage 1 kV and Over. Where instruments, meters, and relays have current-carrying parts of 1 kV and over to ground, they shall be isolated by elevation or protected by suitable barriers, grounded metal, or insulating covers or guards. Their cases shall not be grounded.

Exception: Cases of electrostatic ground detectors where the internal ground segments of the instrument are connected to the instrument case and grounded and the ground detector is isolated by elevation.

250-125. Instrument Grounding Conductor. The grounding conductor for secondary circuits of instrument transformers and for instrument cases shall not be smaller than No. 12 copper or No. 10 aluminum. Cases of instrument transformers, instruments, meters, and relays that are mounted directly on grounded metal surfaces of enclosures or grounded metal switchboard panels shall be considered to be grounded, and no additional grounding conductor shall be required.

M. Grounding of Systems and Circuits of 1 kV and Over (High Voltage)

250-150. General. Where high-voltage systems are grounded, they shall comply with all applicable provisions of the preceding sections of this article and with the following sections, which supplement and modify the preceding sections.

250-151. Derived Neutral Systems. A system neutral derived from a grounding transformer shall be permitted to be used for grounding high-voltage systems.

250-152. Solidly Grounded Neutral Systems.

(a) Neutral Conductor. The minimum insulation level for neutral conductors of solidly grounded systems shall be 600 volts.

Exception No. 1: Bare copper conductors shall be permitted to be used for the neutral of service entrances and the neutral of direct buried portions of feeders.

Exception No. 2: Bare conductors shall be permitted for the neutral of overhead portions installed outdoors.

(FPN): See Section 225-4 for conductor covering where within 10 feet (3.05 m) of any building or other structure.

(b) Multiple Grounding. The neutral of a solidly grounded neutral system shall be permitted to be grounded at more than one point for:

(1) Services.
(2) Direct buried portions of feeders employing a bare copper neutral.
(3) Overhead portion installed outdoors.

(c) Neutral Grounding Conductor. The neutral grounding conductor shall be permitted to be a bare conductor if isolated from phase conductors and protected from physical damage.

250-153. Impedance Grounded Neutral Systems. Impedance grounded neutral systems shall comply with the provisions of (a) through (d) below.

(a) Location. The grounding impedance shall be inserted in the grounding conductor between the grounding electrode of the supply system and the neutral point of the supply transformer or generator.

(b) Identified and Insulated. Where the neutral conductor of an impedance grounded neutral system is used, it shall be identified, as well as fully insulated with the same insulation as the phase conductors.

(c) System Neutral Connection. The system neutral shall not be connected to ground, except through the neutral grounding impedance.

(d) Equipment Grounding Conductors. Equipment grounding conductors shall be permitted to be bare and shall be connected to the ground bus and grounding electrode conductor at the service-entrance equipment and extended to the system ground.

250-154. Grounding of Systems Supplying Portable or Mobile Equipment. Systems supplying portable or mobile high-voltage equipment, other than substations installed on a temporary basis, shall comply with (a) through (f) below.

"Portable" describes equipment that is easily carried, while "mobile" describes equipment that is easily moved, as on wheels, treads, etc.

(a) Portable or Mobile Equipment. Portable or mobile high-voltage equipment shall be supplied from a system having its neutral grounded through an impedance. Where a delta-connected high-voltage system is used to supply portable or mobile equipment, a system neutral shall be derived.

(b) Exposed Noncurrent-Carrying Metal Parts. Exposed noncurrent-carrying metal parts of portable or mobile equipment shall be connected by an equipment grounding conductor to the point at which the system neutral impedance is grounded.

(c) Ground-Fault Current. The voltage developed between the portable or mobile equipment frame and ground by the flow of maximum ground-fault current shall not exceed 100 volts.

(d) Ground-Fault Detection and Relaying. Ground-fault detection and relaying shall be provided to automatically deenergize any high-voltage system component that has developed a ground fault. The continuity of the equipment grounding conductor shall be continuously monitored so as to deenergize automatically the high-voltage feeder to the portable or mobile equipment upon loss of continuity of the equipment grounding conductor.

(e) Isolation. The grounding electrode to which the portable or mobile equipment system neutral impedance is connected shall be isolated from and separated in the ground by at least 20 feet (6.1 m) from any other system or equipment grounding electrode, and there shall be no direct connection between the grounding electrodes, such as buried pipe, fence, etc.

(f) Trailing Cable and Couplers. High-voltage trailing cable and couplers for interconnection of portable or mobile equipment shall meet the requirements of Part C of Article 400 for cables and Section 710-45 for couplers.

250-155. Grounding of Equipment. All noncurrent-carrying metal parts of fixed, portable, and mobile equipment and associated fences, housings, enclosures, and supporting structures shall be grounded.

Exception No. 1: Where isolated from ground and located so as to prevent any person who can make contact with ground from contacting such metal parts when the equipment is energized.

Exception No. 2: Pole-mounted distribution apparatus as provided in Section 250-42, Exception No. 3.

Grounding conductors not an integral part of a cable assembly shall not be smaller than No. 6 copper or No. 4 aluminum.

ARTICLE 280   Surge Arresters

Contents

A. General

B. Installation

C. Connecting Surge Arresters

280-23. Circuits of 1 kV and Over — Surge-Arrester Conductors.

280-24. Circuits of 1 kV and Over — Interconnections.
  (a) Metallic Interconnections.
  (b) Through Spark Gap or Device.
  (c) By Special Permission.

280-25. Grounding.

Voltage surges with peaks of several thousand volts, even on 120-V circuits, are not uncommon. These surges occur because of induced voltages in power and transmission lines resulting from lightning strikes in the vicinity of the line. They also occur as a result of switching inductive circuits on the premises. Surge arresters for installation as part of an electric service and for use with cord- and plug-connected solid-state electronic equipment are commercially available. See Figures 280-1 and 280-2.

Figure 280-1. *Lightning surge protector for service-entrance installation.*

This device is suitable for mounting in a panel knockout. (*General Electric Co.*)

A. General

280-1. **Scope.** This article covers general requirements, installation requirements, and connection requirements for surge arresters installed on premises wiring systems.

Figure 280-2. *Voltage spike protector suitable for use with 120-V cord- and plug-connected electronic equipment such as TV sets, small computers, medical equipment, and electronic organs. (General Electric Co.)*

280-2. **Definition.** A surge arrester is a protective device for limiting surge voltages by discharging or bypassing surge current, and it also prevents continued flow of follow current while remaining capable of repeating these functions.

280-3. **Number Required.** Where used at a point on a circuit, a surge arrester shall be connected to each ungrounded conductor. A single installation of such surge arresters shall be permitted to protect a number of interconnected circuits provided that no circuit is exposed to surges while disconnected from the surge arresters.

Means are required to be provided for protection of circuits that may be disconnected from the generating station bus. A switch with double-throw action used to disconnect the outside circuits from the station generator and alternatively connect these circuits to ground would satisfy the condition of a single set of arresters protecting more than one circuit.

280-4. **Surge Arrester Selection.**

  (a) On Circuits of Less than 1000 Volts. The rating of the surge arrester shall be equal to or greater than the maximum continuous phase-to-ground power frequency voltage available at the point of application.

(b) On Circuits of 1 kV and Over — Silicon Carbide Types. The rating of a silicon carbide-type surge arrester shall be not less than 125 percent of the maximum continuous phase-to-ground voltage available at the point of application.

(FPN No. 1): For further information on surge arresters, see Guide for the Application of Gapped Silicon—Carbide Surge Arresters for Alternating-Current Systems, C62.2-1988, and Standard for Metal Oxide Surge Arresters for Alternating-Current Power Circuits, ANSI/IEEE C62.11-1986.

(FPN No. 2): The selection of a properly rated metal oxide arrester is based on considerations of maximum continuous operating voltage and the magnitude and duration of overvoltages at the arrester location as affected by phase-to-ground faults, system grounding techniques, switching surges, and other causes. See manufacturer's application rules for selection of the specific arrester to be used at a particular location.

B. Installation

280-11. **Location.** Surge arresters shall be permitted to be located indoors or outdoors and shall be made inaccessible to unqualified persons.

Maximum protection is achieved where the surge protective device is located as close as practical to the equipment to be protected. When a surge passes through an arrester, a wave is reflected in both directions on the conductors connected to the surge arrester. The magnitude of the reflected wave will increase as the distance from the arrester increases. Where the length of the conductor between the protected equipment and the surge arrester is short, the magnitude of the wave reflected through the equipment is minimized.

Exception: Surge arresters listed for installation in accessible locations.

See Figures 280-1 and 280-2 for examples of surge arresters listed for installation in accessible locations.

280-12. **Routing of Surge Arrester Connections.** The conductor used to connect the surge arrester to line or bus and to ground shall not be any longer than necessary and shall avoid unnecessary bends.

Arrester conductors should be as short and be run as straight as practicable, avoiding any sharp bends and turns

that would increase the impedance. High-frequency currents, such as those common to lightning discharges, tend to reduce the effectiveness of a grounding conductor.

C. Connecting Surge Arresters

280-21. **Installed at Services of Less than 1000 Volts.** Line and ground connecting conductors shall not be smaller than No. 14 copper or No. 12 aluminum. The arrester grounding conductor shall be connected to one of the following: (1) the grounded service conductor; (2) the grounding electrode conductor; (3) the grounding electrode for the service; or (4) the equipment grounding terminal in the service equipment.

Single-phase or 3-phase grounded or ungrounded services are permitted to have the surge arrester grounded to the equipment grounding terminal in the service equipment. Figure 280-3 shows three methods of grounding the ground terminals of surge arresters at service entrances.

280-22. **Installed on the Load Side Services of Less than 1000 Volts.** Line and ground connecting conductors shall not be smaller than No. 14 copper or No. 12 aluminum. A surge arrester shall be permitted to be connected between any two conductors (ungrounded conductor(s), grounded conductor, grounding conductor). The grounded conductor and the grounding conductor shall be interconnected only by the normal operation of the surge arrester during a surge.

280-23. **Circuits of 1 kV and Over — Surge-Arrester Conductors.** The conductor between the surge arrester and the line and surge arrester and the grounding connection shall not be smaller than No. 6 copper or aluminum.

280-24. **Circuits of 1 kV and Over — Interconnections.** The grounding conductor of a surge arrester protecting a transformer that supplies a secondary distribution system shall be interconnected as specified in (a), (b), or (c) below.

(a) Metallic Interconnections. A metallic interconnection shall be made to the secondary grounded circuit conductor or the secondary circuit grounding conductor provided that, in addition to the direct grounding connection at the surge arrester:

Figure 280-3. *Three locations of grounding surge arresters at service entrances. Top, arrester connected to neutral service conductor; middle, arrester connected to a grounding electrode conductor; and bottom, arrester connected to a grounding electrode conductor of an ungrounded system.*

(1) The grounded conductor of the secondary has elsewhere a grounding connection to a continuous metal underground water piping system. However, in urban water-pipe areas where there are at least four water-pipe connections on the neutral and not fewer than four such connections in each mile of neutral, the metallic interconnection shall be permitted to be made to the secondary neutral with omission of the direct grounding connection at the surge arrester.

(2) The grounded conductor of the secondary system is a part of a multiground neutral system of which the primary neutral has at least four ground connections in each mile of line in addition to a ground at each service.

(b) Through Spark Gap or Device. Where the surge arrester grounding conductor is not connected as in (a) above or where the secondary is not grounded as in (a) above but is otherwise grounded as in Sections 250-81 and 250-83, an interconnection shall be made through a spark gap or listed device as follows:

(1) For ungrounded or unigrounded primary systems, the spark gap or listed device shall have a 60-hertz breakdown voltage of at least twice the primary circuit voltage but not necessarily more than 10 kV, and there shall be at least one other ground on the grounded conductor of the secondary not less than 20 feet (6.1 m) distant from the surge arrester grounding electrode.

(2) For multigrounded neutral primary systems, the spark gap or listed device shall have a 60-hertz breakdown or not more than 3 kV, and there shall be at least one other ground on the grounded conductor of the secondary not less than 20 feet (6.1 m) distant from the surge arrester grounding electrode.

(c) By Special Permission. An interconnection of the surge arrester ground and the secondary neutral, other than as provided in (a) or (b) above, shall be permitted to be made only by special permission.

280-25. **Grounding.** Except as indicated in this article, surge arrester grounding connections shall be made as specified in Article 250. Grounding conductors shall not be run in metal enclosures unless bonded to both ends of such enclosure.

3

Wiring Methods and Materials

ARTICLE 300   Wiring Methods

Contents

A. General Requirements

300-11. Securing and Supporting.
  (a) Secured in Place.
  (b) Raceways Used as Means of Support.
300-12. Mechanical Continuity — Raceways and Cables.
300-13. Mechanical and Electrical Continuity —
Conductors.
  (a) General.
  (b) Device Removal.
300-14. Length of Free Conductors at Outlets, Junctions,
and Switch Points.
300-15. Boxes or Fittings — Where Required.
  (a) Box or Fitting.
  (b) Box Only.
  (c) Fittings and Connectors.
  (d) Equipment.
300-16. Raceway or Cable to Open or Concealed Wiring.
  (a) Box or Fitting.
  (b) Bushing.
300-17. Number and Size of Conductors in Raceway.
300-18. Raceway Installations.
300-19. Supporting Conductors in Vertical Raceways.
  (a) Spacing Intervals — Maximum.
  (b) Support Methods.
300-20. Induced Currents in Metal Enclosures or Metal
Raceways.
  (a) Conductors Grouped Together.
  (b) Individual Conductors.
300-21. Spread of Fire or Products of Combustion.
300-22. Wiring in Ducts, Plenums, and Other
Air-Handling Spaces.
  (a) Ducts for Dust, Loose Stock, or Vapor Removal.
  (b) Ducts or Plenums Used for Environmental Air.
  (c) Other Space Used for Environmental Air.
  (d) Data Processing Systems.
300-23. Panels Designed to Allow Access.

B. Requirements for Over 600 Volts, Nominal

300-31. Covers Required.
300-32. Conductors of Different Systems.
300-34. Conductor Bending Radius.
300-35. Protection Against Induction Heating.
300-36. Grounding.
300-37. Underground Installations.

A. General Requirements

300-1. Scope.

(a) All Wiring Installations. This article covers wiring methods for all wiring installations.

Exception No. 1: As permitted in Article 504, Intrinsically Safe Systems.

Exception No. 2: Only those sections referenced in Article 725 shall apply to Class 1, Class 2, and Class 3 circuits.

Exception No. 3: Only those sections referenced in Article 760 shall apply to fire protective signaling circuits.

Exception No. 4: Only those sections referenced in Article 770 shall apply to optical fiber cables.

Exception No. 5: Only those sections referenced in Article 800 shall apply to communications systems.

Exception No. 6: Only those sections referenced in Article 810 shall apply to radio and television equipment.

Exception No. 7: Only those sections referenced in Article 820 shall apply to community antenna television and radio distribution systems.

The seven exceptions clearly indicate that Article 300 is not applicable to Articles 504, 725, 760, 770, 800, 810, and 820. For example, the requirement of Section 300-15(a) is not applicable to a power-limited fire protective signaling system wired in accordance with Section 760-28(b)(1), so a box is not necessary at the "outlet" for a heat detector head on such a system. However, certain parts of Article 300 are applicable where they are referenced in Articles 504, 725, 760, 770, 800, 810, and 820. For example, see Sections 725-2(b), 760-2(b), 800-3(b)(3), and 820-15(c), which reference Section 300-22. See also the exceptions to these sections.

(b) Integral Parts of Equipment. The provisions of this article are not intended to apply to the conductors that form an integral part of equipment, such as motors, controllers, motor control centers, or factory-assembled control equipment.

See the *Electrical Standard for Industrial Machinery*, NFPA 79-1991 (ANSI).

300-2. **Limitations.**

(a) Voltage. Wiring methods specified in Chapter 3 shall be used for voltages 600 volts, nominal, or less where not specifically limited in some section of Chapter 3. They shall be permitted for voltages over 600 volts, nominal, where specifically permitted elsewhere in this Code.

(b) Temperature. Temperature limitation of conductors shall be in accordance with Section 310-10.

300-3. **Conductors.**

(a) Single Conductors. Single conductors specified in Table 310-13 shall only be permitted to be installed where part of a recognized wiring method of Chapter 3.

This section, in general, prohibits the use of "building wire" such as THHN outside of a raceway.

(b) Conductors of the Same Circuit. All conductors of the same circuit and, where used, the neutral and all equipment grounding conductors shall be contained within the same raceway, cable tray, trench, cable, or cord.

Exception No. 1: The conductors of single-conductor Type MI cable with a nonmagnetic sheath and installed in accordance with Section 330-16 shall be permitted to be run in separate cables.

Section 300-3(b), Exception No. 1 is new in the 1993 *Code.* It recognizes that Type MI cable in the larger sizes is manufactured only as single-conductor cable. This exception now allows such single-conductor Type MI cable to be installed.

A new section 330-16 has been added to Article 330 to address the issue of induced voltages.

Exception No. 2 to (b): Column type panelboards using auxiliary gutters and pull boxes with neutral terminations.

This new exception recognizes the common practice of supplying narrow column-type panelboard through an auxiliary gutter from an overhead pull box and running only the ungrounded conductors down from the pull box to the panelboard. The feeder and branch-circuit neutral conductors are terminated in the overhead pull box and are not carried with the ungrounded conductors. Inductive heating does not occur, since the load-carrying conductors extend down and back up within the same enclosure.

Figure 300-1. *An installation where an auxiliary gutter extends from the panelboard up to a pull box. The pull box is used as a termination point for the feeder and branch-circuit grounded conductors (neutrals).*

Exception No. 3 to (a) and (b): As permitted in Sections 250-57(b), 250-79(f), 300-5(i), 300-20(a), 318-8(d), and 339-3(a)(2).

This exception recognizes that some types of grounding and bonding conductors can be run as single conductors on the exterior of the raceway. For example, see Sections 250-79(f) and 300-5(i).

(c) Conductors of Different Systems.
   (1) 600 Volts, Nominal, or Less. Conductors of 600 volts, nominal, or less, alternating-current circuits, and direct-current circuits shall be permitted to occupy the same equipment wiring enclosure, cable, or raceway. All conductors shall have an insulation rating equal to at least the maximum circuit voltage applied to any conductor within the enclosure, cable, or raceway.

This section makes it clear that it is THE MAXIMUM CIRCUIT VOLTAGE in the raceway, not the maximum insulation voltage rating of the conductors in the raceway, that determines the minimum voltage rating of conductors for systems of 600 V or less.

The conductors of a 3-phase, 4-wire, 208Y/120-V ac circuit; a 3-phase, 4-wire, 480Y/277-V ac circuit; and a 3-wire, 120/240-V dc circuit may occupy the same equipment wiring enclosure, cable, or raceway where all conductors are insulated for the maximum circuit voltage of any conductor. In this case, the maximum circuit voltage would be 480 V, and 600-V insulation would be required for all of the conductors.

Where a 2-wire, 120-V circuit is included in the same raceway with a 3-wire, 120/240-V circuit having 600-V conductors, the 2-wire, 120-V circuit conductors could utilize 300-V insulation because the maximum circuit voltage is only 240V.

Exception: For solar photovoltaic systems in accordance with Section 690-4(b).

Section 690-4(b) prohibits solar photovoltaic circuits to be located within the same enclosure as conductors of other systems, unless the conductors are separated by a partition or are connected together.

(FPN): See Section 725-52(a)(2) for Class 2 and Class 3 circuit conductors.

Section 725-52(a)(2) prohibits Class 2 and Class 3 circuit conductors in the same enclosure, cable, or raceway as Class 1, electric light, and power conductors, with some exceptions.

(2) Over 600 Volts, Nominal. Conductors of circuits rated over 600 volts, nominal, shall not occupy the same equipment wiring enclosure, cable, or raceway with conductors of circuits rated 600 volts, nominal, or less.

(FPN): See Section 300-32, Conductors of Different Systems — over 600 volts, nominal.

Exception No. 1: Secondary wiring to electric-discharge lamps of 1000 volts or less, if insulated for the secondary voltage involved, shall be permitted to occupy the same fixture enclosure as the branch-circuit conductors.

Exception No. 2: Primary leads of electric-discharge lamp ballasts, insulated for the primary voltage of the ballast, where contained within the individual wiring enclosure, shall be permitted to occupy the same fixture enclosure as the branch-circuit conductors.

Exception No. 3: Excitation, control, relay, and ammeter conductors used in connection with any individual motor or starter shall be permitted to occupy the same enclosure as the motor circuit conductors.

300-4. **Protection Against Physical Damage.** Where subject to physical damage, conductors shall be adequately protected.

(a) Cables and Raceways through Wood Members.

(1) Bored Holes. In both exposed and concealed locations, where a cable or raceway-type wiring method is installed through bored holes in joists, rafters, or wood members, holes shall be bored so that the edge of the hole is not less than 1¼ inches (31.8 mm) from the nearest edge of the wood member. Where this distance cannot be maintained, the cable or raceway shall be protected from penetration by screws or nails by a steel plate or bushing, at least ¹⁄₁₆ inch (1.59 mm) thick, and of appropriate length and width installed to cover the area of the wiring.

The intent of this section is to prevent nails from being driven into cables. By keeping the edge of the drilled hole 1¼ inch from the nearest edge of the stud, nails would not be likely to penetrate the stud far enough to injure the cables. The model building codes provide maximum requirements for bored or notched holes in studs, and Section 300-4(a)(2) indicates that consideration should be given to the size of notches in studs so as not to affect the strength of the structure. See Figure 300-2.

Exception: Raceways as covered in Articles 345, 346, 347, and 348.

(2) Notches in Wood. Where there is no objection because of weakening the building structure, in both exposed and concealed locations, cables or raceways shall be permitted to be laid in notches in wood studs, joists, rafters, or other wood members where the cable or raceway at those points is protected against nails or screws by a steel plate at least ¹⁄₁₆ inch (1.59 mm) thick installed before the building finish is applied.

Figure 300-2. Steel plate to protect nonmetallic-sheathed cables within 1¼ inch of the edge of a stud. (RACO)

Exception: Raceways as covered in Articles 345, 346, 347, and 348.

The exceptions to Sections 300-4(a)(1) and 300-4(a)(2) permit intermediate metal conduit, rigid metal conduit, rigid nonmetallic conduit, and electrical metallic tubing to be installed through bored holes or laid in notches less than 1¼ inch from the nearest edge of the stud without a steel plate or bushing.

(b) Nonmetallic-Sheathed Cables and Electrical Nonmetallic Tubing through Metal Framing Members.

(1) Nonmetallic-Sheathed Cable. In both exposed and concealed locations where nonmetallic-sheathed cables pass through either factory or field punched, cut or drilled slots or holes in metal members, the cable shall be protected by bushings or grommets securely fastened in the opening prior to installation of the cable.

(2) Nonmetallic-Sheathed Cable and Electrical Nonmetallic Tubing. Where nails or screws are likely to penetrate nonmetallic-sheathed cable, or electrical nonmetallic tubing, a steel sleeve, steel plate, or steel clip not less than ⅟₁₆ inch (1.59 mm) in thickness shall be used to protect the cable or tubing.

(c) Cables through Spaces Behind Panels Designed to Allow Access. Cables, or raceway-type wiring methods, installed behind panels designed to allow access shall be supported according to their applicable articles.

Cable- or raceway-type wiring methods installed above suspended ceilings with lift-up panels cannot be laid on the suspended ceiling. They are required to be supported according to Section 300-11(a), Section 300-23, and the requirements in the article applicable to the wiring method involved. These support rules do not apply to many low-voltage cable wiring systems, such as most computer, telephone, and cable TV systems. See Section 90-3 and Section 300-1(a), Exception Nos. 1 through 5. However, such low-voltage cables are not permitted to block access to equipment above the suspended ceiling. Examples of this requirement (new in the 1993 *Code*) are found in Sections 725-6 and 760-7.

(d) Cables and Raceways Parallel to Framing Members. In both exposed and concealed locations, where a cable- or raceway-type wiring method is installed parallel to framing members, such as joists, rafters, or studs, the cable or raceway shall be installed and supported so that the nearest outside surface of the cable or raceway is not less than 1¼ inches (31.8 mm) from the nearest edge of the framing member where nails or screws are likely to penetrate. Where this distance cannot be maintained, the cable or raceway shall be protected from penetration by nails or screws by a steel plate, sleeve, or equivalent at least ⅟₁₆ inch (1.59 mm) thick.

Exception No. 1: Raceways as covered in Articles 345, 346, 347, and 348.

This section was new in the 1990 *Code*. The intent is to prevent mechanical damage to cables and raceways from nails. The *Code* offers two means of protection. The first method is to fasten the cable or raceway so that it is 1¼ inches from the edge of the framing member. See Figure 300-3. The second method permits the cable or raceway to be installed closer to the edge of the framing member if physical protection such as a steel plate or a sleeve is provided. The requirement does not apply to rigid metal conduit, rigid nonmetallic conduit, intermediate metal conduit, or electrical metallic tubing wiring methods, as these methods provide physical protection for the conductors.

Figure 300-3. *Parallel installation of cables and raceways and cables in accordance with Section 300-4(d). This requirement generally applies to exposed and concealed work. The cables can be installed closer than 1¼ inches from the edge of the framing member if physical protection is provided.*

Exception No. 2: For concealed work in finished buildings, or finished panels for prefabricated buildings where such supporting is impracticable, it shall be permissible to fish the cables between access points.

Exception No. 3: For mobile homes and recreational vehicles.

300-5. Underground Installations.

(a) Minimum Cover Requirements. Direct buried cable or conduit or other raceways shall be installed to meet the minimum cover requirements of Table 300-5.

Conductors under residential driveways must be at least 18 inches below grade. If the conductors are protected by an overcurrent device rated at not more than 20 amperes and provided with ground-fault circuit interrupter protection for personnel, the burial depth may be reduced to 12 inches.

Figure 300-4. *PVC rigid nonmetallic conduit buried in compliance with Section 300-5 and installed in accordance with Section 300-5(a).*

Figure 300-5. *A 20-ampere, GFCI-protected residential branch circuit is permitted to be installed with a minimum burial depth of 12 inches beneath a residential driveway and outdoor parking areas used only for dwelling-related purposes.*

(b) Grounding. All underground installations shall be grounded and bonded in accordance with Article 250 of this Code.

Where rigid nonmetallic conduit elbows are installed in long runs, they are often damaged in the process of pulling the conductors due to friction at the bend. A new

Table 300-5. Minimum Cover Requirements, 0 to 600 Volts, Nominal, Burial in Inches (Cover is defined as the shortest distance measured between a point on the top surface of any direct buried conductor, cable, conduit, or other raceway and the top surface of finished grade, concrete, or similar cover.)

| Location of Wiring Method or Circuit | Type of Wiring Method or Circuit | | | | |
	1 Direct Burial Cables or Conductors	2 Rigid Metal Conduit or Intermediate Metal Conduit	3 Nonmetallic Raceways Listed for Direct Burial without Concrete Encasement or Other Approved Raceways	4 Residential Branch Circuits Rated 120 Volts or less with GFCI Protection and Maximum Overcurrent Protection of 20 Amperes	5 Circuits for Control of Irrigation and Landscape Lighting Limited to Not More than 30 Volts and Installed with Type UF or in Other Identified Cable or Raceway
All Locations Not Specified Below	24	6	18	12	6
In Trench Below 2-Inch Thick Concrete or Equivalent	18	6	12	6	6
Under a Building	0 (In Raceway Only)	0	0	0 (In Raceway Only)	0 (In Raceway Only)
Under Minimum of 4-Inch Thick Concrete Exterior Slab with No Vehicular Traffic and the Slab Extending Not Less than 6 Inches beyond the Underground Installation	18	4	4	6 (Direct Burial) 4 (In Raceway)	6 (Direct Burial) 4 (In Raceway)
Under Streets, Highways, Roads, Alleys, Driveways, and Parking Lots	24	24	24	24	24
One- and Two-Family Dwelling Driveways and Outdoor Parking Areas, and Used Only for Dwelling-Related Purposes	18	18	18	12	18
In or under Airport Runways, Including Adjacent Areas Where Trespassing Prohibited	18	18	18	18	18
In Solid Rock Where Covered by Minimum of 2 Inches Concrete Extending Down to Rock	2 (In Raceway Only)	2	2	2 (In Raceway Only)	2 (In Raceway Only)

Note 1. For SI units: one inch = 25.4 millimeters.
Note 2. Raceways approved for burial only where concrete encased shall require concrete envelope not less than 2 inches thick.
Note 3. Lesser depths shall be permitted where cables and conductors rise for terminations or splices or where access is otherwise required.
Note 4. Where one of the wiring method types listed in columns 1-3 is combined with one of the circuit types in columns 4 and 5, the shallower depth of burial shall be permitted.

Figure 300-6. *A new exception in the 1993 Code permits the metal elbow to be ungrounded provided it is isolated from possible contact by a minimum cover of 18 inches to any part of the elbow.*

exception in Article 250 permits a metal elbow to be installed without being grounded, provided it is isolated from contact by at least 18 inches of cover.

See Exception to Section 250-32.

(c) Underground Cables Under Buildings. Underground cable installed under a building shall be in a raceway that is extended beyond the outside walls of the building.

(d) Protection from Damage. Direct buried conductors and cables emerging from the ground shall be protected by enclosures or raceways extending from the minimum cover distance required by Section 300-5(a) below grade to a point at least 8 feet (2.44 m) above finished grade. In no case shall the protection be required to exceed 18 inches (457 mm) below finished grade.

Conductors entering a building shall be protected to the point of entrance.

Where the enclosure or raceway is subject to physical damage, the conductors shall be installed in rigid metal conduit, intermediate metal conduit, Schedule 80 rigid nonmetallic conduit, or equivalent.

(e) Splices and Taps. Direct buried conductors or cables shall be permitted to be spliced or tapped without the use of splice boxes. The splices or taps shall be made by approved methods and with identified materials.

Electrical splicing kit for single conductor direct buried cables
(King Technology Inc.)

Figure 300-7. *Examples of underground splicing methods.*

(f) Backfill. Backfill containing large rock, paving materials, cinders, large or sharply angular substance, or corrosive material shall not be placed in an excavation where materials may damage raceways, cables, or other substructures or prevent adequate compaction of fill or contribute to corrosion of raceways, cables, or other substructures.

Where necessary to prevent physical damage to the raceway or cable, protection shall be provided in the form of granular or selected material, suitable running boards, suitable sleeves, or other approved means.

(g) Raceway Seals. Conduits or raceways through which moisture may contact energized live parts shall be sealed or plugged at either or both ends.

(FPN): Presence of hazardous gases or vapors may also necessitate sealing of underground conduits or raceways entering buildings.

Figure 300-8. Conduit sealing bushing used to prevent the entrance of gas or moisture. See Section 230-8 for sealing service raceways. (O.Z./Gedney Co.)

(h) Bushing. A bushing, or terminal fitting, with an integral bushed opening shall be used at the end of a conduit or other raceway that terminates underground where the conductors or cables emerge as a direct burial wiring method. A seal incorporating the physical protection characteristics of a bushing shall be permitted to be used in lieu of a bushing.

(i) Single Conductors. All conductors of the same circuit and, where used, the neutral and all equipment grounding conductors shall be installed in the same raceway or shall be installed in close proximity in the same trench.

Exception No. 1: Conductors in parallel in raceways shall be permitted, but each raceway shall contain all conductors of the same circuit including grounding conductors.

This exception permits the installation of paralleled conductors in different raceways. See Section 310-4 for more information.

Exception No. 2: Isolated phase installations shall be permitted in nonmetallic raceways in close proximity where conductors are paralleled as permitted in Section 310-4 and the conditions of Section 300-20 are met.

Isolated phase installations are those in which there is only one phase per raceway. There may be some advantages to

Figure 300-9. Type UF cable buried in compliance with Table 300-5. Note the protective bushing where the cable is used with metal conduit.

such an installation, where there are many large conductors in parallel, as it avoids crossing conductors in the close quarters of the termination compartment of a switchboard or in unit substation and transformer enclosures. The spacing between isolated phase raceways should be as small as possible and the length of the run limited in order to avoid the increased circuit impedance and resulting increase in voltage drop inherent in an installation involving alternating-current circuits.

Isolated phase installations present an inherent hazard of overheating that must be understood and carefully controlled. This hazard is a result of induced currents in metal surrounding a raceway with only one phase in the raceway. See Sections 300-20(a) and 300-20(b). The surrounding metal acts as a shorted transformer turn. In underground installations it is unlikely that metal will surround a single raceway or that there will be a fire hazard even if this situation exists. This is not true, however, for aboveground raceways, and it is the reason isolated phase installations are not permitted aboveground.

See Sections 300-3(b), Exception No. 1 and 330-16, which recognize single-conductor MI cable.

300-6. **Protection Against Corrosion.** Metal raceways, cable armor, boxes, cable sheathing, cabinets, elbows, couplings, fittings, supports, and support hardware shall be of materials suitable for the environment in which they are to be installed.

(a) General. Ferrous raceways, cable armor, boxes, cable sheathing, cabinets, metal elbows, couplings, fittings, supports, and support hardware shall be suitably protected against corrosion inside and outside (except threads at joints) by a coating of approved corrosion-resistant material such as zinc, cadmium, or enamel. Where protected from corrosion solely by enamel, they shall not be used out-of-doors or in wet locations as described in (c) below. Where boxes or cabinets have an approved system of organic coatings and are marked "Raintight," "Rainproof" or "Outdoor Type," they shall be permitted out-of-doors.

Exception: Threads at joints shall be permitted to be coated with an identified electrically conductive compound.

Zinc chromate paste is one type of electrically conductive compound that can be used.

(b) In Concrete or in Direct Contact with the Earth. Ferrous or nonferrous metal raceways, cable armor, boxes, cable sheathing, cabinets, elbows, couplings, fittings, supports, and support hardware shall be permitted to be installed in concrete or in direct contact with the earth, or in areas subject to severe corrosive influences where made of material judged suitable for the condition, or where provided with corrosion protection approved for the condition.

Section 300-6 applies generally. For specific applications, see the particular article covering the various cables, raceways, or enclosures.

(c) Indoor Wet Locations. In portions of dairies, laundries, canneries, and other indoor wet locations, and in locations where walls are frequently washed or where there are surfaces of absorbent materials, such as damp paper or wood, the entire wiring system, where installed exposed, including all boxes, fittings, conduits, and cable used therewith, shall be mounted so that there is at least ¼-inch (6.35-mm) air space between it and the wall or supporting surface.

Exception: Nonmetallic raceways, boxes, and fittings shall be permitted to be installed without the airspace on a concrete, masonry, tile, or similar surface.

This exception is in harmony with Section 547-4, permitting nonmetallic boxes, fittings, conduit, and cables to be installed without the airspace in corrosive locations of agricultural buildings.

(FPN): In general, areas where acids and alkali chemicals are handled and stored may present such corrosive conditions, particularly when wet or damp. Severe corrosive conditions may also be present in portions of meat-packing plants, tanneries, glue houses, and some stables; installations immediately adjacent to a seashore and swimming pool areas; areas where chemical de-icers are used; and storage cellars or rooms for hides, casings, fertilizer, salt, and bulk chemicals.

Ferrous or nonferrous metal conduit may be installed in concrete, in contact with the earth, or in areas exposed to severe corrosive influences where it has corrosion protection and is judged suitable for the condition. Special precautions are normally necessary for installing aluminum conduits in concrete, and specific approval by the authority having jurisdiction may be necessary.

To help avoid deterioration, metal raceways installed in the earth can be coated with an asphalt compound, plastic sheath, or other equivalent protection.

Galvanized rigid steel conduit and steel intermediate metal conduit do not generally require supplementary corrosion protection.

300-7. Raceways Exposed to Different Temperatures.

(a) **Sealing.** Where portions of an interior raceway system are exposed to widely different temperatures, as in refrigerating or cold-storage plants, circulation of air from a warmer to a colder section through the raceway shall be prevented.

Where a raceway is used to enclose the lighting and refrigeration branch-circuit conductors within a walk-in chest, for example, the circulation of air through the raceway from a warmer to a colder section would cause condensation within the raceway. This can be prevented by sealing the raceway with a suitable, pliable compound at a conduit body or junction box, usually installed in the raceway before it enters the colder section. Special sealing fittings, such as those used in hazardous (classified) locations, are not necessary.

(b) **Expansion Joints.** Raceways shall be provided with expansion joints where necessary to compensate for thermal expansion and contraction.

300-8. Installation of Conductors with Other Systems.

Raceways or cable trays containing electric conductors shall not contain any pipe, tube, or equal for steam, water, air, gas, drainage, or any service other than electrical.

Section 300-8 specifically prohibits installation of an electrical conductor in a raceway or cable tray that includes a drain, water, or air pipe, etc. See fine print note for definition of "raceway" in Article 100. This section does not apply to those conductors that Section 300-1 exempts from the requirements of Article 300.

300-9. Grounding Metal Enclosures.

Metal raceways, boxes, cabinets, cable armor, and fittings shall be grounded as required in Article 250.

300-10. Electrical Continuity of Metal Raceways and Enclosures.

Metal raceways, cable armor, and other metal enclosures for conductors shall be metallically joined together into a continuous electric conductor and shall be so connected to all boxes, fittings, and cabinets as to provide effective electrical continuity. Raceways and cable assemblies shall be mechanically secured to boxes, fittings, cabinets, and other enclosures.

Section 250-51 requires that metal raceways; metal armor or sheaths of cable; metal outlet or junction boxes; and fittings, such as connectors, couplings, locknuts, bushings, etc., must form an effective low-impedance path to ground to conduct safely any fault current and facilitate the operation of overcurrent devices protecting the enclosed circuit conductors.

Exception No. 1: As provided in Section 370-17(c) for nonmetallic boxes.

Exception No. 2: As provided in Section 250-33, Exception No. 2 for metal enclosures.

Exception No. 3: As provided in Section 250-75, Exception where permitted for reduction of electrical noise.

300-11. Securing and Supporting.

(a) **Secured in Place.** Raceways, cable assemblies, boxes, cabinets, and fittings shall be securely fastened in place. Support wires that do not provide secure support shall not be permitted as the sole support.

Branch-circuit wiring associated with equipment that is located within, supported by, or secured to a fire-rated floor or roof/ceiling assembly shall not be secured to the ceiling support wires.

Branch-circuit wiring associated with equipment that is located within, supported by, or secured to a non-fire-rated floor or roof/ceiling assembly shall be permitted to be supported by the ceiling support wires.

Exception: As permitted elsewhere in this Code.

This section makes it clear that support wires, such as those used to hang suspended ceilings, may be used for the support of branch-circuit wiring that supplies equipment located within, supported by, or secured to a suspended ceiling, provided the support wires are not part of a fire-rated ceiling assembly. See Figure 300-8. It is not intended to permit other wiring to be supported solely by suspended ceiling support wires.

Fire-rated floor–ceiling assembly

Damper

Electric fixture

A

Non fire–rated ceiling

B

Figure 300-10. Examples of "fire-rated" and non fire-rated suspended ceilings. See also Sections 300-23 and 370-23(b) and (c). Ceiling support wires of fire-rated floor/ceiling assemblies shown in Figure 300-10A are not permitted to support the branch-circuit wiring supplying the electric fixture.

This section also prohibits the use of ceiling support wires to secure wiring methods, if they do not provide secure support. This is intended to prevent loss of grounding continuity and damage to the wiring raceway or equipment, which could result from frequent movement. See Sections 370-23(b) and (c) for support of outlet boxes.

(b) Raceways Used as Means of Support. Raceways shall not be used as a means of support for other raceways, cables, or nonelectric equipment.

The intent of this section is to prevent cables from being attached to the exterior of a raceway. Cables, such as telephone and computer cables, wrapped around a raceway can prevent the dissipation of heat from the raceway and can affect the temperature of the conductors in the raceway. This section also prevents the use of a raceway to support nonelectric

equipment such as suspended ceilings, water pipes, etc., which could cause a mechanical failure of the raceway.

Exception No. 1: Where the raceways or means of support are identified for the purpose.

(FPN):   See Article 318 for cable trays.

Exception No. 2: Raceways containing power supply conductors for electrically controlled equipment shall be permitted to support Class 2 circuit conductors or cables that are solely for the purpose of connection to the equipment control circuits.

This exception permits, for example, the Class 2 thermostat conductors for a boiler or an air conditioner unit to be supported by the conduit supplying power to the unit. See Figure 300-10.

Figure 300-11. Raceway used to support Class 2 thermostat wires.

Exception No. 3: As permitted in Section 370-23 for boxes or conduit bodies or Section 410-16(f) for fixtures.

300-12. Mechanical Continuity — Raceways and Cables. Metal or nonmetallic raceways, cable armors, and cable sheaths shall be continuous between cabinets, boxes, fittings, or other enclosures or outlets.

Exception: Short sections of raceways used to provide support or protection of cable assemblies from physical damage.

300-13. Mechanical and Electrical Continuity — Conductors.

(a) **General.** Conductors in raceways shall be continuous between outlets, devices, etc., and there shall be no splice or tap within a raceway itself.

Exception No. 1: As provided in Section 374-8 for auxiliary gutters.

Exception No. 2: As provided in Section 362-7 for wireways.

Exception No. 3: As provided in Section 300-15(a), Exception No. 1 for boxes or fittings.

Exception No. 4: As provided in Section 352-7 for surface metal raceways.

Exception No. 5: Busways as covered in Article 364.

Splices or taps are prohibited within raceways, unless the raceways are equipped with hinged or removable covers according to the five exceptions.

(b) **Device Removal.** In multiwire branch circuits, the continuity of a grounded conductor shall not be dependent upon device connections, such as lampholders, receptacles, etc., where the removal of such devices would interrupt the continuity.

Grounded conductors (neutral) of multiwire branch circuits supplying receptacles, lampholders, etc., are not permitted to depend on terminal connections for continuity. For such installations (3- or 4-wire circuits), a splice is made and a jumper is connected to the terminal unless "looped" (see commentary to Section 300-14); that is, a receptacle or lampholder could be replaced without interrupting the continuity of energized downstream line-to-neutral loads. See Figure 370-1. Opening the neutral could cause unbalanced voltages, and a considerably higher voltage would be impressed on one part of a multiwire branch circuit, especially if the downstream line-to-neutral loads are appreciably unbalanced. This requirement does not apply to individual 2-wire circuits or to other circuits that do not contain a grounded (neutral) conductor.

300-14. Length of Free Conductors at Outlets, Junctions, and Switch Points. At least 6 inches (152 mm) of free conductor shall be left at each outlet, junction, and switch point for splices or the connection of fixtures or devices.

Exception: Conductors that are not spliced or terminated at the outlet, junction, or switch point.

A conductor looping through an outlet box and intended for connection to receptacles, switches, lampholders, etc., requires slack so that terminal connections may be made easily.

Conductors running through a box should have sufficient slack to prevent physical damage from the insertion of devices or from the use of fixture studs, hickeys, or other fixture supports within the box.

300-15. Boxes or Fittings — Where Required.

(a) **Box or Fitting.** A box or fitting shall be installed at each conductor splice connection point, outlet, switch point, junction point, or pull point for the connection of conduit, electrical metallic tubing, surface raceway, or other raceways.

Exception No. 1: A box or fitting shall not be required for a conductor splice connection in surface raceways, wireways, header-ducts, multioutlet assemblies, auxiliary gutters, cable trays, and conduit bodies complying with Sections 370-16(c) and 370-28 and having removable covers that are accessible after installation.

Conduit bodies (Types T, L, etc.) are a part of the conduit or tubing system and are not permitted to contain more conductors than permitted for the raceway. Conduit bodies other than short radius type (see Section 370-5) are permitted to contain splices in accordance with Section 370-16(c) provided they have adequate volume in accordance with Section 370-16(b).

Exception No. 2: As permitted in Section 410-31 where a fixture is used as a raceway.

(b) Box Only. A box shall be installed at each conductor splice connection point, outlet, switch point, junction point, or pull point for the connection of Type AC cable, Type MC cable, mineral-insulated, metal-sheathed cable, nonmetallic-sheathed cable, or other cables, at the connection point between any such cable system and a raceway system and at each outlet and switch point for concealed knob-and-tube wiring.

Exception No. 1: Where cables enter or exit from conduit or tubing that is used to provide cable support or protection against physical damage. A fitting shall be provided on the end(s) of the conduit or tubing to protect the wires or cables from abrasion.

Exception No. 1 permits conduit or tubing to be used as support and protection against physical damage without terminating in a box. This exception also permits conduit or tubing to be used as physical protection for underground cables that exit from buildings or that are located outdoors on poles, without a box being required on the end of the conduit. A fitting to protect the wires or cables against physical damage is required on the ends of the conduit or tubing. See Figure 300-9. See Sections 250-32 and 250-33 for grounding requirements.

Exception No. 2: As permitted by Section 336-16 for insulated outlet devices supplied by nonmetallic-sheathed cable.

Exception No. 3: Where accessible fittings are used for straight-through splices in mineral-insulated, metal-sheathed cable.

Exception No. 4: A wiring device with integral enclosure identified for the use having brackets that securely fasten the device to walls or ceilings of conventional on-site frame construction for

use with nonmetallic-sheathed cable shall be permitted without a separate box.

Exception No. 4 applies to a device with an integral enclosure (boxless device).

(FPN): See Sections 336-15, Exception No. 2, 545-10, 550-10(j), and 551-47(e), Exception No. 1.

Exception No. 5: Where metallic manufactured wiring systems are used.

See Article 604, Manufactured Wiring Systems.

Exception No. 6: A conduit body shall be permitted in lieu of a box where installed to comply with Section 370-16(c) and Section 370-28.

Exception No. 7: Where a device identified and listed as suitable for installation without a box is used with a closed-loop power distribution system.

See Article 780, Closed-Loop and Programmed Power Distribution.

Exception No. 8: A fitting identified for the use shall be permitted in lieu of a box where accessible after installation and where the conductors are not spliced or terminated.

This exception permits the use of a fitting instead of a box where a cable system makes a transition to a raceway for the purpose of providing mechanical protection against damage. For example, where nonmetallic-sheathed cable that is run overhead on floor joists and drops down on a concrete wall to supply a receptacle needs to be protected from physical damage, a short length of raceway is installed to the outlet device box. The cable sheath is removed for the length of the raceway, inserted in the raceway, and secured by a combination fitting that is secured to the raceway and also clamps and secures the cable. Section 300-15(c) requires that a proper fitting be used.

(c) Fittings and Connectors. Fittings and connectors shall be used only with the specific wiring methods for which they are designed and listed.

(d) Equipment. An integral junction box or wiring compartment as part of listed equipment shall be permitted at an outlet in lieu of a box.

300-16 . Raceway or Cable to Open or Concealed Wiring.

(a) Box or Fitting. A box or terminal fitting having a separately bushed hole for each conductor shall be used wherever a change is made from conduit, electrical metallic tubing, nonmetallic-sheathed cable, Type AC cable, Type MC cable, or mineral-insulated, metal-sheathed cable and surface raceway wiring to open wiring or to concealed knob-and-tube wiring. A fitting used for this purpose shall contain no taps or splices and shall not be used at fixture outlets.

(b) Bushing. A bushing shall be permitted in lieu of a box or terminal fitting at the end of a conduit or electrical metallic tubing where the raceway terminates behind an open (unenclosed) switchboard or at an unenclosed control and similar equipment. The bushing shall be of the insulating type for other than lead-sheathed conductors.

300-17 . Number and Size of Conductors in Raceway. The number and size of conductors in any raceway shall not be more than will permit dissipation of the heat and ready installation or withdrawal of the conductors without damage to the conductors or to their insulation.

(FPN): See the following sections of this Code: electrical nonmetallic tubing, 331-6; conduit, 345-7 and 346-6; electrical metallic tubing, 348-6; rigid nonmetallic conduit, 347-11; flexible metallic tubing, 349-12; flexible metal conduit, 350-3; liquidtight flexible metal conduit, 351-6; liquidtight nonmetallic flexible conduit, 351-25; surface raceways, 352-4 and 352-25; underfloor raceways, 354-5; cellular metal floor raceways, 356-5; cellular concrete floor raceways, 358-11; wireways, 362-5; auxiliary gutters, 374-5; fixture wire, 402-7; theaters, 520-5; signs, 600-21(d); elevators, 620-33; sound recording, 640-3 and 640-4; Class 1, Class 2, and Class 3 circuits, Article 725; fire protective signaling circuits, Article 760, and optical fiber cables, Article 770.

Listed wire-pulling compounds are available for use to assist in the process of pulling wires into raceways.

300-18 . Raceway Installations. Raceways shall be installed complete between outlet, junction, or splicing points prior to the installation of conductors.

Exception No. 1: Exposed raceways having a removable cover.

Exception No. 2: Where required to facilitate the installation of utilization equipment.

Exception No. 3: Prewired assemblies in accordance with Articles 349 and 350.

One of the primary functions of a raceway is to provide physical protection for conductors. If the raceways are incomplete at the time of installation, there is a greater possibility of damage to the conductors.

Exception No. 2 permits the installation of conductors in a raceway prior to the complete installation of the raceway up to the point of utilization. A typical application of this exception would be a motor installation where the motor is to be supplied through liquidtight flexible metal conduit that will terminate in the motor terminal box through a 90° angle connector. See Figure 300-12.

Figure 300-12. Section 300-18, Exception No. 2 permits conductors to be installed prior to completion of the raceway, such as the conductors supplying a motor through liquidtight flexible metal conduit.

Exception No. 3 permits the use of fixture whips to supply lighting fixtures.

300-19 . Supporting Conductors in Vertical Raceways.

(a) Spacing Intervals — Maximum. Conductors in vertical raceways shall be supported if the vertical rise exceeds the values in Table 300-19(a). One cable support shall be provided at the top of the vertical raceway or as close to the top as practical. Intermediate supports shall be provided as necessary to limit supported conductor lengths to not greater than those values specified in Table 300-19(a).

Table 300-19(a). Spacings for Conductor Supports

AWG or Circular-Mil Size of Wire	Conductors Support of Conductors in Vertical Raceways	Aluminum or Copper-Clad Aluminum	Copper
18 AWG through 8 AWG	Not greater than	. . . 100 feet	. . . 100 feet
6 AWG through 1/0 AWG	" " "	. . . 200 feet	. . . 100 feet
2/0 AWG through 4/0 AWG	" " "	. . . 180 feet	. . . 80 feet
Over 4/0 AWG through 350 kcmil	" " "	. . . 135 feet	. . . 60 feet
Over 350 kcmil through 500 kcmil	" " "	. . . 120 feet	. . . 50 feet
Over 500 kcmil through 750 kcmil	" " "	. . . 95 feet	. . . 40 feet
Over 750 kcmil	" " "	. . . 85 feet	. . . 35 feet

For SI units: one foot = 0.3048 meter.

Exception: Steel wire armor cable shall be supported at the top of the riser with a cable support that clamps the steel wire armor. A safety device shall be permitted at the lower end of the riser to hold the cable in the event there is slippage of the cable in the wire armored cable support. Additional wedge-type supports shall be permitted to relieve the strain on the equipment terminals caused by expansion of the cable under load.

(b) Support Methods. One of the following methods of support shall be used:

(1) By clamping devices constructed of or employing insulating wedges inserted in the ends of the conduits. Where clamping of insulation does not adequately support the cable, the conductor also shall be clamped.

(2) By inserting boxes at the required intervals in which insulating supports are installed and secured in a satisfactory manner to withstand the weight of the conductors attached thereto, the boxes being provided with covers.

(3) In junction boxes, by deflecting the cables not less than 90 degrees and carrying them horizontally to a distance not less than twice the diameter of the cable, the cables being carried on two or more insulating supports, and additionally secured thereto by tie wires if desired. Where this method is used, cables shall be supported at intervals not greater than 20 percent of those mentioned in the preceding tabulation.

(4) By a method of equal effectiveness.

Conductors in long vertical runs are required to be supported to prevent the weight of the conductors from dam-aging the insulation where leaving the conduit and to prevent the conductors from being pulled out of the terminals. Supports such as those shown in Figures 300-12 and 300-13 may be used in addition to many other types of grips manufactured for this purpose.

Example: A vertical raceway contains No. 1/0 copper conductors. One cable support near the top of the run would be required if the vertical run exceeds 100 feet. Intermediate supports may be required to limit the supported length to the table values. If the vertical run were less than 100 feet, cable supports would not be required.

Figure 300-13. A support bushing located at the top of a vertical conduit at a cabinet or pull box, which prevents the weight of the conductors from damaging the insulation or placing a strain on termination points. (O.Z./Gedney Co.)

Figure 300-14. Another method of supporting vertical conductors.

300-20. **Induced Currents in Metal Enclosures or Metal Raceways.**

(a) **Conductors Grouped Together.** Where conductors carrying alternating current are installed in metal enclosures or metal raceways, they shall be so arranged as to avoid heating the surrounding metal by induction. To accomplish this, all phase conductors and, where used, the neutral and all equipment grounding conductors shall be grouped together.

Exception No. 1: As permitted in Section 250-50, Exception for equipment grounding connections.

Exception No. 2: As permitted in Section 426-42 and Section 427-47 for skin effect heating.

By its very nature, skin effect heating uses induced currents in metal raceways to heat pipelines. Significantly, the temperature of the raceway is known and bears a definite relationship to the pipeline temperature and the overall thermal parameters of the system.

(b) **Individual Conductors.** Where a single conductor carrying alternating current passes through metal with magnetic properties, the inductive effect shall be minimized by (1) cutting slots in the metal between the individual holes through which the individual conductors pass, or (2) passing all the conductors in the circuit through an insulating wall sufficiently large for all of the conductors of the circuit.

Exception: In the case of circuits supplying vacuum or electric-discharge lighting systems or signs, or X-ray apparatus, the currents carried by the conductors are so small that the inductive heating effect can be ignored where these conductors are placed in metal enclosures or pass through metal.

(FPN): Because aluminum is not a magnetic metal, there will be no heating due to hysteresis; however, induced currents will be present. They will not be of sufficient magnitude to require grouping of conductors or special treatment in passing conductors through aluminum wall sections.

A new exception in the 1993 *Code* to Section 300-3(b) permits SINGLE conductor Type MI cable provided it complies with Section 330-16. This section requires the installation to conform to Section 300-20 regarding inductive effects.

300-21. **Spread of Fire or Products of Combustion.** Electrical installations in hollow spaces, vertical shafts, and ventilation or air-handling ducts shall be so made that the possible spread of fire or products of combustion will not be substantially increased. Openings around electrical penetrations through fire-resistant-rated walls, partitions, floors, or ceilings shall be firestopped using approved methods to maintain the fire resistance rating.

It is the intent of this section that electrical equipment, raceways, cables, etc., be installed in such a manner that they will not contribute to the spread of fire or the products of combustion through the specified component parts of a building. In addition, the fire-stopping method used is required to effectively maintain the fire-resistance rating of the building component that is pierced. See Figures 300-15 and 300-16.

(FPN): Directories of electrical construction materials published by qualified testing laboratories contain many listing installation restrictions necessary to maintain the fire resistive rating of assemblies where penetrations or openings are made. An example is the 24-inch (610-mm) minimum horizontal separation between boxes on opposite sides of the wall. Assistance in complying with Section 300-21 can be found in these directories and product listings.

Figure 300-15. *Fire seals used to maintain the integrity of fire-rated walls, floors, partitions, or ceilings as required by Section 300-21. (O.Z./Gedney Co.)*

Figure 300-16. *Using approved caulking to meet the requirements of Section 300-21. (Electro Products Division, 3M Co.)*

300-22. **Wiring in Ducts, Plenums, and Other Air-Handling Spaces.** The provisions of this section apply to the installation and uses of electric wiring and equipment in ducts, plenums, and other air-handling spaces.

(FPN): See Article 424, Part F, Duct Heaters.

(a) Ducts for Dust, Loose Stock, or Vapor Removal. No wiring systems of any type shall be installed in ducts used to transport dust, loose stock, or flammable vapors. No wiring system of any type shall be installed in any duct, or shaft containing only such ducts, used for vapor removal or for ventilation of commercial-type cooking equipment.

(b) Ducts or Plenums Used for Environmental Air. Only wiring methods consisting of Type MI cable, Type MC cable employing a smooth or corrugated impervious metal sheath without an overall nonmetallic covering, electrical metallic tubing, flexible metallic tubing, intermediate metal conduit, or rigid metal conduit shall be installed in ducts or plenums specifically fabricated to transport environmental air. Flexible metal conduit and liquidtight flexible metal conduit shall be permitted, in lengths not to exceed 4 feet (1.22 m), to connect physically adjustable equipment and devices permitted to be in these ducts and plenum chambers. The connectors used with flexible metal conduit shall effectively close any openings in the connection. Equipment and devices shall be permitted within such ducts or plenum chambers only if necessary for their direct action upon, or sensing of, the contained air. Where equipment or devices are installed and illumination is necessary to facilitate maintenance and repair, enclosed gasketed-type fixtures shall be permitted.

The intent of this section is to limit the use of materials that would contribute smoke and products of combustion during a fire in an area that handles environmental air, and, in the case of paragraph (b), to provide an effective barrier against the spread of products of combustion into the duct or plenum.

Paragraph (b) applies to ducts and plenums, such as sheet metal ducts, that are specifically constructed to transport environmental air. Equipment and devices such as lighting fixtures and motors are not normally permitted in ducts or plenums and, for this reason, wiring methods in paragraph (b) are different from the wiring methods permitted in paragraph (c).

(c) Other Space Used for Environmental Air. Section 300-22(c) applies to space used for environmental air-handling purposes other than ducts and plenums as specified in Sections 300-22(a) and 300-22(b). Only totally enclosed nonventilated insulated busway having no provisions for plug-in connections and wiring methods consisting of Type MI cable, Type MC cable without an overall nonmetallic covering, Type AC cable, or other factory-assembled multiconductor control or power cable that is specifically listed for the use shall be installed in such other space.

Other type cables and conductors shall be installed in electrical metallic tubing, flexible metallic tubing, intermediate metal conduit, rigid metal conduit, flexible metal conduit, or, where accessible, surface metal raceway or wireway with metal covers or solid bottom metal cable tray with solid metal covers.

Electric equipment with a metal enclosure or with a nonmetallic enclosure listed for the use and having adequate fire-resistant and low-smoke-producing characteristics, and associated wiring material suitable for the ambient temperature, shall be permitted to be installed in such other space unless prohibited elsewhere in this Code.

(FPN): The space over a hung ceiling used for environmental air-handling purposes is an example of the type of other space to which Section 300-22(c) applies.

Exception No. 1: Liquidtight flexible metal conduit in single lengths not exceeding 6 feet (1.83 m).

Exception No. 2: Integral fan systems specifically identified for such use.

Exception No. 3: This section does not include habitable rooms or areas of buildings, the prime purpose of which is not air handling.

Exception No. 3 applies to habitable rooms and other areas being used as portions of air-return systems in buildings, the prime purpose of which is not air handling, such as area A below.

It is not intended that the limitation of wiring methods be applied to these parts of a building.

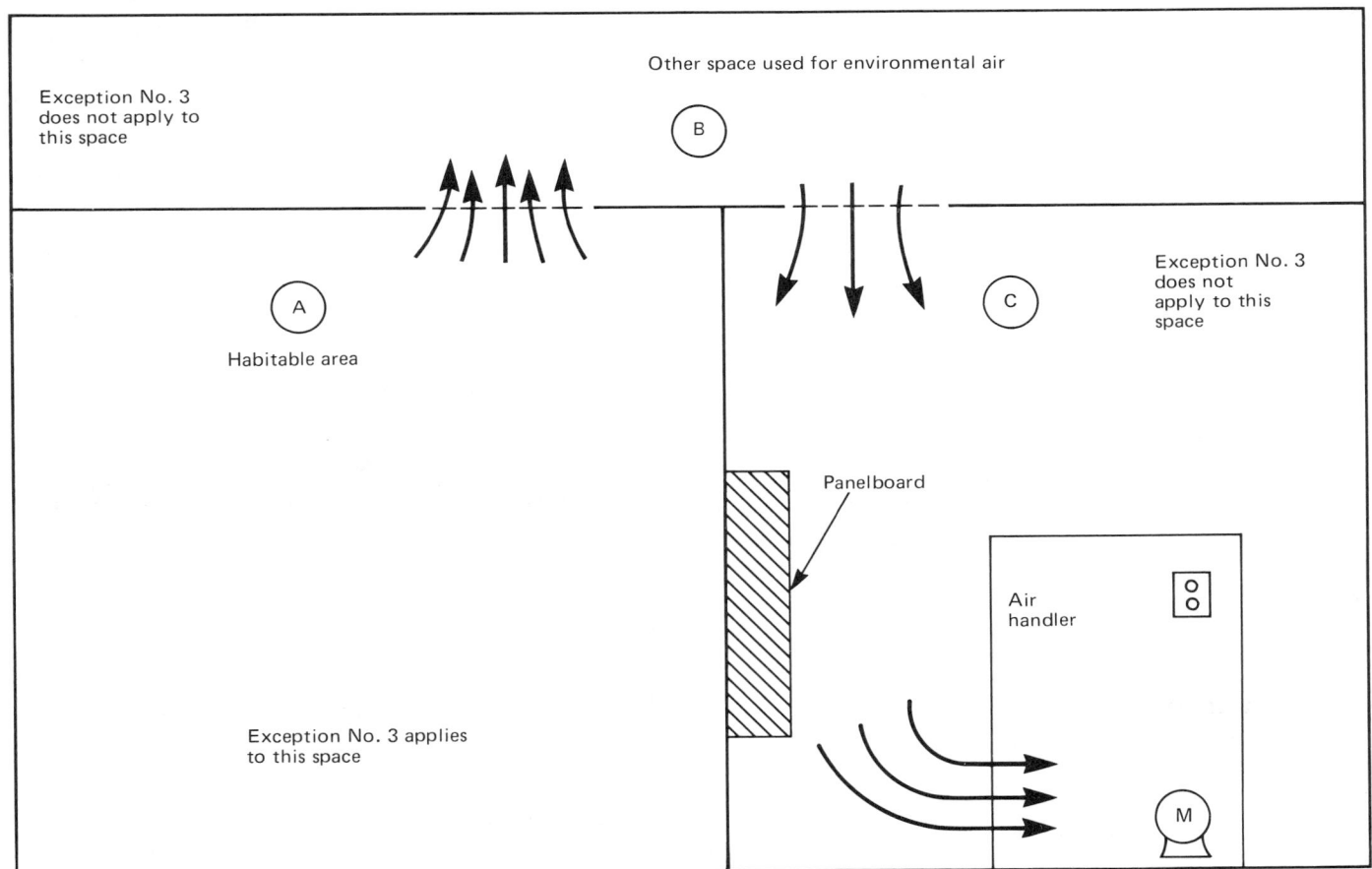

Figure 300-17. *Paragraph (c) of Section 300-22 applies to other spaces used to transport environmental air that are not specifically manufactured as ducts or plenums, such as suspended (hung) ceilings. Many suspended ceilings are intended to transport return air;* *some are also used for supply air, but these are not nearly as common as those used for return air, such as area B in Figure 300-17.*

If the *prime* purpose of the room or space is air-handling, such as area C of Figure 300-17, then the restrictions in Section 300-22(c) apply whether or not electrical equipment is located in the room. See Section 300-22(c), paragraph 3.

Exception No. 4: Listed prefabricated cable assemblies of metallic manufactured wiring systems without nonmetallic sheath shall be permitted where listed for this use.

Note that the cable assembly is required to be listed for use in space used for environmental air. See Article 604.

Exception No. 5: This section does not include the joist or stud spaces in dwelling units where wiring passes through such spaces perpendicular to the long dimension of such spaces.

See Figure 300-18.

Figure 300-18. A cable passing through joist spaces of a dwelling unit. The joist space is covered with sheet metal and used as a cold-air return for a forced warm-air central heating system. Equipment such as junction boxes or device enclosures are not permitted in this location.

(d) Data Processing Systems. Electric wiring in air-handling areas beneath raised floors for data processing systems shall comply with Article 645.

It is not intended that the requirements of Section 300-22(b) or 300-22(c) apply to air-handling areas beneath raised floors in computer rooms. See Article 645.

300-23. **Panels Designed to Allow Access.** Cables, raceways, and equipment installed behind panels designed to allow access including suspended ceiling panels shall be so arranged and secured as to allow the removal of panels and access to the equipment.

This section, new in the 1993 *Code*, is intended to prevent the excess accumulation of wires and cables that could limit access to electrical equipment by preventing the removal of access panels.

B. Requirements for Over 600 Volts, Nominal

300-31. **Covers Required.** Suitable covers shall be installed on all boxes, fittings, and similar enclosures to prevent accidental contact with energized parts or physical damage to parts or insulation.

300-32. **Conductors of Different Systems.** Conductors of high-voltage and low-voltage systems shall not occupy the same wiring enclosure or pull and junction boxes.

Exception No. 1: In motors, switchgear and control assemblies, and similar equipment.

Exception No. 2: In manholes, if extra-low or low-voltage conductors are separated from high-voltage conductors.

300-34. **Conductor Bending Radius.** The conductor shall not be bent to a radius less than eight times the overall diameter for nonshielded conductors or twelve times the diameter for shielded or lead-covered conductors during or after installation.

300-35. **Protection Against Induction Heating.** Metallic raceways and associated conductors shall be so arranged as to avoid heating of the raceway in accordance with the applicable provisions of Section 300-20.

300-36. **Grounding.** Wiring and equipment installations shall be grounded in accordance with the applicable provisions of Article 250.

300-37. **Underground Installations.** The minimum cover requirements shall be in accordance with Section 710-4(b).

ARTICLE 305   Temporary Wiring

Contents

305-1.   **Scope.** The provisions of this article apply to temporary electrical power and lighting wiring methods that may be of a class less than would be required for a permanent installation.

305-2.   **Other Articles.** Except as specifically modified in this article, all other requirements of this Code for permanent wiring shall apply to temporary wiring installations.

305-3.   **Time Constraints.**

(a) During the Period of Construction. Temporary electrical power and lighting installations shall be permitted during the period of construction, remodeling, maintenance, repair, or demolition of buildings, structures, equipment, or similar activities.

(b) 90 Days. Temporary electrical power and lighting installations shall be permitted for a period not to exceed 90 days for Christmas decorative lighting, carnivals, and similar purposes.

Note that the temporary wiring applications of paragraphs (a) and (c) are not restricted to 90 days.

(c) Emergencies and Tests. Temporary electrical power and lighting installations shall be permitted during emergencies and for tests, experiments, and developmental work.

(d) Removal. Temporary wiring shall be removed immediately upon completion of construction or purpose for which the wiring was installed.

Note that the temporary wiring must be removed, not just disconnected.

305-4.   **General.**

(a) Services. Services shall be installed in conformance with Article 230.

(b) Feeders. Feeders shall be protected as provided in Article 240. They shall originate in an approved distribution center. Conductors shall be permitted within cable assemblies; or, cords or cables of a type identified in Table 400-4 for hard usage or extra-hard usage. Where the voltage does not exceed 150 volts to ground and where not subject to physical damage, feeders shall be permitted to be run as open conductors if supported on insulators at intervals of not more than 10 feet (3.05 m).

The term "multiconductor" was deleted from this section in the 1993 *Code*. The change now permits the use of single conductor cords or cables for feeders, such as Type W.

Exception: Where installed for the purposes specified in Section 305-3(c).

(c) Branch Circuits. All branch circuits shall originate in an approved power outlet or panelboard. Conductors shall be permitted within cable assemblies; or, multiconductor cord or cable of a type identified in Table 400-4 for hard usage or extra-hard usage. All conductors shall be protected as provided in Article 240. Where the voltage does not exceed 150 volts to ground and where not subject to physical damage, branch circuits shall be permitted to be run as open conductors if supported on insulators at intervals of not more than 10 feet (3.05 m). No open wiring branch circuit conductors shall be laid on the floor or ground.

Exception: Where installed for the purposes specified in Section 305-3(c).

The basic requirement for safety in Section 305-4(c) is that temporary wiring be located and installed so that it will not be physically damaged. Section 305-2 requires wiring methods to be installed in accordance with the appropriate article (unless modified).

Note that hard usage or extra hard usage extension cords are permitted to be laid on the floor.

(d) Receptacles. All receptacles shall be of the grounding type. Unless installed in a continuous grounded metal raceway or metal-covered cable, all branch circuits shall contain a separate equipment grounding conductor, and all receptacles shall be electrically connected to the equipment grounding conductors. Receptacles on construction sites shall not be installed on branch circuits that supply temporary lighting. Receptacles shall not be connected to the same ungrounded conductor of multiwire circuits that supply temporary lighting.

The intent of this paragraph is to require separate ungrounded conductors for lighting and receptacle loads so that the activation of a fuse, circuit breaker, or ground-fault circuit-interrupter due to a fault or overload of equipment will not deenergize the lighting circuit.

(e) Disconnecting Means. Suitable disconnecting switches or plug connectors shall be installed to permit the disconnection of all ungrounded conductors of each temporary circuit. Multiwire branch circuits shall be provided with a means to disconnect simultaneously all ungrounded conductors at the power outlet or panelboard where the branch circuit originated. Approved handle ties shall be permitted.

(f) Lamp Protection. All lamps for general illumination shall be protected from accidental contact or breakage by a suitable fixture or lampholder with a guard.

Brass shell, paper-lined sockets, or other metal-cased sockets shall not be used unless the shell is grounded.

(g) Splices. On construction sites, a box shall not be required for splices or junction connections where the circuit conductors are multiconductor cord or cable assemblies or open conductors. See Sections 110-14(b) and 400-9. A box, conduit body, or terminal fitting having a separately bushed hole for each conductor shall be used wherever a change is made to a conduit or tubing system or a metal-sheathed cable system.

(h) Protection from Accidental Damage. Flexible cords and cables shall be protected from accidental damage. Sharp corners and projections shall be avoided. Where passing through doorways or other pinch points, protection shall be provided to avoid damage.

Note that, unlike Section 400-8, Section 305-4(h) permits flexible cords and cables, because of the nature of their use, to pass through doorways.

(i) Termination(s) at Devices. Cables entering enclosures containing devices requiring termination shall be secured to the box with fittings designed for the purpose.

This section is not intended to apply to attachment plug and cord connectors.

305-5. **Grounding.** All grounding shall conform with Article 250.

305-6. **Ground-Fault Protection for Personnel.** Ground-fault protection for personnel on construction sites shall be provided to comply with (a) or (b) below.

(a) Ground-Fault Circuit-Interrupters. All 125-volt, single-phase, 15- and 20-ampere receptacle outlets that are not a part of the permanent wiring of the building or structure and that are in use by personnel shall have ground-fault circuit-interrupter protection for personnel. If a receptacle or receptacles are installed as part of the permanent wiring of the building or structure and used for temporary electric power, GFCI protection for personnel shall be provided.

Exception: Receptacles on a 2-wire, single-phase portable or vehicle-mounted generator rated not more than 5 kW, where the circuit conductors of the generator are insulated from the generator frame and all other grounded surfaces.

Where an assured equipment grounding conductor program is not in place, receptacle outlets that are NOT part of the permanent wiring and that are used by construction personnel are required to be GFCI-type receptacles, be supplied through a GFCI-type receptacle, or be protected by a GFCI circuit breaker. The new second sentence (1993 *Code*) requires GFCI protection for construction personnel using receptacles that ARE part of the permanent wiring. Such protection for personnel is permitted to be accomplished with the use of portable GFCIs.

(b) Assured Equipment Grounding Conductor Program. A written procedure shall be continuously enforced at the construction site by one or more designated persons to assure that equipment grounding conductors for all cord sets, receptacles that are not a part of the permanent wiring of the building or structure, and equipment connected by cord and plug are installed and maintained in accordance with the applicable requirements of Sections 210-7(c), 250-45, 250-59, and 305-4(d).

(1) The following tests shall be performed on all cord sets, receptacles that are not part of the permanent wiring of the building or structure, and cord- and plug-connected equipment required to be grounded.

a. All equipment grounding conductors shall be tested for continuity and shall be electrically continuous.

b. Each receptacle and attachment plug shall be tested for correct attachment of the equipment grounding conductor. The equipment grounding conductor shall be connected to its proper terminal.

c. All required tests shall be performed:

1. Before first use on the construction site.

2. When there is evidence of damage.

3. Before equipment is returned to service following any repairs.

4. At intervals not exceeding 3 months.

Figure 305-1. *Temporary power outlet units commonly used on construction sites with a variety of configurations. Some are available with ground-fault circuit-interrupter protection. (Hubbell)*

Figure 305-2. *Tripping of ground-fault circuit-interrupter protective devices by wet or damp weather conditions can be avoided by using watertight plugs and connectors. (Hubbell)*

(2) The tests required in (1) above shall be recorded and made available to the authority having jurisdiction.

305-7. Guarding. For wiring over 600 volts, nominal, suitable fencing, barriers, or other effective means shall be provided to prevent access of other than authorized and qualified personnel.

ARTICLE 310   Conductors for General Wiring

Contents

310-1. **Scope.** This article covers general requirements for conductors and their type designations, insulations, markings, mechanical strengths, ampacity ratings, and uses. These requirements do not apply to conductors that form an integral part of equipment, such as motors, motor controllers, and similar equipment, or to conductors specifically provided for elsewhere in this Code.

(FPN): For flexible cords and cables, see Article 400. For fixture wires, see Article 402.

310-2. **Conductors.**

(a) **Insulated.** Conductors shall be insulated.

Exception: Where covered or bare conductors are specifically permitted elsewhere in this Code.

(FPN): See Section 250-152 for insulation of neutral conductors of a solidly grounded high-voltage system.

(b) **Conductor Material.** Conductors in this article shall be of aluminum, copper-clad aluminum, or copper unless otherwise specified.

310-3. **Stranded Conductors.** Where installed in raceways, conductors of size No. 8 and larger shall be stranded.

Larger sized conductors are required to be stranded to provide greater flexibility. This requirement does not apply to busbars and the conductors of Type MI mineral-insulated metal-sheathed cable. In addition, the bonding conductors of a common bonding grid of a permanently installed swimming pool are required to be solid, nonstranded conductors of No. 8 or larger.

Exception: As permitted or required elsewhere in this Code.

310-4. **Conductors in Parallel.** Aluminum, copper-clad aluminum, or copper conductors of size No. 1/0 and larger, comprising each phase, neutral or grounded circuit conductor, shall be permitted to be connected in parallel (electrically joined at both ends to form a single conductor).

Conductors that are connected in parallel, in accordance with Section 310-4, are considered as a single conductor with a total cross-sectional area of all conductors in parallel. Therefore, where individual conductors are

tapped from conductors in parallel, the tap connection must include all of the conductors in parallel for that particular phase.

Tapping into only one of the parallel conductors will result in an unbalance in the distribution of the tap load current between parallel conductors. This will result in one of the conductors carrying more than its share of the load. This can result in overheating and conductor insulation failure. For example, where a 250 kcmil conductor is tapped from a set of two 500 kcmil conductors in parallel, the splicing device must include both 500 kcmil conductors and the single 250 kcmil tap conductor.

Exception No. 1: As permitted in Section 620-12(a)(1), Exception.

Exception No. 2: Conductors in sizes smaller than No. 1/0 shall be permitted to be run in parallel to supply control power to indicating instruments, contactors, relays, solenoids, and similar control devices provided (a) they are contained within the same raceway or cable; (b) the ampacity of each individual conductor is sufficient to carry the entire load current shared by the parallel conductors; and (c) the overcurrent protection is such that the ampacity of each individual conductor will not be exceeded if one or more of the parallel conductors become inadvertently disconnected.

Exception No. 3: Conductors in sizes smaller than No. 1/0 shall be permitted to be run in parallel for frequencies of 360 hertz and higher where conditions (a),(b), and (c) of Exception No. 2 are met.

For example, in control wiring and circuits that operate at frequencies greater than 360 Hz, it may be necessary to reduce cable capacitance or voltage drop in long lengths of wire. A No. 14 conductor may have more than sufficient capacity to carry the load, but by installing two conductors in parallel, the voltage drop can be reduced to acceptable limits. This method is permissible, provided the safeguards listed in Exception No. 2 are followed.

The paralleled conductors in each phase, neutral or grounded circuit conductor shall:

(1) Be the same length;
(2) Have the same conductor material;
(3) Be the same size in circular mil area;
(4) Have the same insulation type;
(5) Be terminated in the same manner.

Where run in separate raceways or cables, the raceways or cables shall have the same physical characteristics.

(FPN): Differences in inductive reactance and unequal division of current can be minimized by choice of materials, methods of construction, and orientation of conductors. It is not the intent to require that conductors of one phase, neutral or grounded circuit conductor be the same as those of another phase, neutral or grounded circuit conductor to achieve balance.

For example, the conductors in Phases A and B may be copper, and those in Phase C may be aluminum. However, all raceways or cables must be of the same size, material, and length. Cables, in this case, means cables such as Type MC.

Where equipment grounding conductors are used with conductors in parallel, they shall comply with the requirements of this section except that they shall be sized in accordance with Section 250-95.

Where conductors are used in parallel, space in enclosures shall be given consideration (see Articles 370 and 373).

Conductors installed in parallel shall comply with the provisions of Article 310, Note 8(a), Notes to Ampacity Tables of 0 to 2000 Volts.

This section permits a practical means for installing large-capacity conductors for feeders or services. The paralleling of two or more conductors in place of one large conductor to ensure equal division of current depends on a number of factors. Therefore, several conditions must be satisfied so as not to overload any of the individual paralleled conductors. Other than as permitted in Section 250-95 and the exceptions to Section 310-4, there does not appear to be any practical need to parallel conductors smaller than No. 1/0.

To avoid excessive voltage drop and also to ensure equal division of current, it is essential that unlike phase conductors be located close together and that each phase conductor and the neutral, grounded, and grounding conductors, if used, be grouped together in each raceway or cable. However, isolated phase installations are permitted underground where the phase conductors are run in nonmetallic raceways in close proximity.

The impedance of a circuit in an aluminum raceway or aluminum-sheathed cable will be different from the impedance of the same circuit in a steel raceway or steel-sheathed cable; hence, it is required that separate raceways and cables have the same physical characteristics. See Section 300-20.

Note that all of the conductors of the same phase or neutral are required to be of the same conductor material. For example, if 12 conductors are paralleled for a 3-phase, 4-wire, 480Y/277-V ac circuit, four conductors could be installed in each of three raceways. The *Code* does not intend that all 12 conductors be of copper or aluminum, but does intend that the individual conductors in parallel for each phase, grounded conductor, and neutral be of the same material, insulation type, length, etc. Also, it is intended that the three raceways have the same physical characteristics, i.e., three rigid aluminum conduits or three steel IMC conduits or three EMTs or three nonmetallic conduits, not a mixture of two rigid aluminum conduits and one rigid steel conduit.

It is neither economical nor practical to use conductors larger than 1,000 kcmil in raceways, unless the conductor size is governed by voltage drop. The ampacity of larger sizes would increase very little in proportion to the increase in the size of the conductor. Therefore, where the size of a conductor increases 50 percent, for example, from 1,000 to 1,500 kcmil, a Type THW conductor increases 80 A (less than 15 percent). An increase from 1,000 to 2,000 kcmil (100 percent increase) causes an increase of only 120 A (approximately 2 percent). Generally, in situations where economics is a factor, the installation of two (or more) conductors per phase in parallel may be more beneficial.

310-5. **Minimum Size of Conductors.** The minimum size of conductors shall be as shown in Table 310-5.

Exception No. 1: For flexible cords as permitted by Section 400-12.

Exception No. 2: For fixture wire as permitted by Section 410-24.

Table 310-5.

Voltage Rating of Conductor — Volts	Minimum Conductor Size — AWG
0 through 2000	14 Copper
	12 Aluminum or Copper-Clad Aluminum
2001 through 5000	8
5001 through 8000	6
8001 through 15000	2
15001 through 28000	1
28001 through 35000	1/0

Exception No. 3: For fractional horsepower motors as permitted by Section 430-22.

Exception No. 4: For cranes and hoists as permitted by Section 610-14.

Exception No. 5: For elevator control and signaling circuits as permitted by Section 620-12.

Exception No. 6: For Class 1, Class 2, and Class 3 circuits as permitted by Sections 725-16 and 725-37.

Exception No. 7: For fire protective signaling circuits as permitted by Sections 760-16, 760-25, and 760-51.

Exception No. 8: For Type V cables, the minimum conductor sizes are: No. 12 for 2000-volt rating, No. 10 for 3000-volt rating, and No. 8 for 4000-volt rating.

Exception No. 9: For motor control circuits as permitted by Section 430-72.

310-6. Shielding. Solid dielectric insulated conductors operated above 2000 volts in permanent installations shall have ozone-resistant insulation and shall be shielded. All metallic insulation shields shall be grounded through an effective grounding path meeting the requirements of Section 250-51. Shielding shall be for the purpose of confining the voltage stresses to the insulation.

Exception: Nonshielded insulated conductors listed by a qualified testing laboratory shall be permitted for use up to 8000 volts under the following conditions:

a. Conductors shall have insulation resistant to electric discharge and surface tracking, or the insulated conductor(s) shall be covered with a material resistant to ozone, electric discharge, and surface tracking.

b. Where used in wet locations, the insulated conductor(s) shall have an overall nonmetallic jacket or a continuous metallic sheath.

c. Where operated at 5001 to 8000 volts, the insulated conductor(s) shall have a nonmetallic jacket over the insulation. The insulation shall have a specific inductive capacity no greater than 3.6, and the jacket shall have a specific inductive capacity no greater than 10 and no less than 6.

d. Insulation and jacket thicknesses shall be in accordance with Table 310-63.

Solid dielectric insulated conductors that are permanently installed and that operate at greater than 2,000 V are

required to have ozone-resistant insulation and must be shielded with a grounded metallic shield (note exception).

Shielding is accomplished by the application of a metal tape or nonmetallic semiconducting tape around the conductor surface, which will prevent corona from forming and will reduce high-voltage stresses. Corona is a faint glow adjacent to the surface of the electrical conductor at high voltage. If there are high-voltage stresses and a charging current flowing between the conductor and ground (usually due to moisture), the surrounding atmosphere is ionized and ozone, which is generated by an electric discharge in ordinary oxygen or air, is formed, which will attack the conductor jacket and insulation and may eventually break them down. The shield is at ground potential; therefore, no voltage above ground is present on the jacket outside the shield, thus preventing a discharge from the jacket and the subsequent formation of ozone.

Figure 310-1 shows a three-conductor cable of the shielded type.

Figure 310-2 illustrates a stress-relief cone for an indoor cable terminator.

Figure 310-3 illustrates a stress cone on a single-conductor shielded cable terminating inside a pothead. Notice that a clamping ring provides a grounding connection between the copper shielding tape and the shield to the metallic base of the pothead.

Specialized training and close adherence to manufacturer's instructions are absolutely essential for high-voltage cable installations.

Figure 310-1. Three-conductor cable of the shielded type.

Figure 310-2. One-piece, premolded stress-relief cone is for indoor cable terminations of up to 35 kV phase-to-phase. (ITT Blackburn Co.)

— Conductor terminal

— Insulator

— Solid dielectric rubber or silicone polyethylene
— Filling compound
— High voltage rubber insulating tape copper
— Shielding tape
— Copper shield, tape, wire, sheath
— Clamping ring

Figure 310-3. A stress cone on a single-conductor shielded cable terminating inside a pothead.

310-7. **Direct Burial Conductors.** Conductors used for direct burial applications shall be of a type identified for such use. Cables rated above 2000 volts shall be shielded.

Exception: Nonshielded multiconductor cables rated 2001-5000 volts shall be permitted if the cable has an overall metallic sheath or armor.

The metallic shield, sheath, or armor shall be grounded through an effective grounding path meeting the requirements of Section 250-51.

(FPN No. 1): See Section 300-5 for installation requirements for conductors rated 600 volts or less.

(FPN No. 2): See Section 710-4(b) for installation requirements for conductors rated over 600 volts.

310-8. **Wet Locations.**

(a) Insulated Conductors. Insulated conductors used in wet locations shall be (1) lead-covered; (2) Types RHW, TW, THW, THHW, THWN, XHHW; or (3) of a type listed for use in wet locations.

(b) Cables. Cables of one or more conductors used in wet locations shall be of a type listed for use in wet locations.

Conductors used for direct burial applications shall be of a type listed for such use.

310-9. **Corrosive Conditions.** Conductors exposed to oils, greases, vapors, gases, fumes, liquids, or other substances having a deleterious effect upon the conductor or insulation shall be of a type suitable for the application.

See commentary following Section 501-13.

310-10. **Temperature Limitation of Conductors.** No conductor shall be used in such a manner that its operating temperature will exceed that designated for the type of insulated conductor involved. In no case shall conductors be associated together in such a way with respect to type of circuit, the wiring method employed, or the number of conductors that the limiting temperature of any conductor is exceeded.

Most terminations are normally designed only for 60°C (140°F) or 75°C (167°F) maximum temperatures, although some are now being designed for 90°C (194°F); therefore, the higher rated ampacities for conductors of 90°C (194°F), 110°C (230°F), etc., cannot be utilized unless the terminals at which the conductors terminate have comparable ratings.

Tables 310-16 through 310-19 have ampacity correction factors for ambient temperatures that are greater or less than the ambient temperature identified in the table heading. To assign the proper ampacity to a conductor in an ambient above 30°C, the appropriate correction factor must be used. This correction factor is applied in addition to any derating factor, such as in Note 8(a) to the ampacity tables of 0 to 2,000 volts (Tables 310-16 through 310-19).

Example: No. 2 AWG THHN copper conductors are to be installed in a raceway in an ambient temperature of 50°C (122°F). According to Table 310-16, the allowable ampacity of the conductor at 30°C is 130 A, which is multiplied by 0.82 (taken from the correction factors at the bottom of the table); thus the allowable ampacity of the No. 2 conductor at 50°C is reduced to 106.6 A (130 A × 0.82 = 106.6 A).

If six of these conductors were run in a raceway, Note 8(a) to the tables would require the allowable ampacity to be further reduced to 80 percent, which, in this case, would be 106.6 A × 0.8 = 85.28 A. Under these conditions, the No. 2 conductors would be suitable for an 80-A circuit.

The basis for determining the ampacities of conductors for Tables 310-16 and 310-17 was the "NEMA Report of Determination of Maximum Permissible Current-Carrying Capacity of Code Insulated Wires and Cables for Building Purposes" dated June 27, 1938. The basis for determining the ampacities of conductors for Tables 310-18 through 310-19 and the ampacity tables in Appendix B was the Neher-McGrath Method. See commentary for Section 310-15(b).

The temperature rating of a conductor (see Table 310-13) is the maximum temperature, at any location along its length, that the conductor can withstand over a prolonged time period without serious degradation.

Conductors should be chosen that have a rating above the anticipated maximum ambient temperature. The operating temperature of conductors should be controlled at or below the conductor rating by coordinating conductor size, number of associated conductors, and ampacity for the particular conductor rating and ambient temperature. All tabulations should be corrected for the anticipated ambient temperature using the ampacity correction factors at the bottom of the tables. Where more than three conductors are associated together, the additional correction shown in Note 8(a) is required to be applied.

(FPN): The temperature rating of a conductor (see Tables 310-13 and 310-61) is the maximum temperature, at any location along its length, that the conductor can withstand over a prolonged time period without serious degradation. The allowable ampacity tables, the ampacity tables of Article 310 and the ampacity tables of Appendix B, the correction factors at the bottom of these tables, and the notes to the tables provide guidance for coordinating conductor sizes, types, allowable ampacities, ampacities, ambient temperatures, and number of associated conductors.

The fine print note is intended to focus attention on the necessity for derating conductors where high ambient temperatures are encountered and to provide users with helpful information in coordinating ampacities, ambient temperatures, conductor size and number, etc., to assure operation at or below rating.

The principal determinants of operating temperature are:

1. Ambient temperature. Ambient temperature may vary along the conductor length as well as from time to time.

2. Heat generated internally in the conductor as the result of load current flow.

3. The rate at which generated heat dissipates into the ambient medium. Thermal insulation that covers or surrounds conductors will affect the rate of heat dissipation.

4. Adjacent load-carrying conductors. Adjacent conductors have the dual effect of raising the ambient temperature and impeding heat dissipation.

310-11. Marking.

(a) **Required Information.** All conductors and cables shall be marked to indicate the following information, using the applicable method described in (b) below.

(1) The maximum rated voltage for which the conductor was listed.

(2) The proper type letter or letters for the type of wire or cable as specified elsewhere in this Code.

(3) The manufacturer's name, trademark, or other distinctive marking by which the organization responsible for the product can be readily identified.

(4) The AWG size or circular-mil area.

(b) **Method of Marking.**

(1) **Surface Marking.** The following conductors and cables shall be durably marked on the surface. The AWG size or

circular mil area shall be repeated at intervals not exceeding 24 inches (610 mm). All other markings shall be repeated at intervals not exceeding 40 inches (1.02 m).

    a. Single- and multiconductor rubber- and thermoplastic-insulated wire and cable.

    b. Nonmetallic-sheathed cable.

    c. Service-entrance cable.

    d. Underground feeder and branch-circuit cable.

    e. Tray cable.

    f. Irrigation cable.

    g. Power-limited tray cable.

(2) Marker Tape. Metal-covered multiconductor cables shall employ a marker tape located within the cable and running for its complete length.

Exception No. 1: Mineral-insulated, metal-sheathed cable.

Exception No. 2: Type AC cable.

Exception No. 3: The information required in Section 310-11(a) shall be permitted to be durably marked on the outer nonmetallic covering of Type MC or Type PLTC cables at intervals not exceeding 40 inches (1.02 m).

Exception No. 4: The information required in Section 310-11(a) shall be permitted to be durably marked on a nonmetallic covering under the metallic sheath of Type PLTC cable at intervals not exceeding 40 inches (1.02 m).

Type PLTC cable is permitted to have a metallic sheath or armor over a nonmetallic jacketed cable. A second nonmetallic jacket covering the metallic sheath is optional. Exception Nos. 3 and 4 define the marking requirements for either case.

(FPN): Included in the group of metal-covered cables are Type AC cable (Article 333), Type MC cable (Article 334), and lead-sheathed cable.

(3) Tag Marking. The following conductors and cables shall be marked by means of a printed tag attached to the coil, reel, or carton:

    a. Mineral-insulated, metal-sheathed cable.

    b. Switchboard wires.

    c. Metal-covered, single-conductor cables.

    d. Conductors having outer surface of asbestos.

    e. Type AC cable.

(4) Optional Marking of Wire Size. For the following multiconductor cables, the information required in (a) (4) above shall be permitted to be marked on the surface of the individual insulated conductors:

    a. Type MC cable.

    b. Tray cable.

    c. Irrigation cable.

    d. Power-limited tray cable.

    e. Power-limited fire protective signaling cable.

(c) Suffixes to Designate Number of Conductors. A type letter or letters used alone shall indicate a single insulated conductor. The following letter suffixes shall indicate the following:

D—For two insulated conductors laid parallel within an outer nonmetallic covering.

M—For an assembly of two or more insulated conductors twisted spirally within an outer nonmetallic covering.

(d) Optional Markings. Conductor types listed in Table 310-13 shall be permitted to be surface marked to indicate special characteristics of the cable materials.

This section is new in the 1993 *Code*. New cable insulations that have special characteristics are frequently developed. Recent developments have resulted in a new family of limited-smoke cables. These cables are permitted to be marked "LS." Other materials have been developed or are in development that have other characteristics, such as low corrosivity. This section is intended to allow these new developments without the need to have each characteristic identified in the *Code*.

(FPN): Examples of these markings include but are not limited to "LS" for limited-smoke and markings such as "sunlight-resistant."

310-12. **Conductor Identification.**

(a) Grounded Conductors. Insulated conductors of No. 6 or smaller, intended for use as grounded conductors of circuits, shall have an outer identification of a white or natural gray color. Multiconductor flat cable No. 4 or larger shall be permitted to employ an external ridge on the grounded conductor.

Exception No. 1: Fixture wires as outlined in Article 402.

Exception No. 2: Mineral-insulated, metal-sheathed cable.

Exception No. 3: A conductor identified as required by Section 210-5(a) for branch circuits.

Exception No. 4: Where the conditions of maintenance and supervision assure that only qualified persons will service the installation, grounded conductors in multiconductor cables shall be permitted to be permanently identified at their terminations at the time of installation by a distinctive white marking or other equally effective means.

For aerial cable, the identification shall be as above, or by means of a ridge so located on the exterior of the cable as to identify it.

Wires having their outer covering finished to show a white or natural gray color but having colored tracer threads in the braid, identifying the source of manufacture, shall be considered as meeting the provisions of this section.

(FPN): For identification requirements for conductors larger than No. 6, see Section 200-6.

(b) Equipment Grounding Conductors. Bare, covered, or insulated grounding conductors shall be permitted. Individually covered or insulated grounding conductors shall have a continuous outer finish that is either green, or green with one or more yellow stripes.

Exception No. 1: An insulated or covered conductor larger than No. 6 shall, at the time of installation, be permitted to be permanently identified as a grounding conductor at each end and at every point where the conductor is accessible. Identification shall be accomplished by one of the following means:

a. Stripping the insulation or covering from the entire exposed length;

b. Coloring the exposed insulation or covering green; or

c. Marking the exposed insulation or covering with green colored tape or green colored adhesive labels.

Exception No. 2: Where the conditions of maintenance and supervision assure that only qualified persons will service the installation, an insulated conductor in a multiconductor cable shall, at the time of installation, be permitted to be permanently identified as a grounding conductor at each end and at every point where the conductor is accessible by one of the following means:

a. Stripping the insulation from the entire exposed length;

b. Coloring the exposed insulation green; or

c. Marking the exposed insulation with green colored tape or green colored adhesive labels.

(c) Ungrounded Conductors. Conductors that are intended for use as ungrounded conductors, whether used as single conductors or in multiconductor cables, shall be finished to be clearly distinguishable from grounded and grounding conductors. Ungrounded conductors shall be distinguished by colors other than white, natural gray, or green; or by a combination of color plus distinguishing marking. Distinguishing markings shall also be in a color other than white, natural gray, or green, and shall consist of a stripe or stripes or a regularly spaced series of identical marks. Distinguishing markings shall not conflict in any manner with the surface markings required by Section 310-11(b)(1).

Exception: As permitted by Section 200-7.

Ungrounded conductors with white or natural gray colored insulation are permitted where the conductors are permanently reidentified at termination points and where even the conductor is visible and accessible. The normal methods of reidentification include colored tape, tagging, or paint. Other applications where white conductors are permitted include 3-way and 4-way switch loops, flexible cords, and circuits less than 50 volts. See Section 200-7, Exceptions.

310-13. **Conductor Constructions and Applications.** Insulated conductors shall comply with the applicable provisions of one or more of the following: Tables 310-13, 310-61, 310-62, 310-63, and 310-64.

These conductors shall be permitted for use in any of the wiring methods recognized in Chapter 3 and as specified in their respective tables.

(FPN): Thermoplastic insulation may stiffen at temperatures colder than minus 10°C (plus 14°F), requiring that care be exercised during installation at such temperatures. Thermoplastic insulation may also be deformed at normal temperatures where subjected to pressure, requiring care be exercised during installation and at points of support. Thermoplastic insulation, where used on dc circuits in wet locations, may result in electroendosmosis between conductor and insulation.

Table 310-13 lists the various types of insulated conductors as covered by the requirements of this *Code*. More detailed wire classification information from sizes No. 14 through 2,000 kcmil may be obtained from standards or directories, such as those published by the Underwriters Laboratories Inc.

Table 310-13. Conductor Application and Insulations

Trade Name	Type Letter	Max. Operating Temp.	Application Provisions	Insulation	AWG or kcmil	Thickness of Insulation	Mils	Outer Covering****
Fluorinated Ethylene Propylene	FEP or FEPB	90° C 194° F 200° C 392° F	Dry and damp locations. Dry locations — special applications.†	Fluorinated Ethylene Propylene	14-10 8-2		20 30	None
				Fluorinated Ethylene Propylene	14-8 6-2		14 14	Glass braid Asbestos or other suitable braid material
Mineral Insulation (Metal Sheathed)	MI	90° F 194° F 250° C 482° F	Dry and wet locations. For special application.†	Magnesium Oxide	18-16***** 16-10 9-4 3-500		23 36 50 55	Copper or Alloy Steel
Moisture-, Heat-, and Oil-Resistant Thermoplastic	MTW††	60° C 140° F 90° C 194° F	Machine tool wiring in wet locations as permitted in NFPA 79. (See Article 670). Machine tool wiring in dry locations as permitted in NFPA 79. (See Article 670.)	Flame-Retardant, Moisture-, Heat-, and Oil-Resistant Thermoplastic	22-12 10 8 6 4-2 1-4/0 213-500 501-1000	(A) 30 30 45 60 60 80 95 110	(B) 15 20 30 30 40 50 60 70	(A) None (B) Nylon jacket or equivalent
Paper		85° C 185° F	For underground service conductors, or by special permission.	Paper				Lead sheath
Perfluoro-alkoxy	PFA	90° C 194° F 200° C 392° F	Dry and damp locations. Dry locations — special applications.†	Perfluoro-alkoxy	14-10 8-2 1-4/0		20 30 45	None
Perfluoro-alkoxy	PFAH	250° C 482° F	Dry locations only. Only for leads within apparatus or within raceways connected to apparatus. (Nickel or nickel-coated copper only.)	Perfluoro-alkoxy	14-10 8-2 1-4/0		20 30 45	None
Heat-Resistant or Cross-Linked Synthetic Polymer	RH	75° C 167° F	Dry and damp locations.	Heat Resistant or Cross-Linked Synthetic Polymer	14-12** 10 8-2 1-4/0 213-500 501-1000 1001-2000 For 601-2000 volts, see Table 310-62.		30 45 60 80 95 110 125	Moisture-resistant, flame-retardant, non-metallic covering*
Heat-Resistant or Cross-Linked Synthetic Polymer	RHH††	90° C 194° F	Dry and damp locations.					

*Some rubber insulations do not require an outer covering.
**For size Nos. 14-12, RHH shall be 45 mils thickness insulation.
****Some insulations do not require an outer covering.
*****For signaling circuits permitting 300-volt insulation.
†Where environmental conditions require maximum conductor operating temperatures above 90°C.
††Insulation and outer coverings that meet the requirements of flame-retardant, limited-smoke and are so listed shall be permitted to be designated limited-smoke with the suffix /LS after the Code type designation.

Table 310-13, continued

Trade Name	Type Letter	Max. Operating Temp.	Application Provisions	Insulation	AWG or kcmil	Thickness of Insulation		Mils	Outer Covering****
Moisture- and Heat-Resistant or Cross-Linked Synthetic Polymer	RHW††, †††	75° C 167° F	Dry and wet locations. Where over 2000 volts insulation, shall be ozone-resistant	Moisture- and Heat-Resistant or Cross-Linked Synthetic Polymer	14-10 8-2 1-4/0 213-500 501-1000 1001-2000 For 601-2000 volts, see Table 310-62.			45 60 80 95 110 125	Moisture-resistant, flame-retardant, non-metallic covering*
Moisture- and Heat-Resistant or Cross-Linked Synthetic Polymer	RHW-2	90° C 194° F	Dry and wet locations.	Moisture- and Heat-Resistant or Cross-Linked Synthetic Polymer	14-10 8-2 1-4/0 213-500 501-1000 1001-2000 For 601-2000 volts, see Table 310-62.			45 60 80 95 110 125	Moisture-resistant, flame-retardant, nonmetallic covering*
Silicone-Asbestos	SA	90° C 194° F / 125° C 257° F	Dry and damp locations. / For special application.†	Silicone Rubber	14-10 8-2 1-4/0 213-500 501-1000 1001-2000			45 60 80 95 110 125	Asbestos, glass, or other suitable braid material
Synthetic Heat-Resistant	SIS††	90° C 194° F	Switchboard wiring only.	Heat-Resistant Cross-Linked Synthetic Polymer	14-10 8 6-2 1-4/0			30 45 60 80	None
Thermoplastic and Asbestos	TA	90° C 194° F	Switchboard wiring only.	Thermoplastic and Asbestos	14-8 6-2 1-4/0	Th'pl'. 20 30 40	Asb. 20 25 30		Flame-retardant, nonmetallic covering
Thermoplastic and Fibrous Outer Braid	TBS	90° C 194° F	Switchboard wiring only.	Thermoplastic	14-10 8 6-2 1-4/0			30 45 60 80	Flame-retardant, nonmetallic covering

*Some rubber insulations do not require an outer covering.
****Some insulations do not require an outer covering.
†Where environmental conditions require maximum conductor operating temperatures above 90°C.
††Insulation and outer coverings that meet the requirements of flame-retardant, limited-smoke and are so listed shall be permitted to be designated limited-smoke with the suffix /LS after the Code type designation.
†††Listed wire types designated with the suffix "-2 ," such as RHW-2 , shall be permitted to be used at a continuous 90°C-operating temperature, wet or dry.

Table 310-13, continued

Trade Name	Type Letter	Max. Operating Temp.	Application Provisions	Insulation	AWG or kcmil	Thickness of Insulation Mils	Outer Covering****
Extended Polytetra-fluoroethylene	TFE	250° C 482° F	Dry locations only. Only for leads within apparatus or within raceways connected to apparatus, or as open wiring. (Nickel or nickel-coated copper only.)	Extruded Polytetra-fluoro-ethylene	14-10 8-2 1-4/0	20 30 45	None
Heat-Resistant Thermoplastic	THHN††	90° C 194° F	Dry and damp locations.	Flame-Retardant, Heat-Resistant Thermo-plastic	14-12 10 8-6 4-2 1-4/0 250-500 501-1000	15 20 30 40 50 60 70	Nylon jacket or equivalent
Moisture- and Heat-Resistant Thermoplastic	THHW	75° C 167° F 90° C 194° F	Wet location. Dry location.	Flame-Retardant, Moisture- and Heat-Resistant Thermo-plastic	14-10 8-2 1-4/0 213-500 501-1000	45 60 80 95 110	None
Moisture- and Heat-Resistant Thermoplastic	THW††, †††	75° C 167° F 90° C 194° F	Dry and wet locations. Special applications within electric discharge lighting equipment. Limited to 1000 open-circuit volts or less. (Size 14-8 only as permitted in Section 410-31.)	Flame-Retardant, Moisture- and Heat-Resistant Thermoplastic	14-10 8-2 1-4/0 213-500 501-1000 1001-2000	45 60 80 95 110 125	None
Moisture- and Heat-Resistant Thermoplastic	THWN ††, †††	75° C 167° F	Dry and wet locations.	Flame-Retardant, Moisture- and Heat-Resistant Thermoplastic	14-12 10 8-6 4-2 1-4/0 250-500 501-1000	15 20 30 40 50 60 70	Nylon jacket or equivalent
Moisture-Resistant Thermoplastic	TW††	60° C 140° F	Dry and wet locations.	Flame-Retardant, Moisture-Resistant Thermo-plastic	14-10 8 6-2 1-4/0 213-500 501-1000 1001-2000	30 45 60 80 95 110 125	None

****Some insulations do not require an outer covering.
††Insulation and outer coverings that meet the requirements of flame-retardant, limited-smoke and are so listed shall be permitted to be designated limited-smoke with the suffix /LS after the Code type designation.
†††Listed wire types designated with the suffix "-2," such as RHW-2, shall be permitted to be used at a continuous 90°C-operating temperature, wet or dry.

Table 310-13, continued

Trade Name	Type Letter	Max. Operating Temp.	Application Provisions	Insulation	AWG or kcmil	Thickness of Insulation Mils	Outer Covering****
Underground Feeder and Branch-Circuit Cable—Single Conductor. (For Type UF cable employing more than one conductor, see Article 339.)	UF	60° C 140° F ——— 75° C 167° F**	See Article 339.	Moisture-Resistant ——— Moisture- and Heat-Resistant	14-10 8-2 1-4/0	60* 80* 95*	Integral with insulation
Underground Service-Entrance Cable—Single Conductor. (For Type USE cable employing more than one conductor, see Article 338.)	USE†††	75° C 167° F	See Article 338.	Heat- and Moisture-Resistant	12-10 8-2 1-4/0 213-500 501-1000 1001-2000	45 60 80 95*** 110 125	Moisture-resistant non-metallic covering [See Section 338-1(b).]
Heat-Resistant Cross-Linked Synthetic Polymer	XHH ††	90° C 194° F	Dry and damp locations.	Flame-Retardant Cross-Linked Synthetic Polymer	14-10 8-2 1-4/0 213-500 501-1000 1001-2000	30 45 55 65 80 95	None
Moisture- and Heat-Resistant Cross-Linked Synthetic Polymer	XHHW ††, †††	90° C 194° F 75° C 167° F	Dry and damp locations. Wet locations.	Flame-Retardant Cross-Linked Synthetic Polymer	14-10 8-2 1-4/0 213-500 501-1000 1001-2000	30 45 55 65 80 95	None
Moisture- and Heat-Resistant Cross-Linked Synthetic Polymer	XHHW-2	90° C 194° F	Dry and wet locations.	Flame-Retardant Cross-Linked Synthetic Polymer	14-10 8-2 1-4/0 213-500 501-1000 1001-2000	30 45 55 65 80 95	None

*Includes integral jacket.
**For ampacity limitation, see Section 339-5.
***Insulation thickness shall be permitted to be 80 mils for listed Type USE conductors that have been subjected to special investigations.
****Some insulations do not require an outer covering.
††Insulation and outer coverings that meet the requirements of flame-retardant, limited-smoke and are so listed shall be permitted to be designated limited-smoke with the suffix /LS after the Code type designation.
†††Listed wire types designated with the suffix "-2 ," such as RHW-2 , shall be permitted to be used at a continuous 90°C-operating temperature, wet or dry.

Table 310-13, continued

Trade Name	Type Letter	Max. Operating Temp.	Application Provisions	Insulation	AWG or kcmil	Thickness of Insulation Mils	Outer Covering****
Modified Ethylene Tetrafluoro-ethylene	Z	90° C 194° F 150° C 302° F	Dry and damp locations. Dry locations—special appli-cations.†	Modified Ethylene Tetrafluoro-ethylene	14-12 10 8-4 3-1 1/0-4/0	15 20 25 35 45	None
Modified Ethylene Tetrafluoro-ethylene	ZW†††	75° C 167° F 90° C 194° F 150° C 302° F	Wet locations. Dry and damp locations. Dry locations—special appli-cations.†	Modified Ethylene Tetrafluoro-ethylene	14-10 8-2	30 45	None

****Some insulations do not require an outer covering.
†Where environmental conditions require maximum conductor operating temperatures above 90°C.
†††Listed wire types designated with the suffix "-2," such as RHW-2 , shall be permitted to be used at a continuous 90°C-operating temperature, wet or dry.

Table 310-13 also includes conductor applications and maximum operating temperatures. Some conductors have dual ratings. For example, Type XHHW is rated 90°C (194°F) for dry and damp locations and 75°C (167°F) for wet locations; or Type THW, which is rated 75°C (167°F) for dry and wet locations and 90°C (194°F) for special applications within electric-discharge lighting equipment.

Two new catagories of conductors were added to Table 310-13 in the 1990 *NEC*. Types RHW-2, XHHW-2, and other types identified by the suffix "-2" are conductors that are rated 90°C (194°F) for wet locations as well as dry and damp locations. Conductors permitted to be identified by the suffix "-2," other than Types RHW-2 and XHHW-2, are identified in the table by a triple obelisk (†††).

Some conductors are also permitted to be identified by the suffix "/LS" (meaning "low smoke") after the *Code* type designation (e.g., "THWN/LS"). These types are identified in the table by a double obelisk (††). Although the specific performance requirements for conductors identified by the suffix "/LS" had not been established at the time this commentary was prepared, the "/LS" identifier indicates a conductor that has been tested under fire conditions and found to propagate flame more slowly (if at all) and to generate less smoke than permitted for conductors not identified by the "/LS" suffix.

The maximum continuous ampacities for 0-2,000-volt copper, copper-clad aluminum, and aluminum are listed in Tables 310-16 through 310-19 and accompanying Notes 1 through 11, or they can be calculated in accordance with Section 310-15(b).

Copper-clad aluminum conductors are drawn from a copper-clad aluminum rod with the copper metallurgically bonded to an aluminum core. The copper forms a minimum of 10 percent of the cross-sectional area of a solid conductor or each strand of a stranded conductor. See also comments following Section 110-14.

The following table compares the characteristics of copper-clad aluminum with copper and aluminum conductors.

Conductor Characteristics

	Copper	Cu/Al	Aluminum
Density lbs/in³	0.323	0.121	0.098
Density gm/cm³	8.91	3.34	2.71
Resistivity ohms/CMF	10.37	16.08	16.78
Resistivity Microhm-CM	1.724	2.673	2.790
Conductivity (IACS%)	100	61-63	61
Weight % Copper	100	26.8	. . . . .
Tensile K psi-Hard	65.0	30.0	27.0
Tensile kg/mm²-Hard	45.7	21.1	19.0
Tensile K psi-Annealed	35.0	17.0	17.0*
Tensile kg/mm²-Annealed	24.6	12.0	12.0
Specific Gravity	8.91	3.34	2.71

*Semi-annealed

310-14. **Aluminum Conductor Material.** Solid aluminum conductors No. 8, 10, and 12 shall be made of an AA-8000 series electrical grade aluminum alloy conductor material. Stranded aluminum conductors No. 8 through 1000 kcmil marked as Type XHHW, THW, THHW, THWN, THHN, service-entrance Type SE Style U and SE Style R shall be made of an AA-8000 series electrical grade aluminum alloy conductor material.

This section provides proper recognition of approved aluminum alloy conductor material to coordinate with the ANSI/UL listing requirements for testing terminations suitable for use with aluminum conductors, such as CO/ALR devices.

310-15. **Ampacities.** Ampacities for conductors shall be permitted to be determined by (a) or (b) below.

Section 310-15 permits either of two methods of determining conductor ampacity for conductors rated 0 through 2,000 volts (0 through 5,000 volts for Type V conductors). The methods are: (1) to select the ampacity from a table, using correction factors in the table or notes where necessary; or (2) to calculate the ampacity. The latter method can be complex and time-consuming and requires engineering supervision. However, it can also result in lower installation costs in some cases, and, if calculation is done properly, it provides a mathematically exact ampacity. See commentary following Section 310-15(b) and accompanying Appendix B.

(FPN): Ampacities provided by this section do not take voltage drop into consideration. Conductors of circuits as defined in Article 100, sized to prevent a voltage drop exceeding 5 percent, will provide reasonable efficiency of operation.

(a) **General.** Ampacities for conductors rated 0 to 2000 volts shall be as specified in the Allowable Ampacity Tables 310-16 through 310-19 and their accompanying notes. Ampacities for solid dielectric insulated conductors rated 2001 through 35,000 volts shall be as specified in Tables 310-67 through 310-84 and their accompanying notes.

Tables 310-16 and 310-17 are based on a method of calculation developed by Sam J. Rosch and published in March 1938 in a paper entitled "The Current-Carrying Capacity of Rubber-Insulated Conductors," which appeared in "Electrical Engineering," a monthly publication of the American Institute of Electrical Engineers (predecessor of the Institute of Electrical and Electronic Engineers — IEEE). A copy of the paper was reprinted in the January/February 1981 issue of *IAEI News*, a publication of the International Association of Electrical Inspectors.

The ampacities in Tables 310-18 and 310-19 are based on the Neher-McGrath method of calculating current-carrying capacity. This is the same method used for calculation of the ampacities of the high-voltage conductors in Tables 310-69 through 310-84. See commentary following Section 310-15(b).

(FPN): Tables 310-16 through 310-19 are application tables that are for use in determining conductor sizes on loads calculated in accordance with Article 220. Allowable ampacities result from consideration of one or more of the following:

1. Temperature compatibility with connected equipment, especially at the connection points.
2. Coordination with circuit and system overcurrent protection.
3. Compliance with the requirements of product listings or certifications. See Section 110-3(b).
4. Preservation of the safety benefits of established industry practices and standardized procedures.

The ampacities in Table 310-16, in particular, do not take into account all of the many factors affecting ampacity. See commentary following Section 310-15(b) and accompanying Appendix B. However, experience over many years has proven the table values to be adequate where loads are calculated in accordance with Article 220. This is because not all of the diversity factors and load factors in most actual installations are specifically provided for in Article 220. If loads are not calculated in accordance with the requirements of Article 220, the table ampacities, even when corrected in accordance with ambient correction factors and the notes to the tables, may be too high. This can be particularly true where many cables or raceways are routed close to each other underground.

(b) **Engineering Supervision.** Under engineering supervision, conductor ampacities shall be permitted to be calculated by means of the following general formula:

$$I = \sqrt{\frac{TC - (TA + DELTA\ TD)}{RDC\ (1 + YC)RCA}}$$

Where:

TC = Conductor temperature in degrees C.

TA = Ambient temperature in degrees C.

DELTA TD = Dielectric loss temperature rise.

RDC = DC resistance of conductor at temperature TC.

YC = Component ac resistance resulting from skin effect and proximity effect.

RCA = Effective thermal resistance between conductor and surrounding ambient.

(FPN):   See Appendix B for examples of formula applications.

The formula in Section 310-15(b) was developed by Messrs. Neher and McGrath to determine conductor ampacity. It is actually a composite of a number of separate formulas. A description of this method of calculation was given in AIEE paper No. 5-660, "The Calculation of the Temperature Rise and Load Capability of Cable Systems" by J. H. Neher and M. H. McGrath. This paper was presented to the AIEE General Meeting in Montreal, Quebec, Canada on June 24-28, 1956, and was published in "AIEE Transactions," Part III (Power Apparatus and Systems), Vol. 76, October, 1957, pp. 752 through 772. AIEE is now IEEE (Institute of Electrical and Electronic Engineers).

The so-called Neher-McGrath formula in Section 310-15(b) is a heat transfer formula, composed of a series of heat transfer calculations, that takes into account all heat sources and the thermal resistances between the heat source and free air. The most common use for the Neher-McGrath formula is to calculate the ampacity of conductors in underground electrical ducts (raceways), although the formula is applicable to all conductor installations.

It is not the intent of the following to provide instruction on the use of the Neher-McGrath method of calculation. It is, rather, the intent to identify the many factors affecting the calculations. It is because of these many variables, and the complexities of the many formulas involved, that the *Code* requires that the calculation be made under engineering supervision.

Current passsing through a conductor produces I²R losses in the form of heat, which results from conductor losses and appears as a temperature rise in the conductor. This heat must pass through the cable insulation, the air in the raceway, and the raceway itself to the surrounding medium, usually earth or concrete, where it is dissipated into the air by radiation and convection. Unless the heat is dissipated, the temperature in the conductor will exceed the rating of the conductor insulation.

The conductor's ampacity is based on the rate of heat dissipation through the thermal resistances surrounding the conductor. Current traveling through a material with a specific resistance at a specified temperature generates this heat. Additional heat is caused by skin and proximity effects, since the current is usually alternating current and there are other conductors in the same duct.

For conductors in underground electrical ducts, there are several heat sources, as follows (see Figure 310-4):

1. Conductor losses due to the load current I²R. These vary with the load current, conductor material, and conductor cross-sectional area (conductor size).

2. Skin effect heating, if the current is alternating current. The heat developed by the skin effect is due to the shape of the conductor and based on the configuration of the conductors, i.e., solid, stranded, or compact.

3. Hysteresis losses, if the duct is steel or other magnetic material. These losses are dependent upon the magnetic properties of the electrical duct and the shape of the duct.

4. Heating from other conductors in the duct. This heating is based on the number, location, and proximity of other conductors, as well as the losses in the other conductors. The more conductors in the raceway, the greater the heating effect from these conductors is likely to be. This factor replaces the derating factors in Note 8(a) to the tables.

5. Mutual heating from other ducts, cables, etc. in the vicinity. The closer the other heat sources, and the more they surround the duct for which calculations are being made, the greater the heating effect. For example, in the case of a symmetrical 9-duct bank, 3 ducts high and 3 wide, the center duct will receive the most heat as a result of mutual heating.

Heat generated by these various types of losses is conducted through the different thermal resistances, which consist of conductor insulation, the air surrounding the

Figure 310-4. *Heat sources.*

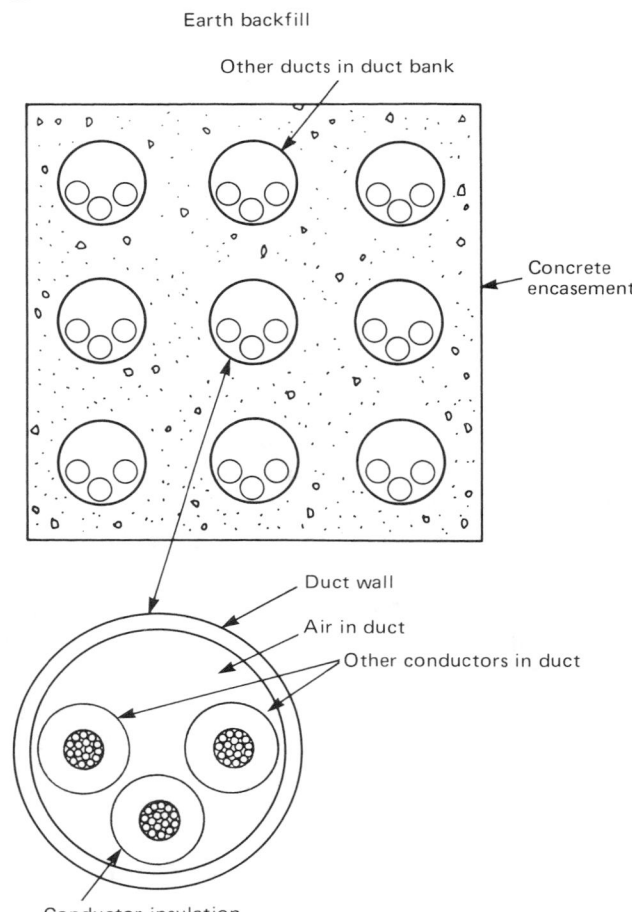

Figure 310-5. *Thermal barriers (resistances). The installation is the same as in Figure 310-4.*

conductors within the duct, the duct material, and the surrounding earth or concrete. To prevent the temperature of the conductors from exceeding the rated temperature of the insulation, heat dissipation through these thermal resistances must be equal to, or greater than, the heat developed. Thus, the thermal resistances of all the components of a conductor must be determined, and the allowable temperature differential above the ambient temperature, and between the conductors and the surface of the earth, must be known. See Figure 310-5.

The conductor insulation, which is designed to perform as a good electrical insulator, also serves as a good thermal insulator. It presents a thermal resistance to heat generated by the conductor due to the I^2R losses, including any dielectric losses. This thermal resistance value depends on the thickness of the insulation and the type of insulating material used. Materials such as polyvinyl chloride, used in Type THW and other conductors; cross-linked polyethylene, used in Type XHHW and other conductors; and rubber, used in Type RHW and other conductors, have different thermal resistivities. In addition, the thickness of the conductor insulation varies from one type of insulation to another, even for the same size conductor.

The next thermal barrier encountered by the heat flow generated in the conductor is the air space between the con ductor insulation and the surrounding wall or raceway. The thermal resistance of this air space is based on the number of conductors in the duct, the assumed mean value of the temperature of the air in the duct, and the constants provided in the Neher-McGrath paper, which were determined from experimental data.

After it passes through the air space around the conductors, the heat encounters the thermal resistance of the duct wall. This thermal resistance is based on the thermal resistivity of the type of material used and the thickness of the duct wall. Metallic materials have less thermal resistance than nonmetallic materials. The thicker the wall, the greater the thermal resistance.

The thermal resistance that must be considered next is that offered by the earth or other backfill material above the duct. This incorporates not only the resistivity of the earth and ambient temperature of the earth, but also the number of current-carrying conductors within the duct, the outside diameter of the duct, the burial depth, a loss factor, and the mutual heating factor caused by other nearby ducts. The deeper the duct is buried, the greater the thermal resistance.

In addition to the Neher-McGrath paper itself, as described in the first paragraph of this commentary, reference can be made to the following for more detailed information on use of this method of calculation.

"Power Cable Ampacities," Insulated Power Cable Engineers Association, IPCEA P-46-426 (IEEE S-135-1).

"Neher-McGrath Calculations for Insulated Power Cables," Peter Pollak, IEEE Paper No. CH2040-4/84/0000-0172, presented at the 1984 IEEE Industrial and Commercial Power Systems Technical Conference, Atlanta, GA, May 9, 1984.

"Cable Ampacities, the *NEC* and Computerized Applications," M.T. Brown, et. al., IEEE paper No. CH2207-9/85/00000-0323.

"How to Use the Neher-McGrath Method to Calculate Ampacity of Underground Conductors," John M. Caloggero, NFPA *Fire Journal*, pp. 17-18, May/June 1988.

(c) **Selection of Ampacity.** Where more than one calculated or tabulated ampacity could apply for a given circuit length, the lowest value shall be used.

Exception: Where two different ampacities apply to adjacent portions of a circuit, the higher ampacity shall be permitted to be used beyond the point of transition, a distance equal to 10 feet (3.05 m) or 10 percent of the circuit length figured at the higher ampacity, whichever is less.

For example, three 500 kcmil THW conductors in a rigid conduit are run from a motor control center for 12 feet past a heat-treating furnace to a pump motor located 150 feet from the motor control center. Where run in a 26°-30°C ambient, the conductors have an ampacity of 380 amperes, per Table 310-16.

The ambient temperature near the furnace, where the conduit is run, is found to be 45°C, and the length of this particular part of the run is greater than 10 feet and more than 10 percent of the total length of the run at the 26-30°C ambient.

In accordance with the ampacity correction factors for Table 310-16, the ampacity is 0.82 × 380 amperes, or 311.6 amperes. This, therefore, is the ampacity of the total run in accordance with Section 310-15(c).

Had the run near the furnace at the 45°C ambient been 10 feet or less in length, the ampacity of the entire run would have been 380 amperes, in accordance with the exception to Section 310-15(c). The heat-sinking effect of the run at the lower ambient temperature would have been sufficient to reduce the temperature of the conductor near the furnace.

(FPN): See Section 110-14(c) for conductor temperature limitations due to termination provisions.

(d) **Electrical Ducts.** Electrical ducts as used in Article 310 shall include any of the electrical conduits recognized in Chapter 3 as suitable for use underground; and other raceways round in cross section, listed for underground use; embedded in earth or concrete.

The term "electrical duct" is used to differentiate from "ducts" used for air handling, for example. It is intended to include nonmetallic electrical ducts commonly used for underground wiring as well as other raceways (e.g. rigid metal conduit, intermediate metal conduit, rigid nonmetallic conduit, etc.) listed for use underground in earth or concrete.

Table 310-16. Allowable Ampacities of Insulated Conductors Rated 0-2000 Volts, 60° to 90°C (140° to 194°F) Not More Than Three Conductors in Raceway or Cable or Earth (Directly Buried), Based on Ambient Temperature of 30°C (86°F)

Size	Temperature Rating of Conductor. See Table 310-13.						Size
	60°C (140°F)	75°C (167°F)	90°C (194°F)	60°C (140°F)	75°C (167°F)	90°C (194°F)	
AWG kcmil	TYPES TW†, UF†	TYPES FEPW†, RH†, RHW†, THHW†, THW†, THWN†, XHHW† USE†, ZW†	TYPES TA, TBS, SA SIS, FEP†, FEPB†, MI RHH†, RHW-2, THHN†, THHW†, THW-2, THWN-2, USE-2, XHH, XHHW† XHHW-2, ZW-2	TYPES TW†, UF†	TYPES RH†, RHW†, THHW†, THW†, THWN†, XHHW†, USE†	TYPES TA, TBS, SA, SIS, THHN†, THHW†, THW-2, THWN-2, RHH†, RHW-2, USE-2 XHH, XHHW, XHHW-2, ZW-2	AWG kcmil
	COPPER			ALUMINUM OR COPPER-CLAD ALUMINUM			
18	....	....	14	....	....	....	....
16	....	....	18	....	....	....	....
14	20†	20†	25†	....	....	....	....
12	25†	25†	30†	20†	20†	25†	12
10	30	35†	40†	25	30†	35†	10
8	40	50	55	30	40	45	8
6	55	65	75	40	50	60	6
4	70	85	95	55	65	75	4
3	85	100	110	65	75	85	3
2	95	115	130	75	90	100	2
1	110	130	150	85	100	115	1
1/0	125	150	170	100	120	135	1/0
2/0	145	175	195	115	135	150	2/0
3/0	165	200	225	130	155	175	3/0
4/0	195	230	260	150	180	205	4/0
250	215	255	290	170	205	230	250
300	240	285	320	190	230	255	300
350	260	310	350	210	250	280	350
400	280	335	380	225	270	305	400
500	320	380	430	260	310	350	500
600	355	420	475	285	340	385	600
700	385	460	520	310	375	420	700
750	400	475	535	320	385	435	750
800	410	490	555	330	395	450	800
900	435	520	585	355	425	480	900
1000	455	545	615	375	445	500	1000
1250	495	590	665	405	485	545	1250
1500	520	625	705	435	520	585	1500
1750	545	650	735	455	545	615	1750
2000	560	665	750	470	560	630	2000

CORRECTION FACTORS

Ambient Temp. °C	For ambient temperatures other than 30°C (86°F), multiply the allowable ampacities shown above by the appropriate factor shown below.						Ambient Temp. °F
21-25	1.08	1.05	1.04	1.08	1.05	1.04	70-77
26-30	1.00	1.00	1.00	1.00	1.00	1.00	78-86
31-35	.91	.94	.96	.91	.94	.96	87-95
36-40	.82	.88	.91	.82	.88	.91	96-104
41-45	.71	.82	.87	.71	.82	.87	105-113
46-50	.58	.75	.82	.58	.75	.82	114-122
51-55	.41	.67	.76	.41	.67	.76	123-131
56-60	....	.58	.71	....	.58	.71	132-140
61-70	....	.33	.58	....	.33	.58	141-158
71-80	....	....	.41	....	....	.41	159-176

† Unless otherwise specifically permitted elsewhere in this Code, the overcurrent protection for conductor types marked with an obelisk (†) shall not exceed 15 amperes for No. 14, 20 amperes for No. 12, and 30 amperes for No. 10 copper; or 15 amperes for No. 12 and 25 amperes for No. 10 aluminum and copper-clad aluminum after any correction factors for ambient temperature and number of conductors have been applied.

Table 310-17. Allowable Ampacities of Single Insulated Conductors, Rated 0 through 2000 Volts, In Free Air Based on Ambient Air Temperature of 30°C (86°F)

Size	Temperature Rating of Conductor. See Table 310-13.						Size
	60°C (140°F)	75°C (167°F)	90°C (194°F)	60°C (140°F)	75°C (167°F)	90°C (194°F)	
AWG kcmil	TYPES TW†, UF†	TYPES FEPW†, RH†, RHW†, THHW†, THW†, THWN†, XHHW†, ZW†	TYPES TA, TBS, SA, SIS, FEP†, FEPB†, MI, RHH†, RHW-2, THHN†, THHW†, THW-2, THWN-2, USE-2, XHH, XHHW†, XHHW-2, ZW-2	TYPES TW†, UF†	TYPES RH†, RHW†, THHW†, THW†, THWN†, XHHW†	TYPES TA, TBS, SA, SIS, THHN†, THHW†, THW-2, THWN-2, RHH†, RHW-2, USE-2, XHH, XHHW†, XHHW-2, ZW-2	AWG kcmil
	COPPER			ALUMINUM OR COPPER-CLAD ALUMINUM			
18	. . . .	. . . .	18	. . . .	. . . .	. . . .	. . . .
16	. . . .	. . . .	24	. . . .	. . . .	. . . .	. . . .
14	25†	30†	35†	. . . .	. . . .	. . . .	. . . .
12	30†	35†	40†	25†	30†	35†	12
10	40†	50†	55†	35†	40†	40†	10
8	60	70	80	45	55	60	8
6	80	95	105	60	75	80	6
4	105	125	140	80	100	110	4
3	120	145	165	95	115	130	3
2	140	170	190	110	135	150	2
1	165	195	220	130	155	175	1
1/0	195	230	260	150	180	205	1/0
2/0	225	265	300	175	210	235	2/0
3/0	260	310	350	200	240	275	3/0
4/0	300	360	405	235	280	315	4/0
250	340	405	455	265	315	355	250
300	375	445	505	290	350	395	300
350	420	505	570	330	395	445	350
400	455	545	615	355	425	480	400
500	515	620	700	405	485	545	500
600	575	690	780	455	540	615	600
700	630	755	855	500	595	675	700
750	655	785	885	515	620	700	750
800	680	815	920	535	645	725	800
900	730	870	985	580	700	785	900
1000	780	935	1055	625	750	845	1000
1250	890	1065	1200	710	855	960	1250
1500	980	1175	1325	795	950	1075	1500
1750	1070	1280	1445	875	1050	1185	1750
2000	1155	1385	1560	960	1150	1335	2000

CORRECTION FACTORS

Ambient Temp. °C	For ambient temperatures other than 30°C (86°F), multiply the allowable ampacities shown above by the appropriate factor shown below.						Ambient Temp. °F
21-25	1.08	1.05	1.04	1.08	1.05	1.04	70-77
26-30	1.00	1.00	1.00	1.00	1.00	1.00	78-86
31-35	.91	.94	.96	.91	.94	.96	87-95
36-40	.82	.88	.91	.82	.88	.91	96-104
41-45	.71	.82	.87	.71	.82	.87	105-113
46-50	.58	.75	.82	.58	.75	.82	114-122
51-55	.41	.67	.76	.41	.67	.76	123-131
56-60	. . . .	.58	.71	. . . .	.58	.71	132-140
61-70	. . . .	.33	.58	. . . .	.33	.58	141-158
71-80	. . . .	. . . .	.41	. . . .	. . . .	.41	159-176

† Unless otherwise specifically permitted elsewhere in this Code, the overcurrent protection for conductor types marked with an obelisk (†) shall not exceed 15 amperes for No. 14, 20 amperes for No. 12, and 30 amperes for No. 10 copper; or 15 amperes for No. 12 and 25 amperes for No. 10 aluminum and copper-clad aluminum.

Table 310-18. Allowable Ampacities of Three Single Insulated Conductors Rated 0 through 2000 Volts, 150° to 250°C (302° to 482°F), in Raceway or Cable Based on Ambient Air Temperature of 40°C (104°F)

Size	Temperature Rating of Conductor. See Table 310-13.				Size
AWG kcmil	150°C (302°F) TYPE Z	200°C (392°F) TYPES FEP, FEPB, PFA	250°C (482°F) TYPES PFAH, TFE	150°C (302°F) TYPE Z	AWG kcmil
	COPPER		NICKEL OR NICKEL-COATED COPPER	ALUMINUM OR COPPER-CLAD ALUMINUM	
14	34	36	39	. . . .	14
12	43	45	54	30	12
10	55	60	73	44	10
8	76	83	93	57	8
6	96	110	117	75	6
4	120	125	148	94	4
3	143	152	166	109	3
2	160	171	191	124	2
1	186	197	215	145	1
1/0	215	229	244	169	1/0
2/0	251	260	273	198	2/0
3/0	288	297	308	227	3/0
4/0	332	346	361	260	4/0
250	. . . .	. . . .	. . . .	. . . .	250
300	. . . .	. . . .	. . . .	. . . .	300
350	. . . .	. . . .	. . . .	. . . .	350
400	. . . .	. . . .	. . . .	. . . .	400
500	. . . .	. . . .	. . . .	. . . .	500
600	. . . .	. . . .	. . . .	. . . .	600
700	. . . .	. . . .	. . . .	. . . .	700
750	. . . .	. . . .	. . . .	. . . .	750
800	. . . .	. . . .	. . . .	. . . .	800
1000	. . . .	. . . .	. . . .	. . . .	1000
1500	. . . .	. . . .	. . . .	. . . .	1500
2000	. . . .	. . . .	. . . .	. . . .	2000

CORRECTION FACTORS

Ambient Temp. °C	For ambient temperatures other than 40°C (104°F), multiply the allowable ampacities shown above by the appropriate factor shown below.				Ambient Temp. °F
41-50	.95	.97	.98	.95	105-122
51-60	.90	.94	.95	.90	123-140
61-70	.85	.90	.93	.85	141-158
71-80	.80	.87	.90	.80	159-176
81-90	.74	.83	.87	.74	177-194
91-100	.67	.79	.85	.67	195-212
101-120	.52	.71	.79	.52	213-248
121-140	.30	.61	.72	.30	249-284
141-160	. . . .	.50	.65	. . . .	285-320
161-180	. . . .	.35	.58	. . . .	321-356
181-200	. . . .	. . . .	.49	. . . .	357-392
201-225	. . . .	. . . .	.35	. . . .	393-437

Table 310-19. Allowable Ampacities for Single Insulated Conductors Rated 0 through 2000 Volts, 150° to 250°C (302° to 482°F), in Free Air Based on Ambient Air Temperature of 40°C (104°F)

Size	Temperature Rating of Conductor. See Table 310-13.						Size
AWG kcmil	150°C (302°F) TYPE Z	200°C (392°F) TYPES FEP, FEPB, PFA	Bare or covered conductors	250°C (482°F) TYPES PFAH, TFE	150°C (302°F) TYPE Z	Bare or covered conductors	AWG kcmil
	COPPER			NICKEL OR NICKEL-COATED COPPER	ALUMINUM OR COPPER-CLAD ALUMINUM		
14	46	54	30	59	. . . .	25	14
12	60	68	35	78	47	30	12
10	80	90	50	107	63	35	10
8	106	124	70	142	83	55	8
6	155	165	95	205	112	75	6
4	190	220	125	278	148	100	4
3	214	252	150	327	170	120	3
2	255	293	175	381	198	135	2
1	293	344	200	440	228	160	1
1/0	339	399	235	532	263	185	1/0
2/0	390	467	275	591	305	215	2/0
3/0	451	546	320	708	351	250	3/0
4/0	529	629	370	830	411	285	4/0
250	. . . .	. . . .	415	. . . .	. . . .	325	250
300	. . . .	. . . .	460	. . . .	. . . .	360	300
350	. . . .	. . . .	520	. . . .	. . . .	405	350
400	. . . .	. . . .	560	. . . .	. . . .	435	400
500	. . . .	. . . .	635	. . . .	. . . .	495	500
600	. . . .	. . . .	710	. . . .	. . . .	560	600
700	. . . .	. . . .	780	. . . .	. . . .	615	700
750	. . . .	. . . .	805	. . . .	. . . .	635	750
800	. . . .	. . . .	835	. . . .	. . . .	660	800
900	. . . .	. . . .	865	. . . .	. . . .	715	900
1000	. . . .	. . . .	895	. . . .	. . . .	770	1000
1500	. . . .	. . . .	1205	. . . .	. . . .	980	1500
2000	. . . .	. . . .	1420	. . . .	. . . .	1215	2000

CORRECTION FACTORS

Ambient Temp. °C	For ambient temperatures other than 40°C (104°F), multiply the allowable ampacities shown above by the appropriate factor shown below.						Ambient Temp. °F
41-50	.95	.97	. . . .	.98	.95	. . . .	105-122
51-60	.90	.94	. . . .	.95	.90	. . . .	123-140
61-70	.85	.90	. . . .	.93	.85	. . . .	141-158
71-80	.80	.87	. . . .	.90	.80	. . . .	159-176
81-90	.74	.83	. . . .	.87	.74	. . . .	177-194
91-100	.67	.79	. . . .	.85	.67	. . . .	195-212
101-120	.52	.71	. . . .	.79	.52	. . . .	213-248
121-140	.30	.61	. . . .	.72	.30	. . . .	249-284
141-160	. . . .	.50	. . . .	.65	. . . .	. . . .	285-320
161-180	. . . .	.35	. . . .	.58	. . . .	. . . .	321-356
181-200	. . . .	. . . .	. . . .	.49	. . . .	. . . .	357-392
201-225	. . . .	. . . .	. . . .	.35	. . . .	. . . .	393-437

Notes to Ampacity Tables of 0 to 2000 Volts

1. Explanation of Tables. For explanation of type letters and for recognized size of conductors for the various conductor insulations, see Section 310-13. For installation requirements, see Sections 310-1 through 310-10 and the various articles of this Code. For flexible cords, see Tables 400-4, 400-5(A), and 400-5(B).

3. 120/240 Volts, 3-Wire, Single-Phase Dwelling Services and Feeders. For dwelling units, conductors, as listed below, shall be permitted to be utilized as 120/240-volt, 3-wire, single-phase service-entrance conductors, service lateral conductors, and feeder conductors that supply the total load to a dwelling unit and installed in raceway or cable with or without an equipment grounding conductor. The grounded conductor shall be permitted to be not more than two AWG sizes smaller than the ungrounded conductors for application of this note, provided the requirements of Sections 215-2, 220-22, and 230-42 are met.

Conductor Types and Sizes
RH-RHH-RHW-THHW-THW-THWN-THHN-XHHW-USE

Copper	Aluminum or Copper-Clad AL	Rating in Amps
AWG	AWG	
4	2	100
3	1	110
2	1/0	125
1	2/0	150
1/0	3/0	175
2/0	4/0	200
3/0	250 kcmil	225
4/0	300 kcmil	250
250 kcmil	350 kcmil	300
350 kcmil	500 kcmil	350
400 kcmil	600 kcmil	400

If a single set of 3-wire, single-phase, service-entrance conductors in raceway or cable supplies a one-family, two-family, or multifamily dwelling, the reduced conductor size permitted by Note 3 is applicable to the service-entrance conductors, service lateral conductors, or any feeder conductors that supply the total load to a dwelling unit. If there are panelboards on the load side of the main service-entrance equipment supplied by feeders, Note 3 does not permit a reduction in the conductor size if the feeder does not supply the total load of the dwelling unit. For example, the feeder conductors supplying a subpanel for a swimming pool would not be permitted to be reduced in accordance with Note 3 as a result of a revision for the 1993 *NEC*. See Figures 310-6 and 310-7.

Other sections of the *Code* must also be applied for determining the size of service or feeder conductors. Section 230-42 requires service conductors to be of sufficient size to carry the load calculated in accordance with Article 220. It should not be taken for granted that the grounded (neutral) conductor can be automatically reduced two sizes. The grounded (neutral) conductor must provide a low impedance fault path capable of conducting fault current back to the transformer. Section 250-23(b) provides the requirements for determining the minimum size grounded (neutral) conductor.

Section 250-23(b) is not applicable to the grounded (neutral) conductor of *feeders*; therefore, the minimum size is governed by Section 220-22. This section requires the grounded (neutral) conductor to be large enough to carry the maximum unbalance of the net computed load connected to the neutral and any one ungrounded conductor. In the event that there are no 240-volt loads, the neutral, under severe unbalanced conditions, will carry the same current as the ungrounded conductor supplying the load.

5. Bare Conductors. Where bare conductors are used with insulated conductors, their allowable ampacities shall be limited to those permitted for the adjacent insulated conductors.

6. Mineral-Insulated, Metal-Sheathed Cable. The temperature limitation on which the ampacities of mineral-insulated, metal-sheathed cable are based is determined by the insulating materials used in the end seal. Termination fittings incorporating unimpregnated, organic, insulating materials are limited to 90°C (194°F) operation.

7. Type MTW Machine Tool Wire.

(FPN): For the allowable ampacities of Type MTW wire, see Table 13-5(a) in the Electrical Standard for Industrial Machinery, NFPA 79-1991.

8. Adjustment Factors.

(a) More than Three Current-Carrying Conductors in a Raceway or Cable. Where the number of current-carrying conductors in a raceway or cable exceeds three, the allowable ampacities shall be reduced as shown in the following table:

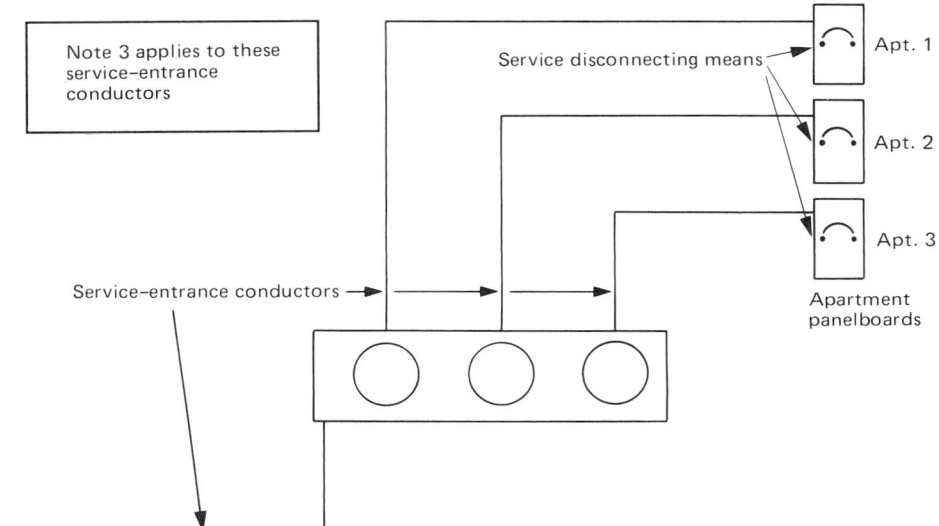

Figure 310-6. *The reduced conductor size permitted in Note 3 of Notes to Ampacity Tables of 0 to 2000 Volts is applicable to the conductors run to each apartment from the meters.*

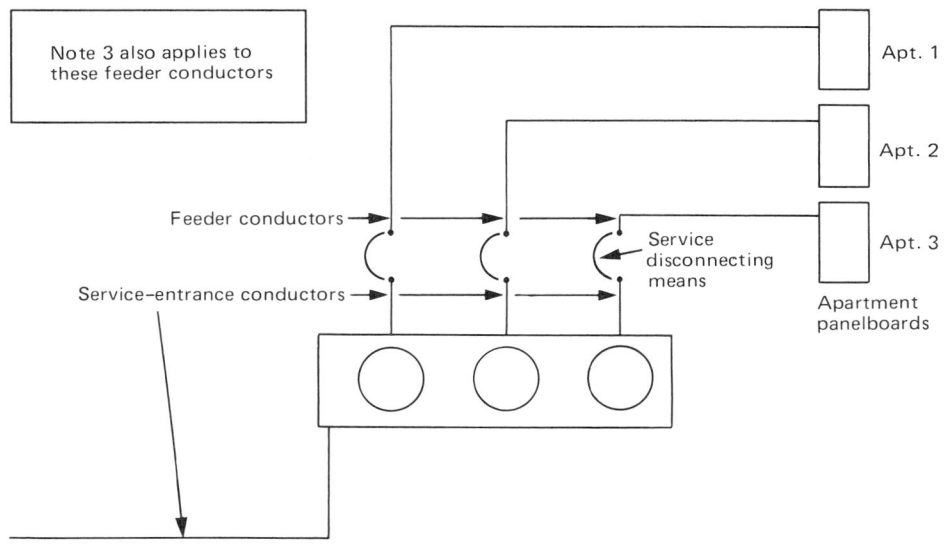

Figure 310-7. *The reduced conductor size permitted in Note 3 of Notes to Ampacity Tables of 0 to 2000 Volts is also applicable to the feeder conductors run to each apartment from the service disconnecting means because these feeders carry the entire load to each apartment.*

Number of Current-Carrying Conductors	Percent of Values in Tables as Adjusted for Ambient Temperature if Necessary
4 through 6	80
7 through 9	70
10 through 20	50
21 through 30	45
31 through 40	40
41 and above	35

The table in Note 8(a) was revised for the 1993 *Code.* The adjustment factors in the second column of the table are the factors that appeared in Column B of the 1990 edition. These factors are based on no diversity. This means that all conductors in the raceway or cable are loaded to their maximum rated load. The calculation of ampacity where there is load diversity is still permitted. However, it must be calculated under engineering supervision in accordance with Section 310-15(b). See Appendix B.

Where single conductors or multiconductor cables are stacked or bundled longer than 24 inches (610 mm) without maintaining spacing and are not installed in raceways, the allowable ampacity of each conductor shall be reduced as shown in the above table.

Exception No. 1: Where conductors of different systems, as provided in Section 300-3, are installed in a common raceway or cable, the derating factors shown above shall apply to the number of power and lighting (Articles 210, 215, 220, and 230) conductors only.

It is assumed that the watt loss (heating) from any control and signal conductors in the same raceway or cable will not be enough to significantly increase the temperature of the power and lighting conductors. See Sections 725-15 and 725-52(b)(2) for limitations on the installation of control and signal conductors in the same raceway or cable as power and lighting conductors.

Exception No. 2: For conductors installed in cable trays, the provisions of Section 318-11 shall apply.

Exception No. 3: Derating factors shall not apply to conductors in nipples having a length not exceeding 24 inches (610 mm).

Exception No. 4: Derating factors shall not apply to underground conductors entering or leaving an outdoor trench if those conductors have physical protection in the form of rigid metal conduit, intermediate metal conduit, or rigid nonmetallic conduit having a length not exceeding 10 feet (3.05 m) above grade and the number of conductors does not exceed four.

Exception No. 5: For other loading conditions, adjustment factors and ampacities shall be permitted to be calculated under Section 310-15(b).

(FPN): See Appendix B, Table B-310-11 for adjustment factors for more than three current-carrying conductors in a raceway or cable with load diversity.

(b) More than One Conduit, Tube, or Raceway. Spacing between conduits, tubing, or raceways shall be maintained.

Spacing is normally maintained between individual conduits in groups of conduit runs from junction box to junction box because of the need to separate the conduits where they enter the junction box to allow room for locknuts and bushings. Field experience has indicated this degree of spacing between runs has not caused any problems.

Figure 310-8. Application of Exception No. 4.

9. Overcurrent Protection. Where the standard ratings and settings of overcurrent devices do not correspond with the ratings and settings allowed for conductors, the next higher standard rating and setting shall be permitted.

Exception: As limited in Section 240-3.

10. Neutral Conductor.

(a) A neutral conductor that carries only the unbalanced current from other conductors of the same circuit need not be counted when applying the provisions of Note 8.

(b) In a 3-wire circuit consisting of 2-phase wires and the neutral of a 4-wire, 3-phase wye-connected system, a common conductor carries approximately the same current as the other conductors and shall be counted when applying the provisions of Note 8.

(c) On a 4-wire, 3-phase wye circuit where the major portion of the load consists of nonlinear loads such as electric-discharge lighting, electronic computer/data processing, or similar equipment, there are harmonic currents present in the neutral conductor, and the neutral shall be considered to be a current-carrying conductor.

Third harmonic currents in 3-phase, 4-wire, wye-connected power systems supplying electronic data processing and similar equipment are capable of causing the current in the neutral to exceed that in the phase conductor.

Third harmonics in this type of equipment are a result of the use of diodes charging capacitors on the input of power supplies. The current waveforms characteristic of such a load are very high in third harmonics. Third harmonics, in contrast to the fundamental, are not reduced by balancing the load. As a result, the neutral conductor, in areas of concentrated electronic loads such as computer installations, production test areas, etc., should not have its ampacity reduced. See also commentary following Section 210-4(a)FPN.

11. Grounding or Bonding Conductor. A grounding or bonding conductor shall not be counted when applying the provisions of Note 8.

Table 310-61. Conductor Application and Insulation

Trade Name	Type Letter	Maximum Operating Temperature	Application Provision	Insulation	Outer Covering
Medium voltage solid dielectric	MV-75* MV-85* MV-90*	75° C 85° C 90° C	Dry or wet locations rated 2001 volts and higher	Thermoplastic or Thermosetting	Jacket, Sheath, or Armor

*Insulation and outer coverings that meet the requirements as flame-retardant limited-smoke and are so listed shall be permitted to be designated limited-smoke with the suffix LS after the Code type designation.

Table 310-62. Thickness of Insulation for 601-2000-Volt Nonshielded Types RHH and RHW, in Mils

Conductor Size AWG-kcmil	A	B
14-10	80	60
8	80	70
6-2	95	70
1-2/0	110	90
3/0-4/0	110	90
213-500	125	105
501-1000	140	120

Note: Column A insulations are limited to natural, SBR, and butyl rubbers.
Note: Column B insulations are materials such as cross-linked polyethylene, ethylene propylene rubber, and composites thereof.

Table 310-63. Thickness of Insulation and Jacket for Nonshielded Solid Dielectric Insulated Conductors Rated 2001 to 8000 Volts, in Mils

Conductor-Size AWG-kcmil	2001-5000 Volts						5001-8000 Volts 100 Percent Insulation Level Wet or Dry Locations		
	Dry Locations Single Conductor			Wet or Dry Locations			Single Conductor		Multi-Conductor*
	Without Jacket	With Jacket		Single Conductor		Multi-Conductor*			
	Insulation	Insulation	Jacket	Insulation	Jacket	Insulation	Insulation	Jacket	Insulation
8	110	90	30	125	80	90	180	80	180
6	110	90	30	125	80	90	180	80	180
4-2	110	90	45	125	80	90	180	95	180
1-2/0	110	90	45	125	80	90	180	95	180
3/0-4/0	110	90	65	125	95	90	180	110	180
213-500	120	90	65	140	110	90	210	110	210
501-750	130	90	65	155	125	90	235	125	235
751-1000	130	90	65	155	125	90	250	140	250

*Note: Under a common overall covering such as a jacket, sheath, or armor.

Table 310-64. Thickness of Insulation for Shielded Solid Dielectric Insulated Conductors Rated 2001 to 35,000 Volts, in Mils

Conductor Size AWG-kcmil	2001-5000 Volts	5001-8000		8001-15,000		15,001-25,000		25,001-28,000	28,001-35,000
		100 Percent insula-tion level	133 Percent insula-tion level	100 Percent insula-tion level	133 Percent insula-tion level	100 Percent insula-tion level	133 Percent insula-tion level	100 Percent insulation level	100 Percent insulation level
8	90	—	—	—	—	—	—	—	—
6-4	90	115	140	—	—	—	—	—	—
2	90	115	140	175	215	—	—	—	—
1	90	115	140	175	215	260	345	280	—
1/0-1000	90	115	140	175	215	260	345	280	345

*Definitions:

100 Percent Insulation Level. Cables in this category shall be permitted to be applied where the system is provided with relay protection such that ground faults will be cleared as rapidly as possible but, in any case, within 1 minute. While these cables are applicable to the great majority of cable installations that are on grounded systems, they shall be permitted to be used also on other systems for which the application of cables is acceptable, provided the above clearing requirements are met in completely deenergizing the faulted section.

133 Percent Insulation Level. This insulation level corresponds to that formerly designated for ungrounded systems. Cables in this category shall be permitted to be applied in situations where the clearing time requirements of the 100 percent level category cannot be met, and yet there is adequate assurance that the faulted section will be deenergized in a time not exceeding 1 hour. Also, they shall be permitted to be used where additional insulation strength over the 100 percent level category is desirable.

Table 310-67. Ampacities of Insulated Single Copper Conductor Cables Triplexed in Air Based on Conductor Temperature of 90°C (194°F) and Ambient Air Temperature of 40°C (104°F)

Conductor Size AWG-kcmil	2001-5000 Volts Ampacity	5001-35,000 Volts Ampacity
8	65	—
6	90	100
4	120	130
2	160	170
1	185	195
1/0	215	225
2/0	250	260
3/0	290	300
4/0	335	345
250	375	380
350	465	470
500	580	580
750	750	730
1000	880	850

Table 310-68. Ampacities of Insulated Single Aluminum Conductor Cables Triplexed in Air Based on Conductor Temperature of 90°C (194°F) and Ambient Air Temperature of 40°C (104°F)

Conductor Size AWG-kcmil	2001-5000 Volts Ampacity	5001-35,000 Volts Ampacity
8	50	—
6	70	75
4	90	100
2	125	130
1	145	150
1/0	170	175
2/0	195	200
3/0	225	230
4/0	265	270
250	295	300
350	365	370
500	460	460
750	600	590
1000	715	700

Table 310-69. Ampacities of Insulated Single Copper Conductor Isolated in Air Based on Conductor Temperature of 90°C (194°F) and Ambient Air Temperature of 40°C (104°F)

Conductor Size AWG-kcmil	2001-5000 Volts Ampacity	5001-15,000 Volts Ampacity	15,001-35,000 Volts Ampacity
8	83	—	—
6	110	110	—
4	145	150	—
2	190	195	—
1	225	225	225
1/0	260	260	260
2/0	300	300	300
3/0	345	345	345
4/0	400	400	395
250	445	445	440
350	550	550	545
500	695	685	680
750	900	885	870
1000	1075	1060	1040
1250	1230	1210	1185
1500	1365	1345	1315
1750	1495	1470	1430
2000	1605	1575	1535

Table 310-71. Ampacities of an Insulated Three-Conductor Copper Cable Isolated in Air Based on Conductor Temperature of 90°C (194°F) and Ambient Air Temperature of 40°C (104°F)

Conductor Size AWG-kcmil	2001-5000 Volts Ampacity	5001-35,000 Volts Ampacity
8	59	—
6	79	93
4	105	120
2	140	165
1	160	185
1/0	185	215
2/0	215	245
3/0	250	285
4/0	285	325
250	320	360
350	395	435
500	485	535
750	615	670
1000	705	770

Table 310-70. Ampacities of Insulated Single Aluminum Conductor Isolated in Air Based on Conductor Temperature of 90°C (194°F) and Ambient Air Temperature of 40°C (104°F)

Conductor Size AWG-kcmil	2001-5000 Volts Ampacity	5001-15,000 Volts Ampacity	15,001-35,000 Volts Ampacity
8	64	—	—
6	85	87	—
4	115	115	—
2	150	150	—
1	175	175	175
1/0	200	200	200
2/0	230	235	230
3/0	270	270	270
4/0	310	310	310
250	345	345	345
350	430	430	430
500	545	535	530
750	710	700	685
1000	855	840	825
1250	980	970	950
1500	1105	1085	1060
1750	1215	1195	1165
2000	1320	1295	1265

Table 310-72. Ampacities of an Insulated Three-Conductor Aluminum Cable Isolated in Air Based on Conductor Temperature of 90°C (194°F) and Ambient Air Temperature of 40°C (104°F)

Conductor Size AWG-kcmil	2001-5000 Volts Ampacity	5001-35,000 Volts Ampacity
8	46	—
6	61	72
4	81	95
2	110	125
1	125	145
1/0	145	170
2/0	170	190
3/0	195	220
4/0	225	255
250	250	280
350	310	345
500	385	425
750	495	540
1000	585	635

Table 310-73. Ampacities of an Insulated Triplexed or Three Single Conductor Copper Cables in Isolated Conduit in Air Based on Conductor Temperature of 90°C (194°F) and Ambient Air Temperature of 40°C (104°F)

Conductor Size AWG-kcmil	2001-5000 Volts Ampacity	5001-35,000 Volts Ampacity
8	55	—
6	75	83
4	97	110
2	130	150
1	155	170
1/0	180	195
2/0	205	225
3/0	240	260
4/0	280	295
250	315	330
350	385	395
500	475	480
750	600	585
1000	690	675

Table 310-75. Ampacities of an Insulated Three-Conductor Copper Cable in Isolated Conduit in Air Based on Conductor Temperature of 90°C (194°F) and Ambient Air Temperature of 40°C (104°F)

Conductor Size AWG-kcmil	2001-5000 Volts Ampacity	5001-35,000 Volts Ampacity
8	52	—
6	69	83
4	91	105
2	125	145
1	140	165
1/0	165	195
2/0	190	220
3/0	220	250
4/0	255	290
250	280	315
350	350	385
500	425	470
750	525	570
1000	590	650

Table 310-74. Ampacities of Insulated Triplexed or Three Single Conductor Aluminum Cables in Isolated Conduit in Air Based on Conductor Temperature of 90°C (194°F) and Ambient Air Temperature of 40°C (104°F)

Conductor Size AWG-kcmil	2001-5000 Volts Ampacity	5001-35,000 Volts Ampacity
8	43	—
6	58	65
4	76	84
2	100	115
1	120	130
1/0	140	150
2/0	160	175
3/0	190	200
4/0	215	230
250	250	255
350	305	310
500	380	385
750	490	485
1000	580	565

Table 310-76. Ampacities of an Insulated Three-Conductor Aluminum Cable in Isolated Conduit in Air Based on Conductor Temperature of 90°C (194°F) and Ambient Air Temperature of 40°C (104°F)

Conductor Size AWG-kcmil	2001-5000 Volts Ampacity	5001-35,000 Volts Ampacity
8	41	—
6	53	64
4	71	84
2	96	115
1	110	130
1/0	130	150
2/0	150	170
3/0	170	195
4/0	200	225
250	220	250
350	275	305
500	340	380
750	430	470
1000	505	550

Table 310-77. Ampacities of Three Single Insulated Copper Conductors in Underground Electrical Ducts (Three Conductors per Electrical Duct) Based on Ambient Earth Temperature of 20°C (68°F), Electrical Duct Arrangement per Figure 310-1, 100 percent Load Factor, Thermal Resistance (RHO) of 90, Conductor Temperature 90°C (194°F)

Size AWG-kcmil	2001-5000 Volts Ampacity	5001-35,000 Volts Ampacity
One Circuit (See Figure 310-1, Detail 1)		
8	64	—
6	85	90
4	110	115
2	145	155
1	170	175
1/0	195	200
2/0	220	230
3/0	250	260
4/0	290	295
250	320	325
350	385	390
500	470	465
750	585	565
1000	670	640
Three Circuits (See Figure 310-1, Detail 2) Size		
8	56	—
6	73	77
4	95	99
2	125	130
1	140	145
1/0	160	165
2/0	185	185
3/0	210	210
4/0	235	240
250	260	260
350	315	310
500	375	370
750	460	440
1000	525	495
Six Circuits (See Figure 310-1, Detail 3) Size		
8	48	—
6	62	64
4	80	82
2	105	105
1	115	120
1/0	135	135
2/0	150	150
3/0	170	170
4/0	195	190
250	210	210
350	250	245
500	300	290
750	365	350
1000	410	390

Table 310-78. Ampacities of Three Single Insulated Aluminum Conductors in Underground Electrical Ducts (Three Conductors per Electrical Duct) Based on Ambient Earth Temperature of 20°C (68°F), Electrical Duct Arrangement per Figure 310-1, 100 percent Load Factor, Thermal Resistance (RHO) of 90, Conductor Temperature of 90°C (194°F)

Size AWG-kcmil	2001-5000 Volts Ampacity	5001-35,000 Volts Ampacity
One Circuit (See Figure 310-1, Detail 1)		
8	50	—
6	66	70
4	86	91
2	115	120
1	130	135
1/0	150	155
2/0	170	175
3/0	195	200
4/0	225	230
250	250	250
350	305	305
500	370	370
750	470	455
1000	545	525
Three Circuits (See Figure 310-1, Detail 2) Size		
8	44	—
6	57	60
4	74	77
2	96	100
1	110	110
1/0	125	125
2/0	145	145
3/0	160	165
4/0	185	185
250	205	200
350	245	245
500	295	290
750	370	355
1000	425	405
Six Circuits (See Figure 310-1, Detail 3) Size		
8	38	—
6	48	50
4	62	64
2	80	80
1	91	90
1/0	105	105
2/0	115	115
3/0	135	130
4/0	150	150
250	165	165
350	195	195
500	240	230
750	290	280
1000	335	320

Table 310-79. Ampacities of Three Insulated Copper Conductors Cabled within an Overall Covering (Three-Conductor Cable) in Underground Electrical Ducts (One Cable per Electrical Duct) Based on Ambient Earth Temperature of 20°C (68°F), Electrical Duct Arrangement per Figure 310-1, 100 percent Load Factor, Thermal Resistance (RHO) of 90, Conductor Temperature 90°C (194°F)

Size AWG-kcmil	2001-5000 Volts Ampacity	5001-35,000 Volts Ampacity
One Circuit (See Figure 310-1, Detail 1)		
8	59	—
6	78	88
4	100	115
2	135	150
1	155	170
1/0	175	195
2/0	200	220
3/0	230	250
4/0	265	285
250	290	310
350	355	375
500	430	450
750	530	545
1000	600	615
Three Circuits (See Figure 310-1, Detail 2) Size		
8	53	—
6	69	75
4	89	97
2	115	125
1	135	140
1/0	150	160
2/0	170	185
3/0	195	205
4/0	225	230
250	245	255
350	295	305
500	355	360
750	430	430
1000	485	485
Six Circuits (See Figure 310-1, Detail 3) Size		
8	46	—
6	60	63
4	77	81
2	98	105
1	110	115
1/0	125	130
2/0	145	150
3/0	165	170
4/0	185	190
250	200	205
350	240	245
500	290	290
750	350	340
1000	390	380

Table 310-80. Ampacities of Three Insulated Aluminum Conductors Cabled within an Overall Covering (Three-Conductor Cable) in Underground Electrical Ducts (One Cable per Electrical Duct) Based on Ambient Earth Temperature of 20°C (68°F), Electrical Duct Arrangement per Figure 310-1, 100 percent Load Factor, Thermal Resistance (RHO) of 90, Conductor Temperature 90°C (194°F)

Size AWG-kcmil	2001-5000 Volts Ampacity	5001-35,000 Volts Ampacity
One Circuit (See Figure 310-1, Detail 1)		
8	46	—
6	61	69
4	80	89
2	105	115
1	120	135
1/0	140	150
2/0	160	170
3/0	180	195
4/0	205	220
250	230	245
350	280	295
500	340	355
750	425	440
1000	495	510
Three Circuits (See Figure 310-1, Detail 2) Size		
8	41	—
6	54	59
4	70	75
2	90	100
1	105	110
1/0	120	125
2/0	135	140
3/0	155	160
4/0	175	180
250	190	200
350	230	240
500	280	285
750	345	350
1000	400	400
Six Circuits (See Figure 310-1, Detail 3) Size		
8	36	—
6	46	49
4	60	63
2	77	80
1	87	90
1/0	99	105
2/0	110	115
3/0	130	130
4/0	145	150
250	160	160
350	190	190
500	230	230
750	280	275
1000	320	315

Table 310-81. Ampacities of Single Insulated Copper Conductors Directly Buried in Earth Based on Ambient Earth Temperature of 20°C (68°F), Arrangement per Figure 310-1, 100 percent Load Factor, Thermal Resistance (RHO) of 90, Conductor Temperature 90°C (194°F)

Conductor Size AWG-kcmil	2001-5000 Volts Ampacity	5001-35,000 Volts Ampacity
One Circuit— 3 Conductors (See Figure 310-1, Detail 9)		
8	110	—
6	140	130
4	180	170
2	230	210
1	260	240
1/0	295	275
2/0	335	310
3/0	385	355
4/0	435	405
250	470	440
350	570	535
500	690	650
750	845	805
1000	980	930
Two Circuits— 6 Conductors (See Figure 310-1, Detail 10)		
8	100	—
6	130	120
4	165	160
2	215	195
1	240	225
1/0	275	255
2/0	310	290
3/0	355	330
4/0	400	375
250	435	410
350	520	495
500	630	600
750	775	740
1000	890	855

For SI units: one inch = 25.4 millimeters.

Table 310-82. Ampacities of Single Insulated Aluminum Conductors Directly Buried in Earth Based on Ambient Earth Temperature of 20°C (68°F), Arrangement per Figure 310-1, 100 percent Load Factor, Thermal Resistance (RHO) of 90, Conductor Temperature 90°C (194°F)

Conductor Size AWG-kcmil	2001-5000 Volts Ampacity	5001-35,000 Volts Ampacity
One Circuit— 3 Conductors (See Figure 310-1, Detail 9)		
8	85	—
6	110	100
4	140	130
2	180	165
1	205	185
1/0	230	215
2/0	265	245
3/0	300	275
4/0	340	315
250	370	345
350	445	415
500	540	510
750	665	635
1000	780	740
Two Circuits— 6 Conductors (See Figure 310-1, Detail 10)		
8	80	—
6	100	95
4	130	125
2	165	155
1	190	175
1/0	215	200
2/0	245	225
3/0	275	255
4/0	310	290
250	340	320
350	410	385
500	495	470
750	610	580
1000	710	680

For SI units: one inch = 25.4 millimeters.

Table 310-83. Ampacities of Three Insulated Copper Conductors Cabled within an Overall Covering (Three-Conductor Cable), Directly Buried in Earth Based on Ambient Earth Temperature of 20°C (68°F), Arrangement per Figure 310-1, 100 percent Load Factor, Thermal Resistance (RHO) of 90, Conductor Temperature 90°C (194°F)

Conductor Size AWG-kcmil	2001-5000 Volts Ampacity	5001-35,000 Volts Ampacity
One Circuit (See Figure 310-1, Detail 5)		
8	85	—
6	105	115
4	135	145
2	180	185
1	200	210
1/0	230	240
2/0	260	270
3/0	295	305
4/0	335	350
250	365	380
350	440	460
500	530	550
750	650	665
1000	730	750
Two Circuits (See Figure 310-1, Detail 10)		
8	80	—
6	100	105
4	130	135
2	165	170
1	185	195
1/0	215	220
2/0	240	250
3/0	275	280
4/0	310	320
250	340	350
350	410	420
500	490	500
750	595	605
1000	665	675

For SI units: one inch = 25.4 millimeters.

Table 310-84. Ampacities of Three Insulated Aluminum Conductors Cabled within an Overall Covering (Three-Conductor Cable), Directly Buried in Earth Based on Ambient Earth Temperature of 20°C (68°F), Arrangement per Figure 310-1, 100 percent Load Factor, Thermal Resistance (RHO) of 90, Conductor Temperature 90°C (194°F)

Conductor Size AWG-kcmil	2001-5000 Volts Ampacity	5001-35,000 Volts Ampacity
One Circuit (See Figure 310-1, Detail 5)		
8	65	—
6	80	90
4	105	115
2	140	145
1	155	165
1/0	180	185
2/0	205	210
3/0	230	240
4/0	260	270
250	285	300
350	345	360
500	420	435
750	520	540
1000	600	620
Two Circuits (See Figure 310-1, Detail 6)		
8	60	—
6	75	80
4	100	105
2	130	135
1	145	150
1/0	165	170
2/0	190	195
3/0	215	220
4/0	245	250
250	265	275
350	320	330
500	385	395
750	480	485
1000	550	560

For SI units: one inch = 25.4 millimeters.

Notes to Tables 310-69 through 310-84

(FPN): For ampacities calculated in accordance with the following Notes 1 and 2, reference IEEE/ICEA "Power Cable Ampacities," Vol. I and II (IPCEA Pub. No. P-46-426) and the "References" therein for availability of all factors and constants.

1. Ambients Not in Tables. Ampacities at ambient temperatures other than those shown in the tables shall be determined by means of the following formula:

$$I_2 = I_1 \sqrt{\frac{TC - TA_2 - DELTA\ TD}{TC - TA_1 - DELTA\ TD}}$$

Where:

I_1 = Ampacity from tables at ambient TA_1.

I_2 = Ampacity at desired ambient TA_2.

TC = Conductor temperature in degrees C.

TA_1 = Surrounding ambient from tables in degrees C.

TA_2 = Desired ambient in degrees C.

DELTA TD = Dielectric loss temperature rise.

2. Grounded Shields. Ampacities shown in Tables 310-69, 310-70, 310-81, and 310-82 are for cable with shields grounded at one point only. Where shields are grounded at more than one point, ampacities shall be adjusted to take into consideration the heating due to shield currents.

3. Electrical Duct Bank Configuration. Ampacities shown in Tables 310-77, 310-78, 310-79, and 310-80 shall apply only where the cables are located in the outer electrical ducts of the electrical duct bank. Ampacities for cables located in the inner electrical ducts of the electrical duct bank shall be determined by special calculations.

4. Burial Depth of Underground Circuits. For applications where burial depths must be deeper than shown in the underground ampacity tables, the following ampacity derating factor shall be permitted to be used: 6 percent per increased foot of depth for all values of Rho. No rating change is required where the burial depth is decreased.

5. Thermal Resistivity. Thermal resistivity, as used in this Code, refers to the heat transfer capability through a substance by conduction. It is the reciprocal of thermal conductivity and is designated Rho and expressed in the units °C-cm/watt.

6. Electrical Ducts Utilized in Figure 310-1. Spacings between electrical ducts (raceways) as defined in Figure 310-1 shall be permitted to be less than specified in Figure 310-1, where ducts (raceways) enter equipment enclosures from underground, without reducing the ampacity of conductors contained within such ducts (raceways).

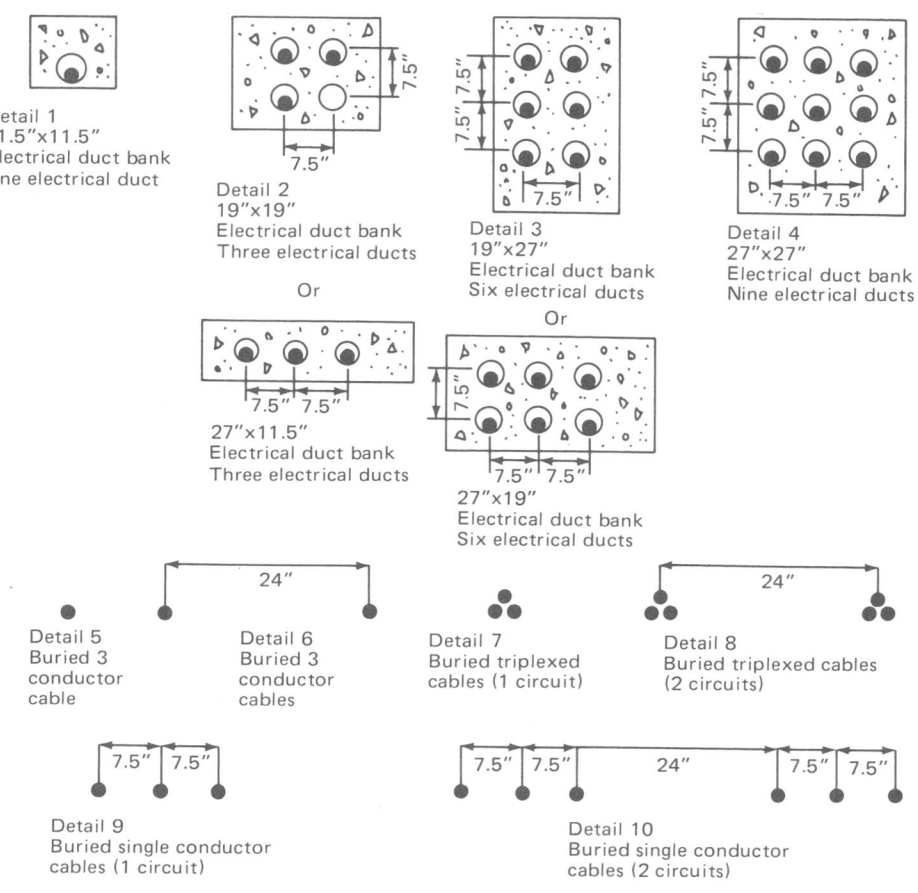

Figure 310-1. *Cable Installation Dimensions for Use with Tables 310-77 through 310-84.*

Detail 1
11.5"x11.5"
Electrical duct bank
One electrical duct

Detail 2
19"x19"
Electrical duct bank
Three electrical ducts

Or

27"x11.5"
Electrical duct bank
Three electrical ducts

Detail 3
19"x27"
Electrical duct bank
Six electrical ducts

Or

27"x19"
Electrical duct bank
Six electrical ducts

Detail 4
27"x27"
Electrical duct bank
Nine electrical ducts

Detail 5
Buried 3
conductor
cable

Detail 6
Buried 3
conductor
cables

Detail 7
Buried triplexed
cables (1 circuit)

Detail 8
Buried triplexed cables
(2 circuits)

Detail 9
Buried single conductor
cables (1 circuit)

Detail 10
Buried single conductor
cables (2 circuits)

Notes for all details:
1. Minimum burial depths to top electrical ducts or cables shall be in accordance with Section 710-4(b). Maximum depth to the top of electrical duct banks shall be 30 inches and maximum depth to the top of direct buried cables shall be 36 inches.

2. Burial depths shall be permitted to be increased in part(s) of the duct run to avoid underground obstructions without decreasing the rated ampacity of the conductors. The total length of parts of the duct run increased in depth to avoid obstructions must be less than 25 percent of the total run length, or else the ampacity reduction factor of Note 4 of Tables 310–69 through 310–84 shall be applied.

3. For SI units: one inch = 25.4 millimeters; one foot = 305 millimeters.

Legend

▢ Backfill
(earth or concrete)

◯ Electrical duct

● Cable or cables

ARTICLE 318   Cable Trays

Contents

318-1. **Scope.** This article covers cable tray systems including ladders, troughs, channels, solid bottom trays, and other similar structures.

Cable trays are not considered raceways. However, grounding is required in accordance with Section 318-7. See definition of "Raceway" in Article 100.

318-2. **Definition.**

Cable Tray System. A unit or assembly of units or sections, and associated fittings, forming a rigid structural system used to support cables and raceways.

318-3. **Uses Permitted.**

(a) Wiring Methods. The following shall be permitted to be installed in cable tray systems under the conditions described in their respective articles:

(1) Mineral-insulated, metal-sheathed cable (Article 330); (2) electrical nonmetallic tubing (Article 331); (3) armored cable (Article 333); (4) metal-clad cable (Article 334); (5) nonmetallic-sheathed cable (Article 336); (6) shielded, nonmetallic-sheathed cable (Article 337); (7) multiconductor service-entrance cable (Article 338); (8) multiconductor underground feeder and branch-circuit cable (Article 339); (9) power and control tray cable (Article 340); (10) power-limited tray cable

(Sections 725-50, 725-51, and 725-53); (11) other factory-assembled, multiconductor control, signal, or power cables that are specifically approved for installation in cable trays; (12) intermediate metal conduit (Article 345); (13) rigid metal conduit (Article 346); (14) rigid nonmetallic conduit (Article 347); (15) electrical metallic tubing (Article 348); (16) flexible metallic tubing (Article 349); (17) flexible zmetal conduit (Article 350); or (18) liquidtight flexible metal conduit and liquidtight flexible nonmetallic conduit (Article 351).

This section has been revised for the 1993 edition of the *NEC* to permit the use of cable trays as a support method for specific types of raceways.

(b) In Industrial Establishments. In industrial establishments only, where conditions of maintenance and supervision assure that only qualified persons will service the installed cable tray system, any of the cables in (1) and (2) below shall be permitted to be installed in ladder, ventilated trough, 4-inch (102-mm) ventilated channel cable trays, or 6-inch (152-mm) ventilated channel cable trays.

(1) Single Conductor. Single conductor cable shall be No. 1/0 or larger and shall be of a type listed and marked on the surface for use in cable trays. Where Nos. 1/0 through 4/0 single conductor cables are installed in ladder cable tray, the maximum allowable rung spacing for the ladder cable tray shall be 9 inches (229 mm). Where exposed to direct rays of the sun, cables shall be identified as being sunlight-resistant.

This section was revised for the 1990 edition of the *NEC* to permit single conductors as small as No. 1/0, provided they are listed and marked for use in cable trays. Previously, the minimum size was 250 kcmil (MCM).

A new Exception No. 2 has been added to this section for the 1993 *Code*. Single conductors used as equipment grounding conductors smaller than No. 1/0, but not less than No. 4, are allowed in cable trays with rung spacing not greater than 9 inches.

Exception No. 1: Welding cables as permitted in Article 630, Part E.

Cable trays used to support welding cable are required to be dedicated only for welding cable. See Section 630-42.

Exception No. 2: Single conductors used as equipment grounding conductors shall be permitted to be No. 4 or larger.

(2) Multiconductor. Multiconductor cables Type MV (Article 326) where exposed to direct rays of the sun shall be identified as being sunlight-resistant.

(c) Equipment Grounding Conductors. Metal in cable trays, as defined in Table 318-7(b) (2), shall be permitted to be used as equipment grounding conductors in commercial and industrial establishments, only where continuous maintenance and supervision assure that qualified persons will service the installed cable tray system.

The cross-sectional area of the grounding metal is marked on the outer surface of the sidewall of cable trays listed by UL.

(d) Hazardous (Classified) Locations. Cable trays in hazardous (classified) locations shall contain only the cable types permitted in Sections 501-4, 502-4, 503-3, and 504-20.

(e) Nonmetallic Cable Tray. Nonmetallic cable tray shall be permitted in corrosive areas and in areas requiring voltage isolation.

Fiberglass cable trays are often used to support cables between an energized cell in an electrolytic cell room (see Article 668) and the grounded frame of the cell room to assure voltage isolation.

(FPN): It is not the intent of this article to limit the use of cable trays to industrial establishments only.

318-4. **Uses Not Permitted.** Cable tray systems shall not be used in hoistways or where subject to severe physical damage. Cable tray systems shall not be used in environmental air-handling spaces except to support wiring methods recognized in Section 300-22(c).

Only wiring methods recognized in Section 300-22(c) are permitted in environmental air-handling spaces.

318-5. **Construction Specifications.**

(a) Strength and Rigidity. Cable trays shall have suitable strength and rigidity to provide adequate support for all contained wiring.

(b) Smooth Edges. Cable trays shall not have sharp edges, burrs, or projections that may damage the insulation or jackets of the wiring.

(c) Corrosion Protection. Cable trays shall be made of corrosion-resistant material or, if made of metal, shall be adequately protected against corrosion.

(d) Side Rails. Cable trays shall have side rails or equivalent structural members.

(e) Fittings. Cable trays shall include fittings or other suitable means for changes in direction and elevation of runs.

(f) Nonmetallic Cable Tray. Nonmetallic cable trays shall be made of flame-retardant material.

318-6. Installation.

(a) Complete System. Cable trays shall be installed as a complete system. Field bends or modifications shall be so made that the electrical continuity of the cable tray system and support for the cables shall be maintained.

(FPN): It is the intent to permit discontinuous segments and termination of cable tray installations where the system provides for the support of cables in accordance with their corresponding articles and where adequate bonding is provided in the cable tray system design.

Cable trays are required to be installed as a complete system for that portion of the cable tray system that is intended to support the cables. This does not mean that the cable tray has to be 100 percent mechanically continuous. For example, cables in cable trays that are installed one above the other or at crossovers are allowed to make the transition from one cable tray to the other even though the cable trays are not mechanically connected, provided the cables or wiring method used is supported as required by the article for that specific wiring method and the equipment grounding continuity for the circuit is maintained. See Figure 318-1.

(b) Completed Before Installation. Each run of cable tray shall be completed before the installation of cables.

(c) Supports. Supports shall be provided to prevent stress on cables where they enter raceways or other enclosures from cable tray systems.

(d) Covers. In portions of runs where additional protection is required, covers or enclosures providing the required protection shall be of a material compatible with the cable tray.

(e) Multiconductor Cables Rated 600 Volts or Less. Multiconductor cables rated 600 volts or less shall be permitted to be installed in the same cable tray.

(f) Cables Rated Over 600 Volts. Cables rated over 600 volts shall not be installed in the same cable tray with cables rated 600 volts or less.

Exception No. 1: Where separated by a solid fixed barrier of a material compatible with the cable tray.

High voltage x-ray cables are permitted to be installed in cable trays and troughs along with equipment control and power supply conductors without the need for barriers to separate the wiring.

Exception No. 2: Where cables over 600 volts are Type MC.

(g) Through Partitions and Walls. Cable trays shall be permitted to extend transversely through partitions and walls or vertically through platforms and floors in wet or dry locations where the installations, complete with installed cables, are made in accordance with the requirements of Section 300-21.

See Figure 300-15.

(h) Exposed and Accessible. Cable trays shall be exposed and accessible except as permitted by Section 318-6(g).

(i) Adequate Access. Sufficient space shall be provided and maintained about cable trays to permit adequate access for installing and maintaining the cables.

(FPN): See Section 310-10 for temperature limitation of conductors.

This fine print note is intended to caution the user that the heat dissipation of conductors installed in thermal insulation is reduced.

(j) Incidental Support from Cable Tray. Where approved and designed to support the load, cable trays shall be permitted as a means of incidental support for raceways that are supported in accordance with Articles 345, 346, 347, and 348.

(FPN): See Section 300-11(b) for restrictions concerning raceways used as a means of support.

318-7. Grounding.

(a) Metallic Cable Trays. Metallic cable trays that support electrical conductors shall be grounded as required for conductor enclosures in Article 250.

Bonding jumper not required for rigidly bolted tray joints

Discontinuous joints require bonding

Cable ground wires are not required if rating of the feeder overcurrent device permits using the tray for equipment grounding

Switchgear transformer

XO

Neutral bus

Ground wires in cable

Ground bus, bonded to enclosure

System grounding electrode conductor

Bond

Bond

Bond

Equipment grounding conductors

Power distribution panel, motor control center, etc.

Ground bus, bonded to enclosure

Conduit

Motor installation

Figure 318-1. *An example of multiconductor nonmetallic jacketed cables in cable trays with conduit runs to power equipment. Bonding is provided in accordance with Section 318-7(b)(4). (Cable Tray Institute)*

(b) Steel or Aluminum Cable Tray Systems. Steel or aluminum cable tray systems shall be permitted to be used as equipment grounding conductors provided that all the following requirements are met:

(1) The cable tray sections and fittings shall be identified for grounding purposes.

(2) The minimum cross-sectional area of cable trays shall conform to the requirements in Table 318-7(b)(2).

(3) All cable tray sections and fittings shall be legibly and durably marked to show the cross-sectional area of metal in channel cable trays, or cable trays of one-piece construction, and the total cross-sectional area of both side rails for ladder or trough cable trays.

(4) Cable tray sections, fittings, and connected raceways shall be bonded in accordance with Section 250-75 using bolted mechanical connectors or bonding jumpers sized and installed in accordance with Section 250-79.

Much the same as the *Code* requires metal raceways and metal enclosures to be grounded, cable trays made of metal are also required to be grounded. Ground continuity is permitted to be maintained with the use of bonding jumpers. See Figure 318-1.

318-8. Cable Installation.

(a) Cable Splices. Cable splices made and insulated by approved methods shall be permitted to be located within a cable tray provided they are accessible and do not project above the side rails.

(b) Fastened Securely. In other than horizontal runs, the cables shall be fastened securely to transverse members of the cable trays.

(c) Bushed Conduit and Tubing. A box shall not be required where cables or conductors are installed in bushed conduit and tubing used for support or for protection against physical damage.

Table 318-7(b)(2). Metal Area Requirements for Cable Trays Used as Equipment Grounding Conductors

Maximum Fuse Ampere Rating, Circuit Breaker Ampere Trip Setting, or Circuit Breaker Protective Relay Ampere Trip Setting for Ground-Fault Protection of Any Cable Circuit in the Cable Tray System	Minimum Cross-Sectional Area of Metal* in Square Inches	
	Steel Cable Trays	**Aluminum Cable Trays**
60	0.20	0.20
100	0.40	0.20
200	0.70	0.20
400	1.00	0.40
600	1.50**	0.40
1000	—	0.60
1200	—	1.00
1600	—	1.50
2000	—	2.00**

For SI units: one square inch = 645 square millimeters.
*Total cross-sectional area of both side rails for ladder or trough cable trays; or the minimum cross-sectional area of metal in channel cable trays or cable trays of one-piece construction.
**Steel cable trays shall not be used as equipment grounding conductors for circuits with ground-fault protection above 600 amperes. Aluminum cable trays shall not be used as equipment grounding conductors for circuits with ground-fault protection above 2000 amperes.

(d) Connected in Parallel. Where single conductor cables comprising each phase or neutral of a circuit are connected in parallel as permitted in Section 310-4, the conductors shall be installed in groups consisting of not more than one conductor per phase or neutral to prevent current unbalance in the paralleled conductors due to inductive reactance.

Single conductors shall be securely bound in circuit groups to prevent excessive movement due to fault-current magnetic forces.

Exception: Where single conductors are cabled together, such as triplexed assemblies.

318-9. Number of Multiconductor Cables, Rated 2000 Volts or Less, in Cable Trays. The number of multiconductor cables, rated 2000 volts or less, permitted in a single cable tray shall not exceed the requirements of this section. The conductor sizes herein apply to both aluminum and copper conductors.

(a) Any Mixture of Cables. Where ladder or ventilated trough cable trays contain multiconductor power or lighting cables, or any mixture of multiconductor power, lighting, control, and signal cables, the maximum number of cables shall conform to the following:

(1) Where all of the cables are No. 4/0 or larger, the sum of the diameters of all cables shall not exceed the cable tray width, and the cables shall be installed in a single layer.

(2) Where all of the cables are smaller than No. 4/0, the sum of the cross-sectional areas of all cables shall not exceed the maximum allowable cable fill area in Column 1 of Table 318-9, for the appropriate cable tray width.

(3) Where No. 4/0 or larger cables are installed in the same cable tray with cables smaller than No. 4/0, the sum of the cross-sectional areas of all cables smaller than No. 4/0 shall not exceed the maximum allowable fill area resulting from the computation in Column 2 of Table 318-9, for the appropriate cable tray width. The No. 4/0 and larger cables shall be installed in a single layer, and no other cables shall be placed on them.

(b) Multiconductor Control and/or Signal Cables Only. Where a ladder or ventilated trough cable tray, having a usable inside depth of 6 inches (152 mm) or less, contains multiconductor control and/or signal cables only, the sum of the cross-sectional areas of all cables at any cross section shall not exceed 50 percent of the interior cross-sectional area of the cable tray. A depth of 6 inches (152 mm) shall be used to compute the allowable interior cross-sectional area of any cable tray that has a usable inside depth of more than 6 inches (152 mm).

(c) Solid Bottom Cable Trays Containing Any Mixture. Where solid bottom cable trays contain multiconductor power or lighting cables, or any mixture of multiconductor power, lighting, control, and signal cables, the maximum number of cables shall conform to the following:

(1) Where all of the cables are No. 4/0 or larger, the sum of the diameters of all cables shall not exceed 90 percent of the cable tray width, and the cables shall be installed in a single layer.

(2) Where all of the cables are smaller than No. 4/0, the sum of the cross-sectional areas of all cables shall not exceed the maximum allowable cable fill area in Column 3 of Table 318-9 for the appropriate cable tray width.

(3) Where No. 4/0 or larger cables are installed in the same cable tray with cables smaller than No. 4/0, the sum of the cross-sectional areas of all cables smaller than No. 4/0 shall not exceed the maximum allowable fill area resulting from the computation in Column 4 of Table 318-9 for the appropriate cable tray width. The No. 4/0 and larger cables shall be installed in a single layer, and no other cables shall be placed on them.

(d) Solid Bottom Cable Tray Multiconductor Control and Signal Cables Only. Where a solid bottom cable tray, having a usable inside depth of 6 inches (152 mm) or less, contains multiconductor control and/or signal cables only, the sum of the cross-sectional areas of all cables at any cross section shall not exceed 40 percent of the interior cross-sectional area of the cable tray. A depth of 6 inches (152 mm) shall be used to compute the allowable interior cross-sectional area of any cable tray that has a usable inside depth of more than 6 inches (152 mm).

Table 318-9. Allowable Cable Fill Area for Multiconductor Cables in Ladder, Ventilated Trough, or Solid Bottom Cable Trays for Cables Rated 2000 Volts or Less

	Maximum Allowable Fill Area in Square Inches for Multiconductor Cables			
	Ladder or Ventilated Trough Cable Trays, Section 318-9(a)		Solid Bottom Cable Trays, Section 318-9(c)	
Inside Width of Cable Tray (Inches)	Column 1 Applicable for Section 318-9(a)(2) Only (Square Inches)	Column 2* Applicable for Section 318-9(a)(3) Only (Square Inches)	Column 3 Applicable for Section 318-9(c)(2) Only (Square Inches)	Column 4* Applicable for Section 318-9(c)(3) Only (Square Inches)
6	7	7−(1.2 Sd)**	5.5	5.5−Sd**
12	14	14−(1.2 Sd)	11.0	11.0−Sd
18	21	21−(1.2 Sd)	16.5	16.5−Sd
24	28	28−(1.2 Sd)	22.0	22.0−Sd
30	35	35−(1.2 Sd)	27.5	27.5−Sd
36	42	42−(1.2 Sd)	33.0	33.0−Sd

For SI units: one square inch = 645 square millimeters.
* The maximum allowable fill areas in Columns 2 and 4 shall be computed. For example, the maximum allowable fill, in square inches, for a 6-inch (152-mm) wide cable tray in Column 2 shall be: 7 minus (1.2 multiplied by Sd).
** The term Sd in Columns 2 and 4 is equal to the sum of the diameters, in inches, of all Nos. 4/0 AWG and larger multiconductor cables in the same cable tray with smaller cables.

(e) Ventilated Channel Cable Trays. Where ventilated channel cable trays contain multiconductor cables of any type, the combined cross-sectional area of all cables shall not exceed 1.3 square inches (839 sq mm) in 3-inch (76-mm) wide channel trays, 2.5 square inches (1613 sq mm) in 4-inch (102-mm)

wide channel trays, or 3.8 square inches (2452 sq mm) in 6-inch (152-mm) wide channel trays.

Exception: Where only one multiconductor cable is installed in a ventilated channel tray, the cross-sectional area of the cable shall not exceed 2.3 square inches (1484 sq mm) in a 3-inch (76-mm) wide channel tray, 4.5 square inches (2903 sq mm) in a 4-inch (102-mm) wide channel tray, or 7.0 square inches (4516 sq mm) in a 6-inch (152-mm) wide channel tray.

Cable trays may be ladder or ventilated trough, solid bottom, ventilated channel-type, unventilated, covered, etc., and of various widths and depths. Therefore, inspectors or contractors are not expected to compute the various combinations of cable tray fill in the field. Installation handbooks for cable tray applications are available from various cable tray manufacturers.

318-10. **Number of Single Conductor Cables, Rated 2000 Volts or Less, in Cable Trays.** The number of single conductor cables, rated 2000 volts or less, permitted in a single cable tray section shall not exceed the requirements of this section. The single conductors, or conductor assemblies, shall be evenly distributed across the cable tray. The conductor sizes herein apply to both aluminum and copper conductors.

(a) Ladder or Ventilated Trough Cable Trays. Where ladder or ventilated trough cable trays contain single conductor cables, the maximum number of single conductors shall conform to the following:

(1) Where all of the cables are 1000 kcmil or larger, the sum of the diameters of all single conductor cables shall not exceed the cable tray width.

(2) Where all of the cables are from 250 kcmil up to 1000 kcmil, the sum of the cross-sectional areas of all single conductor cables shall not exceed the maximum allowable cable fill area in Column 1 of Table 318-10, for the appropriate cable tray width.

(3) Where 1000 kcmil or larger single conductor cables are installed in the same cable tray with single conductor cables smaller than 1000 kcmil, the sum of the cross-sectional areas of all cables smaller than 1000 kcmil shall not exceed the maximum allowable fill area resulting from the computation in Column 2 of Table 318-10, for the appropriate cable tray width.

(4) Where any of the conductor cables are Nos. 1/0 through 4/0, the sum of the diameters of all single conductor cables shall

Table 318-10. Allowable Cable Fill Area for Single Conductor Cables in Ladder or Ventilated Trough Cable Trays For Cables Rated 2000 Volts or Less

Inside Width of Cable Tray (Inches)	Maximum Allowable Fill Area in Square Inches for Single Conductor Cables in Ladder or Ventilated Trough Cable Trays	
	Column 1 Applicable for Section 318-10(a)(2) Only (Square Inches)	Column 2* Applicable for Section 318-10(a)(3) Only (Square Inches)
6	6.50	6.50 − (1.1 Sd)**
12	13.0	13.0 − (1.1 Sd)
18	19.5	19.5 − (1.1 Sd)
24	26.0	26.0 − (1.1 Sd)
30	32.5	32.5 − (1.1 Sd)
36	39.0	39.0 − (1.1 Sd)

For SI units: one square inch = 645 square millimeters.
*The maximum allowable fill areas in Column 2 shall be computed. For example, the maximum allowable fill, in square inches, for a 6-inch (152-mm) wide cable tray shall be: 6.5 minus (1.1 multiplied by Sd).
**The term Sd in Column 2 is equal to the sum of the diameters, in inches, of all 1000 kcmil and larger single conductor cables in the same ladder or ventilated trough cable tray with small cables.

not exceed the cable tray width, and they shall be installed in a single layer.

(b) Ventilated Channel Cable Trays. Where 3-inch (76-mm), 4-inch (102-mm), or 6-inch (152-mm) wide ventilated channel cable trays contain single conductor cables, the sum of the diameters of all single conductors shall not exceed the inside width of the channel.

318-11. Ampacity of Cables, Rated 2000 Volts or Less, in Cable Trays.

(a) Multiconductor Cables. The ampacity of multiconductor cables, nominally rated 2000 volts or less, installed according to the requirements of Section 318-9, shall comply with the allowable ampacities of Tables 310-16 and 310-18. The derating factors of Article 310, Note 8(a) of the Notes to Ampacity Tables of 0 to 2000 Volts shall apply only to multiconductor cables with more than three current-carrying conductors. Derating shall be limited to the number of current-carrying conductors in the cable and not to the number of conductors in the cable tray.

Exception No. 1: Where cable trays are continuously covered for more than 6 feet (1.83 m) with solid unventilated covers, not over 95 percent of the allowable ampacities of Tables 310-16 and 310-18 shall be permitted for multiconductor cables.

Exception No. 2: Where multiconductor cables are installed in a single layer in uncovered trays, with a maintained spacing of not less than one cable diameter between cables, the ampacity shall not exceed the allowable ambient temperature corrected ampacities of multiconductor cables, with not more than three insulated conductors rated 0-2000 volts in free air, in accordance with Section 310-15(b).

Not less than one cable diameter.

Figure 318-2. *Multiconductor cables, 2,000 volts or less. Not more than three conductors per cable. Ampacity of conductors can be determined from Table B-310-3, in Appendix B.*

(FPN): See Table B-310-3 in Appendix B.

(b) Single Conductor Cables. The derating factors of Article 310, Note 8 (a) of the Notes to Ampacity Tables of 0 to 2000 Volts shall not apply to the ampacity of cables in cable trays. The ampacity of single conductor cables, or single conductors cabled together (triplexed, quadruplexed, etc.), nominally rated 2000 volts or less, shall comply with the following:

(1) Where installed according to the requirements of Section 318-10, the ampacities for 600 kcmil and larger single conductor cables in uncovered cable trays shall not exceed 75 percent of the allowable ampacities in Tables 310-17 and 310-19. Where cable trays are continuously covered for more than 6 feet (1.83 m) with solid unventilated covers, the ampacities for 600 kcmil and larger cables shall not exceed 70 percent of the allowable ampacities in Tables 310-17 and 310-19.

(2) Where installed according to the requirements of Section 318-10, the ampacities for No. 1/0 through 500 kcmil single conductor cables in uncovered cable trays shall not exceed 65 percent of the allowable ampacities in Tables 310-17 and

310-19. Where cable trays are continuously covered for more than 6 feet (1.83 m) with solid unventilated covers, the ampacities for No. 1/0 through 500 kcmil cables shall not exceed 60 percent of the allowable ampacities in Tables 310-17 and 310-19.

(3) Where single conductors are installed in a single layer in uncovered cable trays, with a maintained space of not less than one cable diameter between individual conductors, the ampacity of Nos. 1/0 and larger cables shall not exceed the allowable ampacities in Tables 310-17 and 310-19.

(4) Where single conductors are installed in a triangular configuration in uncovered cable trays, with a maintained space of not less than 2.15 times one conductor diameter (2.15 m⁻ O.D.) between circuits, the ampacity of Nos. 1/0 and larger cables shall not exceed the allowable ampacities of two or three single insulated conductors rated 0 through 2000 volts supported on a messenger in accordance with Section 310-15(b).

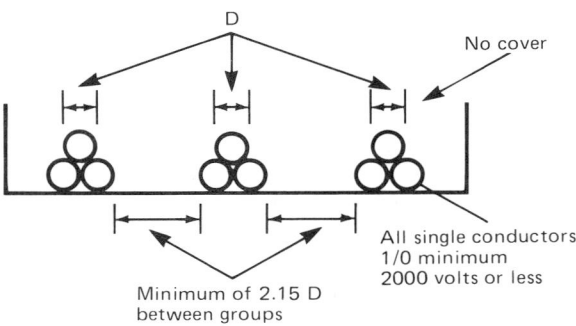

Figure 318-3. Three single conductors installed in a triangular configuration with spacing between the groups of not less than 2.15 times the diameter of the conductor. See Table B-310-2 in Appendix B for ampacities of conductors in this configuration.

This section recognizes the use of single conductors in a triangular configuration installed in a cable tray with maintained spacing as having the same ampacity as three single insulated conductors on a messenger. The maintained spacing allows air to circulate around the cable.

Where two single conductors or three single conductors, nominally rated 2,000 volts or less, are cabled together in a triangular configuration, the ampacity of the conductors is determined in accordance with the method in Section 310-15(b), the Neher-McGrath calculations. However, the FPN to Section 318-11(b)(4) refers to Table B-310-2 in

Appendix B, which was originally Table 310-23 in the 1987 edition of the *NEC*. The ampacity values listed in Table B-310-2 can be used, since they were derived from the Neher-McGrath formulas.

(FPN): See Table B-310-2 in Appendix B.

318-12. **Number of Type MV and Type MC Cables (2001 Volts or Over) in Cable Trays.** The number of cables, rated 2001 volts or over, permitted in a single cable tray shall not exceed the requirements of this section.

The sum of the diameters of single conductor and multiconductor cables shall not exceed the cable tray width, and the cables shall be installed in a single layer. Where single conductor cables are triplexed, quadruplexed, or bound together in circuit groups, the sum of the diameters of the single conductors shall not exceed the cable tray width, and these groups shall be installed in single layer arrangement.

318-13. **Ampacity of Type MV and Type MC Cables (2001 Volts or Over) in Cable Trays.** The ampacity of cables, rated 2001 volts, nominal, or over, installed according to Section 318-12 shall not exceed the requirements of this section.

(a) Multiconductor Cables (2001 Volts or Over). The ampacity of multiconductor cables shall comply with the allowable ampacities of Tables 310-75 and 310-76.

Exception No. 1: Where cable trays are continuously covered for more than 6 feet (1.83 m) with solid unventilated covers, not more than 95 percent of the allowable ampacities of Tables 310-75 and 310-76 shall be permitted for multiconductor cables.

Exception No. 2: Where multiconductor cables are installed in a single layer in uncovered cable trays, with a maintained spacing of not less than one cable diameter between cables, the ampacity shall not exceed the allowable ampacities of Tables 310-71 and 310-72.

(b) Single Conductor Cables (2001 Volts or Over). The ampacity of single conductor cables, or single conductors cabled together (triplexed, quadruplexed, etc.), shall comply with the following:

(1) The ampacities for Nos. 1/0 and larger single conductor cables in uncovered cable trays shall not exceed 75 percent of the allowable ampacities in Tables 310-69 and 310-70. Where the cable trays are covered for more than

6 feet (1.83 m) with solid unventilated covers, the ampacities for Nos. 1/0 and larger single conductor cables shall not exceed 70 percent of the allowable ampacities in Tables 310-69 and 310-70.

(2) Where single conductor cables are installed in a single layer in uncovered cable trays, with a maintained space of not less than one cable diameter between individual conductors, the ampacity of Nos. 1/0 and larger cables shall not exceed the allowable ampacities in Tables 310-69 and 310-70.

(3) Where single conductors are installed in a triangular configuration in uncovered cable trays, with a maintained space of not less than 2.15 times one conductor diameter (2.15 × O.D.) between circuits, the ampacity of Nos. 1/0 and larger cables shall not exceed the allowable ampacities in Tables 310-67 and 310-68.

ARTICLE 320 Open Wiring on Insulators

Contents

320-1. **Definition.** Open wiring on insulators is an exposed wiring method using cleats, knobs, tubes, and flexible tubing for the protection and support of single insulated conductors run in or on buildings, and not concealed by the building structure.

Open wiring on insulators is an exposed wiring method that is not permitted to be concealed by the structure or finish of the building. It is permitted indoors or outdoors, in dry or wet locations, and where subject to corrosive vapors. Any of the general-use conductors listed in Table 310-13, such as Types RH, THW, and XHHW, can be installed as open wiring. The selection, of course, depends on whether the location is wet or dry, temperature considerations, ampacities, etc.

This method of wiring may be used for temporary lighting and power circuits on construction sites and lighting and power circuits in agricultural buildings. It may also be used for services. It is also commonly used for feeders in industrial locations. See Sections 230-43, 305-4, and 547-4.

320-2. **Other Articles.** Open wiring on insulators shall comply with this article and also with the applicable provisions of other articles in this Code, especially Articles 225 and 300.

320-3. **Uses Permitted.** Open wiring on insulators shall be permitted on systems of 600 volts, nominal, or less, only for industrial or agricultural establishments, indoors or outdoors, in wet or dry locations, where subject to corrosive vapors, and for services.

320-5. **Conductors.**

(a) Type. Conductors shall be of a type specified by Article 310.

(b) Ampacity. The ampacity shall comply with Section 310-15.

See Tables 310-17 and 310-19.

320-6. **Conductor Supports.** Conductors shall be rigidly supported on noncombustible, nonabsorbent insulating materials and shall not contact any other objects. Supports shall be installed as follows: (1) within 6 inches (152 mm) from a tap or splice; (2) within 12 inches (305 mm) of a dead-end connection to a lampholder or receptacle; (3) at intervals not exceeding 4½ feet (1.37 m) and at closer intervals sufficient to provide adequate support where likely to be disturbed.

Exception No. 1: Supports for conductors No. 8 or larger installed across open spaces shall be permitted up to 15 feet (4.57 m) apart if noncombustible, nonabsorbent insulating spacers are used at least every 4½ feet (1.37 m) to maintain at least 2½ inches (64 mm) between conductors.

Exception No. 2: Where not likely to be disturbed in buildings of mill construction, No. 8 and larger conductors shall be permitted to be run across open spaces if supported from each wood cross member on approved insulators maintaining 6 inches (152 mm) between conductors.

Mill construction is generally considered to be a building where the floors and ceilings are supported by wood beams or wood cross members spaced approximately 15 feet apart. No. 8 and larger conductors are allowed to span this distance where the ceilings are high and free of obstructions and the conductors are unlikely to come into contact with other objects.

Exception No. 3: In industrial establishments only, where conditions of maintenance and supervision assure that only qualified persons will service the system, conductors of sizes 250 kcmil and larger shall be permitted to be run across open spaces where supported on intervals up to 30 fee (9.1 m) apart.

It is common practice in industrial buildings to install open feeders on insulators, which are mounted on the bottom of roof trusses at every bay location. Many bays are more than 15 feet wide. Therefore, Exception No. 3 permits size 250 kcmil and larger conductors to be supported at 30-foot intervals, where it is assured that qualified persons will service the system.

In addition to the ease and economy of installations or alterations of open wiring, it is to be noted that, by close spacing of conductors, the reactance of a circuit is reduced; hence, the voltage drop is reduced.

320-7. **Mounting of Conductor Supports.** Where nails are used to mount knobs, they shall not be smaller than 10 penny. Where screws are used to mount knobs, or where nails or screws are used to mount cleats, they shall be of a length sufficient to penetrate the wood to a depth equal to at least one-half the height of the knob and the full thickness of the cleat. Cushion washers shall be used with nails.

320-8. **Tie Wires.** No. 8 or larger conductors supported on solid knobs shall be securely tied thereto by tie wires having an insulation equivalent to that of the conductor.

320-10. **Flexible Nonmetallic Tubing.** In dry locations where not exposed to severe physical damage, conductors shall be permitted to be separately enclosed in flexible nonmetallic tubing. The tubing shall be in continuous lengths not exceeding 15 feet (4.57 m) and secured to the surface by straps at intervals not exceeding 4½ feet (1.37 m).

320-11. **Through Walls, Floors, Wood Cross Members, etc.** Open conductors shall be separated from contact with walls, floors, wood cross members, or partitions through which they pass by tubes or bushings of noncombustible, nonabsorbent insulating material. Where the bushing is shorter than the hole, a waterproof sleeve of noninductive material shall be inserted in the hole and an insulating bushing slipped into the sleeve at each end in such a manner as to keep the conductors absolutely out of contact with the sleeve. Each conductor shall be carried through a separate tube or sleeve.

(FPN): See Section 310-10 for temperature limitation of conductors.

320-12. **Clearance from Piping, Exposed Conductors, etc.** Open conductors shall be separated at least 2 inches (50.8 mm) from metal raceways, piping, or other conducting material, and from any exposed lighting, power, or signaling conductor, or shall be separated therefrom by a continuous and firmly fixed nonconductor in addition to the insulation of the conductor. Where any insulating tube is used, it shall be secured at the ends. Where practicable, conductors shall pass over rather than under any piping subject to leakage or accumulations of moisture.

The provision for additional protective insulation on open wiring is to prevent contact with metal piping, metal objects, or exposed conductors of other circuits.

320-13. **Entering Spaces Subject to Dampness, Wetness, or Corrosive Vapors.** Conductors entering or leaving locations subject to dampness, wetness, or corrosive vapors shall have drip loops formed on them and shall then pass upward and inward from the outside of the buildings, or from the damp, wet, or corrosive location, through noncombustible, nonabsorbent insulating tubes.

(FPN): See Section 230-52 for individual conductors entering buildings or other structures.

320-14. **Protection from Physical Damage.** Conductors within 7 feet (2.13 m) from the floor shall be considered exposed to physical damage. Where open conductors cross ceiling joists and wall studs and are exposed to physical damage, they shall be protected by one of the following methods: (1) by guard strips not less than 1 inch (25.4 mm) nominal in thickness and at least as high as the insulating supports, placed on each side of and close to the wiring; (2) by a substantial running board at least ½ inch (12.7 mm) thick back of the conductors with side protections. Running boards shall extend at least 1 inch (25.4 mm) outside the conductors, but not more than 2 inches (50.8 mm), and the protecting sides shall be at least 2 inches (50.8 mm) high and at least 1 inch (25.4 mm) nominal in thickness; (3) by boxing made as above and furnished with a cover kept at least 1 inch (25.4 mm) away from the conductors within. Where protecting vertical conductors on side walls, the boxing shall be closed at the top and the holes through which the conductors pass shall be bushed; (4) by rigid metal conduit, intermediate metal conduit, rigid nonmetallic conduit, or electrical metallic tubing, in which case the rules of Article 345, 346, 347, or 348 shall apply; or by metal piping, in which case the conductors shall be encased in continuous lengths of approved flexible tubing. The conductors passing through metal enclosures shall be so grouped that current in both directions is approximately equal.

320-15. **Unfinished Attics and Roof Spaces.** Conductors in unfinished attics and roof spaces shall comply with (a) or (b) below.

(a) **Accessible by Stairway or Permanent Ladder.** Conductors shall be installed along the side of or through bored holes in floor joists, studs, or rafters. Where run through bored holes, conductors in the joists and in studs or rafters to a height of not less than 7 feet (2.13 m) above the floor or floor joists shall be protected by substantial running boards extending not less than 1 inch (25.4 mm) on each side of the conductors. Running boards shall be securely fastened in place. Running boards and guard strips shall not be required for conductors installed along the sides of joists, studs, or rafters.

(b) **Not Accessible by Stairway or Permanent Ladder.** Conductors shall be installed along the sides of or through bored holes in floor joists, studs, or rafters.

Exception: In buildings completed before wiring is installed and having head room at all points of less than 3 feet (914 mm).

320-16. **Switches.** Surface-type snap switches shall be mounted in accordance with Section 380-10(a), and boxes shall not be required. Other type switches shall be installed in accordance with Section 380-4.

ARTICLE 321   Messenger Supported Wiring

Contents

321-1. **Definition.** Messenger supported wiring is an exposed wiring support system using a messenger wire to support insulated conductors by any one of the following: (1) a messenger with rings and saddles for conductor support; (2) a messenger with a field-installed lashing material for conductor support; (3) factory-assembled aerial cable; (4) multiplex cables utilizing a bare conductor, factory assembled and twisted with one or more insulated conductors, such as duplex, triplex, or quadruplex type of construction.

Messenger supported wiring systems have been manufactured and successfully used in industrial installations for many years. They have also been used for many years as service drops by utilities for commercial and residential installations.

See reference to messenger supported wiring in Section 225-6(b), Exception.

321-2. **Other Articles.** Messenger supported wiring shall comply with this article and also with the applicable provisions of other articles in this Code, especially Articles 225 and 300.

321-3. **Uses Permitted.**

(a) **Cable Types.** The following shall be permitted to be installed in messenger supported wiring under the conditions described in the article referenced for each: (1) mineral-insulated, metal-sheathed cable (Article 330); (2) metal-clad cable (Article 334); (3) multiconductor service-entrance cable (Article 338);

(4) multiconductor underground feeder and branch-circuit cable (Article 339); (5) power and control tray cable (Article 340); (6) power-limited tray cable (Sections 725-51 and 725-53); (7) other factory-assembled, multiconductor control, signal, or power cables that are identified for the use.

(b) In Industrial Establishments. In industrial establishments only, where conditions of maintenance and supervision assure that only competent individuals will service the installed messenger supported wiring, the following shall be permitted:

(1) Any of the conductor types shown in Table 310-13 or Table 310-62.

Some of the triplex and quadruplex cable used by utilities as service-drop cable, does not utilize conductors recognized in Table 310-13 and does not meet the requirements of Article 310. Such triplex and quadruplex cable would, therefore, be acceptable only when approved by the authority having jurisdiction.

(2) MV Cable.

Where exposed to weather, conductors shall be listed for use in wet locations.

Where exposed to direct rays of the sun, conductors or cables shall be sunlight-resistant.

(c) Hazardous (Classified) Locations. Messenger supported wiring shall be permitted to be used in hazardous (classified) locations where the contained cables are permitted for such use in Sections 501-4, 502-4, 503-3, and 504-20.

321-4. **Uses Not Permitted.** Messenger supported wiring shall not be used in hoistways or where subject to severe physical damage.

321-5. **Ampacity.** The ampacity shall be determined by Section 310-15.

See Section 310-15(b) and Appendix B, Tables B-310-2 and B-310-3.

321-6. **Messenger Support.** The messenger shall be supported at dead ends and at intermediate locations so as to eliminate tension on the conductors. The conductors shall not be permitted to come into contact with the messenger supports or any structural members, walls, or pipes.

321-7. **Grounding.** The messenger shall be grounded as required by Sections 250-32 and 250-33 for enclosure grounding.

321-8. **Conductor Splices and Taps.** Conductor splices and taps made and insulated by approved methods shall be permitted in messenger supported wiring.

ARTICLE 324   Concealed Knob-and-Tube Wiring

Contents

324-1. **Definition.** Concealed knob-and-tube wiring is a wiring method using knobs, tubes, and flexible nonmetallic tubing for the protection and support of single insulated conductors concealed in hollow spaces of walls and ceilings of buildings.

Open wiring on insulators (Article 320) is required to be exposed, whereas knob-and-tube wiring is allowed to be concealed. Conductors used for knob-and-tube work may be of any general-use type specified by Article 310.

324-2. **Other Articles.** Concealed knob-and-tube wiring shall comply with this article and also with the applicable provisions of other articles in this Code, especially Article 300.

324-3. **Uses Permitted.** Concealed knob-and-tube wiring shall be permitted to be used only for extensions of existing installations and elsewhere only by special permission under the following conditions:

(1) In the hollow spaces of walls and ceilings.

(2) In unfinished attic and roof spaces as provided in Section 324-11.

Knob-and-tube wiring is permitted to be installed for extensions of existing installations where special permission is granted by the authority having jurisdiction of enforcement of the *Code*. See definition of "Special Permission" in Article 100.

324-4. **Uses Not Permitted.** Concealed knob-and-tube wiring shall not be used in commercial garages, theaters and similar locations, motion picture studios, hazardous (classified) locations, or in the hollow spaces of walls, ceilings, and attics where such spaces are insulated by loose, rolled, or foamed-in-place insulating material that envelops the conductors.

Concealed knob-and-tube wiring is designed for use in hollow spaces of walls, ceilings, and attics and utilizes the free air in such spaces for heat dissipation. Weatherization of hollow spaces by blown-in, foamed-in, or rolled insulation prevents the dissipation of heat into the free air space. This will result in higher conductor temperature, which could cause insulation breakdown and possible ignition of the insulation.

324-5. **Conductors.**

(a) Type. Conductors shall be of a type specified by Article 310.

(b) Ampacity. The ampacity shall be determined by Section 310-15.

See Tables 310-17 and 310-19.

324-6. **Conductor Supports.** Conductors shall be rigidly supported on noncombustible, nonabsorbent insulating materials and shall not contact any other objects. Supports shall be installed as follows: (1) within 6 inches (152 mm) of each side of each tap or splice, and (2) at intervals not exceeding 4½ feet (1.37 m).

Exception: If it is not practicable to provide supports in dry locations, it shall be permissible to fish conductors through hollow

spaces if each conductor is individually enclosed in flexible nonmetallic tubing. The tubing shall be in continuous lengths between supports, between boxes, or between a support and a box.

324-7. **Tie Wires.** Where solid knobs are used, conductors shall be securely tied thereto by tie wires having insulation equivalent to that of the conductor.

324-8. **Conductor Clearances.** A clearance of not less than 3 inches (76 mm) shall be maintained between conductors and of not less than 1 inch (25.4 mm) between the conductor and the surface over which it passes.

Exception: Where space is too limited to provide the above minimum clearances, such as at meters, panelboards, outlets, and switch points, the conductors shall be individually enclosed in flexible nonmetallic tubing, which shall be in continuous lengths between the last support or box and the terminal point.

324-9. **Through Walls, Floors, Wood Cross Members, etc.** Conductors shall comply with Section 320-11 where passing through holes in structural members. Where passing through wood cross members in plastered partitions, conductors shall be protected by noncombustible, nonabsorbent, insulating tubes extending not less than 3 inches (76 mm) beyond the wood member.

The provision for insulated tubes for use with knob-and-tube wiring where passing through wood cross members in plastered partitions is to protect the wire from contact with plaster that is likely to accumulate on horizontal wood members.

324-10. **Clearance from Piping, Exposed Conductors, etc.** Conductors shall comply with Section 320-12 for clearances from other exposed conductors, piping, etc.

324-11. **Unfinished Attics and Roof Spaces.** Conductors in unfinished attics and roof spaces shall comply with (a) or (b) below.

(FPN): See Section 310-10 for temperature limitation of conductors.

(a) Accessible by Stairway or Permanent Ladder. Conductors shall be installed along the side of or through bored holes in floor joists, studs, or rafters. Where run through bored holes, conductors in the joists and in studs or rafters to a height of not less than 7 feet (2.13 m) above the floor or floor joists shall be protected by substantial running boards extending not less than 1 inch (25.4 mm) on each side of the conductors. Running boards shall be securely fastened in place. Running boards and guard strips shall not be required where conductors are installed along the sides of joists, studs, or rafters.

(b) Not Accessible by Stairway or Permanent Ladder. Conductors shall be installed along the sides of or through bored holes in floor joists, studs, or rafters.

Exception: In buildings completed before wiring is installed and having head room at all points of less than 3 feet (914 mm).

Figure 324-1 illustrates the "running board" method of protecting open-type conductors in an accessible attic. This method is applied in attics that are accessible by stairways or permanent ladders and where such spaces are generally used for storage.

Figure 324-1. *Open wiring in accessible attic. Wires run through rafters and through joists where there is no floor.*

324-12. Splices. Splices shall be soldered unless approved splicing devices are used. In-line or strain splices shall not be used.

324-13. Boxes. Outlet boxes shall comply with Article 370.

324-14. Switches. Switches shall comply with Sections 380-4 and 380-10(b).

ARTICLE 325   Integrated Gas Spacer Cable

Type IGS

Contents

A. General

325-1. Definition.
325-2. Other Articles.
325-3. Uses Permitted.
325-4. Uses Not Permitted.

B. Installation

325-11. Bending Radius.
325-12. Bends.
325-13. Fittings.
325-14. Ampacity.

C. Construction Specifications

325-20. Conductors.
325-21. Insulation.
325-22. Conduit.
325-23. Grounding.
325-24. Marking.

A. General

325-1. Definition. Type IGS cable is a factory assembly of one or more conductors, each individually insulated and enclosed in a loose fit nonmetallic flexible conduit as an integrated gas spacer cable rated 0-600 volts.

Type IGS conductors consist of solid aluminum rods, 250 kcmil minimum. These conductors are insulated with dry kraft paper and are factory-installed in a medium-density polyethylene gas pipe, 2-inch minimum trade size, which is then filled with sulfur hexafluoride gas at a pressure of approximately 20 psi. See Figure 325-1.

325-2. Other Articles. The Type IGS cable shall comply with this article and also with the applicable provisions of other articles in this Code.

Figure 325-1. *Cross section of single-conductor, 4,750 kcmil, Type IGS cable.*

325-3. **Uses Permitted.** The Type IGS cable shall be permitted for use underground, including direct burial in the earth, as service-entrance conductors, or as feeder or branch-circuit conductors.

325-4. **Uses Not Permitted.** The Type IGS cable shall not be used as interior wiring or exposed in contact with buildings.

B. Installation

325-11. **Bending Radius.** Where the coilable nonmetallic conduit and cable is bent for installation purposes or is flexed or bent during shipment or installation, the radii of bends measured to the inside of the bend shall not be less than specified in Table 325-11.

Table 325-11. Minimum Radii of Bends

Conduit Trade Size	Minimum Radii
2 inch	24 inches (610 mm)
3 inch	35 inches (889 mm)
4 inch	45 inches (1.14 m)

325-12. **Bends.** A run of Type IGS cable between pull boxes or terminations shall not contain more than the equivalent of four quarter bends (360 degrees, total), including those bends located immediately at the pull box or terminations.

325-13. **Fittings.** Terminations and splices for the Type IGS cable shall be identified as a type that is suitable for maintaining the gas pressure within the conduit. A valve and cap shall be provided for each length of the cable and conduit to check the gas pressure or to inject gas into the conduit.

325-14. **Ampacity.** The ampacity of the Type IGS cable and conduit shall not exceed values shown in Table 325-14 for single conductor or multiconductor cable.

Table 325-14. Ampacity Type IGS

Size kcmil	Amperes
250	119
500	168
750	206
1000	238
1250	266
1500	292
1750	315
2000	336
2250	357
2500	376
3000	412
3250	429
3500	445
3750	461
4000	476
4250	491
4500	505
4750	519

C. Construction Specifications

325-20. **Conductors.** The conductors shall be solid aluminum rods, laid parallel, consisting of one to nineteen ½-inch (12.7-mm) diameter rods.

The minimum conductor size shall be 250 kcmil and the maximum size shall be 4750 kcmil.

325-21. **Insulation.** The insulation shall be dry kraft paper tapes and a pressurized sulfur hexafluoride gas (SF_6), both approved for electrical use. The nominal gas pressure shall be 20 pounds per square inch gauge (psig) (138 kPa gauge).

The thickness of the paper spacer shall be as specified in Table 325-21.

Table 325-21. Paper Spacer Thickness

Size kcmil	Thickness Inches (mm)
250-1000	.040 (1.02)
1250-4750	.060 (1.52)

325-22. **Conduit.** The conduit shall be an approved medium density polyethylene identified as suitable for use with natural gas rated pipe in 2 inches, 3 inches, or 4 inches trade size. The percent fill dimensions for the conduit are shown in Table 325-22.

The size of the conduit permitted for each conductor size shall be calculated for a percent fill not to exceed Table 1, Chapter 9.

Table 325-22. Conduit Dimensions

Conduit Trade Size, Inches	Outside Diameter, Inches (mm)	Inside Diameter, Inches (mm)
2	2.375 (60)	1.947 (49.46)
3	3.500 (89)	2.886 (73.30)
4	4.500 (114)	3.710 (94.23)

325-23. **Grounding.** The Type IGS cable shall comply with Article 250.

325-24. **Marking.** The provisions of Section 310-11 shall apply for the Type IGS cable.

ARTICLE 326 Medium Voltage Cable

Type MV

Contents

326-1. Definition.
326-2. Other Articles.
326-3. Uses Permitted.
326-4. Uses Not Permitted.
326-5. Construction.
326-6. Ampacity.
326-7. Marking.

326-1. **Definition.** Type MV is a single or multiconductor solid dielectric insulated cable rated 2001 volts or higher.

Medium-voltage cables are rated 2,001 to 35,000 V. Cables rated 2,001 to 8,000 V may be shielded or non-shielded. All insulated conductors 8,001 V and higher have electrostatic shielding. When nonshielded cables are used,

they must comply with Section 310-6, Exception. If these cables are installed in underground conduits, they must be encased in 3 inches of concrete. See Section 710-4(b).

326-2. **Other Articles.** In addition to the provisions of this article, Type MV cable shall comply with the applicable provisions of this Code, especially those of Articles 300, 305, 310, 318, 501, and 710.

326-3. **Uses Permitted.** Type MV cables shall be permitted for use on power systems rated up to 35,000 volts, nominal, in wet or dry locations, in raceways, cable trays as specified in Section 318-3(b)(1), or directly buried in accordance with Section 710-4(b) and in messenger supported wiring.

326-4. **Uses Not Permitted.** Type MV cable shall not be used unless identified for the use (1) where exposed to direct sunlight, and (2) in cable trays.

Cables intended for installation in cable trays in accordance with Article 318 are marked "for CT Use" or "Cable Tray Use."

326-5. **Construction.** Type MV cables shall have copper, aluminum, or copper-clad aluminum conductors and shall be constructed in accordance with Article 310.

Cables with aluminum conductors are marked with the word "aluminum" or the letters "AL."

326-6. **Ampacity.** The ampacity of Type MV cable shall be in accordance with Section 310-15.

Exception: The ampacity of Type MV cable installed in cable tray shall be in accordance with Section 318-13.

This exception is required to provide the correct ampacities for conductors and multiconductor cables where installed in cable tray.

326-7. **Marking.** Medium voltage cable shall be marked as required in Section 310-11.

Cables are marked with their conductor size, voltage rating, and insulation level (100 percent or 133 percent).

ARTICLE 328   Flat Conductor Cable

Type FCC

Contents

A. General

328-1. Scope. This article covers a field-installed wiring system for branch circuits incorporating Type FCC cable and associated accessories as defined by the article. The wiring system is designed for installation under carpet squares.

The flat conductor cable system is designed to provide a completely accessible, flexible power system. It also provides an easy method for reworking obsolete wiring systems currently in use in many office facilities. See Figure 328-1.

The carpet squares are not permitted to be larger than 36 inches by 36 inches. See Section 328-10. This limitation is judged necessary to provide ready access to the cable by lifting a carpet square. It also reduces the likelihood of damage to the cable by an individual cutting through the carpet above the cable with a knife or razor blade and possibly penetrating the top shield of the cable in the process.

Figure 328-1.   Installing flat conductor cable. (AMP Products Corp.)

328-2. Definitions.

Type FCC Cable: Type FCC cable consists of three or more flat copper conductors placed edge-to-edge and separated and enclosed within an insulating assembly.

FCC System: A complete wiring system for branch circuits that is designed for installation under carpet squares. The FCC system includes Type FCC cable and associated shielding, connectors, terminators, adapters, boxes, and receptacles.

Cable Connector: A connector designed to join Type FCC cables without using a junction box.

Insulating End: An insulator designed to electrically insulate the end of a Type FCC cable.

Top Shield: A grounded metal shield covering undercarpet components of the FCC system for the purposes of providing protection against physical damage.

Bottom Shield: A protective layer that is installed between the floor and Type FCC flat conductor cable to protect the cable from physical damage and may or may not be incorporated as an integral part of the cable.

Transition Assembly: An assembly to facilitate connection of the FCC system to other approved wiring systems, incorporating (1) a means of electrical interconnection, and (2) a suitable box or covering for providing electrical safety and protection against physical damage.

Metal Shield Connections: Means of connection designed to electrically and mechanically connect a metal shield to another metal shield, to a receptacle housing or self-contained device, or to a transition assembly.

328-3. Other Articles. The FCC systems shall conform with applicable provisions of Articles 210, 220, 240, 250, and 300.

328-4. Uses Permitted.

(a) Branch Circuits. Use of FCC systems shall be permitted both for general-purpose and appliance branch circuits and for individual branch circuits.

(b) Floors. Use of FCC systems shall be permitted on hard, sound, smooth, continuous floor surfaces made of concrete, ceramic, or composition flooring, wood, and similar materials.

(c) Walls. Use of FCC systems shall be permitted on wall surfaces in surface metal raceways.

(d) Damp Locations. Use of FCC systems in damp locations shall be permitted.

(e) Heated Floors. Materials used for floors heated in excess of 30°C (86°F) shall be identified as suitable for use at these temperatures.

328-5. Uses Not Permitted. FCC systems shall not be used (1) outdoors or in wet locations; (2) where subject to corrosive vapors; (3) in any hazardous (classified) location; or (4) in residential, school, and hospital buildings.

Section 328-5(4) prohibits Type FCC wiring systems throughout school and hospital buildings, even though parts of these buildings may be office or administrative spaces.

328-6. Branch-Circuit Ratings.

(a) Voltage. Voltage between ungrounded conductors shall not exceed 300 volts. Voltage between ungrounded conductors and the grounded conductor shall not exceed 150 volts.

(b) Current. General-purpose and appliance branch circuits shall have ratings not exceeding 20 amperes. Individual branch circuits shall have ratings not exceeding 30 amperes.

B. Installation

328-10. Coverings. Floor-mounted Type FCC cable, cable connectors, and insulating ends shall be covered with carpet squares no larger than 36 inches (914 mm) square. Those carpet squares that are adhered to the floor shall be attached with release-type adhesives.

328-11. Cable Connections and Insulating Ends. All Type FCC cable connections shall use connectors identified for their use, installed such that electrical continuity, insulation, and sealing against dampness and liquid spillage are provided. All bare cable ends shall be insulated and sealed against dampness and liquid spillage using listed insulating ends.

328-12. Shields.

(a) Top Shield. A metal top shield shall be installed over all floor-mounted Type FCC cable, connectors, and insulating ends. The top shield shall completely cover all cable runs, corners, connectors, and ends.

(b) Bottom Shield. A bottom shield shall be installed beneath all Type FCC cable, connectors, and insulating ends.

328-13. **Enclosure and Shield Connections.** All metal shields, boxes, receptacle housings, and self-contained devices shall be electrically continuous to the equipment grounding conductor of the supplying branch circuit. All such electrical connections shall be made with connectors identified for this use. The electrical resistivity of such shield system shall not be more than that of one conductor of the Type FCC cable used in the installation.

328-14. **Receptacles.** All receptacles, receptacle housings, and self-contained devices used with the FCC system shall be identified for this use and shall be connected to the Type FCC cable and metal shields. Connection from any grounding conductor of the Type FCC cable shall be made to the shield system at each receptacle.

328-15. **Connection to Other Systems.** Power feed, grounding connection, and shield system connection between the FCC system and other wiring systems shall be accomplished in a transition assembly identified for this use.

328-16. **Anchoring.** All FCC system components shall be firmly anchored to the floor or wall using an adhesive or mechanical anchoring system identified for this use. Floors shall be prepared to assure adherence of the FCC system to the floor until the carpet squares are placed.

328-17. **Crossings.** Crossings of more than two Type FCC cable runs shall not be permitted at any one point. Crossings of a Type FCC cable over or under a flat communications or signal cable shall be permitted. In each case, a grounded layer of metal shielding shall separate the two cables, and crossings of more than two flat cables shall not be permitted at any one point.

328-18. **System Height.** Any portion of an FCC system with a height above floor level exceeding 0.090 inches (2.29 mm) shall be tapered or feathered at the edges to floor level.

328-19. **FCC Systems Alterations.** Alterations to FCC systems shall be permitted. New cable connectors shall be used at new connection points to make alterations. It shall be permitted to leave unused cable runs and associated cable connectors in place and energized. All cable ends shall be covered with insulating ends.

328-20. **Polarization of Connections.** All receptacles and connections shall be constructed and installed so as to maintain proper polarization of the system.

C. Construction

328-30. **Type FCC Cable.** Type FCC cable shall be approved for use with the FCC system and shall consist of three, four, or five flat copper conductors, one of which shall be an equipment grounding conductor. The insulating material of the cable shall be moisture-resistant and flame-retardant.

328-31. **Markings.** Type FCC cable shall be clearly and durably marked on both sides at intervals of not more than 24 inches (610 mm) with the information required by Section 310-11(a) and with the following additional information: (1) material of conductors; (2) maximum temperature rating; and (3) ampacity.

328-32. **Conductor Identification.**

(a) Colors. Conductors shall be clearly and durably marked on both sides throughout their length as specified in Section 310-12.
(b) Order. For a 2-wire FCC system with grounding, the grounding conductor shall be central.

328-33. **Corrosion Resistance.** Metal components of the system shall be either (1) corrosion-resistant; (2) coated with corrosion-resistant materials; or (3) insulated from contact with corrosive substances.

328-34. **Insulation.** All insulating materials in the FCC systems shall be identified for their use.

328-35. **Shields.**

(a) Materials and Dimensions. All top and bottom shields shall be of designs and materials identified for their use. Top shields shall be metal. Both metallic and nonmetallic materials shall be permitted for bottom shields.
(b) Resistivity. Metal shields shall have cross-sectional areas that provide for electrical resistivity of not more than that of one conductor of the Type FCC cable used in the installation.

(c) Metal-Shield Connectors. Metal shields shall be connected to each other and to boxes, receptacle housings, self-contained devices, and transition assemblies using metal-shield connectors.

328-36. **Receptacles and Housings.** Receptacle housings and self-contained devices designed either for floor mounting or for in- or on-wall mounting shall be permitted for use with the FCC system. Receptacle housings and self-contained devices shall incorporate means for facilitating entry and termination of Type FCC cable and for electrically connecting the housing or device with the metal shield. Receptacles and self-contained devices shall comply with Section 210-7. Power and communications outlets installed together in common housing shall be permitted in accordance with Section 800-52(c)(2), Exception No. 2.

328-37. **Transition Assemblies.** All transition assemblies shall be identified for their use. Each assembly shall incorporate means for facilitating entry of the Type FCC cable into the assembly, for connecting the Type FCC cable to grounded conductors, and for electrically connecting the assembly to the metal cable shields and to equipment grounding conductors.

ARTICLE 330 Mineral-Insulated, Metal-Sheathed Cable

Type MI

Contents

A. General

B. Installation

C. Construction Specifications

A. General

330-1. **Definition.** Type MI mineral-insulated, metal-sheathed cable is a factory assembly of one or more conductors insulated with a highly compressed refractory mineral insulation and enclosed in a liquidtight and gastight continuous copper or alloy steel sheath.

330-2. **Other Articles.** Type MI cable shall comply with this article and also with the applicable provisions of other articles in this Code, especially Article 300.

Mineral-insulated, metal-sheathed cable consists of one or more solid copper conductors insulated with highly compressed magnesium oxide and enclosed in a continuous copper or alloy steel, e.g., stainless steel sheath. It is manufactured in size Nos. 16 to 250 kcmil, one conductor; Nos. 16 to 4, two- and three-conductor; Nos. 16 to 6, four-conductor; and Nos. 16 to 10, seven-conductor. The cable is rated 600 V.

Terminations especially investigated for use with this cable are listed as "Mineral-Insulated Cable Fittings."

Supplementary nonmetallic coatings presently used have not been investigated for resistance to corrosion.

Fittings for use on Type MI mineral-insulated cable are suitable for use at a maximum operating temperature of 85°C (185°F) in dry locations and 60°C (140°F) in wet locations. A complete box connector consists of a connector body and a screw-on potting fitting.

The screw-on potting fitting to be used with the connector may be used separately as an end fitting for change to open wiring. The screw-on potting fitting is to be assembled with a special tool and consists of a screw-on pot, insulating cap, insulating sleeving, anchoring bead, and sealing compound. See Figure 330-1.

Threaded Gland ——— End Seal ———

Figure 330-1. Type MI cable fitting used for terminating cable at box or equipment. (Pyrotenax USA, Inc.)

Brass gland nut
Brass compression ring
Brass gland body
N.P.T. taper thread
Brass screw-on pot cuts its own thread as it screws on to the cable sheath
Anchoring bead securing sleeving
Insulating cap
Insulating sleeving may be color coded

330-3. **Uses Permitted.** Type MI cable shall be permitted as follows: (1) for services, feeders, and branch circuits; (2) for power, lighting, control, and signal circuits; (3) in dry, wet, or continuously moist locations; (4) indoors or outdoors; (5) where exposed or concealed; (6) embedded in plaster, concrete, fill, or other masonry, whether above or below grade; (7) in any hazardous (classified) location; (8) where exposed to oil and gasoline; (9) where exposed to corrosive conditions not deteriorating to its sheath; (10) in underground runs where suitably protected against physical damage and corrosive conditions.

Type MI mineral-insulated, metal-sheathed cable is suitable for all power and control circuits up to 600 V and may be used for services, feeders, and branch circuits in exposed and concealed work. It is permitted to be installed in dry and wet locations; and in plaster, in masonry, concrete, or fill; or underground. It may be installed where exposed to weather, continuous moisture, exposed to oil or gasoline, in any hazardous (classified) location; or other conditions not having a deteriorating effect on the metal sheath.

330-4. **Uses Not Permitted.** Type MI cable shall not be used where exposed to destructive corrosive conditions.

Exception: Where protected by materials suitable for the conditions.

B. Installation

330-10. **Wet Locations.** Where installed in wet locations, Type MI cable shall comply with Section 300-6(c).

330-11. **Through Joists, Studs, or Rafters.** Type MI cable shall comply with Section 300-4 where installed through studs, joists, rafters, or similar wood members.

330-12. **Supports.** Type MI cable shall be securely supported at intervals not exceeding 6 feet (1.83 m) by straps, staples, hangers, or similar fittings so designed and installed as not to damage the cable.

Exception: Where cable is fished in.

330-13. **Bends.** Bends in Type MI cable shall be so made as not to damage the cable. The radius of the inner edge of any bend shall not be less than shown below.

(1) Five times the external diameter of the metallic sheath for cable not more than ¾ inch (19 mm) in external diameter.

(2) Ten times the external diameter of the metallic sheath for cable greater than ¾ inch (19 mm) but not more than 1 inch (25.4 mm) in external diameter.

This section was revised for the 1993 *Code.* The minimum bending radius for cables with an external diameter that is greater than ¾ inch but not more than 1 inch has been increased to 10 times the external diameter of the cable. The cables that have an external diameter of ¾ inch and smaller have a minimum bending radius of five times the external diameter of the cable.

The minimum bending radius is intended to prevent mechanical damage to the conductor or the sheath that could result in cracking or a hot spot at the point of damage or both.

330-14. **Fittings.** Fittings used for connecting Type MI cable to boxes, cabinets, or other equipment shall be identified for such use. Where single-conductor cables enter ferrous metal boxes or cabinets, the installation shall comply with Section 300-20 to prevent inductive heating.

330-15. **Terminal Seals.** Where Type MI cable terminates, an approved seal shall be provided immediately after stripping to prevent the entrance of moisture into the insulation. The conductors extending beyond the sheath shall be individually provided with an approved insulating material.

330-16. **Single Conductors.** Where single-conductor cables are used, all phase conductors and, where used, the neutral conductor shall be grouped together to minimize induced voltage on the sheath. Where single-conductor cables enter ferrous enclosures, the installation shall comply with Section 300-20 to prevent heating from induction.

Figure 330-2. Minimum bending radius for external diameter of not more than ³/₄ inches. R = 5 X external diameter for external diameter greater than ³/₄ inches but not more than 1 inch, R = 1X external diameter.

This section is new in the 1993 *Code*. It permits Type MI cable to be used as single conductors. The larger sizes of Type MI cable are only available as single conductor cables. Single conductors in a metal sheath can result in induced voltage on the sheath. Therefore, Section 330-16 requires all conductors of the circuit to be grouped together to minimize the voltage on the sheath.

Where single conductors enter a ferrous metal enclosure, inductive heating can occur. This is due to hysteresis loss caused by the magnetic flux that will occur in ferrous metals and I^2R losses from the currents induced by the conductor. Section 300-20 requires additional measures to minimize the magnetic heating of enclosure through which single conductors enter. The additional measures may consist of slots cut in the metal between the individual holes for each conductor or by passing all of the conductors in the circuit through an insulating wall in the enclosure. The insulating wall must be large enough to allow all of the conductors to pass through.

C. Construction Specifications

330-20. **Conductors.** Type MI cable conductors shall be of solid copper or nickel-clad copper with a resistance corresponding to standard AWG sizes.

330-21. **Insulation.** The conductor insulation in Type MI cable shall be a highly compressed refractory mineral that provides proper spacing for all conductors.

330-22. **Outer Sheath.** The outer sheath shall be of a continuous construction to provide mechanical protection and moisture seal. Where made of copper, it shall provide an adequate path for equipment grounding purposes. Where made of steel, an equipment grounding conductor in accordance with Article 250 shall be provided.

ARTICLE 331   Electrical Nonmetallic Tubing

Contents

A. General

B. Installation

A. General

331-1. **Definition.** Electrical nonmetallic tubing is a pliable corrugated raceway of circular cross-section with integral or associated couplings, connectors and fittings listed for the installation of electric conductors. It is composed of a material that is resistant to moisture, chemical atmospheres, and is flame-retardant.

A pliable raceway is a raceway that can be bent by hand with a reasonable force, but without other assistance.

(FPN): It is intended that the material used has ignitibility, flammability, smoke generation, and toxicity characteristics that do not exceed those of rigid (nonplasticized) polyvinyl chloride.

Electrical nonmetallic tubing (ENT) is made of the same material (PVC) used for rigid nonmetallic conduit suitable for aboveground use. See Article 347. Because of the corrugations, the raceway can be bent by hand and has some degree of flexibility, but it is not intended for use where flexibility is necessary, as at motor terminations to prevent transmission of noise and vibration, or for connection of adjustable fixtures or moving parts. See Figure 331-1.

ENT is suitable for the installation of conductors having a temperature rating as indicated on the product. The maximum allowable ambient temperature is 50°C (122°F).

The outside diameters of ENT are such that standard couplings and other fittings for rigid PVC conduit can be employed.

331-2. **Other Articles.** Installations for electrical nonmetallic tubing shall comply with the provisions of the applicable sections of Article 300. Where equipment grounding is required by Article 250, a separate equipment grounding conductor shall be installed in the raceway.

331-3. **Uses Permitted.** The use of electrical nonmetallic tubing and fittings shall be permitted:

(1) In any building not exceeding three floors above grade.

  a. For exposed work, where not subject to physical damage.
  b. Concealed within walls, floors, and ceilings.

(FPN): See Section 336-4(a) for definition of first floor.

Electrical nonmetallic tubing is permitted to be installed, concealed, or exposed. If it is used exposed and it is subject to physical damage, it is required to be protected and is limited to use in buildings not exceeding three floors [as defined in Section 336-4(a)] above grade. [See definition of exposed (as applied to wiring methods) in Article 100.] Where used concealed or above a suspended ceiling, ENT is permitted to be installed within walls, floors, or ceilings in buildings of three floors or less without the need for fire-rated construction. The three-floor limitation is based on the likelihood that only a small quantity of ENT will be exposed to fire and that the occupants will have adequate time to exit the building before the products of combustion make the building untenable.

Figure 331-1. *Electrical nonmetallic tubing is permitted in ¹/₂-inch through 2-inch trade sizes only. (Carlon, a Lamson & Sessions Co.)*

Electrical nonmetallic tubing is permitted to be installed within the walls, floors, or ceilings of a building of *any* height where the walls, floors, or ceilings provide a thermal barrier of material that has at least a 15-minute finish rating. See commentary following Section 331-3(2). It is not permitted or intended that ENT be used exposed in the first three floors of a building that exceeds three floors except as permitted in Section 331-3(5). Where installed in a building over three floors, ENT must be installed behind the 15-minute thermal barrier on all floors.

(2) In any building exceeding three floors above grade, electrical nonmetallic tubing shall be concealed within walls, floors, and ceilings where the walls, floors, and ceilings provide a thermal barrier of material that has at least a 15-minute finish rating as identified in listings of fire-rated assemblies.

Interior finish is generally considered to consist of those materials or combinations of materials that form the exposed interior surface of walls and ceilings in a building. Common interior finish materials include plaster, gypsum wallboard, wood, plywood paneling, fibrous ceiling tiles, and a variety of wall coverings. Ordinary paint, wallpaper, or other similar wall coverings not exceeding $\frac{1}{28}$ inch in thickness are generally considered as incidental to interior finish, except where the authority having jurisdiction deems them to be a hazard.

The finish rating of a wall or ceiling finish is the time required for the unexposed wall surface to reach an average temperature of 121°C (250°F) above ambient with a temperature rise at any one point not exceeding 163°C (325°F), when the assembly is tested in accordance with NFPA 251, *Standard Methods of Fire Tests of Building Construction and Materials* (also known as ANSI/UL 263).

The finish rating of wall and ceiling assemblies tested and rated by UL can be found in the UL Fire Resistance Directory immediately following the assembly rating and just below the design number. However, only assemblies containing combustible support members have published finish ratings. Obviously, it is not the intent to limit ENT to constructions consisting of combustible support members. This section is intended to provide a 15-minute thermal barrier as a minimum threshold of acceptability.

The fire resistance rating of an assembly or finish is the length of time the finish or assembly withstands the fire test without the unexposed side exceeding an average temperature rise of 121°C (250°F) and without the single point temperature exceeding 163°C (325°F). It is, in effect, the finish rating.

The chart below was reproduced from the NFPA *Fire Protection Handbook* (16th edition). It provides fire resistance ratings for common finishes.

If the finish rating concealing the ENT is unknown or is less than 15 minutes, the ENT can still be used if the installation meets the criteria in Section 331-3, including the 3-floor limitation, where required and the installation is not prohibited by Section 331-4. For assemblies and finishes not tested and rated, or not given a finish rating because they include no combustible supports, see the following chart.

Material	Fire Resistance Rating* Min
Fiberboard, $\frac{1}{2}$ in. thick	5
Fiberboard, flameproofed, $\frac{1}{2}$ in. thick	10
Fiberboard, $\frac{1}{2}$ in. thick, with $\frac{1}{2}$ in. 1:2, 1:2 gypsum-sand plaster	15
Gypsum wallboard, $\frac{3}{8}$ in. thick	10
Gypsum wallboard, $\frac{1}{2}$ in. thick	15
Gypsum wallboard, $\frac{5}{8}$ in. thick	20
Gypsum wallboards, laminated, two $\frac{3}{8}$ in. thick	28
Gypsum wallboards, laminated, one $\frac{3}{8}$ in. plus one $\frac{1}{2}$ in. thick	37
Gypsum wallboards, laminated, two $\frac{1}{2}$ in. thick	47
Gypsum wallboards, laminated, two $\frac{5}{8}$ in. thick	60
Gypsum lath, plain or indented, $\frac{3}{8}$ in. thick, with $\frac{1}{2}$ in. 1:2, 1:2 gypsum-sand plaster	20
Gypsum lath, perforated, $\frac{3}{8}$ in. thick, with $\frac{1}{2}$ in. 1:2, 1:2 gypsum-sand plaster	30
Gypsum-sand plaster, 1:2, 1:3, $\frac{1}{2}$ in. thick, on wood lath	15
Lime-sand plaster, 1:5, 1:7.5, $\frac{1}{2}$ in. thick, on wood lalth	15
Gypsum-sand plaster, 1:2, 1:2, $\frac{3}{4}$ in. thick, on metal lath (no paper backing)	15
Neat gypsum plaster, $\frac{3}{4}$ in. thick on metal lath (no paper backing)†	30
Neat gypsum plaster, 1 in. thick, on metal lath (no paper backing)†	35
Lime-sand plaster, 1:5, 1:7.5, $\frac{3}{4}$ in. thick, on metal lath (no paper backing)	10
Portland cement plaster, $\frac{3}{4}$ in. thick, on metal lath (no paper backing)	10
Gypsum-sand plaster, 1:2, 1:3, $\frac{3}{4}$ in. thick, on paper-backed metal lath	20

*From National Bureau of Standards, BMS-92.
†Unsanded wood-fiber plaster.
SI units: 1 in. = 25.4 mm.

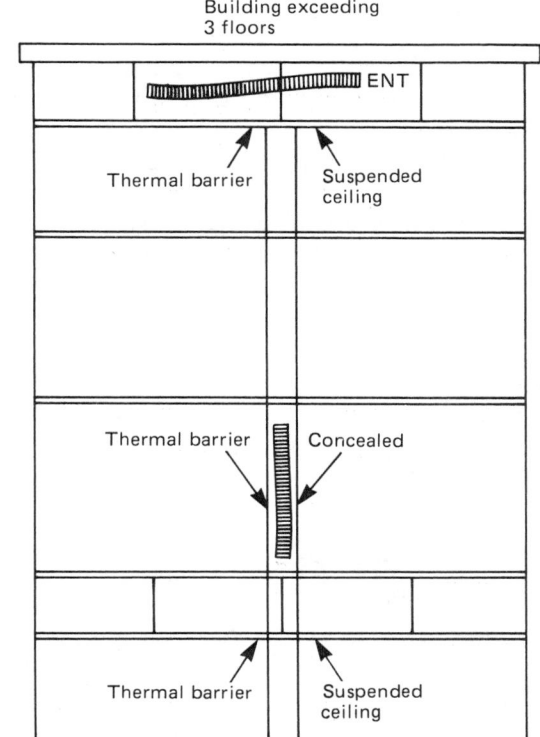

Figure 331-2. Some examples of permitted uses of electrical nonmetallic tubing in buildings of 3 floors or less and buildings exceeding 3 floors.

(3) In locations subject to severe corrosive influences as covered in Section 300-6 and where subject to chemicals for which the materials are specifically approved.

(4) In concealed, dry, and damp locations not prohibited by Section 331-4.

(5) Above suspended ceilings where the suspended ceilings provide a thermal barrier of material that has at least a 15-minute finish rating as identified in listings of fire-rated assemblies, except as permitted in Section 331-3(1)a.

(6) Embedded in poured concrete, provided fittings identified for this purpose are used for connections.

(7) For wet locations indoors or in a concrete slab on or below grade, with fittings listed for the purpose.

(FPN): Extreme cold may cause some types of nonmetallic conduits to become brittle and, therefore, more susceptible to damage from physical contact.

331-4. **Uses Not Permitted.** Electrical nonmetallic tubing shall not be used:

(1) In hazardous (classified) locations.

Exception: Except as permitted by Section 504-20.

(2) For the support of fixtures and other equipment.

(3) Where subject to ambient temperatures exceeding those for which the tubing is listed.

(4) For conductors whose insulation temperature limitations would exceed those for which the tubing is listed.

(5) For direct earth burial.

(6) Where the voltage is over 600 volts.

(7) In exposed locations, except as permitted by Sections 331-3(1), 331-3(5), and 331-3(7).

(8) In theaters and similar locations, except as provided in Articles 518 and 520.

See Sections 518-4 and 520-4.

B. Installation

331-5. **Size.**

(a) Minimum. Tubing smaller than ½-inch electrical trade size shall not be used.

(b) Maximum. Tubing larger than 2-inch electrical trade size shall not be used.

This section has been revised for the 1993 *Code* to permit a maximum 2-inch electrical trade size. The maximum size was formerly 1-inch electrical trade size.

331-6. **Number of Conductors in Tubing.** The number of conductors in a single tubing shall not exceed that permitted by the percentage fill in Table 1, Chapter 9.

331-7. **Trimming.** All cut ends of tubing shall be trimmed inside and outside to remove rough edges.

331-8. **Joints.** All joints between lengths of tubing and between tubing and couplings, fittings and boxes shall be by an approved method.

331-9. **Bends — How Made.** Bends of electrical nonmetallic tubing shall be so made that the tubing will not be damaged and that the internal diameter of the tubing will not be effectively reduced. Bends shall be permitted to be made manually without auxiliary equipment, and the radius of the curve of the inner edge of such bends shall not be less than shown in Table 346-10.

331-10. **Bends — Number in One Run.** There shall not be more than the equivalent of four quarter bends (360 degrees total) between pull points, e.g., conduit bodies and boxes.

331-11. **Supports.** Electrical nonmetallic tubing shall be installed as a complete system as provided in Article 300 and shall be securely fastened in place within 3 feet (914 mm) of each outlet box, device box, junction box, cabinet, or fitting.

Tubing shall be secured at least every 3 feet (914 mm).

Exception No. 1: Where support is being provided at least every 3 feet (914 mm) by openings through framing members.

Exception No. 2: Lengths not exceeding a distance of 6 feet (1.83 m) from a fixture terminal connection for tap connections to lighting fixtures.

331-12. **Boxes and Fittings.** Boxes and fittings shall comply with the applicable provisions of Article 370.

331-13. **Splices and Taps.** Splices and taps shall be made only in junction boxes, outlet boxes, device boxes, or conduit bodies. See Article 370.

Figure 331-3. *Where ENT is run on the surface of framing members, it is required to be fastened to the framing member every 3 feet and within 3 feet of every box. See also Section 300-4(d) for protection against physical damage.*

Figure 331-4. *ENT is permitted to be used as a fixture whip without support for lengths not exceeding 6 feet. See also Section 410-67(c).*

331-14. **Bushings.** Where a tubing enters a box, fitting, or other enclosure, a bushing or adapter shall be provided to protect the wire from abrasion unless the box, fitting, or enclosure design provides equivalent protection.

(FPN): See Section 373-6(c) for the protection of conductors size No. 4 or larger.

C. Construction Specifications

331-15. General. Electrical nonmetallic tubing shall be clearly and durably marked at least every 10 feet (3.05 m) as required in the first sentence of Section 110-21. The type of material shall also be included in the marking. Tubing that has limited-smoke-producing characteristics shall be permitted to be identified with the suffix LS.

ARTICLE 333   Armored Cable

Type AC

Contents

A. General

A. General

333-1. Definition. Type AC cable is a fabricated assembly of insulated conductors in a flexible metallic enclosure. See Section 333-19.

Armored cable is listed by Underwriters Laboratories Inc. in sizes No. 14 through No. 1 copper and No. 12 through No. 1 aluminum or copper-clad aluminum and is rated at 600 V or less.

333-2. Other Articles. Type AC cable shall comply with this article and also with the applicable provisions of other articles in this Code, especially Article 300.

333-3. Uses Permitted. Except where otherwise specified in this Code and where not subject to physical damage, Type AC cable shall be permitted for branch circuits and feeders in both exposed and concealed work and in cable trays where identified for such use.

Type AC cable shall be permitted in dry locations and embedded in plaster finish on brick or other masonry, except in damp or wet locations. It shall be permissible to run or fish this cable in the air voids of masonry block or tile walls where such walls are not exposed or subject to excessive moisture or dampness or are below grade line.

333-4. Uses Not Permitted. Type AC cable shall not be used where prohibited elsewhere in this Code, including (1) in theaters and similar locations, except as provided in Article 518, Places of Assembly; (2) in motion picture studios; (3) in any hazardous (classified) location except as permitted by Sections 501-4(b) and 504-20; (4) where exposed to corrosive fumes or vapors; (5) on cranes or hoists, except as provided in Section 610-11, Exception No. 3; (6) in storage battery rooms; (7) in hoistways or on elevators, except as provided in Section 620-21; or (8) in commercial garages where prohibited in Article 511.

B. Installation

333-7. Support. Type AC cable shall be secured by approved staples, straps, hangers, or similar fittings so designed and installed as not to damage the cable at intervals not exceeding 4½ feet (1.37 m) and within 12 inches (305 mm) of every outlet box, junction box, cabinet or fitting.

This section requires that the cable be SECURED. Simply draping the cable over air ducts, lower members of bar joists, pipes, and ceiling grid members is not permitted. Exception No. 3 permits unsecured lengths up to 6 feet from accessible outlets above (suspended) ceilings. See also Section 300-4(c).

Exception No. 1: Where cable is fished.

Exception No. 2: Lengths of not more than 2 feet (610 mm) at terminals where flexibility is necessary.

Exception No. 3: Lengths of not more than 6 feet (1.83 m) from an outlet for connections within an accessible ceiling to lighting fixtures or equipment.

Exception No. 4: Where installed in cable trays, Type AC cable shall comply with Section 318-8(b).

333-8. **Bending Radius.** All bends shall be made so that the cable will not be damaged, and the radius of the curve of the inner edge of any bend shall not be less than five times the diameter of the Type AC cable.

333-9. **Boxes and Fittings.** At all points where the armor of AC cable terminates, a fitting shall be provided to protect wires from abrasion, unless the design of the outlet boxes or fittings is such as to afford equivalent protection, and, in addition, an approved insulating bushing or its equivalent approved protection shall be provided between the conductors and the armor. The connector or clamp by which the Type AC cable is fastened to boxes or cabinets shall be of such design that the insulating bushing or its equivalent will be visible for inspection. This bushing shall not be required with lead-covered cables where so installed that the lead sheath will be visible for inspection. Where change is made from Type AC cable to other cable or raceway wiring methods, a box, fitting, or conduit body shall be installed at junction points as required in Section 300-15.

Armored cable connectors are considered suitable for equipment grounding.

333-10. **Through or Parallel to Framing Members.** Type AC cable shall comply with Section 300-4 where installed through or parallel to studs, joists, rafters, or similar wood or metal members.

333-11. **Exposed Work.** Exposed runs of cable shall closely follow the surface of the building finish or of running boards.

Exception No. 1: Lengths of not more than 24 inches (610 mm) at terminals where flexibility is necessary.

Exception No. 2: On the underside of floor joists in basements where supported at each joist and so located as not to be subject to physical damage.

Exception No. 3: Lengths of not more than 6 feet (1.83 m) from an outlet for connection within an accessible ceiling to lighting fixtures or other equipment.

333-12. **In Accessible Attics.** Type AC cables in accessible attics or roof spaces shall be installed as specified in (a) and (b) below.

(a) **Where Run Across the Top of Floor Joists.** Where run across the top of floor joists, or within 7 feet (2.13 m) of floor or floor joists across the face of rafters or studding, in attics and roof spaces that are accessible, the cable shall be protected by substantial guard strips that are at least as high as the cable. Where this space is not accessible by permanent stairs or ladders, protection shall only be required within 6 feet (1.83 m) of the nearest edge of the scuttle hole or attic entrance.

(b) **Cable Installed Parallel to Framing Members.** Where the cable is installed parallel to the sides of rafters, studs, or floor joists, neither guard strips nor running boards shall be required, and the installation shall also comply with Section 300-4(d).

C. Construction Specifications

333-19. **Construction.** Type AC cable shall have an armor of flexible metal tape. The insulated conductors shall be in accordance with Section 333-20. Cables of the AC type shall have an internal bonding strip of copper or aluminum in intimate contact with the armor for its entire length.

The armor of Type AC cable is recognized as an equipment grounding conductor by Section 250-91(b). The required internal bonding strip can be simply cut off at the termination of the armored cable, or it can be bent back on the armor. It is not necessary to connect it to an equipment grounding terminal. Its use is to reduce the inductive reactance of the spiral armor and increase its effectiveness as an equipment grounding means. Many installers use this strip to help prevent the insulating bushing required by Section 333-9 (the "red head") from falling out during rough wiring.

333-20. **Conductors.** Insulated conductors shall be of a type listed in Table 310-13 or those identified for use in this cable. In addition, the conductors shall have an overall moisture-resistant and fire retardant fibrous covering. For Type ACT, a moisture-resistant fibrous covering shall be required only on the individual conductors. The ampacity shall be determined by Section 310-15.

Exception: Armored cable installed in thermal insulation shall have conductors rated at 90°C (194°F). The ampacity of cable installed in these applications shall be that of 60°C (140°F) conductors.

The marking of cables follows. ACT indicates an armored cable employing conductors having thermoplastic insulation. AC indicates an armored cable employing conductors having thermosetting insulation.

No suffix indicates 60°C (140°F) rating. H indicates 75°C (167°F) rating. HH indicates 90°C (194°F) rating.

The exception recognizes the decrease in heat dissipation capability of cables installed in a space that is provided with thermal insulation.

333-21. **Grounding.** Type AC cable shall provide an adequate path for equipment grounding as required by Section 250-51.

333-22. **Marking.** The provisions of Section 310-11 shall apply, except that Type AC cable shall have ready identification of the manufacturer by distinctive external markings on the cable sheath throughout its entire length. Cables that are flame-retardant and have limited-smoke characteristics shall be permitted to be identified with the suffix LS.

ARTICLE 334   Metal-Clad Cable

Type MC

Contents

A. General

A. General

334-1. **Definition.** Type MC cable is a factory assembly of one or more conductors, each individually insulated and enclosed in a metallic sheath of interlocking tape, or a smooth or corrugated tube.

Type MC cable is available in three designs: (1) interlocked metal tape, (2) corrugated tube, and (3) smooth tube. All are intended for aboveground use, except where marked for direct burial. Cables that are suitable for use in cable trays, in direct sunlight, or directly buried are so marked. Type MC cables include Type CS (copper sheath) and Type ALS (aluminum sheath).

334-2. **Other Articles.** Metal-clad cable shall comply with this article and also with the applicable provisions of other articles in this Code, especially Article 300.

Type MC cable is rated for use up to 5,000 V and listed in sizes No. 18 and larger for copper and No. 12 and larger for aluminum or copper-clad aluminum. It employs thermoset, thermoplastic, varnished cloth, or composite varnished cloth-thermoplastic insulated conductors. The latter is designated as Type VT and rated 85°C (185°F).

Type MC cable shall be permitted for systems in excess of 600 volts, nominal. See Section 300-2(a).

334-3. **Uses Permitted.** Except where otherwise specified in this Code and where not subject to physical damage, Type MC cables shall be permitted as follows: (1) for services, feeders, and branch circuits; (2) for power, lighting, control, and signal circuits; (3) indoors or outdoors; (4) where exposed or concealed; (5) direct buried where identified for such use; (6) in cable tray; (7) in any approved raceway; (8) as open runs of cable; (9) as aerial cable on a messenger; (10) in hazardous (classified) locations as permitted in Articles 501, 502, 503, and 504; (11) in dry locations; and (12) in wet locations where any of the following conditions are met:

(1) The metallic covering is impervious to moisture.

(2) A lead sheath or moisture-impervious jacket is provided under the metal covering.

(3) The insulated conductors under the metallic covering are approved for use in wet locations.

Exception: See Section 501-4(b), Exception.

(FPN): See Section 300-6 for protection against corrosion.

334-4. **Uses Not Permitted.** Type MC cable shall not be used where exposed to destructive corrosive conditions, such as direct burial in the earth, in concrete, or where exposed to cinder fills, strong chlorides, caustic alkalis, or vapors of chlorine or of hydrochloric acids.

Exception: Where the metallic sheath is suitable for the conditions or is protected by material suitable for the conditions.

B. Installation

334-10. **Installation.** Type MC cable shall be installed in compliance with Articles 300, 710, and 725 as applicable.

(a) **Support.** Type MC cable shall be supported and secured at intervals not exceeding 6 feet (1.83 m).

New work

Figure 334-1. *For new installations, Type MC cable is required to be supported and secured at intervals not exceeding 6 feet. In dwelling units, it is required to be secured within 12 inches from an outlet box.*

Exception No. 1: Where installed as branch circuits in dwelling units, Type MC cable shall be secured within 12 inches (305 mm) from every outlet box, junction box, cabinet, or fitting.

Exception No. 2: Where Type MC cable is fished.

This section has been revised for the 1993 *Code*. Two new exceptions were added. Exception No. 1 modifies the support requirements for MC cable used in dwelling units. Support is still required at intervals not exceeding 6 feet. In addition, MC cable must be supported within 12 inches of every fitting or every junction box, outlet box, or cabinet that the cable enters. See Figure 334-1. Exception No. 2 permits Type MC cable to be fished. See Figure 334-2.

(b) **Cable Tray.** Type MC cable installed in cable tray shall comply with Article 318.

Figure 334-2. For existing installations, Type MC cable is permitted to be fished in walls, floors, or ceilings.

(c) Direct Buried. Direct buried cable shall comply with Section 300-5 or 710-4, as appropriate.

(d) Installed as Service-Entrance Cable. Type MC cable installed as service-entrance cable shall comply with Article 230.

(e) Installed Outside of Buildings or as Aerial Cable. Type MC cable installed outside of buildings or as aerial cable shall comply with Article 225 and Article 321.

(f) Through or Parallel to Joists, Studs, and Rafters. Type MC cable shall comply with Section 300-4 where installed through or parallel to joists, studs, rafters, or similar wood or metal members.

(g) In Accessible Attics. The installation of Type MC cable in accessible attics or roof spaces shall also comply with Section 333-12.

In accessible attics, Type MC cable that is installed across the top of floor joists or within 7 feet of the floor or floor joists across the face of rafters or studs must be protected

by guard strips. Where the attic is not accessible by a permanent ladder or stairs, guard strips are only required within 6 feet of the scuttle hole or opening.

334-11. **Bending Radius.** All bends shall be so made that the cable will not be damaged, and the radius of the curve of the inner edge of any bend shall not be less than shown below.

(a) Smooth Sheath.

(1) Ten times the external diameter of the metallic sheath for cable not more than ¾ inch (19 mm) in external diameter;

(2) Twelve times the external diameter of the metallic sheath for cable more than ¾ inch (19 mm) but not more than 1½ inches (38 mm) in external diameter; and

See commentary following Section 334-11(c).

(3) Fifteen times the external diameter of the metallic sheath for cable more than 1½ inches (38 mm) in external diameter.

(b) Interlocked-type Armor or Corrugated Sheath. Seven times the external diameter of the metallic sheath.

(c) Shielded Conductors. Twelve times the overall diameter of one of the individual conductors or seven times the overall diameter of the multiconductor cable, whichever is greater.

The minimum bending radius of 12 times the overall diameter of a single shielded conductor [Section 334-11(a)(2)] is consistent with ICEA (formerly IPCEA) requirements and good engineering practice; however, the same minimum on a multiconductor cable would be excessive.

For example, consider 500 kcmil, 15 kV, 100 percent insulation level (0.175 in. insulation):

	O.D.	12 × O.D.	7 × O.D.
Single Conductor	1.50 in.	18 in.	—
Three Conductor	3.15 – 3.50 in.	38 – 42 in.	22 – 24 in.

334-12. **Fittings.** Fittings used for connecting Type MC cable to boxes, cabinets, or other equipment shall be identified for such use. Where single-conductor cables enter ferrous metal boxes or cabinets, the installation shall comply with Section 300-20 to prevent inductive heating.

Connectors should be selected in accordance with the size and type of cable for which they are designed. Bronze connectors are intended for use only with cable employing corrugated copper armor. Some Type MC cable connectors are also acceptable for AC cables.

334-13. **Ampacity.** The ampacity of Type MC cable shall be in accordance with Section 310-15.

Exception No. 1: The ampacities for Type MC cable installed in cable tray shall be determined in accordance with Sections 318-11 and 318-13.

Exception No. 2: The ampacities of No. 18 and No. 16 conductors shall be in accordance with Table 402-5.

(FPN): See Section 310-10 for temperature limitation of conductors.

C. Construction Specifications

334-20. **Conductors.** The conductors shall be of copper, aluminum, or copper-clad aluminum, solid or stranded.

The minimum conductor size shall be No. 18 copper and No. 12 aluminum or copper-clad aluminum.

334-21. **Insulation.** The insulated conductors shall comply with (a) or (b) below.

(a) 600 Volts. Insulated conductors in sizes No. 18 and 16 shall be of a type listed in Table 402-3, with a maximum operating temperature not less than 90°C (194°F), and as permitted by Section 725-16. Conductors larger than No. 16 shall be of a type listed in Table 310-13 or of a type identified for use in MC cable.

(b) Over 600 Volts. Insulated conductors shall be of a type listed in Tables 310-61 through 310-67.

334-22. **Metallic Sheath.** The metallic covering shall be one of the following types: smooth metallic sheath, welded and corrugated metallic sheath, interlocking metal tape armor. The metallic sheath shall be continuous and close fitting.

Supplemental protection of an outer covering of corrosion-resistant material shall be permitted and shall be required where such protection is needed. The sheath shall not be used as a current-carrying conductor.

(FPN): See Section 300-6 for protection against corrosion.

334-23. **Grounding.** Type MC cable shall provide an adequate path for equipment grounding as required by Article 250.

The armor of interlocking Type MC cable is not recognized by UL as the sole means of providing an equipment grounding circuit, but may be used to supplement the internal grounding conductor.

334-24. **Marking.** The provisions of Section 310-11 shall apply. Cables that are flame-retardant and have limited-smoke characteristics shall be permitted to be identified with the suffix LS.

Type MC cable is required to be marked with the maximum working voltage, proper type letter or letters for the type of wire, and the AWG size or circular mil area. This marking may be on a marker tape located within the cable and running its complete length, or, if the metallic covering is of smooth construction that permits surface marking, the MC cable may be durably marked on the outer covering at intervals not exceeding 24 inches. See Section 310-11 for marking requirements.

ARTICLE 336 Nonmetallic-Sheathed Cable

Types NM and NMC

Contents

A. General

C. Construction Specifications

336-25. Construction.
  (a) Type NM.
  (b) Type NMC.
336-26. Conductors.
336-27. Marking.

A. General

336-1. Definition. Nonmetallic-sheathed cable is a factory assembly of two or more insulated conductors having an outer sheath of moisture-resistant, flame-retardant, nonmetallic material.

Nonmetallic-sheathed cable may be used for either exposed or concealed wiring. Where exposed, it should not be exposed to physical damage. It was first recognized in the 1928 *NEC* as a substitute for concealed knob-and-tube wiring (Article 324) and open wiring on insulators (Article 320). The basic advantages of nonmetallic-sheathed cable (Type NM and Type NMC) are that the outer sheath provides continuous protection in addition to the insulation applied to the conductors; the cable is easily fished in partitions of finished buildings; no insulating supports are required; and only one hole need be bored that can accommodate more than one cable passing through a wood cross member. If multiple cables are grouped together and routed through a single hole, see Note 8(a) to the Notes to Ampacity Tables of 0 to 2000 Volts, second paragraph, and commentary following Section 336-2.

Where the cable passes through factory- or field-punched holes in metal studs or similar members, it is required to be protected by bushings or grommets securely fastened in the opening, unless the slots or holes are formed so that no metal edge can cut or tear the cable. See Section 300-4(b).

336-2. Other Articles. In addition to the provisions of this article, installations of nonmetallic-sheathed cable shall comply with the other applicable provisions of this Code, especially Articles 300 and 310.

The second paragraph of Note 8(a) to the Notes to Ampacity Tables of 0 to 2000 Volts states: "Where single conductors or multiconductor cables are stacked or bundled longer than 24 inches (610 mm) without maintaining spacing and are not installed in raceways, the allowable

ampacity of each conductor shall be reduced as shown in the above table."

Failure to comply with the appropriate ampacity derating called for by Note 8(a), where Types NM and NMC cables may be stacked or bundled, can lead to overheating of conductors.

The requirements of Note 8(a) also apply to other wiring methods.

336-3. Uses Permitted. Type NM and Type NMC cables shall be permitted to be used in one- and two-family dwellings, multifamily dwellings, and other structures, except as prohibited in Section 336-4. Where installed in cable trays, cables shall be identified for this use.

(FPN): See Section 310-10 for temperature limitation of conductors.

This fine print note referencing Section 310-10 alerts the installer to temperature limitations along the entire length of the cable.

(a) Type NM. Type NM cable shall be permitted for both exposed and concealed work in normally dry locations. It shall be permissible to install or fish Type NM cable in air voids in masonry block or tile walls where such walls are not exposed or subject to excessive moisture or dampness.

(b) Type NMC. Type NMC cable shall be permitted (1) for both exposed and concealed work in dry, moist, damp, or corrosive locations; (2) in outside and inside walls of masonry block or tile; (3) in a shallow chase in masonry, concrete, or adobe protected against nails or screws by a steel plate at least $1/16$ inch (1.59 mm) thick and covered with plaster, adobe, or similar finish.

Where exposed to fumes, vapors, or liquids such as ammonia and barnyard acids, type NMC (corrosion-resistant) cable is required for installations in dairy barns and similar farm buildings (see Article 547) where ordinary types of nonmetallic-sheathed cables have in some cases deteriorated rapidly due to ammonia fumes or the growth of fungus or mold.

In addition to insulated conductors, nonmetallic-sheathed cable may have an insulated, covered, or bare conductor for equipment grounding purposes only. See Section 250-57 and Table 250-95.

336-4. Uses Not Permitted.

(a) Type NM or NMC. Types NM and NMC cables shall not be used (1) in any dwelling or structure exceeding three floors above grade; (2) as service-entrance cable; (3) in commercial garages having hazardous (classified) locations as provided in Section 511-3; (4) in theaters and similar locations, except as provided in Article 518, Places of Assembly; (5) in motion picture studios; (6) in storage battery rooms; (7) in hoistways; (8) embedded in poured cement, concrete, or aggregate; or (9) in any hazardous (classified) location except as permitted by Sections 501-4(b), Exception and 504-20. For the purpose of this article, the first floor of a building shall be that floor that has 50 percent or more of the exterior wall surface area level with or above finished grade. One additional level that is the first level and not designed for human habitation and used only for vehicle parking, storage, or similar use shall be permitted.

Type NM and Type NMC cables are permitted for dwellings and other structures such as stores, professional offices, motels, industrial occupancies, etc., provided these dwellings or structures do not exceed three floors above grade. See Figures 336-1 and 336-2. The word "floor" as used in Section 336-4 means the entire story of the building, from floor to ceiling. It is required that the calculations for determining the first story be based on 50 percent of the area of the lower story exterior wall surfaces.

There were two significant changes in this requirement in the 1990 *NEC.* First, the requirement was modified in accordance with Formal Interpretation No. 70-87-1 in the 1987 *Code* to clarify that the 50 percent figure in the definition of the first floor of a building is based on the area of the external wall surface, rather than the perimeter. Second, only a single "not for human habitation" floor is permitted before the first floor starts.

(b) Type NM. Type NM cable shall not be installed (1) where exposed to corrosive fumes or vapors; (2) where embedded in masonry, concrete, adobe, fill, or plaster; (3) in a shallow chase in masonry, concrete, or adobe and covered with plaster, adobe, or similar finish.

For concealed work, nonmetallic-sheathed cable should be installed where it is protected from physical damage that is often caused by nails or screws. Where practical, care should be taken to avoid areas where trim, door and window casings, baseboards, moldings, etc., are likely to be nailed. See Section 300-4.

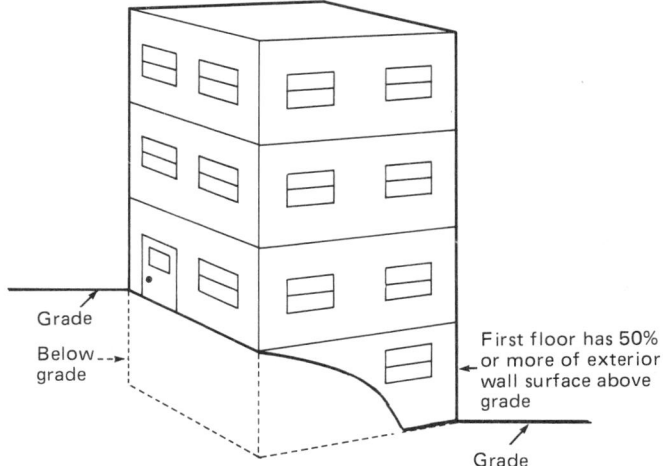

Figure 336-1. *A representation of a first floor of a building that is level with or above finished grade for 50 percent or more of its exterior wall surface area between grade and the floor above.*

Figure 336-2. *A representation of a building where the first level is a parking area so that, for the purposes of Section 336-4(a), the first floor is the first level above the parking area.*

B. Installation

336-10. Exposed Work — General. In exposed work, except as provided in Sections 300-11(a), 336-12, and 336-13, the cable shall be installed as specified in (a) and (b) below.

(a) To Follow Surface. The cable shall closely follow the surface of the building finish or of running boards.

(b) Protection from Physical Damage. The cable shall be protected from physical damage where necessary by conduit, electrical metallic tubing, Schedule 80 PVC rigid nonmetallic conduit, pipe, guard strips, or other means. Where passing through a floor, the cable shall be enclosed in rigid metal conduit, intermediate metal conduit, electrical metallic tubing, Schedule 80 PVC rigid nonmetallic conduit, or other metal pipe extending at least 6 inches (152 mm) above the floor.

336-11. **Through or Parallel to Joists, Studs, and Rafters.** Type NM or NMC cable shall comply with Section 300-4 where installed through or parallel to joists, studs, rafters, or similar wood or metal members.

336-12. **In Unfinished Basements.** Where the cable is run at angles with joists in unfinished basements, it shall be permissible to secure cables not smaller than two No. 6 or three No. 8 conductors directly to the lower edges of the joists. Smaller cables shall either be run through bored holes in joists or on running boards. Where run parallel to the joists, cable of any size shall be secured to the sides of joists in accordance with Section 300-4(d).

Figure 336-3. Nonmetallic-sheathed cable installed in an unfinished basement. The cable can be run through joists (A), and attached to the side or face of joists or beams (B) and to the running boards (C). Section 300-4(d) requires cables that are run parallel to framing members be installed at least 1¼ inch from the nearest edge of studs, joists, or rafters.

336-13. **In Accessible Attics.** The installation of cable in accessible attics or roof spaces shall also comply with Section 333-12.

336-14. **Bends.** Bends in cable shall be so made, and other handling shall be such, that the protective coverings of the cable will not be damaged, and no bend shall have a radius less than five times the diameter of the cable.

336-15. **Supports.** Nonmetallic-sheathed cable shall be secured by staples, cable ties, straps, or similar fittings so designed and installed as not to damage the cable. Cable shall be secured in place at intervals not exceeding 4½ feet (1.37 m) and within 12 inches (305 mm) from every cabinet, box, or fitting. Two conductor cables shall not be stapled on edge. Cables run through holes in wooden joists, rafters, or studs shall be considered to be supported.

This section requires that the cable be SECURED. Simply draping the cable over air ducts or lower members of bar joists, pipes, and ceiling grid members is not permitted, except where fished as permitted by Exception No. 1. See also Section 300-4(c).

This section has been revised for the 1993 *Code*. It prohibits 2-conductor, Type NM cable from being stapled on edge. The intent is to prohibit the cable from being installed with its short dimension against a wooden joist. When stapled in this manner, two cables are usually placed side by side under the staple. If the staple is driven too far into the stud, damage to the insulation and conductors can occur.

(FPN): See Section 370-17(c) for support where nonmetallic boxes are used.

Exception No. 1: For concealed work in finished buildings or finished panels for prefabricated buildings where such supporting is impracticable, it shall be permissible to fish the cable between access points.

Exception No. 2: A wiring device identified for the use, without a separate outlet box, incorporating an integral cable clamp shall be permitted where the cable is secured in place at intervals not exceeding 4½ feet (1.37 m) and within 12 inches (305 mm) from the wiring device wall opening, and there shall be at least a 12-inch (305-mm) loop of unbroken cable or 6 inches (152 mm) of a cable end available on the interior side of the finished wall to permit replacement.

336-16. **Devices of Insulating Material.** Switch, outlet, and tap devices of insulating material shall be permitted to be used without boxes in exposed cable wiring and for rewiring in existing buildings where the cable is concealed and fished. Openings in such devices shall form a close fit around the outer covering of the cable, and the device shall fully enclose that part of the cable from which any part of the covering has been removed.

Where connections to conductors are by binding-screw terminals, there shall be available as many terminals as conductors.

Exception: Where cables are clamped within the structure and terminals are of a type identified for use with multiconductors.

336-17. **Boxes of Insulating Material.** Nonmetallic outlet boxes shall be permitted as provided in Section 370-3.

Nonmetallic boxes and nonmetallic wiring systems are recommended for use in corrosive atmospheres. See Sections 370-3, 370-17(c), 555-6, and Article 547.

336-18. **Devices with Integral Enclosures.** Wiring devices with integral enclosures identified for such use shall be permitted as provided in Section 300-15(b), Exception No. 4.

The *Code* recognizes wiring devices with integral enclosures for use in conventional on-site frame construction.

C. Construction Specifications

336-25. **Construction.** The insulated conductors of Types NM and NMC cable shall be in conformity with Section 336-26. The conductors shall be sizes No. 14 through 2 with copper conductors or sizes No. 12 through 2 with aluminum or copper-clad aluminum conductors. In addition to the insulated conductors, the cable shall be permitted to have an insulated or bare conductor for equipment grounding purposes only. Where provided, the grounding conductor shall be sized in accordance with Article 250.

(a) **Type NM.** The overall covering shall be flame-retardant and moisture-resistant.

(b) **Type NMC.** The overall covering shall be flame-retardant, moisture-resistant, fungus-resistant, and corrosion-resistant.

336-26. **Conductors.** The insulated conductors shall be one of the types listed in Table 310-13 that is suitable for branch-circuit wiring or one that is identified for use in these cables.

Cables with conductors rated 90°C (194°F) are designated by testing agencies as Type NM-B or NMC-B. The ampacities of nonmetallic-sheathed cable types, regardless of the conductor temperature rating, are limited to those of 60°C (140°F) conductors.

Conductors shall be rated at 90°C (194°F). The ampacity of Types NM and NMC cable shall be that of 60°C- (140°F-) conductors and shall comply with Section 310-15.

336-27. **Marking.** In addition to the provisions of Section 310-11, the cable shall have a distinctive marking on the exterior for its entire length specifying the cable type. Cables that are flame-retardant and have limited-smoke characteristics shall be permitted to be identified with the suffix LS.

The "LS" (Low Smoke) marking is permitted on cables with such characteristics.

ARTICLE 337　　Shielded Nonmetallic-Sheathed Cable

Type SNM

Contents

337-1. **Definition.** Type SNM shielded nonmetallic-sheathed cable is a factory assembly of two or more insulated conductors in an extruded core of moisture-resistant, flame-resistant nonmetallic material, covered with an overlapping spiral metal tape and wire shield and jacketed with an extruded moisture-, flame-, oil-, corrosion-, fungus-, and sunlight-resistant nonmetallic material.

Type SNM cables are multiconductor cables in an extruded core of nonmetallic material covered with an overlapping spiral metal tape and wire shield with an overall nonmetallic material jacketing. They are commonly installed in cable trays or in raceways.

Figure 337-1 is a simplified illustration of a Type SNM cable, and Figure 337-2 is an exploded view illustrating fittings for connecting SNM cable to rigid metal conduit or intermediate metal conduit.

Figure 337-1. A seven-conductor No. 12 Type SNM cable typical for use in cable trays or raceways.

Figure 337-2. A CGSJ fitting used to connect type SNM cable to ¾-inch rigid metal conduit in Class I or Class II, Division 2 hazardous (classified) locations.

337-2. Other Articles. In addition to the provisions of this article, installation of Type SNM cable shall conform to other applicable provisions, such as Articles 300, 318, 501, and 502.

337-3. Uses Permitted. Type SNM cable shall be used only as follows: (1) where operating temperatures do not exceed the rating marked on the cable; (2) in cable trays or in raceways; (3) in hazardous (classified) locations where permitted in Articles 500 through 516; or (4) as permitted in Article 547.

(FPN): See Section 310-10 for temperature limitation of conductors.

337-4. Bends. Bends in Type SNM cable shall be so made as not to damage the cable or its covering. The radius of the inner edge shall not be less than five times the cable diameter.

337-5. Handling. Type SNM cable shall be handled in such a manner as not to damage the cable or its covering.

337-6. Fittings. Fittings for connecting Type SNM cable to enclosures or equipment shall be identified for this use.

337-7. Bonding. The wire shield shall be bonded to the frame or enclosure of the utilization equipment and to the ground bus or connection at the power supply point. This bonding shall be accomplished using fittings (Section 337-6) or by other approved bonding methods [Section 501-16(a)].

337-8. Construction. The conductors of Type SNM cable shall be Type TFN, TFFN, THHN, or THWN in sizes No. 18 through No. 2 copper and No. 12 through No. 2 in aluminum or copper-clad aluminum. Conductor sizes shall be permitted to be mixed in individual cables. The flat overlapping metal tapes shall be spiraled with a long lay. The shield wires shall have a total cross-sectional area as required by Article 250 and not less than the largest circuit conductor in the cable.

The outer jacket shall be water-, oil-, flame-, corrosion-, fungus-, and sunlight-resistant, and suitable for installation in cable trays.

337-9. Marking. Type SNM cable shall have a distinctive marking on its exterior surface for its entire length indicating its type and maximum operating temperature. It shall comply with the general marking requirements of Section 310-11. Cables that are flame-retardant and have limited-smoke characteristics shall be permitted to be identified with the suffix LS.

The conductors shall each be numbered for identification from each other by durable marking on two sides 180 degrees apart every 6 inches (152 mm) of length, with alternate legends inverted to facilitate reading from both sides.

ARTICLE 338   Service-Entrance Cable

Types SE and USE

Contents

338-1. **Definition.** Service-entrance cable is a single conductor or multiconductor assembly provided with or without an overall covering, primarily used for services, and is of the following types:

(a) Type SE. Type SE, having a flame-retardant, moisture-resistant covering.

(b) Type USE. Type USE, identified for underground use, having a moisture-resistant covering, but not required to have a flame-retardant covering.

Cabled single-conductor Type USE constructions recognized for underground use may have a bare copper conductor cabled with the assembly. Type USE single, parallel, or cabled conductor assemblies recognized for underground use may have a bare copper concentric conductor applied. These constructions do not require an outer overall covering.

Exception: Type USE shall be permitted for service laterals above ground outside of buildings.

This exception is new in the 1993 *Code*. It recognizes that Type USE cable may rise out of the ground to terminate in a meter base above ground.

(FPN No. 1):   See Section 230-41, Exception, item b for directly buried, uninsulated service-entrance conductors.

(FPN No. 2):   See Section 300-5(d) for protection from physical damage.

(c) One Uninsulated Conductor. If Type SE or USE cable consists of two or more conductors, one shall be permitted to be uninsulated.

Service-entrance cable is labeled in sizes No. 12 and larger for copper and No. 10 and larger for aluminum or copper-clad aluminum with Type RH, RHW, RHH, or XHHW conductors. If the type designation for the conductors is marked on the outside surface of the cable, the temperature rating of the cable corresponds to the rating of the individual conductors. Where this marking does not appear, the temperature rating of the cable is 75°C (167°F).

The cables are classified as follows:

Type SE — Cable for aboveground installation.

Type USE — Cable for underground installation including burial directly in the earth. Type USE size No. 4/0 and smaller where used as a branch circuit or feeder for underground installation, including direct burial, is required to have all circuit conductors insulated. The equipment grounding conductor, where required, is permitted to be bare. See Section 230-41 for service-entrance conductor insulation requirements.

Some Type USE cables are provided in a flat or twisted assembly of 2, 3, or 4 single conductors and are surface-marked "Pump Cable." The cable tag on these cables, and others not so marked, may read: "For use within the well casing for wiring deep-well water pumps where the cable is not subject to repetitive handling caused by frequent servicing of the pump units. Such Type USE cables have been investigated as submersible water pump cables for the use indicated on the tag marking."

338-2. **Uses Permitted as Service-Entrance Conductors.** Service-entrance cable used as service-entrance conductors shall be installed as required by Article 230.

338-3. **Uses Permitted as Branch Circuits or Feeders.**

(a) Grounded Conductor Insulated. Type SE service-entrance cables shall be permitted in interior wiring systems where all of the circuit conductors of the cable are of the rubber-covered or thermoplastic type.

(b) Grounded Conductor Not Insulated. Type SE service-entrance cables without individual insulation on the grounded circuit conductor shall not be used as a branch circuit or as a feeder within a building, except a cable that has a final nonmetallic outer covering and is supplied by alternating current at not over 150 volts to ground shall be permitted (1) as a branch circuit to supply only a range, wall-mounted oven, counter-mounted cooking unit, or clothes dryer as covered in Section 250-60 or (2) as a feeder to supply only other buildings on the same premises.

According to the UL *Electrical Construction Materials Directory*, based on tests that have been made involving the maximum heating that can be produced, an uninsulated conductor employed in a service cable assembly is considered to have the same current-carrying capacity as the insulated conductor even though it may be smaller in size.

Type SE service-entrance cable shall be permitted for use where the fully insulated conductors are used for circuit wiring and the uninsulated conductor is used for equipment grounding purposes.

(c) **Temperature Limitations.** Type SE service-entrance cable used to supply appliances shall not be subject to conductor temperatures in excess of the temperature specified for the type of insulation involved.

338-4. **Interior Installation Methods.** In addition to the provisions of this article, Type SE service-entrance cable used for interior wiring shall be installed in accordance with the provisions of Article 336 and shall comply with the applicable provisions of Article 300.

(FPN): See Section 310-10 for temperature limitation of conductors.

Section 336-4 prohibits the use of nonmetallic-sheathed cables in dwellings and other structures exceeding three floors above grade (an additional level, that is the first level that is not for human habitation and is used only for vehicle storage, parking, etc., is permitted.) Type SE cable (unarmored), which is similar in construction to Types NM and NMC, where used for interior branch circuits and feeders, should also meet the provisions of Sections 336-3 and 336-4.

The same restriction applies to Type UF where used for interior wiring. See Section 339-3(a)(4).

338-5. **Marking.** Service-entrance cable shall be marked as required in Section 310-11. Cable with the neutral conductor smaller than the ungrounded conductors shall be so marked.

ARTICLE 339   Underground Feeder and Branch-Circuit Cable

Type UF

Contents

339-1. Description and Marking.
(a) Description.
(b) Marking.
339-2. Other Articles.
339-3. Use.
(a) Uses Permitted.
(b) Uses Not Permitted.
339-4. Overcurrent Protection.
339-5. Ampacity.

339-1. **Description and Marking.**

(a) **Description.** Underground feeder and branch-circuit cable shall be an approved Type UF cable in sizes No. 14 copper or No. 12 aluminum or copper-clad aluminum through No. 4/0. The conductors of Type UF shall be one of the moisture-resistant types listed in Table 310-13 that is suitable for branch-circuit wiring or one that is identified for such use. In addition to the insulated conductors, the cable shall be permitted to have an approved size of insulated or bare conductor for equipment grounding purposes only. The overall covering shall be flame-retardant, moisture-, fungus-, and corrosion-resistant, and suitable for direct burial in the earth.

(b) **Marking.** In addition to the provisions of Section 310-11, the cable shall have a distinctive marking on the exterior for its entire length specifying the cable type.

339-2. **Other Articles.** In addition to the provisions of this article, installations of underground feeder and branch-circuit cable (Type UF) shall comply with other applicable provisions of this Code, especially Article 300 and Section 310-13.

Underground feeder and branch-circuit cable is rated 600 V and is listed in sizes No. 14 to 4/0, copper, and No. 12 to 4/0, aluminum or copper-clad aluminum, for single and multiple conductor cables. The ampacity of multi-conductor cables with or without the suffix "B" following the cable type designation is that of conductors rated 60°C (140°F).

Submersible water pump cable is a multiconductor cable in which 2, 3, or 4 single-conductor Type UF cables are twisted together without an outer covering. The cable is labeled in sizes from Nos. 14 to 4/0, copper, and from Nos. 12 to 4/0, aluminum or copper-clad aluminum. The cable is tag marked: "For use within the well casing for wiring deep-well water pumps where the cable is not subject to repetitive handling caused by frequent servicing of the pump units." The insulation may be surface-marked "Pump Cable."

This cable may employ copper, aluminum, or copper-clad aluminum conductors. Cables with copper-clad aluminum conductors are surface-printed "AL (CU-CLAD)" or "Cu-Clad Al."

If single-conductor Type UF cable is terminated with a fitting not specifically recognized for use with single-conductor cable, special care should be taken to ensure it is properly secured and not subject to damage.

339-3. Use.

(a) Uses Permitted.

(1) Type UF cable shall be permitted for use underground, including direct burial in the earth, as feeder or branch-circuit cable where provided with overcurrent protection of the rated ampacity as required in Section 339-4.

(2) Where single-conductor cables are installed, all cables of the feeder circuit, subfeeder circuit, or branch circuit, including the neutral and equipment grounding conductor, if any, shall be run together in the same trench or raceway.

Exception: For solar photovoltaic systems in accordance with Section 690-31.

(3) For underground requirements, see Section 300-5.

(4) Type UF cable shall be permitted for interior wiring in wet, dry, or corrosive locations under the recognized wiring methods of this Code, and, where installed as nonmetallic-sheathed cable, the installation and conductor requirements shall comply with the provisions of Article 336 and shall be of the multiconductor type.

See commentary following Sections 336-4(a) and (b), and 338-4.

Exception: Single-conductor cables shall be permitted as the nonheating leads for heating cables as provided in Section

424-43 and in solar photovoltaic systems in accordance with Section 690-31.

Type UF cable supported by cable trays shall be of the multiconductor type.

(FPN):   See Section 310-10 for temperature limitation of conductors.

(b) Uses Not Permitted. Type UF cable shall not be used (1) as service-entrance cables; (2) in commercial garages; (3) in theaters; (4) in motion picture studios; (5) in storage battery rooms; (6) in hoistways; (7) in any hazardous (classified) location; (8) embedded in poured cement, concrete, or aggregate, except where embedded in plaster as nonheating leads as provided in Article 424; (9) where exposed to direct rays of the sun, unless identified as sunlight-resistant.

Exception: See Section 501-4(b), Exception.

Type UF cables suitable for exposure to the direct rays of the sun are indicated by tag marking and marking on the surface of the cable with the designation "Sunlight Resistant."

339-4. Overcurrent Protection. Overcurrent protection shall be provided in accordance with provisions of Section 240-3.

339-5. Ampacity. The ampacity of Type UF cable shall be that of 60°C (140°F) conductors in accordance with Section 310-15.

ARTICLE 340   Power and Control Tray Cable

Type TC

Contents

340-1. **Definition.** Type TC power and control tray cable is a factory assembly of two or more insulated conductors, with or without associated bare or covered grounding conductors under a nonmetallic sheath, approved for installation in cable trays, in raceways, or where supported by a messenger wire.

340-2. **Other Articles.** In addition to the provisions of this article, installations of Type TC tray cable shall comply with other applicable articles of this Code, especially Articles 300 and 318.

340-3. **Construction.** The insulated conductors of Type TC tray cable shall be in sizes No. 18 through 1000 kcmil copper and sizes No. 12 through 1000 kcmil aluminum or copper-clad aluminum. Insulated conductors of sizes No. 14 and larger copper and sizes No. 12 and larger aluminum or copper-clad aluminum shall be one of the types listed in Table 310-13 or 310-62 that is suitable for branch circuit and feeder circuits or one that is identified for such use. Insulated conductors of sizes No. 18 and No. 16 copper shall be in accordance with Section 725-16. The outer sheath shall be a flame-retardant, nonmetallic material. A metallic sheath shall not be permitted either under or over the nonmetallic sheath. Where installed in wet locations, Type TC cable shall be resistant to moisture and corrosive agents.

Exception: Where used for fire protective signaling systems, conductors shall be in accordance with Section 760-16.

340-4. **Use Permitted.** Type TC tray cable shall be permitted to be used (1) for power, lighting, control, and signal circuits; (2) in cable trays, or in raceways, or where supported in outdoor locations by a messenger wire; (3) in cable trays in hazardous (classified) locations as permitted in Articles 318, 501, 502, and 504 in industrial establishments where the conditions of maintenance and supervision assure that only qualified persons will service the installation; (4) for Class 1 circuits as permitted in Article 725; (5) for nonpower-limited fire protective signaling circuits if conductors comply with the requirements of Section 760-16.

This section was revised for the 1993 *Code* to permit Type TC tray cable to be used for nonpower-limited fire-protective signaling circuits. The conductors must be copper. Aluminum and copper-clad aluminum are not permitted. In addition, the stranding requirements of Section 760-16(c) must be complied with. See Section 760-16.

(FPN): See Section 310-10 for temperature limitation of conductors.

The restriction that requires maintenance and supervision to be performed under conditions that ensure that only qualified persons will service the installation of Type TC cable applies only where the cable is to be used in a hazardous (classified) location.

340-5. **Uses Not Permitted.** Type TC tray cable shall not be (1) installed where they will be exposed to physical damage; (2) installed as open cable on brackets or cleats; (3) used where exposed to direct rays of the sun, unless identified as sunlight-resistant; (4) direct buried, unless identified for such use.

Where identified for the use, Type TC cable is permitted to be directly buried. See definition of "identified" in Article 100.

340-6. **Marking.** The cable shall be marked in accordance with Section 310-11. Cables that are flame-retardant and have limited-smoke characteristics shall be permitted to be identified with the suffix LS.

340-7. **Ampacity.** The ampacities of the conductors of Type TC tray cable shall be determined from Section 402-5 for conductors smaller than No. 14 and from Section 318-11.

340-8. **Bends.** Bends in Type TC cable shall be made so as not to damage the cable.

ARTICLE 342 Nonmetallic Extensions

Contents

342-1. **Definition.** Nonmetallic extensions are an assembly of two insulated conductors within a nonmetallic jacket or an extruded thermoplastic covering. The classification includes both surface extensions, intended for mounting directly on the surface of walls or ceilings, and aerial cable, containing a supporting messenger cable as an integral part of the cable assembly.

342-2. **Other Articles.** In addition to the provisions of this article, nonmetallic extensions shall be installed in accordance with the applicable provisions of this Code.

342-3. **Uses Permitted.** Nonmetallic extensions shall be permitted only where all of the following conditions are met:

(a) **From an Existing Outlet.** The extension is from an existing outlet on a 15- or 20-ampere branch circuit in conformity with the requirements of Article 210.

(b) **Exposed and in a Dry Location.** The extension is run exposed and in a dry location.

(c) **Nonmetallic Surface Extensions.** For nonmetallic surface extensions, the building is occupied for residential or office purposes and does not exceed the height limitations specified in Section 336-4(a).

Nonmetallic surface extensions are permitted to be installed only in residential or office buildings no higher than three floors above grade in accordance with 336-4(2). However, it is permitted as an aerial cable in industrial occupancies where a highly flexible means for connecting equipment is necessary. See Sections 342-4(a) and 342-7(b).

(c1) [(**Alternate to (c)**]. For aerial cable, the building is occupied for industrial purposes, and the nature of the occupancy requires a highly flexible means for connecting equipment.

A nonmetallic extension is an assembly of two insulated circuit conductors with or without an equipment grounding conductor within a nonmetallic jacket or extruded thermoplastic covering. Assemblies without a grounding conductor are marked "intended for replacement use only."

(FPN): See Section 310-10 for temperature limitation of conductors.

342-4. **Uses Not Permitted.** Nonmetallic extensions shall not be used:

(a) **Aerial Cable.** As aerial cable to substitute for one of the general wiring methods specified by this Code.

(b) **Unfinished Areas.** In unfinished basements, attics, or roof spaces.

(c) **Voltage Between Conductors.** Where the voltage between conductors exceeds 150 volts for nonmetallic surface extension and 300 volts for aerial cable.

(d) **Corrosive Vapors.** Where subject to corrosive vapors.

(e) **Through a Floor or Partition.** Where run through a floor or partition, or outside the room in which it originates.

342-5. **Splices and Taps.** Extensions shall consist of a continuous unbroken length of the assembly, without splices, and without exposed conductors between fittings. Taps shall be permitted where approved fittings completely covering the tap connections are used. Aerial cable and its tap connectors shall be provided with an approved means for polarization. Receptacle-type tap connectors shall be of the locking-type.

342-6. **Fittings.** Each run shall terminate in a fitting that covers the end of the assembly. All fittings and devices shall be of a type identified for the use.

342-7. **Installation.** Nonmetallic extensions shall be installed as specified in (a) and (b) below.

(a) **Nonmetallic Surface Extensions.**

(1) One or more extensions shall be permitted to be run in any direction from an existing outlet, but not on the floor or within 2 inches (50.8 mm) from the floor.

(2) Nonmetallic surface extensions shall be secured in place by approved means at intervals not exceeding 8 inches (203 mm).

Exception: Where connection to the supplying outlet is made by means of an attachment plug, the first fastening shall be permitted 12 inches (305 mm) or less from the plug.

There shall be at least one fastening between each two adjacent outlets supplied. An extension shall be attached only to woodwork or plaster finish, and shall not be in contact with any metal work or other conductive material other than with metal plates on receptacles.

(3) A bend that reduces the normal spacing between the conductors shall be covered with a cap to protect the assembly from physical damage.

(b) Aerial Cable.

(1) Aerial cable shall be supported by its messenger cable and securely attached at each end with approved clamps and turnbuckles. Intermediate supports shall be provided at not more than 20-foot (6.1-m) intervals. Cable tension shall be adjusted to eliminate excessive sag. The cable shall have a clearance of not less than 2 inches (50.8 mm) from steel structural members or other conductive material.

(2) Aerial cable shall have a clearance of not less than 10 feet (3.05 m) above floor areas accessible to pedestrian traffic, and not less than 14 feet (4.27 m) above floor areas accessible to vehicular traffic.

(3) Cable suspended over work benches, not accessible to pedestrian traffic, shall have a clearance of not less than 8 feet (2.44 m) above the floor.

(4) Aerial cables shall be permitted as a means to support lighting fixtures where the total load on the supporting messenger cable does not exceed that for which the assembly is intended.

(5) The supporting messenger cable, where installed in conformity with the applicable provisions of Article 250 and if properly identified as an equipment grounding conductor, shall be permitted to ground equipment. The messenger cable shall not be used as a branch-circuit conductor.

342-8. **Marking.** Nonmetallic extensions shall be marked in accordance with Section 110-21.

ARTICLE 343 Preassembled Cable in Nonmetallic Conduit

Contents

A. General

B. Installation

C. Construction

A. General

343-1. **Description.** Preassembled cable in nonmetallic conduit is a listed factory assembly of conductors or cables inside a nonmetallic, smooth wall conduit with a circular cross section.

The nonmetallic conduit shall be composed of a material that is resistant to moisture and corrosive agents. It shall also be capable of being supplied on reels without damage or distortion and shall be of sufficient strength to withstand abuse, such as impact or crushing, in handling and during installation without damage to conduit or conductors.

Article 343 is new in the 1993 *Code*. Preassembled cable in conduit has been used by electric utilities for outdoor lighting for several years. It is supplied in continuous lengths on coils, reels, or cartons. It consists of nonmetallic conduit with the conductors preinstalled by the manufacturer. The intent of preassembly is to minimize the damage to conductors and raceways that can result from pulling. The product is designed to allow conductors to be removed and reinserted; therefore, future maintenance is not precluded.

The use of preassembled cable in nonmetallic conduit is restricted and is not permitted inside buildings. The conductors may enter the building for termination, but the raceway may not. See Section 343-3 for uses permitted.

343-2. Other Articles. Installations for preassembled cable in nonmetallic conduit shall comply with the provisions of the applicable sections of Article 300. Where equipment grounding is required by Article 250, an assembly containing a separate equipment grounding conductor shall be used.

343-3. Uses Permitted. The use of preassembled cable in nonmetallic conduit and fittings shall be permitted:

(1) For direct burial underground installation. For minimum cover requirements, see Tables 300-5 and 710-4(b) under rigid nonmetallic conduit.

(2) Encased or embedded in concrete.

(3) In cinder fill.

(4) In underground locations subject to severe corrosive influences as covered in Section 300-6 and where subject to chemicals for which the assembly is specifically approved.

343-4. Uses Not Permitted. Preassembled cable in nonmetallic conduit shall not be used:

(1) In exposed locations.

(2) Inside buildings.

Exception: The conductor portion of the assembly shall be permitted to extend within the building for termination purposes.

(3) In hazardous (classified) locations.

Exception: As covered in Sections 503-3(a), 504-20, 514-8, and 515-5, and in Class I, Division 2 locations as permitted in the exception to Section 501-4(b).

B. Installation

343-5. Size.

(a) **Minimum.** Preassembled cable in nonmetallic conduit smaller than 1/2-inch (13-mm) electrical trade size shall not be used.

(b) **Maximum.** Preassembled cable in nonmetallic conduit larger than 2-inch (50-mm) electrical trade size shall not be used.

343-6. Trimming. For termination, the conduit shall be trimmed away from the conductors or cables using an approved method that will not damage the conductor or cable insulation or jacket. All ends shall be trimmed inside and out to remove rough edges.

343-7. Joints. All joints between conduit, fittings, and boxes shall be made by an approved method.

343-8. Conductor Terminations. All terminations between the conductors or cables and equipment shall be made by an approved method for that type of conductor or cable.

343-9. Bushings. Where the preassembled cable in nonmetallic conduit enters a box, fitting, or other enclosure, a bushing or adapter shall be provided to protect the conductor or cable from abrasion unless the design of the box, fitting, or enclosure provides equivalent protection.

(FPN): See Section 373-6(c) for the protection of conductors size No. 4 or larger.

343-10. Bends — How Made. Bends of preassembled cable in nonmetallic conduit shall be manually made so that the conduit will not be damaged and the internal diameter of the conduit will not be effectively reduced.

343-11. Bends — Number in One Run. There shall not be more than the equivalent of four quarter bends (360 degrees total) between termination points.

343-12. Splices and Taps. Splices and taps shall be made in junction boxes or other enclosures. See Article 370.

C. Construction

343-13. **General.** Preassembled cable in nonmetallic conduit is an assembly that is provided in continuous lengths shipped in a coil, reel, or carton.

343-14. **Conductors and Cables.** Conductors and cables used in preassembled cable in nonmetallic conduit shall be as follows:

(a) Conductors or cables of 600 volts or less shall be suitable for use in wet locations. Alternating-current and direct-current circuits shall be permitted. All conductors shall have an insulation rating equal to at least the maximum nominal circuit voltage of any conductor or cable within the conduit.

(b) **Over 600 Volts.** Conductors or cables rated over 600 volts shall not occupy the same conduit with conductors or cables of circuits rated 600 volts or less. All conductors or cables shall be suitable for use in wet locations.

(FPN): See Section 300-3.

343-15. **Conductor Fill.** The maximum number of conductors or cables in preassembled cable in nonmetallic conduit shall not exceed the number indicated in Table 1 of Chapter 9 for the sizes involved.

343-16. **Marking.** Preassembled cable in nonmetallic conduit shall be clearly and durably marked at least every 10 feet (3.05 m) as required by Section 110-21. The type of conduit material shall also be included in the marking.

Identification of conductors or cables used in the assembly shall be provided on a tag attached to each end of the assembly or to the side of a reel.

ARTICLE 345 Intermediate Metal Conduit

Contents

A. General

B. Installation

C. Construction Specifications

A. General

345-1. **Definition.** Intermediate metal conduit is a metal raceway of circular cross section with integral or associated couplings, connectors, and fittings approved for the installation of electrical conductors.

Intermediate metal conduit (IMC) is a thinner-walled rigid metal conduit and is satisfactory for use in all locations where rigid metal conduit is permitted to be used. Also, threaded and unthreaded fittings, couplings, connectors, etc., are interchangeable for either IMC or rigid metal conduit.

Galvanized IMC installed in concrete does not require supplementary corrosion protection. Wherever ferrous metal conduit runs directly from concrete encasement to soil burial, severe corrosive effects are likely to occur on the metal raceway at the location where the concrete meets the soil. In the absence of experience with the corrosive effects of soil in a specific location, soils producing severe corrosive effects are generally characterized by low resistivity, less than 2,000 ohm-centimeters.

345-2. Other Articles. Installations for intermediate metal conduit shall comply with the provisions of the applicable sections of Article 300.

345-3. Uses Permitted.

(a) All Atmospheric Conditions and Occupancies. Use of intermediate metal conduit shall be permitted under all atmospheric conditions and occupancies. Where practicable, dissimilar metals in contact anywhere in the system shall be avoided to eliminate the possibility of galvanic action. Intermediate metal conduit shall be permitted as an equipment grounding conductor.

(FPN):   See Section 250-91(b) for types of equipment grounding conductors.

Exception: Aluminum fittings and enclosures shall be permitted to be used with steel intermediate metal conduit.

(b) Corrosion Protection. Intermediate metal conduit, elbows, couplings, and fittings shall be permitted to be installed in concrete, in direct contact with the earth, or in areas subject to severe corrosive influences where protected by corrosion protection and judged suitable for the condition.

(FPN):   See Section 300-6 for protection against corrosion.

(c) Cinder Fill. Intermediate metal conduit shall be permitted to be installed in or under cinder fill where subject to permanent moisture where protected on all sides by a layer of noncinder concrete not less than 2 inches (50.8 mm) thick; where the conduit is not less than 18 inches (457 mm) under the fill; or where protected by corrosion protection and judged suitable for the condition.

(FPN):   See Section 300-6 for protection against corrosion.

B. Installation

345-5. Wet Locations. All supports, bolts, straps, screws, etc., shall be of corrosion-resistant materials or protected against corrosion by corrosion-resistant materials.

(FPN):   See Section 300-6 for protection against corrosion.

345-6. Size.

(a) Minimum. Conduit smaller than 1/2-inch electrical trade size shall not be used.

(b) Maximum. Conduit larger than 4-inch electrical trade size shall not be used.

345-7. Number of Conductors in Conduit. The number of conductors in a single conduit shall not exceed that permitted by the percentage fill specified in Table 1, Chapter 9, using the conduit dimensions of Table 4, Chapter 9.

345-8. Reaming and Threading. All cut ends of conduits shall be reamed or otherwise finished to remove rough edges. Where conduit is threaded in the field, a standard cutting die with a 3/4-inch taper per foot (1 in 16) shall be used.

See commentary following Section 348-11.

(FPN):   See Standards for Pipe Threads, General Purpose (Inch), ANSI/ASME B.1.20.1-1983.

345-9. Couplings and Connectors.

(a) Threadless. Threadless couplings and connectors used with conduit shall be made tight. Where buried in masonry or concrete, they shall be the concrete-tight type. Where installed in wet locations, they shall be the raintight type.

(b) Running Threads. Running threads shall not be used on conduit for connection at couplings.

See commentary following Section 346-9.

345-10. Bends — How Made. Bends of intermediate metal conduit shall be so made that the conduit will not be damaged and that the internal diameter of the conduit will not be effectively reduced. The radius of the curve of the inner edge of any field bend shall not be less than indicated in Table 346-10.

See commentary following Section 346-10.

Exception: For field bends for conductors without lead sheath and made with a single operation (one shot) bending machine designed for the purpose, the minimum radius shall not be less than that indicated in Table 346-10, Exception.

345-11. **Bends — Number in One Run.** There shall not be more than the equivalent of four quarter bends (360 degrees total) between pull points, e.g., conduit bodies and boxes.

See commentary following Section 346-11.

345-12. **Supports.** Intermediate metal conduit shall be installed as a complete system as provided in Article 300 and shall be securely fastened in place. Conduit shall be supported at least every 10 feet (3.05 m). In addition, conduit shall be securely fastened within 3 feet (914 mm) of each outlet box, junction box, device box, cabinet, conduit body, or other conduit termination. Fastening shall be permitted to be increased to a distance of 5 feet (1.52 m) where structural members do not readily permit fastening within 3 feet (914 mm).

See Figure 345-1. Intermediate metal conduit is required to be securely fastened at least every 10 feet. Support is also required within 3 feet of outlet boxes, junction boxes, cabinets, and conduit bodies. However, where structural support members don't permit fastening within 3 feet, the support may be located 5 feet away. This section has been revised for the 1993 *Code* so that it no longer requires support within 3 feet of every coupling. Coupling support is assured by the requirements in the third sentence of this section.

(FPN): Support provided by a bored or punched hole in a framing member is intended to meet the support requirements of this section.

Exception No. 1: If made up with threaded couplings, it shall be permissible to support straight runs of intermediate metal conduit in accordance with Table 346-12, provided such supports prevent transmission of stresses to termination where conduit is deflected between supports.

Exception No. 2: The distance between supports shall be permitted to be increased to 20 feet (6.1 m) for exposed vertical risers from industrial machinery, provided that the conduit is made up with threaded couplings, is firmly supported at the top and bottom of the riser, and no other means of intermediate support is readily available.

345-13. **Boxes and Fittings.** See Article 370.

345-14. **Splices and Taps.** Splices and taps shall be made only in junction boxes, outlet boxes, device boxes, or conduit bodies. See Article 370.

345-15. **Bushings.** Where a conduit enters a box, fitting, or other enclosure, a bushing shall be provided to protect the wire from abrasion unless the design of the box, fitting, or enclosure is such as to afford equivalent protection.

(FPN): See Section 373-6(c) for the protection of conductors Nos. 4 and larger at bushings.

See commentary following Section 373-6.

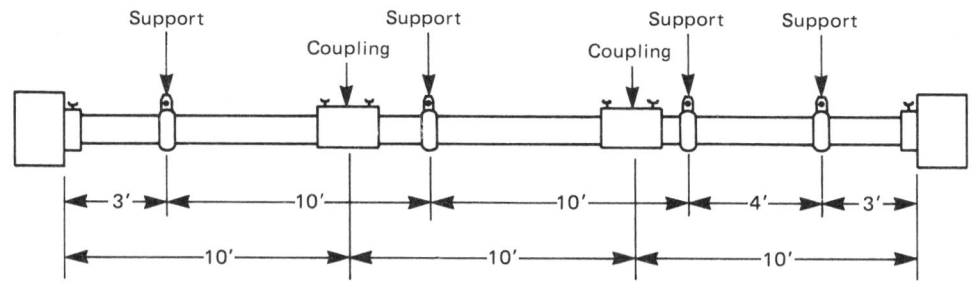

Figure 345-1. Minimum support required. Note that support is not required on each side of a coupling. See also the last sentence of Section 345-12.

C. Construction Specifications

345-16. **General.** Intermediate metal conduit shall comply with (a) through (c) below.

(a) Standard Lengths. Intermediate metal conduit as shipped shall be in standard lengths of 10 feet (3.05 m), including coupling, one coupling to be furnished with each length. For specific applications or use, it shall be permissible to ship lengths shorter or longer than 10 feet (3.05 m), with or without couplings.

(b) Corrosion-Resistant Material. Nonferrous conduit of corrosion-resistant material shall have suitable markings.

(c) Marking. Each length shall be clearly and durably identified at 2½-foot (762-mm) intervals with the letters IMC. Each length shall be marked as required in the first sentence of Section 110-21.

ARTICLE 346   Rigid Metal Conduit

Contents

346-1. **Use.** The use of rigid metal conduit shall be permitted under all atmospheric conditions and occupancies subject to the following:

(a) Protected by Enamel. Ferrous raceways and fittings protected from corrosion solely by enamel shall be permitted only indoors and in occupancies not subject to severe corrosive influences.

(b) Dissimilar Metals. Where practicable, dissimilar metals in contact anywhere in the system shall be avoided to eliminate the possibility of galvanic action.

Exception: Aluminum fittings and enclosures shall be permitted to be used with steel rigid metal conduit, and steel fittings and enclosures shall be permitted to be used with aluminum rigid metal conduit.

(c) Corrosion Protection. Ferrous or nonferrous metal conduit, elbows, couplings, and fittings shall be permitted to be installed in concrete, in direct contact with the earth, or in areas subject to severe corrosive influences where protected by corrosion protection and judged suitable for the condition.

(FPN):   See Section 300-6 for protection against corrosion.

This section indicates the permitted uses for ferrous and nonferrous conduit, including their use in concrete, in direct contact with the earth, and in corrosive areas. The fine print note references Section 300-6 for additional information on protection against corrosion and specific types of corrosion-resistant materials.

The exception to Section 346-1(b) makes it clear that aluminum rigid conduit can be used with steel fittings and enclosures as can aluminum fittings and enclosures be used with steel rigid conduit. It has been shown by test that the galvanic corrosion at steel and aluminum interfaces is minor in comparison to the natural corrosion on the combination of steel and steel or aluminum and aluminum.

It is advisable to consult with the authority enforcing this *Code* for approval of corrosion-resistant materials and/or for requirements prior to the installation of nonferrous metal (aluminum) conduit in concrete, since chloride additives in the concrete mix may cause corrosion.

346-2. **Other Articles.** Installations of rigid metal conduit shall comply with the applicable provisions of Article 300.

A. Installation

346-3. **Cinder Fill.** Conduit shall not be used in or under cinder fill where subject to permanent moisture.

Exception No. 1: Where of corrosion-resistant material suitable for the purpose.

Exception No. 2: Where protected on all sides by a layer of noncinder concrete at least 2 inches (50.8 mm) thick.

Exception No. 3: Where the conduit is at least 18 inches (457 mm) under the fill.

Although cinder fill is not commonly used in modern construction, it is still encountered at older building sites. Care should be taken to ensure the proper installation of rigid metal conduit as permitted by the exceptions. Where cinders have been used as fill, they may contain sulfur, and where they have combined with moisture, sulfuric acid is formed, which can corrode metal raceways.

346-4. **Wet Locations.** All supports, bolts, straps, screws, etc., shall be of corrosion-resistant materials or protected against corrosion by corrosion-resistant materials.

(FPN): See Section 300-6 for protection against corrosion.

346-5. **Minimum Size.** Conduit smaller than $\frac{1}{2}$-inch electrical trade size shall not be used.

Exception: For enclosing the leads of motors as permitted in Section 430-145(b).

346-6. **Number of Conductors in Conduit.** The number of conductors permitted in a single conduit shall not exceed the percentage fill specified in Table 1, Chapter 9.

(FPN): For conductor cross-sectional area, see Tables 5, 5A, 6, and 8 and the applicable Notes to Tables at the beginning of Chapter 9.

In Chapter 9, Tables 3A, 3B, and 3C are based on the allowable percentages of Chapter 9, Table 1, for conduit or tubing fill; that is, 53 percent for 1 conductor, 31 percent for 2 conductors, and 40 percent for 3 or more conductors. Percentages for lead-covered conductors vary somewhat from other conductor types. See Chapter 9, Table 1.

346-7. **Reaming and Threading.**

(a) Reamed. All cut ends of conduits shall be reamed or otherwise finished to remove rough edges.

See commentary following Section 348-11.

(b) Threaded. Where conduit is threaded in the field, a standard conduit cutting die with a $\frac{3}{4}$-inch taper per foot (1 in 16) shall be used.

(FPN): See Standards for Pipe Threads, General Purpose (Inch), ANSI/ASME, B.1.20.1-1983.

346-8. **Bushings.** Where a conduit enters a box, fitting, or other enclosure, a bushing shall be provided to protect the wire from abrasion unless the box, fitting, or enclosure design provides equivalent protection.

(FPN): See Section 373-6(c) for the protection of conductors at bushings.

346-9. **Couplings and Connectors.**

(a) Threadless. Threadless couplings and connectors used with conduit shall be made tight. Where buried in masonry or concrete, they shall be of the concrete-tight type. Where installed in wet locations, they shall be of the raintight type.

(b) Running Threads. Running threads shall not be used on conduit for connection at couplings.

Figure 346-1 illustrates a threadless connection integral to a conduit body, FS box, etc. This type of connection may be separate from the conduit body or box as an individual fitting of the compression type (raintight) suitable for wet locations or of the setscrew type.

Threadless fittings are not intended for use over threads as the fitting will not properly seat. The threaded end of the conduit should be cut off and reamed before installation.

Figure 346-2 illustrates an Erickson coupling (the electrical equivalent of a pipe union), which is used to join two lengths of conduit where it is impossible to turn either length, such as in underground or concrete-slab construction. Another fitting for joining lengths of conduit is a bolted split couplings. Running threads are not permitted to join two conduits, but may be permitted to join two boxes where electrical and mechanical connections are assured (locknuts and bushings).

Figure 346-1. Conduit body with threadless connector. (Appleton Electric Co.)

Figure 346-2. Erickson or union-type coupling. (Appleton Electric Co.)

346-10. Bends — How Made. Bends of rigid metal conduit shall be so made that the conduit will not be damaged, and that the internal diameter of the conduit will not be effectively reduced. The radius of the curve of the inner edge of any field bend shall not be less than shown in Table 346-10.

Exception: For field bends for conductors without lead sheath and made with a single operation (one shot) bending machine designed for the purpose, the minimum radius shall not be less than indicated in Table 346-10, Exception.

The term "field bend" means any bend or offset made by installers, using proper tools and equipment, during the installation of conduit systems.

346-11. Bends — Number in One Run. There shall not be more than the equivalent of four quarter bends (360 degrees total) between pull points, e.g., conduit bodies and boxes.

Limiting the number of bends in a conduit run reduces pulling tension on conductors and helps ensure easy

Table 346-10. Radius of Conduit Bends (Inches)

Size of Conduit (In.)	Conductors without Lead Sheath (In.)	Conductors with Lead Sheath (In.)
$^1/_2$	4	6
$^3/_4$	5	8
1	6	11
$1^1/_4$	8	14
$1^1/_2$	10	16
2	12	21
$2^1/_2$	15	25
3	18	31
$3^1/_2$	21	36
4	24	40
5	30	50
6	36	61

For SI units: (Radius) one inch = 25.4 millimeters.

Table 346-10, Exception. Radius of Conduit Bends (Inches)

Size of Conduit (In.)	Radius to Center of Conduit (In.)
$^1/_2$	4
$^3/_4$	$4^1/_2$
1	$5^3/_4$
$1^1/_4$	$7^1/_4$
$1^1/_2$	$8^1/_4$
2	$9^1/_2$
$2^1/_2$	$10^1/_2$
3	13
$3^1/_2$	15
4	16
5	24
6	30

For SI units: (Radius) one inch = 25.4 millimeters.

insertion or removal of conductors during later phases of construction when the conduit may be permanently enclosed by the finish of the building. Adjustments during that time are often impossible.

The *Code* does not limit the pull points to conduit bodies and boxes; these are only examples of pull points.

346-12. Supports. Rigid metal conduit shall be installed as a complete system as provided in Article 300 and shall be securely fastened in place. Conduit shall be supported at least every 10 feet (3.05 m). In addition, conduit shall be securely fastened within 3 feet (914 mm) of each outlet box, junction box, device box, cabinet, conduit body, or other conduit termination. Fastening shall be permitted to be increased to a distance of 5 feet (1.52 m) where structural members do not readily permit fastening within 3 feet (914 mm).

See Figure 346-3. Rigid metal conduit is required to be securely fastened at least every 10 feet. Support is also required within 3 feet of outlet boxes, junction boxes, cabinets, and conduit bodies. However, where structural support members don't permit fastening within 3 feet, the support may be located 5 feet away. This section has been revised for the 1993 *Code* so that it no longer requires support within 3 feet of every coupling. Coupling support is assured by the requirement in the third sentence of this section.

(FPN): Support provided by a bored or punched hole in a framing member is intended to meet the support requirements of this section.

Exception No. 1: If made up with threaded couplings, it shall be permissible to support straight runs of rigid metal conduit in accordance with Table 346-12, provided such supports prevent transmission of stresses to termination where conduit is deflected between supports.

Exception No. 2: The distance between supports shall be permitted to be increased to 20 feet (6.1 m) for exposed vertical risers from industrial machinery, provided that the conduit is made up with threaded couplings, is firmly supported at the top and bottom of the riser, and no other means of intermediate support is readily available.

346-13 . **Boxes and Fittings.** Boxes and fittings shall comply with the applicable provisions of Article 370.

Table 346-12. **Supports for Rigid Metal Conduit**

Conduit Size (Inches)	Maximum Distance Between Rigid Metal Conduit Supports (Feet)
$^1/_2$-$^3/_4$	10
1	12
1 $^1/_4$-1 $^1/_2$	14
2-2 $^1/_2$	16
3 and larger	20

For SI units: (Supports) one foot = 0.3048 meter.

346-14 . **Splices and Taps.** Splices and taps shall be made only in junction boxes, outlet boxes, device boxes, or conduit bodies. See Article 370.

B. Construction Specifications

346-15 . **General.** Rigid metal conduit shall comply with (a) through (c) below.

(a) Standard Lengths. Rigid metal conduit as shipped shall be in standard lengths of 10 feet (3.05 m), including coupling, one coupling to be furnished with each length. Each length shall be reamed and threaded on each end. For specific applications or uses, it shall be permissible to ship standard lengths or lengths shorter or longer than 10 feet (3.05 m) with or without couplings and with or without threads.

(b) Corrosion-Resistant Material. Nonferrous conduit of corrosion-resistant material shall have suitable markings.

(c) Durably Identified. Each length shall be clearly and durably identified in every 10 feet (3.05 m) as required in the first sentence of Section 110-21.

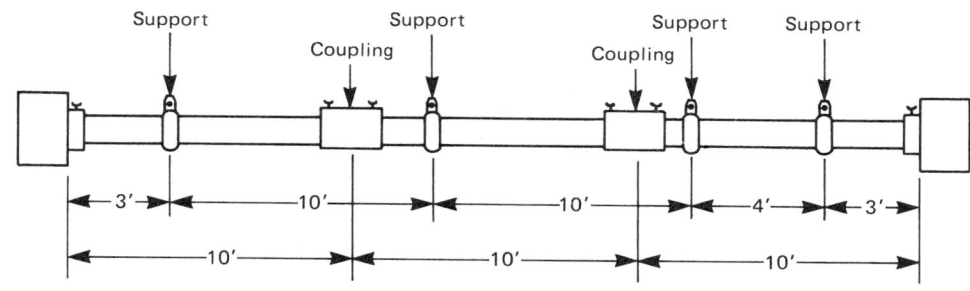

Figure 346-3. Minimum support required. Note that support is not required on each side of a coupling. See also the last sentence of Section 346-12.

ARTICLE 347   Rigid Nonmetallic Conduit

Contents

347-1. **Description.** This article shall apply to a type of conduit and fittings of suitable nonmetallic material that is resistant to moisture and chemical atmospheres. For use aboveground, it shall also be flame-retardant, resistant to impact and crushing, resistant to distortion from heat under conditions likely to be encountered in service, and resistant to low temperature and sunlight effects. For use underground, the material shall be acceptably resistant to moisture and corrosive agents and shall be of sufficient strength to withstand abuse, such as by impact and crushing, in handling and during installation. Conduits listed for the purpose shall be permitted to be installed underground in continuous lengths from a reel. Where intended for direct burial, without encasement in concrete, the material shall also be capable of withstanding continued loading that is likely to be encountered after installation.

Three types of rigid nonmetallic conduit are listed by UL: (1) rigid nonmetallic plastic Schedule 40 and 80 PVC, (2) rigid nonmetallic underground plastic, and (3) rigid nonmetallic, underground, other than plastic, fiber type. Only the rigid nonmetallic plastic Schedule 40 and 80 PVC are recognized by the *Code* as suitable for use aboveground.

Rigid nonmetallic plastic (Schedule 40 and 80 PVC), unless marked for a higher temperature, is intended for use with wires rated 75°C (167°F) or less including where it is encased in concrete within buildings and where ambient temperature is 50°C (122°F) or less. Where encased in concrete in trenches outside of buildings it is suitable for use with wires rated 90°C (194°F) or less.

The UL listings of rigid nonmetallic underground plastic include three types: (1) polyvinyl chloride (PVC) Type A or Type EB; (2) high-density polyethylene (HDPE) Schedule 40; and (3) fiberglass reinforced epoxy. The various conduit types differ in their inside and outside diameters.

This type of conduit is designed for use in underground work under the following conditions, as indicated on the product: (1) where laid with its entire length in concrete (Type A); (2) where laid with its entire length in concrete in outdoor trenches (Type EB); and (3) where directly buried with or without being encased in concrete (HDPE Schedule 40 and fiberglass reinforced epoxy). This type of conduit is intended for use in ambient temperatures of 50°C (122°F) or less, and, unless marked otherwise, Type A and HDPE Schedule 40 conduit are intended for use with wires rated 75°C (167°F) or less. Type EB conduit and Type A conduit, encased in concrete in trenches outside of buildings, may be used with wires rated 90°C (194°F) or less. HDPE Schedule 40 conduit, where directly buried or encased in concrete, may be used with wire rated 90°C (194°F) or less. Fiberglass-reinforced epoxy conduit may be used with wires rated 90°C (194°F) or less.

The underground fiber conduit is listed in two types: Type I for use where laid with its entire length in concrete, and Type II for use without concrete encasement.

Rigid nonmetallic conduit is listed in sizes ½ to 6 inches, inclusive.

Listed PVC conduit is inherently resistant to atmospheres containing common industrial corrosive agents and will also withstand vapors or mist of caustic, pickling acids, hydrofluoric and chromic acids, and plating baths.

PVC conduit is designed for connection to couplings, fittings, and boxes by the use of a suitable solvent-type cement. Instructions supplied by the manufacturer describe the method of assembly and precautions to be followed.

For use of Schedule 80, see Sections 300-5(d), 551-80(b), and 710-3(b)(1).

This section has been revised for the 1993 *Code*. It recognizes a new type of rigid nonmetallic conduit that has a limited degree of bendability. It is usually shipped to the job site on reels. The use of this conduit is limited to underground installations.

347-2. Uses Permitted. The use of listed rigid nonmetallic conduit and fittings shall be permitted under the following conditions:

(FPN): Extreme cold may cause some nonmetallic conduits to become brittle and therefore more susceptible to damage from physical contact.

(a) **Concealed.** In walls, floors, and ceilings.

(b) **Corrosive Influences.** In locations subject to severe corrosive influences as covered in Section 300-6 and where subject to chemicals for which the materials are specifically approved.

(c) **Cinders.** In cinder fill.

(d) **Wet Locations.** In portions of dairies, laundries, canneries, or other wet locations and in locations where walls are frequently washed, the entire conduit system including boxes and fittings used therewith shall be so installed and equipped as to prevent water from entering the conduit. All supports, bolts, straps, screws, etc., shall be of corrosion-resistant materials or be protected against corrosion by approved corrosion-resistant materials.

(e) **Dry and Damp Locations.** In dry and damp locations not prohibited by Section 347-3.

(f) **Exposed.** For exposed work where not subject to physical damage if identified for such use.

(g) **Underground Installations.** For underground installations, see Sections 300-5 and 710-4(b).

347-3. Uses Not Permitted. Rigid nonmetallic conduit shall not be used:

(a) **Hazardous (Classified) Locations.** In hazardous (classified) locations, except as covered in Sections 503-3(a), 504-20, 514-8, and 515-5; and in Class I, Division 2 locations as permitted in the exception to Section 501-4(b).

(b) **Support of Fixtures.** For the support of fixtures or other equipment.

Exception: Rigid nonmetallic conduit shall be permitted to support nonmetallic conduit bodies no larger than the largest trade size of an entering raceway. The conduit bodies shall not contain devices or support fixtures.

(c) **Physical Damage.** Where subject to physical damage unless identified for such use.

(d) **Ambient Temperatures.** Where subject to ambient temperatures exceeding those for which the conduit is approved.

(e) **Insulation Temperature Limitations.** For conductors whose insulation temperature limitations would exceed those for which the conduit is approved.

(f) **Theaters and Similar Locations.** In theaters and similar locations, except as provided in Articles 518 and 520.

See commentary following Section 347-1.

Nonmetallic conduits are not permitted to be installed in ducts, plenums, and other air-handling spaces. See Section 300-22.

They are not permitted in theaters and similar locations, except as provided in Sections 518-4 and 520-4. This restriction was new in Article 347 of the 1990 *NEC*, but did not represent a change in *Code* requirements, since the restrictions in the use of rigid nonmetallic conduit in Sections 518-4 and 520-4 has not changed from the 1987 *NEC* requirements.

In addition, nonmetallic conduits should not be used where their use would substantially increase the possible spread of fire or products of combustion through fire-rated, fire-resistant, or fire-stopped walls, partitions, ceilings and floors, hollow spaces, vertical shafts, and ventilating or air-handling ducts. See Section 300-21 for requirements covering the prevention of the spread of fire or products of combustion.

347-4. Other Articles. Installation of rigid nonmetallic conduit shall comply with the applicable provisions of Article 300. Where equipment grounding is required by Article 250, a separate equipment grounding conductor shall be installed in the conduit.

Exception: As permitted in Section 250-91(b), Exception No. 3 for direct-current circuits.

A. Installations

347-5. Trimming. All cut ends shall be trimmed inside and outside to remove rough edges.

See commentary following Section 348-11.

347-6. Joints. All joints between lengths of conduit, and between conduit and couplings, fittings, and boxes, shall be made by an approved method.

347-8. Supports. Rigid nonmetallic conduit shall be installed as a complete system as provided in Section 300-18 and shall be supported as required in Table 347-8. In addition, conduit shall be securely fastened within 3 feet (914 mm) of each outlet box, junction box, device box, conduit body, or other conduit termination. Rigid nonmetallic conduit shall be fastened so that movement from thermal expansion or contraction will be permitted.

The requirement in Section 347-8 for a support within 3 feet of each conduit termination is consistent with the minimum support spacing in Table 347-8.

It is recognized that these requirements are fairly stringent because they are based on ambient temperatures higher than normally encountered and utilize horizontal support tests only. Expansion can cause damage to the raceway or its supports. Therefore, expansion joints should be used and the fastening to the mounting means should allow expansion/contraction cycles without damage. See commentary following Section 347-9.

347-9. Expansion Joints. Expansion joints for rigid nonmetallic conduit shall be provided to compensate for thermal expansion and contraction.

Exception: Where the computed length change due to thermal expansion or contraction, according to Table 10, Chapter 9, is less than .25 inches (6.36 mm) in a straight run between securely

Table 347-8. Support of Rigid Nonmetallic Conduit

Conduit Size (Inches)	Maximum Spacing Between Supports (Feet)
¹/₂-1	3
1 ¹/₄-2	5
2 ¹/₂-3	6
3 ¹/₂-5	7
6	8

For SI units: (Supports) one foot = 0.3048 meter.

mounted items such as boxes, cabinets, elbows, or other conduit terminations, an expansion joint shall not be required.

(FPN): See Table 10 in Chapter 9 for expansion characteristics of PVC rigid nonmetallic conduit.

Expansion joints or expansion couplings are generally provided in exposed runs of nonmetallic rigid conduit where: (1) the run is long; (2) the run is subjected to large temperature variations during installation or afterwards; and (3) expansion and contraction measures are provided for the building structure. Rigid nonmetallic conduit exhibits a considerably greater change in length per degree change in temperature than metal raceway systems.

In some parts of the United States and other countries, outdoor temperature variations of over 38°C (100°F) are common. According to Chapter 9, Table 10, a 100-foot run of PVC rigid nonmetallic conduit will change 4.1 inches in length if the temperature change is 38°C (100°F).

The normal expansion range of most larger sizes of rigid nonmetallic conduit expansion couplings is generally 6 inches. Information concerning installation and application of this type of coupling may be obtained from manufacturer's instructions.

Expansion couplings are seldom used underground where temperatures are relatively constant. Where rigid nonmetallic conduit is buried or covered immediately, expansion and contraction are not a problem.

347-10. Minimum Size. No conduit smaller than ¹/₂-inch electrical trade size shall be used.

347-11. Number of Conductors. The number of conductors permitted in a single conduit shall not exceed the percentage fill specified in Table 1, Chapter 9.

Schedule 80 PVC conduit has less cross-sectional area than Schedule 40, rigid metal conduit, or EMT, so Chapter 9, Tables 3A, 3B, and 3C are not applicable to Schedule 80.

(FPN): For conductor cross-sectional area, see Tables 5, 5A, 6, and 8 and the applicable Notes to Tables at the beginning of Chapter 9.

See commentary following Section 346-6.

347-12. Bushings. Where a conduit enters a box or other fitting, a bushing or adapter shall be provided to protect the wire from abrasion unless the design of the box or fitting is such as to provide equivalent protection.

(FPN): See Section 373-6(c) for the protection of conductors No. 4 and larger at bushings.

347-13. Bends — How Made. Bends of rigid nonmetallic conduit shall be so made that the conduit will not be damaged and that the internal diameter of the conduit will not be effectively reduced. Field bends shall be made only with bending equipment identified for the purpose, and the radius of the curve of the inner edge of such bends shall not be less than shown in Table 346-10.

See commentary following Section 346-10.

347-14. Bends — Number in One Run. There shall not be more than the equivalent of four quarter bends (360 degrees total) between pull points, e.g., conduit bodies and boxes.

See commentary following Section 346-11.

347-15. Boxes and Fittings. Boxes and fittings shall comply with the applicable provisions of Article 370.

347-16. Splices and Taps. Splices and taps shall be made only in junction boxes, outlet boxes, device boxes, or conduit bodies. See Article 370.

B. Construction Specifications

347-17. General. Rigid nonmetallic conduit shall comply with the following:

Marking. Each length of nonmetallic conduit shall be clearly and durably marked at least every 10 feet (3.05 m) as required in the first sentence of Section 110-21. The type of material shall also be included in the marking unless it is visually identifiable. For conduit recognized for use aboveground, these markings shall be permanent. For conduit limited to underground use only, these markings shall be sufficiently durable to remain legible until the material is installed. Conduit shall be permitted to be surface marked to indicate special characteristics of the material.

(FPN): Examples of these optional markings include but are not limited to "LS" for limited-smoke and markings such as "sunlight-resistant."

ARTICLE 348　Electrical Metallic Tubing

Contents

348-1. **Use.** The use of electrical metallic tubing shall be permitted for both exposed and concealed work. Electrical metallic tubing shall not be used (1) where, during installation or afterward, it will be subject to severe physical damage; (2) where protected from corrosion solely by enamel; (3) in cinder concrete or cinder fill where subject to permanent moisture unless protected on all sides by a layer of noncinder concrete at least 2 inches (50.8 mm) thick or unless the tubing is at least 18 inches (457 mm) under the fill; (4) in any hazardous (classified) location except as permitted by Sections 502-4, 503-3, and 504-20; or (5) for the support of fixtures or other equipment. Where practicable, dissimilar metals in contact anywhere in the system shall be avoided to eliminate the possibility of galvanic action.

This section was revised for the 1993 *Code* to clarify that EMT is not permitted to support fixtures or equipment.

Exception: Aluminum fittings and enclosures shall be permitted to be used with steel electrical metallic tubing.

Ferrous or nonferrous electrical metallic tubing, elbows, couplings, and fittings shall be permitted to be installed in concrete, in direct contact with the earth, or in areas subject to severe corrosive influences where protected by corrosion protection and judged suitable for the condition.

(FPN): See Section 300-6 for protection against corrosion.

Galvanized steel electrical metallic tubing installed in concrete on grade or above grade generally requires no supplementary corrosion protection. EMT installed in concrete below grade level or installed in contact with soil generally requires supplementary corrosion protection.

348-2. **Other Articles.** Installations of electrical metallic tubing shall comply with the applicable provisions of Article 300.

A. Installation

348-4. **Wet Locations.** All supports, bolts, straps, screws, etc., shall be of corrosion-resistant materials or protected against corrosion by corrosion-resistant materials.

(FPN): See Section 300-6 for protection against corrosion.

348-5. **Size.**

(a) **Minimum.** Tubing smaller than ½-inch electrical trade size shall not be used.

Exception: For enclosing the leads of motors as permitted in Section 430-145(b).

(b) **Maximum.** The maximum size of tubing shall be the 4-inch electrical trade size.

348-6. **Number of Conductors in Tubing.** The number of conductors permitted in a single tubing shall not exceed the percentage fill specified in Table 1, Chapter 9.

(FPN): For conductor cross-sectional area, see Tables 5, 5A, 6, and 8 and the applicable Notes to Tables at the beginning of Chapter 9.

348-7. **Threads.** Electrical metallic tubing shall not be threaded. Where integral couplings are utilized, such couplings shall be permitted to be factory threaded.

348-8. **Couplings and Connectors.** Couplings and connectors used with tubing shall be made up tight. Where buried in masonry or concrete, they shall be concrete-tight type. Where installed in wet locations, they shall be of the raintight type.

UL-listed fittings that are suitable for use in poured concrete or where exposed to rain are so indicated on the fitting or carton. The term "raintight" or the equivalent on the carton indicates suitability for use where directly exposed to rain. The term "concretetight" or equivalent on the carton indicates suitability for use in poured concrete. See Sections 225-22 and 230-53.

Fittings have been tested for use with steel tubing only unless marked on the device or carton to indicate suitability for use with aluminum or other material.

Indentor-type fittings are for use with metallic-coated electrical metallic tubing only and require a special tool supplied by the manufacturer for proper installation. Diametrically opposed indentor-type tools require two sets of indentations nominally 90 degrees apart. Triple indent tools require one set of indentations.

348-9. **Bends — How Made.** Bends in the tubing shall be so made that the tubing will not be damaged and the internal diameter of the tubing will not be effectively reduced. The radius of the curve of the inner edge of any field bend shall not be less than shown in Table 346-10.

Exception: For field bends made with a bending machine designed for the purpose, the minimum radius shall not be less than indicated in Table 346-10, Exception.

348-10. **Bends — Number in One Run.** There shall not be more than the equivalent of four quarter bends (360 degrees total) between pull points, e.g., conduit bodies and boxes.

See commentary following Section 346-11.

348-11. **Reaming.** All cut ends of electrical metallic tubing shall be reamed or otherwise finished to remove rough edges.

In addition to a reamer, a half-round file has proved practical for removing rough edges. Using the handle of a pair of "Channel Lock" (pump) pliers, the nose of side-cutting pliers or an electrician's knife can be effective.

348-12. **Supports.** Electrical metallic tubing shall be installed as a complete system as provided in Article 300 and shall be securely fastened in place at least every 10 feet (3.05 m) and within 3 feet (914 mm) of each outlet box, junction box, device box, cabinet, conduit body, or other tubing terminations.

Electrical metallic tubing is required to be securely fastened at least every 10 feet. Support is also required within 3 feet of outlet boxes, junction boxes, device boxes, cabinets, and conduit bodies. This section has been revised for the 1993 *Code* so that it no longer requires fastening within 3 feet of every coupling. Coupling support is assured by the 10-foot support requirement in this section.

Exception: Fastening of unbroken lengths shall be permitted to be increased to a distance of 5 feet (1.52 m) where structural members do not readily permit fastening within 3 feet (914 mm).

For example, the exception permits boxes that are secured to ceiling or roof support structural members, spaced not more than five feet apart, to serve as support for runs of EMT perpendicular to the axis of the roof or ceiling support members. See Figure 348-2.

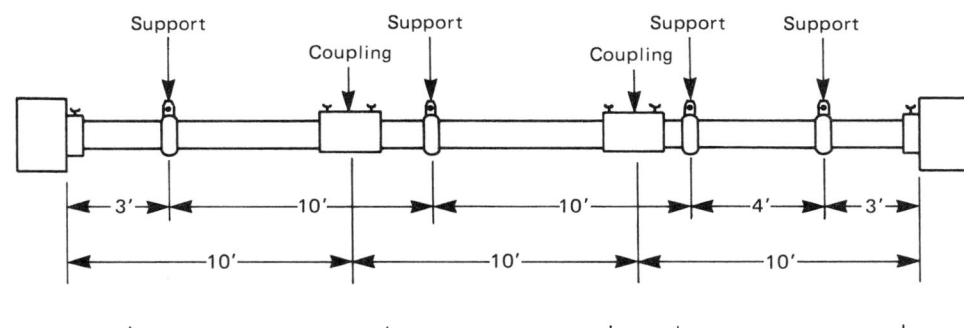

Figure 348-1. Minimum support required unless exception applies. Note that support is not required within 3 feet on each side of a coupling.

Figure 348-2. Illustration of an installation complying with Section 348-12, Exception.

348-13. **Boxes and Fittings.** Boxes and fittings shall comply with the applicable provisions of Article 370.

348-14. **Splices and Taps.** Splices and taps shall be made only in junction boxes, outlet boxes, device boxes, or conduit bodies. See Article 370.

B. Construction Specifications

348-15. **General.** Electrical metallic tubing shall comply with (a) through (d) below.

(a) Cross Section. The tubing, and elbows and bends for use with the tubing, shall have a circular cross section.

(b) Finish. Tubing shall have such a finish or treatment of outer surfaces as will provide an approved durable means of readily distinguishing it, after installation, from rigid metal conduit.

(c) Connectors. Where the tubing is coupled together by threads, the connector shall be so designed as to prevent bending of the tubing at any part of the thread.

(d) Marking. Electrical metallic tubing shall be clearly and durably marked at least every 10 feet (3.05 m) as required in the first sentence of Section 110-21.

ARTICLE 349   Flexible Metallic Tubing

Contents

A. General

349-1. **Scope.** The provisions of this article apply to a raceway for electric conductors that is circular in cross section, flexible, metallic, and liquidtight without a nonmetallic jacket.

Flexible metallic tubing is a type of raceway used for certain specific applications, particularly for use under the requirements of Sections 300-22(b) and (c) for wiring in ducts, plenums, and other air-handling spaces. Flexible metallic tubing is a material that is very flexible and is rarely affected by conditions of vibration or other movement. It is an effective barrier to gases and products of combustion where installed with matching fittings and is of adequate mechanical strength for use where not exposed to physical damage.

Flexible metallic tubing in length not greater than 6 feet is suitable for use as a raceway for tap conductors supplying lighting fixtures where outlet boxes are located not less than 1 foot from the fixture. Flexible metallic tubing has advantages over the use of liquidtight flexible metal conduit where installed in ducts and plenums because it does not have a nonmetallic outer sheath that could introduce smoke and other products of combustion into the ventilation system in the event of a fire.

349-2. **Other Articles.** Installations of flexible metallic tubing shall comply with the provisions of the applicable sections of Article 300 and Section 110-21.

349-3. **Uses Permitted.** Flexible metallic tubing shall be permitted to be used (1) in dry locations; (2) in accessible locations where protected from physical damage or concealed, such as above suspended ceilings; (3) for 1000 volts maximum; and (4) in branch circuits.

A common application of flexible metallic tubing is as a wiring method for equipment or lighting fixtures mounted on, or above, suspended ceilings.

349-4. **Uses Not Permitted.** Flexible metallic tubing shall not be used (1) in hoistways; (2) in storage battery rooms; (3) in hazardous (classified) locations unless otherwise permitted under other articles in this Code; (4) underground for direct earth burial, or embedded in poured concrete or aggregate; (5) where subject to physical damage; and (6) in lengths over 6 feet (1.83 m).

Unlike flexible metal conduit or liquidtight flexible metal conduit, flexible metallic tubing is limited in use to 6-foot lengths.

B. Construction and Installation

349-10. **Size.**

(a) **Minimum.** Flexible metallic tubing smaller than 1/2-inch electrical trade size shall not be used.

Exception No. 1: 3/8-inch trade size shall be permitted to be installed in accordance with Sections 300-22(b) and (c).

Exception No. 2: 3/8-inch trade size shall be permitted in lengths not in excess of 6 feet (1.83 m) as part of an approved assembly or for lighting fixtures. See Section 410-67(c).

(b) **Maximum.** The maximum size of flexible metallic tubing shall be the 3/4-inch trade size.

349-12. **Number of Conductors.**

(a) **1/2-Inch and 3/4-Inch Flexible Metallic Tubing.** The number of conductors permitted in 1/2-inch and 3/4-inch trade sizes of flexible metallic tubing shall not exceed the percentage of fill specified in Table 1, Chapter 9.

(b) **3/8-Inch Flexible Metallic Tubing.** The number of conductors permitted in 3/8-inch trade size flexible metallic tubing shall not exceed that permitted in Table 350-3.

(FPN): For conductor cross-sectional area, see Tables 5, 5A, 6, and 8 and the applicable Notes to Tables at the beginning of Chapter 9.

349-16. **Grounding.** See Section 250-91(b), Exception No. 1.

349-17. **Splices and Taps.** Splices and taps shall be made only in junction boxes, outlet boxes, device boxes, or conduit bodies. See Article 370.

349-18. **Fittings.** Flexible metallic tubing shall be used only with approved terminal fittings. Fittings shall effectively close any openings in the connection.

(FPN): See Sections 300-22(b) and (c) for use in ducts, plenums, and other spaces used for environmental air.

349-20. **Bends.**

(a) **Infrequent Flexing Use.** Where the flexible metallic tubing shall be infrequently flexed in service after installation, the radii of bends measured to the inside of the bend shall not be less than specified in Table 349-20(a).

Table 349-20(a). Minimum Radii for Flexing Use

Trade Size	Minimum Radii
3/8 inch	10 inches
1/2 inch	12 1/2 inches
3/4 inch	17 1/2 inches

For SI units: (Radii) one inch = 25.4 millimeters.

(b) **Fixed Bends.** Where the flexible metallic tubing is bent for installation purposes and is not flexed or bent as required by use after installation, the radii of bends measured to the inside of the bend shall not be less than specified in Table 349-20(b).

Table 349-20(b). Minimum Radii for Fixed Bends

Trade Size	Minimum Radii
3/8 inch	3 1/2 inches
1/2 inch	4 inches
3/4 inch	5 inches

For SI units: (Radii) one inch = 25.4 millimeters.

ARTICLE 350   Flexible Metal Conduit

Contents

350-4. Supports.
350-5. Grounding.
350-6. Bends — Number in One Run.
350-7. Number of Conductors.
350-8. Fittings.
350-9. Trimming.
350-10. Splices and Taps.

350-1. **Other Articles.** Installations of flexible metal conduit shall comply with the applicable provisions of Article 300.

350-2. **Uses Not Permitted.** Flexible metal conduit shall not be used (1) in wet locations unless conductors are of lead-covered type or of other types approved for the specific conditions and the installation is such that water is not likely to enter other raceways or enclosures to which the conduit is connected; (2) in hoistways, other than provided in Section 620-21; (3) in storage-battery rooms; (4) in any hazardous (classified) location other than permitted in Sections 501-4(b) and 504-20; (5) where rubber-covered conductors are exposed to oil, gasoline, or other materials having a deteriorating effect on rubber; (6) underground or embedded in poured concrete or aggregate; or (7) where subject to physical damage.

Flexible metal conduit is permitted for use in wet locations, provided the completed installation prevents water from entering enclosures or other raceways to which the conduit is connected and the conductors are suitable for wet locations. See Figure 350-1.

Listed flexible metal conduit ½ inches and larger may be installed in unlimited lengths where an equipment grounding conductor is installed with the circuit conductors. See Section 350-5, Exception No. 2 for the use of flexible metal conduit in lengths of 6 feet or less.

350-3. **Minimum Size.** Flexible metal conduit less than ½-inch electrical trade size shall not be used.

Exception No. 1: For enclosing the leads of motors as permitted in Section 430-145(b).

Exception No. 2: Flexible metal conduit of ⅜-inch nominal trade size shall be permitted in lengths not in excess of 6 feet (1.83 m) as a part of a listed assembly, or for tap connections

Figure 350-1. *An example of one acceptable application of flexible metal conduit on the exterior of a building. The branch-circuit supply conductors are suitable for use in a wet location, and the junction box is listed for use in a wet location.*

to lighting fixtures as required in Section 410-67(c), or for utilization equipment.

This exception makes it clear that ⅜-inch flexible metal conduit is permitted to be used as the manufactured or field-installed metal raceway (4 to 6 feet in length) to enclose tap conductors between the outlet box and the fixture terminal housing of recessed lighting fixtures.

Flexible metal conduit is also permitted to be used as a 6-foot fixture whip from an outlet box to a lighting fixture that is secured to, and supported by, a suspended ceiling.

Exception No. 3: Flexible metal conduit of ⅜-inch nominal trade size shall be permitted for manufactured wiring systems as permitted in Section 604-6(a).

This exception permits a smaller minimum size for manufactured wiring systems because the conductors are not as prone to physical damage when assembled under factory-controlled conditions.

Exception No. 4: As permitted in Section 620-21, Exception No. 5.

Exception No. 5: Flexible metal conduit of ⅜-inch nominal trade size shall be permitted as part of a listed assembly to connect wired fixture sections as permitted in Section 410-77(c).

Section 410-77 describes a wired fixture section and limits the length of ⅜-in. flexible metal conduit to 25 feet for this purpose.

Table 350-3. **Maximum Number of Insulated Conductors in ⅜-Inch Flexible Metal Conduit***

Col. A = With fitting inside conduit.
Col. B = With fitting outside conduit.

Size AWG	Types RFH-2, SF-2		Types TF, XHHW, AF, TW		Types TFN, THHN, THWN		Types FEP, FEPB, PF, PGF	
	A	B	A	B	A	B	A	B
18	..	3	3	7	4	8	5	8
16	..	2	2	4	3	7	4	8
14	..	..	..	4	3	7	3	7
12	..	..	..	3	..	4	..	4
10	..	..	..	..	..	2	..	3

* In addition, one uninsulated equipment grounding conductor of the same size shall be permitted.

350-4. **Supports.** Flexible metal conduit shall be secured by an approved means at intervals not exceeding 4½ feet (1.37 m) and within 12 inches (305 mm) on each side of every outlet box, junction box, cabinet, or fitting.

Exception No. 1: Where flexible metal conduit is fished.

Exception No. 2: Lengths not exceeding 3 feet (914 mm) at terminals where flexibility is necessary.

Exception No. 3: Lengths not exceeding 6 feet (1.83 m) from a fixture terminal connection for tap connections to lighting fixtures as required in Section 410-67(c).

Flexible metal conduit is permitted to be concealed (rendered inaccessible by the finish of a building). However, unlike other raceways such as rigid metal conduit, intermediate metal conduit, or electrical metallic tubing, which are required to be supported every 10 feet and within 3 feet of every box or fitting, flexible metal conduit is required to be supported at least every 4½ feet and within 12 inches of every box or fitting.

350-5. **Grounding.** Flexible metal conduit shall be permitted as a grounding means as covered in Section 250-91(b). Where an equipment bonding jumper is required around flexible metal conduit, it shall be installed in accordance with Section 250-79.

In general, flexible metal conduit requires the inclusion of an equipment grounding conductor. The conduit must be listed and terminated in listed fittings. See Exception No. 2 and commentary for conditions permitting short lengths of flexible conduit to serve as the equipment grounding conductor. Note that Exception No. 1 requires an equipment grounding conductor to be installed where the connection is to provide flexibility.

Where used in hazardous (classified) locations, a bonding jumper is specifically required. See Sections 501-16(b), 502-16(b), and 503-16(b).

Exception No. 1: Where used to connect equipment where flexibility is required, an equipment grounding conductor shall be installed.

Where flexible metal conduit is installed to minimize the transmission of vibration from equipment such as motors or to provide flexibility for equipment that requires adjustment such as floodlights or spotlights, a separate equipment grounding conductor is required to be installed regardless of the length of the flexible conduit.

Exception No. 2: Listed flexible metal conduit shall be permitted as a grounding means if the total length in any ground return path is 6 feet (1.83 m) or less, the conduit is terminated in fittings listed for grounding, and the circuit conductors contained therein are protected by overcurrent devices rated at 20 amperes or less.

Section 350-5, Exception No. 2 has been revised in the 1993 *Code* to clarify that only *listed* flexible metal conduit terminated in listed fittings is allowed to be used as a grounding means. It is limited to lengths no longer than six feet and must be protected by an overcurrent device rated at 20 amperes or less.

Where the length of the total ground-fault return path exceeds six feet or the circuit overcurrent exceeds 20 amperes, a separate equipment grounding conductor must be installed with the circuit conductors. However, Section 250-79(f) permits the equipment grounding conductor to be routed on the outside of the raceway in lengths no longer than six feet and bonded at each end.

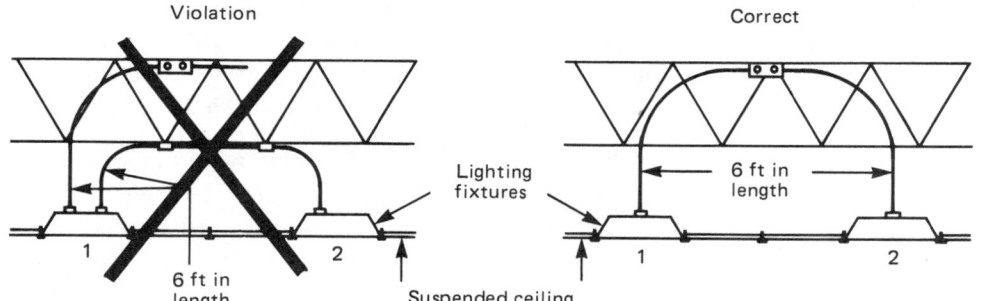

Figure 350-2. *The sketch on the right shows the proper application of flexible metal conduit where the total length of any ground return path is limited to 6 feet. The sketch on the left shows an application that is in violation, as the grounding return path for fixture No. 2 is 12 feet.*

350-6. **Bends — Number in One Run.** There shall not be more than the equivalent of four quarter bends (360 degrees total) between pull points, e.g., conduit bodies and boxes.

Similar to other raceways, a run of flexible metal conduit installed between boxes, conduit bodies, etc., is not permitted to contain more than the equivalent of four quarter bends (360 degrees total). Proper shaping and support of this flexible wiring method will assure that conductors can be easily installed or withdrawn at any time.

350-7. **Number of Conductors.** The number of conductors permitted in a single ½-inch through 4-inch trade size shall not exceed the percentage of fill specified in Table 1, Chapter 9. See Table 350-3 for ⅜-inch flexible metal conduit.

350-8. **Fittings.** Fittings listed for flexible metal conduit shall be used. Angle connectors shall not be used for concealed raceway installations.

350-9. **Trimming.** All cut ends of conduit shall be trimmed or otherwise finished to remove rough edges, except where fittings that thread into the convolutions are used.

350-10. **Splices and Taps.** Splices and taps shall be made only in junction boxes, outlet boxes, device boxes, or conduit bodies.

ARTICLE 351 Liquidtight Flexible Metal Conduit and Liquidtight Flexible Nonmetallic Conduit

Contents

351-1. Scope.

A. Liquidtight Flexible Metal Conduit

351-2. Definition.
351-3. Other Articles.
351-4. Use.
  (a) Permitted.
  (b) Not Permitted.
351-5. Size.
  (a) Minimum.
  (b) Maximum.
351-6. Number of Conductors.
  (a) Single Conduit.
  (b) ⅜-Inch Liquidtight Flexible Metal Conduit.
351-7. Fittings.
351-8. Supports.
351-9. Grounding.
351-10. Bends — Number in One Run.
351-11. Splices and Taps.

B. Liquidtight Flexible Nonmetallic Conduit

351-22. Definition.
351-23. Use.
  (a) Permitted.
  (b) Not Permitted.

351-1. **Scope.** This article covers liquidtight flexible metal conduit and liquidtight flexible nonmetallic conduit.

Liquidtight flexible metal conduit is intended for use in wet locations or where exposed to mineral oil, both at a maximum temperature of 60°C (140°F). It is not intended for use where exposed to gasoline or similar light petroleum solvents unless so marked on the product.

Liquidtight flexible nonmetallic conduit is used extensively in the machine tool and related industries. See Section 15-8 in NFPA 79-1991, *Electrical Standard for Industrial Machinery*.

A. Liquidtight Flexible Metal Conduit

351-2. **Definition.** Liquidtight flexible metal conduit is a raceway of circular cross section having an outer liquidtight, nonmetallic, sunlight-resistant jacket over an inner flexible metal core with associated couplings, connectors, and fittings and approved for the installation of electric conductors.

351-3. **Other Articles.** Installations of liquidtight flexible metal conduit shall comply with the applicable provisions of Article 300 and with the specific sections of Articles 350, 501, 502, 503, and 553 referenced below.

(FPN):   For marking requirements, see Section 110-21.

351-4. **Use.**

(a) **Permitted.** Liquidtight flexible metal conduit shall be permitted to be used in exposed or concealed locations:

(1) Where conditions of installation, operation, or maintenance require flexibility or protection from liquids, vapors, or solids.

(2) As permitted by Sections 501-4(b), 502-4, 503-3, and 504-20 and in other hazardous (classified) locations where specifically approved, and by Section 553-7(b).

(3) For direct burial where listed and marked for the purpose.

"Listed and marked" liquidtight flexible metal conduit is permitted for direct burial in the earth. Note that the requirements of Section 300-5 are applicable to liquidtight flexible metal conduit where installed underground.

Liquidtight flexible metal conduit may be installed in unlimited lengths, provided an equipment grounding conductor is installed with the circuit conductors. See Section 351-9, Exception No. 2.

Liquidtight flexible metal conduit has been added in the 1993 *Code* as a new wiring method for services, where the length does not exceed six feet and an equipment bonding jumper is installed. See Section 351-9, Exception No. 2.

(b) **Not Permitted.** Liquidtight flexible metal conduit shall not be used:

(1) Where subject to physical damage.

(2) Where any combination of ambient and conductor temperature will produce an operating temperature in excess of that for which the material is approved.

351-5. **Size.**

(a) **Minimum.** Liquidtight flexible metal conduit smaller than $\frac{1}{2}$-inch electrical trade size shall not be used.

Exception: $\frac{3}{8}$-inch size shall be permitted as covered in Section 350-3.

(b) **Maximum.** The maximum size of liquidtight flexible metal conduit shall be the 4-inch trade size.

351-6. **Number of Conductors.**

(a) **Single Conduit.** The number of conductors permitted in a single conduit, $\frac{1}{2}$- through 4-inch trade sizes, shall not exceed the percentage of fill specified in Table 1, Chapter 9.

(b) $\frac{3}{8}$-**Inch Liquidtight Flexible Metal Conduit.** The number of conductors permitted in $\frac{3}{8}$-inch liquidtight flexible metal conduit shall not exceed that permitted in Table 350-3.

351-7. **Fittings.** Liquidtight flexible metal conduit shall be used only with approved terminal fittings. Angle connectors shall not be used for concealed raceway installations.

351-8. **Supports.** Where liquidtight flexible metal conduit is installed as a fixed raceway, it shall be secured at intervals not exceeding 4½ feet (1.37 m) and within 12 inches (305 mm) on each side of every outlet box, junction box, cabinet, or fitting.

Exception No. 1: Where liquidtight flexible metal conduit is fished.

Exception No. 2: Lengths not exceeding 3 feet (914 mm) at terminals where flexibility is necessary.

Exception No. 3: Lengths not exceeding 6 feet (1.83 m) from a fixture terminal connection for tap conductors to lighting fixtures as required in Section 410-67(c).

Section 410-67(c) is part of the special provisions for flush and recessed fixtures. The support requirements are modified where the liquidtight flexible metal conduit encloses tap conductors.

351-9. **Grounding.** Liquidtight flexible metal conduit shall be permitted as a grounding conductor where both the conduit and the fittings are approved for grounding. Where an equipment bonding jumper is required around liquidtight flexible metal conduit, it shall be installed in accordance with Section 250-79.

Exception No. 1: Where used to connect equipment and flexibility is required, an equipment grounding conductor shall be installed.

See commentary following Section 250-91(b), Exception No. 2.

Exception No. 2: Listed liquidtight flexible metal conduit shall be permitted as a grounding means in the 1¼-inch and smaller trade sizes if the total length of all liquidtight flexible metal conduit in any ground return path is 6 feet (1.83 m) or less, the conduit is terminated in fittings listed for grounding, and the circuit conductors contained therein are protected by overcurrent devices rated at 20 amperes or less for ⅜-inch and ½-inch trade sizes and 60 amperes or less for ¾-inch through 1¼-inch trade sizes.

See commentary following Section 350-5, Exception No. 2.

(FPN): See Sections 501-16(b), 502-16(b), and 503-16(b) for types of equipment grounding conductors.

Where liquidtight flexible metal conduit is installed in hazardous (classified) locations, a bonding jumper may be required. However, there are some exceptions, as indicated in the exceptions to Sections 501-16(b), 502-16(b), and 503-16(b).

351-10. **Bends — Number in One Run.** There shall not be more than the equivalent of four quarter bends (360 degrees total) between pull points, e.g., conduit bodies and boxes.

351-11. **Splices and Taps.** Splices and taps shall be made only in junction boxes, outlet boxes, device boxes, or conduit bodies. See Article 370.

B. Liquidtight Flexible Nonmetallic Conduit

351-22. **Definition.** Liquidtight flexible nonmetallic conduit is a raceway of circular cross section of various types:

(1) A smooth seamless inner core and cover bonded together and having one or more reinforcement layers between the core and cover.

(2) A smooth inner surface with integral reinforcement within the conduit wall.

(3) A corrugated internal and external surface without integral reinforcement within the conduit wall.

This conduit is flame-resistant and, with fittings, is approved for the installation of electrical conductors.

351-23. **Use.**

(a) Permitted. Liquidtight flexible nonmetallic conduit shall be permitted to be used in exposed or concealed locations:

(FPN): Extreme cold may cause some types of nonmetallic conduits to become brittle and therefore more susceptible to damage from physical contact.

(1) Where flexibility is required for installation, operation, or maintenance;

(2) Where protection of the contained conductors is required from vapors, liquids, or solids;

(3) For outdoor locations where listed and marked as suitable for the purpose.

(FPN): For marking requirements, see Section 110-21.

(4) For direct burial where listed and marked for the purpose.

(b) Not Permitted. Liquidtight flexible nonmetallic conduit shall not be used:

(1) Where subject to physical damage;

(2) Where any combination of ambient and conductor temperatures is in excess of that for which the liquidtight flexible nonmetallic conduit is approved;

(3) In lengths longer than 6 feet (1.83 m).

Exception: Where longer length is essential for a required degree of flexibility.

(4) Where voltage of the contained conductors is in excess of 600 volts, nominal.

Exception: As permitted in Section 600-31(a), Exception for electric signs over 600 volts.

351-24. **Size.** The sizes of liquidtight flexible nonmetallic conduit shall be electrical trade sizes ½ inch to 4 inch inclusive.

Exception No. 1: ⅜-inch size for enclosing the leads of motors as permitted in Section 430-145(b).

Exception No. 2: ⅜-inch trade size shall be permitted in lengths not in excess of 6 feet (1.83 m) as a part of a listed assembly, for tap connections to lighting fixtures as required in Section 410-67(c), or for utilization equipment. See Table 350-3 for conduit fill.

Exception No. 3: ⅜-inch trade size for electric sign conductors on insulators in accordance with Section 600-31(a).

351-25. **Number of Conductors.** The number of conductors permitted in a single conduit shall be in accordance with the percentage fill specified in Table 1, Chapter 9.

351-26. **Fittings.** Liquidtight flexible nonmetallic conduit shall be used only with terminal fittings identified for such use. Angle connectors shall not be used for concealed raceway installations.

351-28. **Equipment Grounding.** Where an equipment grounding conductor is required for the circuits installed in liquidtight flexible nonmetallic conduit, it shall be permitted to be installed on the inside or outside of the conduit. Where installed on the outside, the length of the equipment grounding conductor shall not exceed 6 feet (1.83 m) and shall be routed with the raceway or enclosure. Fittings and boxes shall be bonded or grounded in accordance with Article 250.

351-29. **Splices and Taps.** Splices and taps shall be made only in junction boxes, outlet boxes, device boxes, or conduit bodies. See Article 370.

351-30. **Bends — Number in One Run.** There shall not be more than the equivalent of four quarter bends (360 degrees total) between pull points, e.g., conduit bodies and boxes.

ARTICLE 352   Surface Metal Raceways and Surface Nonmetallic Raceways

Contents

A. Metal Surface Raceways

B. Surface Nonmetallic Raceways

A. Surface Metal Raceways

352-1. **Use.** The use of surface metal raceways shall be permitted in dry locations. They shall not be used (1) where subject to severe physical damage unless otherwise approved; (2) where the voltage is 300 volts or more between conductors unless the metal has a thickness of not less than .040 inch (1.02 mm); (3) where subject to corrosive vapors; (4) in hoistways;

(5) in any hazardous (classified) location except Class I, Division 2 locations as permitted in the exception to Section 501-4(b); nor (6) concealed except as follows:

Exception No. 1: Surface metal raceways shall be permitted for underplaster extensions where identified for such use.

Exception No. 2: As permitted in Section 645-5(d)(2).

(FPN): See definition of "Exposed — (As applied to wiring methods)" in Article 100.

352-2. **Other Articles.** Surface metal raceways shall comply with the applicable provisions of Article 300.

352-3. **Size of Conductors.** No conductor larger than that for which the raceway is designed shall be installed in surface metal raceway.

The number, type, and size of conductors that are permitted to be installed in a listed raceway are marked on the raceway or on the package in which they are shipped.

Raceways that have been listed for use with lighting fixtures or other devices are so marked on the raceways or on the package in which they are shipped.

The listing mark is applied to each length or package of complete raceway, raceway cover, or raceway base.

Some lighting fixtures covered under the UL categories of "fixtures" and "recessed-type fixtures" are suitable for use as raceways. See Section 250-91(b)(11).

See Figures 352-3 and 352-4.

352-4. **Number of Conductors in Raceways.** The number of conductors installed in any raceway shall be no greater than the number for which the raceway is designed.

The derating factors of Article 310, Note 8 (a) of Notes to Ampacity Tables of 0 to 2000 Volts shall not apply to conductors installed in surface metal raceways where all of the following conditions are met: (1) the cross-sectional area of the raceway exceeds 4 square inches (2580 sq mm); (2) the current-carrying conductors do not exceed thirty in number; (3) the sum of the cross-sectional areas of all contained conductors does not exceed 20 percent of the interior cross-sectional area of the surface metal raceway.

Figure 352-1. Surface metal raceway used as an extension from an existing receptacle. This installation is typical of how surface raceways can be used.

(FPN): For conductor cross-sectional area, see Tables 5, 5A, 6, and 8 and the applicable Notes to Tables at the beginning of Chapter 9.

352-5. **Extension Through Walls and Floors.** It shall be permissible to extend unbroken lengths of surface metal raceways through dry walls, dry partitions, and dry floors.

(FPN): See Section 353-3 for multioutlet assemblies.

352-6. **Combination Raceways.** Where combination surface metal raceways are used both for signaling and for lighting and power circuits, the different systems shall be run in separate compartments identified by sharply contrasting colors of the interior finish, and the same relative position of compartments shall be maintained throughout the premises.

352-7. **Splices and Taps.** Splices and taps shall be permitted in surface metal raceway having a removable cover that is accessible after installation. The conductors, including splices and taps, shall not fill the raceway to more than 75 percent of its area at that point. Splices and taps in surface metal raceways without removable covers shall be made only in junction boxes. All splices and taps shall be made by approved methods.

352-8 . **General.** Surface metal raceways shall be of such construction as will distinguish them from other raceways. Surface metal raceways and their elbows, couplings, and similar fittings shall be so designed that the sections can be electrically and mechanically coupled together and installed without subjecting the wires to abrasion.

Where covers and accessories of nonmetallic materials are used on surface metal raceways, they shall be identified for such use.

352-9 . **Grounding.** Surface metal raceway enclosures providing a transition from other wiring methods shall have a means for connecting an equipment grounding conductor.

Figure 352-2. An example of providing a means for terminating an equipment grounding conductor at surface metal raceway.

A new Section 352-9, "Grounding," has been added to the 1993 *Code*. Where surface metal raceways are supplied from a different wiring method, or where surface metal raceways supply a different wiring method, a means must be provided at the surface metal raceway for terminating an equipment grounding conductor at the point where a change of wiring method occurs.

For example, where surface metal raceways are supplied by Type NM or MC cable, a means must be available at the surface metal raceway for terminating the equipment grounding conductor provided within the cables. See Figure 352-3.

B. Surface Nonmetallic Raceways

352-21 . **Description.** Part B of this article shall apply to a type of surface nonmetallic raceway and fittings of suitable nonmetallic material that is resistant to moisture and chemical atmospheres. It shall also be flame-retardant, resistant to impact and crushing, resistant to distortion from heat under conditions likely to be encountered in service, and resistant to low-temperature effects. Surface nonmetallic raceways that have limited-smoke-producing characteristics shall be permitted to be identified with the suffix LS.

352-22 . **Use.** The use of surface nonmetallic raceways shall be permitted in dry locations. They shall not be used (1) where concealed; (2) where subject to severe physical damage; (3) where the voltage is 300 volts or more between conductors, unless listed for higher voltage; (4) in hoistways; (5) in any hazardous (classified) location except Class I, Division 2 locations as permitted in the exception to Section 501-4(b); (6) where subject to ambient temperatures exceeding those for which the non-metallic raceway is listed; nor (7) for conductors whose insulation temperature limitations would exceed those for which the non-metallic raceway is listed.

352-23 . **Other Articles.** Surface nonmetallic raceways shall comply with the applicable provisions of Article 300.

352-24 . **Size of Conductors.** No conductor larger than that for which the raceway is designed shall be installed in surface nonmetallic raceway.

352-25 . **Number of Conductors in Raceways.** The number of conductors installed in any raceway shall be no greater than the number for which the raceway is designed.

Type of raceway		Wire size gauge No.	Number of wires			
			Types RHH, RHW	Type THW	Type TW	Types THHN, THWN
No. 200	$\frac{1''}{2}$ $\frac{11''}{32}$	12 14		2 2	3 3	3 5
No. 500	$\frac{3''}{4}$ $\frac{17''}{32}$	8 10 12 14	 2 2 2	 2 3 4	2 3 4 6	2 4 7 9
No. 700	$\frac{3''}{4}$ $\frac{21''}{32}$	6 8 10 12 14	 2 2 3	 2 3 4 5	 2 4 6 7	2 3 5 8 11
No.1 1500	$1\frac{9''}{16}$ $\frac{11''}{32}$	6 8 10 12 14	 2 2 2	 3 3 4	 2 4 5 6	2 3 5 7 10
No. 2000†	$1\frac{9''}{32}$ $\frac{3''}{4}$	12 14			7 7	7 7
No. 2100†	$1\frac{1''}{4}$ $\frac{7''}{8}$	6 8 10 12 14	2 4 7 8 10	4 6 10 13 15	4 8 14 19 24	6 10 17 28 37
No. 2200†	$2\frac{3''}{8}$ $\frac{3''}{4}$	6 8 10 12 14	5 8 13 15 18	7 11 19 23 29	3* 7 7* 14 10* 26 10* 34 10* 44	11 19 32 51 69

†Figures for Nos. 2000, 2100, 2200, G–3000, G–4000, and G–6000 are without receptacles, except where noted.
*With receptacles.

Figure 352-3. *Surface metal raceway. (The Wiremold Co.)*

Type of raceway		Wire size gauge No.	Number of wires							
			Types RHH, RHW		Type THW		Type TW		Types THHN, THWN	
No. 2600	(2 7/32″ × 23/32″)	6 8 10 12 14	2 4 6 7 9		3 5 9 11 14		3 7 12 16 21		5 9 15 24 33	
G-3000	(2 3/4″ × 1 17/32″)	6 8 10 12 14	4* 6* 10* 14* 16*	11 18 30 36 42	6* 8* 10* 18* 26*	19 26 45 55 67	6* 8* 10* 18* 26*	17 34 62 81 103	6* 8* 10* 18* 26*	27 44 76 119 160
G-4000—With divider	(4 3/4″ × 1 3/4″)	2 3 4 6 8 10 12 14	– – – 4* 7* 11* 15* 17*	7 8 9 12 19 32 39 45	– – – 4* 7* 11* 15* 17*	10 11 13 18 28 48 59 72	– – – 4* 7* 11* 15* 17*	10 11 13 18 36 66 86 110	– – – 7* 8* 15* 24* 32*	12 15 17 28 47 81 128 171
Without divider	(4 3/4″ × 1 3/4″)	2 3 4 6 8 10 12 14	– – – 8* 10* 15* 21* 21*	14 16 18 24 39 65 78 91	– – – 8* 10* 15* 21* 21*	20 23 27 36 57 96 119 145	– – – 8* 10* 12* 16* 17*	20 23 27 36 78 133 174 222	– – – 10* 15* 18* 34* 34*	25 30 35 57 94 163 256 344
G-6000	(4 3/4″ × 3 9/16″)	2/0 1/0 1 2 3 4 6 8 10 12 14	10* 11* 12* 16* 19* 21* 27* 40* 75* 90* 105*	17 20 23 30 34 39 51 74 137 164 193	12* 14* 17* 23* 27* 32* 42* 57* 111* 137* 167*	22 26 31 43 50 58 77 106 203 252 307	12* 14* 17* 23* 27* 32* 42* 73* 154* 200* 255*	22 26 31 43 50 58 77 134 282 368 469	15* 18* 21* 29* 34* 40* 66* 92* 187* 295* 396*	27 33 39 53 63 74 122 169 343 540 726

†Figures for Nos. 2000, 2100, 2200, G-3000, G-4000, and G-6000 are without receptacles, except where noted.
*With receptacles.

Figure 252-3. (continued)

Type of raceway	Wire size gauge No.	Number of wires in one raceway									
		Types RHH, RHW		Type RH		Type THW		Types T, TW		Types THHN, THWN	
No. 111 $\frac{17}{64}$ in. $\frac{35}{64}$ in.	12							2		3	
	14							2		3	
No. 222 $\frac{3}{8}$ in. $\frac{7}{8}$ in.	8							2		2	
	10	2				2		4		4	
	12	2				3		5		7	
	14	3				4		6		10	
No. 333 $\frac{7}{16}$ in. 1 in.	6					2		2		2	
	8					3		5		3	
	10	2		2		3		5		6	
	12	2		4		4		6		9	
	14	3		4		5		8		12	
No. 888 $\frac{11}{16}$ in. $1\frac{23}{64}$ in.	6	2		2		3		3		5	
	8	3		3		5		7		9	
	10	6		6		9		13		16	
	12	7		10		11		17		25	
	14	9		12		14		22		34	
No. 711 $\frac{3}{8}$ in. $1\frac{1}{8}$ in.	8							2		2	
	10					2		3		4	
	12	2		2		3		4		7	
	14	2		3		4		6		9	
No. 733 $\frac{11}{16}$ in. $2\frac{1}{32}$ in.	6	3		3		4		4		7	
	8	4		4		7		9		11	
	10	8		8		11		16		20	
	12	9		13		14		21		31	
	14	11		16		17		27		42	
No. 1700† $1\frac{5}{8}$ in. $2\frac{1}{8}$ in.	6	3*	8	3*	8	5*	13	5*	13	8*	21
	8	5*	14	5*	14	8*	21	10*	27	13*	34
	10	9*	24	9*	24	13*	35	19*	49	23*	60
	12	11*	28	15*	39	17*	43	24*	64	36*	94
	14	13*	33	18*	48	20*	53	31*	81	49*	126
No. 3400		Catalog No. 3400 is a raceway consisting of two No. 1700 housings in a common cover. Each channel has the same wire fill as 1700.									
No. 5100		Catalog No. 5100 is a raceway consisting of three No. 1700 housings in a common cover. Each channel has the same wire fill as 1700.									

†Figures for No. 1700 are without devices, except where noted.
*With devices.

Figure 352-4. *Types of surface metal raceways. (Walker Div. of Butler Mfg. Co.)*

Figure 352-5. *An example of nonmetallic surface raceway extending from an existing outlet. (The Wiremold Co.)*

352-26 . **Combination Raceways.** Where combination surface nonmetallic raceways are used both for signaling and for lighting and power circuits, the different systems shall be run in separate compartments, identified by printed legend or by sharply contrasting colors of the interior finish, and the same relative position of compartments shall be maintained throughout the premises.

352-27 . **General.** Surface nonmetallic raceways shall be of such construction as will distinguish them from other raceways. Surface nonmetallic raceways and their elbows, couplings, and similar fittings shall be so designed that the sections can be mechanically coupled together and installed without subjecting the wires to abrasion.

Figure 352-6. *An example of nonmetallic surface raceway supplying a lighting outlet. (The Wiremold Co.)*

352-28 . **Extension Through Walls and Floors.** It shall be permissible to extend unbroken lengths of surface nonmetallic raceways through dry walls, dry partitions, and dry floors.

(FPN): See Section 353-3 for multioutlet assemblies.

352-29 . **Splices and Taps.** Splices and taps shall be permitted in surface nonmetallic raceways having a removable cover that is accessible after installation. The conductors, including splices and taps, shall not fill the raceway to more than 75 percent of its area at that point. Splices and taps in surface nonmetallic raceways without removable covers shall be made only in junction boxes. All splices and taps shall be made by approved methods.

ARTICLE 353   Multioutlet Assembly

Contents

353-1. **Other Articles.** A multioutlet assembly shall comply with applicable provisions of Article 300.

(FPN): See definition in Article 100.

Multioutlet assemblies are metal raceways that are usually surface mounted and designed to contain branch-circuit conductors and receptacles. Receptacles may be spaced at desired intervals and may be assembled at the factory or in the field. See Section 220-3(c), Exception No. 1 and Figure 220-4.

353-2. **Use.** The use of a multioutlet assembly shall be permitted in dry locations. It shall not be installed (1) where concealed, except that it shall be permissible to surround the back and sides of a metal multioutlet assembly by the building finish or recess a nonmetallic multioutlet assembly in a baseboard; (2) where subject to severe physical damage; (3) where the voltage is 300 volts or more between conductors unless the assembly is of metal having a thickness of not less than .040 inch (1.02 mm); (4) where subject to corrosive vapors; (5) in hoistways; nor (6) in any hazardous (classified) locations except Class I, Division 2 locations as permitted in the exception to Section 501-4(b).

353-3. **Metal Multioutlet Assembly Through Dry Partitions.** It shall be permissible to extend a metal multioutlet assembly through (not run within) dry partitions, if arrangements are made for removing the cap or cover on all exposed portions and no outlet is located within the partitions.

ARTICLE 354   Underfloor Raceways

Contents

354-1. **Other Articles.** Underfloor raceways shall comply with the applicable provisions of Article 300.

354-2. **Use.** The installation of underfloor raceways shall be permitted beneath the surface of concrete or other flooring material or in office occupancies, where laid flush with the concrete floor and covered with linoleum or equivalent floor covering. Underfloor raceways shall not be installed (1) where subject to corrosive vapors, nor (2) in any hazardous (classified) locations, except as permitted by Section 504-20 and in Class I, Division 2 locations as permitted in the exception to Section 501-4(b). Unless made of a material judged suitable for the condition or unless corrosion protection approved for the condition is provided, ferrous or nonferrous metal underfloor raceways, junction boxes, and fittings shall not be installed in concrete or in areas subject to severe corrosive influences.

An underfloor raceway is a practical means of bringing light, power, and signal and communications systems to desks, work benches, or tables that are not located adjacent to wall space. This wiring method offers flexibility in layout where used with movable partitions and is commonly used in large retail stores and office buildings to supply power at any desired location.

Underfloor raceways are permitted beneath the surface of concrete, wood, or other flooring material. The wiring method between cabinets, raceway junction boxes, and outlet boxes may be rigid metal conduit, intermediate metal conduit, rigid nonmetallic conduit, liquidtight flexible nonmetallic conduit, electrical nonmetallic tubing, or electrical metallic tubing. Flexible metal conduit may be used where not installed in concrete.

354-3. **Covering.** Raceway coverings shall comply with (a) through (d) below.

(a) Raceways Not Over 4 Inches (102 mm) Wide. Half-round and flat-top raceways not over 4 inches (102 mm) in width shall have not less than ¾ inch (19 mm) of concrete or wood above the raceway.

Exception: As permitted in (c) and (d) below for flat-top raceways.

(b) Raceways Over 4 Inches (102 mm) Wide but Not Over 8 Inches (203 mm) Wide. Flat-top raceways over 4 inches (102 mm) but not over 8 inches (203 mm) wide with a minimum of 1 inch (25.4 mm) spacing between raceways shall be covered with concrete to a depth of not less than 1 inch (25.4 mm). Raceways spaced less than 1 inch (25.4 mm) apart shall be covered with concrete to a depth of 1½ inches (38 mm).

(c) Trench-type Raceways Flush with Concrete. Trench-type flush raceways with removable covers shall be permitted to be laid flush with the floor surface. Such approved raceways shall be so designed that the cover plates will provide adequate mechanical protection and rigidity equivalent to junction box covers.

Approved flush-type underfloor raceways may be installed flush with the floor surface provided they have covers at least equal to those of junction box covers. Coverings for underfloor raceways are illustrated in Figures 354-1, 354-2, and 354-3.

(d) Other Raceways Flush with Concrete. In office occupancies, approved metal flat-top raceways, if not over 4 inches (102 mm) in width, shall be permitted to be laid flush with the concrete floor surface, provided they are covered with substantial linoleum not less than 1/16 inch (1.59 mm) in thickness or with equivalent floor covering. Where more than one and not more than three single raceways are each installed flush with the concrete, they shall be contiguous with each other and joined to form a rigid assembly.

354-4. **Size of Conductors.** No conductor larger than that for which the raceway is designed shall be installed in underfloor raceways.

354-5. **Maximum Number of Conductors in Raceway.** The combined cross-sectional area of all conductors or cables shall not exceed 40 percent of the interior cross-sectional area of the raceway.

(FPN): For conductor cross-sectional area, see Tables 5, 5A, 6, and 8 and the applicable Notes to Tables at the beginning of Chapter 9.

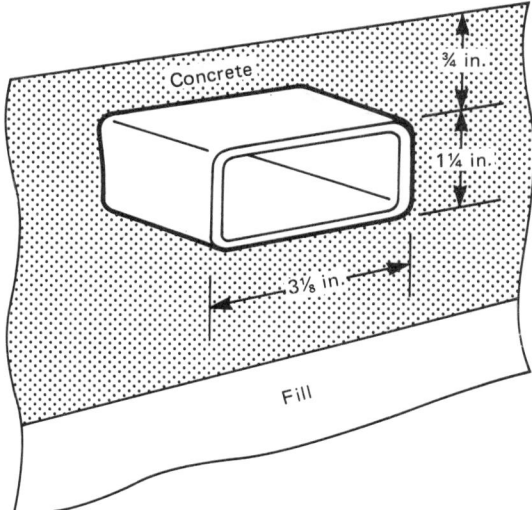

Figure 354-1. A ¾-inch wood or concrete covering is required over underfloor raceways, except for trench-type flush raceways. See Section 354-3(a). (Walker, Div. of Butler Mfg. Co.)

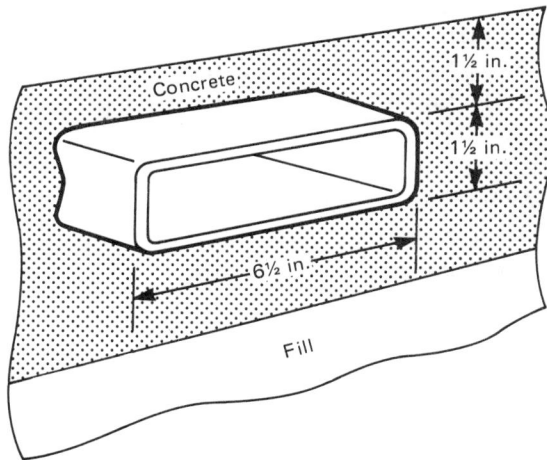

Figure 354-2. Flat-top underfloor raceways over 4 inches in width and spaced less than 1 inch apart must be covered with at least 1½ inches of concrete. See Section 354-3(b). (Walker, Div. of Butler Mfg. Co.)

354-6. **Splices and Taps.** Splices and taps shall be made only in junction boxes.

For the purposes of this section, so-called loop wiring (continuous, unbroken conductor connecting the individual outlets) shall not be considered to be a splice or tap.

Figure 354-3. *A receptacle outlet supplied from an underfloor raceway by the loop method of wiring.*

Exception: Splices and taps shall be permitted in trench-type flush raceway having a removable cover that is accessible after installation. The conductors, including splices and taps, shall not fill the raceway more than 75 percent of its area at that point.

354-7. **Discontinued Outlets.** When an outlet is abandoned, discontinued, or removed, the sections of circuit conductors supplying the outlet shall be removed from the raceway. No splices or reinsulated conductors, such as would be the case with abandoned outlets on loop wiring, shall be allowed in raceways.

Loop wiring (continuous, unbroken conductors) is recognized where it runs from the underfloor raceway up to the terminals of attached receptacles, back into the raceway, and then on to the next device. See Figure 354-3.

When an outlet is removed, the sections of conductors supplying the outlet must be removed from the raceway as well. As is the case with abandoned outlets on loop wiring, reinsulated or spliced conductors are not allowed in raceways except trench-type raceways as covered in the exception to Section 354-6.

354-8. **Laid in Straight Lines.** Underfloor raceways shall be laid so that a straight line from the center of one junction box to the center of the next junction box will coincide with the centerline of the raceway system. Raceways shall be firmly held in place to prevent disturbing this alignment during construction.

354-9. **Markers at Ends.** A suitable marker shall be installed at or near each end of each straight run of raceways to locate the last insert.

354-10. **Dead Ends.** Dead ends of raceways shall be closed.

354-13. **Junction Boxes.** Junction boxes shall be leveled to the floor grade and sealed to prevent the free entrance of water

or concrete. Junction boxes used with metal raceways shall be metal and shall be electrically continuous with the raceways.

354-14. **Inserts.** Inserts shall be leveled and sealed to prevent the entrance of concrete. Inserts used with metal raceways shall be metal and shall be electrically continuous with the raceway. Inserts set in or on fiber raceways before the floor is laid shall be mechanically secured to the raceway. Inserts set in fiber raceways after the floor is laid shall be screwed into the raceway. When cutting through the raceway wall and setting inserts, chips and other dirt shall not be allowed to remain in the raceway, and tools shall be used that are so designed as to prevent the tool from entering the raceway and damaging conductors that may be in place.

354-15. **Connections to Cabinets and Wall Outlets.** Connections between raceways and distribution centers and wall outlets shall be made by means of flexible metal conduit where not installed in concrete, rigid metal conduit, intermediate metal conduit, electrical metallic tubing, or approved fittings. Where a metallic underfloor raceway system provides for the termination of an equipment grounding conductor, rigid nonmetallic conduit, electrical nonmetallic tubing, or liquidtight flexible nonmetallic conduit where not installed in concrete, shall be permitted.

ARTICLE 356 Cellular Metal Floor Raceways

Contents

356-1. Definitions.
356-2. Uses Not Permitted.
356-3. Other Articles.

A. Installation

356-4. Size of Conductors.
356-5. Maximum Number of Conductors in Raceway.
356-6. Splices and Taps.
356-7. Discontinued Outlets.
356-8. Markers.
356-9. Junction Boxes.
356-10. Inserts.
356-11. Connection to Cabinets and Extensions from Cells.

B. Construction Specifications

356-12. General.

356-1. **Definitions.** For the purposes of this article, a "cellular metal floor raceway" shall be defined as the hollow spaces of cellular metal floors, together with suitable fittings, that may be approved as enclosures for electric conductors. A "cell" shall be defined as a single, enclosed tubular space in a cellular metal floor member, the axis of the cell being parallel to the axis of the metal floor member. A "header" shall be defined as a transverse raceway for electric conductors, providing access to predetermined cells of a cellular metal floor, thereby permitting the installation of electric conductors from a distribution center to the cells.

Cellular metal floor raceways are a form of metal floor deck construction designed for use in steel frame buildings and consisting of sheet metal formed into shapes combining to form cells or raceways. The cells extend across the building and, depending on the structural strength required, can have various shapes and sizes.

One type of cellular metal floor is illustrated in Figure 356-1. See Figure 356-2 for installation of header ducts (one for power conductors and one for telephone conductors) prior to the concrete being poured.

356-2. **Uses Not Permitted.** Conductors shall not be installed in cellular metal floor raceways (1) where subject to corrosive

Figure 356-1. One type of cellular metal floor construction as viewed in the so-called "slab" stage of installation. (Square D Co.)

Figure 356-2. Telephone and power header ducts feeding a Cellufloor distribution system. (Square D Co.)

vapor; (2) in any hazardous (classified) location except as permitted by Section 504-20, and in Class I, Division 2 locations as permitted in the exception to Section 501-4(b); nor (3) in commercial garages, other than for supplying ceiling outlets or extensions to the area below the floor but not above.

(FPN): See Section 300-8 for installation of conductors with other systems.

Section 300-8 prohibits the installation of electric conductors in raceways or cable trays containing any pipes, tubes, etc., for steam, water, air, gas, drainage, or any service other than electrical.

356-3. **Other Articles.** Cellular metal floor raceways shall comply with the applicable provisions of Article 300.

A. Installation

356-4. **Size of Conductors.** No conductor larger than No. 1/0 shall be installed, except by special permission.

356-5. **Maximum Number of Conductors in Raceway.** The combined cross-sectional area of all conductors or cables shall not exceed 40 percent of the interior cross-sectional area of the cell or header.

(FPN): For conductor cross-sectional area, see Tables 5, 5A, 6, and 8 and the applicable Notes to Tables at the beginning of Chapter 9.

Connections to the cells are made by means of headers extending across the cells and connecting only to those cells that are to be used as raceways for the conductors. Two or three separate headers, connecting to different sets of cells, may be used for different systems, such as light and power systems, signaling systems, and communication systems.

Figure 356-3 shows the cells with a header in place. The header is extended up to a cabinet or distribution center on a wall or column by means of a special elbow fitting. A junction box or access fitting is provided at each point where the header crosses a cell to which it connects.

See Figure 354-3 and commentary following Section 354-7.

Figure 356-3. A typical cellular metal floor raceway installation showing cells, header ducts, junction boxes, and special elbow fittings. (Square D Co.)

356-6. **Splices and Taps.** Splices and taps shall be made only in header access units or junction boxes.

For the purposes of this section, so-called loop wiring (continuous unbroken conductor connecting the individual outlets) shall not be considered to be a splice or tap.

356-7. **Discontinued Outlets.** When an outlet is abandoned, discontinued, or removed, the sections of circuit conductors supplying the outlet shall be removed from the raceway. No splices or reinsulated conductors, such as would be the case with abandoned outlets on loop wiring, shall be allowed in raceways.

356-8. **Markers.** A suitable number of markers shall be installed for the future locating of cells.

Markers are brass flat-head screws set into the top side of the cells and so adjusted that their heads are flush with the floor finish and are exposed in order to aid in the location of cells for future installations.

356-9. **Junction Boxes.** Junction boxes shall be leveled to the floor grade and sealed against the free entrance of water or concrete. Junction boxes used with these raceways shall be of metal and shall be electrically continuous with the raceway.

356-10. **Inserts.** Inserts shall be leveled to the floor grade and sealed against the entrance of concrete. Inserts shall be of metal and shall be electrically continuous with the raceway. In cutting through the cell wall and setting inserts, chips and other dirt shall not be allowed to remain in the raceway, and tools shall be used that are designed to prevent the tool from entering the cell and damaging the conductors.

Figure 356-3 illustrates cells connected to headers with junction boxes for future access and a special elbow fitting for connecting the header to a cabinet. Connections to wall outlets are to be made with metal raceways unless there are provisions for equipment grounding termination. See Section 356-11.

Installation instructions are supplied by the manufacturer for use by the general contractor, erector, electrical contractor, inspector, and others concerned with the installation.

Figure 356-4 illustrates a preset dual insert, installed prior to concrete being applied, used with cellular metal floor raceways. To install an insert after concrete has been applied, markers should be checked to locate a cell. See Section 356-8. Then, a properly sized concrete-boring drill is used to cut through the concrete to expose the top of the cell. At this point, a properly sized metal-cutting hole saw is used to cut through the cell wall. The saw depth is preset to prevent the tool from entering the cell and damaging the conductors. The insert threads into the hole providing an electrical, mechanical, and bushed connection.

Outlet fitting box — Flush floor service fitting

Power cell

Telephone/ signal cell

Dual pre-set insert

Figure 356-4. A preset dual insert used with a cellular metal floor raceway to provide access to the power and telephone signal cells in the floor. Note separation. (Square D Co.)

356-11. Connection to Cabinets and Extensions from Cells. Connections between raceways and distribution centers and wall outlets shall be made by means of flexible metal conduit where not installed in concrete, rigid metal conduit, intermediate metal conduit, electrical metallic tubing, or approved fittings. Where there are provisions for the termination of an equipment grounding conductor, nonmetallic conduit, electrical nonmetallic tubing, or liquidtight flexible nonmetallic conduit where not installed in concrete, shall be permitted.

B. Construction Specifications

356-12. General. Cellular metal floor raceways shall be so constructed that adequate electrical and mechanical continuity of the complete system will be secured. They shall provide a complete enclosure for the conductors. The interior surfaces shall be free from burrs and sharp edges, and surfaces over which conductors are drawn shall be smooth. Suitable bushings or fittings having smooth rounded edges shall be provided where conductors pass.

ARTICLE 358 Cellular Concrete Floor Raceways

Contents

358-1. Scope. This article covers cellular concrete floor raceways, the hollow spaces in floors constructed of precast cellular concrete slabs, together with suitable metal fittings designed to provide access to the floor cells.

Cellular concrete floor raceways are a form of floor deck construction and are commonly used in high-rise office buildings. This method is very similar in design, application, and adaptation to cellular metal floor raceways.

Basically, this wiring method consists of floor cells (that are part of the structural floor system), header ducts laid at right angles to the cells and used to carry conductors from cabinets to cells, and junction boxes as shown in Figure 358-1.

358-2. Definitions. A "cell" shall be defined as a single, enclosed tubular space in a floor made of precast cellular concrete slabs, the direction of the cell being parallel to the direction of the floor member. A "header" shall be defined as transverse metal raceways for electric conductors, providing access to predetermined cells of a precast cellular concrete floor, thereby permitting the installation of electric conductors from a distribution center to the floor cells.

358-3. Other Articles. Cellular concrete floor raceways shall comply with the applicable provisions of Article 300.

358-4. Uses Not Permitted. Conductors shall not be installed in precast cellular concrete floor raceways (1) where subject to corrosive vapor; (2) in any hazardous (classified) location except as permitted by Section 504-20, and in Class I, Division 2 locations as permitted in the exception to Section 501-4(b); nor (3) in commercial garages, other than for supplying ceiling outlets or extensions to the area below the floor but not above.

Figure 358-1. Standard underfloor duct used on precast cellular concrete floor raceway. (Square D Co.)

(FPN): See Section 300-8 for installation of conductors with other systems.

Section 300-8 prohibits the installation of electric conductors in raceways or cable trays containing any pipes, tubes, etc. for steam, water, air, gas, drainage, or any service other than electrical.

358-5. **Header.** The header shall be installed in a straight line at right angles to the cells. The header shall be mechanically secured to the top of the precast cellular concrete floor. The end joints shall be closed by a metal closure fitting and sealed against the entrance of concrete. The header shall be electrically continuous throughout its entire length and shall be electrically bonded to the enclosure of the distribution center.

358-6. **Connection to Cabinets and Other Enclosures.** Connections from headers to cabinets and other enclosures shall be made by means of metal raceways and approved fittings.

358-7. **Junction Boxes.** Junction boxes shall be leveled to the floor grade and sealed against the free entrance of water or concrete. Junction boxes shall be of metal and shall be mechanically and electrically continuous with the header.

Figure 358-2 illustrates a trench-type raceway with a rigid cover plate extending at a right angle across the cells, with access to predetermined cells.

358-8. **Markers.** A suitable number of markers shall be installed for the future location of cells.

358-9. **Inserts.** Inserts shall be leveled and sealed against the entrance of concrete. Inserts shall be of metal and shall be fitted with receptacles of the grounded type. A grounding conductor shall connect the insert receptacles to a positive ground connection provided on the header. When cutting through the cell wall for setting inserts or other purposes (such as providing access openings between header and cells), chips and other dirt shall not be allowed to remain in the raceway, and the tool used shall be so designed as to prevent the tool from entering the cell and damaging the conductors.

358-10. **Size of Conductors.** No conductor larger than No. 1/0 shall be installed, except by special permission.

358-11. **Maximum Number of Conductors.** The combined cross-sectional area of all conductors or cables shall not exceed 40 percent of the cross-sectional area of the cell or header.

358-12. **Splices and Taps.** Splices and taps shall be made only in header access units or junction boxes.

For the purposes of this section, so-called loop wiring (continuous unbroken conductor connecting the individual outlets) shall not be considered to be a splice or tap.

Figure 358-2. Trench-type raceway with removable cover shown extending at right angles across the cells of cellular concrete floor construction. (Bargar Metal Fabricating Co.)

358-13. **Discontinued Outlets.** When an outlet is abandoned, discontinued, or removed, the sections of circuit conductors supplying the outlet shall be removed from the raceway. No splices or reinsulated conductors, such as would be the case of abandoned outlets on loop wiring, shall be allowed in raceways.

ARTICLE 362   Metal Wireways and Nonmetallic Wireways

Contents

A. Metal Wireways

B. Nonmetallic Wireways

A. Metal Wireways

362-1. **Definition.** Wireways are sheet-metal troughs with hinged or removable covers for housing and protecting electric wires and cable and in which conductors are laid in place after the wireway has been installed as a complete system.

Wireways are sheet-metal enclosures equipped with hinged or removable covers and are manufactured in 1- to 10-foot lengths and various widths and depths. Couplings, elbows, end plates, and accessories such as "T" and "X" fittings are available.

Unlike auxiliary gutters, which are not permitted to extend more than 30 feet from the equipment they supplement, wireways may be run throughout an entire area, as shown in Figure 362-1.

The total of the cross-sectional areas of all conductors is not permitted to exceed 20 percent of the interior cross-sectional area of the wireway. Where not more than 30 conductors are installed, the derating factors of Note 8(a) of Notes to Ampacity Tables of 0 to 2000 Volts are not applicable.

Example: A wireway contains 24 TW conductors, eight No. 3/0 ($8 \times 0.3288 = 2.6304$), three No. 6 ($3 \times 0.0819 = 0.2457$), three No. 8 ($3 \times 0.0471 = 0.1413$), and 10 No. 12 ($10 \times 0.0172 = 0.172$), which total 3.1894 sq in. (dimensions of conductors are from Chapter 9, Table 5). Twenty percent of the cross-sectional area of the wireway is required to be 3.19 sq in. or greater. Therefore, 3.19 sq in. $\div 0.20 = 15.95$ sq in. A 4-inch $\times$ 4-inch or larger wireway is permitted to contain these conductors.

362-2. **Use.** Wireways shall be permitted only for exposed work. Wireways installed in wet locations shall be of raintight construction. Wireways shall not be installed (1) where subject to severe physical damage or corrosive vapor, nor (2) in any hazardous (classified) location except as permitted by Sections 501-4(b), 502-4(b), and 504-20.

Exception: Wireways shall be permitted in concealed spaces in accordance with Section 640-4, Exception, item c.

This exception permits wireways to be used in concealed spaces for sound recording and similar equipment, provided they are run in a straight line between outlets or junction boxes. In addition, covers of the boxes must be accessible,

Figure 362-1. A worker installing conductors in a sheet-metal wireway after the complete wireway has been installed. (Square D Co.)

and all sharp edges that could cause abrasion of the cable must be smoothed.

362-3. **Other Articles.** Installations of wireways shall comply with the applicable provisions of Article 300.

362-4. **Size of Conductors.** No conductor larger than that for which the wireway is designed shall be installed in any wireway.

362-5. **Number of Conductors.** Wireways shall not contain more than thirty current-carrying conductors at any cross section. Conductors for signaling circuits or controller conductors between a motor and its starter and used only for starting duty shall not be considered as current-carrying conductors.

The sum of cross-sectional areas of all contained conductors at any cross section of the wireway shall not exceed 20 percent of the interior cross-sectional area of the wireway.

The derating factors specified in Article 310, Note 8 (a) of Notes to Ampacity Tables of 0 to 2000 Volts shall not be applicable to the thirty current-carrying conductors at 20 percent fill specified above.

Exception No. 1: Where the derating factors specified in Article 310, Note 8 (a) of Notes to Ampacity Tables of 0 to 2000 Volts are applied, the number of current-carrying conductors shall not be limited, but the sum of the cross-sectional areas of all contained conductors at any cross section of the wireway shall not exceed 20 percent of the interior cross-sectional area of the wireway.

The number of current-carrying conductors in a wireway is permitted to exceed 30, provided the sum of the cross-sectional areas of all the conductors does not exceed 20 percent of the interior cross-sectional area of the wireway and the derating factors in Article 310, Note 8(a) of the Notes to the Ampacity Tables of 0 to 2,000 Volts are applied.

Exception No. 2: As provided in Section 520-5, the thirty-conductor limitation shall not apply to theaters and similar locations.

Exception No. 3: As provided in Section 620-32, the 20-percent fill limitation shall not apply to elevators and dumbwaiters.

(FPN): For conductor cross-sectional area, see Tables 5, 5A, 6, and 8 and the applicable Notes to Tables at the beginning of Chapter 9.

362-6. **Deflected Insulated Conductors.** Where insulated conductors are deflected within a wireway, either at the ends or where conduits, fittings, or other raceways or cables enter or leave the wireway, or where the direction of the wireway is deflected greater than 30 degrees, dimensions corresponding to Section 373-6 shall apply.

The intent is to provide adequate space for bending conductors without damage to the insulation.

362-7. **Splices and Taps.** Splices and taps shall be permitted within a wireway provided they are accessible. The conductors, including splices and taps, shall not fill the wireway to more than 75 percent of its area at that point.

Conductors in wireways are accessible through hinged or removable covers. Circuits, taps, or splices may be added or altered, if necessary.

See Section 362-5. See also Chapter 9, Table 5, for the dimensions of all common sizes of conductors.

362-8. **Supports.** Wireways shall be supported at intervals not to exceed 5 feet (1.52 m), or for individual lengths longer than 5 feet (1.52 m) at each end or joint, unless listed for other support intervals. In no case shall the distance between supports exceed 10 feet (3.05 m).

Exception: Vertical runs of wireways shall be securely supported at intervals not exceeding 15 feet (4.57 m) and shall have not more than one joint between supports. Adjoining wireway sections shall be securely fastened together to provide a rigid joint.

362-9. **Extension Through Walls.** Unbroken lengths of wireway shall be permitted to pass transversely through walls if in unbroken lengths where passing through.

362-10. **Dead Ends.** Dead ends of wireways shall be closed.

362-11. **Extensions from Wireways.** Extensions from wireways shall be made with cord pendants or any wiring method in Chapter 3 that includes a means for equipment grounding. Where a separate equipment grounding conductor is employed, connection of the equipment grounding conductors in the wiring method to the wireway shall comply with Sections 250-113 and 250-118. Where rigid nonmetallic conduit, electrical nonmetallic tubing, or liquidtight flexible nonmetallic conduit is used, connection of the equipment grounding conductor in the nonmetallic raceway to a metal wireway shall comply with Sections 250-113 and 250-118.

Extensions from wireways using metal raceways, metal-sheathed cables, and nonmetallic-sheathed cables are made through knockouts provided on the wireway or that are field-punched. Rigid nonmetallic conduit, electrical nonmetallic tubing, and liquidtight flexible nonmetallic conduit may also be used. Cables and nonmetallic raceways are required to include a means for equipment grounding. Where an equipment grounding conductor is used, it is required to be connected to the metal wireway in accordance with Sections 250-113 and 250-118.

Sections of wireways, including accessory fittings (elbows, endplates, flanges, etc.), are bolted together assuring a rigid mechanical and electrical connection.

See Section 250-91(b)(11).

362-12. **Marking.** Wireways shall be marked so that their manufacturer's name or trademark will be visible after installation.

362-13. **Grounding.** Grounding shall be according to the provisions of Article 250.

B. Nonmetallic Wireways

362-14. **Definition.** Nonmetallic wireways are flame-retardant, nonmetallic troughs with removable covers for housing and protecting electric wires and cables in which conductors are laid in place after the wireway has been installed as a complete system.

A new Part B has been added to Article 362 for the 1993 *Code* to provide installation requirements for nonmetallic wireways.

Nonmetallic wireways are troughs with removable covers in which conductors are laid in place after the wireway has been installed as a complete system. The wireway must be installed on the surface of the structure not concealed. It is allowed to pass through walls provided it is an unbroken length passing through the wall.

362-15. **Uses Permitted.** The use of nonmetallic wireways shall be permitted:

(1) Only for exposed work.

Exception: Nonmetallic wireways shall be permitted in concealed spaces in accordance with Section 640-4, Exception, item c.

(2) Where subject to corrosive vapors.

(3) In wet locations where listed for the purpose.

(FPN): Extreme cold may cause nonmetallic wireways to become brittle and, therefore, more susceptible to damage from physical contact.

362-16. **Uses Not Permitted.** Nonmetallic wireways shall not be used:

(1) Where subject to physical damage.

(2) In any hazardous (classified) location.

Exception: As permitted in Section 504-20.

(3) Where exposed to sunlight unless listed and marked as suitable for the purpose.

(4) Where subject to ambient temperatures other than those for which nonmetallic wireway is listed.

362-17. **Other Articles.** Installations of nonmetallic wireways shall comply with the applicable provisions of Article 300. Where equipment grounding is required by Article 250, a separate equipment grounding conductor shall be installed in the nonmetallic wireway.

362-18. **Size of Conductors.** No conductor larger than that for which the nonmetallic wireway is designed shall be installed in any nonmetallic wireway.

362-19. **Number of Conductors.** The sum of cross-sectional areas of all contained conductors at any cross section of the nonmetallic wireway shall not exceed 20 percent of the interior cross-sectional area of the nonmetallic wireway. Conductors for signaling circuits or controller conductors between a motor and its starter and used only for starting duty shall not be considered as current-carrying conductors.

The derating factors specified in Article 310, Note 8(a) of Notes to Ampacity Tables of 0 to 2000 Volts shall be applicable to the current-carrying conductors at the 20 percent fill specified above.

(FPN): For conductor cross-sectional area, see Tables 5, 5A, 6, and 8 and the applicable Notes to Tables at the beginning of Chapter 9.

362-20. **Deflected Insulated Conductors.** Where insulated conductors are deflected within a nonmetallic wireway, either at the ends or where conduits, fittings, or other raceways or cables enter or leave the nonmetallic wireway, or where the direction of the nonmetallic wireway is deflected greater than 30 degrees, dimensions corresponding to Section 373-6 shall apply.

362-21. **Splices and Taps.** Splices and taps shall be permitted within a nonmetallic wireway provided they are accessible. The conductors, including splices and taps, shall not fill the nonmetallic wireway to more than 75 percent of its area at that point.

362-22. **Supports.** Nonmetallic wireways shall be supported at intervals not to exceed 3 feet (914 mm), and at each end or joint, unless listed for other support intervals. In no case shall the distance between supports exceed 10 feet (3.05 m).

Exception: Vertical runs of nonmetallic wireways shall be securely supported at intervals not exceeding 4 feet (1.22 m), unless listed for other support intervals, and shall have not more than one joint between supports. Adjoining nonmetallic wireway sections shall be securely fastened together to provide a rigid joint.

362-23. **Expansion Joints.** Expansion joints for nonmetallic wireway shall be provided for thermal expansion and contraction.

Exception: Where the length change due to thermal expansion or contraction is less than 0.25 inch (6.35 mm) in a straight run, an expansion joint shall not be required.

362-24. **Extension Through Walls.** Unbroken lengths of nonmetallic wireway shall be permitted to pass transversely through walls if in unbroken lengths where passing through.

362-25. **Dead Ends.** Dead ends of nonmetallic wireways shall be closed.

362-26. **Extensions from Nonmetallic Wireways.** Extensions from nonmetallic wireways shall be made using any wiring method in Chapter 3. A separate equipment grounding conductor shall be installed in any of the wiring methods used for the extension.

362-27. **Marking.** Nonmetallic wireways shall be marked so that the manufacturer's name or trademark and interior cross-sectional area in square inches shall be visible after installation. Nonmetallic wireways that have limited-smoke-producing characteristics shall be permitted to be identified with the suffix LS.

ARTICLE 363   Flat Cable Assemblies

Type FC

Contents

363-1. **Definition.** Type FC, a flat cable assembly, is an assembly of parallel conductors formed integrally with an insulating material web specifically designed for field installation in surface metal raceway.

Type FC cable is an assembly of two, three, or four parallel No. 10 special stranded copper wires formed integrally with an insulating material web. The cable is marked with the size of the maximum branch circuit to which it may be connected, the cable type designation, manufacturer's identification, maximum working voltage, conductor size, and temperature rating. A marking accompanying the cable on a tag or reel indicates the special metal raceways and specific type of FC cable fittings with which the cable is intended to be used.

Figures 363-1 and 363-2 show the basic components of this wiring method.

363-2. **Other Articles.** In addition to the provisions of this article, installation of Type FC cable shall conform with the applicable provisions of Articles 210, 220, 250, 300, 310, and 352.

363-3. **Uses Permitted.** Flat cable assemblies shall be permitted only as branch circuits to supply suitable tap devices for lighting, small appliances, or small power loads. Flat cable assemblies shall be installed for exposed work only. Flat cable assemblies shall be installed in locations where they will not be subjected to severe physical damage.

Splice
plate

Terminal box
With color–coded
terminal block

Insulating
end cap

Fixture
hanger

Cable pull–in guide

Figure 363-1. *The basic components and accessories used for an installation of Type FC (flat) cable assembly. (The Wiremold Co.)*

Figure 363-2. *Fixture hanger used with Type FC cable assembly. (The Wiremold Co.)*

The channel portion of the surface metal raceway systems shall be installed as complete systems before the flat cable assemblies are pulled into the raceways.

363-6. **Number of Conductors.** The flat cable assemblies shall consist of either two, three, or four conductors.

363-7. **Size of Conductors.** Flat cable assemblies shall have conductors of No. 10 special stranded copper wires.

363-8. **Conductor Insulation.** The entire flat cable assembly shall be formed to provide a suitable insulation covering all of the conductors and using one of the materials recognized in Table 310-13 for general branch-circuit wiring.

363-9. **Splices.** Splices shall be made in approved junction boxes using approved wiring methods.

363-10. **Taps.** Taps shall be made between any phase conductor and the neutral or any other phase conductor by means of devices and fittings identified for the use. Tap devices shall be rated at not less than 15 amperes, or more than 300 volts to ground, and they shall be color-coded in accordance with the requirements of Section 363-20.

363-4. **Uses Not Permitted.** Flat cable assemblies shall not be installed (1) where subject to corrosive vapors unless suitable for the application; (2) in hoistways; (3) in any hazardous (classified) location; or (4) outdoors or in wet or damp locations unless identified for use in wet locations.

363-5. **Installation.** Flat cable assemblies shall be installed in the field only in surface metal raceways identified for the use.

363-11. Dead Ends. Each flat cable assembly dead end shall be terminated in an end-cap device identified for the use.

The dead-end fitting for the enclosing surface metal raceway shall be identified for the use.

363-12. Fixture Hangers. Fixture hangers installed with the flat cable assemblies shall be identified for the use.

363-13. Fittings. Fittings to be installed with flat cable assemblies shall be designed and installed to prevent physical damage to the cable assemblies.

363-14. Extensions. All extensions from flat cable assemblies shall be made by approved wiring methods, within the junction boxes, installed at either end of the flat cable assembly runs.

363-15. Supports. The flat cable assemblies shall be supported by means of their special design features, within the surface metal raceways.

The surface metal raceways shall be supported as required for the specific raceway to be installed.

363-16. Rating. The rating of the branch circuit shall not exceed 30 amperes.

363-17. Marking. In addition to the provisions of Section 310-11, Type FC cable shall have the temperature rating durably marked on the surface at intervals not exceeding 24 inches (610 mm).

363-18. Protective Covers. Where a flat cable assembly is installed less than 8 feet (2.44 m) from the floor, it shall be protected by a metal cover identified for the use.

363-19. Identification. The grounded conductor shall be identified throughout its length by means of a distinctive and durable white or natural gray marking.

363-20. Terminal Block Identification. Terminal blocks identified for the use shall have distinctive and durable markings for color or word coding. The grounded conductor section shall have a white marking or other suitable designation. The next adjacent section of the terminal block shall have a black marking or other suitable designation. The next section shall have a red marking or other suitable designation. The final or outer section, opposite the grounded conductor section of the terminal block, shall have a blue marking or other suitable designation.

ARTICLE 364 Busways

Contents

A. General Requirements

B. Requirements for Over 600 Volts, Nominal

A. General Requirements

364-1. Scope. This article covers service-entrance, feeder, and branch-circuit busways and associated fittings.

364-2. Definition. For the purpose of this article, a busway is considered to be a grounded metal enclosure containing factory-mounted, bare or insulated conductors, which are usually copper or aluminum bars, rods, or tubes.

(FPN): For cablebus, refer to Article 365.

The maximum rating of a UL-listed busway is 600 V.

A busway that has been investigated to determine its suitability for installation in a specified position, or for use in vertical runs, or for support at intervals greater than 5 feet, or for outdoor use, is so marked.

A busway that is intended to supply and support industrial and commercial lighting fixtures is classified as lighting busway and is so marked. Trolley busway is marked "Trolley Busway" and is additionally marked "Lighting Busway" if intended to supply and support industrial and commercial lighting fixtures. A busway with provision for insertion of plug-in devices at any point along the length of the busway and intended for general use is classified as "Continuous Plug-In Busway" and is so marked. The marking is contiguous with the marking of the manufacturer's name and the electrical rating.

Short-run busways are marked to limit the run to 30 feet or less, and no more than 10 feet vertically, and are intended primarily for a feed to switchboards. Except for transformer stubs, short-run busways are not intended to have intermediate taps. Short-run busways are not ventilated and may be marked for outdoor use.

Busways and associated fittings marked "Short Circuit Current Rating(s) Maximum RMS Symmetrical Amperes _____ Volts _____" have been investigated for the rating indicated.

A busway marked "Lighting Busway" and protected by overcurrent devices rated in excess of 20 amperes is intended for use only with fixtures employing heavy-duty lampholders unless additional overcurrent protection is provided for the fixture in accordance with this *Code*.

A trolley busway should be installed out of the reach of persons, or it should be otherwise installed to prevent accidental contact with exposed conductors. See Figures 364-1 and 364-2.

364-3. **Other Articles.** Installations of busways shall comply with the applicable provisions of Article 300.

364-4. **Use.**

(a) **Use Permitted.** Busways shall be installed only where they are located in the open and are visible.

Figure 364-1. *A trolley busway with the trolley in place. (Amerace Corp.)*

Figure 364-2. *A plug-in device for stationary use on a trolley busway. (Amerace Corp.)*

Exception No. 1: Busways shall be permitted to be installed behind panels if means of access are provided and if all the following conditions are met.

a. No overcurrent devices are installed on the busway other than for individual fixtures or other loads.

b. The space behind the access panels is not used for air-handling purposes.

c. The busway is totally enclosed, nonventilating type.

d. Busway is so installed that the joints between sections and fittings are accessible for maintenance purposes.

Exception No. 1 permits busways to be located behind panels that are designed to allow access, such as suspended ceilings *not* used for air-handling purposes, provided the busway is of the totally enclosed nonventilated type, joints and fittings are accessible for maintenance, and no overcurrent device (other than for an individual fixture) is installed.

Busways are commonly used as feeders, mounted horizontally in industrial buildings or mounted vertically in highrise buildings.

See Figure 100-1.

Figure 364-3. A schematic of a "potentializer plug" and its connections to a busway.

Where busways are employed for ungrounded systems, an abnormal potential may build up on one of the conductors and cause a flashover on the system. Figure 364-3 is a diagram of a potentializer plug and its connection to a busway. This device is a complete assembly in a metal enclosure designed to plug into a busway. It consists of three 18,000-ohm resistors that serve to maintain each of the

conductors at a normal potential to ground. A tap is connected to each resistor, providing 120 V to three 7.5-W lamps that serve as ground detectors.

Exception No. 2: Busways shall be permitted to be installed behind access panels in accordance with Section 300-22(c).

Exception No. 2 permits busways to be installed in air-handling spaces, such as above suspended ceilings where the space is used for environmental air return, if the busway is of the totally enclosed nonventilated type having *insulated busbars* and no provision for plug-in connections.

(b) Use Prohibited. Busways shall not be installed (1) where subject to severe physical damage or corrosive vapors; (2) in hoistways; (3) in any hazardous (classified) location, unless specifically approved for such use [see Section 501-4(b)]; nor (4) outdoors or in wet or damp locations unless identified for such use.

364-5. **Support.** Busways shall be securely supported at intervals not exceeding 5 feet (1.52 m) unless otherwise designed and marked.

364-6. **Through Walls and Floors.** It shall be permissible to extend unbroken lengths of busway through dry walls. It shall be permissible to extend busways vertically through dry floors if totally enclosed (unventilated) where passing through and for a minimum distance of 6 feet (1.83 m) above the floor to provide adequate protection from physical damage.

A busway or fitting containing a vapor seal is so marked, but, unless marked otherwise, the busway or fitting has not been investigated for passage through a fire-rated wall.

364-7. **Dead Ends.** A dead end of a busway shall be closed.

364-8. **Branches from Busways.** Branches from busways shall be made with busways, rigid metal conduit, intermediate metal conduit, rigid nonmetallic conduit, electrical nonmetallic tubing, flexible metal conduit, liquidtight flexible metal conduit, electrical metallic tubing, metal surface raceway, metal-clad cable, or listed bus drop cable; or with suitable cord assemblies approved for hard usage for the connection of portable equipment or for the connection of stationary equipment to facilitate their interchange. Flexible cord assembly connections shall be permitted to be made directly to the load end terminals of a busway plug-in device, provided a suitable tension take-up device is employed on the cord and the length of the cord from the busway plug-in device to the tension take-up device does not exceed 6 feet (1.83 m). Where a nonmetallic raceway is used, connection of equipment grounding conductors in the nonmetallic raceway to the busway shall comply with Sections 250-113 and 250-118.

364-9. Overcurrent Protection. Overcurrent protection shall be provided in accordance with Sections 364-10 through 364-14.

364-10. Rating of Overcurrent Protection — Feeders. Where the allowable current rating of the busway does not correspond to a standard rating of the overcurrent device, the next higher rating shall be permitted.

The rated ampacity of a busway is based on the allowable temperature rise of the conductors and can be determined in the field only by reference to the nameplate data.

364-11. Reduction in Ampacity Size of Busway. Overcurrent protection shall be required where busways are reduced in ampacity.

Exception: For industrial establishments only, omission of overcurrent protection shall be permitted at points where busways are reduced in ampacity, provided that the length of the busway having the smaller ampacity does not exceed 50 feet (15.2 m) and has an ampacity at least equal to $1/3$ the rating or setting of the overcurrent device next back on the line, and provided further that such busway is free from contact with combustible material.

In industrial establishments, where the size of the smaller busway is kept within the specified limits, the additional cost of providing overcurrent protection at the point where the size is changed is not warranted. For example, busway protected by a 1200-A overcurrent device may be reduced in size, provided the smaller busway has a current rating of 400 A ($1/3$ of 1,200 A) and does not extend more than 50 feet. In this case, overcurrent protection would be required if the smaller busway were rated less than 400 A; e.g., 200 A, 300 A, etc.

364-12. Feeder or Branch Circuits. Where a busway is used as a feeder, devices or plug-in connections for tapping off feeder or branch circuits from the busway shall contain the overcurrent devices required for the protection of the feeder or branch circuits. The plug-in device shall consist of an externally operable

circuit breaker or an externally operable fusible switch. Where such devices are mounted out of reach and contain disconnecting means, suitable means such as ropes, chains, or sticks shall be provided for operating the disconnecting means from the floor.

Exception No. 1: As permitted in Section 240-21 for taps.

Exception No. 2: For fixed or semi-fixed lighting fixtures, where the branch-circuit overcurrent device is part of the fixture cord plug on cord-connected fixtures.

Exception No. 3: Where fixtures without cords are plugged directly into the busway and the overcurrent device is mounted on the fixture.

Externally operated fused switches and circuit breakers plugged into busways that are mounted out of reach, are to be considered accessible where operated by means such as ropes, chains, or hooksticks. See Figure 100-2.

364-13. Rating of Overcurrent Protection — Branch Circuits. A busway shall be permitted as a branch circuit of any one of the types described in Article 210. When so used, the rating or setting of the overcurrent device protecting the busway shall determine the ampere rating of the branch circuit, and the circuit shall in all respects conform with the requirements of Article 210 that apply to branch circuits of that rating.

364-14. Length of Busways Used as Branch Circuits. Busways used as branch circuits and designed so that loads can be connected at any point shall be limited to such lengths as will provide that in normal use the circuits will not be overloaded.

364-15. Marking. Busways shall be marked with the voltage and current rating for which they are designed, and with the manufacturer's name or trademark in such manner as to be visible after installation.

B. Requirements for Over 600 Volts, Nominal

364-21. Identification. Each bus run shall be provided with a permanent nameplate on which the following information shall be provided: (1) rated voltage; (2) rated continuous current; if bus is forced-cooled, both the normal forced-cooled rating and the self-cooled (not forced-cooled) rating for the same temperature rise shall be given; (3) rated frequency; (4) rated impulse withstand voltage; (5) rated 60-Hz withstand voltage (dry); (6) rated momentary current; and (7) manufacturer's name or trademark.

(FPN): See Switchgear Assemblies, ANSI C37.20-1969 (R1982), for construction and testing requirements for metal-enclosed buses.

364-22. **Grounding.** Metal-enclosed bus shall be grounded in accordance with Article 250.

364-23. **Adjacent and Supporting Structures.** Metal-enclosed busways shall be installed so that temperature rise from induced circulating currents in any adjacent metallic parts will not be hazardous to personnel or constitute a fire hazard.

Figure 364-4. A 10-foot section of feeder busway. (Square D Co.)

364-24. **Neutral.** Neutral bus, where required, shall be sized to carry all neutral load current, including harmonic currents, and shall have adequate momentary and short-circuit rating consistent with system requirements.

364-25. **Barriers and Seals.** Bus runs having sections located both inside and outside of buildings shall have a vapor seal at the building wall to prevent interchange of air between indoor and outdoor sections.

See also Section 300-21.

Exception: Vapor seals shall not be required in forced-cooled bus.

Fire barriers shall be provided where fire walls, floors, or ceilings are penetrated.

(FPN): See Section 300-21 for information concerning the spread of fire or products of combustion.

364-26. **Drain Facilities.** Drain plugs, filter drains, or similar methods shall be provided to remove condensed moisture from low points in bus run.

364-27. **Ventilated Bus Enclosures.** Ventilated bus enclosures shall be installed in accordance with Article 710, Part D, unless designed so that foreign objects inserted through any opening will be deflected from energized parts.

364-28. **Terminations and Connections.** Where bus enclosures terminate at machines cooled by flammable gas, seal-off bushings, baffles, or other means shall be provided to prevent accumulation of flammable gas in the bus enclosures.

Flexible or expansion connections shall be provided in long, straight runs of bus to allow for temperature expansion or contraction, or where the bus run crosses building vibration insulation joints.

All conductor termination and connection hardware shall be accessible for installation, connection, and maintenance.

364-29. **Switches.** Switching devices or disconnecting links provided in the bus run shall have the same momentary rating as the bus. Disconnecting links shall be plainly marked to be removable only when bus is deenergized. Switching devices that are not load break shall be interlocked to prevent operation under load, and disconnecting link enclosures shall be interlocked to prevent access to energized parts.

364-30. **Wiring 600 Volts or Less, Nominal.** Secondary control devices and wiring that are provided as part of the metal-enclosed bus run shall be insulated by fire-retardant barriers from all primary circuit elements with the exception of short lengths of wire, such as at instrument transformer terminals.

ARTICLE 365 Cablebus

Contents

(b) Ampacity of Conductors.

(c) Size and Number of Conductors.

(d) Conductor Supports.

365-5. Overcurrent Protection.

365-6. Support and Extension Through Walls and Floors.

(a) Support.

(b) Transversely Routed.

(c) Through Dry Floors and Platforms.

(d) Through Floors and Platforms in Wet Locations.

365-7. Fittings.

365-8. Conductor Terminations.

365-9. Grounding.

365-10. Marking.

365-1. **Definition.** Cablebus is an approved assembly of insulated conductors with fittings and conductor terminations in a completely enclosed, ventilated protective metal housing. The assembly is designed to carry fault current and to withstand the magnetic forces of such current.

Cablebus consists of a metal structure or framework that is installed in a manner similar to a cable tray support system. Insulated conductors, No. 1/0 or larger, are field-installed within the framework on special insulating blocks at specified intervals to provide controlled spacing between conductors. To completely enclose the conductors, a ventilated top cover is attached to the framework. See Figure 365-1.

(FPN): Cablebus is ordinarily assembled at the point of installation from components furnished or specified by the manufacturer in accordance with instructions for the specific job.

365-2. **Use.**

(a) **600 Volts or Less.** Cablebus shall be permitted at any voltage or current for which spaced conductors are rated and shall be installed for exposed work only. Cablebus installed outdoors or in corrosive, wet, or damp locations shall be identified for such use. Cablebus shall not be installed in hoistways or hazardous (classified) locations unless specifically approved for such use. Cablebus shall be permitted to be used for branch circuits, feeders, and services.

Cablebus framework, where adequately bonded, shall be permitted as the equipment grounding conductor for branch circuits and feeders.

Figure 365-1. *A section of cablebus with conductors in place and the ventilated top cover ready to be attached to the busway frame.* (Husky Cabl-Bus)

(b) **Over 600 Volts.** Cablebus shall be permitted for systems in excess of 600 volts, nominal. See Section 710-4(a).

365-3. **Conductors.**

(a) **Types of Conductors.** The current-carrying conductors in cablebus shall have an insulation rating of 75°C or higher of an approved type and suitable for the application in accordance with Articles 310 and 710.

(b) **Ampacity of Conductors.** The ampacity of conductors in cablebus shall be in accordance with Tables 310-17 and 310-19.

(c) **Size and Number of Conductors.** The size and number of conductors shall be that for which the cablebus is designed, and in no case smaller than No. 1/0.

(d) **Conductor Supports.** The insulated conductors shall be supported on blocks or other mounting means designed for the purpose.

The individual conductors in a cablebus shall be supported at intervals not greater than 3 feet (914 mm) for horizontal runs and 1½ feet (457 mm) for vertical runs. Vertical and horizontal spacing between supported conductors shall not be less than one conductor diameter at the points of support.

365-5. **Overcurrent Protection.** Where the allowable ampacity of cablebus conductors does not correspond to a standard rating of an overcurrent device, the next higher ampere-rated overcurrent device shall be permitted.

365-6. **Support and Extension Through Walls and Floors.**

(a) **Support.** Cablebus shall be securely supported at intervals not exceeding 12 feet (3.66 m).

Exception: Where spans longer than 12 feet (3.66 m) are required, the structure shall be specifically designed for the required span length.

(b) **Transversely Routed.** It shall be permissible to extend cablebus transversely through partitions or walls, other than fire walls, provided the section within the wall is continuous, protected against physical damage, and unventilated.

(c) **Through Dry Floors and Platforms.** Except where fire stops are required, it shall be permissible to extend cablebus vertically through dry floors and platforms, provided the cablebus is totally enclosed at the point where it passes through the floor or platform and for a distance of 6 feet (1.83 m) above the floor or platform.

(d) **Through Floors and Platforms in Wet Locations.** Except where fire stops are required, it shall be permissible to extend cablebus vertically through floors and platforms in wet locations where (1) there are curbs or other suitable means to prevent water flow through the floor or platform opening, and (2) where the cablebus is totally enclosed at the point where it passes through the floor or platform and for a distance of 6 feet (1.83 m) above the floor or platform.

365-7. **Fittings.** A cablebus system shall include approved fittings for (1) changes in horizontal or vertical direction of the run; (2) dead ends; (3) terminations in or on connected apparatus or equipment or the enclosures for such equipment; and (4) additional physical protection where required, such as guards for severe mechanical exposure.

365-8. **Conductor Terminations.** Approved terminating means shall be used for connections to cablebus conductors.

365-9. **Grounding.** Sections of cablebus shall be electrically bonded either by inherent design of the mechanical joints or by applied bonding means.

(FPN): See Section 250-75 for bonding of metal noncurrent-carrying parts.

A cablebus installation shall be grounded in accordance with Sections 250-32 and 250-33.

365-10. **Marking.** Each section of cablebus shall be marked with the manufacturer's name or trade designation and the maximum diameter, number, voltage rating, and ampacity of the conductors to be installed. Markings shall be so located as to be visible after installation.

ARTICLE 370 Outlet, Device, Pull and Junction Boxes, Conduit Bodies and Fittings

Contents

A. Scope and General

B. Installation

A. Scope and General

370-1. **Scope.** This article covers the installation and use of all boxes, conduit bodies, and fittings as required by Section 300-15, and boxes, conduit bodies, and fittings referred to in Section 300-15 used as outlet, junction, or pull boxes, depending on their use. Cast, sheet metal, nonmetallic, and other boxes such as FS, FD, and larger boxes are not classified as conduit bodies.

(FPN): For systems over 600 volts, nominal, see Part D of this article.

370-2. **Round Boxes.** Round boxes shall not be used where conduits or connectors requiring the use of locknuts or bushings are to be connected to the side of the box.

This rule requires the use of rectangular or octagonal boxes having a flat bearing surface at each knockout for locknuts and bushings to ensure effective grounding continuity. However, round boxes can be used where the conduit or cable is secured by clamps within the box, or where the cable does not need attachment to the box. See Section 370-17(c), Exception.

370-3. **Nonmetallic Boxes.** Nonmetallic boxes shall be permitted only with open wiring on insulators, concealed knob-and-tube wiring, nonmetallic-sheathed cable, and nonmetallic raceways.

Exception No. 1: Where internal bonding means are provided between all entries, nonmetallic boxes shall be permitted to be used with metal raceways or metal-jacketed cables.

Exception No. 2: Where integral bonding means with a provision for attaching a grounding jumper inside the box are provided between all threaded entries in nonmetallic boxes listed for the purpose, nonmetallic boxes shall be permitted to be used with metal raceways or metal-jacketed cables.

Exception No. 1 applies to nonmetallic boxes without threaded entries and permits the use of metal raceways and/or metal-jacketed cables with nonmetallic boxes. Internal bonding means is required to be installed to ensure ground continuity between the metal raceways or metal-jacketed cables.

Exception No. 2 permits the use of metal raceways and/or metal-jacketed cables with listed nonmetallic boxes equipped with threaded entries. Integral bonding means is required to ensure ground continuity between the threaded entries. The requirement for means to attach a grounding jumper is intended to accommodate devices or equipment attached to the box.

370-4. **Metal Boxes.** All metal boxes shall be grounded in accordance with the provisions of Article 250.

370-5. **Short Radius Conduit Bodies.** Conduit bodies such as capped elbows and service-entrance elbows enclosing conductors No. 6 or smaller, and that are only intended to enable the installation of the raceway and the contained conductors, shall not contain splices, taps, or devices and shall be of sufficient size to provide free space for all conductors enclosed in the fitting.

The term "Short Radius Conduit Bodies" is new in the 1993 *Code*. This type of conduit body is not permitted to contain splices.

B. Installation

370-15. **Damp, Wet, or Hazardous (Classified) Locations.**

(a) Damp or Wet Locations. In damp or wet locations, boxes, conduit bodies, and fittings shall be so placed or equipped as to prevent moisture from entering or accumulating within the box, conduit body, or fitting. Boxes, conduit bodies, and fittings installed in wet locations shall be listed for use in wet locations.

Article 100 defines "weatherproof" as "so constructed or protected that exposure to the weather will not interfere with successful operation." Rainproof, raintight, or watertight equipment can fulfill the requirements for the definition of weatherproof where varying weather conditions other than wetness, such as snow, ice, dust, or temperature extremes, are not a factor.

A weatherhead fitting is considered to be weatherproof because the openings for the conductors are placed in a downward position so that rain or snow cannot enter the fitting.

See definitions of "damp location" and "wet location" under "Location" in Article 100.

(b) Hazardous (Classified) Locations. Installations in hazardous (classified) locations shall conform to Articles 500 through 517.

(FPN No. 1): For boxes in floors, see Section 370-27(b).

(FPN No. 2): For protection against corrosion, see Section 300-6.

370-16. **Number of Conductors in Outlet, Device, and Junction Boxes, and Conduit Bodies.** Boxes shall be of sufficient size to provide free space for all conductors enclosed in the box.

The provisions of this section shall not apply to terminal housings supplied with motors. See Section 430-12.

Boxes and conduit bodies containing conductors, size No. 4 or larger, shall also comply with the provisions of Section 370-28.

(a) Standard Boxes. The maximum number of conductors permitted in standard boxes shall be as is listed in Table 370-16(a). See Section 370-28 where boxes or conduit bodies are used as junction or pull boxes.

(1) Table 370-16(a) shall apply where no fittings or devices, such as fixture studs, cable clamps, hickeys, switches, or receptacles, are contained in the box and where no equipment grounding conductors are part of the wiring within the box. Where one or more of these types of fittings, such as fixture studs, cable clamps, or hickeys are contained in the box, the number of conductors shown in the table shall be reduced by one for each type of fitting; an additional deduction of two conductors shall be made for each mounting yoke or strap containing one or more devices or equipment; and a further deduction of one conductor shall be made for one or more equipment grounding conductors entering the box. Where a second set of equipment grounding conductors, as permitted by Section 250-74, Exception No. 4, is present in the box, then an additional deduction of one conductor shall be made. A conductor running through the box shall be counted as one conductor, and each conductor originating outside of the box and terminating inside the box is counted as one conductor. Conductors, no part of which leaves the box, shall not be counted. The volume of a wiring enclosure (box)

shall be the total volume of the assembled sections, and, where used, the space provided by plaster rings, domed covers, extension rings, etc., that are marked with their volume in cubic inches, or are made from boxes the dimensions of which are listed in Table 370-16(a).

Exception: Where an equipment grounding conductor or not over four fixture wires smaller than No. 14, or both, enter a box from a fixture canopy and terminate within that box, it shall be permitted to omit these conductors from the calculations. Where branch-circuit conductors enter a fixture canopy from a box and terminate within that canopy, it shall be permitted to count these conductors as not leaving the box.

(2) For combinations of conductor sizes shown in Table 370-16(a), the maximum number of conductors permitted shall be computed using the volume per conductor listed in Table 370-16(b), with the deductions provided for in Section 370-16(a)(1). For fixture studs, cable clamps, or hickeys, these deductions shall be based on the largest conductor entering the box; for each yoke or strap containing one or more devices or equipment, the deduction shall be based on the largest conductor connected to device(s) or equipment supported by that yoke or strap; and for equipment grounding conductors, the deductions shall be based on the largest equipment grounding conductor entering the box. The maximum number and size of conductors listed in Table 370-16(a) shall not be exceeded.

(b) **Other Boxes.** Boxes 100 cubic inches (1640 cm³) or less other than those described in Table 370-16(a) and nonmetallic boxes shall be durably and legibly marked by the manufacturer with their cubic inch capacity. The maximum number of conductors permitted shall be computed using the volume per conductor listed in Table 370-16(b), with the deductions provided for in Section 370-16(a)(1). For fixture studs, cable clamps, or hickeys, these deductions shall be based on the largest conductor entering the box; for each yoke or strap containing one or more devices or equipment, the deduction shall be based on the largest conductor connected to device(s) or equipment supported by that yoke or strap; and for equipment grounding conductors, the deductions shall be based on the largest equipment grounding conductor entering the box. Boxes described in Table 370-16(a) that have a larger cubic inch capacity than is designated in the table shall be permitted to have their cubic inch capacity marked as required by this section, and the maximum number of conductors permitted shall be computed using the volume per conductor listed in Table 370-16(b).

Figure 370-1 Part A is an example of a box that requires no deductions. All that is necessary to determine the number of conductors is to compare the marked cubic inch capacity of the box (10.3 cubic inches) with Table 370-16(a). Each unspliced conductor running through the box is counted as one. Four No. 14 conductors require 8 cubic inches. *THE BOX IS ADEQUATELY SIZED.*

Figure 370-1 Part B illustrates a box containing one clamp, one device, several equipment grounding conductors, and four circuit conductors, all of the same size. Table 370-16(a) indicates that an 18 cubic inch box is permitted to contain 9 No. 14 conductors. Section 370-16(a) requires the following deductions:

Deductions	
1 cable clamp	minus 1 conductor
1 yoke or strap	minus 2 conductors
All equipment grounding conductors	minus 1 conductor
Required Total Deductions	4 conductors

After deducting the 4 conductors from the 9 permitted, there is space for 5 conductors. Since there are only 4 circuit conductors, *THE BOX IS ADEQUATELY SIZED.*

Figure 370-2 is an example of the required deductions when the box contains conductors of *different* sizes. In this type of installation, it is necessary to make the calculation in accordance with Section 370-16(a)(2). Deductions for equipment grounding conductors and fittings (such as fixture studs, cable clamps, or hickeys) are made on the basis of the *largest size conductor.* The two conductor deduction for devices or equipment is made based on the *largest conductor* attached to the device or equipment yoke or strap. The calculations for Figure 370-2 are as follows:

Deductions	
2 cable clamps minus 1 No. 12	= *2.25 cubic inches
2 equipment grounding conductors minus 1 No. 12	= 2.25 cubic inches
1 yoke with No. 12 conductors (2 × 2.25 cubic inches)	= 4.50 cubic inches
1 yoke with No. 14 conductors (2 × 2 cubic inches)	= 4.00 cubic inches
Total	13.00 cubic inches
36 cubic inches (total box volume) minus 13	= 23 cubic inches available

Required

2 No. 14 conductors	= 4 cubic inches
4 No. 12 conductors	= 9 cubic inches
13 cubic inches minimum required	
13 cubic inch minimum required,	
23 cubic inches available	

THE BOX IS ADEQUATELY SIZED.

*See Table 370-16(b) for cubic inch requirements for conductors. The cubic inch capacity of boxes can be increased with the use of various extension boxes, domed attachments, or extension rings.

A   Standard 10.3 cu. in. box no. 14 conductors

(c) Conduit Bodies. Conduit bodies enclosing No. 6 conductors or smaller other than short radius conduit bodies as described in Section 370-5 shall have a cross-sectional area not less than twice the cross-sectional area of the largest conduit or tubing to which it is attached. The maximum number of conductors permitted shall be the maximum number permitted by Table 1 of Chapter 9 for the conduit to which it is attached.

Conduit bodies shall not contain splices, taps, or devices unless they are durably and legibly marked by the manufacturer with their cubic inch capacity. The maximum number of conductors permitted shall be computed using the provisions of Section 370-16(b) for other than standard boxes. Conduit bodies shall be supported in a rigid and secure manner.

All conduit bodies other than the short-radius type are permitted to contain splices or taps, provided the conduit bodies are marked with their cubic inch capacity. Such conduit bodies are required to have a cross-sectional area not less than twice that of the conduit to which they are attached and are not permitted to contain more conductors than the attached raceway. The volume requirements for splicing or taping are provided in Section 370-16(b).

B   Standard 18 cu. in. box

Figure 370-1. Part A of this figure is an example of a standard size box containing no fittings or devices such as fixture studs, cable clamps, switches, receptacles, or equipment grounding conductors. Section 370-16(2) applies to this box. Part B is an example of a device box containing items requiring deductions in accordance with Section 370-16(a)(1).

Figure 370-2. An example of volume requirement calculations in accordance with Section 370-16(a)(2) for a box containing conductors of different sizes.

Conduit bodies must be rigidly supported. See exceptions to Sections 370-23(d) and (e), which permit the raceway to support the conduit body, provided the conduit body is not larger than the attached raceway.

See Figure 370-2. See Section 370-28 for requirements where conduit bodies are used as pull and junction boxes.

370-17. Conductors Entering Boxes, Conduit Bodies, or Fittings.
Conductors entering boxes, conduit bodies, or fittings shall be protected from abrasion and shall comply with (a) through (d) below.

(a) Openings to Be Closed. Openings through which conductors enter shall be adequately closed.

(b) Metal Boxes, Conduit Bodies, and Fittings. Where metal outlet boxes, conduit bodies, or fittings are installed with open wiring or concealed knob-and-tube wiring, conductors shall enter through insulating bushings or, in dry locations, through flexible tubing extending from the last insulating support and firmly secured to the box, conduit body, or fitting. Where raceway or cable is installed with metal outlet boxes, conduit bodies, or fittings, the raceway or cable shall be secured to such boxes, conduit bodies, and fittings.

Table 370-16(a). Metal Boxes

Box Dimension, Inches Trade Size or Type	Min. Cu. In. Cap.	Maximum Number of Conductors						
		No. 18	No. 16	No. 14	No. 12	No. 10	No. 8	No. 6
4 x 1 1/4 Round or Octagonal	12.5	8	7	6	5	5	4	2
4 x 1 1/2 Round or Octagonal	15.5	10	8	7	6	6	5	3
4 x 2 1/8 Round or Octagonal	21.5	14	12	10	9	8	7	4
4 x 1 1/4 Square	18.0	12	10	9	8	7	6	3
4 x 1 1/2 Square	21.0	14	12	10	9	8	7	4
4 x 2 1/8 Square	30.3	20	17	15	13	12	10	6
4 11/16 x 1 1/4 Square	25.5	17	14	12	11	10	8	5
4 11/16 x 1 1/2 Square	29.5	19	16	14	13	11	9	5
4 11/16 x 2 1/8 Square	42.0	28	24	21	18	16	14	8
3 x 2 x 1 1/2 Device	7.5	5	4	3	3	3	2	1
3 x 2 x 2 Device	10.0	6	5	5	4	4	3	2
3 x 2 x 2 1/4 Device	10.5	7	6	5	4	4	3	2
3 x 2 x 2 1/2 Device	12.5	8	7	6	5	5	4	2
3 x 2 x 2 3/4 Device	14.0	9	8	7	6	5	4	2
3 x 2 x 3 1/2 Device	18.0	12	10	9	8	7	6	3
4 x 2 1/8 x 1 1/2 Device	10.3	6	5	5	4	4	3	2
4 x 2 1/8 x 1 7/8 Device	13.0	8	7	6	5	5	4	2
4 x 2 1/8 x 2 1/8 Device	14.5	9	8	7	6	5	4	2
3 3/4 x 2 x 2 1/2 Masonry Box/Gang	14.0	9	8	7	6	5	4	2
3 3/4 x 2 x 3 1/2 Masonry Box/Gang	21.0	14	12	10	9	8	7	4
FS—Minimum Internal Depth 1 3/4 Single Cover/Gang	13.5	9	7	6	6	5	4	2
FD—Minimum Internal Depth 2 3/8 Single Cover/Gang	18.0	12	10	9	8	7	6	3
FS—Minimum Internal Depth 1 3/4 Multiple Cover/Gang	18.0	12	10	9	8	7	6	3
FD—Minimum Internal Depth 2 3/8 Multiple Cover/Gang	24.0	16	13	12	10	9	8	4

For SI units: one cubic inch = 16.4 cm.^{3}

Table 370-16(b). Volume Required per Conductor

Size of Conductor	Free Space within Box for Each Conductor
No. 18	1.5 cubic inches
No. 16	1.75 cubic inches
No. 14	2. cubic inches
No. 12	2.25 cubic inches
No. 10	2.5 cubic inches
No. 8	3. cubic inches
No. 6	5. cubic inches

For SI units: one cubic inch = 16.4 cm.^{3}

Figure 370-3. An example of splices in a raceway supported conduit body. See Section 370-16(b) for volume calculations.

(c) Nonmetallic Boxes. Nonmetallic boxes shall be suitable for the lowest temperature rated conductor entering the box. Where nonmetallic boxes are used with open wiring or concealed knob-and-tube wiring, the conductors shall enter the box through individual holes. Where flexible tubing is used to encase the conductors, the tubing shall extend from the last insulating support to no less than $^1/_4$ inch (6.35 mm) inside the box. Where nonmetallic-sheathed cable is used, the cable assembly, including the sheath, shall extend into the box no less than $^1/_4$ inch (6.35 mm) through a nonmetallic-sheathed cable knockout opening. In all instances, all permitted wiring methods shall be secured to the boxes.

Standard nonmetallic boxes are permitted for use with 90°C (194°F) insulated conductors. A nonmetallic box used for splicing a conductor of a higher temperature rating to a conductor of a lower temperature rating is required to be identified as suitable for the temperature rating of the lower-rated conductor. The intent is to avoid the necessity of giving a high temperature rating to boxes in a normal temperature location simply because high temperatureconductors enter or exit the box from, or to, a high temperature location. However, where insulated conductors rated at higher temperatures are necessary in a high temperature environment, the box is required to be suitably identified by marking on the box or in the listing of the box. See Section 110-3(b).

Exception: Where nonmetallic-sheathed cable is used with boxes no larger than a nominal size 2$^1/_4$ inch by 4 inch mounted in walls and where the cable is fastened within 8 inches (203 mm) of the box measured along the sheath and where the sheath extends into the box no less than $^1/_4$ inch (6.35 mm), securing the cable to the box shall not be required. Multiple cable entries shall be permitted in a single knockout opening.

Cable securing means is required in ceiling boxes and all other boxes larger than 2$^1/_4$ inches by 4 inches. The requirement is based on the width of the box and the likelihood that the cable will be pushed back out of the box when the conductors and device, if any, are folded back into the box during installation of receptacles, switches, etc. The last sentence, which permits multiple cable entries in a single knockout opening, is new in the 1993 *Code*.

(d) Conductors No. 4 or Larger. Installation shall comply with Section 373-6(c).

370-18. **Unused Openings.** Unused openings in boxes, conduit bodies, and fittings shall be effectively closed to afford protection substantially equivalent to that of the wall of the box, conduit body, or fitting. Metal plugs or plates used with nonmetallic boxes, conduit bodies, or fittings shall be recessed at least $^1/_4$ inch (6.35 mm) from the outer surface.

370-19. **Boxes Enclosing Flush Devices.** Boxes used to enclose flush devices shall be of such design that the devices will be completely enclosed on back and sides, and that substantial support for the devices will be provided. Screws for supporting the box shall not be used in attachment of the device contained therein.

370-20. **In Wall or Ceiling.** In walls or ceilings of concrete, tile, or other noncombustible material, boxes and fittings shall be so installed that the front edge of the box or fitting will not set back of the finished surface more than $^1/_4$ inch (6.35 mm). In walls and ceilings constructed of wood or other combustible material, outlet boxes and fittings shall be flush with the finished surface or project therefrom.

Plaster and gypsum board are "other noncombustible materials." A wall with wood studs covered by plaster or gypsum board is considered a "wall of noncombustible material" for the purposes of Section 370-20.

370-21. **Repairing Plaster and Dry Wall or Plasterboard.** Plaster, dry wall, or plasterboard surfaces that are broken or incomplete shall be repaired so there will be no gaps or open spaces greater than ⅛ inch (3.18 mm) at the edge of the box or fitting.

370-22. **Exposed Surface Extensions.** Surface extensions from an outlet box of a concealed wiring system shall be made by mounting and mechanically securing a box or extension ring over the concealed box. Where required, equipment grounding shall be in accordance with Article 250.

Exception: A surface extension shall be permitted to be made from the cover of a concealed box where the cover is designed so that it cannot fall off, or be removed if its security means becomes loose, and if the wiring method is flexible and so arranged that any required grounding continuity is independent of the connection between the box and cover.

Figure 370-4. An example of a flexible surface extension from a concealed outlet box. The Exception to Section 370-22 permitting this technique requires the use of a cover that will not fall off if the securing screws become loose.

370-23. **Supports.** Enclosures within the scope of Article 370 shall be rigidly and securely fastened in place in accordance with (a) through (g) below.

(a) Surface Mounting. They shall be fastened to the surface upon which they are mounted unless such surface does not provide adequate support, in which case they shall be supported in accordance with (b).

Support of a box on a suspended-type ceiling is one example of where a rod should be attached to the box and structural member.

(b) Structural Mounting. They shall be rigidly supported from a structural member of the building either directly or by using a metal or wood brace. Support wires that do not provide rigid support shall not be permitted as the sole support.

Figure 370-5 illustrates one method of supporting a box where the ceiling construction affords no support. See also Section 410-16(a).

Box rod and plate hanger used when a fixture weighing more than 50 lbs. is to be installed, or when a box is installed in a large opening of a tile ceiling.

Figure 370-5. A plate and threaded-rod hanger used to support an outlet box in a tile arch ceiling.

(1) Nails, where used as a fastening means, shall be permitted to pass through the interior of the enclosure if located within ¼ inch (6.35 mm) of the back or ends of the enclosure.

This prevents the nails from interfering with the installation of devices. Permitting nails inside the box within ¼ inch of the ends prevents splitting of the smaller wooden studs used in some frame-type construction. Splitting sometimes occurs where nails are within ¼ inch of the back of the box.

(2) Metal braces shall be protected against corrosion and formed from metal not less than .020 inch (508 micrometers) thick uncoated. Wood braces shall have a cross section not less than nominal 1 inch (25.4 mm) by 2 inches (50.8 mm).

(c) Nonstructural Mounting. It shall be permissible to make a flush installation in existing covered surfaces where adequate support is provided by clamps, anchors, or fittings. Framing members of suspended ceiling systems shall be permitted as the support if the framing members are adequately supported and securely fastened to each other and to the building structure. Enclosures so supported shall be fastened to the framing member by mechanical means such as bolts, screws, or rivets. Clips identified for use with the type of ceiling framing member(s) and enclosure(s) shall also be permitted.

Where there are no structural members, or where cut into existing walls, boxes are permitted to be secured by clamps or anchors. See Figure 370-6 for one example of an acceptable mounting method.

Figure 370-6.   This is one type of service box used for old work. Shown in the bottom figure is a device box mounted in an opening in an existing wall be means of a securing bracket that is part of the box.

(d) Raceway Supported Enclosure(s), Without Devices or Fixtures. Enclosures that are not over 100 cubic inches (1640 cm³) in size and that have threaded entries or have hubs identified for the purpose, and that do not contain devices or support fixtures, shall be considered to be adequately supported where two or more conduits are threaded wrenchtight into the enclosure or hubs, and where each conduit is supported within 3 feet (914 mm) of the enclosure on two or more sides so as to provide the rigid and secure installation intended by this section of the Code.

Exception: Conduit or electrical metallic tubing shall be permitted to support conduit bodies provided the conduit bodies are not larger than the largest trade size of the conduit or electrical metallic tubing.

Boxes are not permitted to be supported by rigid raceways using a locknut and bushing connection, nor is a box permitted to be supported by a single raceway. However, enclosures without devices or fixtures are considered to be adequately supported, provided the threaded conduits enter the box on two or more sides and are supported within 3 feet of the enclosure.

Such enclosures shall also be considered to be adequately supported if they comply with subsection (e) following.

(e) Raceway Supported Enclosures, With Devices or Fixtures. Enclosures that are not over 100 cubic inches (1640 cm³) in size and that have threaded entries or have hubs identified for the purpose, and that support fixtures or contain devices, or both, shall be considered adequately supported where two or more conduits are threaded wrenchtight into the enclosure or hubs and where each conduit is supported within 18 inches (457 mm) of the enclosure so as to provide the rigid and secure installation intended by this section of the Code.

Exception: Conduit shall be permitted to support conduit bodies provided the conduit bodies are not larger than the largest trade size of the conduit.

The conduit is required to be supported within 18 inches if the enclosure contains devices or fixtures. See commentary following Section 370-23(d).

(f) Enclosure(s) in Concrete or Masonry. Enclosure(s) shall be permitted to be supported by being embedded.

Boxes are permitted to be embedded in masonry or concrete, provided they are rigid and secure. See Figure 370-7.

(g) Pendant Boxes. Boxes shall be supported from a multiconductor cord or cable in an approved manner that protects the conductors against strain, such as a strain relief connector threaded into a box with a hub.

Figure 370-7. A mud box installed in a concrete ceiling. Additional support is not required.

See Sections 517-61(b)(3), Exception No. 2 and 517-61(c)(1), Exception for examples of locations where pendant boxes may be used. They are also commonly used around cranes and hoists and in many industrial applications.

370-24. **Depth of Outlet Boxes.** No box shall have an internal depth of less than $1/2$ inch (12.7 mm). Boxes intended to enclose flush devices shall have an internal depth of not less than $15/16$ inch (23.8 mm).

The use of a shallow box may become necessary because of old work or existing construction where very shallow partitions, plumbing pipes, or ductwork is encountered within the partition, etc. The selection of a box used in this type of situation is required to be based on its having sufficient cubic inch capacity.

370-25. **Covers and Canopies.** In completed installations, each outlet box shall have a cover, faceplate, or fixture canopy.

(a) Nonmetallic or Metal Covers and Plates. Nonmetallic or metal covers and plates shall be permitted with nonmetallic outlet boxes. Where metal covers or plates are used, they shall comply with the grounding requirements of Section 250-42.

(FPN): See Sections 410-18(a) and 410-56(c) for metal faceplates.

(b) Exposed Combustible Wall or Ceiling Finish. Where a fixture canopy or pan is used, any combustible wall or ceiling finish exposed between the edge of the canopy or pan and the outlet box shall be covered with noncombustible material.

Because of the possibility that heat from a short circuit, overlamping, or ground fault within a fixture canopy or pan could create a fire hazard, any exposed combustible wall or ceiling space between the edge of the outlet box and the perimeter of the fixture is required to be covered with noncombustible material. The noncombustible material need not be metal. Glass fiber pads commonly provided as thermal barriers on ceiling pan fixtures can be used to meet this requirement. Where the wall or ceiling finish is concrete, tile, plaster, or other noncombustible material, the requirements of this section do not apply. See Section 370-21.

(c) Flexible Cord Pendants. Covers of outlet boxes and conduit bodies having holes through which flexible cord pendants pass shall be provided with bushings designed for the purpose or shall have smooth, well-rounded surfaces on which the cords may bear. So-called hard-rubber or composition bushings shall not be used.

370-27. **Outlet Boxes.**

(a) Boxes at Lighting Fixture Outlets. Boxes used at lighting fixture outlets shall be designed for the purpose. At every outlet used exclusively for lighting, the box shall be so designed or installed that a lighting fixture may be attached.

Device boxes are designed for the mounting of devices such as snap-switches and receptacles, usually by 6-32 screws. They are not suitable for the support of other than very lightweight lighting fixtures, such as some wall-bracket types. See Section 410-16, Means of Support for Lighting Fixtures. The outlet box is required to provide "adequate" support.

(b) Floor Boxes. Boxes listed specifically for this application shall be used for receptacles located in the floor.

Exception: Boxes located in elevated floors of show windows and similar locations where the authority having jurisdiction judges them to be free from physical damage, moisture, and dirt.

(c) Boxes at Fan Outlets. Outlet boxes shall not be used as the sole support for ceiling (paddle) fans.

Exception: Boxes listed for the application shall be permitted as the sole means of support.

See also Section 422-18, Support of Ceiling Fans.
One method of supporting a ceiling fan so that the box does not serve as the sole support is shown in Figure 370-8.

Figure 370-8. Ceiling fan supported without depending on box for sole support.

370-28. **Pull and Junction Boxes.** Boxes and conduit bodies used as pull or junction boxes shall comply with (a) through (d) of this section.

(a) Minimum Size. For raceways containing conductors of No. 4 or larger, and for cables containing conductors of No. 4 or larger, the minimum dimensions of pull or junction boxes installed in a raceway or cable run shall comply with the following:

(1) Straight Pulls. In straight pulls, the length of the box shall not be less than eight times the trade diameter of the largest raceway.

This section applies to minimum dimensions of pull and junction boxes or conduit bodies used with raceways (¾ inch or larger) or cables containing conductors No. 4 or larger.

For straight pulls, for example, a 2-inch conduit containing four No. 4/0 conductors (see Chapter 9, Table 3B) requires a 16-inch-long pull box [8 × 2 inches = 16 inches per 370-28 (a)(1)]. It should be understood that 16 inches is the required *minimum* length; however, for maximum ease in handling this size conductor, a longer length pull box may be desired.

(2) Angle or U Pulls. Where angle or U pulls are made, the distance between each raceway entry inside the box and the opposite wall of the box shall not be less than six times the trade diameter of the largest raceway in a row. This distance shall be increased for additional entries by the amount of the sum of the diameters of all other raceway entries in the same row on the same wall of the box. Each row shall be calculated individually, and the single row that provides the maximum distance shall be used.

Exception: Where a raceway or cable entry is in the wall of a box or conduit body opposite to a removable cover and where the distance from that wall to the cover is in conformance with the column for one wire per terminal in Table 373-6(a).

Figures 370-9(a) and (b) provide examples of calculations required by Section 370-18(a) and (b).

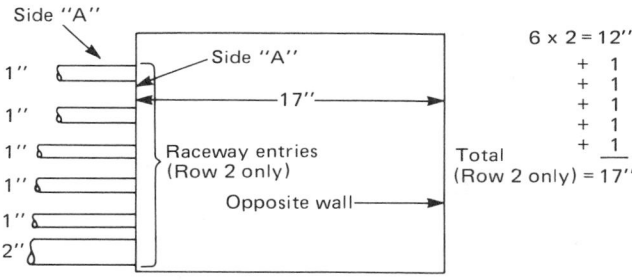

Figure 370-9(a). Where angle or U pulls are made, the distance between each raceway entry inside the box and the opposite wall of the box must not be less than six times the trade diameter of the largest raceway. This distance must be increased for additional entries by the amount of the sum of the diameters of the maximum number of all other raceway entries in one row on the same side of the box.

The distance between raceway entries enclosing the same conductor shall not be less than six times the trade diameter of the larger raceway.

When transposing cable size into raceway size in (a)(1) and (a)(2) above, the minimum trade size raceway required for the number and size of conductors in the cable shall be used.

(3) Boxes or conduit bodies of dimensions less than those required in (a)(1) and (a)(2) above shall be permitted for installations of combinations of conductors that are less than the maximum conduit or tubing fill (of conduits or tubing being used) permitted by Table 1 of Chapter 9, provided the box

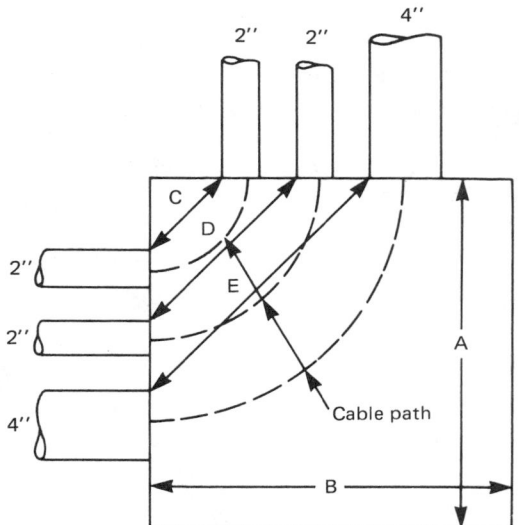

A = 6 x 4'' + (2 + 2'') = 28'' min.
B = 6 x 4'' + (2 + 2'') = 28'' min.
C = 6 x 2'' = 12'' min. required between raceways enclosing
    the same conductor
D = 6 x 2'' = 12'' min. required between raceways enclosing
    the same conductor
E = 6 x 4'' = 24'' min. required between raceways enclosing
    the same conductor

Figure 370-9(b). Raceway entries enclosing the same conductor are required to have a minimum separation between them. The intent is to provide adequate space for the conductors to make the bend.

or conduit body has been approved for and is permanently marked with the maximum number and maximum size of conductors permitted.

Exception: Terminal housings supplied with motors, which shall comply with the provisions of Section 430-12.

(b) Conductors in Pull or Junction Boxes. In pull boxes or junction boxes having any dimension over 6 feet (1.83 m), all conductors shall be cabled or racked up in an approved manner.

(FPN): See Section 373-6(c) for insulation of conductors at bushings.

(c) Covers. All pull boxes, junction boxes, conduit bodies, and fittings shall be provided with covers compatible with the box, conduit body, or fitting construction and suitable for the conditions of use. Where metal covers are used, they shall comply with the grounding requirements of Section 250-42.

(d) Permanent Barriers. Where permanent barriers are installed in a box, each section shall be considered as a separate box.

370-29. **Conduit Bodies, Junction, Pull, and Outlet Boxes to Be Accessible.** Conduit bodies, junction, pull, and outlet boxes shall be so installed that the wiring contained in them can be rendered accessible without removing any part of the building or, in underground circuits, without excavating sidewalks, paving, earth, or other substance that is to be used to establish the finished grade.

Exception: Listed boxes shall be permitted where covered by gravel, light aggregate, or noncohesive granulated soil if their location is effectively identified and accessible for excavation.

Consideration should also be given to the accessibility of junction boxes installed on a structural ceiling above a suspended ceiling.

A covered box is permitted to be used at any point for the connection of conduit, tubing, or cable, provided it is not rendered inaccessible. See Article 100 for definition of "Accessible (as applied to wiring methods)." See also Section 300-15.

C. Construction Specifications

370-40. **Metal Boxes, Conduit Bodies, and Fittings.**

(a) Corrosion-Resistant. Metal boxes, conduit bodies, and fittings shall be corrosion-resistant or shall be well-galvanized, enameled, or otherwise properly coated inside and out to prevent corrosion.

(FPN): See Section 300-6 for limitation in the use of boxes and fittings protected from corrosion solely by enamel.

(b) Thickness of Metal. Sheet steel boxes not over 100 cubic inches (1640 cm³) in size shall be made from steel not less than 0.0625 inch (1.59 mm) thick. The wall of a malleable iron box or conduit body and a die-cast or permanent-mold cast aluminum, brass, bronze, or zinc box or conduit body shall not be less than $\frac{3}{32}$ inch (2.38 mm) thick. Other cast metal boxes or conduit bodies shall have a wall thickness not less than $\frac{1}{8}$ inch (3.17 mm).

Exception No. 1: Listed boxes and conduit bodies shown to have equivalent strength and characteristics shall be permitted to be made of thinner or other metals.

Exception No. 2: The walls of listed short radius conduit bodies, as covered in Section 370-5, shall be permitted to be made of thinner metal.

The exceptions permitting thinner wall thickness for listed boxes and conduit bodies is new in the 1993 *Code.*

(c) Metal Boxes Over 100 Cubic Inches. Metal boxes over 100 cubic inches (1640 cm³) in size shall be constructed so as to be of ample strength and rigidity. If of sheet steel, the metal thickness shall not be less than 0.053 inch (1.35 mm) uncoated.

(d) Grounding Provisions. A means shall be provided in each metal box, designed for use with nonmetallic raceways and nonmetallic cable systems, for the connection of an equipment grounding conductor.

The "means provided" by the box manufacturer is usually in the form of a 10-32 tapped hole marked "GR" or "GRD," or the equivalent, next to the hole. It should be noted, however, that the "means provided" may not necessarily be utilized. See Figure 250-38 and the commentary following Section 250-114.

370-41. **Covers.** Metal covers shall be of the same material as the box or fitting with which they are used, or they shall be lined with firmly attached insulating material not less than ¹/₃₂ inch (0.79 mm) thick, or they shall be listed for the purpose. Metal covers shall be the same thickness as the boxes or fittings for which they are used, or they shall be listed for the purpose. Covers of porcelain or other approved insulating materials shall be permitted if of such form and thickness as to afford the required protection and strength.

370-42. **Bushings.** Covers of outlet boxes, conduit bodies, and outlet fittings having holes through which flexible cord pendants may pass shall be provided with approved bushings or shall have smooth, well-rounded surfaces upon which the cord may bear. Where conductors other than flexible cord may pass through a metal cover, a separate hole equipped with a bushing of suitable insulating material shall be provided for each conductor. Such separate holes shall be connected by a slot as required by Section 300-20.

(FPN): For alternating-current conductors, see Section 300-20(b).

370-43. **Nonmetallic Boxes.** Provisions for supports or other mounting means for nonmetallic boxes shall be outside of the box, or the box shall be so constructed as to prevent contact between the conductors in the box and the supporting screws.

370-44. **Marking.** All boxes and conduit bodies, covers, extension rings, plaster rings, and the like shall be durably and legibly marked with the manufacturer's name or trademark.

D. Pull and Junction Boxes for Use on Systems Over 600 Volts, Nominal

370-70. **General.** In addition to the generally applicable provisions of Article 370, the rules in Sections 370-71 and 370-72 shall apply.

370-71. **Size of Pull and Junction Boxes.** Pull and junction boxes shall provide adequate space and dimensions for the installation of conductors in accordance with the following:

(a) For Straight Pulls. The length of the box shall not be less than forty-eight times the outside diameter, over sheath, of the largest shielded or lead-covered conductor or cable entering the box. The length shall not be less than thirty-two times the outside diameter of the largest nonshielded conductor or cable.

(b) For Angle or U Pulls. The distance between each cable or conductor entry inside the box and the opposite wall of the box shall not be less than thirty-six times the outside diameter, over sheath, of the largest cable or conductor. This distance shall be increased for additional entries by the amount of the sum of the outside diameters, over sheath, of all other cables or conductor entries through the same wall of the box.

The distance between a cable or conductor entry and its exit from the box shall be not less than thirty-six times the outside diameter, over sheath, of that cable or conductor.

Exception No. 1: Terminal housings supplied with motors, which shall comply with the provisions of Section 430-12.

Exception No. 2: Where cables are nonshielded and not lead-covered, the distance of thirty-six times the outside diameter shall be permitted to be reduced to twenty-four times the outside diameter.

Exception No. 3: Where a conductor or cable entry is in the wall of a box opposite to a removable cover and where the distance from that wall to the cover is in conformance with the provisions of Section 300-34.

(c) Removable Sides. One or more sides of any pull box shall be removable.

370-72. Construction and Installation Requirements.

(a) Corrosion Protection. Boxes shall be made of material inherently resistant to corrosion or shall be suitably protected, both internally and externally, by enameling, galvanizing, plating, or other means.

(b) Passing Through Partitions. Suitable bushings, shields, or fittings having smooth, rounded edges shall be provided where conductors or cables pass through partitions and at other locations where necessary.

(c) Complete Enclosure. Boxes shall provide a complete enclosure for the contained conductors or cables.

(d) Wiring Is Accessible. Boxes shall be so installed that the wiring is accessible without removing any part of the building. Working space shall be provided in accordance with Section 110-34.

(e) Suitable Covers. Boxes shall be closed by suitable covers securely fastened in place. Underground box covers that weigh over 100 pounds (45.4 kg) shall be considered as meeting this requirement. Covers for boxes shall be permanently marked "DANGER HIGH VOLTAGE — KEEP OUT." The marking shall be on the outside of the box cover and shall be readily visible. Letters shall be block type at least ½ inch (12.7 mm) in height.

(f) Suitable for Expected Handling. Boxes and their covers shall be capable of withstanding the handling to which they may likely be subjected.

ARTICLE 373   Cabinets, Cutout Boxes, and Meter Socket Enclosures

Contents

373-1. Scope.

A. Installation

373-1. Scope.
This article covers the installation and construction specifications of cabinets, cutout boxes, and meter socket enclosures.

See Section 373-6(b)(1) Exception No. 2 for the requirement in Article 373 relating to meter socket enclosures.

See definitions of "Cabinet" and "Cutout Box" in Article 100. Cabinets and cutout boxes are designed with a swinging door(s) to enclose switches, overcurrent devices, or control equipment. Some cabinets for circuit breaker panelboards or load centers do not have doors as permitted by Exception No. 2 to Section 240-30. Cabinets and cutout boxes are required to be of sufficient size to accommodate all devices and conductors without overcrowding or jamming. This condition can be prevented by the use of auxiliary gutters. See Article 374.

A. Installation

373-2. Damp, Wet, or Hazardous (Classified) Locations.

(a) **Damp and Wet Locations.** In damp or wet locations, cabinets and cutout boxes of the surface type shall be so placed or equipped as to prevent moisture or water from entering and accumulating within the cabinet or cutout box, and shall be mounted so there is at least ¼-inch (6.35-mm) air space between the enclosure and the wall or other supporting surface. Cabinets or cutout boxes installed in wet locations shall be weatherproof.

(FPN): For protection against corrosion, see Section 300-6.

(b) **Hazardous (Classified) Locations.** Installations in hazardous (classified) locations shall conform to Articles 500 through 517.

See Section 430-91 for motor controller enclosure selection table for indoor and outdoor use.

373-3. Position in Wall.
In walls of concrete, tile, or other noncombustible material, cabinets shall be so installed that the front edge of the cabinet will not set back of the finished surface more than ¼ inch (6.35 mm). In walls constructed of wood or other combustible material, cabinets shall be flush with the finished surface or project therefrom.

373-4. Unused Openings.
Unused openings in cabinet or cutout boxes shall be effectively closed to afford protection substantially equivalent to that of the wall of the cabinet or cutout box. Where metal plugs or plates are used with nonmetallic cabinets or cutout boxes, they shall be recessed at least ¼ inch (6.35 mm) from the outer surface.

373-5. Conductors Entering Cabinets or Cutout Boxes.
Conductors entering cabinets or cutout boxes shall be protected from abrasion and shall comply with (a) through (c) below.

See Section 373-6(c).

(a) **Openings to Be Closed.** Openings through which conductors enter shall be adequately closed.

(b) **Metal Cabinets and Cutout Boxes.** Where metal cabinets or cutout boxes are installed with open wiring or concealed knob-and-tube wiring, conductors shall enter through insulating bushings or, in dry locations, through flexible tubing extending from the last insulating support and firmly secured to the cabinet or cutout box.

(c) **Cables.** Where cable is used, each cable shall be secured to the cabinet or cutout box.

This section prohibits the installation of several cables bunched together and run through a knockout or chase nipple. Individual cable clamps or connectors are required to be used with only one cable per clamp or connector unless the clamp or connector is approved for more than a single cable.

373-6. Deflection of Conductors.
Conductors at terminals or conductors entering or leaving cabinets or cutout boxes and the like shall comply with (a) through (c) below.

(a) **Width of Wiring Gutters.** Conductors shall not be deflected within a cabinet or cutout box unless a gutter having a width in accordance with Table 373-6(a) is provided. Conductors in parallel in accordance with Section 310-4 shall be judged on the basis of the number of conductors in parallel.

Table 373-6(a). Minimum Wire-Bending Space at Terminals and Minimum Width of Wiring Gutters in Inches

AWG or Circular-Mil Size of Wire	Wires per Terminal				
	1	2	3	4	5
14-10	Not Specified	—	—	—	—
8-6	1½	—	—	—	—
4-3	2	—	—	—	—
2	2½	—	—	—	—
1	3	—	—	—	—
1/0-2/0	3½	5	7	—	—
3/0-4/0	4	6	8	—	—
250 kcmil	4½	6	8	10	—
300-350 kcmil	5	8	10	12	—
400-500 kcmil	6	8	10	12	14
600-700 kcmil	8	10	12	14	16
750-900 kcmil	8	12	14	16	18
1000-1250 kcmil	10	—	—	—	—
1500-2000 kcmil	12	—	—	—	—

For SI units: one inch = 25.4 millimeters.
Bending space at terminals shall be measured in a straight line from the end of the lug or wire connector (in the direction that the wire leaves the terminal) to the wall, barrier, or obstruction.

(b) Wire Bending Space at Terminals. Wire bending space at each terminal shall be provided in accordance with (1) or (2) below.

(1) Table 373-6(a) shall apply where the conductor does not enter or leave the enclosure through the wall opposite its terminal.

Exception No. 1: A conductor shall be permitted to enter or leave an enclosure through the wall opposite its terminal provided the conductor enters or leaves the enclosure where the gutter joins an adjacent gutter that has a width that conforms to Table 373-6(b) for that conductor.

Exception No. 2: A conductor not larger than 350 kcmil shall be permitted to enter or leave an enclosure containing only a meter socket(s) through the wall opposite its terminal, provided the terminal is a lay-in type where either:

a. The terminal is directly facing the enclosure wall and off-set is not greater than 50 percent of the bending space specified in Table 373-6(a), or

b. The terminal is directed toward the opening in the enclosure and is within a 45-degree angle of directly facing the enclosure wall.

(FPN): Offset is the distance measured along the enclosure wall from the axis of the centerline of the terminal to a line passing through the center of the opening in the enclosure.

(2) Table 373-6(b) shall apply where the conductor enters or leaves the enclosure through the wall opposite its terminal.

Section 373-6(b)(2) and Table 373-6(b) provide the requirements for wire bending space where straight-in wiring or offset (double bends) is employed at terminals. Section 373-6(b)(1) is for use where only 90-degree bends are involved.

The footnotes to Table 373-6(b) are intended to permit a reduction in required bending space for *removable* and *lay-in* wire terminals. These terminal wire connectors are required to be of the type that is intended for a single conductor (single barrel). To make wiring easier, one type of terminal may be removed and placed on the stripped end of the conductor, which has been cut to the proper length. The terminal is then crimped or lightly torqued on the conductor as intended, and then remounted. If a mechanical

Figure 373-1. The following rules apply where wiring as shown.

T1, Section 373-6(b)(2): Table 373-6(b) applies for conductors M.

T2, Section 373-6(b)(2): Table 373-6(b) applies for conductors BR2 unless in accordance with Section 373-6(b)(1), Exception. Conductors enter a second wiring space G, conforming to Table 373-6(b) for conductors BR2.

T3, Section 373-6(b)(2): Table 373-6(b) applies for conductors BR3.

T4, Section 373-6(b)(1): Table 373-6(a) applies for conductor N.

G1, Section 373-6(a): Table 373-6(a) applies for conductors M. Table 373-6(b) applies for conductors BR2 where T2 does not comply with Table 373-6(b).

G2, Section 373-6(a): Table 373-6(a) applies for conductors BR2.

G3, Section 373-6(a): Table 373-6(a) applies for conductors BR3.

G4, Section 373-6(a): Table 373-6(a) applies for conductor N.

screw connector is involved, the screw should then be torqued to the proper value. See commentary following the fine print note under Section 110-14.

Figure 373-2. *Conditions under which Section 373-6(b)(1), Exception No. 2 is applicable.*

Note that in accordance with the footnotes to Tables 373-6(a) and 373-6(b), when using Table 373-6(a), bending space is measured in the direction that the wire leaves the terminal and, when using Table 373-6(b), it is measured in a direction perpendicular to the enclosure wall.

A lay-in-type terminal is a pressure wire connector in which part of the connector is removeable or swings away so that the stripped end of the conductor can be laid into the fixed portion of the connector. The removeable or swing-away portion is then put back in place and the connector tightened down on the conductor.

See Figures 373-1 and 373-2. See also Figure 430-1.

(c) Insulated Fittings. Where ungrounded conductors of No. 4 or larger enter a raceway in a cabinet, pull box, junction box, or auxiliary gutter, the conductors shall be protected by a substantial fitting providing a smoothly rounded insulating surface, unless the conductors are separated from the raceway fitting by substantial insulating material securely fastened in place.

Where No. 4 or larger ungrounded conductors enter a cabinet or cutout box from metal raceways, a smoothly

rounded insulating bushing or fitting is required to protect the conductors from abrasion during and after installation. See Sections 345-15, 346-8, and 347-12.

Metal conduit bushings or fittings provided with insulated sleeves or linings are commonly used. It is also possible to use a separate insulating sleeve or lining to separate the conductors from the raceway fitting.

Listed insulating bushings provided separately, or as part of a fitting are colored black or brown if they are suitable for a temperature of 150°C and any other color for 90°C unless specifically marked for a higher temperature. See Figure 373-3.

Exception: Where threaded hubs or bosses that are an integral part of an enclosure provide a smoothly rounded or flared entry for conductors.

Conduit bushings constructed wholly of insulating material shall not be used to secure a raceway. The insulating fitting or insulating material shall have a temperature rating not less than the insulation temperature rating of the installed conductors.

Table 373-6(b).   Minimum Wire-Bending Space at Terminals for Section 373-6(b)(2) in Inches

Wire Size (AWG or kcmil)	Wires per Terminal			
	1	2	3	4 or More
14-10	Not Specified	—	—	—
8	1 1/2	—	—	—
6	2	—	—	—
4	3	—	—	—
3	3	—	—	—
2	3 1/2	—	—	—
1	4 1/2	—	—	—
1/0	5 1/2	5 1/2	7	—
2/0	6	6	7 1/2	—
3/0	6 1/2 (1/2)	6 1/2 (1/2)	8	—
4/0	7 (1)	7 1/2 (1 1/2)	8 1/2 (1/2)	—
250	8 1/2 (2)	8 1/2 (2)	9 (1)	10
300	10 (3)	10 (2)	11 (1)	12
350	12 (3)	12 (3)	13 (3)	14 (2)
400	13 (3)	13 (3)	14 (3)	15 (3)
500	14 (3)	14 (3)	15 (3)	16 (3)
600	15 (3)	16 (3)	18 (3)	19 (3)
700	16 (3)	18 (3)	20 (3)	22 (3)
750	17 (3)	19 (3)	22 (3)	24 (3)
800	18	20	22	24
900	19	22	24	24
1000	20	—	—	—
1250	22	—	—	—
1500	24	—	—	—
1750	24	—	—	—
2000	24	—	—	—

For SI units: one inch = 25.4 millimeters.
Bending space at terminals shall be measured in a straight line from the end of the lug or wire connector in a direction perpendicular to the enclosure wall.
For removable and lay-in wire terminals intended for only one wire, bending space shall be permitted to be reduced by the number of inches shown in parentheses.

373-7. **Space in Enclosures.** Cabinets and cutout boxes shall have sufficient space to accommodate all conductors installed in them without crowding.

373-8. **Enclosures for Switches or Overcurrent Devices.** Enclosures for switches or overcurrent devices shall not be used as junction boxes, auxiliary gutters, or raceways for conductors feeding through or tapping off to other switches or overcurrent devices.

Exception: Where adequate space is provided so that the conductors do not fill the wiring space at any cross section to more than 40 percent of the cross-sectional area of the space, and so that the conductors, splices, and taps do not fill the wiring space at any cross section to more than 75 percent of the cross-sectional area of the space.

Figure 373-3.   An insulating bushing to protect conductors from chafing against a metal conduit fitting.

Insulated thermoplastic or fiber bushing (Note: double locknut)

Most enclosures are intended to accommodate only those conductors that will be connected to terminals for switches or overcurrent devices within the enclosures themselves. Where adequate space is provided for additional conductors, such as control circuits, the total conductor fill in the enclosure is not permitted to exceed 40 percent of the cross section of the wiring space in the enclosure, and no more than 75 percent if splices or taps are necessary.

Example: If an enclosure has a wiring space of 4 inches × 3 inches, the cross-sectional area is 12 square inches. Thus, the total conductor fill (see Chapter 9, Table 5 for dimensions of conductors) at any cross section cannot exceed 4.8 square inches (40 percent of 12 square inches), and the maximum space for conductors and splices or taps at any cross section cannot exceed 9 square inches (75 percent of 12 square inches).

In general, the best way to avoid overcrowding enclosures is to use properly sized auxiliary gutters (Sections 374-5 and 374-8) or junction boxes (Sections 370-16 and 370-28). See Section 430-10 and commentary for wiring space in enclosures for motor controllers and disconnecting means. See also Section 710-59 for installations over 600 volts.

373-9. **Side or Back Wiring Spaces or Gutters.** Cabinets and cutout boxes shall be provided with back wiring spaces, gutters, or wiring compartments as required by Section 373-11(c) and (d).

B. Construction Specifications

373-10. **Material.** Cabinets and cutout boxes shall comply with (a) through (c) below.

(a) Metal Cabinets and Cutout Boxes. Metal cabinets and cutout boxes shall be protected both inside and outside against corrosion.

(FPN): For protection against corrosion, see Section 300-6.

(b) Strength. The design and construction of cabinets and cutout boxes shall be such as to secure ample strength and rigidity. If constructed of sheet steel, the metal thickness shall not be less than 0.053 inch (1.35 mm) uncoated.

(c) Nonmetallic Cabinets. Nonmetallic cabinets shall be listed or they shall be submitted for approval prior to installation.

373-11. **Spacing.** The spacing within cabinets and cutout boxes shall comply with (a) through (d) below.

(a) General. Spacing within cabinets and cutout boxes shall be sufficient to provide ample room for the distribution of wires and cables placed in them, and for a separation between metal parts of devices and apparatus mounted within them as follows:

(1) Base. Other than at points of support, there shall be an air space of at least 1/16 inch (1.59 mm) between the base of the device and the wall of any metal cabinet or cutout box in which the device is mounted.

(2) Doors. There shall be an air space of at least 1 inch (25.4 mm) between any live metal part, including live metal parts of enclosed fuses, and the door.

Exception: Where the door is lined with an approved insulating material or is of a thickness of metal not less than 0.093 inches (2.36 mm) uncoated, the air space shall not be less than 1/2 inch (12.7 mm).

(3) Live Parts. There shall be an air space of at least 1/2 inch (12.7 mm) between the walls, back, gutter partition, if of metal, or door of any cabinet or cutout box and the nearest exposed current-carrying part of devices mounted within the cabinet where the voltage does not exceed 250. This spacing shall be increased to at least 1 inch (25.4 mm) for voltages 251 to 600, nominal.

Exception: As permitted in (2) above.

(b) Switch Clearance. Cabinets and cutout boxes shall be deep enough to allow the closing of the doors when 30-ampere branch-circuit panelboard switches are in any position; when combination cutout switches are in any position; or when other single-throw switches are opened as far as their construction will permit.

(c) Wiring Space. Cabinets and cutout boxes that contain devices or apparatus connected within the cabinet or box to more than eight conductors, including those of branch circuits, meter loops, feeder circuits, power circuits, and similar circuits, but not including the supply circuit or a continuation thereof, shall have back-wiring spaces or one or more side-wiring spaces, side gutters, or wiring compartments.

(d) Wiring Space — Enclosure. Side-wiring spaces, side gutters, or side-wiring compartments of cabinets and cutout boxes shall be made tight enclosures by means of covers, barriers, or partitions extending from the bases of the devices, contained in the cabinet to the door, frame, or sides of the cabinet.

Exception: Where the enclosure contains only those conductors that are led from the cabinet at points directly opposite their terminal connections to devices within the cabinet.

Partially enclosed back-wiring spaces shall be provided with covers to complete the enclosure. Wiring spaces that are required by (c) above, and that are exposed when doors are open, shall be provided with covers to complete the enclosure. Where adequate space is provided for feed-through conductors and for splices as required in Section 373-8, Exception, additional barriers shall not be required.

ARTICLE 374 Auxiliary Gutters

Contents

374-8. Splices and Taps.
    (a) Within Gutters.
    (b) Bare Conductors.
    (c) Suitably Identified.
    (d) Overcurrent Protection.
374-9. Construction and Installation.
    (a) Electrical and Mechanical Continuity.
    (b) Substantial Construction.
    (c) Smooth Rounded Edges.
    (d) Deflected Insulated Conductors.
    (e) Outdoor Use.
    (f) Grounding.

374-1. **Use.** Auxiliary gutters shall be permitted to supplement wiring spaces at meter centers, distribution centers, switchboards, and similar points of wiring systems and may enclose conductors or busbars but shall not be used to enclose switches, overcurrent devices, appliances, or other similar equipment.

Auxiliary gutter sections and associated fittings are identical to those of wireways, and, if listed by UL, each bears the single UL listing mark, "Listed Wireway or Auxiliary Gutter." They differ only in their intended use. See commentary following Section 362-1. Gutters (and wireways) are required to be constructed and installed to ensure adequate electrical and mechanical continuity of the complete system. See Section 250-91(b)(11).

Auxiliary gutters for outdoor use are required to be of raintight construction. See Section 620-35 for elevator uses and Section 640-4 for sound-recording equipment uses.

374-2. **Extension Beyond Equipment.** An auxiliary gutter shall not extend a greater distance than 30 feet (9.14 m) beyond the equipment that it supplements.

Exception: As provided in Section 620-35 for elevators.

(FPN): For wireways, see Article 362. For busways, see Article 364.

374-3. **Supports.** Gutters shall be supported throughout their entire length at intervals not exceeding 5 feet (1.52 m).

374-4. **Covers.** Covers shall be securely fastened to the gutter.

374-5. **Number of Conductors.** Auxiliary gutters shall not contain more than thirty current-carrying conductors at any

cross section. The sum of the cross-sectional areas of all contained conductors at any cross section of an auxiliary gutter shall not exceed 20 percent of the interior cross-sectional area of the auxiliary gutter.

Exception No. 1: As provided in Section 620-35 for elevators.

Exception No. 2: Conductors for signaling circuits or controller conductors between a motor and its starter and used only for starting duty shall not be considered as current-carrying conductors.

Exception No. 3: Where the correction factors specified in Article 310, Note 8(a) of Notes to Ampacity Tables of 0 to 2000 Volts are applied, there shall be no limit on the number of current-carrying conductors, but the sum of the cross-sectional area of all contained conductors at any cross section of the auxiliary gutter shall not exceed 20 percent of the interior cross-sectional area of the auxiliary gutter.

(FPN): For conductor cross-sectional area, see Tables 5, 5A, 6, and 8 and the applicable Notes to Tables at the beginning of Chapter 9.

The dimensions of rubber- and thermoplastic-insulated conductors given in Chapter 9, Tables 5 and 5A may be used to compute the size of gutters required to contain a given combination of such conductors.

Where auxiliary gutters contain 30 or fewer current-carrying conductors, the correction factors in Article 310, Note 8(a) of Notes to Ampacity Tables of 0 to 2000 Volts do not apply. If Note 8(a) is applied there is no limit on the number of current-carrying conductors; however, the contained conductors are not permitted to exceed 20 percent of the interior cross-sectional area of the gutter. See example given in the commentary following Section 362-1 for method of calculating number of conductors within a wireway, which is also applicable to auxiliary gutters.

No limit is placed on the size of conductors that may be installed in an auxiliary gutter; however, see Section 374-6 for ampacity limitations of bare copper or aluminum busbars enclosed in gutters.

374-6. **Ampacity of Conductors.** Where the number of current-carrying conductors contained in the auxiliary gutter is thirty or less, the correction factors specified in Article 310, Note 8(a) of Notes to Ampacity Tables of 0 to 2000 Volts shall not apply. The current carried continuously in bare copper bars in auxiliary gutters shall not exceed 1000 amperes per square inch (645 sq mm) of cross section of the conductor. For aluminum bars, the current carried continuously shall not exceed 700 amperes per square inch (645 sq mm) of cross section of the conductor.

374-7. **Clearance of Bare Live Parts.** Bare conductors shall be securely and rigidly supported so that the minimum clearance between bare current-carrying metal parts of opposite polarities mounted on the same surface will not be less than 2 inches (50.8 mm), nor less than 1 inch (25.4 mm) for parts that are held free in the air. A clearance not less than 1 inch (25.4 mm) shall be secured between bare current-carrying metal parts and any metal surface. Adequate provisions shall be made for the expansion and contraction of busbars.

374-8. **Splices and Taps.** Splices and taps shall comply with (a) through (d) below.

(a) Within Gutters. Splices or taps shall be permitted within gutters where they are accessible by means of removable covers or doors. The conductors, including splices and taps, shall not fill the gutter to more than 75 percent of its area.

(b) Bare Conductors. Taps from bare conductors shall leave the gutter opposite their terminal connections, and conductors shall not be brought in contact with uninsulated current-carrying parts of opposite polarity.

(c) Suitably Identified. All taps shall be suitably identified at the gutter as to the circuit or equipment that they supply.

(d) Overcurrent Protection. Tap connections from conductors in auxiliary gutters shall be provided with overcurrent protection as required in Section 240-21.

Precautions are required to be taken by providing suitable bushings, shields, etc., where conductors pass around bends or between gutters and cabinets and other locations to prevent abrasion of the conductor insulation. Also, conductors are required to be shaped or formed in a permanent manner so that they are not in contact with bare busbars within the gutter.

Per subparagraphs (c) and (d), all taps from gutters are required to be identified (as to circuits or equipment) and be protected with overcurrent devices per Section 240-21.

374-9. **Construction and Installation.** Auxiliary gutters shall comply with (a) through (f) below.

(a) Electrical and Mechanical Continuity. Gutters shall be so constructed and installed that adequate electrical and mechanical continuity of the complete system will be secured.

(b) Substantial Construction. Gutters shall be of substantial construction and shall provide a complete enclosure for the contained conductors. All surfaces, both interior and exterior, shall be suitably protected from corrosion. Corner joints shall be made tight and, where the assembly is held together by rivets or bolts, shall be spaced not more than 12 inches (305 mm) apart.

(c) Smooth Rounded Edges. Suitable bushings, shields, or fittings having smooth, rounded edges shall be provided where conductors pass between gutters, through partitions, around bends, between gutters and cabinets or junction boxes, and at other locations where necessary to prevent abrasion of the insulation of the conductors.

(d) Deflected Insulated Conductors. Where insulated conductors are deflected within an auxiliary gutter, either at the ends or where conduits, fittings, or other raceways or cables enter or leave the gutter, or where the direction of the gutter is deflected greater than 30 degrees, dimensions corresponding to Section 373-6 shall apply.

(e) Outdoor Use. Auxiliary gutters installed in wet locations shall be of raintight construction.

This section correlates with Section 362-2 and provides for auxiliary gutters that may be installed in wet locations that may not be outdoors; for example, in a car washing area inside of a building.

(f) Grounding. Grounding shall be according to the provisions of Article 250.

ARTICLE 380   Switches

Contents

A. Installation

A. Installation

380-1. Scope. The provisions of this article shall apply to all switches, switching devices, and circuit breakers where used as switches.

380-2. Switch Connections.

(a) Three-Way and Four-Way Switches. Three-way and four-way switches shall be so wired that all switching is done only in the ungrounded circuit conductor. Where in metal raceways or metal-jacketed cables, wiring between switches and outlets shall be in accordance with Section 300-20(a).

Exception: Switch loops shall not require a grounded conductor.

Although the *NEC* does not specifically prohibit use of two 2-conductor nonmetallic-sheathed cables for wiring 3-way and 4-way switches instead of a single 3-conductor cable, use of two 2-conductor cables could easily result in a violation of Section 300-20 if metal boxes are used and the cables enter the box through separate knockouts. Use of the same clamp or section of a clamp for both cables would, in most cases, be in violation of Section 110-3(b) because clamps have been tested for only one cable per clamp or section of clamp.

The grounded conductor is not needed [see Section 300-20(a)] because the ungrounded conductor both enters and leaves the enclosure in the same cable or raceway, thus avoiding inductive heating.

(b) Grounded Conductors. Switches or circuit breakers shall not disconnect the grounded conductor of a circuit.

Exception No. 1: Where the switch or circuit breaker simultaneously disconnects all conductors of the circuit.

Exception No. 2: Where the switch or circuit breaker is so arranged that the grounded conductor cannot be disconnected until all the ungrounded conductors of the circuit have been disconnected.

380-3. Enclosure. Switches and circuit breakers shall be of the externally operable type mounted in an enclosure listed for the intended use. The minimum wire bending space at terminals and minimum gutter space provided in switch enclosures shall be as required in Section 373-6.

Exception: Pendant- and surface-type snap switches and knife switches mounted on an open-face switchboard or panelboard.

380-4. Wet Locations. A switch or circuit breaker in a wet location or outside of a building shall be enclosed in a weatherproof enclosure or cabinet that shall comply with Section 373-2(a). Switches shall not be installed within wet locations in tub or shower spaces unless installed as part of a listed assembly.

The requirement for switches in wet locations is new in the 1993 *Code*.

380-5. **Time Switches, Flashers, and Similar Devices.** Time switches, flashers, and similar devices shall be of the enclosed type or shall be mounted in cabinets or boxes or equipment enclosures. Energized parts shall be barriered to prevent operator exposure when making manual adjustments or switching.

Exception: Where mounted so they are accessible only to qualified persons and so located in an enclosure that any energized parts within 6 inches (152 mm) of the manual adjustment or switch are covered by suitable barriers.

380-6. **Position of Knife Switches.**

(a) **Single-Throw Knife Switches.** Single-throw knife switches shall be so placed that gravity will not tend to close them. Single-throw knife switches, approved for use in the inverted position, shall be provided with a locking device that will ensure that the blades remain in the open position when so set.

(b) **Double-Throw Knife Switches.** Double-throw knife switches shall be permitted to be mounted so that the throw will be either vertical or horizontal. Where the throw is vertical, a locking device shall be provided to hold the blades in the open position when so set.

(c) **Connection of Knife Switches.** Single-throw knife switches shall be so connected that the blades are deenergized when the switch is in the open position.

Exception: Where the load side of the switch is connected to circuits or equipment, the inherent nature of which may provide a backfeed source of power. For such installations, a permanent sign shall be installed on the switch enclosure or immediately adjacent to open switches that reads: "WARNING—LOAD SIDE OF SWITCH MAY BE ENERGIZED BY BACKFEED."

Typical backfeed sources are batteries, generators, and double-ended switchboard ties. These may cause the switch blades to be energized when the switch is in the open position, a condition inherent to the circuitry.

380-7. **Indicating.** General-use and motor-circuit switches and circuit breakers, where mounted in an enclosure as described in Section 380-3, shall clearly indicate whether they are in the open "off" or closed "on" position.

Where these switch or circuit breaker handles are operated vertically rather than rotationally or horizontally, the up position of the handle shall be the "on" position.

Exception: Double-throw switches.

380-8. **Accessibility and Grouping.**

(a) **Location.** All switches and circuit breakers used as switches shall be so located that they may be operated from a readily accessible place. They shall be so installed that the center of the grip of the operating handle of the switch or circuit breaker, when in its highest position, will not be more than 6½ feet (1.98 m) above the floor or working platform.

Exception No. 1: On busway installations, fused switches and circuit breakers shall be permitted to be located at the same level as the busway. Suitable means shall be provided to operate the handle of the device from the floor.

Exception No. 2: Switches installed adjacent to motors, appliances, or other equipment that they supply shall be permitted to be located higher than specified in the foregoing and to be accessible by portable means.

Exception No. 3: Hookstick operable isolating switches shall be permitted at greater heights.

(b) **Voltage Between Adjacent Switches.** Snap switches shall not be grouped or ganged in enclosures unless they can be so arranged that the voltage between adjacent switches does not exceed 300, or unless they are installed in enclosures equipped with permanently installed barriers between adjacent switches.

380-9. **Faceplates for Flush-Mounted Snap Switches.** Flush snap switches, that are mounted in ungrounded metal boxes and located within reach of conducting floors or other conducting surfaces, shall be provided with faceplates of nonconducting, noncombustible material. Metal faceplates shall be of ferrous metal not less than 0.030 inch (0.762 mm) in thickness or of nonferrous metal not less than 0.040 inch (1.016 mm) in thickness. Faceplates of insulating material shall be noncombustible and not less than 0.10 inch (2.54 mm) in thickness, but they shall be permitted to be less than 0.10 inch (2.54 mm) in thickness if formed or reinforced to provide adequate mechanical strength. Faceplates shall be installed so as to completely cover the wall opening and seat against the wall surface.

Switch plates attached to ungrounded metal boxes are required to be made of insulating material and are required to have no exposed conductive parts.

380-10. **Mounting of Snap Switches.**

(a) **Surface-type.** Snap switches used with open wiring on insulators shall be mounted on insulating material that will separate the conductors at least ½ inch (12.7 mm) from the surface wired over.

(b) **Box Mounted.** Flush-type snap switches mounted in boxes that are set back of the wall surface as permitted in Section 370-20 shall be installed so that the extension plaster ears are seated against the surface of the wall. Flush-type snap switches mounted in boxes that are flush with the wall surface or project therefrom shall be so installed that the mounting yoke or strap of the switch is seated against the box.

Cooperation is necessary among the building trades (carpenters, dry-wall installers, plasterers, etc.) in order for electricians to properly set device boxes flush with the finish surface, thereby ensuring a secure seating of the switch yoke and permitting the maximum projection of switch handles through the installed switch plate.

380-11. **Circuit Breakers as Switches.** A hand-operable circuit breaker equipped with a lever or handle, or a power-operated circuit breaker capable of being opened by hand in the event of a power failure, shall be permitted to serve as a switch if it has the required number of poles. Note: See provisions contained in Section 240-81 and Section 240-83.

Circuit breakers capable of being hand-operated are required to clearly indicate whether they are in the open, "off," or closed, "on," position.

See Section 240-83(d) for marking (SWD) for circuit breakers used as switches for 120-V and 277-V fluorescent lighting circuits. Also see Section 380-7.

380-12. **Grounding of Enclosures.** Metal enclosures for switches or circuit breakers shall be grounded as specified in Article 250. Where nonmetallic enclosures are used with metal-sheathed cables or metallic conduits, provision shall be made for grounding continuity. Metal face plates for snap switches shall be effectively grounded where used with a wiring method that includes or provides an equipment ground.

380-13. **Knife Switches.**

(a) **Isolating Switches.** Knife switches rated at over 1200 amperes at 250 volts or less, and at over 600 volts at 251 to 600 volts, shall be used only as isolating switches and shall not be opened under load.

Figure 380-1. *The effective grounding of metal face plates can be accomplished by connecting the equipment grounding conductor provided with the wiring method to a grounding terminal on a metal yoke or strap.*

(b) **To Interrupt Currents.** To interrupt currents over 1200 amperes at 250 volts, nominal, or less, or over 600 amperes at 251 to 600 volts, nominal, a circuit breaker or a switch of special design listed for such purpose shall be used.

(c) **General-Use Switches.** Knife switches of ratings less than specified in (a) and (b) above shall be considered general-use switches.

(FPN): See definition of general-use switch in Article 100.

(d) **Motor-Circuit Switches.** Motor-circuit switches shall be permitted to be of the knife-switch type.

(FPN): See definition of a motor-circuit switch in Article 100.

380-14. **Rating and Use of Snap Switches.** Snap switches shall be used within their ratings and as indicated in (a) through (c) below:

(a) AC General-Use Snap Switch. A form of general-use snap switch suitable only for use on alternating-current circuits for controlling the following:

(1) Resistive and inductive loads, including electric-discharge lamps, not exceeding the ampere rating of the switch at the voltage involved.

(2) Tungsten-filament lamp loads not exceeding the ampere rating of the switch at 120 volts.

(3) Motor loads not exceeding 80 percent of the ampere rating of the switch at its rated voltage.

(b) AC-DC General-Use Snap Switch. A form of general-use snap switch suitable for use on either ac or dc circuits for controlling the following:

(1) Resistive loads not exceeding the ampere rating of the switch at the voltage applied.

(2) Inductive loads not exceeding 50 percent of the ampere rating of the switch at the applied voltage. Switches rated in horsepower are suitable for controlling motor loads within their rating at the voltage applied.

(3) Tungsten-filament lamp loads not exceeding the ampere rating of the switch at the applied voltage if "T" rated.

(FPN No. 1): For switches on signs and outline lighting, see Section 600-2.

(FPN No. 2): For switches controlling motors, see Sections 430-83, 430-109, and 430-110.

(c) CO/ALR Snap Switches. Snap switches rated 20 amperes or less directly connected to aluminum conductors shall be listed and marked CO/ALR.

B. Construction Specifications

380-15. **Marking.** Switches shall be marked with the current and voltage and, if horsepower rated, the maximum rating for which they are designed.

380-16. **600-Volt Knife Switches.** Auxiliary contacts of a renewable or quick-break type or the equivalent shall be provided on all knife switches rated 600 volts designed for use in breaking current over 200 amperes.

380-17. **Fused Switches.** A fused switch shall not have fuses in parallel except as permitted in Section 240-8, Exception.

380-18. **Wire Bending Space.** The wire bending space required by Section 380-3 shall meet Table 373-6(b) spacings to the enclosure wall opposite the line and load terminals.

ARTICLE 384   Switchboards and Panelboards

Contents

A. Switchboards

B. Panelboards

384-16. Overcurrent Protection.
  (a) Lighting and Appliance Branch-Circuit Panelboard
      Individually Protected.
  (b) Snap Switches Rated at 30 Amperes or Less.
  (c) Continuous Load.
  (d) Supplied through a Transformer.
  (e) Delta Breakers.
  (f) Back-Fed Devices.
384-17. Panelboards in Damp or Wet Locations.
384-18. Enclosure.
384-19. Relative Arrangement of Switches and Fuses.
384-20. Grounding of Panelboards.

C. Construction Specifications

384-30. Panels.
384-31. Busbars.
384-32. Protection of Instrument Circuits.
384-33. Component Parts.
384-34. Knife Switches.
384-35. Wire Bending Space in Panelboards.
384-36. Minimum Spacings.

384-1. **Scope.** This article covers (1) all switchboards, panelboards, and distribution boards installed for the control of light and power circuits, and (2) battery-charging panels supplied from light or power circuits.

Exception: Switchboards or portions thereof used exclusively to control signaling circuits operated by batteries.

Installation requirements for motor control centers are included in Article 384, in accordance with Exception No. 1 of Section 430-1.

384-2. **Other Articles.** Switches, circuit breakers, and overcurrent devices used on switchboards, panelboards, and distribution boards, and their enclosures, shall comply with this article and also with the requirements of Articles 240, 250, 370, 373, 380, and other articles that apply. Switchboards and panelboards in hazardous (classified) locations shall comply with the requirements of Articles 500 through 517.

See definitions of "Panelboard" and "Switchboard" in Article 100.

384-3. **Support and Arrangement of Busbars and Conductors.**

(a) **Conductors and Busbars on a Switchboard, Panelboard, or Control Board.** Conductors and busbars on a switchboard, panelboard, or control board shall be so located as to be free from physical damage and shall be held firmly in place. Other than the required interconnections and control wiring, only those conductors that are intended for termination in a vertical section of a switchboard shall be located in that section. Barriers shall be placed in all service switchboards that will isolate the service busbars and terminals from the remainder of the switchboard.

Exception: Conductors shall be permitted to travel horizontally through vertical sections of switchboards where such conductors are isolated from busbars by a barrier.

It is often impractical to disconnect or deenergize the service conductors supplying a service switchboard. For this reason, qualified electricians work on these switchboards with the service bus energized. Barriers are required in all UL-listed service switchboards to isolate the service busbars and terminals from the remainder of the switchboard, thus providing some measure of safety against contact with line energized parts during maintenance and installation of new feeders or branch circuits. It must be remembered that deenergizing the load side of a switchboard, by operation of the disconnecting means, does not deenergize the ungrounded service conductors. Installers should also be careful to remove tools that may have been left on the inside of the gear in order to prevent ground faults or short circuits due to tools coming in contact with busbars.

The exception permits conductors to travel horizontally through vertical sections of a switchboard where barriers are provided to isolate the conductors from the busbars.

(b) **Overheating and Inductive Effects.** The arrangement of busbars and conductors shall be such as to avoid overheating due to inductive effects.

(c) **Used As Service Equipment.** Each switchboard, or panelboard, if used as service equipment shall be provided with a main bonding jumper sized in accordance with Section 250-79(d) or the equivalent placed within the panelboard or one of the sections of the switchboard for connecting the grounded service conductor on its supply side to the switchboard or panelboard frame. All sections of a switchboard shall be bonded together using an equipment grounding conductor sized in accordance with Table 250-95.

Exception: As covered in Section 250-27 for high-impedance grounded neutral system connections.

(d) Terminals. Terminals in switchboards and panelboards shall be so located that it will not be necessary to reach across or beyond an ungrounded line bus in order to make connections.

(e) High-Leg Marking. On a switchboard or panelboard supplied from a 4-wire delta-connected system, where the midpoint of one phase is grounded, that phase busbar or conductor having the higher voltage to ground shall be durably and permanently marked by an outer finish that is orange in color, or by other effective means.

The high leg marking is required to be the color orange or other means and is intended to prevent problems due to the lack of complete standardization where metered and nonmetered equipment is installed in the same installation. Electricians should always test each phase to ground with suitable equipment in order to know exactly where this high leg is located in the system.

(f) Phase Arrangement. The phase arrangement on 3-phase buses shall be A, B, C from front to back, top to bottom, or left to right, as viewed from the front of the switchboard or panelboard. The B phase shall be that phase having the higher voltage to ground on 3-phase, 4-wire delta-connected systems. Other busbar arrangements shall be permitted for additions to existing installations and shall be marked.

Exception: Equipment within the same single section or multi-section switchboard or panelboard as the meter on 3-phase, 4-wire delta-connected systems shall be permitted to have the same phase configuration as the metering equipment.

The exception permits the phase leg having the higher voltage to ground to be located at the right hand position (C phase). The exception recognizes the fact that metering compartments have been standardized with the high leg at the right position (C phase) and this makes it unnecessary to transpose the busbar arrangement ahead of and beyond a metering compartment. See also Sections 215-8 and 230-56. Other busbar arrangements for addition to existing installations are permitted by the main rule.

(g) Minimum Wire Bending Space. The minimum wire bending space at terminals and minimum gutter space provided in panelboards and switchboards shall be as required in Section 373-6.

This section requires that installations in the field comply with Section 373-6. See also commentary following Section 384-35, which covers the size of the enclosure.

384-4. **Installation.** Equipment within the scope of Article 384 shall be located in rooms or spaces dedicated to such equipment. Such space shall include that space described in Section 110-16 and, in addition, shall include an exclusively dedicated space extending 25 feet (7.62 m) from the floor or to the structural ceiling with a width and depth that of the equipment. No piping, ducts, or equipment foreign to the electrical equipment or architectural appurtenances shall be permitted to be installed in, enter, or pass through such spaces or rooms.

(FPN No. 1):   It is not the intent to mandate a dedicated room.

(FPN No. 2):   This section is not intended to prohibit sprinkler protection for the electrical installation.

(FPN No. 3):   For the purpose of this section, dropped, suspended, and similar ceilings not intended to add strength to the building structure are not structural ceilings.

(FPN No. 4):   It is not the intent that any of the provisions of this rule or the exceptions thereto allow any equipment to be located in the working space described in Section 110-16.

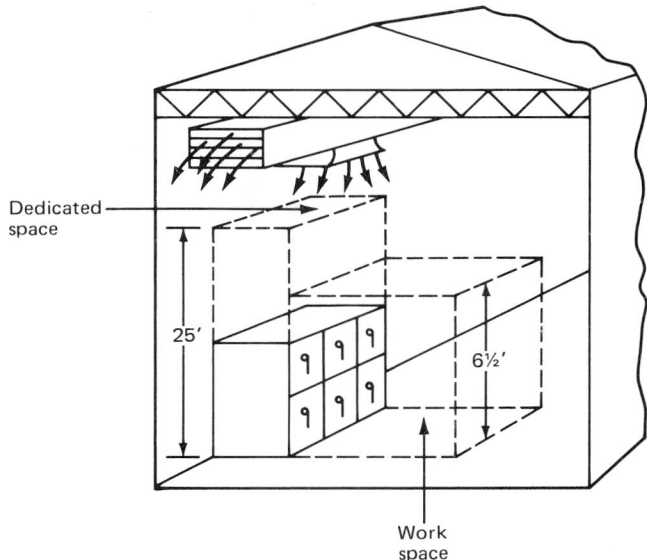

Figure 384-1. Section 384-4 is intended to require the space outlined by the footprint of the panelboard or switchboard to be reserved for the installation of electrical equipment or for the installation of conduits, cable trays, etc., entering or exiting the equipment.

Formal Interpretation 81-3
Reference: 384-2 (384-4 in this edition)

Statement: A building has one or more closets located so as to feed electric and communication services to areas of the building. Each closet is entered by one door and it has no partitions. A portion of the closet is dedicated to a panelboard serving branch circuits for that area. Another portion of the closet is dedicated to telephone equipment. The telephone equipment and wiring do not encroach on the dedicated space for the panelboard.

Question: Is it the intent of Section 384-2 (Section 384-4 in this edition) of the 1981 *National Electrical Code* to prohibit such an installation?

Answer: No.

Statement: It has been common practice to flush-mount panelboards in the walls of corridors and hallways in buildings and residences.

Question: Is it the intent of Section 384-2 of the 1981 *National Electrical Code* to prohibit such installation?

Answer: No.

Issue Edition: 1981
Date: June 1981 ■

Formal Interpretation 81-5
Reference: 384-2 (384-4 in this edition)

Question: Is it the intent of Section 384-2 (Section 384-4 of this edition) of the *National Electrical Code* to prohibit automatic sprinkler protection in rooms containing switchboards and panelboards?

Answer: No.

Issue Edition: 1981
Date: August 1982 ■

The required space includes the space described in Section 110-16 and an exclusively dedicated space extending 25 feet from floor or to the structural ceiling over the equipment. See Figures 384-2 and 384-3. A suspended ceiling over the equipment would not be considered as being the structural ceiling described in this section. See FPN No. 3.

It is not the intent of this section to prohibit suspended ceilings over equipment.

Automatic sprinklers and their associated piping are permitted in rooms dedicated exclusively to panelboards and switchboards if their purpose is the protection of the panelboards and switchboards. See the second fine print note following the main rule.

Where the room in which electrical equipment is located is not a room dedicated only for switchboards and panelboards, automatic sprinklers and their associated piping are permitted in the room, provided they do not enter or pass through the dedicated space or work space required by Section 110-16.

If a room does not contain equipment within the scope of Article 384, it is not considered a dedicated electrical room. However, the installation of motor control centers must comply with the requirements of Section 384-4.

Exception No. 1: Control equipment that by its very nature or because of other rules of this Code must be adjacent to or within sight of its operating machinery.

Exception No. 2: Ventilating, heating, or cooling equipment that serves the electrical rooms or spaces.

Exception No. 3: Equipment located throughout industrial plants that is isolated from foreign equipment by height or physical enclosures or covers that will afford adequate mechanical protection from vehicular traffic, accidental contact by unauthorized personnel, or accidental spillage or leakage from piping systems.

Exception No. 4: Outdoor electrical equipment located in weatherproof enclosures protected from accidental contact by unauthorized personnel or vehicular traffic or accidental spillage or leakage from piping systems.

Side view   Front view

Figure 384-2. This figure illustrates the work space required in front of the panelboard by Section 110-16. This is working space. Fine Print Note No. 4 to Section 384-4 (new in the 1993 Code) emphasizes that no equipment, electrical or otherwise, is allowed in the work space. See Figure 384-3 for additional space required by Section 384-4.

Side view   Front view

Figure 384-3. This figure illustrates the additional exclusively dedicated space required over and under the panelboard by Section 384-4. This space is for the cables, raceways, etc., that run to and from the panelboard.

A. Switchboards

384-5. Location of Switchboards. Switchboards that have any exposed live parts shall be located in permanently dry locations and then only where under competent supervision and accessible only to qualified persons. Switchboards shall be so located that the probability of damage from equipment or processes is reduced to a minimum.

384-6. Switchboards in Damp or Wet Locations. Switchboards in damp or wet locations shall be installed to comply with Section 373-2(a).

384-7. Location Relative to Easily Ignitible Material. Switchboards shall be so placed as to reduce to a minimum the probability of communicating fire to adjacent combustible materials. Where installed over a combustible floor, suitable protection thereto shall be provided.

Installation of switchboards on a combustible wood floor is prohibited. One method of compliance with this rule is to form and set a piece of sheet steel or other suitable noncombustible material on the floor under the equipment.

384-8. Clearances.

(a) From Ceiling. A space of 3 feet (914 mm) or more shall be provided between the top of any switchboard and any combustible ceiling.

Exception No. 1: Where a noncombustible shield is provided between the switchboard and the ceiling.

Exception No. 2: Totally enclosed switchboards.

Building designers should consider these rules when designing areas in which switchboards will be located.

(b) Around Switchboards. Clearances around switchboards shall comply with the provisions of Section 110-16.

Sufficient access and working space is required to permit ready and safe operation and maintenance of such equipment. Table 110-16(a) indicates minimum working clearances from 0 to 600 V.

For work space clearances of switchboards operating at over 600 V, see Table 110-34(a).

384-9. Conductor Insulation. An insulated conductor used within a switchboard shall be listed, flame-retardant, and shall be rated not less than the voltage applied to it and not less than the voltage applied to other conductors or busbars with which it may come in contact.

384-10. Clearance for Conductors Entering Bus Enclosures. Where conduits or other raceways enter a switchboard, floor standing panelboard, or similar enclosure at the bottom, sufficient space shall be provided to permit installation of conductors in the enclosure. The wiring space shall not be less than shown in the following table where the conduit or raceways enter or leave the enclosure below the busbars, their supports, or other obstructions. The conduit or raceways, including their end fittings, shall not rise more than 3 inches (76 mm) above the bottom of the enclosure.

Conductor	Minimum Spacing Between Bottom of Enclosure and Busbars, Their Supports, or Other Obstructions (Inches)
Insulated busbars, their supports, or other obstructions	8 (203 mm)
Noninsulated busbars	10 (254 mm)

This section should be carefully considered where installing underground conduit or raceways that will terminate in the bottom of an open switchboard. For example, if larger sizes of conduit are employed for service laterals or feeders and terminate where they extend more than 3 inches above the bottom of the enclosure, it will be difficult to cut them after it is discovered that they are too long. On the other hand, conduits or raceways should not be installed flush with the finished floor under switchboards that are located on the outside of buildings or in other locations where water could enter the raceways.

384-11. Grounding Switchboard Frames. Switchboard frames and structures supporting switching equipment shall be grounded.

Exception: Frames of 2-wire, direct-current switchboards shall not be required to be grounded if effectively insulated from ground.

384-12 . Grounding of Instruments, Relays, Meters, and Instrument Transformers on Switchboards. Instruments, relays, meters, and instrument transformers located on switchboards shall be grounded as specified in Sections 250-121 through 250-125.

B. Panelboards

384-13 . General. All panelboards shall have a rating not less than the minimum feeder capacity required for the load computed in accordance with Article 220. Panelboards shall be durably marked by the manufacturer with the voltage and the current rating and the number of phases for which they are designed and with the manufacturer's name or trademark in such a manner as to be visible after installation, without disturbing the interior parts or wiring. All panelboard circuits and circuit modifications shall be legibly identified as to purpose or use on a circuit directory located on the face or inside of the panel doors.

Some panelboards are suitable for use as service equipment and are so marked.

UL-listed panelboards are for use with copper conductors unless marked to indicate which terminals are suitable for use with aluminum conductors. Such marking is required to be independent of any marking on terminal connectors and is required to appear on a wiring diagram or other readily visible location. If all terminals are suitable for use with aluminum conductors as well as with copper conductors, the panelboard will be marked "Use Copper or Aluminum Wire." A panelboard employing terminals or main or branch-circuit units individually marked "AL-CU" will be marked as noted above or will be marked "Use Copper Wire Only." The latter marking indicates that wiring space or other factors make the panelboard unsuitable for aluminum conductors. See Section 110-14(c).

Panelboards to which units (circuit breakers, switches, etc.) may be added in the field are marked with the name or trademark of the manufacturer and the catalog number or equivalent of those units intended for installation in the field.

Unless the panelboard is marked to indicate otherwise, the termination provisions are based on the use of 60°C (140°F) ampacities for wire sizes No. 14 through 1 and 75°C (167°F) ampacities for wire sizes No. 1/0 and larger.

(FPN): See Section 110-22 for additional requirements.

384-14 . Lighting and Appliance Branch-Circuit Panelboard. For the purposes of this article, a lighting and appliance branch-circuit panelboard is one having more than 10 percent of its overcurrent devices rated 30 amperes or less, for which neutral connections are provided.

A lighting and appliance branch-circuit panelboard is a panelboard having a maximum of 42 overcurrent devices (see Section 384-15), where more than 10 percent of the installed overcurrent devices (10 percent of $42 = 4.2$; rounded off to 5) are rated 30 A or less and for which circuit and neutral connections are provided. Lighting circuits rated 30 A or less without a neutral connection are not considered.

384-15 . Number of Overcurrent Devices on One Panelboard. Not more than forty-two overcurrent devices (other than those provided for in the mains) of a lighting and appliance branch-circuit panelboard shall be installed in any one cabinet or cutout box.

Class CTL panelboards are identified by the words "Class CTL" on the Underwriters Laboratories Inc. listing mark.

Class CTL panelboards incorporate physical features that, in conjunction with the physical size, configuration, or other means provided in Class CTL circuit breakers, fuseholders, or fusible switches, are designed to prevent the installation of more overcurrent protective poles than that number for which the panelboard is designed and rated.

Class CTL is the Underwriters Laboratories Inc. designation for the *Code* requirement for circuit limitation within a lighting and appliance branch-circuit panelboard and means "circuit limiting."

A lighting and appliance branch-circuit panelboard shall be provided with physical means to prevent the installation of more overcurrent devices than that number for which the panelboard was designed, rated, and approved.

For the purposes of this article, a 2-pole circuit breaker shall be considered two overcurrent devices; a 3-pole breaker shall be considered three overcurrent devices.

384-16 . Overcurrent Protection.

(a) Lighting and Appliance Branch-Circuit Panelboard Individually Protected. Each lighting and appliance branch-circuit panelboard shall be individually protected on the supply side by not more than two main circuit breakers or two sets of fuses having a combined rating not greater than that of the panelboard.

Exception No. 1: Individual protection for a lighting and appliance panelboard shall not be required if the panelboard feeder has overcurrent protection not greater than the rating of the panelboard.

Main overcurrent protection may be an integral part of a panelboard or located remote from the panelboard. See Figures 384-4, 384-5, and 384-6. See also commentary following Section 384-15.

Figure 384-4 shows a panelboard with a 200-A main circuit breaker. Figure 384-5 shows a panelboard without main overcurrent protection but it may be protected by overcurrent protection as illustrated in Figure 384-6.

Exception No. 2: For existing installations, individual protection for lighting and appliance branch-circuit panelboards shall not be required where such panelboards are used as service equipment in supplying an individual residential occupancy.

The phrase "for existing installations" in Exception No. 2 means the existing panelboard. It is not intended that a split-bus panelboard used in an individual dwelling occupancy be replaced if a circuit is added to the existing panelboard. However, it does mean that for installation of new panelboards in new or existing residential occupancies, a split-bus six disconnect panelboard (with more than two circuit breakers or sets of fuses protecting the panelboard) is not permitted for the service equipment.

An individual residential occupancy could be a dwelling unit in a multifamily dwelling where the panelboard is used as service equipment. See the definition of "Dwelling Unit" in Article 100.

(b) Snap Switches Rated at 30 Amperes or Less. Panelboards equipped with snap switches rated at 30 amperes or less shall have overcurrent protection not in excess of 200 amperes.

This requirement is limited to snap switches; it does not apply to panelboards equipped with circuit breakers.

(c) Continuous Load. The total load on any overcurrent device located in a panelboard shall not exceed 80 percent of

Figure 384-4. *A panelboard with main circuit breaker disconnect suitable for use as service equipment. (Square D Co.)*

its rating where, in normal operation, the load will continue for three hours or more.

Exception: Where the assembly, including the overcurrent device, is listed for continuous operation at 100 percent of its rating.

Figure 384-5. A panelboard with main lugs only. (Square D Co.)

(d) Supplied through a Transformer. Where a panelboard is supplied through a transformer, the overcurrent protection required in (a) and (b) above shall be located on the secondary side of the transformer.

Exception: A panelboard supplied by the secondary side of a single-phase transformer having a 2-wire (single-voltage) secondary shall be considered as protected by overcurrent protection provided on the primary (supply) side of the transformer, provided this protection is in accordance with Section 450-3(b)(1) and does not exceed the value determined by multiplying the panelboard rating by the secondary-to-primary voltage ratio.

(e) Delta Breakers. A 3-phase disconnect or overcurrent device shall not be connected to the bus of any panelboard that has less than 3-phase buses.

(FPN): This is intended to prohibit the use of "delta breakers" in panelboards.

(f) Back-Fed Devices. Plug-in-type overcurrent protection devices or plug-in-type main lug assemblies that are back fed shall be secured in place by an additional fastener that requires other than a pull to release the device from the mounting means on the panel.

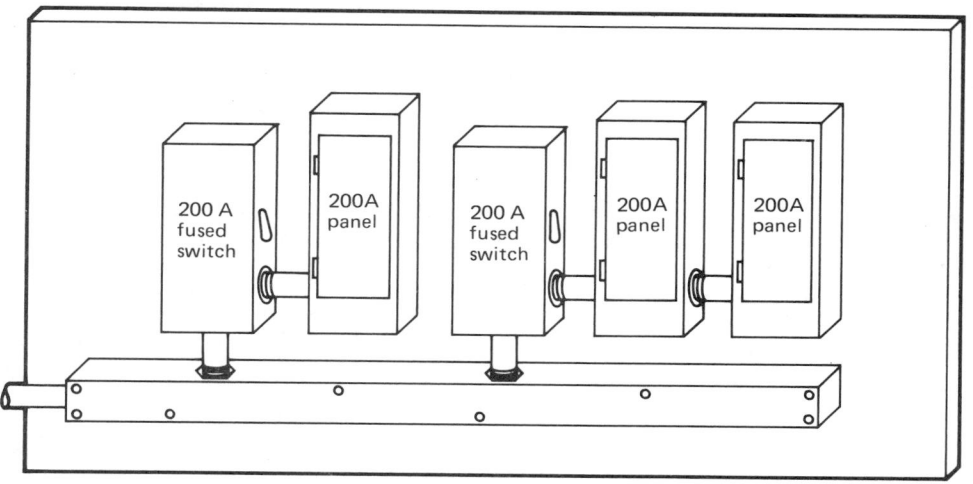

Figure 384-6. An arrangement of three individual lighting and appliance branch-circuit panelboards with main overcurrent protection remote from the panelboards. Note that the panelboard feeders have overcurrent protection not greater than the rating of the panelboard.

Figure 384-7. *The upper panel has two 100-A main breakers installed as disconnecting means and 200-A main lugs. The lower is a split-bus panel with 150-A main lugs and six main breaker disconnecting means. The 150-A panelboard is suitable for use as service equipment only if it is not a lighting and appliance panelboard or if it presently exists in an individual residential occupancy.*

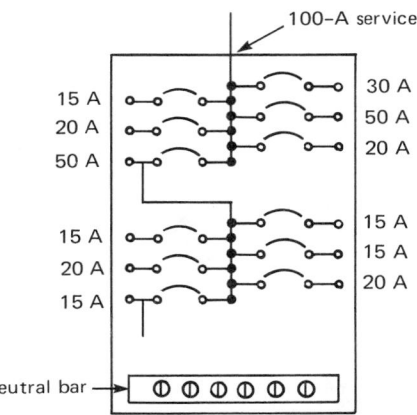

Figure 384-8. *A split-bus lighting and appliance branch-circuit panelboard supplying an individual residential occupancy.*

384-17. **Panelboards in Damp or Wet Locations.** Panelboards in damp or wet locations shall be installed to comply with Section 373-2(a).

384-18. **Enclosure.** Panelboards shall be mounted in cabinets, cutout boxes, or enclosures designed for the purpose and shall be dead front.

Exception: Panelboards other than of the dead-front externally operable type shall be permitted where accessible only to qualified persons.

384-19. **Relative Arrangement of Switches and Fuses.** In panelboards, fuses of any type shall be installed on the load side of any switches.

Exception: As provided in Section 230-94 for use as service equipment.

Section 230-94 permits the service switch on either the supply side or load side of fuses. Where fuses of panelboards are accessible to other than qualified persons, such as occupants of a multifamily dwelling, Section 240-40 requires that disconnecting means be located on the supply side of all fuses in circuits of over 150 volts to ground and cartridge-type fuses in circuits of any voltage. Thus, when the disconnect switch is opened, the fuses are deenergized and danger from shock is reduced.

384-20. **Grounding of Panelboards.** Panelboard cabinets and panelboard frames, if of metal, shall be in physical contact with each other and shall be grounded in accordance with Article 250 or Section 384-3(c). Where the panelboard is used with nonmetallic raceway or cable or where separate grounding conductors are provided, a terminal bar for the grounding conductors shall be secured inside the cabinet. The terminal bar shall be bonded to the cabinet and panelboard frame, if of metal, otherwise it shall be connected to the grounding conductor that is run with the conductors feeding the panelboard.

A separate equipment grounding conductor terminal bar is required to be installed and bonded to the panelboard for the termination of feeder and branch-circuit equipment grounding conductors. Where installed within service equipment, this terminal is permitted to be bonded to the neutral terminal bar. Any other connection between the equipment grounding terminal bar and the neutral bar, other than as permitted by Exception No. 2, would raise the potential of all exposed dead metal parts of equipment, since current flow in the neutral or grounded conductor would allow a potential difference of several volts, and would also permit neutral current to take parallel paths back to the service equipment, one being through the equipment grounding conductor (the raceway, for example). This is important where subpanels are used, since arcing and/or loose connections at connectors, raceway fittings, etc., could serve to create a potential fire or shock hazard.

Grounding conductors shall not be connected to a terminal bar provided for grounded conductors (may be a neutral) unless the bar is identified for the purpose and is located where connection is made from the grounded conductor to a grounding electrode as permitted or required by Article 250.

Exception: Where an isolated equipment grounding conductor is provided as permitted by Section 250-74, Exception No. 4, this insulated equipment grounding conductor that is run with the circuit conductors shall be permitted to pass through the panelboard without being connected to the panelboard's equipment grounding terminal bar.

Electronic equipment, which is often used in data processing systems, hospitals, laboratories, etc., may fail to perform properly due to electromagnetic interference present in the electrical supply.

Where required for the reduction of electrical noise (electromagnetic interference) on the grounding circuit, an isolated equipment grounding terminal is permitted. This equipment grounding terminal is required to be grounded by an insulated equipment grounding conductor that is run with the circuit conductors. It is also permitted to pass through one or more panelboards (without connection to the panelboard grounding terminal), but it is very important that it terminate directly at the applicable separately derived system or service grounding terminal. However, if the isolated equipment grounding conductor is run in a separate building, Section 250-74, Exception No. 4 requires the isolated equipment grounding conductor to terminate at a panelboard within the same building. Connection to only a separate grounding electrode places earth in the fault return path and may prevent sufficient current for opening overcurrent protection when a ground fault occurs. See commentary following Section 250-74, Fine Print Note and Section 250-91(c).

C. Construction Specifications

384-30. **Panels.** The panels of switchboards shall be made of moisture-resistant, noncombustible material.

384-31. **Busbars.** Insulated or bare busbars shall be rigidly mounted.

384-32. **Protection of Instrument Circuits.** Instruments, pilot lights, potential transformers, and other switchboard devices with potential coils shall be supplied by a circuit that is protected by standard overcurrent devices rated 15 amperes or less.

Exception No. 1: Where the operation of the overcurrent device might introduce a hazard in the operation of devices.

Exception No. 2: For ratings of 2 amperes or less, special types of enclosed fuses shall be permitted.

384-33. **Component Parts.** Switches, fuses, and fuseholders used on panelboards shall comply with the applicable requirements of Articles 240 and 380.

384-34. **Knife Switches.** Exposed blades of knife switches shall be deenergized when open.

384-35. **Wire Bending Space in Panelboards.** The enclosure for a panelboard shall have the top and bottom wire bending space sized in accordance with Table 373-6(b) for the largest conductor entering or leaving the enclosure. Side wire bending space shall be in accordance with Table 373-6(a) for the largest conductor to be terminated in that space.

Exception No. 1: Either the top or bottom wire bending space shall be permitted to be sized in accordance with Table 373-6(a) for a lighting and appliance branch-circuit panelboard rated 225 amperes or less.

Exception No. 2: Either the top or bottom wire bending space for any panelboard shall be permitted to be sized in accordance with Table 373-6(a) where at least one side wire bending space is sized in accordance with Table 373-6(b) for the largest conductor to be terminated in any side wire bending space.

Exception No. 3: The top and bottom wire bending space shall be permitted to be sized in accordance with Table 373-6(a) spacings if the panelboard is designed and constructed for wiring using only one single 90-degree bend for each conductor, including the neutral, and the wiring diagram shows and specifies the method of wiring that shall be used.

Exception No. 4: Either the top or the bottom wire bending space, but not both, shall be permitted to be sized in accordance with Table 373-6(a) where there are no conductors terminated in that space.

This section covers the size of the enclosure for a panelboard. With reference to Figure 373-1 (see Section 373-6), the general rule calls for wire bending space T1 and T4 to be in accordance with Table 373-6(b) for Size M conductors (assuming these are the largest conductors entering the enclosure). Side wire bending space T2 shall be in accordance with Table 373-6(a) for the wire size to be used with the largest rated unit facing that side space, and T3 shall be similarly sized for the largest rated unit facing the right side of the enclosure. Exception No. 1 of Section 384-35 permits either T1 or T4 (not both) to be reduced to the space required by Table 373-6(a) for size M conductors for a panelboard rated 225 A or less. Exception No. 2 of Section 384-35 permits either T1 or T4 (not both) to be reduced to the space required by Table 373-6(a) for size M conductors for any panelboard where either T2 or T3 (or both) is sized in accordance with Table 373-6(b) for the largest conductor to be terminated in either the left or

right side spaces. Under the construction rules of Section 384-35, a panelboard enclosure might not be of adequate size for all manner of wiring, and Section 373-6 must be considered when wiring is planned.

Exception No. 3 of Section 384-35 permits both the top and bottom wire bending space to be reduced as noted. A single 90 degree bend, meaning one and only one 90 degree bend, is required to be present for the ungrounded conductors. A grounded conductor is permitted to be wired straight in if Table 373-6(b) spacing is provided for the grounded conductor.

Exception No. 4 permits a reduction to the Table 373-6(a) spacings for the top or bottom space where there are no terminals facing that space. In this case, the space is a gutter space, and measurement is on a line perpendicular to the wall of the enclosure and to the closest barrier post or side of a switch, fuse, or circuit breaker unit that is, or may be, installed.

384-36. **Minimum Spacings.** The distance between bare metal parts, busbars, etc., shall not be less than specified in Table 384-36.

Exception No. 1: At switches or circuit breakers.

Exception No. 2: Inherent spacings in listed components.

Where close proximity does not cause excessive heating, parts of the same polarity at switches, enclosed fuses, etc., shall be permitted to be placed as close together as convenience in handling will allow.

Table 384-36. **Minimum Spacings Between Bare Metal Parts**

	Opposite Polarity Where Mounted on the Same Surface	Opposite Polarity Where Held Free in Air	Live Parts to Ground*
Not over 125 volts, nominal	$3/4$ inch	$1/2$ inch	$1/2$ inch
Not over 250 volts, nominal	$1\,1/4$ inch	$3/4$ inch	$1/2$ inch
Not over 600 volts, nominal	2 inches	1 inch	1 inch

For SI units: one inch = 25.4 millimeters.
*For spacing between live parts and doors of cabinets, see Sections 373-11(a) (1), (2), and (3).

4

Equipment for General Use

ARTICLE 400 Flexible Cords and Cables

Contents

A. General

B. Construction Specifications

C. Portable Cables Over 600 Volts, Nominal

(a) Conductors.

(b) Shields.

(c) Equipment Grounding Conductor(s).

400-32. Shielding.

400-33. Grounding.

400-34. Minimum Bending Radii.

400-35. Fittings.

400-36. Splices and Terminations.

A. General

400-1. **Scope.** This article covers general requirements, applications, and construction specifications for flexible cords and flexible cables.

Flexible cords and cables as covered by Article 400 are not considered a wiring method. Wiring methods are covered in Chapter 3 of the *Code*.

400-2. **Other Articles.** Flexible cords and flexible cables shall comply with this article and with the applicable provisions of other articles of this Code.

400-3. **Suitability.** Flexible cords and cables and their associated fittings shall be suitable for the conditions of use and location.

400-4. **Types.** Flexible cords and flexible cables shall conform to the description in Table 400-4. Types of flexible cords and flexible cables other than those listed in the table shall be the subject of special investigation.

Notes to Table 400-4

1. Except for Types HPN, SP-1, SP-2, SP-3, SPE-1, SPE-2, SPE-3, SPT-1, SPT-2, SPT-3, TPT, and 3-conductor parallel versions of SRD, SRDE, SRDT, individual conductors are twisted together.

2. Types TPT, TS, and TST shall be permitted in lengths not exceeding 8 feet (2.44 m) where attached directly, or by means of a special type of plug, to a portable appliance rated at 50 watts or less and of such nature that extreme flexibility of the cord is essential.

3. Rubber-filled or varnished cambric tapes shall be permitted as a substitute for the inner braids.

4. Types G, S, SC, SCE, SCT, SE, SEO, SEOO, SO, SOO, ST, STO, STOO, and W shall be permitted for use on theater

stages, in garages, and elsewhere where flexible cords are permitted by this Code.

5. Elevator traveling cables for operating control and signal circuits shall contain nonmetallic fillers as necessary to maintain concentricity. Cables shall have steel supporting members as required for suspension by Section 620-41. In locations subject to excessive moisture or corrosive vapors or gases, supporting members of other materials shall be permitted. Where steel supporting members are used, they shall run straight through the center of the cable assembly and shall not be cabled with the copper strands of any conductor.

In addition to conductors used for control and signaling circuits, Types E, EO, ET, ETLB, ETP, and ETT elevator cables shall be permitted to incorporate in the construction one or more No. 20 telephone conductor pairs, one or more coaxial cables, and/or one or more optical fibers. The No. 20 conductor pairs shall be permitted to be covered with suitable shielding for telephone, audio, or higher frequency communication circuits; the coaxial cables consist of a center conductor, insulation, and shield for use in video or other radio frequency communication circuits. The optical fiber shall be suitably covered with flame-retardant thermoplastic. The insulation of the conductors shall be rubber or thermoplastic of thickness not less than specified for the other conductors of the particular type of cable. Metallic shields shall have their own protective covering. Where used, these components shall be permitted to be incorporated in any layer of the cable assembly but shall not run straight through the center.

6. The third conductor in these cables shall be used for equipment grounding purposes only.

7. The individual conductors of all cords, except those of heat-resistant cords, shall have a thermoset or thermoplastic insulation, except that the grounding conductor where used shall be in accordance with Section 400-23(b). Unvulcanized rubber compounds shall be permitted to be used for all sizes of heater cord Types HSJ and HSJO, and for sizes No. 18 and 16 Type HPD.

8. Where the voltage between any two conductors exceeds 300, but does not exceed 600, flexible cord of Nos. 10 and smaller shall have thermoset or thermoplastic insulation on the individual conductors at least 45 mils in thickness, unless Type S, SE, SEO, SEOO, SO, SOO, ST, STO, or STOO cord is used.

9. Insulations and outer coverings that meet the requirements as flame-retardant, limited-smoke, and are so listed, shall be permitted to be designated limited-smoke with the suffix /LS after the Code type designation.

Table 400-4. Flexible Cords and Cables (See Section 400-4)

Trade Name	Type Letter	Size AWG	No. of Conductors	Insulation	Nominal Insulation Thickness*		Braid on Each Conductor	Outer Covering	Use		
					AWG	Mils					
Lamp Cord	C	18-10	2 or more	Thermoset or Thermoplastic	18-16 / 14-10	30 / 45	Cotton	None	Pendant or Portable	Dry Locations	Not Hard Usage
Elevator Cable	E See Note 5. See Note 9.	20-14	2 or more	Thermoset	20-16 / 20-16	20 / 20	Cotton / Flexible Nylon Jacket	Three Cotton, Outer one Flame-Retardant & Moisture-Resistant, See Note 3.	Elevator Lighting and Control	Nonhazardous Locations	
Elevator Cable	EO See Note 5.	20-14	2 or more	Thermoset	20-16 / 14	20 / 30	Cotton	Three Cotton, Outer one Flame-Retardant & Moisture-Resistant. See Note 3. / One Cotton and a Neoprene Jacket See Note 3.	/ Elevator Lighting and Control	Nonhazardous Locations / Hazardous (Classified) Locations	
Elevator Cable	ET See Note 5.	20-14	2 or more	Thermoplastic	20-16 / 14	20 / 30	Rayon	Three Cotton or equivalent, Outer one Flame-Retardant & Moisture-Resist. See Note 3.	Nonhazardous Locations		
	ETLB See Note 5.						None				
	ETP See Note 5.			Thermoplastic			Rayon	Thermoplastic	Hazardous (Classified) Locations		
	ETT See Note 5.			Thermoplastic			None	One Cotton or equivalent and a Thermoplastic Jacket	Hazardous (Classified) Locations		

See Notes 1 through 9.
*See Note 8.

Table 400-4, continued

Trade Name	Type Letter	Size AWG	No. of Conductors	Insulation	Nominal Insulation Thickness*		Braid on Each Conductor	Outer Covering	Use		
					AWG	Mils					
Portable Power Cable	G	8-500 kcmil	2-6 plus Grounding Conductor(s)	Thermoset	8-2 1-4/0 250 kcmil-500 kcmil	60 80 95		Oil-Resistant Thermoset	Portable, Extra Hard Usage, and as Permitted in Sections 520-68(a) and 530-12.		
Heater Cord	HPD	18-12	2, 3, or 4	Thermoset with Asbestos or All Thermoset	Thermost 18-16 14-12	 15 30	None	Cotton or Rayon	Portable Heaters	Dry Locations	Not Hard Usage
Parallel Heater Cord	HPN See Note 6.	18-12	2 or 3	Thermo-setting	18-16 14 12	45 80 95	None	Thermosetting	Portable	Damp Locations	Not Hard Usage
Thermoset Jacketed Heater Cord	HS	14-12	2, 3, or 4	Thermoset with Asbestos or All Thermoset	18-16 (Thermoset/Asbestos)	15	None	Cotton and Thermoset	Portable or Portable Heaters		Extra Hard Usage
	HSJ See Note 7.	18-12			18-16 (All Thermoset)	30				Damp Locations	Hard Usage
	HSJO See Note 7.				14-12 (Thermoset/Asbestos)	30		Cotton and Oil-Resistant			
	HSO	14-12			14-12 (All Thermoset)	45					Extra Hard Usage
Twisted Portable Cord	PD	18-10	2 or more	Thermoset or Thermoplastic	18-16 14-10	30 45	Cotton	Cotton or Rayon	Pendant or Portable	Dry Locations	Not Hard Usage
Hard Service Cord	S See Note 4.	18-2	2 or more	Thermoset	18-16 14-10 8-2	30 45 60	None	Thermoset	Pendant or Portable	Damp Locations	Extra Hard Usage
Flexible Stage and Lighting Power Cable	SC	8-250 kcmil	1 or more	Thermoset	8-2 1-4/0 250 kcmil	60 80 95		Thermoset**	Portable, Extra Hard Usage, and as permitted in Articles 520 and 530		

See Notes 1 through 9.
* See Note 8.
** The required outer covering on some single-conductor cables may be integral with the insulation.

Table 400-4, continued

Trade Name	Type Letter	Size AWG	No. of Conduc-tors	Insulation	Nominal Insulation Thickness*		Braid on Each Conductor	Outer Covering	Use		
					AWG	Mils					
Flexible Stage and Lighting Power Cable	SCE	8-250 kcmil	1 or more	Thermo-plastic Elastomer	8-2 1-4/0 250 kcmil	60 80 95		Thermoplastic Elastomer**	Portable, Extra Hard Usage, and as permitted in Articles 520 and 530		
Flexible Stage and Lighting Power Cable	SCT	8-250 kcmil	1 or more	Thermo-plastic	8-2 1-4/0 250 kcmil	60 80 95		Thermoplastic**	Portable, Extra Hard Usage, and as permitted in Articles 520 and 530		
Hard Service Cord	SE See Note 4.	18-2	2 or more	Thermo-plastic Elastomer	18-16 14-10	30 45	None	Thermoplastic Elastomer	Pendant or Portable	Damp Locations	Extra Hard Usage
	SEO See Note 4.				8-2	60		Oil-Resistant Thermo-plastic Elastomer			
	SEOO See Note 4.			Oil-Resistant Thermo-plastic Elastomer							
Junior Hard Service Cord	SJ			Thermoset				Thermoset	Pendant or Portable	Damp Locations	Hard Usage
	SJE			Thermo-plastic Elastomer	8-12	30	None	Thermoplastic Elastomer			
	SJEO							Oil-Resistant Thermoplastic Elastomer			
	SJEOO			Oil-Resistant Thermo-plastic Elastomer							
	SJO	18-10	2,3,4, or 5	Thermoset				Oil-Resistant Thermoset			
	SJOO	18-10	2, 3, 4, or 5	Oil-Resistant Thermoset	8-12	30	None	Oil-Resistant Thermoset	Pendant or Portable	Damp Locations	Extra Hard Usage
	SJT			Thermo-plastic or Thermoset	10	45		Thermoplastic			
	SJTO			Thermoset or Thermo-plastic				Oil-Resistant Thermoplastic			

See Notes 1 through 9.
* See Note 8.
**The required outer covering on some single-conductor cables may be integral with the insulation.

Table 400-4, continued

Trade Name	Type Letter	Size AWG	No. of Conduc-tors	Insulation	Nominal Insulation Thickness*		Braid on Each Conductor	Outer Covering	Use		
					AWG	Mils					
Junior Hard Service Cord	SJTOO			Oil-Resistant Thermo-plastic or Thermoset				Oil-Resistant Thermoplastic			
Hard Service Cord	SO See Note 4.	18-2	2 or more	Thermoset	18-16	30		Oil-Resistant Thermoset	Pendant or Portable	Damp Locations	Extra Hard Usage
	SOO See Note 4.			Oil-Resistant Thermoset	14-10	45		Oil-Resistant Thermoset			
					8-2	60					
All Thermoset Parallel Cord	SP-1 See Note 6.	18		Thermoset	18	30	None	Thermoset	Pendant or Portable	Damp Locations	Not Hard Usage
	SP-2 See Note 6.	18-16	2 or 3		18-16	45					
	SP-3 See Note 6.	18-10		Thermoset	18-16 14 12 10	60 80 95 110	None	Thermoset	Refrigerators, Room Air Conditioners, and as per-mitted in Sec-tion 422-8(d)	Damp Locations	Not Hard Usage
All Elastomer (Thermo-plastic) Parallel Cord	SPE-1 See Note 6.	18		Thermo-plastic Elastomer	18	30	None	Thermoplastic Elastomer	Pendant or Portable	Damp Locations	Not Hard Usage
	SPE-2 See Note 6.	18-16	2 or 3		18-16	45					
	SPE-3 See Note 6.	18-10			18-16 14 12 10	60 80 95 110	None	Thermoplastic Elastomer	Refrigerators, Room Air Conditioners, and as per-mitted in Sec-tion 422-8(d)	Damp Locations	Not Hard Usage

See Notes 1 through 9.
*See Note 8.

Table 400-4, continued

Trade Name	Type Letter	Size AWG	No. of Conductors	Insulation	Nominal Insulation Thickness*		Braid on Each Conductor	Outer Covering	Use		
					AWG	Mils					
All Plastic Parallel Cord	SPT-1 See Note 6.	18		Thermoplastic	18	30	None	Thermoplastic	Pendant or Portable	Damp Locations	Not Hard Usage
	SPT-2 See Note 6.	18-16	2 or 3	Thermoplastic	18-16	45	None	Thermoplastic	Pendant or Portable	Damp Locations	Not Hard Usage
	SPT-3 See Note 6.	18-10		Thermoplastic	18-16 14 12 10	60 80 95 110	None	Thermoplastic	Refrigerators, Room Air Conditioners, and as permitted in Section 422-8(d)	Damp Locations	Not Hard Usage
Range, Dryer Cable	SRD	10-4	3 or 4	Thermoset	10-4	45	None	Thermoset	Portable	Damp Locations	Ranges, Dryers
	SRDE	10-4	3 or 4	Thermoplastic Elastomer			None	Thermoplastic Elastomer	Portable	Damp Locations	Ranges, Dryers
	SRDT	10-4	3 or 4	Thermoplastic			None	Thermoplastic	Portable	Damp Locations	Ranges, Dryers
Hard Service Cord	ST See Note 4.	18-2	2 or more	Thermoplastic or Thermoset	18-16 14-10 8-2	30 45 60	None	Thermoplastic	Pendant or Portable	Damp Locations	Extra Hard Usage
	STO See Note 4.							Oil-Resistant Thermoplastic			
	STOO See Note 4.			Oil-Resistant Thermoplastic or Thermoset							
Vacuum Cleaner Cord	SV See Note 6.	18-17	2 or 3	Thermoset	18-17	15	None	Thermoset	Pendant or Portable	Damp Locations	Not Hard Usage
	SVE See Note 6.			Thermoplastic Elastomer				Thermoplastic Elastomer			
	SVEO See Note 6.							Oil-Resistant Thermoplastic Elastomer			
	SVEOO See Note 6.			Oil-Resistant Thermoplastic Elastomer							

See Notes 1 through 9.
* See Note 8.

Table 400-4, continued

Trade Name	Type Letter	Size AWG	No. of Conduc-tors	Insulation	Nominal Insulation Thickness*		Braid on Each Conductor	Outer Covering	Use		
					AWG	Mils					
Vacuum Cleaner Cord	SVO			Thermoset				Oil-Resistant Thermoset			
	SVOO			Oil-Resistant Thermoset				Oil-Resistant Thermoset			
	SVT See Note 6.			Thermoset or Thermo-plastic				Thermoplastic			
	SVTO See Note 6.			Thermoset or Thermo-plastic				Oil-Resistant Thermoplastic			
	SVTOO			Oil-Resistant Thermo-plastic or Thermoset				Oil-Resistant Thermoplastic			
Parallel Tinsel Cord	TPT See Note 2.	27	2	Thermoplastic	27	30	None	Thermoplastic	Attached to an Appliance	Damp Locations	Not Hard Usage
Jacketed Tinsel Cord	TS See Note 2.	27	2	Thermoset	27	15	None	Thermoset	Attached to an Appliance	Damp Locations	Not Hard Usage
	TST See Note 2.	27	2	Thermoplastic			None	Thermoplastic	Attached to an Appliance	Damp Locations	Not Hard Usage
Portable Power Cable	W	8-500 kcmil	1-6	Thermoset	8-2 1-4/0 250 kcmil-500 kcmil	60 80 95		Oil-Resistant Thermoset	Portable, Extra Hard Usage, and as Permitted in Sections 520-68 and 530-12.		

See Notes 1 through 9.
* See Note 8.

400-5. **Ampacities for Flexible Cords and Cables.** Table 400-5(A) provides the allowable ampacities and Table 400-5(B) provides the ampacities for flexible cords and cables with not more than three current-carrying conductors. If the number of current-carrying conductors exceeds three, the allowable ampacity or the ampacity of each conductor shall be reduced from the 3-conductor rating as shown in the following table:

Number of Conductors	Percent of Value in Tables 400-5(A) and 400-5(B)
4 through 6	80
7 through 9	70
10 through 20	50
21 through 30	45
31 through 40	40
41 and above	35

Ultimate Insulation Temperature. In no case shall conductors be associated together in such a way with respect to the kind of circuit, the wiring method used, or the number of conductors such that the limiting temperature of the conductors is exceeded.

A neutral conductor that carries only the unbalanced current from other conductors of the same circuit need not be considered as a current-carrying conductor.

In a 3-wire circuit consisting of two phase wires and the neutral of a 4-wire, 3-phase wye-connected system, a common conductor carries approximately the same current as the other conductors and shall be considered a current-carrying conductor.

On a 4-wire, 3-phase wye circuit where the major portion of the load consists of nonlinear loads such as electric-discharge lighting, electronic computer/data processing, or similar equipment, there are harmonic currents present in the neutral conductor, and the neutral shall be considered to be a current-carrying conductor.

An equipment grounding conductor shall not be considered a current-carrying conductor.

Where a single conductor is used for both equipment grounding and to carry unbalanced current from other conductors, as provided for in Section 250-60 for electric ranges and electric clothes dryers, it shall not be considered as a current-carrying conductor.

Table 400-5(A). **Allowable Ampacity for Flexible Cords and Cables [Based on Ambient Temperature of 30°C (86°F). See Section 400-13 and Table 400-4.]**

Size AWG	Thermoset Type TS / Thermoplastic Types TPT, TST	Thermoset Types C, E, EO, PD, S, SJ, SJO, SJOO, SO, SOO, SP-1, SP-2, SP-3, SRD, SV, SVO, SVOO / Thermoplastic Types ET, ETLB, ETT, SE, SEO, SJE, SJEO, SJT, SJTO, SJTOO, SPE-1, SPE-2, SPE-3, SPT-1, SPT-2, SPT-3, ST, SRDE, SRDT, STO. STOO, SVE, SVEO, SVT, SVTO, SVTOO		Types AFS, AFSJ, HPD, HPN, HS, HSJ, HSJO, HSO
		A†	B†	
27*	0.5	..	..	..
20	..	5**	7**	..
18	..	7	10	10
17	..	..	12	..
16	..	10	13	15
15	..	..	..	17
14	..	15	18	20
12	..	20	25	30
10	..	25	30	35
8	..	35	40	..
6	..	45	55	..
4	..	60	70	..
2	..	80	95	..

* Tinsel cord.
** Elevator cables only.
† The allowable currents under subheading A apply to 3-conductor cords and other multiconductor cords connected to utilization equipment so that only 3 conductors are current-carrying. The allowable currents under subheading B apply to 2-conductor cords and other multiconductor cords connected to utilization equipment so that only 2 conductors are current-carrying.
(FPN): It is intended that this table be used in conjunction with applicable end-use product standards to ensure selection of the proper size and type.

Exception: For other loading conditions, adjustment factors shall be permitted to be calculated under Section 310-15(b).

See commentary following Section 310-15(b).

(FPN): See Appendix B, Table B-310-11 for adjustment factors for more than three current-carrying conductors in a raceway or cable with load diversity.

Table 400-5(B). Ampacity of Cable Types SC, SCE, SCT, G, and W. [Based on Ambient Temperature of 30°C (86°F). See Table 400-4.] Temperature Rating of Cable

Size AWG/ kcmil	60°C (140°F)			75°C (167°F)			90°C (194°F)		
	D	E	F	D	E	F	D	E	F
8	60	55	48	70	65	57	80	74	65
6	80	72	63	95	88	77	105	99	87
4	105	96	84	125	115	101	140	130	114
3	120	113	99	145	135	118	165	152	133
2	140	128	112	170	152	133	190	174	152
1	165	150	131	195	178	156	220	202	177
1/0	195	173	151	230	207	181	260	234	205
2/0	225	199	174	265	238	208	300	271	237
3/0	260	230	201	310	275	241	350	313	274
4/0	300	265	232	360	317	277	405	361	316
250	340	296	259	405	354	310	455	402	352
300	375	330	289	445	395	346	505	449	393
350	420	363	318	505	435	381	570	495	433
400	455	392	343	545	469	410	615	535	468
500	515	448	392	620	537	470	700	613	536

The ampacities under subheading D are permitted for single-conductor Types SC, SCE, SCT, and W cable only where the individual conductors are not installed in raceways and are not in physical contact with each other except in lengths not to exceed 24 inches (610 mm) where passing through the wall of an enclosure.

The ampacities under subheading E apply to 2-conductor cables and other multiconductor cables connected to utilization equipment so that only 2 conductors are current-carrying. The ampacities under subheading F apply to 3-conductor cables and other multiconductor cables connected to utilization equipment so that only 3 conductors are current-carrying.

400-6. Markings.

(a) Standard Markings. Flexible cords and cables shall be marked by means of a printed tag attached to the coil reel or carton. The tag shall contain the information required in Section 310-11(a).

Types S, SC, SCE, SCT, SE, SEO, SEOO, SJ, SJE, SJEO, SJEOO, SJO, SJT, SJTO, SJTOO, SO, SOO, ST, STO, and STOO flexible cords and G and W flexible cables shall be durably marked on the surface at intervals not exceeding 24 inches (610 mm) with the type designation, size, and number of conductors.

(b) Optional Markings. Flexible cords and cable types listed in Table 400-4 shall be permitted to be surface marked to indicate special characteristics of the cable materials.

(FPN): Examples of these markings include, but are not limited to, "LS" for limited-smoke and markings such as "sunlight-resistant."

400-7. Uses Permitted.

(a) Uses. Flexible cords and cables shall be used only for (1) pendants; (2) wiring of fixtures; (3) connection of portable lamps or appliances; (4) elevator cables; (5) wiring of cranes and hoists; (6) connection of stationary equipment to facilitate their frequent interchange; (7) prevention of the transmission of noise or vibration; (8) appliances where the fastening means and mechanical connections are specifically designed to permit ready removal for maintenance and repair, and the appliance is intended or identified for flexible cord connection; (9) data processing cables as permitted by Section 645-5; (10) connection of moving parts; or (11) temporary wiring as permitted in Sections 305-4(b) and 305-4(c).

(b) Attachment Plugs. Where used as permitted in subsections (a)(3), (a)(6), and (a)(8) of this section, each flexible cord shall be equipped with an attachment plug and shall be energized from a receptacle outlet.

The flexible cords and cables referred to in this article are not limited to use with portable equipment. However, they are not permitted to be used as a substitute for the fixed wiring of a structure or where concealed behind building walls, ceilings, or floors. See Section 400-8. Also see Article 305 for the requirement for the use of extension cords as temporary wiring. See Section 240-4 for overcurrent protection requirements for flexible cord.

Exception: As permitted in Section 364-8.

400-8. Uses Not Permitted.
Unless specifically permitted in Section 400-7, flexible cords and cables shall not be used (1) as a substitute for the fixed wiring of a structure; (2) where run through holes in walls, ceilings, or floors; (3) where run through doorways, windows, or similar openings; (4) where attached to building surfaces; (5) where concealed behind building walls, ceilings, or floors; or (6) where installed in raceways, except as otherwise permitted in this Code.

Exception: Flexible cord and cable shall be permitted to have one connection to the building surface for a suitable tension take-up device. Length of the cord or cable from the supply termination to the take-up device shall be limited to 6 feet (1.83 m).

400-9. **Splices.** Flexible cord shall be used only in continuous lengths without splice or tap when initially installed in applications permitted by Section 400-7(a). The repair of hard-service cord (see Column 1, Table 400-4) Nos. 14 and larger shall be permitted if conductors are spliced in accordance with Section 110-14(b) and the completed splice retains the insulation, outer sheath properties, and usage characteristics of the cord being spliced.

400-10. **Pull at Joints and Terminals.** Flexible cords shall be so connected to devices and to fittings that tension will not be transmitted to joints or terminals.

(FPN): Some methods of preventing pull on a cord from being transmitted to joints or terminals are (1) knotting the cord, (2) winding with tape, and (3) fittings designed for the purpose.

400-11. **In Show Windows and Show Cases.** Flexible cords used in show windows and show cases shall be Type AFS, S, SE, SEO, SEOO, SJ, SJE, SJEO, SJEOO, SJO, SJOO, SJT, SJTO, SJTOO, SO, SOO, ST, STO, or STOO.

Exception No. 1: For the wiring of chain-supported lighting fixtures.

Exception No. 2: As supply cords for portable lamps and other merchandise being displayed or exhibited.

Flexible cords listed for hard usage or extra hard usage should be used in show windows and showcases. Precautions should be taken to ensure that these cords are maintained in good condition because they may come in contact with combustible materials usually present at these locations. In addition, they are exposed to wear and tear from continuous housekeeping and display changes.

400-12. **Minimum Size.** The individual conductors of a flexible cord or cable shall not be smaller than the sizes in Table 400-4.

400-13. **Overcurrent Protection.** Flexible cords not smaller than No. 18, and tinsel cords or cords having equivalent characteristics of smaller size approved for use with specific appliances, shall be considered as protected against overcurrent by the overcurrent devices described in Section 240-4.

400-14. **Protection from Damage.** Flexible cords and cables shall be protected by bushings or fittings where passing through holes in covers, outlet boxes, or similar enclosures.

There are a variety of bushings and fittings available for this purpose, both insulated and noninsulated. Some include strain-relief means as required in Section 400-10. Many insulating bushings are listed by Underwriters Laboratories Inc. in the product categories Conduit Fittings (bushings and fittings for use on the ends of conduit in boxes, gutters, etc.); Insulating Devices and Materials; Bushings (bushings for the protection of cords where they pass through walls or barriers of metal); or Outlet Bushings and Fittings (bushings and fittings for use on the ends of conduit, EMT, or armored cable where a change to open wiring is made).

B. Construction Specifications

400-20. **Labels.** Flexible cords shall be examined and tested at the factory and labeled before shipment.

See definition of "Labeled" in Article 100.

400-21. **Nominal Insulation Thickness.** The nominal thickness of insulation for conductors of flexible cords and cables shall not be less than specified in Table 400-4.

400-22. **Grounded-Conductor Identification.** One conductor of flexible cords that is intended to be used as a grounded circuit conductor shall have a continuous marker readily distinguishing it from the other conductor or conductors. The identification shall consist of one of the methods indicated in (a) through (f) below.

(a) **Colored Braid.** A braid finished to show a white or natural gray color and the braid on the other conductor or conductors finished to show a readily distinguishable solid color or colors.

(b) **Tracer in Braid.** A tracer in a braid of any color contrasting with that of the braid and no tracer in the braid of the other conductor or conductors. No tracer shall be used in the braid of any conductor of a flexible cord that contains a conductor having a braid finished to show white or natural gray.

Exception: In the case of Types C and PD, and cords having the braids on the individual conductors finished to show white or natural gray. In such cords, the identifying marker shall be permitted to consist of the solid white or natural gray finish on one conductor, provided there is a colored tracer in the braid of each other conductor.

(c) Colored Insulation. A white or natural gray insulation on one conductor and insulation of a readily distinguishable color or colors on the other conductor or conductors for cords having no braids on the individual conductors.

For jacketed cords furnished with appliances, one conductor having its insulation colored light blue, with the other conductors having their insulation of a readily distinguishable color other than white or natural gray.

Exception: Cords that have insulation on the individual conductors integral with the jacket.

It shall be permissible to cover the insulation with an outer finish to provide the desired color.

(d) Colored Separator. A white or natural gray separator on one conductor and a separator of a readily distinguishable solid color on the other conductor or conductors of cords having insulation on the individual conductors integral with the jacket.

(e) Tinned Conductors. One conductor having the individual strands tinned and the other conductor or conductors having the individual strands untinned for cords having insulation on the individual conductors integral with the jacket.

(f) Surface Marking. One or more stripes, ridges, or grooves so located on the exterior of the cord as to identify one conductor for cords having insulation on the individual conductors integral with the jacket.

400-23. **Equipment Grounding-Conductor Identification.** A conductor intended to be used as an equipment grounding conductor shall have a continuous identifying marker readily distinguishing it from the other conductor or conductors. Conductors having a continuous green color or a continuous green color with one or more yellow stripes shall not be used for other than equipment grounding purposes. The identifying marker shall consist of one of the methods in (a) or (b) below.

(a) Colored Braid. A braid finished to show a continuous green color or a continuous green color with one or more yellow stripes.

(b) Colored Insulation or Covering. For cords having no braids on the individual conductors, an insulation of a continuous green color or a continuous green color with one or more yellow stripes.

400-24. **Attachment Plugs.** Where a flexible cord is provided with an equipment grounding conductor and equipped with an attachment plug, the attachment plug shall comply with Sections 250-59(a) and (b).

C. Portable Cables Over 600 Volts, Nominal

400-30. **Scope.** This part applies to multiconductor portable cables used to connect mobile equipment and machinery.

400-31. **Construction.**

(a) Conductors. The conductors shall be No. 8 copper or larger and shall employ flexible stranding.

(b) Shields. Cables operated at over 2000 volts shall be shielded. Shielding shall be for the purpose of confining the voltage stresses to the insulation.

(c) Equipment Grounding Conductor(s). Equipment grounding conductor(s) shall be provided. The total area shall not be less than that of the size of the equipment grounding conductor required in Section 250-95.

400-32. **Shielding.** All shields shall be grounded.

400-33. **Grounding.** Grounding conductors shall be connected in accordance with Part K of Article 250.

400-34. **Minimum Bending Radii.** The minimum bending radii for portable cables during installation and handling in service shall be adequate to prevent damage to the cable.

400-35. **Fittings.** Connectors used to connect lengths of cable in a run shall be of a type that lock firmly together. Provisions shall be made to prevent opening or closing these connectors while energized. Suitable means shall be used to eliminate tension at connectors and terminations.

400-36. **Splices and Terminations.** Portable cables shall not contain splices unless the splices are of the permanent molded, vulcanized types in accordance with Section 110-14(b). Terminations on portable cables rated over 600 volts, nominal, shall be accessible only to authorized and qualified personnel.

ARTICLE 402   Fixture Wires

Contents

402-1. **Scope.** This article covers general requirements and construction specifications for fixture wires.

402-2. **Other Articles.** Fixture wires shall comply with this article and also with the applicable provisions of other articles of this Code.

(FPN):   For application in lighting fixtures, see Article 410.

402-3. **Types.** Fixture wires shall be of a type listed in Table 402-3, and they shall comply with all requirements of that table. The fixture wires listed in Table 402-3 are all suitable for service at 600 volts, nominal, unless otherwise specified.

(FPN):   Thermoplastic insulation may stiffen at temperatures colder than minus 10°C (plus 14°F), requiring care be exercised during installation at such temperatures. Thermoplastic insulation may also be deformed at normal temperatures where subjected to pressure, requiring care be exercised during installation and at points of support.

Table 402-5.

Size (AWG)	Allowable Ampacity
18	6
16	8
14	17
12	23
10	28

402-5. **Allowable Ampacities for Fixture Wires.** The ampacity of fixture wire shall be as specified in Table 402-5.

No conductor shall be used under such conditions that its operating temperature will exceed the temperature specified in Table 402-3 for the type of insulation involved.

(FPN):   See Section 310-10 for temperature limitation of conductors.

402-6. **Minimum Size.** Fixture wires shall not be smaller than No. 18.

402-7. **Number of Conductors in Conduit or Tubing.** The number of fixture wires permitted in a single conduit or tubing shall be as shown in Table 2 of Chapter 9.

402-8. **Grounded-Conductor Identification.** One conductor of fixture wires that is intended to be used as a grounded conductor shall be identified by means of stripes or by the means described in Sections 400-22(a) through (e).

402-9. **Marking.**

(a) **Required Information.** All fixture wires shall be marked to indicate the information required in Section 310-11(a).

(b) **Method of Marking.** Thermoplastic-insulated fixture wire shall be durably marked on the surface at intervals not exceeding 24 inches (610 mm). All other fixture wire shall be marked by means of a printed tag attached to the coil, reel, or carton.

(c) **Optional Marking.** Fixture wire types listed in Table 402-3 shall be permitted to be surface marked to indicate special characteristics of the cable materials.

(FPN):   Examples of these markings include, but are not limited to, "LS" for limited-smoke or markings such as "sunlight-resistant."

402-10. **Uses Permitted.** Fixture wires shall be permitted (1) for installation in lighting fixtures and in similar equipment where enclosed or protected and not subject to bending or twisting in use, or (2) for connecting lighting fixtures to the branch-circuit conductors supplying the fixtures.

402-11. **Uses Not Permitted.** Fixture wires shall not be used as branch-circuit conductors.

Exception: As permitted by Section 725-16 for Class 1 circuits and Section 760-16 for fire protective signaling circuits.

402-12. **Overcurrent Protection.** Overcurrent protection for fixture wires shall be as specified in Section 240-4.

Table 402-3. Fixture Wire

Trade Name	Type Letter	Insulation	AWG	Thickness of Insulation	Mils	Outer Covering	Max. Operating Temp.	Application Provisions
				Thickness of Moisture-Resistant Insulation Mils	Thickness of Asbestos Mils			
Asbestos Covered Heat-Resistant Fixture Wire	AF	Impregnated Asbestos or Moisture-Resistant Insulation and Impregnated Asbestos	18-14 12-10	— 20 — 25	30 10 45 20	None	150°C 302°F	Fixture wiring. Limited to 300 volts and indoor dry locations.
Heat-Resistant Rubber-Covered Fixture Wire — Flexible Stranding	FFH-2	Heat-Resistant Rubber Heat-Resistant Latex Rubber	18-16 18-16		30 18	Nonmetallic Covering	75°C 167°F	Fixture wiring, and as permitted in Section 725-16.
ECTFE Solid or 7-Strand	HF	Ethylene Chloro-Trifluoro Ethylene	18-14		15	None	150°F 302°F	Fixture wiring, and as permitted in Section 725-16
ECTFE Flexible Stranding	HFF	Ethylene Chloro-Trifluoro-Ethylene	18-14		15	None	150°C 302°F	Fixture wiring, and as permitted in Section 725-16.
Tape Insulated Fixture Wire — Solid or 7-Strand	KF-1	Aromatic Polyimide Tape	18-10		5.5	None	200°C 392°F	Fixture Wiring. Limited to 300 volts.
	KF-2	Aromatic Polyimide Tape	18-10		8.4	None	200°C 392°F	Fixture wiring, and as permitted in Sections 725-16 and 760-16.
Tape Insulated Fixture Wire — Flexible Stranding	KFF-1	Aromatic Polyimide Tape	18-10		5.5	None	200°C 392°F	Fixture Wiring. Limited to 300 volts.
	KFF-2	Aromatic Polyimide Tape	18-10		8.4	None	200°C 392°F	Fixture wiring, and as permitted in Section 725-16.
Perfluoro-alkoxy — Solid or 7-Strand (Nickel or Nickel-Coated Copper)	PAF	Perfluoroalkoxy	18-14		20	None	250°C 482°F	Fixture wiring, and as permitted in Sections 725-16 and 760-16. (Nickel or nickel-coated copper)

Table 402-3, continued

Trade Name	Type Letter	Insulation	AWG	Thickness of Insulation	Mils	Outer Covering	Max. Operating Temp.	Application Provisions
Perfluoro-alkoxy — Flexible Stranding	PAFF	Perfluoro-alkoxy	18-14		20	None	150°C 302°F	Fixture wiring, and as permitted in Section 725-16.
Fluorinated Ethylene Propylene Fixture Wire — Solid or 7-Strand	PF	Fluorinated Ethylene Propylene	18-14		20	None	200°C 392°F	Fixture wiring, and as permitted in Sections 725-16 and 760-16.
Fluorinated Ethylene Propylene Fixture Wire — Flexible Stranding	PFF	Fluorinated Ethylene Propylene	18-14		20	None	150°C 302°F	Fixture witing, and as permitted in Section 725-16.
Fluorinated Ethylene Propylene Fixture Wire — Solid or 7-Strand	PGF	Fluorinated Ethylene Propylene	18-14		14	Glass Braid	200°C 392°F	Fixture wiring, and as permitted in Sections 725-16 and 760-16.
Fluorinated Ethylene Propylene Fixture Wire — Flexible Stranding	PGFF	Fluorinated Ethylene Propylene	18-14		14	Glass Braid	150°C 302°F	Fixture wiring, and as permitted in Section 725-16.
Extruded Polytetra-Fluoroethylene Solid or 7-Strand (Nickel or Nickel-Coated Copper)	PTF	Extruded Polytetra-Fluoro-ethylene	18-14		20	None	250°C 482°F	Fixture wiring, and as permitted in Sections 725-16 and 760-16. (Nickel or nickel-coated copper)
Extruded Polytetra-Fluoroethylene Flexible Stranding 26-36 AWG Silver or Nickel-Coated Copper)	PTFF	Extruded Polytetra-Fluoroeth-ylene	18-14		20	None	150°C 302°F	Fixture wiring, and as permitted in Section 725-16. (Silver or nickel-coated copper)

Table 402-3, continued

Trade Name	Type Letter	Insulation	AWG	Thickness of Insulation	Mils	Outer Covering	Max. Operating Temp.	Application Provisions
Heat-Resistant Rubber-Covered Fixture Wire — Solid or 7-Strand	RFH-1	Heat-Resistant Rubber	18		15	Nonmetallic Covering	75°C 167°F	Fixture wiring. Limited to 300 volts.
	RFH-2	Heat-Resistant Rubber	18-16		30	Nonmetallic Covering	75°C 167°F	Fixture wiring, and as permitted in Sections 725-16 and 760-16.
		Heat-Resistant Latex Rubber	18-16		18			
Heat-Resistant Cross-Linked Synthetic Polymer-Insulated Fixture Wire — Solid or Stranded	RFHH-2*	Cross-Linked Synthetic Polymer	18-16		30	None or Nonmetallic Covering	90°C 194°F	Fixture wiring, and as permitted in Sections 725-16 and 760-16. Multiconductor cable as permitted in Sections 725-16 and 760-16.
			18-16		45			
	RFHH-3*							
Silicone Insulated Fixture Wire — Solid or 7-Strand	SF-1	Silicone Rubber	18		15	Nonmetallic Covering	200°C 392°F	Fixture wiring. Limited to 300 volts.
	SF-2	Silicone Rubber	18-14		30	Nonmetallic Covering	200°C 392°F	Fixture wiring, and as permitted in Sections 725-16 and 760-16.
Silicone Insulated Fixture Wire — Flexible Stranding	SFF-1	Silicone Rubber	18		15	Nonmetallic Covering	150°C 302°F	Fixture wiring. Limited to 300 volts.
	SFF-2	Silicone Rubber	18-14		30	Nonmetallic Covering	150°C 302°F	Fixture wiring, and as permitted in Section 725-16.
Thermoplastic Covered Fixture Wire — Solid or 7-Strand	TF*	Thermoplastic	18-16		30	None	60°C 140°F	Fixture wiring, and as permitted in Sections 725-16 and 760-16.
Thermoplastic Covered Fixture Wire — Flexible Stranding	TFF*	Thermoplastic	18-16		30	None	60°C 140°F	Fixture wiring, and as permitted in Section 725-16.

*Insulations and outer coverings that meet the requirements of flame-retardant, limited-smoke and are so listed shall be permitted to be designated limited-smoke with the suffix /LS after the Code type designation.

Table 402-3, continued

Trade Name	Type Letter	Insulation	AWG	Thickness of Insulation	Mils	Outer Covering	Max. Operating Temp.	Application Provisions
Heat-Resistant Thermoplastic-Covered Fixture Wire — Solid or 7-Strand	TFN*	Thermoplastic	18-16		15	Nylon-Jacketed or equivalent	90°C 194°F	Fixture wiring, and as permitted in Sections 725-16 and 760-16.
Heat-Resistant Thermoplastic Covered Fixture Wire — Flexible Stranded	TFFN*	Thermoplastic	18-16		15	Nylon-Jacketed or equivalent	90°C 194°F	Fixture wiring, and as permitted in Section 725-16.
Cross-Linked Polyolefin Insulated Fixture Wire — Solid or 7-Strand	XF*	Cross-Linked Polyolefin	18-14 12-10		30 45	None	150°C 302°F	Fixture wiring. Limited to 300 volts.
Cross-Linked Polyolefin Insulated Fixture Wire — Flexible Stranded	XFF*	Cross-Linked Polyolefin	18-14 12-10		30 45	None	150°C 302°F	Fixture wiring. Limited to 300 volts.
Modified ETFE Solid or 7-Strand	ZF	Modified Ethylene Tetrafluoro-Ethylene	18-14		15	None	150°C 302°F	Fixture wiring, and as permitted in Sections 725-16 and 760-16.
Flexible Stranding	ZFF	Modified Ethylene Tetrafluoro-Ethylene	18-14		15	None	150°C 302°F	Fixture wiring, and as permitted in Section 725-16.
High Temp. Modified ETFE — Solid or 7-Strand	ZHF	Modified Ethylene Tetrafluoro-ethylene	18-14		15	None	200°C 392°F	Fixture wiring, and as permitted in Sections 725-16 and 760-16

*Insulations and outer coverings that meet the requirements of flame-retardant, limited-smoke and are so listed shall be permitted to be designated limited-smoke with the suffix /LS after the Code type designation.

ARTICLE 410   Lighting Fixtures, Lampholders, Lamps, and Receptacles

Contents

A. General

410-1. Scope. This article covers lighting fixtures, lampholders, pendants, receptacles, incandescent filament lamps, arc lamps, electric-discharge lamps, the wiring and equipment forming part of such lamps, fixtures, and lighting installations.

410-2. Application to Other Articles. Equipment for use in hazardous (classified) locations shall conform to Articles 500 through 517.

410-3. Live Parts. Fixtures, lampholders, lamps, and receptacles shall have no live parts normally exposed to contact. Exposed accessible terminals in lampholders, receptacles, and switches shall not be installed in metal fixture canopies or in open bases of portable table or floor lamps.

Exception: Cleat-type lampholders and receptacles located at least 8 feet (2.44 m) above the floor shall be permitted to have exposed contacts.

B. Fixture Locations

410-4. Fixtures in Specific Locations.

Underwriters Laboratories Inc. publishes a pamphlet titled "Fixture Marking Guide." This pamphlet was developed to help authorities having jurisdiction quickly determine whether common types of UL-listed fluorescent, high-intensity discharge and incandescent fixtures are installed correctly. It is available from UL.

(a) Wet and Damp Locations. Fixtures installed in wet or damp locations shall be so installed that water cannot enter or accumulate in wiring compartments, lampholders, or other electrical parts. All fixtures installed in wet locations shall be marked, "Suitable for Wet Locations." All fixtures installed in damp locations shall be marked, "Suitable for Wet Locations" or "Suitable for Damp Locations."

Installations underground or in concrete slabs or masonry in direct contact with the earth, and locations subject to saturation with water or other liquids, such as locations exposed to weather and unprotected, vehicle washing areas, and like locations, shall be considered to be wet locations with respect to the above requirement.

Interior locations protected from weather but subject to moderate degrees of moisture, such as some basements, some barns, some cold-storage warehouses and the like, the partially protected locations under canopies, marquees, roofed open porches, and the like, shall be considered to be damp locations with respect to the above requirement.

(FPN): See Article 680 for lighting fixtures in swimming pools, fountains, and similar installations.

Fixtures marked "Suitable for Wet Locations" are required where exposed to the weather or where subject to water saturation. Construction, design, and installation are to be such as to prevent the entrance of rain, snow, ice, and dust. Outdoor parks and parking lots, outdoor recreational areas (tennis, golf, baseball, etc.), car wash areas, and building exteriors are examples of wet locations.

Locations protected from the weather and not subject to water saturation but still exposed to moisture, such as the underside of store or gasoline station canopies or theater marquees, some cold-storage warehouses, some agricultural buildings, some basements, and roofed open porches and carports, may be considered damp locations. Fixtures used in these locations are required to be marked "Suitable for Damp Locations." See definitions of "damp location," "dry location," and "wet location" under "Location" in Article 100.

(b) Corrosive Locations. Fixtures installed in corrosive locations shall be of a type suitable for such locations.

(FPN): See Section 210-7 for receptacles in fixtures.

(c) In Ducts or Hoods. Fixtures shall be permitted to be installed in cooking hoods of nonresidential occupancies where all of the following conditions are met:

(1) The fixture shall be identified for use within commercial cooking hoods and installed so that the temperature limits of the materials used are not exceeded.

(2) The fixture shall be so constructed that all exhaust vapors, grease, oil or cooking vapors are excluded from the lamp and wiring compartment. Diffusers shall be resistant to thermal shock.

(3) Parts of the fixture exposed within the hood shall be corrosion-resistant or protected against corrosion, and the surface shall be smooth so as not to collect deposits and facilitate cleaning.

(4) Wiring methods and materials supplying the fixture(s) shall not be exposed within the cooking hood.

(FPN): See Section 110-11 for conductors and equipment exposed to deteriorating agents.

The requirements for this section were initially taken from NFPA 96, *Standard for the Installation of Equipment for the Removal of Smoke and Grease-Laden Vapors from Commercial Cooking Equipment*. NFPA 96 covers the basic requirements for the design, installation, and use of exhaust system components including (1) hoods, (2) grease-removal devices, (3) exhaust ducts, (4) dampers, (5) air-moving devices, (6) auxiliary equipment, and (7) fire extinguishing equipment for the exhaust system and its accompanying cooking equipment in commercial, industrial, institutional, and similar cooking applications. This standard does not apply to installations for normal residential use.

Grease can cause short circuits or ground faults in wiring, hence the requirement prohibiting wiring methods and materials (raceways, cables, lampholders, etc.) within ducts or hoods. Conventional enclosed and gasketed fixtures located in the path of travel of exhaust products are not permitted because a fire could result from the high temperatures on grease-coated glass bowls or globes enclosing the lamps. Recessed or surface fixtures intended for location within hoods are required to be identified as suitable for the specific purpose, and should be installed with the required clearances maintained. Note that wiring systems, including rigid metal conduit, are not permitted to be run exposed within the cooking hood.

(d) Pendants. No parts of cord-connected fixtures, hanging fixtures, or pendants shall be located within a zone measured 3 feet (914 mm) horizontally and 8 feet (2.44 m) vertically from the top of the bathtub rim. This zone is all encompassing and includes the zone directly over the tub.

The intent of this section is to keep the cord-connected, hanging, or pendant fixture out of an individual's reach while standing on a bathtub rim.

See Figure 410-1. This requirement applies to hydromassage bathtubs as defined in Section 680-4 as well as other bathtub types. See Section 680-41 for installation requirements for spas and hot tubs (as defined in Section 680-4) installed indoors.

Figure 410-1. Fixtures located near bathtubs.

410-5. **Fixtures Near Combustible Material.** Fixtures shall be so constructed, or installed, or equipped with shades or guards that combustible material will not be subjected to temperatures in excess of 90°C (194°F).

410-6. **Fixtures Over Combustible Material.** Lampholders installed over highly combustible material shall be of the unswitched type. Unless an individual switch is provided for each

fixture, lampholders shall be located at least 8 feet (2.44 m) above the floor, or shall be so located or guarded that the lamps cannot be readily removed or damaged.

This section refers to pendants and fixed lighting equipment installed above highly combustible material. Where the lamp cannot be located out of reach, the requirement can be met by equipping the lamp with a suitable guard. This section is not applicable to portable lamps.

410-7. **Fixtures in Show Windows.** Externally wired fixtures shall not be used in a show window.

Exception: Fixtures of the chain-supported type shall be permitted to be externally wired.

410-8. **Fixtures in Clothes Closets.**

(a) Definition.

Storage Space: Storage space shall be defined as a volume bounded by the sides and back closet walls and planes extending from the closet floor vertically to a height of 6 feet (1.83 m) or the highest clothes-hanging rod and parallel to the walls at a horizontal distance of 24 inches (610 mm) from the sides and back of the closet walls respectively, and continuing vertically to the closet ceiling parallel to the walls at a horizontal distance of 12 inches (305 mm) or the width of the shelf, whichever is greater.

(FPN): See Figure 410-8.

The 24-inch rule is intended to cover the clothes-hanging space, even if no clothes-hanging rod is installed. If a clothes-hanging rod is installed, the space extends from the floor to the top of the highest rod. If no clothes-hanging rod is installed, it extends from the floor to a height of 6 feet.

The 12-inch rule in the first paragraph is intended to cover the shelf space if shelving is not installed at the time of fixture installation. If shelving is installed, and the shelves are wider than 12 inches, the greater width applies.

The 12-inch rule in the second paragraph is intended to cover the clothes-hanging space in closets where there is access to both sides of a hanging rod.

For a closet that permits access to both sides of a hanging rod, the storage space shall include the volume below the

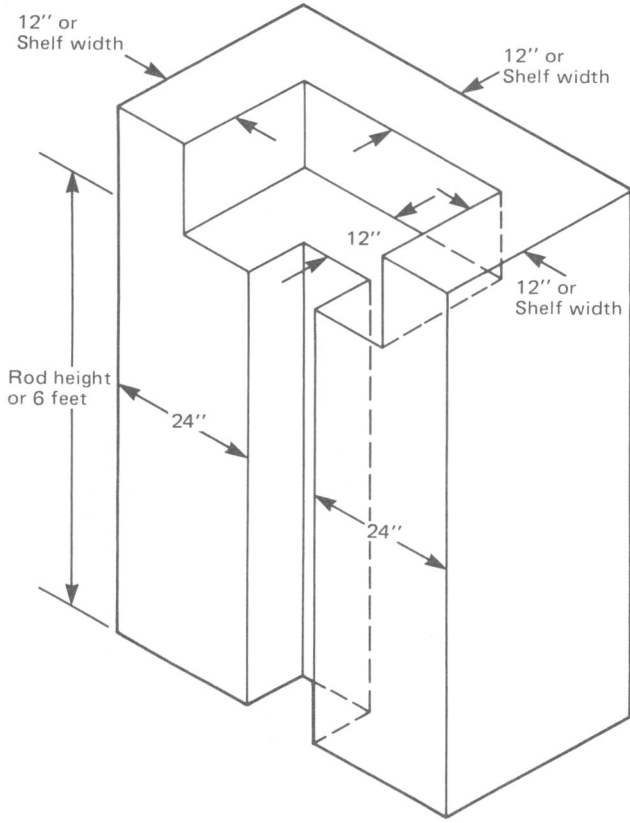

12'' or
Shelf width

12'' or
Shelf width

12''

12'' or
Shelf width

Rod height
or 6 feet

24''

24''

For SI units: one inch = 25.4 millimeters; one foot = 0.3048 meter.

Figure 410-8. Closet Storage Space.

highest rod extending 12 inches (305 mm) on either side of the rod on a plane horizontal to the floor extending the entire length of the rod.

(b) Fixture Types Permitted. Listed fixtures of the following types shall be permitted to be installed in a closet:

(1) A surface-mounted or recessed incandescent fixture with a completely enclosed lamp.

(2) A surface-mounted or recessed fluorescent fixture.

(c) Fixture Types Not Permitted. Incandescent fixtures with open or partially enclosed lamps and pendant fixtures or lampholders shall not be permitted.

See commentary following Section 410-8(d)(3).

(d) Location. Fixtures in clothes closets shall be permitted to be installed as follows:

(1) Surface-mounted incandescent fixtures installed on the wall above the door or on the ceiling, provided there is a minimum clearance of 12 inches (305 mm) between the fixture and the nearest point of a storage space.

(2) Surface-mounted fluorescent fixtures installed on the wall above the door or on the ceiling, provided there is a minimum clearance of 6 inches (152 mm) between the fixture and the nearest point of a storage space.

Note that the clearance measurement is to the fixture, not to the lamp itself.

(3) Recessed incandescent fixtures with a completely enclosed lamp installed in the wall or the ceiling, provided there is a minimum clearance of 6 inches (152 mm) between the fixture and the nearest point of a storage space.

This requirement is the result of tests that have shown that hot filament falling from a broken incandescent lamp can ignite combustible material below the fixture in which the lamp is installed. Note that the clearance measurement is to the fixture, not the lamp itself.

(4) Recessed fluorescent fixtures installed in the wall or on the ceiling, provided there is a minimum clearance of 6 inches (152 mm) between the fixture and the nearest point of a storage space.

It is not mandatory to install a lighting fixture in a clothes closet; if one is installed, however, the conditions for installation are as required by this section.

The requirements here apply to incandescent and fluorescent lighting in clothes closets of various kinds of occupancies. The intent is to prevent hot lamps, or parts of broken lamps, from coming in contact with cartons, blankets, etc., stored on shelves and clothing hung in closets.

410-9. **Space for Cove Lighting.** Coves shall have adequate space and shall be so located that lamps and equipment can be properly installed and maintained.

Adequate space is necessary for easy access for relamping fixtures or replacing lampholders, ballasts, etc., and adequate space also improves ventilation.

C. Provisions at Fixture Outlet Boxes, Canopies, and Pans

410-10. **Space for Conductors.** Canopies and outlet boxes taken together shall provide adequate space so that fixture conductors and their connecting devices can be properly installed.

410-11. **Temperature Limit of Conductors in Outlet Boxes.** Fixtures shall be of such construction or so installed that the conductors in outlet boxes shall not be subjected to temperatures greater than that for which the conductors are rated.

Branch-circuit wiring shall not be passed through an outlet box that is an integral part of an incandescent fixture unless the fixture is identified for through-wiring.

Branch-circuit conductors run to a lighting outlet box are not permitted to be subjected to greater temperatures than those for which they are rated. For example, conductors are rated 60°C and are to supply a ceiling outlet box for the connection of a surface-mounted incandescent fixture or attached outlet box of a recessed fixture. The design and installation of the fixture should be such that the heat of the incandescent lamps does not subject the conductors to a greater temperature than 60°C. These types of fixtures are listed by Underwriters Laboratories Inc. based on a heat-contributing factor of the supply conductors of not more than the maximum permitted lamp wattage of the fixture.

Figure 410-2 illustrates recessed fixtures listed by UL for one set of supply conductors, and Figure 410-3 illustrates fixtures listed for a feed-through installation.

Figure 410-2. Branch-circuit conductors terminating at each fixture (no feed-through).

410-12. **Outlet Boxes to Be Covered.** In a completed installation, each outlet box shall be provided with a cover unless covered by means of a fixture canopy, lampholder, receptacle, or similar device.

Figure 410-3. Recessed lighting fixtures that are designed for feed-through branch-circuit conductors.

410-13. **Covering of Combustible Material at Outlet Boxes.** Any combustible wall or ceiling finish exposed between the edge of a fixture canopy or pan and an outlet box shall be covered with noncombustible material.

Lighting fixtures are required to be designed and installed not only to prevent overheating of conductors but also to prevent overheating of adjacent combustible wall or ceiling finishes. Hence, it is required that any combustible finish between the edge of a fixture canopy and an outlet box be covered with a noncombustible material or fixture accessory. See Section 370-21 for requirements covering noncombustible finishes.

Where lighting fixtures are not directly mounted on outlet boxes, suitable outlet box covers are required.

410-14. **Connection of Electric-Discharge Lighting Fixtures.**

(a) Independently of the Outlet Box. Where electric-discharge lighting fixtures are supported independently of the outlet box, they shall be connected through metal raceways, nonmetallic raceways, Type MC cable, Type AC cable, Type MI cable, or nonmetallic-sheathed cables.

Exception: Cord-connected fixtures shall be permitted as provided in Sections 410-30(b) and (c).

(b) Access to Boxes. Electric-discharge lighting fixtures surface-mounted over concealed outlet, pull, or junction boxes shall be installed with suitable openings in back of the fixture to provide access to the boxes.

D. Fixture Supports

410-15. **Supports.**

(a) General. Fixtures, lampholders, and receptacles shall be securely supported. A fixture that weighs more than 6 pounds

(2.72 kg) or exceeds 16 inches (406 mm) in any dimension shall not be supported by the screw shell of a lampholder.

(b) Metal Poles Supporting Lighting Fixtures. Metal poles shall be permitted to be used to support lighting fixtures and enclose supply conductors, provided that the following conditions are met:

(1) An accessible handhole, not less than 2 inches 50.8 mm) × 4 inches (102 mm), having a raintight cover, shall provide access to the supply raceway or cable termination within the pole or pole base. Where raceway risers or cable is not installed within the pole, a threaded fitting or nipple shall be brazed or welded to the pole opposite the handhole for the supply connection. Other poles shall be permitted to be field-welded, brazed, or tapped. Such poles shall be capped or covered.

Exception: It shall be permitted to omit the handhole required in (b)(1) above on a metal pole 20 feet (6.10 m) or less in height above grade if the pole is provided with a hinged base. The grounding terminal shall be accessible and be within the hinged base. Both parts of the hinged pole shall be bonded in accordance with Section 250-75.

This exception recognizes metal light poles that do not have a handhole. These poles use a hinged base pole to permit access to splices made in the pole base. The height of the pole is limited to 20 feet. Both parts of the pole must be bonded in accordance with Section 250-75. See Figure 410-4.

(2) A terminal for grounding the pole shall be provided; it shall be accessible from the handhole.

Exception: It shall be permitted to omit the handhole and grounding terminal required in (b)(1) and (b)(2) above where the supply wiring method continues without splice or pull point to a fixture mounted on a metal pole 8 feet (2.44 m) or less in height above grade, and where the interior of the pole and any splices are accessible by the removal of the fixture.

This exception is typically used for pole lights at dwellings.

(3) Metal raceways or other equipment grounding conductors shall be bonded to the pole with an equipment grounding conductor recognized by Section 250-91(b) and sized in accordance with Section 250-95.

Figure 410-4. A hinged base metal pole supporting a lighting fixture. A handhole is not necessary because the pole can be tilted to allow access to terminations in the base.

(4) Conductors in vertical metal poles used as raceways shall be supported as provided in Section 300-19.

410-16. Means of Support.

(a) Outlet Boxes. Where the outlet box or fitting will provide adequate support, a fixture shall be attached thereto or be supported as required by Section 370-23 for boxes. A fixture that weighs more than 50 pounds (22.7 kg) shall be supported independently of the outlet box.

(b) Inspection. Fixtures shall be so installed that the connections between the fixture conductors and the circuit conductors can be inspected without requiring the disconnection of any part of the wiring.

Exception: Fixtures connected by attachment plugs and receptacles.

(c) Suspended Ceilings. Framing members of suspended ceiling systems used to support fixtures shall be securely fastened to each other and shall be securely attached to the building structure at appropriate intervals. Fixtures shall be securely fastened to the ceiling framing member by mechanical means, such as bolts, screws, or rivets. Clips identified for use with the type of ceiling framing member(s) and fixture(s) shall also be permitted.

(d) Fixture Studs. Fixture studs that are not a part of outlet boxes, hickeys, tripods, and crowfeet shall be made of steel, malleable iron, or other material suitable for the application.

(e) Insulating Joints. Insulating joints that are not designed to be mounted with screws or bolts shall have an exterior metal casing, insulated from both screw connections.

(f) Raceway Fittings. Raceway fittings used to support lighting fixture(s) shall be capable of supporting the weight of the complete fixture assembly and lamp(s).

Regardless of whether a lighting fixture is attached to an outlet box or supported independently of the outlet box, care should be taken to securely fasten the outlet box or support the independent rod or pipe hanger, as shown in Figure 370-5.

So-called "drop-in" fixtures or surface-mounted fixtures are required to be securely fastened to the framing members of hung or suspended ceilings by mechanical means, such as bolts, screws, or rivets, or clips identified for use with the type of ceiling framing member(s) and fixture(s), and no other support of the fixture is necessary. However, the suspended ceiling framing members must be securely attached to each other and to the building structure; also, additional supporting wires, rods, etc., may be necessary to provide ample support of the ceiling in areas where fixtures are installed.

(g) Busways. Fixtures shall be permitted to be connected to busways in accordance with Section 364-12.

(h) Trees. Outdoor lighting fixtures and associated equipment shall be permitted to be supported by trees.

(FPN No. 1): See Section 225-26.

Section 225-26 prohibits the support of overhead conductor spans on trees.

(FPN No. 2): See Section 300-5(d).

E. Grounding

410-17. **General.** Fixtures and lighting equipment shall be grounded as provided in Part E of this article.

410-18. **Exposed Fixture Parts.**

(a) With Exposed Conductive Parts. The exposed conductive parts of lighting fixtures and equipment directly wired or attached to outlets supplied by a wiring method that provides an equipment ground shall be grounded.

(b) Made of Insulating Material. Fixtures directly wired or attached to outlets supplied by a wiring method that does not provide a ready means for grounding shall be made of insulating material and shall have no exposed conductive parts.

410-19. **Equipment Over 150 Volts to Ground.**

(a) Metal Fixtures, Transformers, and Transformer Enclosures. Metal fixtures, transformers, and transformer enclosures on circuits operating at over 150 volts to ground shall be grounded.

(b) Other Exposed Metal Parts. Other exposed metal parts shall be grounded or insulated from ground and other conducting surfaces and inaccessible to unqualified persons.

Exception: Lamp tie wires, mounting screws, clips, and decorative bands on glass lamps spaced not less than 1½ inches (38 mm) from lamp terminals shall not be required to be grounded.

410-20. **Equipment Grounding Conductor Attachment.** Fixtures with exposed metal parts shall be provided with a means for connecting an equipment grounding conductor for such fixtures.

410-21. **Methods of Grounding.** Fixtures and equipment shall be considered grounded where mechanically connected to an equipment grounding conductor as specified in Section 250-91(b) and sized in accordance with Section 250-95.

F. Wiring of Fixtures

410-22. **Fixture Wiring — General.** Wiring on or within fixtures shall be neatly arranged and shall not be exposed to physical damage. Excess wiring shall be avoided. Conductors shall be so arranged that they shall not be subjected to temperatures above those for which they are rated.

410-23. **Polarization of Fixtures.** Fixtures shall be so wired that the screw shells of lampholders will be connected to the same fixture or circuit conductor or terminal. The grounded conductor, where connected to a screw-shell lampholder, shall be connected to the screw shell.

410-24. **Conductors.**

(a) **Insulation.** Fixtures shall be wired with conductors having insulation suitable for the environmental conditions, current, voltage, and temperature to which the conductors will be subjected.

(b) **Conductor Size.** Fixture conductors shall not be smaller than No. 18.

(FPN No. 1): For ampacity of fixture wire, see Section 402-5.

(FPN No. 2): For maximum operating temperature and voltage limitation of fixture wires, see Section 402-3.

410-25. **Conductors for Certain Conditions.**

(a) **Mogul-Base Lampholders.** Fixtures provided with mogul-base, screw-shell lampholders and operating at not over 300 volts between conductors shall be wired with Type AF, SF-1, SF-2, SFF-1, SFF-2, PF, PGF, PFF, PGFF, PTF, PTFF, PAF, PAFF, XF, XFF, ZF, or ZFF fixture wire.

(b) **Other than Mogul-Base, Screw-Shell Lampholders.** Fixtures provided with other than mogul-base, screw-shell lampholders and operating at not over 300 volts between conductors shall be wired with Type AF, SF-1, SF-2, PF, PGF, PFF, PGFF, PTF, PTFF, PAF, PAFF, XF, XFF, ZF, or ZFF fixture wire or Type AFC or AFPD flexible cord.

Exception No. 1: Where temperatures do not exceed 90°C (194°F), Types TFN and TFFN fixture wire shall be permitted.

Exception No. 2: Where temperatures exceed 60°C (140°F) but are not higher than 75°C (167°F), Types RH and RHW rubber-covered wire and Types RFH-1, RFH-2, and FFH-2 fixture wire shall be permitted.

Exception No. 3: Where temperatures do not exceed 60°C (140°F), Type TW thermoplastic wire, Types TF and TFF fixture wire shall be permitted, including fixtures of decorative types on

which lamps of not over 60-watt rating are used in connection with imitation candles.

(FPN): See Table 402-3 and Section 402-3 for fixture wires and conductors; and Table 400-5(A) for flexible cords.

410-27. **Pendant Conductors for Incandescent Filament Lamps.**

(a) **Support.** Pendant lampholders with permanently attached leads, where used for other than festoon wiring, shall be hung from separate stranded rubber-covered conductors that are soldered directly to the circuit conductors but supported independently thereof.

(b) **Size.** Such pendant conductors shall not be smaller than No. 14 for mogul-base or medium-base screw-shell lampholders, nor smaller than No. 18 for intermediate or candelabra-base lampholders.

Exception: Listed Christmas tree and decorative lighting outfits shall be permitted to be smaller than No. 18.

(c) **Twisted or Cabled.** Pendant conductors longer than 3 feet (914 mm) shall be twisted together where not cabled in a listed assembly.

410-28. **Protection of Conductors and Insulation.**

(a) **Properly Secured.** Conductors shall be secured in a manner that will not tend to cut or abrade the insulation.

(b) **Protection through Metal.** Conductor insulation shall be protected from abrasion where it passes through metal.

(c) **Fixture Stems.** Splices and taps shall not be located within fixture arms or stems.

(d) **Splices and Taps.** No unnecessary splices or taps shall be made within or on a fixture.

(FPN): For approved means of making connections, see Section 110-14.

(e) **Stranding.** Stranded conductors shall be used for wiring on fixture chains and on other movable or flexible parts.

(f) **Tension.** Conductors shall be so arranged that the weight of the fixture or movable parts will not put a tension on the conductors.

410-29. **Cord-Connected Showcases.** Individual showcases, other than fixed, shall be permitted to be connected by flexible cord to permanently installed receptacles, and groups of not more than six such showcases shall be permitted to be coupled together by flexible cord and separable locking-type connectors with one of the group connected by flexible cord to a permanently installed receptacle.

The installation shall comply with (a) through (e) of this section.

(a) Cord Requirements. Flexible cord shall be hard-service type, having conductors not smaller than the branch-circuit conductors, having ampacity at least equal to the branch-circuit overcurrent device, and having an equipment grounding conductor.

(FPN): See Table 250-95 for size of equipment grounding conductor.

(b) Receptacles, Connectors, and Attachment Plugs. Receptacles, connectors, and attachment plugs shall be of a listed grounding type rated 15 or 20 amperes.

(c) Support. Flexible cords shall be secured to the undersides of showcases so that (1) wiring will not be exposed to mechanical damage; (2) a separation between cases not in excess of 2 inches (50.8 mm), nor more than 12 inches (305 mm) between the first case and the supply receptacle, will be assured; and (3) the free lead at the end of a group of showcases will have a female fitting not extending beyond the case.

(d) No Other Equipment. Equipment other than showcases shall not be electrically connected to showcases.

(e) Secondary Circuit(s). Where showcases are cord-connected, the secondary circuit(s) of each electric-discharge lighting ballast shall be limited to one showcase.

410-30. Cord-Connected Lampholders and Fixtures.

(a) Lampholders. Where a metal lampholder is attached to a flexible cord, the inlet shall be equipped with an insulating bushing that, if threaded, shall not be smaller than nominal ⅜-inch pipe size. The cord hole shall be of a size appropriate for the cord, and all burrs and fins shall be removed in order to provide a smooth bearing surface for the cord.

Metal (brass-shell and aluminum-shell-type) lampholders used with flexible cord pendants should be equipped with smooth and permanently secured insulating bushings. Nonmetallic-type lampholders do not require a bushing because the material and design afford equivalent protection.

Bushing having holes ⁹⁄₃₂ inch (7.14 mm) in diameter shall be permitted for use with plain pendant cord and holes ¹³⁄₃₂ inch (10.3 mm) in diameter with reinforced cord.

(b) Adjustable Fixtures. Fixtures that require adjusting or aiming after installation shall not be required to be equipped with an attachment plug or cord connector provided the exposed cord is of the hard usage or extra-hard usage type and is not longer than that required for maximum adjustment. The cord shall not be subject to strain or physical damage.

(c) Electric-Discharge Fixtures.

(1) A listed fixture or a listed fixture assembly shall be permitted to be cord-connected if located directly below the outlet box and the cord is continuously visible for its entire length outside the fixture and is not subject to strain or physical damage. Such cord-equipped fixtures shall terminate at the outer end of the cord in a grounding-type attachment plug (cap) or busway plug.

This section was revised for the 1993 *Code* to clarify that the rule applies to listed cord- and plug-connected electric discharge lighting fixtures or electric discharge lighting fixture assemblies. See Figure 410-5.

The supply cord is not permitted to penetrate a suspended ceiling since it is required to be visible for its entire length.

Such cords can not be used as a supporting means and the fixtures are suspended directly below the outlet boxes supplying each fixture. Electric-discharge lighting fixtures are not permitted to be supplied by cord where installed in lift-out-type suspended ceilings. If the electric discharge fixture is suspended below the lift-out-type ceiling, the cord is not permitted to penetrate the ceiling. Electric-discharge fixtures are permitted to be connected to busways by cords plugged directly into the busway or suspended from the busway as permitted in Section 364-12.

Exception: A listed fixture or a listed fixture assembly incorporating cord and canopy shall not be required to terminate at the outer end in an attachment plug or busway plug.

This exception is new in the 1993 *Code*. It permits listed cord- and canopy-connected fixtures. Such fixtures are not required to terminate in an attachment plug. However, the cord is required to be visible along its entire length. See Figure 410-6.

Figure 410-5. A listed fluorescent lighting fixture that is cord-and plug-connected. The cord must be continuously visible along its entire length.

(2) Electric-discharge lighting fixtures provided with mogul-base, screw-shell lampholders shall be permitted to be connected to branch circuits of 50 amperes or less by cords complying with Section 240-4. Receptacles and attachment plugs shall be permitted to be of lower ampere rating than the branch circuit but not less than 125 percent of the fixture full-load current.

(3) Electric-discharge lighting fixtures equipped with a flanged surface inlet shall be permitted to be supplied by cord pendants equipped with cord connectors. Inlets and connectors shall be permitted to be of lower ampere rating than the branch circuit but not less than 125 percent of the fixture load current.

410-31. **Fixtures as Raceways.** Fixtures shall not be used as a raceway for circuit conductors.

Exception No. 1: Fixtures listed for use as a raceway.

Fixtures listed for use as raceways are marked as suitable for use as raceways.

Exception No. 2: Fixtures designed for end-to-end assembly to form a continuous raceway or fixtures connected together by recognized wiring methods shall be permitted to carry through conductors of a 2-wire or multiwire branch circuit supplying the fixtures.

Exception No. 3: One additional 2-wire branch circuit separately supplying one or more of the connected fixtures described in

Exception No. 2 shall be permitted to be carried through the fixtures.

(FPN): See Article 100 for definition of "Multiwire Branch Circuit."

Exception No. 3 permits an additional 2-wire circuit to be carried through the fixtures to supply switched night lighting commonly used to conserve energy.

Branch-circuit conductors within 3 inches (76 mm) of a ballast within the ballast compartment shall have an insulation temperature rating not lower than 90°C (194°F), such as Types RHH, THW, THHN, THHW, FEP, FEPB, SA, and XHHW.

See conductor application provisions for these insulation types in Table 310-13. Note the 90°C rating that may be applied to Type THW conductors for special application in electric discharge lighting equipment.

G. Construction of Fixtures

410-34. **Combustible Shades and Enclosures.** Adequate air space shall be provided between lamps and shades or other enclosures of combustible material.

410-35. **Fixture Rating.**

(a) **Marking.** All fixtures requiring ballasts or transformers shall be plainly marked with their electrical rating and the manufacturer's name, trademark, or other suitable means of identification. A fixture requiring supply wire rated higher than 90°C (194°F) shall be so marked, in letters 1/4 inch (6.35 mm) high prominently displayed on the fixture and shipping carton or equivalent.

(b) **Electrical Rating.** The electrical rating shall include the voltage and frequency and shall indicate the current rating of the unit, including the ballast, transformer, or autotransformer.

410-36. **Design and Material.** Fixtures shall be constructed of metal, wood, or other material suitable for the application and shall be so designed and assembled as to secure requisite mechanical strength and rigidity. Wiring compartments, including their entrances, shall be such that conductors may be drawn in and withdrawn without physical damage.

410-37. **Nonmetallic Fixtures.** In all fixtures not made entirely of metal or noncombustible material, wiring compartments shall be lined with metal.

Exception: Where armored or lead-covered conductors with suitable fittings are used.

410-38. Mechanical Strength.

(a) Tubing for Arms. Tubing used for arms and stems where provided with cut threads shall not be less than 0.040 inch (0.1 mm) in thickness and where provided with rolled (pressed) threads shall not be less than 0.025 inch (0.635 mm) in thickness. Arms and other parts shall be fastened to prevent turning.

(b) Metal Canopies. Metal canopies supporting lampholders, shades, etc., exceeding 8 pounds (3.63 kg), or incorporating attachment-plug receptacles, shall not be less than 0.020 inch (508 micrometers) in thickness. Other canopies shall not be less than 0.016 inch (406 micrometers) if made of steel and not less than 0.020 inch (508 micrometers) if of other metals.

(c) Canopy Switches. Pull-type canopy switches shall not be inserted in the rims of metal canopies that are less than 0.025 inch (635 micrometers) in thickness unless the rims are reinforced by the turning of a bead or the equivalent. Pull-type canopy switches, whether mounted in the rims or elsewhere in sheet metal canopies, shall not be located more than 3½ inches (89 mm) from the center of the canopy. Double set-screws, double canopy rings, a screw ring, or equal method shall be used where the canopy supports a pull-type switch or pendant receptacle.

The above thickness requirements shall apply to measurements made on finished (formed) canopies.

410-39. Wiring Space.
Bodies of fixtures, including portable lamps, shall provide ample space for splices and taps and for the installation of devices, if any. Splice compartments shall be of nonabsorbent, noncombustible material.

410-42. Portable Lamps.

(a) General. Portable lamps shall be wired with flexible cord, recognized by Section 400-4, and an attachment plug of the polarized or grounding type. Where used with Edison-base lampholders, the grounded conductor shall be identified and attached to the screw shell and the identified blade of the attachment plug.

(b) Portable Handlamps. In addition to the provisions of Section 410-42(a), portable handlamps shall comply with the following: (1) metal shell, paper-lined lampholders shall not be used;

Figure 410-6. A portable handlamp with a grounded metal guard and reflector, and a swivel-type hook that permits the lamp to be adjusted in different positions. (Daniel Woodhead Co.)

(2) handlamps shall be equipped with a handle of molded composition or other insulating material; (3) handlamps shall be equipped with a substantial guard attached to the lampholder or handle; (4) metallic guards shall be grounded by the means of an equipment grounding conductor run with circuit conductors within the power-supply cord.

410-44. Cord Bushings.
A bushing or the equivalent shall be provided where flexible cord enters the base or stem of a portable lamp. The bushing shall be of insulating material unless a jacketed type of cord is used.

410-45. Tests.
All wiring shall be free from short circuits and grounds and shall be tested for these defects prior to being connected to the circuit.

410-46. **Live Parts.** Exposed live parts within porcelain fixtures shall be suitably recessed and so located as to make it improbable that wires will come in contact with them. There shall be a spacing of at least ½ inch (12.7 mm) between live parts and the mounting plane of the fixture.

H. Installation of Lampholders

410-47. **Screw-Shell Type.** Lampholders of the screw-shell type shall be installed for use as lampholders only. Where supplied by a circuit having a grounded conductor, the grounded conductor shall be connected to the screw shell.

Many years ago it was common practice to install screw-shell lampholders with screw-shell adapters in baseboards and walls to connect cord-connected appliances and lighting equipment. This now prohibited practice permitted exposed live parts to be contacted by persons when the adapters were removed.

See Section 410-56(a) for permitted uses of receptacles.

410-48. **Double-Pole Switched Lampholders.** Where supplied by the ungrounded conductors of a circuit, the switching device of lampholders of the switched type shall simultaneously disconnect both conductors of the circuit.

Single-pole switching may be used to interrupt the ungrounded conductor of a 2-wire circuit having one conductor grounded. The grounded conductor is required to be connected to the screw shell of the lampholder.

Where a 2-wire circuit is derived from two ungrounded conductors of a multiwire circuit (3- or 4-wire system), or from the two ungrounded conductors of a 2-wire circuit (3-wire system), and used with switched lampholders, the switching device is required to be double-pole and to simultaneously disconnect both ungrounded conductors of the circuit. See Section 410-52.

410-49. **Lampholders in Wet or Damp Locations.** Lampholders installed in wet or damp locations shall be of the weatherproof type.

J. Construction of Lampholders

410-50. **Insulation.** The outer metal shell and the cap shall be lined with insulating material that shall prevent the shell and cap

from becoming a part of the circuit. The lining shall not extend beyond the metal shell more than ⅛ inch (3.17 mm), but shall prevent any current-carrying part of the lamp base from being exposed when a lamp is in the lampholding device.

410-51. **Lead Wires.** Lead wires, furnished as a part of weatherproof lampholders and intended to be exposed after installation, shall be of approved stranded, rubber-covered conductors not smaller than No. 14 and shall be sealed in place or otherwise made raintight.

Exception: No. 18 rubber-covered conductors shall be permitted for candelabra sockets.

410-52. **Switched Lampholders.** Switched lampholders shall be of such construction that the switching mechanism interrupts the electrical connection to the center contact. The switching mechanism shall also be permitted to interrupt the electrical connection to the screw shell if the connection to the center contact is simultaneously interrupted.

K. Lamps and Auxiliary Equipment

410-53. **Bases, Incandescent Lamps.** An incandescent lamp for general use on lighting branch circuits shall not be equipped with a medium base if rated over 300 watts, nor with a mogul base if rated over 1500 watts. Special bases or other devices shall be used for over 1500 watts.

410-54. **Electric-Discharge Lamp Auxiliary Equipment.**

(a) Enclosures. Auxiliary equipment for electric-discharge lamps shall be enclosed in noncombustible cases and treated as sources of heat.

(b) Switching. Where supplied by the ungrounded conductors of a circuit, the switching device of auxiliary equipment shall simultaneously disconnect all conductors.

Underwriters Laboratories Inc. provides the following information under Electric-Discharge Lamp Control Equipment, Ballasts, in the UL *Electrical Construction Materials Directory*.

Open Type

Open core and coil constructions (i.e. ballasts without complete metal enclosures) are intended for use within suitable enclosures.

Indoor Ballasts

An indoor ballast is suitable for use in an indoor, dry location only.

Outdoor Ballasts

Type 1—Outdoor ballast is suitable for use in (1) outdoor equipment, (2) fixtures intended for wet or damp locations or (3) an outdoor sign if the ballast is within an overall electrical enclosure. Ballasts of this type are marked "Type 1 Outdoor" or "Type 1."

Type 2—Outdoor ballast, Type 2, is suitable for use in (1) outdoor fixtures, (2) fixtures intended for wet or damp locations or (3) an outdoor sign if the ballast, in addition to its own enclosure, is within an overall enclosure. Ballasts of this type are marked "Type 2 Outdoor" or "Type 2."

Weatherproof Ballast

A weatherproof ballast is suitable for use where completely exposed to the weather without an additional enclosure and is marked "Weatherproof" or "WP."

410-55. Arc Lamps.

Arc lamps used in theaters shall comply with Section 520-61, and arc lamps used in projection machines shall comply with Section 540-20. Arc lamps used on constant-current systems shall comply with the general requirements of Article 710.

L. Receptacles, Cord Connectors, and Attachment Plugs (Caps)

410-56. Rating and Type.

(a) Receptacles. Receptacles installed for the attachment of portable cords shall be rated at not less than 15 amperes, 125 volts, or 15 amperes, 250 volts, and shall be of a type not suitable for use as lampholders.

Exception: The use of receptacles of 10-ampere, 250-volt rating used in nonresidential occupancies for the supply of equipment other than portable hand tools, portable handlamps, and extension cords shall be permitted.

(b) CO/ALR Receptacles. Receptacles rated 20 amperes or less and directly connected to aluminum conductors shall be marked CO/ALR.

This section requires that 15- and 20-ampere receptacles directly connected to aluminum conductors be suitable for such use. If the receptacle is not of the CO/ALR type, it can be connected with a copper pigtail to an aluminum branch-circuit conductor if a pressure wire connector suitable for such a connection, and marked with the letters "AL" and "CU," is used. See commentary on Section 110-14(b).

(c) Isolated Ground Receptacles. Receptacles intended for the reduction of electrical noise (electromagnetic interference) as permitted in Section 250-74, Exception No. 4 shall be identified by an orange color or an orange triangle located on the face of the receptacle.

Although this requirement was new in the 1990 *NEC*, the orange color or orange triangle has been used for a number of years to identify isolated ground receptacles.

(d) Faceplates. Metal faceplates shall be of ferrous metal not less than 0.030 inch (762 micrometers) in thickness or of nonferrous metal not less than 0.040 inch (1 mm) in thickness. Metal faceplates shall be grounded. Faceplates of insulating material shall be noncombustible and not less than 0.10 inch (2.54 mm) in thickness but shall be permitted to be less than 0.10 inch (2.54 mm) in thickness if formed or reinforced to provide adequate mechanical strength.

(e) Position of Receptacle Faces. After installation, receptacle faces shall be flush with or project from faceplates of insulating material and shall project a minimum of 0.015 inch (381 micrometers) from metal faceplates. Faceplates shall be installed so as to completely cover the opening and seat against the mounting surface. Receptacles mounted in boxes that are set back of the wall surface, as permitted in Section 370-20, shall be installed so that the mounting yoke or strap of the receptacle is held rigidly at the surface of the wall. Receptacles mounted in boxes that are flush with the wall surface or project therefrom shall be so installed that the mounting yoke or strap of the receptacle is seated against the box or raised box cover.

Paragraph (e) requires boxes to be properly and securely mounted to provide a solid backing for receptacles so that attachment plugs can be inserted or removed without movement of the box or receptacle. This is also intended to provide for secure mounting of the receptacle in order to maintain effective grounding continuity for contact devices or yokes listed for the purpose, where the box is installed flush with the wall surface or projects therefrom. See Section 380-10(b).

The reason for requiring receptacles to project from metal faceplates is to prevent faults between the blades of attachment plugs and metal faceplates. The design requirements of paragraph (f) for attachment plugs (dead-front construction) should minimize such faults at metal plates with new devices; however, existing attachment plugs with terminal screws exposed on the face are still in use.

Mounting boxes properly (Sections 370-20 and 370-23) requires the cooperation of other construction trades (plasterers, dry-wall applicators, carpenters, building designers, etc.). The proper installation of receptacles and faceplates ensures that attachment plugs can be fully inserted, thus providing a better contact.

(f) Attachment Plugs. All 15- and 20-ampere attachment plugs and connectors shall be so constructed that there are no exposed current-carrying parts except the prongs, blades, or pins. The cover for wire terminations shall be a part, which is essential for the operation of an attachment plug or connector (dead-front construction).

(g) Attachment Plug Ejector Mechanisms. Attachment plug ejector mechanisms shall not adversely affect engagement of the blades of the attachment plug with the contacts of the receptacle.

Section 410-56(g) permits a device designed for use by the aged, infirm, and the blind to reduce the likelihood of damage to the cord when pulling on the cord to remove the plug.

(h) Noninterchangeability. Receptacles, cord connectors, and attachment plugs shall be constructed so that the receptacle or cord connectors will not accept an attachment plug with a different voltage or current rating than that for which the device is intended. Nongrounding-type receptacles and connectors shall not accept grounding-type attachment plugs.

See Figures 210-7 and 210-8 for ANSI C73 standard configuration chart.

Exception: A 20-ampere T-slot receptacle or cord connector shall be permitted to accept a 15-ampere attachment plug of the same voltage rating.

(i) Receptacles in Raised Covers. Receptacles installed in raised covers shall not be secured solely by a single screw.

Figure 410-7. Receptacles mounted on a raised cover are not permitted to be secured by a single screw, unless listed and identified for the use.

Exception: Devices or assemblies listed and identified for such use.

410-57. Receptacles in Damp or Wet Locations.

(a) Damp Locations. A receptacle installed outdoors in a location protected from the weather or in other damp locations shall have an enclosure for the receptacle that is weatherproof when the receptacle is covered (attachment plug cap not inserted and receptacle covers closed).

An installation suitable for wet locations shall also be considered suitable for damp locations.

A receptacle shall be considered to be in a location protected from the weather where located under roofed open porches, canopies, marquees, and the like, and will not be subjected to a beating rain or water run-off.

(b) Wet Locations. A receptacle installed outdoors where exposed to weather or in other wet locations shall be in a weatherproof enclosure, the integrity of which is not affected when the receptacle is in use (attachment plug cap inserted).

Exception: An enclosure that is weatherproof only when a self-closing receptacle cover is closed shall be permitted to be used for a receptacle installed outdoors where the receptacle is provided for use with portable tools or other portable equipment normally connected to the outlet only when attended.

This exception was revised for the 1993 *Code*. The main rule of this section applies to receptacles for cord- and plug-connected equipment that is likely to be used outdoors for long periods of time, including pump motors, vending machines, etc. The intent is that the receptacle remain weatherproof with the plug inserted. The exception applies to receptacles for cord- and plug-connected portable tools or other portable equipment that is likely to be used outdoors for a specific purpose and then removed. Examples include gardening tools, television sets, radios, etc. See Figures 410-8 and 410-9.

Figure 410-8. *The receptacle on the left is permitted to be used for portable tools and appliances that are normally used only when attended. The receptacle on the right may be used for equipment that is likely to be used when unattended.*

(c) Protection for Floor Receptacles. Standpipes of floor receptacles shall allow floor-cleaning equipment to be operated without damage to receptacles.

(d) Flush Mounting with Faceplate. The enclosure for a receptacle installed in an outlet box flush-mounted on a wall surface shall be made weatherproof by means of a weatherproof faceplate assembly that provides a watertight connection between the plate and the wall surface.

(e) Installation. A receptacle outlet installed outdoors shall be located so that water accumulation is not likely to touch the outlet cover or plate.

Outdoor receptacle outlets are required for one-family and two-family dwellings and for swimming pool areas. They are also very common at other locations, such as shopping centers for children's rides and decorative lighting, truck terminals for refrigeration units and engine heaters, marinas, mobile home and recreational vehicle sites, etc.

The enclosure for an outdoor receptacle may be flush or surface mounted or supported by conduits in accordance with Section 370-23 and used with a variety of receptacles and covers; however, it is also the installer's responsibility to provide a watertight seal. See Figure 410-9. See also commentary following Section 410-57(b), Exception.

Figure 410-9. *Weatherproof receptacle cover suitable for wet locations. (Crouse-Hinds)*

410-58. **Grounding-type Receptacles, Adapters, Cord Connectors, and Attachment Plugs.**

(a) Grounding Poles. Grounding-type receptacles, cord connectors, and attachment plugs shall be provided with one fixed grounding pole in addition to the circuit poles.

Exception: The grounding contacting pole of grounding-type attachment plugs on the power-supply cords of portable hand-held, hand-guided, or hand-supported tools or appliances shall be permitted to be of the movable, self-restoring type on circuits operating at not over 150 volts between any two conductors nor over 150 volts between any conductor and ground.

(b) Grounding-Pole Identification. Grounding-type receptacles, adapters, cord connections, and attachment plugs shall have a means for connection of a grounding conductor to the grounding pole. A terminal for connection to the grounding pole shall be designated by:

(1) A green-colored hexagonal-headed or shaped terminal screw or nut, not readily removable; or

(2) A green-colored pressure wire connector body (a wire barrel); or

(3) A similar green-colored connection device, in the case of adapters. The grounding terminal of a grounding adapter shall be a green-colored rigid ear, lug, or similar device. The grounding connection shall be so designed that it cannot make contact with current-carrying parts of the receptacle, adapter, or attachment plug. The adapter shall be polarized.

This section requires the grounding terminal of an adapter to be a green-colored ear, lug, or similar device, thereby prohibiting use of an adapter with an attached pigtail grounding wire that has been used for many years.

(4) If the terminal for the equipment grounding conductor is not visible, the conductor entrance hole shall be marked with the word "green" or otherwise identified by a distinctive green color.

(c) Grounding Terminal Use. A grounding terminal or grounding-type device shall not be used for purposes other than grounding.

(d) Grounding-Pole Requirements. Grounding-type attachment plugs and mating cord connectors and receptacles shall be so designed that the grounding connection is made before the current-carrying connections. Grounding-type devices shall be designed so grounding poles of attachment plugs cannot be brought into contact with current-carrying parts of receptacles or cord connectors.

The grounding blade of the attachment plug cap of most grounding-type combinations is longer to ensure a "make-first, break-last" grounding connection. In some non-ANSI pin-and-sleeve types, the grounding contact of the receptacle is closer to the face of the receptacle than other contacts, serving the same purpose.

(e) Use. Grounding-type attachment plugs shall be used only where an equipment ground is to be provided.

M. Special Provisions for Flush and Recessed Fixtures

410-64. **General.** Fixtures installed in recessed cavities in walls or ceilings shall comply with Sections 410-65 through 410-72.

> **Formal Interpretation 81-6**
> Reference: Article 410 Part N (Part M in the 1993 Edition)
>
> *Question:* Is it intended that fixtures installed in suspended ceilings be subject to the requirements of Part N of Article 410?
>
> *Answer:* Yes.
>
> *Issue Edition:* 1981
> *Date:* October 1982 ■

410-65. **Temperature.**

(a) Combustible Material. Fixtures shall be so installed that adjacent combustible material will not be subjected to temperatures in excess of 90°C (194°F).

(b) Fire-Resistant Construction. Where a fixture is recessed in fire-resistant material in a building of fire-resistant construction, a temperature higher than 90°C (194°F), but not higher than 150°C (302°F), shall be considered acceptable if the fixture is plainly marked that it is listed for that service.

(c) Recessed Incandescent Fixtures. Incandescent fixtures shall have thermal protection and shall so be identified as thermally protected.

Because many recessed incandescent fixtures are suitable for a wide variety of lamp sizes and types, and finish trims, the temperature close to the lamp can vary widely. Therefore, many manufacturers have chosen to locate their thermal protectors away from the source of heat, such as in the outlet box, and to design the protector so that it will detect a change in temperature resulting from the addition of thermal insulation around the fixture. This prevents nuisance tripping of the protector as a result of changing lamp wattage, for example, but still provides protection against excessive overheating as a result of thermal insulation around a recessed fixture that is not designed for such use.

Exception No. 1: Recessed incandescent fixtures identified for use and installed in poured concrete.

Exception No. 2: Listed recessed incandescent fixtures that provide, by construction design, the equivalent temperature performance characteristics of thermally protected fixtures and are so identified.

Recessed incandescent fixtures without thermal protection are not permitted unless they are listed and identified as providing equivalent temperature protection by construction design.

Figure 410-10. A listed Type IC recessed fixture suitable for use in insulated ceilings in direct contact with thermal insulation. Thermal protection is provided to deactivate the lamp should the fixture be mislamped so that it overheats. (Thomas Industries Inc.)

410-66 . Clearance and Installation.

(a) **Clearance.** Recessed portions of lighting fixture enclosures, other than at the points of support, shall be spaced at least ½ inch (12.7 mm) from combustible materials.

Exception: Recessed fixtures identified as suitable for insulation to be in direct contact with the fixture.

See Figure 410-10.

(b) **Installation.** Thermal insulation shall not be installed within 3 inches (76 mm) of the recessed fixture enclosure, wiring compartment, or ballast, and shall not be so installed above the fixture so as to entrap heat and prevent the free circulation of air.

Exception: Recessed fixtures identified as suitable for insulation to be in direct contact with the fixture.

410-67 . Wiring.

(a) **General.** Conductors having insulation suitable for the temperature encountered shall be used.

(b) **Circuit Conductors.** Branch-circuit conductors having an insulation suitable for the temperature encountered shall be permitted to terminate in the fixture.

(c) **Tap Conductors.** Tap conductors of a type suitable for the temperature encountered shall be permitted to run from the fixture terminal connection to an outlet box placed at least 1 foot (305 mm) from the fixture. Such tap conductors shall be in suitable raceway or Type AC or MC cable of at least 4 feet (1.22 m) but not more than 6 feet (1.83 m) in length.

N. Construction of Flush and Recessed Fixtures

410-68 . **Temperature.** Fixtures shall be so constructed that adjacent combustible material will not be subject to temperatures in excess of 90°C (194°F).

410-69 . **Housing.** Sheet metal of flush and recessed fixture housings shall be protected against corrosion and shall not be less than No. 22 MSG.

Exception: A wiring compartment cover shall be permitted to be of a thinner material provided it is within the No. 22 MSG housing and does not support any current-carrying components.

410-70 . **Lamp Wattage Marking.** Incandescent lamp fixtures shall be marked to indicate the maximum allowable wattage of lamps. The markings shall be permanently installed, in letters at least ¼ inch (6.35 mm) high, and shall be located where visible during relamping.

410-71 . **Solder Prohibited.** No solder shall be used in the construction of a fixture box.

410-72 . **Lampholders.** Lampholders of the screw-shell type shall be of porcelain or other suitable insulating materials. Where used, cements shall be of the high-heat type.

P. Special Provisions for Electric-Discharge Lighting Systems of 1000 Volts or Less

410-73. General.

(a) Open-Circuit Voltage of 1000 Volts or Less. Equipment for use with electric-discharge lighting systems and designed for an open-circuit voltage of 1000 volts or less shall be of a type intended for such service.

(b) Considered as Energized. The terminals of an electric-discharge lamp shall be considered as energized where any lamp terminal is connected to a circuit of over 300 volts.

(c) Transformers of the Oil-Filled Type. Transformers of the oil-filled type shall not be used.

(d) Additional Requirements. In addition to complying with the general requirements for lighting fixtures, such equipment shall comply with Part P of this article.

(e) Thermal Protection. Where fluorescent fixtures are installed indoors, the ballasts shall have thermal protection integral within the ballast. Replacement ballasts for all fluorescent fixtures installed indoors shall also have thermal protection integral within the ballast.

Exception No. 1: Fluorescent fixtures using straight tubular lamps with simple reactance ballasts.

Exception No. 2: Ballasts for use in exit fixtures and so identified.

Exception No. 3: Egress lighting energized only during an emergency.

Thermal protection integral with the ballast is required for fluorescent fixtures installed indoors. Thermally protected ballasts are required as replacements for nonthermally protected ballasts in older fixtures. Thermally protected fluorescent lamp ballasts intended for use in accordance with Section 410-73(e) are marked "Class P."

As different Class P ballasts have different heating characteristics, the heating characteristics should be considered when selecting replacements for nonthermally protected ballasts.

This type of ballast protection is set to open the circuit at a predetermined temperature to prevent abnormal ballast heat buildup caused by a fault in one or more of the ballast components, or by some lampholder or wiring fault.

Exception Nos. 2 and 3 are new in the 1993 *Code.* Exception No. 2 exempts exit sign fixtures from the thermal protection requirement because overheating during high ambient conditions could cause the thermal protection to operate. This could impair evacuation during a fire.

Exception No. 3 exempts egress lighting from the thermal protection requirement for the same reason. However, this exception applies to egress lighting that is energized only during the emergency condition.

Figure 410-11 illustrates a reactance-type ballast used in series with a 30-W or less preheat-type fluorescent lamp. This type of ballast does not require thermal protection, and the fixture may be equipped with automatic-type starters (such as used with medicine cabinet fixtures) or a manual momentary contact starter (such as used with desk lamps and some small under-cabinet fixtures).

(f) High-Intensity Discharge Fixtures. Recessed high-intensity discharge fixtures shall be thermally protected and shall be so identified. Where fixtures, whether recessed or otherwise, are operated by remote ballasts, the ballasts shall also be thermally protected.

Exception: Recessed high-intensity discharge fixtures identified for use and installed in poured concrete.

(FPN): The thermal protection required by Section 410-73 may be accomplished by means other than a thermal protector.

410-74. Direct-Current Equipment.
Fixtures installed on direct-current circuits shall be equipped with auxiliary equipment and resistors especially designed and for direct-current operation, and the fixtures shall be so marked.

410-75. Open-Circuit Voltage Exceeding 300 Volts.
Equipment having an open-circuit voltage exceeding 300 volts shall not be installed in dwelling occupancies unless such equipment is so designed that there will be no exposed live parts when lamps are being inserted, are in place, or are being removed.

Fixtures intended for use in other-than-dwelling occupancies are so marked. This usually indicates that the fixture has maintenance features that are considered to be beyond the capabilities of the ordinary home owner or involve voltages in excess of those permitted by this *Code* for dwelling occupancies. See Sections 210-6 and 410-80(b).

Figure 410-11. The circuitry for a simple reactance-type ballast for fluorescent lighting.

410-76. **Fixture Mounting.**

(a) Exposed Ballasts. Fixtures having exposed ballasts or transformers shall be so installed that such ballasts or transformers will not be in contact with combustible material.

(b) Combustible Low-Density Cellulose Fiberboard. Where a surface-mounted fixture containing a ballast is to be installed on combustible low-density cellulose fiberboard, it shall be listed for this condition or shall be spaced not less than 1½ inches (38 mm) from the surface of the fiberboard. Where such fixtures are partially or wholly recessed, the provisions of Sections 410-64 through 410-72 shall apply.

(FPN): Combustible low-density cellulose fiberboard includes sheets, panels, and tiles that have a density of 20 pounds per cubic foot (320.36 kg/cu m) or less, and that are formed of bonded plant fiber material but does not include solid or laminated wood, nor fiberboard that has a density in excess of 20 pounds per cubic foot (320.36 kg/cu m) or is a material that has been integrally treated with fire-retarding chemicals to the degree that the flame spread in any plane of the material will not exceed 25, determined in accordance with tests for surface burning characteristics of building materials. See Test Method for Surface Burning Characteristics of Building Materials, ANSI/ASTM E84-1984.

Fluorescent lamp fixtures intended for mounting on combustible low-density cellulose fiberboard ceilings have been evaluated with thermal insulation above the ceiling in the vicinity of the fixture and are marked *"Suitable for Surface Mounting on Combustible Low-Density Cellulose Fiberboard."*

Fluorescent lamp fixtures not so marked may be directly mounted against a ceiling surface of *other-than-combustible, low-density fiberboard* or may be spaced not less than 1½ inches from the surface of the low-density fiberboard.

Further information may be obtained from the Underwriters Laboratories Inc. publication, "Building Materials Directory."

410-77. **Equipment Not Integral with Fixture.**

(a) Metal Cabinets. Auxiliary equipment, including reactors, capacitors, resistors, and similar equipment, where not installed as part of a lighting fixture assembly, shall be enclosed in accessible, permanently installed metal cabinets.

(b) Separate Mounting. Separately mounted ballasts that are intended for direct connection to a wiring system shall not be required to be separately enclosed.

(c) Wired Fixture Sections. Wired fixture sections are paired, with a ballast(s) supplying a lamp or lamps in both. For interconnection between paired units, it shall be permissible to use ⅜-inch flexible metal conduit in lengths not exceeding 25 feet

(7.62 m) in conformance with Article 350. Fixture wire operating at line voltage, supplying only the ballast(s) of one of the paired fixtures, shall be permitted in the same raceway as the lamp supply wires of the paired fixtures.

Wired fixture sections are shipped in pairs and are marked for use in pairs. Each individual unit includes lamps in odd-numbered quantities (1 or 3 is most common) with the odd lamp in each fixture supplied by a two-lamp ballast located in one fixture of the pair. Use of two-lamp ballasts is more energy efficient than use of single-lamp or three-lamp ballasts.

410-78. **Autotransformers.** An autotransformer that is used to raise the voltage to more than 300 volts, as part of a ballast for supplying lighting units, shall be supplied only by a grounded system.

410-79. **Switches.** Snap switches shall comply with Section 380-14.

Q. Special Provisions for Electric-Discharge Lighting Systems of More than 1000 Volts

These sections apply to interior electric-discharge neon-tube-type lighting that contains neon, helium, or argon gas, with or without mercury, at low vapor pressure; long-length fluorescent tube lighting requiring more than 1,000 V; and cold-cathode fluorescent-lamp installations arranged to operate with several tubes in series.

410-80. **General.**

(a) Open-Circuit Voltage Exceeding 1000 Volts. Equipment for use with electric-discharge lighting systems and designed for an open-circuit voltage exceeding 1000 volts shall be of a type intended for such service.

(b) Dwelling Occupancies. Equipment having an open-circuit voltage exceeding 1000 volts shall not be installed in or on dwelling occupancies.

This section specifically prohibits electric-discharge lighting, such as neon-tube, high-intensity discharge, or fluorescent lighting, that has an open circuit voltage greater than 1000 volts to be installed in dwelling occupancies. Such lighting systems are often used as decorative lighting as well as for outline lighting and signs. Where used as outline lighting or signs in nonresidential occupancies, see also Article 600.

(c) Live Parts. The terminal of an electric-discharge lamp shall be considered as a live part where any lamp terminal is connected to a circuit of over 300 volts.

(d) Additional Requirements. In addition to complying with the general requirements for lighting fixtures, such equipment shall comply with Part Q of this article.

(FPN): For signs and outline lighting, see Article 600.

410-81. **Control.**

(a) Disconnection. Fixtures or lamp installations shall be controlled either singly or in groups by an externally operable switch or circuit breaker that opens all ungrounded primary conductors.

(b) Within Sight or Locked Type. The switch or circuit breaker shall be located within sight from the fixtures or lamps, or it shall be permitted elsewhere if it is provided with a means for locking in the open position.

The provision that requires the switch or circuit breaker to be within view or capable of being locked in the "off" position ensures the service person that the disconnecting means will not be closed while servicing the equipment.

410-82. **Lamp Terminals and Lampholders.** Parts that must be removed for lamp replacement shall be hinged or held captive. Lamps or lampholders will be so designed that there shall be no exposed live parts when lamps are being inserted or are being removed.

410-83. **Transformer Ratings.** Transformers and ballasts shall have a secondary open-circuit voltage of not over 15,000 volts with an allowance on test of 1000 volts additional. The secondary-current rating shall be not more than 120 milliamperes if the open-circuit voltage is over 7500 volts, and not more than 240 milliamperes if the open-circuit voltage is 7500 volts or less.

410-84. **Transformer Type.** Transformers shall be enclosed and listed.

410-85. **Transformer Secondary Connections.** The high-voltage windings of transformers shall not be connected in series or in parallel.

Exception: Two transformers, each having one end of its high-voltage winding grounded and connected to the enclosure, shall be permitted to have their high-voltage windings connected in series to form the equivalent of a midpoint grounded transformer. The grounded ends shall be connected by insulated conductors not smaller than No. 14.

410-86. Transformer Locations.

(a) **Accessible.** Transformers shall be accessible after installation.

(b) **Secondary Conductors.** Transformers shall be installed as near to the lamps as practicable to keep the secondary conductors as short as possible.

(c) **Adjacent to Combustible Materials.** Transformers shall be so located that adjacent combustible materials will not be subjected to temperatures in excess of 90°C (194°F).

410-87. Transformer Loading. The lamps connected to any transformer shall be of such length and characteristics as not to cause a condition of continuous overvoltage on the transformer.

Transformers are required to be enclosed and listed, and should be rated to supply the proper current and voltage for the lamp or tube. See Section 600-32.

410-88. Wiring Method — Secondary Conductors. Conductors shall be installed in accordance with Section 600-31.

Table 310-13, which lists various types of insulated conductors, does not include the type of cable required in Sections 410-88 and 600-31(b). There are, however, standards for this type of cable. The following information is an excerpt from the Underwriters Laboratories Inc.'s *Electrical Construction Materials Directory*.

Gas tube sign and ignition cable may be Type GTO-5 (5,000 volts), GTO-10 (10,000 volts), or GTO-15 (15,000 volts), and is listed in sizes Nos. 18 to 10 copper and Nos. 12 to 10 aluminum and copper-clad aluminum. This material is intended for use with gas tube signs, oil burners, and inside lighting.

L — used as a suffix in combination with any of the preceding type letter designations indicates that an outer covering of lead has been applied.

Wires with copper-clad aluminum are surface printed "AL (CU-CLAD)" or "CU-CLAD AL." Wires with aluminum conductors are surface printed "AL."

410-89. Lamp Supports. Lamps shall be adequately supported as required in Section 600-33.

410-90. Exposure to Damage. Lamps shall not be located where normally exposed to physical damage.

410-91. Marking. Each fixture or each secondary circuit of tubing having an open-circuit voltage of over 1000 volts shall have a clearly legible marking in letters not less than 1/4 inch (6.35 mm) high reading "Caution. . . .volts." The voltage indicated shall be the rated open-circuit voltage.

410-92. Switches. Snap switches shall comply with Section 380-14.

R. Lighting Track

410-100. Definition. Lighting track is a manufactured assembly designed to support and energize lighting fixtures that are capable of being readily repositioned on the track. Its length may be altered by the addition or subtraction of sections of track.

410-101. Installation.

(a) **Lighting Track.** Lighting track shall be permanently installed and permanently connected to a branch circuit. Only lighting track fittings shall be installed on lighting track. Lighting track fittings shall not be equipped with general-purpose receptacles.

A lighting track fitting differs from a fitting as defined in Article 100 in that it usually performs both an electrical and a mechanical function.

It is not the intent that such assemblies be a system for locating convenience receptacles or an alternative for required receptacle outlets such as those required in Section 210-62. Lighting track can be removed and relocated and thus is not a substitute for required outlets.

(b) **Connected Load.** The connected load on lighting track shall not exceed the rating of the track. Lighting track shall be supplied by a branch circuit having a rating not more than that of the track.

(c) **Locations Not Permitted.** Lighting track shall not be installed (1) where subject to physical damage; (2) in wet or damp locations; (3) where subject to corrosive vapors; (4) in storage battery rooms; (5) in hazardous (classified) locations; (6) where concealed; (7) where extended through walls or partitions; (8) less than 5 feet (1.52 m) above the finished floor except where protected from physical damage or track operating at less than 30 volts RMS open-circuit voltage.

Low voltage lighting track operating at less than 30 volts is permitted to be installed less than 5 feet above the floor.

(d) Support. Fittings identified for use on lighting track shall be designed specifically for the track on which they are to be installed. They shall be securely fastened to the track, maintain polarization and grounding, and shall be designed to be suspended directly from the track.

410-102. **Track Load.** For branch-circuit calculations, a maximum of 2 feet (609.6 mm) of lighting track or fraction thereof shall be considered 180 VA. Where multicircuit track is installed, the load requirement of this section shall be considered to be divided equally between the circuits.

Exception: Where installed in dwelling unit(s) or the guest rooms of hotels or motels.

Note Section 220-3(c)(5) references this section for computation of branch circuits.

410-103. **Heavy-Duty Track.** Heavy-duty lighting track is lighting track identified for use exceeding 20 amperes. Each fitting attached to a heavy-duty lighting track shall have individual overcurrent protection.

410-104. **Fastening.** Lighting track shall be securely mounted so that each fastening will be suitable for supporting the maximum weight of fixtures that can be installed. Unless identified for supports at greater intervals, a single section 4 feet (1.22 m) or shorter in length shall have two supports, and, where installed in a continuous row, each individual section of not more than 4 feet (1.22 m) in length shall have one additional support.

410-105. **Construction Requirements.**

(a) Construction. The housing for the lighting track system shall be of substantial construction to maintain rigidity. The conductors shall be installed within the track housing permitting insertion of a fixture, and designed to prevent tampering and accidental contact with live parts. Components of lighting track systems of different voltages shall not be interchangeable. The track

conductors shall be a minimum No. 12 or equal, and shall be copper. The track system ends shall be insulated and capped.

Exception: Fittings that incorporate an integral device to reduce the line voltage for a lower voltage lamp.

(b) Grounding. Lighting track shall be grounded in accordance with Article 250, and the track sections shall be securely coupled to maintain continuity of the circuitry, polarization, and grounding throughout.

ARTICLE 422   Appliances

Contents

A. General

(a) 300 Watts or Less.

(b) Over 300 Watts.

(c) Lampholders.

422-16. Grounding.

422-17. Wall-Mounted Ovens and Counter-Mounted
Cooking Units.

    (a) Permitted to Be Cord- and Plug-Connected or
Permanently Connected.

    (b) Separable Connector or a Plug and Receptacle
Combination.

422-18. Support of Ceiling Fans.

422-19. Other Installation Methods.

D. Control and Protection of Appliances

422-20. Disconnecting Means.

422-21. Disconnection of Permanently Connected
Appliances.

    (a) Rated at Not Over 300 Volt Amperes
or ⅛ Horsepower.

    (b) Permanently Connected Appliances of Greater
Rating.

422-22. Disconnection of Cord- and Plug-Connected
Appliances.

    (a) Separable Connector or an Attachment Plug and
Receptacle.

    (b) Connection at the Rear Base of a Range.

    (c) Rating.

    (d) Requirements for Attachment Plugs and Connectors.

422-23. Polarity in Cord- and Plug-Connected Appliances.

422-24. Cord- and Plug-Connected Appliances Subject to
Immersion.

422-25. Unit Switch(es) as Disconnecting Means.

    (a) Multifamily Dwellings.

    (b) Two-Family Dwellings.

    (c) One-Family Dwellings.

    (d) Other Occupancies.

422-26. Switch and Circuit Breaker to Be Indicating.

422-27. Disconnecting Means for Motor-Driven
Appliances.

422-28. Overcurrent Protection.

    (a) Appliances.

    (b) Household-type Appliance with Surface Heating
Elements.

    (c) Infrared Lamp Commercial and Industrial Heating
Appliances.

    (d) Open-Coil or Exposed Sheathed-Coil Types of
Surface Heating Elements in Commercial-type
Heating Appliances.

    (e) Single Nonmotor-Operated Appliance.

    (f) Electric Heating Appliances Employing Resistance-
type Heating Elements Rated More than 48 Amperes.

E. Marking of Appliances

422-29. Cord- and Plug-Connected Pipe Heating
Assemblies.

422-30. Nameplate.

    (a) Nameplate Marking.

    (b) To Be Visible.

422-31. Marking of Heating Elements.

422-32. Appliances Consisting of Motors and Other Loads.

    (a) Marking.

    (b) Alternate Marking Method.

A. General

422-1. **Scope.** This article covers electric appliances used in any occupancy.

This article covers electric appliances that may be used in a dwelling unit or in commercial and industrial locations. It also covers appliances that may be fastened in place, or cord- and plug-connected, such as air-conditioning units, dishwashers, heating appliances, water heaters, infrared heating lamps, etc. See Section 422-3 for requirements of other articles. Also see Article 100 for definition of "Appliance."

422-2. **Live Parts.** Appliances shall have no live parts normally exposed to contact.

Exception: Toasters, grills, or other appliances in which the current-carrying parts at high temperatures are necessarily exposed.

422-3. **Other Articles.** All requirements of this Code shall apply where applicable. Appliances for use in hazardous (classified) locations shall comply with Articles 500 through 517.

The requirements of Article 430 shall apply to the installation of motor-operated appliances and the requirements of Article 440 shall apply to the installation of appliances containing hermetic refrigerant motor-compressor(s), except as specifically amended in this article.

B. Branch-Circuit Requirements

422-4. **Branch-Circuit Sizing.** This section specifies sizes of conductors capable of carrying appliance current without overheating under the conditions specified. This section shall not apply to conductors that form an integral part of an appliance.

Such conductors are tested as part of the listing or labeling process.

(a) Individual Circuits. The rating of an individual branch circuit shall not be less than the marked rating of the appliance or the marked rating of an appliance having combined loads as provided in Section 422-32.

Exception No. 1: For motor-operated appliances not having a marked rating, the branch-circuit size shall be in accordance with Part B of Article 430.

Exception No. 2: For an appliance, other than a motor-operated appliance, that is continuously loaded, the branch-circuit rating shall not be less than 125 percent of the marked rating; or not less than 100 percent if the branch-circuit device and its assembly are listed for continuous loading at 100 percent of its rating.

Exception No. 3: Branch circuits for household cooking appliances shall be permitted to be in accordance with Table 220-19.

If a labeled or listed appliance is provided with installation instructions from the manufacturer, the branch-circuit size is not permitted to be less than the minimum size stated in the installation instructions. See Section 110-3(b).

(b) Circuits Supplying Two or More Loads. For branch circuits supplying appliance and other loads, the rating shall be determined in accordance with Section 210-23.

422-5. **Branch-Circuit Overcurrent Protection.** Branch circuits shall be protected in accordance with Section 240-3.

If a protective device rating is marked on an appliance, the branch-circuit overcurrent device rating shall not exceed the protective device rating marked on the appliance.

C. Installation of Appliances

422-6. **General.** All appliances shall be installed in an approved manner.

422-7. **Central Heating Equipment.** Central heating equipment other than fixed electric space heating equipment shall be supplied by an individual branch circuit.

Exception: Auxiliary equipment such as a pump, valve, humidifier, or electrostatic air cleaner directly associated with the heating equipment shall be permitted to be connected to the same branch circuit.

This section was new in the 1990 *NEC.* It is intended that the electric motors, ignition systems, controls, etc., of fossil-fuel fired central heating equipment be connected to an individual branch circuit as defined in Article 100. See Branch Circuit, Individual.

422-8. **Flexible Cords.**

(a) Heater Cords. All cord- and plug-connected smoothing irons and electrically heated appliances that are rated at more than 50 watts and produce temperatures in excess of 121°C (250°F) on surfaces with which the cord is likely to be in contact shall be provided with one of the types of approved heater cords listed in Table 400-4.

(b) Other Heating Appliances. All other cord- and plug-connected electrically heated appliances shall be connected with one of the approved types of cord listed in Table 400-4, selected in accordance with the usage specified in that table.

(c) Other Appliances. Flexible cord shall be permitted (1) for connection of appliances to facilitate their frequent interchange or to prevent the transmission of noise or vibration or (2) to facilitate the removal or disconnection of appliances that are fastened in place, where the fastening means and mechanical connections are specifically designed to permit ready removal for maintenance or repair, and the appliance is intended or identified for flexible cord connection.

It should be understood that the cord-connected appliance is required to be specifically designed to be readily removable for maintenance and repair, mechanically as well as electrically. See Figure 422-1.

(d) Specific Appliances.

(1) Electrically operated kitchen waste disposers intended for dwelling unit use shall be permitted to be cord-and-plug connected with a flexible cord identified for the purpose, terminated with a grounding-type attachment plug where all of the following conditions are met:

   a. The length of the cord shall not be less than 18 inches (457 mm) and not over 36 inches (914 mm).

   b. Receptacles shall be located to avoid physical damage to the flexible cord.

   c. The receptacle shall be accessible.

Figure 422-1. *An example of a cord- and plug-connected appliance with mechanical connections designed to permit removal. The cord and receptacle are designed and installed in accordance with Section 422-8(d).*

(2) Built-in dishwashers and trash compactors intended for dwelling use shall be permitted to be cord-and-plug connected with a flexible cord identified for the purpose, terminated with a grounding-type attachment plug where all of the following conditions are met:

   a. The length of the cord shall be 3 to 4 feet (0.914 to 1.22 m).

   b. Receptacles shall be located to avoid physical damage to the flexible cord.

   c. The receptacle shall be located in the space occupied by the appliance or adjacent thereto.

   d. The receptacle shall be accessible.

Exception: Listed kitchen waste disposers, dishwashers, and trash compactors protected by a system of double insulation, or its equivalent, shall not be required to be grounded. Where such a system is employed, the equipment shall be distinctively marked.

(3) Cord- and plug-connected high-pressure spray washing machines shall be provided with factory-installed ground-fault circuit-interrupter protection for personnel. The ground-fault circuit-interrupter shall be an integral part of the attachment plug or shall be located in the supply cord within 12 inches (305 mm) of the attachment plug.

Exception No. 1: A high-pressure spray washer protected by a system of double insulation if such a unit is provided with a permanent warning indicating that it shall be connected to a receptacle protected by a ground-fault circuit-interrupter.

Exception No. 2: A high-pressure spray washer rated for a 3-phase supply system.

Exception No. 3: A high-pressure spray washer rated over 250 volts.

Two new exceptions, No. 2 and No. 3, have been added to the 1993 *Code*. These new exceptions permit high-pressure spray washers to be used without a ground-fault circuit-interrupter as part of the supply cord for washers rated 3-phase or over 250 volts. The main rule of Section 422-8(d)(3) remains unchanged.

422-9. **Cord- and Plug-Connected Immersion Heaters.** Electric heaters of the cord- and plug-connected immersion type shall be so constructed and installed that current-carrying parts are effectively insulated from electrical contact with the substance in which they are immersed.

422-10. **Protection of Combustible Material.** Each electrically heated appliance that is intended by size, weight, and service to be located in a fixed position shall be so placed as to provide ample protection between the appliance and adjacent combustible material.

422-11. **Stands for Cord- and Plug-Connected Appliances.** Each smoothing iron and other cord- and plug-connected electrically heated appliance intended to be applied to combustible material shall be equipped with an approved stand, which shall be permitted to be a separate piece of equipment or a part of the appliance.

422-12. **Signals for Heated Appliances.** In other than dwelling-type occupancies, each electrically heated appliance or group of appliances intended to be applied to combustible material shall be provided with a signal.

Exception: If an appliance is provided with an integral temperature-limiting device.

A common way to provide a signal light for electrically heated appliances in commercial or industrial locations is to use a red light so connected to and within sight of the appliance as to indicate that the appliance is energized and operating.

No signal is required for an electrically heated appliance provided with an integral thermostat or equivalent that limits the temperature to which it can heat.

422-13. Flatirons.
Electrically heated smoothing irons shall be equipped with an identified temperature-limiting means.

422-14. Water Heaters.

(a) Storage- and Instantaneous-type Water Heaters. Each storage- or instantaneous-type water heater shall be equipped with a temperature-limiting means in addition to its control thermostat to disconnect all ungrounded conductors, and such means shall be (1) installed to sense maximum water temperature and (2) either a trip-free, manually reset type or a type having a replacement element. Such water heaters shall be marked to require the installation of a temperature and pressure relief valve.

(FPN): See Relief Valves and Automatic Gas Shutoff Devices for Hot Water Supply Systems, ANSI Z21.22-1986.

Exception: Water heaters with supply water temperature of 82°C (180°F) or above and a capacity of 60 kW or above and identified as being suitable for this use; and water heaters with a capacity of 1 gallon (3.785 L) or less and identified as being suitable for such use.

(b) Storage-type Water Heaters. A branch circuit supplying a fixed storage-type water heater having a capacity of 120 gallons (454.2 L) or less shall have a rating not less than 125 percent of the nameplate rating of the water heater.

(FPN): For branch-circuit sizing, see Section 422-4(a), Exception No. 2.

422-15. Infrared Lamp Industrial Heating Appliances.

(a) 300 Watts or Less. Infrared heating lamps rated at 300 watts or less shall be permitted with lampholders of the medium-base, unswitched porcelain type or other types identified as suitable for use with infrared heating lamps rated 300 watts or less.

(b) Over 300 Watts. Screw-shell lampholders shall not be used with infrared lamps over 300 watts rating.

Exception: Lampholders identified as suitable for use with infrared heating lamps rated more than 300 watts.

(c) Lampholders. Lampholders shall be permitted to be connected to any of the branch circuits of Article 210 and, in industrial occupancies, shall be permitted to be operated in series on circuits of over 150 volts to ground provided the voltage rating of the lampholders is not less than the circuit voltage.

Each section, panel, or strip carrying a number of infrared lampholders (including the internal wiring of such section, panel, or strip) shall be considered an appliance. The terminal connection block of each such assembly shall be considered an individual outlet.

Infrared (heat) radiation lamps are tungsten-filament incandescent lamps that are similar in appearance to lighting lamps; however, they are designed to operate at a lower temperature, thus transferring more heat radiation and less light intensity. Infrared lamps are used for a variety of heating and drying purposes in residential, commercial, and industrial locations.

422-16. Grounding.
Appliances required by Article 250 to be grounded shall have exposed noncurrent-carrying metal parts grounded in the manner specified in Article 250.

(FPN): See Sections 250-42, 250-43, and 250-45 for equipment grounding of refrigerators and freezers and Sections 250-57 and 250-60 for equipment grounding of electric ranges, wall-mounted ovens, counter-mounted cooking units, and clothes dryers.

422-17. Wall-Mounted Ovens and Counter-Mounted Cooking Units.

(a) Permitted to Be Cord- and Plug-Connected or Permanently Connected. Wall-mounted ovens and counter-mounted cooking units complete with provisions for mounting and for making electrical connections shall be permitted to be permanently connected or, only for ease in servicing or for installation, cord- and plug-connected.

(b) Separable Connector or a Plug and Receptacle Combination. A separable connector or a plug and receptacle combination in the supply line to an oven or cooking unit shall:

(1) Not be installed as the disconnecting means required by Section 422-20.

(2) Be approved for the temperature of the space in which it is located.

422-18. **Support of Ceiling Fans.** Listed ceiling fans that do not exceed 35 pounds (15.88 kg) in weight, with or without accessories, shall be permitted to be supported by outlet boxes identified for such use and supported in accordance with Sections 370-23 and 370-27.

Section 370-23 requires boxes to be rigid and securely fastened in place. Section 370-27 does not permit standard type boxes to support ceiling fans unless they are provided with supplemental support as shown in Figure 370-8. Supplemental support is not required for listed boxes identified for fan support. Section 422-18 above permits boxes identified for fan support to be used to support listed ceiling fans that do not exceed 35 pounds. See Figure 422-2.

422-19. **Other Installation Methods.** Appliances employing methods of installation other than covered by this article shall be permitted to be used only by special permission.

D. Control and Protection of Appliances

422-20. **Disconnecting Means.** A means shall be provided to disconnect each appliance from all ungrounded conductors in accordance with the following sections of Part D. If an appliance is supplied by more than one source, the disconnecting means shall be grouped and identified.

422-21. **Disconnection of Permanently Connected Appliances.**

(a) Rated at Not Over 300 Volt Amperes or 1/8 Horsepower. For permanently connected appliances rated at not over 300 volt amperes or 1/8 horsepower, the branch-circuit overcurrent device shall be permitted to serve as the disconnecting means.

(b) Permanently Connected Appliances of Greater Rating. For permanently connected appliances of greater rating, the

Figure 422-2. An example of supporting ceiling fans with a box identified for such use. (Raco Inc.)

branch-circuit switch or circuit breaker shall be permitted to serve as the disconnecting means where the switch or circuit breaker is within sight from the appliance or is capable of being locked in the open position.

(FPN No. 1): For motor-driven appliances of more than 1/8 horsepower, see Section 422-27.

(FPN No. 2): For appliances employing unit switches, see Section 422-25.

422-22. Disconnection of Cord- and Plug-Connected Appliances.

(a) Separable Connector or an Attachment Plug and Receptacle. For cord- and plug-connected appliances, an accessible separable connector or an accessible plug and receptacle shall be permitted to serve as the disconnecting means. Other cord- and plug-connected appliances shall be provided with disconnecting means in accordance with Section 422-21.

(b) Connection at the Rear Base of a Range. For cord- and plug-connected household electric ranges, an attachment plug and receptacle connection at the rear base of a range, if it is accessible from the front by removal of a drawer, shall be considered as meeting the intent of Section 422-22(a).

(c) Rating. The rating of a receptacle or of a separable connector shall not be less than the rating of any appliance connected thereto.

Exception: Demand factors authorized elsewhere in this Code shall be permitted to be applied.

(d) Requirements for Attachment Plugs and Connectors. Attachment plugs and connectors shall conform to the following:

(1) **Live Parts.** They shall be so constructed and installed as to guard against inadvertent contact with live parts.

(2) **Interrupting Capacity.** They shall be capable of interrupting their rated current without hazard to the operator.

(3) **Interchangeability.** They shall be so designed that they will not fit into receptacles of lesser rating.

422-23. Polarity in Cord- and Plug-Connected Appliances.

If the appliance is provided with a manually operated, line-connected, single-pole switch for appliance on-off operation, an Edison-base lampholder, or a 15- or 20-ampere receptacle, the attachment plug shall be of the polarized or grounding type.

(FPN): For polarity of Edison-base lampholders, see Section 410-42(a).

422-24. Cord- and Plug-Connected Appliances Subject to Immersion.

Cord- and plug-connected portable freestanding hydromassage units and hand-held hair dryers shall be constructed to provide protection for personnel against electrocution when immersed while in the "on" or "off" position.

This requirement was new in the 1990 *NEC*. Although receptacles in bathrooms of dwelling units have been required to be protected by a ground-fault circuit-interrupter since the 1975 edition of the *Code*, there are still many receptacles in use in existing bathrooms that are not so protected. Cord- and plug-connected appliances such as hand-held hair dryers, curling irons, etc., which can and have accidentally fallen into bathtubs causing fatalities, are required to be provided with some form of protective device that is part of the appliance. There are three types of protectors that can be used to comply with this requirement: ALCIs, IDCIs, and GFCIs.

Appliance-leakage circuit-interrupters (ALCIs) are intended to deenergize the supply to the appliance when leakage current exceeds a predetermined value. Immersion-detector circuit-interrupters (IDCIs) deenergize the supply when a liquid causes a conductive path between a live part and a sensor. Ground-fault circuit-interrupters (GFCIs) deenergize the supply when the current to ground exceeds a predetermined value.

422-25. Unit Switch(es) as Disconnecting Means.

A unit switch(es) with a marked "off" position that is a part of an appliance and disconnects all ungrounded conductors shall be permitted as the disconnecting means required by this article where other means for disconnection are provided in the following types of occupancies:

(a) Multifamily Dwellings. In multifamily dwellings, the other disconnecting means shall be within the dwelling unit, or on the same floor as the dwelling unit in which the appliance is installed, and shall be permitted to control lamps and other appliances.

(b) Two-Family Dwellings. In two-family dwellings, the other disconnecting means shall be permitted either inside or outside of the dwelling unit in which the appliance is installed. In this case, an individual switch or circuit breaker for the dwelling unit shall be permitted and shall also be permitted to control lamps and other appliances.

(c) One-Family Dwellings. In one-family dwellings, the service disconnecting means shall be permitted to be the other disconnecting means.

(d) Other Occupancies. In other occupancies, the branch-circuit switch or circuit breaker, where readily accessible for servicing of the appliance, shall be permitted as the other disconnecting means.

422-26. **Switch and Circuit Breaker to Be Indicating.** Switches and circuit breakers used as disconnecting means shall be of the indicating type.

422-27. **Disconnecting Means for Motor-Driven Appliances.** If a switch or circuit breaker serves as the disconnecting means for a permanently connected motor-driven appliance of more than 1/8 horsepower, it shall be located within sight from the motor controller and shall comply with Part I of Article 430.

Exception: A switch or circuit breaker that serves as the other disconnecting means as required in Section 422-25(a), (b), (c), or (d) shall be permitted to be out of sight from the motor controller of an appliance provided with a unit switch(es) with a marked "off" position and that disconnects all ungrounded conductors.

422-28. **Overcurrent Protection.**

(a) Appliances. Appliances shall be protected against overcurrent in accordance with (b) through (f) below and Sections 422-4 and 422-5.

Exception: Motors of motor-operated appliances shall be provided with overload protection in accordance with Part C of Article 430. Hermetic refrigerant motor-compressors in air-conditioning or refrigerating equipment shall be provided with overload protection in accordance with Part F of Article 440. Where appliance overcurrent protective devices that are separate from the appliance are required, data for selection of these devices shall be marked on the appliance. The minimum marking shall be that specified in Sections 430-7 and 440-4.

(b) Household-type Appliance with Surface Heating Elements. A household-type appliance with surface heating elements having a maximum demand of more than 60 amperes computed in accordance with Table 220-19 shall have its power supply subdivided into two or more circuits, each of which is provided with overcurrent protection rated at not over 50 amperes.

(c) Infrared Lamp Commercial and Industrial Heating Appliances. Infrared lamp commercial and industrial heating appliances shall have overcurrent protection not exceeding 50 amperes.

(d) Open-Coil or Exposed Sheathed-Coil Types of Surface Heating Elements in Commercial-type Heating Appliances. Open-coil or exposed sheathed-coil types of surface heating elements in commercial-type heating appliances shall be protected by overcurrent protective devices rated at not over 50 amperes.

(e) Single Nonmotor-Operated Appliance. If the branch circuit supplies a single nonmotor-operated appliance, the rating of overcurrent protection shall (1) not exceed that marked on the appliance; (2) if the overcurrent protection rating is not marked and the appliance is rated over 13.3 amperes, not exceed 150 percent of the appliance rated current; or (3) if the overcurrent protection rating is not marked and the appliance is rated 13.3 amperes or less, not exceed 20 amperes.

Exception: Where 150 percent of appliance rating does not correspond to a standard overcurrent device ampere rating, the next higher standard rating shall be permitted.

(f) Electric Heating Appliances Employing Resistance-type Heating Elements Rated More than 48 Amperes. Electric heating appliances employing resistance-type heating elements rated more than 48 amperes shall have the heating elements subdivided. Each subdivided load shall not exceed 48 amperes and shall be protected at not more than 60 amperes.

These supplementary overcurrent protective devices shall be (1) factory-installed within or on the heater enclosure or provided as a separate assembly by the heater manufacturer; (2) accessible, but need not be readily accessible; and (3) suitable for branch-circuit protection.

The main conductors supplying these overcurrent protective devices shall be considered branch-circuit conductors.

Exception No. 1: Household-type appliances with surface heating elements as covered in Section 422-28(b) and commercial-type heating appliances as covered in Section 422-28(d).

Exception No. 2: Commercial kitchen and cooking appliances using sheathed-type heating elements not covered in Section 422-28(d) shall be permitted to be subdivided into circuits not exceeding 120 amperes and protected at not more than 150 amperes where one of the following is met:

a. Elements are integral with and enclosed within a cooking surface;

b. Elements are completely contained within an enclosure identified as suitable for this use; or

c. Elements are contained within an ASME rated and stamped vessel.

Exception No. 3: Water heaters and steam boilers employing resistance-type immersion electric heating elements contained in an ASME rated and stamped vessel shall be permitted to be subdivided into circuits not exceeding 120 amperes and protected at not more than 150 amperes.

E. Marking of Appliances

422-29. **Cord- and Plug-Connected Pipe Heating Assemblies.** Cord- and plug-connected pipe heating assemblies intended to prevent freezing of piping shall be listed.

The *listing* requirement is new in the 1993 *Code*. It was included as a result of data submitted substantiating numerous fires initiated by heat tapes.

422-30. **Nameplate.**

(a) Nameplate Marking. Each electric appliance shall be provided with a nameplate giving the identifying name and the rating in volts and amperes, or in volts and watts. If the appliance is to be used on a specific frequency or frequencies, it shall be so marked.

Where motor overload protection external to the appliance is required, the appliance shall be so marked.

(FPN):   See Section 422-28(a), Exception for overcurrent protection requirements.

(b) To Be Visible. Marking shall be located so as to be visible or easily accessible after installation.

422-31. **Marking of Heating Elements.** All heating elements that are rated over one ampere, replaceable in the field, and a part of an appliance shall be legibly marked with the ratings in volts and amperes, or in volts and watts, or with the manufacturer's part number.

422-32. **Appliances Consisting of Motors and Other Loads.** Appliances shall be marked in accordance with (a) or (b) below.

(a) Marking. In addition to the marking required in Section 422-30, the marking on an appliance consisting of a motor with other load(s) or motors with or without other load(s) shall specify the minimum supply circuit conductor ampacity and the maximum rating of the circuit overcurrent protective device.

Exception No. 1: Appliances factory-equipped with cords and attachment plugs, complying with Section 422-30.

Exception No. 2: An appliance where both the minimum supply circuit conductor ampacity and maximum rating of the circuit overcurrent protective device are not more than 15 amperes and complies with Section 422-30.

(b) Alternate Marking Method. An alternate marking method shall be permitted to specify the rating of the largest motor in volts and amperes, and the additional load(s) in volts and amperes, or volts and watts in addition to the marking required in Section 422-30.

Exception No. 1: Appliances factory-equipped with cords and attachment plugs, complying with Section 422-30.

Exception No. 2: The ampere rating of a motor ⅛ horsepower or less or a nonmotor load 1 ampere or less shall be permitted to be omitted unless such loads constitute the principal load.

ARTICLE 424   Fixed Electric Space Heating Equipment

Contents

A. General

B. Installation

C. Control and Protection of Fixed Electric Space Heating Equipment

(a) Heating Equipment with Supplementary Overcurrent Protection.

(b) Heating Equipment without Supplementary Overcurrent Protection.

(c) Unit Switch(es) as Disconnecting Means.

424-20. Thermostatically Controlled Switching Devices.

(a) Serving as Both Controllers and Disconnecting Means.

(b) Thermostats that Do Not Directly Interrupt All Ungrounded Conductors.

424-21. Switch and Circuit Breaker to Be Indicating.

424-22. Overcurrent Protection.

(a) Branch-Circuit Devices.

(b) Resistance Elements.

(c) Overcurrent Protective Devices.

(d) Branch-Circuit Conductors.

(e) Conductors for Subdivided Loads.

D. Marking of Heating Equipment

424-28. Nameplate.

(a) Marking Required.

(b) Location.

424-29. Marking of Heating Elements.

E. Electric Space Heating Cables

424-34. Heating Cable Construction.

424-35. Marking of Heating Cables.

424-36. Clearances of Wiring in Ceilings.

424-37. Location of Branch-Circuit and Feeder Wiring in Exterior Walls.

424-38. Area Restrictions.

(a) Shall Not Extend Beyond the Room or Area.

(b) Uses Prohibited.

(c) In Closet Ceilings as Low Temperature Heat Sources to Control Relative Humidity.

424-39. Clearance from Other Objects and Openings.

424-40. Splices.

424-41. Installation of Heating Cables on Dry Board, in Plaster, and on Concrete Ceilings.

(a) Shall Not Be Installed in Walls.

(b) Adjacent Runs.

(c) Surfaces to Be Applied.

(d) Splices.

(e) Ceiling Surface.

(f) Secured.

(g) Dry Board Installations.

(h) Free from Contact with Conductive Surfaces.

(i) Joists.

(j) Crossing Joists.

424-42. Finished Ceilings.

424-43. Installation of Nonheating Leads of Cables.

(a) Free Nonheating Leads.

(b) Leads in Junction Box.

(c) Excess Leads.

424-44. Installation of Cables in Concrete or Poured Masonry Floors.

(a) Watts per Linear Foot.

(b) Spacing Between Adjacent Runs.

(c) Secured in Place.

(d) Spacings Between Heating Cable and Metal Embedded in the Floor.

(e) Leads Protected.

(f) Bushings or Approved Fittings.

424-45. Inspection and Tests.

F. Duct Heaters

424-57. General.

424-58. Identification.

424-59. Airflow.

424-60. Elevated Inlet Temperature.

424-61. Installation of Duct Heaters with Heat Pumps and Air Conditioners.

424-62. Condensation.

424-63. Fan Circuit Interlock.

424-64. Limit Controls.

424-65. Location of Disconnecting Means.

424-66. Installation.

G. Resistance-type Boilers

424-70. Scope.

424-71. Identification.

424-72. Overcurrent Protection.

(a) Boiler Employing Resistance-type Immersion Heating Elements in an ASME Rated and Stamped Vessel.

(b) Boiler Employing Resistance-type Heating Elements Rated More than 48 Amperes and Not Contained in an ASME Rated and Stamped Vessel.

(c) Supplementary Overcurrent Protective Devices.

A. General

424-1. **Scope.** This article covers fixed electric equipment used for space heating. For the purpose of this article, heating equipment shall include heating cable, unit heaters, boilers, central systems, or other approved fixed electric space heating equipment. This article shall not apply to process heating and room air conditioning.

424-2. **Other Articles.** All requirements of this Code shall apply where applicable. Fixed electric space heating equipment for use in hazardous (classified) locations shall comply with Articles 500 through 517. Fixed electric space heating equipment incorporating a hermetic refrigerant motor-compressor shall also comply with Article 440.

424-3. **Branch Circuits.**

(a) **Branch-Circuit Requirements.** Individual branch circuits shall be permitted to supply any size fixed electric space heating equipment.

Branch circuits supplying two or more outlets for fixed electric space heating equipment shall be rated 15, 20, or 30 amperes.

Exception: In other than residential occupancies, fixed infrared heating equipment shall be permitted to be supplied from branch circuits rated not over 50 amperes.

(b) **Branch-Circuit Sizing.** The ampacity of the branch-circuit conductors and the rating or setting of overcurrent protective devices supplying fixed electric space heating equipment consisting of resistance elements with or without a motor shall not be less than 125 percent of the total load of the motors and the heaters. The rating or setting of overcurrent protective devices shall be permitted in accordance with Section 240-3(b). A contactor, thermostat, relay, or similar device, listed for continuous operation at 100 percent of its rating, shall be permitted to supply its full-rated load as provided in Section 210-22(c), Exception.

The sizing of branch-circuit conductors supplying fixed electric space heating equipment at 125 percent of the total load of the heaters (and motors) is predicated on the need to protect overcurrent devices, particularly in panelboards, from overheating during periods of prolonged operation. See Section 384-16(c). Since the branch-circuit conductors and overcurrent device are required to be rated at 125 percent of the total load, an additional increase of 125 percent is not required for continuous loads. The requirement in this section is phrased to avoid arguments as to whether or not the heating equipment is a "continuous load" as defined in Article 100.

The size of the branch-circuit conductors and overcurrent protective devices supplying fixed electric space heating equipment including a hermetic refrigerant motor-compressor with or without resistance units shall be computed in accordance with Sections 440-34 and 440-35.

The provisions of this section shall not apply to conductors that form an integral part of approved fixed electric space heating equipment.

B. Installation

424-9. General. All fixed electric space heating equipment shall be installed in an approved manner.

Permanently installed electric baseboard heaters equipped with factory-installed receptacle outlets, or outlets provided as a separate listed assembly, shall be permitted in lieu of a receptacle outlet(s) that is required by Section 210-50(b). Such receptacle outlets shall not be connected to the heater circuits.

(FPN): Listed baseboard heaters include instructions that may not permit their installation below receptacle outlets.

A new second paragraph has been added to the 1993 *Code* that restates the permission granted in Section 210-52(b), Exception, to allow factory-installed receptacle outlets in electric baseboard heaters to satisfy the spacing requirements for receptacle outlets according to Section 210-52(b). These outlets are not permitted to be connected to the branch-circuit supplying the baseboard heaters.

Heating equipment and systems often have special installation instructions for spacings, types of supply wires, or special control equipment that must be considered in determining the suitability of the installation.

See also commentary after fine print note at end of Section 210-52(a).

424-10. Special Permission. Fixed electric space heating equipment and systems installed by methods other than covered by this article shall be permitted only by special permission.

424-11. Supply Conductors. Fixed electric space heating equipment requiring supply conductors with over 60°C insulation shall be clearly and permanently marked. This marking shall be plainly visible after installation and shall be permitted to be adjacent to the field-connection box.

Fixed electric space heating equipment may require supply conductors with a temperature rating greater than 60°C.

424-12. Locations.

(a) **Exposed to Severe Physical Damage.** Fixed electric space heating equipment shall not be used where exposed to severe physical damage unless adequately protected.

(b) **Damp or Wet Locations.** Heaters and related equipment installed in damp or wet locations shall be approved for such locations and shall be constructed and installed so that water cannot enter or accumulate in or on wired sections, electrical components, or duct work.

(FPN No. 1): See Section 110-11 for equipment exposed to deteriorating agents.

(FPN No. 2): See Section 680-27 for pool deck areas.

424-13. Spacing from Combustible Materials. Fixed electric space heating equipment shall be installed to provide the required spacing between the equipment and adjacent combustible material, unless it has been found to be acceptable where installed in direct contact with combustible material.

424-14. Grounding. All exposed noncurrent-carrying metal parts of fixed electric space heating equipment likely to become energized shall be grounded as required in Article 250.

C. Control and Protection of Fixed Electric Space Heating Equipment

424-19. Disconnecting Means. Means shall be provided to disconnect the heater, motor controller(s), and supplementary overcurrent protective device(s) of all fixed electric space heating equipment from all ungrounded conductors. Where heating

Figure 424-1. *An electric furnace with cooling coils for air conditioning.*

equipment is supplied by more than one source, the disconnecting means shall be grouped and identified.

(a) Heating Equipment with Supplementary Overcurrent Protection. The disconnecting means for fixed electric space heating equipment with supplementary overcurrent protection shall be within sight from the supplementary overcurrent protective device(s), on the supply side of these devices, if fuses, and, in addition, shall comply with either (1) or (2) below.

(1) Heater Containing No Motor Rated Over ⅛ Horsepower. The above disconnecting means or unit switches complying with Section 424-19(c) shall be permitted to serve as the required disconnecting means for both the motor controller(s) and heater under either item a or b below.

a. The disconnecting means provided is also within sight from the motor controller(s) and the heater; or

b. The disconnecting means provided shall be capable of being locked in the open position.

(2) Heater Containing a Motor(s) Rated Over ⅛ Horsepower. The above disconnecting means shall be permitted to serve as the required disconnecting means for both the motor controller(s) and heater by one of the means specified in items a through d below.

a. Where the disconnecting means is also in sight from the motor controller(s) and the heater.

b. Where the disconnecting means is not within sight from the heater, a separate disconnecting means shall be installed, or the disconnecting means shall be capable of being locked in the open position, or unit switches complying with Section 424-19(c) shall be permitted.

c. Where the disconnecting means is not within sight from the motor controller location, a disconnecting means complying with Section 430-102 shall be provided.

d. Where the motor is not in sight from the motor controller location, Section 430-102(b) shall apply.

(b) Heating Equipment without Supplementary Overcurrent Protection.

(1) Without Motor or with Motor Not Over ⅛ Horsepower. For fixed electric space heating equipment without a motor rated over ⅛ horsepower, the branch-circuit switch or circuit breaker shall be permitted to serve as the disconnecting means, where the switch or circuit breaker is within sight from the heater or is capable of being locked in the open position.

Where electric space heating equipment, without unit switches, that contains a motor rated ⅛ horsepower or less or without a motor are installed, the branch-circuit switch or circuit breaker is allowed to serve as the disconnecting means, provided that it is located *within sight* from the heater. Where the disconnect is not *within sight* of the heater, it must be capable of being *locked in the off position.*

Section 424-19(c) permits a unit switch to serve as the disconnecting means provided it has a marked "off" position and disconnects all ungrounded conductors and OTHER MEANS are also provided in accordance with paragraphs (1), (2), (3), and (4). Such OTHER MEANS are not required to be capable of being locked in the "open position" as required by Section 424-9(b)(1) above.

See Section 424-20 for thermostatically controlled switching devices.

(2) Over 1/8 Horsepower. For motor-driven electric space heating equipment with a motor rated over 1/8 horsepower, a disconnecting means shall be located within sight from the motor controller.

Exception: As permitted by Section 424-19(a)(2).

(c) Unit Switch(es) as Disconnecting Means. A unit switch(es) with a marked "off" position that is part of a fixed heater and disconnects all ungrounded conductors shall be permitted as the disconnecting means required by this article where other means for disconnection are provided in the following types of occupancies.

(1) Multifamily Dwellings. In multifamily dwellings, the other disconnecting means shall be within the dwelling unit, or on the same floor as the dwelling unit in which the fixed heater is installed, and shall also be permitted to control lamps and appliances.

(2) Two-Family Dwellings. In two-family dwellings, the other disconnecting means shall be permitted either inside or outside of the dwelling unit in which the fixed heater is installed. In this case, an individual switch or circuit breaker for the dwelling unit shall be permitted and shall also be permitted to control lamps and appliances.

(3) One-Family Dwellings. In one-family dwellings, the service disconnecting means shall be permitted to be the other disconnecting means.

(4) Other Occupancies. In other occupancies, the branch-circuit switch or circuit breaker, where readily accessible for servicing of the fixed heater, shall be permitted as the other disconnecting means.

424-20. Thermostatically Controlled Switching Devices.

(a) Serving as Both Controllers and Disconnecting Means. Thermostatically controlled switching devices and combination thermostats and manually controlled switches shall be permitted to serve as both controllers and disconnecting means, provided all of the following conditions are met:

(1) Provided with a marked "off" position.

(2) Directly open all ungrounded conductors when manually placed in the "off" position.

(3) Designed so that the circuit cannot be energized automatically after the device has been manually placed in the "off" position.

(4) Located as specified in Section 424-19.

(b) Thermostats that Do Not Directly Interrupt All Ungrounded Conductors. Thermostats that do not directly interrupt all ungrounded conductors and thermostats that operate remote-control circuits shall not be required to meet the requirements of (a). These devices shall not be permitted as the disconnecting means.

424-21. Switch and Circuit Breaker to Be Indicating.
Switches and circuit breakers used as disconnecting means shall be of the indicating type.

424-22. Overcurrent Protection.

(a) Branch-Circuit Devices. Electric space heating equipment, other than such motor-operated equipment as required by Articles 430 and 440 to have additional overcurrent protection, shall be permitted to be protected against overcurrent where supplied by one of the branch circuits in Article 210.

(b) Resistance Elements. Resistance-type heating elements in electric space heating equipment shall be protected at not more than 60 amperes. Equipment rated more than 48 amperes and employing such elements shall have the heating elements subdivided, and each subdivided load shall not exceed 48 amperes. Where a subdivided load is less than 48 amperes, the rating of the supplementary overcurrent protective device shall comply with Section 424-3(b).

Exception: As provided in Section 424-72(a).

(c) Overcurrent Protective Devices. The supplementary overcurrent protective devices for the subdivided loads specified in (b) above shall be (1) factory-installed within or on the heater enclosure or supplied for use with the heater as a separate assembly by the heater manufacturer; (2) accessible, but shall not be required to be readily accessible; and (3) suitable for branch-circuit protection.

(FPN): See Section 240-10.

Where cartridge fuses are used to provide this overcurrent protection, a single disconnecting means shall be permitted to be used for the several subdivided loads.

(FPN No. 1): For supplementary overcurrent protection, see Section 240-10.

(FPN No. 2): For disconnecting means for cartridge fuses in circuits of any voltage, see Section 240-40.

Where subdivided loads are required, the heating equipment manufacturer is required to furnish the necessary overcurrent protective devices.

The main branch-circuit conductors supplying the overcurrent protective devices for subdivided loads are considered as branch circuits to make it clear that the 125 percent requirement in Section 424-3(b) is for the branch circuit only.

(d) Branch-Circuit Conductors. The conductors supplying the supplementary overcurrent protective devices shall be considered branch-circuit conductors.

Exception: For heaters rated 50 kW or more, the conductors supplying the supplementary overcurrent protective devices specified in (c) above shall be permitted to be sized at not less than 100 percent of the nameplate rating of the heater, provided all of the following conditions are met:

a. The heater is marked with a minimum conductor size; and

b. The conductors are not smaller than the marked minimum size; and

c. A temperature-actuated device controls the cyclic operation of the equipment.

(e) Conductors for Subdivided Loads. Field-wired conductors between the heater and the supplementary overcurrent protective devices shall be sized at not less than 125 percent of the load served. The supplementary overcurrent protective devices specified in (c) shall protect these conductors in accordance with Section 240-3.

Exception: For heaters rated 50 kW or more, the ampacity of field-wired conductors between the heater and the supplementary overcurrent protective devices shall be permitted to be not less than 100 percent of the load of their respective subdivided circuits, provided all of the following conditions are met:

a. The heater is marked with a minimum conductor size; and

b. The conductors are not smaller than the marked minimum size; and

c. A temperature-activated device controls the cyclic operation of the equipment.

D. Marking of Heating Equipment

424-28. **Nameplate.**

(a) Marking Required. Each unit of fixed electric space heating equipment shall be provided with a nameplate giving the identifying name and the normal rating in volts and watts, or in volts and amperes.

Electric space heating equipment intended for use on alternating current only or direct current only shall be marked to so indicate. The marking of equipment consisting of motors over 1/8 horsepower and other loads shall specify the rating of the motor in volts, amperes, and frequency, and the heating load in volts and watts, or in volts and amperes.

(b) Location. This nameplate shall be located so as to be visible or easily accessible after installation.

424-29. **Marking of Heating Elements.** All heating elements that are replaceable in the field and are a part of an electric heater shall be legibly marked with the ratings in volts and watts, or in volts and amperes.

E. Electric Space Heating Cables

424-34. **Heating Cable Construction.** Heating cables shall be furnished complete with factory-assembled nonheating leads at least 7 feet (2.13 m) in length.

424-35. **Marking of Heating Cables.** Each unit shall be marked with the identifying name or identification symbol, catalog number, ratings in volts and watts, or in volts and amperes.

Each unit length of heating cable shall have a permanent legible marking on each nonheating lead located within 3 inches (76 mm) of the terminal end. The lead wire shall have the following color identification to indicate the circuit voltage on which it is to be used: 120-volt nominal, yellow; 208-volt nominal, blue; 240-volt nominal, red; and 277-volt nominal, brown.

424-36. **Clearances of Wiring in Ceilings.** Wiring located above heated ceilings shall be spaced not less than 2 inches (50.8 mm) above the heated ceiling and shall be considered as operating at an ambient of 50°C (122°F). The ampacity of conductors shall be computed on the basis of the correction factors shown in the 0-2000 volt ampacity tables of Article 310.

Exception: Wiring above heated ceilings and located above thermal insulation having a minimum thickness of 2 inches (50.8 mm) shall not require correction for temperature.

424-37. **Location of Branch-Circuit and Feeder Wiring in Exterior Walls.** Wiring methods shall comply with Article 300 and Section 310-10.

424-38. **Area Restrictions.**

(a) **Shall Not Extend Beyond the Room or Area.** Heating cables shall not extend beyond the room or area in which they originate.

(b) **Uses Prohibited.** Cables shall not be installed in closets, over walls or partitions that extend to the ceiling, or over cabinets whose clearance from the ceiling is less than the minimum horizontal dimension of the cabinet to the nearest cabinet edge that is open to the room or area.

Exception: Isolated single runs of cable shall be permitted to pass over partitions where they are embedded.

(c) **In Closet Ceilings as Low Temperature Heat Sources to Control Relative Humidity.** This provision shall not prevent the use of cable in closet ceilings as low temperature heat sources to control relative humidity, provided they are used only in those portions of the ceiling that are unobstructed to the floor by shelves or other permanent fixtures.

424-39. **Clearance from Other Objects and Openings.** Heating elements of cables shall be separated at least 8 inches (203 mm) from the edge of outlet boxes and junction boxes that are to be used for mounting surface lighting fixtures. A clearance of not less than 2 inches (50.8 mm) shall be provided from recessed fixtures and their trims, ventilating openings, and other such openings in room surfaces. Sufficient area shall be provided to assure that no heating cable will be covered by any surface-mounted units.

424-40. **Splices.** Embedded cables shall be spliced only where necessary and only by approved means, and in no case shall the length of the heating cable be altered.

424-41. **Installation of Heating Cables on Dry Board, in Plaster, and on Concrete Ceilings.**

(a) **Shall Not Be Installed in Walls.** Cables shall not be installed in walls.

Exception: Isolated single runs of cable shall be permitted to run down a vertical surface to reach a dropped ceiling.

(b) **Adjacent Runs.** Adjacent runs of cable not exceeding $2\frac{3}{4}$ watts per foot (305 mm) shall be installed not less than $1\frac{1}{2}$ inches (38 mm) on centers.

(c) **Surfaces to Be Applied.** Heating cables shall be applied only to gypsum board, plaster lath, or other fire-resistant material. With metal lath or other electrically conductive surfaces, a coat of plaster shall be applied to completely separate the metal lath or conductive surface from the cable.

(FPN): See also (f) below.

(d) **Splices.** All heating cables, the splice between the heating cable and nonheating leads, and 3-inch (76-mm) minimum of the nonheating lead at the splice shall be embedded in plaster or dry board in the same manner as the heating cable.

(e) **Ceiling Surface.** The entire ceiling surface shall have a finish of thermally noninsulating sand plaster having a nominal thickness of $\frac{1}{2}$ inch (12.7 mm), or other noninsulating material identified as suitable for this use and applied according to specified thickness and directions.

(f) **Secured.** Cables shall be secured at intervals not exceeding 16 inches (406 mm) by means of approved stapling, tape, plaster, nonmetallic spreaders, or other approved means. Staples or metal fasteners that straddle the cable shall not be used with metal lath or other electrically conductive surfaces.

Exception: Cables identified to be secured at intervals not to exceed 6 feet (1.83 m).

(g) **Dry Board Installations.** In dry board installations, the entire ceiling below the heating cable shall be covered with gypsum board not exceeding $\frac{1}{2}$ inch (12.7 mm) thickness. The void between the upper layer of gypsum board, plaster lath, or other fire-resistant material and the surface layer of gypsum board shall be completely filled with thermally conductive, nonshrinking plaster or other approved material or equivalent thermal conductivity.

(h) **Free from Contact with Conductive Surfaces.** Cables shall be kept free from contact with metal or other electrically conductive surfaces.

(i) **Joists.** In dry board applications, cable shall be installed parallel to the joist, leaving a clear space centered under the joist of $2\frac{1}{2}$ inches (64 mm) (width) between centers of adjacent runs of cable. A surface layer of gypsum board shall be mounted so that the nails or other fasteners do not pierce the heating cable.

(j) Crossing Joists. Cables shall cross joists only at the ends of the room.

Exception: Where the cable is required to cross joists elsewhere in order to satisfy the manufacturer's instructions that the installer avoid placing the cable too close to ceiling penetrations and light fixtures.

424-42. **Finished Ceilings.** Finished ceilings shall not be covered with decorative panels or beams constructed of materials that have thermal insulating properties, such as wood, fiber, or plastic. Finished ceilings shall be permitted to be covered with paint, wallpaper, or other approved surface finishes.

424-43. **Installation of Nonheating Leads of Cables.**

(a) Free Nonheating Leads. Free nonheating leads of cables shall be installed in accordance with approved wiring methods from the junction box to a location within the ceiling. Such installations shall be permitted to be single conductors in approved raceways, single or multiconductor Type UF, Type NMC, Type MI, or other approved conductors.

(b) Leads in Junction Box. Not less than 6 inches (152 mm) of free nonheating lead shall be within the junction box. The marking of the leads shall be visible in the junction box.

(c) Excess Leads. Excess leads of heating cables shall not be cut but shall be secured to the underside of the ceiling and embedded in plaster or other approved material, leaving only a length sufficient to reach the junction box with not less than 6 inches (152 mm) of free lead within the box.

424-44. **Installation of Cables in Concrete or Poured Masonry Floors.**

(a) Watts per Linear Foot. Heating cables shall not exceed 16½ watts per linear foot (305 mm) of cable.

(b) Spacing Between Adjacent Runs. The spacing between adjacent runs of cable shall not be less than 1 inch (25.4 mm) on centers.

(c) Secured in Place. Cables shall be secured in place by nonmetallic frames or spreaders or other approved means while the concrete or other finish is applied.

Cables shall not be installed where they bridge expansion joints unless protected from expansion and contraction.

(d) Spacings Between Heating Cable and Metal Embedded in the Floor. Spacings shall be maintained between the heating cable and metal embedded in the floor.

Exception: Grounded metal-clad cable shall be permitted to be in contact with metal embedded in the floor.

(e) Leads Protected. Leads shall be protected where they leave the floor by rigid metal conduit, intermediate metal conduit, rigid nonmetallic conduit, electrical metallic tubing, or by other approved means.

(f) Bushings or Approved Fittings. Bushings or approved fittings shall be used where the leads emerge within the floor slab.

424-45. **Inspection and Tests.** Cable installations shall be made with due care to prevent damage to the cable assembly and shall be inspected and approved before cables are covered or concealed.

F. Duct Heaters

424-57. **General.** Part F shall apply to any heater mounted in the air stream of a forced-air system where the air-moving unit is not provided as an integral part of the equipment.

Figure 424-2. An insert-type electric duct heater.

424-58. **Identification.** Heaters installed in an air duct shall be identified as suitable for the installation.

424-59. **Airflow.** Means shall be provided to assure uniform and adequate airflow over the face of the heater in accordance with the manufacturer's instructions.

(FPN): Heaters installed within 4 feet (1.22 m) of the outlet of an air-moving device, heat pump, air conditioner, elbows, baffle plates, or other obstructions in duct work may require turning vanes, pressure plates, or other devices on the inlet side of the duct heater to assure an even distribution of air over the face of the heater.

424-60. **Elevated Inlet Temperature.** Duct heaters intended for use with elevated inlet air temperature shall be identified as suitable for use at the elevated temperatures.

424-61. **Installation of Duct Heaters with Heat Pumps and Air Conditioners.** Heat pumps and air conditioners having duct heaters closer than 4 feet (1.22 m) to the heat pump or air conditioner shall have both the duct heater and heat pump or air conditioner identified as suitable for such installation and so marked.

424-62. **Condensation.** Duct heaters used with air conditioners or other air-cooling equipment that may result in condensation of moisture shall be identified as suitable for use with air conditioners.

424-63. **Fan Circuit Interlock.** Means shall be provided to ensure that the fan circuit is energized when any heater circuit is energized. However, time- or temperature-controlled delay in energizing the fan motor shall be permitted.

424-64. **Limit Controls.** Each duct heater shall be provided with an approved, integral, automatic-reset temperature-limiting control or controllers to deenergize the circuit or circuits.

In addition, an integral independent supplementary control or controllers shall be provided in each duct heater that will disconnect a sufficient number of conductors to interrupt current flow. This device shall be manually resettable or replaceable.

424-65. **Location of Disconnecting Means.** Duct heater controller equipment shall be accessible with the disconnecting means installed at or within sight from the controller.

Exception: As permitted by Section 424-19(a).

424-66. **Installation.** Duct heaters shall be installed in accordance with the manufacturer's instructions in a manner so that operation will not create a hazard to persons or property. Furthermore, duct heaters shall be located with respect to building construction and other equipment so as to permit access to the heater. Sufficient clearance shall be maintained to permit

replacement of controls and heating elements and for adjusting and cleaning of controls and other parts requiring such attention. See Section 110-16.

(FPN): For additional installation information, see Installation of Air Conditioning and Ventilating Systems, NFPA 90A-1989 (ANSI) and Installation of Warm Air Heating and Air Conditioning Systems, NFPA 90B-1989 (ANSI).

G. Resistance-type Boilers

424-70. **Scope.** The provisions in Part G of this article shall apply to boilers employing resistance-type heating elements. Electrode-type boilers shall not be considered as employing resistance-type heating elements. See Part H of this article.

424-71. **Identification.** Resistance-type boilers shall be identified as suitable for the installation.

424-72. **Overcurrent Protection.**

(a) Boiler Employing Resistance-type Immersion Heating Elements in an ASME Rated and Stamped Vessel. A boiler employing resistance-type immersion heating elements contained in an ASME rated and stamped vessel shall have the heating elements protected at not more than 150 amperes. Such a boiler rated more than 120 amperes shall have the heating elements subdivided into loads not exceeding 120 amperes.

Where a subdivided load is less than 120 amperes, the rating of the overcurrent protective device shall comply with Section 424-3(b).

(b) Boiler Employing Resistance-type Heating Elements Rated More than 48 Amperes and Not Contained in an ASME Rated and Stamped Vessel. A boiler employing resistance-type heating elements not contained in an ASME rated and stamped vessel shall have the heating elements protected at not more than 60 amperes. Such a boiler rated more than 48 amperes shall have the heating elements subdivided into loads not exceeding 48 amperes.

Where a subdivided load is less than 48 amperes, the rating of the overcurrent protective device shall comply with Section 424-3(b).

(c) Supplementary Overcurrent Protective Devices. The supplementary overcurrent protective devices for the subdivided loads as required by Sections 424-72(a) and (b) shall be (1) factory-installed within or on the boiler enclosure or provided as a separate assembly by the boiler manufacturer; and (2) accessible, but need not be readily accessible; and (3) suitable for branch-circuit protection.

Where cartridge fuses are used to provide this overcurrent protection, a single disconnecting means shall be permitted for the several subdivided circuits. See Section 240-40.

(d) Conductors Supplying Supplementary Overcurrent Protective Devices. The conductors supplying these supplementary overcurrent protective devices shall be considered branch-circuit conductors.

Exception: Where the heaters are rated 50 kW or more, the conductors supplying the overcurrent protective device specified in (c) above shall be permitted to be sized at not less than 100 percent of the nameplate rating of the heater, provided all of the following conditions are met:

a. The heater is marked with a minimum conductor size; and

b. The conductors are not smaller than the marked minimum size; and

c. A temperature- or pressure-actuated device controls the cyclic operation of the equipment.

(e) Conductors for Subdivided Loads. Field-wired conductors between the heater and the supplementary overcurrent protective devices shall be sized at not less than 125 percent of the load served. The supplementary overcurrent protective devices specified in (c) shall protect these conductors in accordance with Section 240-3.

Exception: For heaters rated 50 kW or more, the ampacity of field-wired conductors between the heater and the supplementary overcurrent protective devices shall be permitted to be not less than 100 percent of the load of their respective subdivided circuits, provided all of the following conditions are met:

a. The heater is marked with a minimum conductor size; and

b. The conductors are not smaller than the marked minimum size; and

c. A temperature-activated device controls the cyclic operation of the equipment.

424-73. Over-Temperature Limit Control. Each boiler designed, so that in normal operation there is no change in state of the heat transfer medium, shall be equipped with a temper-

ature sensitive limiting means. It shall be installed to limit maximum liquid temperature and shall directly or indirectly disconnect all ungrounded conductors to the heating elements. Such means shall be in addition to a temperature regulating system and other devices protecting the tank against excessive pressure.

424-74. Over-Pressure Limit Control. Each boiler designed, so that in normal operation there is a change in state of the heat transfer medium from liquid to vapor, shall be equipped with a pressure sensitive limiting means. It shall be installed to limit maximum pressure and shall directly or indirectly disconnect all ungrounded conductors to the heating elements. Such means shall be in addition to a pressure regulating system and other devices protecting the tank against excessive pressure.

424-75. Grounding. All noncurrent-carrying metal parts shall be grounded in accordance with Article 250. Means for connection of equipment grounding conductor(s) sized in accordance with Table 250-95 shall be provided.

H. Electrode-type Boilers

424-80. Scope. The provisions in Part H of this article shall apply to boilers for operation at 600 volts, nominal, or less, in which heat is generated by the passage of current between electrodes through the liquid being heated.

(FPN): For over 600 volts see Part G of Article 710.

424-81. Identification. Electrode-type boilers shall be identified as suitable for the installation.

424-82. Branch-Circuit Requirements. The size of branch-circuit conductors and overcurrent protective devices shall be calculated on the basis of 125 percent of the total load (motors not included). A contactor, relay, or other device, approved for continuous operation at 100 percent of its rating, shall be permitted to supply its full-rated load. See Section 210-22(c), Exception. The provisions of this section shall not apply to conductors that form an integral part of an approved boiler.

Exception: For an electrode boiler rated 50 kW or more, the conductors supplying the boiler electrode(s) shall be permitted to be sized at not less than 100 percent of the nameplate rating of the electrode boiler, provided all the following conditions are met:

a. The electrode boiler is marked with a minimum conductor size; and

b. The conductors are not smaller than the marked minimum size; and

c. A temperature- or pressure-actuated device controls the cyclic operation of the equipment.

424-83. **Over-Temperature Limit Control.** Each boiler designed, so that in normal operation there is no change in state of the heat transfer medium, shall be equipped with a temperature sensitive limiting means. It shall be installed to limit maximum liquid temperature and shall directly or indirectly interrupt all current flow through the electrodes. Such means shall be in addition to the temperature regulating system and other devices protecting the tank against excessive pressure.

424-84. **Over-Pressure Limit Control.** Each boiler designed, so that in normal operation there is a change in state of the heat transfer medium from liquid to vapor, shall be equipped with a pressure sensitive limiting means. It shall be installed to limit maximum pressure and shall directly or indirectly interrupt all current flow through the electrodes. Such means shall be in addition to a pressure regulating system and other devices protecting the tank against excessive pressure.

424-85. **Grounding.** For those boilers designed such that fault currents do not pass through the pressure vessel, and the pressure vessel is electrically isolated from the electrodes, all exposed noncurrent-carrying metal parts, including the pressure vessel, supply, and return connecting piping, shall be grounded in accordance with Article 250.

For all other designs, the pressure vessel containing the electrodes shall be isolated and electrically insulated from ground.

424-86. **Markings.** All electrode-type boilers shall be marked to show (1) the manufacturer's name; (2) the normal rating in volts, amperes, and kilowatts; (3) the electrical supply required specifying frequency, number of phases, and number of wires; (4) the marking: "Electrode-type Boiler"; (5) a warning marking — "ALL POWER SUPPLIES SHALL BE DISCONNECTED BEFORE SERVICING, INCLUDING SERVICING THE PRESSURE VESSEL."

The nameplate shall be located so as to be visible after installation.

J. Electric Radiant Heating Panels and Heating Panel Sets

424-90. **Scope.** The provisions of Part J of this article shall apply to radiant heating panels and heating panel sets.

424-91. **Definitions.**

(a) Heating Panel. A heating panel is a complete assembly provided with a junction box or a length of flexible conduit for connection to a branch circuit.

(b) Heating Panel Set. A heating panel set is a rigid or nonrigid assembly provided with nonheating leads or a terminal junction assembly identified as being suitable for connection to a wiring system.

424-92. **Markings.**

(1) Markings shall be permanent and in a location that is visible prior to application of panel finish.

(2) Each unit shall be identified as suitable for the installation.

(3) Each unit shall be marked with the identifying name or identification symbol, catalog number, and rating in volts and watts, or in volts and amperes.

(4) The manufacturers of heating panels or heating panel sets shall provide marking labels that indicate that the space heating installation incorporates heating panels or heating panel sets and instructions that the labels shall be affixed to the panelboards to identify which branch circuits supply the circuits to those space heating installations.

Exception: Heating panels and heating panel set installations that are visible and distinguishable after installation shall not be required to have labels provided.

424-93. **Installation.**

(a) General.

(1) Heating panels and heating panel sets shall be installed in accordance with the manufacturer's instructions.

(2) The heating portion shall not:

a. Be installed in or behind surfaces where subject to physical damage.

b. Be run through or above walls, partitions, cupboards, or similar portions of structures that extend to the ceiling.

c. Be run in or through thermal insulation, but shall be permitted to be in contact with the surface of thermal insulation.

(3) Edges of panels and panel sets shall be separated by not less than 8 inches (203 mm) from the edges of any outlet boxes and junction boxes that are to be used for mounting surface lighting fixtures. A clearance of not less than 2 inches (50.8 mm) shall be provided from recessed fixtures and their trims, ventilating openings, and other such openings in room surfaces. Sufficient area shall be provided to assure that no heating panel or heating panel set is to be covered by any surface-mounted units.

Exception: Heating panels and panel sets listed and marked for lesser clearances shall be permitted to be installed at the marked clearances.

(4) After the heating panels or heating panel sets are installed and inspected, it shall be permitted to install a surface that has been identified by the manufacturer's instructions as being suitable for the installation. The surface shall be secured so that the nails or other fastenings do not pierce the heating panels or heating panel sets.

(5) Surfaces permitted by Section 424-93(a)(4) shall be permitted to be covered with paint, wallpaper, or other approved surfaces identified in the manufacturer's instructions as being suitable.

(b) Heating Panel Sets.

(1) Heating panel sets shall be permitted to be secured to the lower face of joists or mounted in between joists, headers, or nailing strips.

(2) Heating panel sets shall be installed parallel to joists or nailing strips.

(3) Nailing or stapling of heating panel sets shall be done only through the unheated portions provided for this purpose. Heating panel sets shall not be cut through or nailed through any point closer than 1/4 inch (6.35 mm) to the element. Nails, staples, or other fasteners shall not be used where they penetrate current-carrying parts.

(4) Heating panel sets shall be installed as complete units unless identified as suitable for field cutting in an approved manner.

424-94. **Clearances of Wiring in Ceilings.** Wiring located above heated ceilings shall be spaced not less than 2 inches (50.8 mm) above the heated ceiling and shall be considered as operating at an ambient of 50°C (122°F). The ampacity shall be computed on the basis of the correction factors given in the 0-2000 volt ampacity tables of Article 310.

Exception: Wiring above heated ceilings and located above thermal insulations having a minimum thickness of 2 inches (50.8 mm) shall not require correction for temperature.

424-95. **Location of Branch-Circuit and Feeder Wiring in Walls.**

(a) Exterior Walls. Wiring methods shall comply with Article 300 and Section 310-10.

(b) Interior Walls. Any wiring behind heating panels or heating panel sets located in interior walls or partitions shall be considered as operating at an ambient of 40°C (104°F), and the ampacity shall be computed on the basis of the correction factors given in the 0-2000 volt ampacity tables of Article 310.

424-96. **Connection to Branch-Circuit Conductors.**

(a) General. Heating panels or heating panel sets assembled together in the field to form a heating installation in one room or area shall be connected in accordance with the manufacturer's instructions.

(b) Heating Panels. Heating panels shall be connected to branch-circuit wiring by an approved wiring method.

(c) Heating Panel Sets.

(1) Heating panel sets shall be connected to branch-circuit wiring by a method identified as being suitable for the purpose.

(2) A heating panel set provided with terminal junction assembly shall be permitted to have the nonheating leads attached at the time of installation in accordance with the manufacturer's instructions.

424-97. **Nonheating Leads.** Excess nonheating leads of heating panels or heating panel sets shall be permitted to be cut to the required length. They shall meet the installation requirements of the wiring method employed in accordance with Section 424-96. Nonheating leads shall be an integral part of a heating panel and a heating panel set and shall not be subjected to the ampacity requirements of Section 424-3(b) for branch circuits.

424-98. Installation in Concrete or Poured Masonry.

(a) **Maximum Heated Area.** Heating panels or heating panel sets shall not exceed 33 watts per square foot (0.093 sq m) of heated area.

(b) **Secured in Place and Identified as Suitable.** Heating panels or heating panel sets shall be secured in place by means specified in the manufacturer's instructions and identified as suitable for the installation.

(c) **Expansion Joints.** Heating panels or heating panel sets shall not be installed where they bridge expansion joints unless provision is made for expansion and contraction.

(d) **Spacings.** Spacings shall be maintained between heating panels or heating panel sets and metal embedded in the floor.

Exception: Grounded metal-clad heating panels shall be permitted to be in contact with metal embedded in the floor.

(e) **Protection of Leads.** Leads shall be protected where they leave the floor by rigid metal conduit, intermediate metal conduit, rigid nonmetallic conduit, electrical metallic tubing, or by other approved means.

(f) **Bushings or Fittings Required.** Bushings or approved fittings shall be used where the leads emerge within the floor slabs.

424-99. Installation Under Floor Covering.

(a) **Identification.** Heating panels or heating panel sets for installation under floor covering shall be identified as suitable for installation under floor covering.

(b) **Maximum Heated Area.** Heating panels or panel sets, installed under floor covering, shall not exceed 15 watts per square foot (0.093 m²) of heated area.

(c) **Installation.** Listed heating panels or panel sets, if installed under floor covering, shall be installed on floor surfaces that are smooth and flat in accordance with the manufacturer's instructions and shall also comply with the following:

(1) **Expansion Joints.** Heating panels or heating panel sets shall not be installed where they bridge expansion joints unless protected from expansion and contraction.

(2) **Connection to Conductors.** Heating panels and heating panel sets shall be connected to branch-circuit and supply wiring by wiring methods recognized in Chapter 3.

(3) **Anchoring.** Heating panels and heating panel sets shall be firmly anchored to the floor using an adhesive or anchoring system identified for this use.

(4) **Coverings.** After heating panels or heating panel sets are installed and inspected, they shall be permitted to be covered by a floor covering that has been identified by the manufacturer as being suitable for the installation. The covering shall be secured to the heating panel or heating panel sets with release-type adhesives or by means identified for this use.

(5) **Fault Protection.** A device to open all ungrounded conductors supplying the heating panels or heating panel sets, provided by the manufacturer, shall function when a low or high resistance line-to-line, line to grounded conductor, or line to ground fault occurs, such as the result of a penetration of the element/element assembly.

An example of a heating system that could be installed in this fashion is a system using conductive film heating elements.

(FPN): An integral grounding shield may be required to provide this protection.

ARTICLE 426   Fixed Outdoor Electric Deicing and Snow-Melting Equipment

Contents

A. General

B. Installation

C. Resistance Heating Elements

(a) Watt Density.

(b) Spacing.

(c) Cover.

(d) Secured.

(e) Expansion and Contraction.

426-21. Exposed Deicing and Snow-Melting Equipment.

(a) Secured.

(b) Overtemperature.

(c) Expansion and Contraction.

(d) Flexural Capability.

426-22. Installation of Nonheating Leads for Embedded Equipment.

(a) Grounding Sheath or Braid.

(b) Raceways.

(c) Bushings.

(d) Expansion and Contraction.

(e) Leads in Junction Boxes.

426-23. Installation of Nonheating Leads for Exposed Equipment.

(a) Nonheating Leads.

(b) Protection.

426-24. Electrical Connection.

(a) Heating Element Connections.

(b) Circuit Connections.

426-25. Marking.

426-26. Corrosion Protection.

426-27. Grounding.

(a) Metal Parts.

(b) Grounding Braid or Sheath.

D. Impedance Heating

426-30. Personnel Protection.

426-31. Voltage Limitations.

426-32. Isolation Transformer.

426-33. Induced Currents.

426-34. Grounding.

E. Skin Effect Heating

426-40. Conductor Ampacity.

426-41. Pull Boxes.

426-42. Single Conductor in Enclosure.

426-43. Corrosion Protection.

426-44. Grounding.

F. Control and Protection

426-50. Disconnecting Means.

(a) Disconnection.

(b) Cord- and Plug-Connected Equipment.

426-51. Controllers.

(a) Temperature Controller with "Off" Position.

(b) Temperature Controller without "Off" Position.

(c) Remote Temperature Controller.

(d) Combined Switching Devices.

426-52. Overcurrent Protection.

426-53. Equipment Protection.

426-54. Cord- and Plug-Connected Deicing and Snow-Melting Equipment.

A. General

426-1. Scope. The requirements of this article shall apply to electrically energized heating systems and the installation of these systems.

(a) Embedded. Embedded in driveways, walks, steps, and other areas.

(b) Exposed. Exposed on drainage systems, bridge structures, roofs, and other structures.

Article 426 includes requirements for resistance heating elements, impedance heating systems, or skin effect heating systems. These systems are defined in Section 426-2. In addition, specific requirements are provided for exposed resistance heating elements of the type commonly used on residences for gutter and roof deicing and snow melting. See Sections 426-21 and 426-23. See commentary following Section 426-11.

426-2. Definitions. For the purpose of this article:

Heating System. A complete system consisting of components such as heating elements, fastening devices, nonheating circuit wiring, leads, temperature controllers, safety signs, junction boxes, raceways, and fittings.

Resistance Heating Element. A specific separate element to generate heat that is embedded in or fastened to the surface to be heated.

(FPN): Tubular heaters, strip heaters, heating cable, heating tape, and heating panels are examples of resistance heaters.

Impedance Heating System. A system in which heat is generated in a pipe or rod, or combination of pipes and rods, by causing current to flow through the pipe or rod by direct connection to an ac voltage source from a dual-winding transformer. The pipe or rod shall be permitted to be embedded in the surface to be heated, or constitute the exposed components to be heated.

Skin Effect Heating System. A system in which heat is generated on the inner surface of a ferromagnetic envelope embedded in or fastened to the surface to be heated.

(FPN): Typically, an electrically insulated conductor is routed through and connected to the envelope at the other end. The envelope and the electrically insulated conductor are connected to an ac voltage source from a dual-winding transformer.

426-3. **Application of Other Articles.** All requirements of this Code shall apply except as specifically amended in this article. Cord- and plug-connected fixed outdoor electric deicing and snow-melting equipment intended for specific use and identified as suitable for this use shall be installed according to Article 422. Fixed outdoor electric deicing and snow-melting equipment for use in hazardous (classified) locations shall comply with Articles 500 through 516.

See Sections 422-6 and 422-8.

426-4. **Branch-Circuit Sizing.** The ampacity of branch-circuit conductors and the rating or setting of overcurrent protective devices supplying fixed outdoor electric deicing and snow-melting equipment shall not be less than 125 percent of the total load of the heaters. The rating or setting of overcurrent protective devices shall be permitted in accordance with Section 240-3(b).

B. Installation

426-10. **General.** Equipment for outdoor electric deicing and snow melting shall be identified as being suitable for:

(1) The chemical, thermal, and physical environment, and
(2) Installation in accordance with the manufacturer's drawings and instructions.

426-11. **Use.** Electrical heating equipment shall be installed in such a manner as to be afforded protection from physical damage.

The instructions required by UL for UL-listed mat or cable deicing and snow-melting equipment intended for burial in concrete specifically indicate that the slab is required to be a double pour (poured in two parts) if that is the only acceptable means of installation. If such a limitation is not specifically mentioned, either a single or double pour may be used. See Section 110-3(b).

426-12. **Thermal Protection.** External surfaces of outdoor electric deicing and snow-melting equipment that operate at temperatures exceeding 60°C (140°F) shall be physically guarded, isolated, or thermally insulated to protect against contact by personnel in the area.

See Section 110-17.

426-13. **Identification.** The presence of outdoor electric deicing and snow-melting equipment shall be evident by the posting of appropriate caution signs or markings where clearly visible.

426-14. **Special Permission.** Fixed outdoor deicing and snow-melting equipment employing methods of construction or installation other than covered by this article shall be permitted only by special permission.

See definition of "Special Permission" in Article 100.

C. Resistance Heating Elements

426-20. **Embedded Deicing and Snow-Melting Equipment.**

(a) **Watt Density.** Panels or units shall not exceed 120 watts per square foot (0.093 sq m) of heated area.

(b) **Spacing.** The spacing between adjacent cable runs is dependent upon the rating of the cable, and shall be not less than 1 inch (25.4 mm) on centers.

(c) **Cover.** Units, panels, or cables shall be installed:

(1) On a substantial asphalt or masonry base at least 2 inches (50.8 mm) thick and have at least 1½ inches (38 mm) of asphalt or masonry applied over the units, panels, or cables; or

(2) They shall be permitted to be installed over other approved bases and embedded within 3½ inches (89 mm) of masonry or asphalt but not less than 1½ inches (38 mm) from the top surface; or

(3) Equipment that has been specially investigated for other forms of installation shall be installed only in the manner for which it has been investigated.

(d) Secured. Cables, units, and panels shall be secured in place by frames or spreaders or other approved means while the masonry or asphalt finish is applied.

(e) Expansion and Contraction. Cables, units, and panels shall not be installed where they bridge expansion joints unless provision is made for expansion and contraction.

426-21. **Exposed Deicing and Snow-Melting Equipment.**

(a) Secured. Heating element assemblies shall be secured to the surface being heated by approved means.

(b) Overtemperature. Where the heating element is not in direct contact with the surface being heated, the design of the heater assembly shall be such that its temperature limitations shall not be exceeded.

(c) Expansion and Contraction. Heating elements and assemblies shall not be installed where they bridge expansion joints unless provision is made for expansion and contraction.

(d) Flexural Capability. Where installed on flexible structures, the heating elements and assemblies shall have a flexural capability compatible with the structure.

426-22. **Installation of Nonheating Leads for Embedded Equipment.**

(a) Grounding Sheath or Braid. Nonheating leads having a grounding sheath or braid shall be permitted to be embedded in the masonry or asphalt in the same manner as the heating cable without additional physical protection.

(b) Raceways. All but 1 to 6 inches (25.4 to 152 mm) of nonheating leads of Type TW and other approved types not having a grounding sheath shall be enclosed in a rigid conduit, electrical metallic tubing, intermediate metal conduit, or other raceways within asphalt or masonry; and the distance from the factory splice to raceway shall be not less than 1 inch (25.4 mm) or more than 6 inches (152 mm).

(c) Bushings. Insulating bushings shall be used in the asphalt or masonry where leads enter conduit or tubing.

See commentary following Section 373-6(c).

(d) Expansion and Contraction. Leads shall be protected in expansion joints and where they emerge from masonry or asphalt by rigid conduit, electrical metallic tubing, intermediate metal conduit, other raceways, or other approved means.

(e) Leads in Junction Boxes. Not less than 6 inches (152 mm) of free nonheating lead shall be within the junction box.

426-23. **Installation of Nonheating Leads for Exposed Equipment.**

(a) Nonheating Leads. Power supply nonheating leads (cold leads) for resistance elements shall be suitable for the temperature encountered. Preassembled nonheating leads on approved heaters shall be permitted to be shortened if the markings specified in Section 426-25 are retained. Not less than 6 inches (152 mm) of nonheating leads shall be provided within the junction box.

(b) Protection. Nonheating power supply leads shall be enclosed in a rigid conduit, intermediate metal conduit, electrical metallic tubing, or other approved means.

426-24. **Electrical Connection.**

(a) Heating Element Connections. Electrical connections, other than factory connections of heating elements to nonheating elements embedded in masonry or asphalt or on exposed surfaces, shall be made with insulated connectors identified for the use.

(b) Circuit Connections. Splices and terminations at the end of the nonheating leads, other than the heating element end, shall be installed in a box or fitting in accordance with Sections 110-14 and 300-15.

426-25. **Marking.** Each factory-assembled heating unit shall be legibly marked within 3 inches (76 mm) of each end of the nonheating leads with the permanent identification symbol, catalog number, and ratings in volts and watts, or in volts and amperes.

426-26. **Corrosion Protection.** Ferrous and nonferrous metal raceways, cable armor, cable sheaths, boxes, fittings, supports, and support hardware shall be permitted to be installed in concrete or in direct contact with the earth, or in areas subject to severe corrosive influences, where made of material suitable for the condition, or where provided with corrosion protection identified as suitable for the condition.

426-27. **Grounding.**

(a) Metal Parts. Exposed noncurrent-carrying metal parts of equipment likely to become energized shall be bonded together and grounded in a manner specified in Article 250.

(b) Grounding Braid or Sheath. Grounding means, such as copper braid, metal sheath, or other approved means, shall be provided as part of the heated section of the cable, panel, or unit.

D. Impedance Heating

426-30. **Personnel Protection.** Exposed elements of impedance heating systems shall be physically guarded, isolated, or thermally insulated with weatherproof jacket to protect against contact by personnel in the area.

426-31. **Voltage Limitations.** The impedance heating elements shall not operate at a voltage greater than 30 volts ac.

Exception: The voltage shall be permitted to be greater than 30 volts, but not more than 80 volts, if a ground-fault circuit-interrupter for personnel protection is provided.

426-32. **Isolation Transformer.** A dual-winding transformer with a grounded shield between the primary and secondary windings shall be used to isolate the distribution system from the heating system.

426-33. **Induced Currents.** All current-carrying components shall be installed in accordance with Section 300-20.

426-34. **Grounding.** An impedance heating system that is operating at a voltage greater than 30, but not more than 80, shall be grounded at designated point(s).

E. Skin Effect Heating

426-40. **Conductor Ampacity.** The current through the electrically insulated conductor inside the ferromagnetic envelope shall be permitted to exceed the ampacity values shown in Article 310, provided it is identified as suitable for this use.

426-41. **Pull Boxes.** Where pull boxes are used, they shall be accessible without excavation by location in suitable vaults or above grade. Outdoor pull boxes shall be of watertight construction.

426-42. **Single Conductor in Enclosure.** The provisions of Section 300-20 shall not apply to the installation of a single conductor in a ferromagnetic envelope (metal enclosure).

426-43. **Corrosion Protection.** Ferromagnetic envelopes, ferrous or nonferrous metal raceways, boxes, fittings, supports, and support hardware shall be permitted to be installed in concrete or in direct contact with the earth, or in areas subjected to severe corrosive influences, where made of material suitable for the condition, or where provided with corrosion protection identified as suitable for the condition. Corrosion protection shall maintain the original wall thickness of the ferromagnetic envelope.

426-44. **Grounding.** The ferromagnetic envelope shall be grounded at both ends; and, in addition, it shall be permitted to be grounded at intermediate points as required by its design.

The provisions of Section 250-26 shall not apply to the installation of skin effect heating systems.

(FPN): For grounding methods, see Section 250-26(d).

F. Control and Protection

426-50. **Disconnecting Means.**

(a) Disconnection. All fixed outdoor deicing and snow-melting equipment shall be provided with a means for disconnection from all ungrounded conductors. Where readily accessible to the user of the equipment, the branch-circuit switch or circuit breaker shall be permitted to serve as the disconnecting means. Switches used as the disconnecting means shall be of the indicating type.

(b) Cord- and Plug-Connected Equipment. The factory-installed attachment plug of cord- and plug-connected equipment rated 20 amperes or less and 150 volts or less to ground shall be permitted to be the disconnecting means.

426-51. **Controllers.**

(a) Temperature Controller with "Off" Position. Temperature controlled switching devices that indicate an "off" position and that interrupt line current shall open all ungrounded conductors when the control device is in the "off" position. These devices shall not be permitted to serve as the disconnecting means unless provided with a positive lockout in the "off" position.

(b) Temperature Controller without "Off" Position. Temperature controlled switching devices that do not have an "off" position shall not be required to open all ungrounded conductors and shall not be permitted to serve as the disconnecting means.

(c) Remote Temperature Controller. Remote controlled temperature-actuated devices shall not be required to meet the requirements of Section 426-51(a). These devices shall not be permitted to serve as the disconnecting means.

(d) Combined Switching Devices. Switching devices consisting of combined temperature-actuated devices and manually controlled switches that serve both as the controller and the disconnecting means shall comply with all of the following conditions:

(1) Open all ungrounded conductors when manually placed in the "off" position; and

(2) Be so designed that the circuit cannot be energized automatically if the device has been manually placed in the "off" position; and

(3) Be provided with a positive lockout in the "off" position.

426-52. **Overcurrent Protection.** Fixed outdoor electric deicing and snow-melting equipment shall be permitted to be protected against overcurrent where supplied by a branch circuit as specified in Section 426-4.

426-53. **Equipment Protection.** Ground-fault protection of equipment shall be provided for branch circuits supplying fixed outdoor electric deicing and snow-melting equipment.

Section 426-53 is a significant new requirement in the 1993 *Code*. It requires branch-circuits that supply fixed outdoor snow-melting and deicing equipment to be protected by a device that provides ground-fault protection of equipment. This is not the same as a ground-fault circuit-interrupter used for personnel protection that trips at 5 milliamperes (± 1 milliampere).

426-54. **Cord- and Plug-Connected Deicing and Snow-Melting Equipment.** Cord- and plug-connected deicing and snow-melting equipment shall be listed.

ARTICLE 427 Fixed Electric Heating Equipment for Pipelines and Vessels

Contents
A. General

A. General

427-1. **Scope.** The requirements of this article shall apply to electrically energized heating systems and the installation of these systems used with pipelines or vessels or both.

Article 427 includes requirements for impedance heating, induction heating, and skin effect heating, in addition to resistance heating elements. Definitions of the various systems are provided in Section 427-2.

427-2. **Definitions.** For the purpose of this article:

Pipeline: A length of pipe including pumps, valves, flanges, control devices, strainers and/or similar equipment for conveying fluids.

Vessel: A container such as a barrel, drum, or tank for holding fluids or other material.

Integrated Heating System: A complete system consisting of components such as pipelines, vessels, heating elements, heat transfer medium, thermal insulation, moisture barrier, nonheating leads, temperature controllers, safety signs, junction boxes, raceways, and fittings.

Resistance Heating Element: A specific separate element to generate heat that is applied to the pipeline or vessel externally or internally.

(FPN): Tubular heaters, strip heaters, heating cable, heating tape, heating blankets, and immersion heaters are examples of resistance heaters.

Impedance Heating System: A system in which heat is generated in a pipeline or vessel wall by causing current to flow through the pipeline or vessel wall by direct connection to an ac voltage source from a dual-winding transformer.

Induction Heating System: A system in which heat is generated in a pipeline or vessel wall by inducing current and hysteresis effect in the pipeline or vessel wall from an external isolated ac field source.

Skin Effect Heating System: A system in which heat is generated on the inner surface of a ferromagnetic envelope attached to a pipeline and/or vessel.

(FPN): Typically, an electrically insulated conductor is routed through and connected to the envelope at the other end. The envelope and the electrically insulated conductor are connected to an ac voltage source from a dual-winding transformer.

427-3. **Application of Other Articles.** All requirements of this Code shall apply except as specifically amended in this article. Cord-connected pipe heating assemblies intended for specific use and identified as suitable for this use shall be installed according to Article 422. Fixed electric pipeline and vessel heating equipment for use in hazardous (classified) locations shall comply with Articles 500 through 516.

427-4. **Branch-Circuit Sizing.** The ampacity of branch-circuit conductors and the rating or setting of overcurrent protective devices supplying fixed electric heating equipment for pipelines and vessels shall be not less than 125 percent of the total load of the heaters. The rating or setting of overcurrent protective devices shall be permitted in accordance with Section 240-3(b).

B. Installation

427-10. **General.** Equipment for pipeline and vessel electrical heating shall be identified as being suitable for (1) the chemical, thermal, and physical environment; and (2) installation in accordance with the manufacturer's drawings and instructions.

427-11. **Use.** Electrical heating equipment shall be installed in such a manner as to be afforded protection from physical damage.

427-12. **Thermal Protection.** External surfaces of pipeline and vessel heating equipment that operate at temperatures exceeding 60°C (140°F) shall be physically guarded, isolated, or thermally insulated to protect against contact by personnel in the area.

427-13. **Identification.** The presence of electrically heated pipelines or vessels, or both, shall be evident by the posting of appropriate caution signs or markings at frequent intervals along the pipeline or vessel.

C. Resistance Heating Elements

427-14. **Secured.** Heating element assemblies shall be secured to the surface being heated by means other than the thermal insulation.

427-15. **Not in Direct Contact.** Where the heating element is not in direct contact with the pipeline or vessel being heated, means shall be provided to prevent overtemperature of the heating element unless the design of the heater assembly is such that its temperature limitations will not be exceeded.

427-16. **Expansion and Contraction.** Heating elements and assemblies shall not be installed where they bridge expansion joints unless provisions are made for expansion and contraction.

427-17. **Flexural Capability.** Where installed on flexible pipelines, the heating elements and assemblies shall have a flexural capability compatible with the pipeline.

427-18. **Power Supply Leads.**

(a) **Nonheating Leads.** Power supply nonheating leads (cold leads) for resistance elements shall be suitable for the temperature encountered. Preassembled nonheating leads on approved heaters shall be permitted to be shortened if the markingsspecified in Section 427-20 are retained. Not less than 6 inches (152 mm) of nonheating leads shall be provided within the junction box.

(b) **Power Supply Leads Protection.** Nonheating power supply leads shall be protected where they emerge from electrically heated pipeline or vessel heating units by rigid metal conduit, intermediate metal conduit, electrical metallic tubing, or other raceways identified as suitable for the application.

(c) **Interconnecting Leads.** Interconnecting nonheating leads connecting portions of the heating system shall be permitted to be covered by thermal insulation in the same manner as the heaters.

427-19. **Electrical Connections.**

(a) **Nonheating Interconnections.** Nonheating interconnections, where required under thermal insulation, shall be made with insulated connectors identified as suitable for this use.

(b) **Circuit Connections.** Splices and terminations outside the thermal insulation shall be installed in a box or fitting in accordance with Sections 110-14 and 300-15.

427-20. **Marking.** Each factory-assembled heating unit shall be legibly marked within 3 inches (76 mm) of each end of the nonheating leads with the permanent identification symbol, catalog number, and ratings in volts and watts, or in volts and amperes.

427-21. **Grounding.** Exposed noncurrent-carrying metal parts of electric heating equipment that are likely to become energized shall be grounded as required in Article 250.

427-22. **Equipment Protection.** Ground-fault protection of equipment shall be provided for branch circuits supplying electric heating equipment not having a metal covering.

The level of ground-fault protection provided by Class A GFCIs, which are normally used for personnel safety is 5 milliamperes (± 1 milliampere). This level may not be practical for an application where capacitive-type leakage, such as on long runs of heat-tracing cable, may be encountered. The intent of this section is to minimize the possibility of fire by providing equipment ground-fault protection as defined in Article 100, and to provide a degree of personnel safety by rapidly deenergizing a circuit that has developed a ground fault. This may be provided by a Class B GFCI, which trips at a higher level.

427-23. **Nonmetallic Pipelines.** Heating assemblies intended for heating nonmetallic pipelines or vessels shall have an overall grounded metal covering.

This requirement was new in the 1990 *NEC*. It is intended to provide a path to ground for fault current in order to trip phase or ground-fault protective devices, thus reducing the potential for fire and electric shock.

D. Impedance Heating

427-25. Personnel Protection. All accessible external surfaces of the pipeline and/or vessel being heated shall be physically guarded, isolated, or thermally insulated (with weatherproof jacket for outside installations) to protect against contact by personnel in the area.

427-26. Voltage Limitations. The secondary winding of the isolation transformer (Section 427-27) connected to the pipeline or vessel being heated shall not have an output voltage greater than 30 volts ac.

Exception: The voltage shall be permitted to be greater than 30 volts but not more than 80 volts if a ground-fault circuit-interrupter for personnel protection is provided.

See commentary following Section 427-22.

427-27. Isolation Transformer. A dual-winding transformer with a grounded shield between the primary and secondary windings shall be used to isolate the distribution system from the heating system.

427-28. Induced Currents. All current-carrying components shall be installed in accordance with Section 300-20.

427-29. Grounding. The pipeline or vessel, or both, being heated that is operating at a voltage greater than 30 but not more than 80 shall be grounded at designated points.

427-30. Secondary Conductor Sizing. The ampacity of the conductors connected to the secondary of the transformer shall be at least 100 percent of the total load of the heater.

E. Induction Heating

427-35. Scope. This part covers the installation of line frequency induction heating equipment and accessories for pipelines and vessels.

(FPN): See Article 665 for other applications.

427-36. Personnel Protection. Induction coils that operate or may operate at a voltage greater than 30 volts ac shall be enclosed in a nonmetallic or split metallic enclosure, isolated or made inaccessible by location to protect personnel in the area.

427-37. Induced Current. Induction coils shall be prevented from inducing circulating currents in surrounding metallic equipment, supports, or structures by shielding, isolation, or insulation of the current paths. Stray current paths shall be bonded to prevent arcing.

F. Skin Effect Heating

427-45. Conductor Ampacity. The ampacity of the electrically insulated conductor inside the ferromagnetic envelope shall be permitted to exceed the values given in Article 310, provided it is identified as suitable for this use.

427-46. Pull Boxes. Pull boxes for pulling the electrically insulated conductor in the ferromagnetic envelope shall be permitted to be buried under the thermal insulation, provided their locations are indicated by permanent markings on the insulation jacket surface and on drawings. For outdoor installations, pull boxes shall be of watertight construction.

427-47. Single Conductor in Enclosure. The provisions of Section 300-20 shall not apply to the installation of a single conductor in a ferromagnetic envelope (metal enclosure).

427-48. Grounding. The ferromagnetic envelope shall be grounded at both ends and, in addition, it shall be permitted to be grounded at intermediate points as required by its design. The ferromagnetic envelope shall be bonded at all joints to assure electrical continuity.

The provisions of Section 250-26 shall not apply to the installation of skin effect heating systems.

(FPN): See Section 250-26(d) for grounding methods.

G. Control and Protection

427-55. Disconnecting Means.

(a) **Switch or Circuit Breaker.** Means shall be provided to disconnect all fixed electric pipeline or vessel heating equipment from all ungrounded conductors. The branch-circuit switch or circuit breaker, where readily accessible to the user of the equipment, shall be permitted to serve as the disconnecting means. The disconnecting means shall be of the indicating type, and shall be provided with a positive lockout in the "off" position.

(b) Cord- and Plug-Connected Equipment. The factory-installed attachment plug of cord- and plug-connected equipment rated 20 amperes or less and 150 volts or less to ground shall be permitted to be the disconnecting means.

427-56. Controls.

(a) Temperature Control with "Off" Position. Temperature controlled switching devices that indicate an "off" position and that interrupt line current shall open all ungrounded conductors when the control device is in this "off" position. These devices shall not be permitted to serve as the disconnecting means unless provided with a positive lockout in the "off" position.

(b) Temperature Control without "Off" Position. Temperature controlled switching devices that do not have an "off" position shall not be required to open all ungrounded conductors and shall not be permitted to serve as the disconnecting means.

(c) Remote Temperature Controller. Remote controlled temperature-actuated devices shall not be required to meet the requirements of Sections 427-56(a) and (b). These devices shall not be permitted to serve as the disconnecting means.

(d) Combined Switching Devices. Switching devices consisting of combined temperature-actuated devices and manually controlled switches that serve both as the controllers and the disconnecting means shall comply with all the following conditions:

(1) Open all ungrounded conductors when manually placed in the "off" position; and

(2) Be so designed that the circuit cannot be energized automatically if the device has been manually placed in the "off" position; and

(3) Be provided with a positive lockout in the "off" position.

427-57. Overcurrent Protection.
Heating equipment shall be considered as protected against overcurrent where supplied by a branch circuit as specified in Section 427-4.

ARTICLE 430   Motors, Motor Circuits, and Controllers

Contents

A. General

A. General

430-1. **Scope.** This article covers motors, motor branch-circuit and feeder conductors and their protection, motor overload protection, motor control circuits, motor controllers, and motor control centers.

Article 430 has been extensively revised by removing the requirements for phase converters and relocating them in a new Article 455. In addition, Part H of Article 430 now contains new material covering the installation of motor control centers.

Exception No. 1: Installation requirements for motor control centers are covered in Section 384-4.

Exception No. 2: Air-conditioning and refrigerating equipment are covered in Article 440.

(FPN): Diagram 430-1 is for information only.

Part A. General, Sections 430-1 through 430-18
Part B. Motor Circuit Conductors, Sections 430-21 through 430-29.
Part C. Motor and Branch-Circuit Overload Protection, Sections 430-31 through 430-44.
Part D. Motor Branch-Circuit Short-Circuit and Ground-Fault Protection, Sections 430-51 through 430-58
Part E. Motor Feeder Short-Circuit and Ground-Fault Protection, Sections 430-61 through 430-63
Part F. Motor Control Circuits, Sections 430-71 through 430-74.
Part G. Motor Controllers, Sections 430-81 through 430-91.
Part H. Motor Control Centers, Sections 430-92 Through 430-98.
Part I. Disconnecting Means, Sections 430-101 through 430-113.
Part J. Over 600 Volts, Nominal, Sections 430-121 through 430-127.
Part K. Protection of Live Parts—All Voltages, Sections 430-131 through 430-133.
Part L. Grounding—All Voltages, Sections 430-141 through 430-145.
Part M. Tables, Tables 430-147 through 430-152.

To supply		
Motor feeder		Part B Sec. 430-24 430-25 and 430-26
Motor feeder short-circuit and ground-fault protection		Part E
Motor disconnecting means		Part I
Motor branch-circuit short-circuit and ground-fault protection		Part D
Motor circuit conductor		Part B
Motor controller		Part G
Motor control circuits		Part F
Motor overload protection		Part C
Motor		Part A
Thermal protection		Part C
Secondary controller Secondary conductors		Part B Sec. 430-23
Secondary resistor		Part B Sec. 430-23 and Art. 470

(FPN) Diagram 430-1.

Diagram 430-1 is intended to assist the user in following the provisions of Article 430. It is explanatory material and not a *Code* requirement.

430-2. **Adjustable Speed Drive Systems.** The incoming branch circuit or feeder to power conversion equipment included as a part of an adjustable speed drive system shall be based on the rated input to the power conversion equipment. If the power conversion equipment provides overload protection for the motor, additional overload protection is not required.

The disconnecting means shall be permitted to be in the incoming line to the conversion equipment and shall have a rating not less than 115 percent of the rated input current of the conversion unit.

430-3. **Part-Winding Motors.** A part-winding-start induction or synchronous motor is one arranged for starting by first energizing part of its primary (armature) winding and, subsequently, energizing the remainder of this winding in one or more steps. The purpose is to reduce the initial values of the starting current drawn or the starting torque developed by the motor. A standard part-winding-start induction motor is arranged so that one-half of its primary winding can be energized initially, and, subsequently, the remaining half can be energized, both halves then carrying equal current. A hermetic refrigerant compressor motor shall not be considered a standard part-winding-start induction motor.

Where separate overload devices are used with a standard part-winding-start induction motor, each half of the motor winding shall be individually protected in accordance with Sections 430-32 and 430-37 with a trip current one-half that specified.

Each motor-winding connection shall have branch-circuit short-circuit and ground-fault protection rated at not more than one-half that specified by Section 430-52.

Exception: A single device having this half rating shall be permitted for both windings if it will allow the motor to start. Where a time-delay (dual-element) fuse is used as a single device for both windings, it shall be permitted to have a rating not exceeding 150 percent of motor full-load current.

430-5. **Other Articles.** Motors and controllers shall also comply with the applicable provisions of the following:

430-6. **Ampacity and Motor Rating Determination.** The size of conductors supplying equipment covered by this article shall be selected from Tables 310-16 through 310-19 or shall be calculated in accordance with Section 310-15(b). The required ampacity and motor ratings shall be determined as specified in (a), (b), and (c) below.

(a) General Motor Applications. Other than as specified for torque motors in (b) below and for ac adjustable voltage motors in (c) below, where the current rating of a motor is used to determine the ampacity of conductors or ampere ratings of switches, branch-circuit short-circuit and ground-fault protection, etc., the values given in Tables 430-147, 430-148, 430-149, and 430-150, including notes, shall be used instead of the actual current rating marked on the motor nameplate. Separate motor overload protection shall be based on the motor nameplate current rating. Where a motor is marked in amperes, but not horsepower, the horsepower rating shall be assumed to be that corresponding to the value given in Tables 430-147, 430-148, 430-149, and 430-150, interpolated if necessary.

Exception No. 1: Multispeed motors shall be in accordance with Sections 430-22(a) and 430-52.

Exception No. 2: For equipment employing a shaded-pole or permanent-split-capacitor-type fan or blower motor that is marked with the motor type, the full-load current for such motor marked on the nameplate of the equipment in which the fan or blower motor is employed shall be used instead of the horsepower rating to determine the ampacity or rating of the disconnecting means, the branch-circuit conductors, the controller, the branch-circuit short-circuit and ground-fault protection, and the separate overload protection. This marking on the equipment nameplate shall not be less than the current marked on the fan or blower motor nameplate.

(b) Torque Motors. For torque motors, the rated current shall be locked-rotor current, and this nameplate current shall be used to determine the ampacity of the branch-circuit conductors covered in Sections 430-22 and 430-24, the ampere rating of the motor overload protection, and the ampere rating of motor branch-circuit and ground-fault protection in accordance with Section 430-52(b).

(FPN): For motor controllers and disconnecting means, see Section 430-83, Exception No. 3 and Section 430-110.

(c) AC Adjustable Voltage Motors. For motors used in alternating-current, adjustable voltage, variable torque drive systems, the ampacity of conductors, or ampere ratings of switches, branch-circuit short-circuit and ground-fault protection, etc., shall be based on the maximum operating current marked on the motor or control nameplate, or both. If the maximum operating current does not appear on the nameplate, the ampacity determination shall be based on 150 percent of the values given in Tables 430-149 and 430-150.

For general motor applications, other than ac adjustable voltage or torque-type motors, the ampacity of motor branch-circuit conductors, branch-circuit and ground-fault protection, and ampere rating of the motor disconnecting means, is determined by the ampere values listed in Tables 430-147 through 430-150. The ampere values are based on the horsepower rating and nominal voltage listed on the motor nameplate.

The ampere rating provided on the motor nameplate is used to size the overload protective devices intended to protect the motor, motor control apparatus, and motor branch-circuit conductors.

430-7. **Marking on Motors and Multimotor Equipment.**

(a) Usual Motor Applications. A motor shall be marked with the following information:

(1) Maker's name.

(2) Rated volts and full-load amperes. For a multispeed motor, full-load amperes for each speed, except shaded-pole and permanent-split capacitor motors where amperes are required only for maximum speed.

(3) Rated frequency and number of phases, if an alternating-current motor.

(4) Rated full-load speed.

(5) Rated temperature rise or the insulation system class and rated ambient temperature.

(6) Time rating. The time rating shall be 5, 15, 30, or 60 minutes, or continuous.

(7) Rated horsepower if ⅛ horsepower or more. For a multispeed motor ⅛ horsepower or more, rated horsepower for each speed, except shaded-pole and permanent-split capacitor motors ⅛ horsepower or more where rated horsepower is required only for maximum speed. Motors of arc welders are not required to be marked with the horsepower rating.

(8) Code letter if an alternating-current motor rated ½ horsepower or more. On polyphase wound-rotor motors the code letter shall be omitted.

(FPN): See (b) below.

(9) Secondary volts and full-load amperes if a wound-rotor induction motor.

(10) Field current and voltage for direct-current excited synchronous motors.

(11) Winding: straight shunt, stabilized shunt, compound, or series, if a direct-current motor. Fractional horsepower dc motors 7 inches (178 mm) or less in diameter shall not be required to be marked.

(12) A motor provided with a thermal protector complying with Sections 430-32(a) (2) or (c) (2) shall be marked "Thermally Protected." Thermally protected motors rated 100 watts or less and complying with Section 430-32(c) (2) shall be permitted to use the abbreviated marking "T.P."

(13) A motor complying with Section 430-32(c) (4) shall be marked "Impedance Protected." Impedance protected motors rated 100 watts or less and complying with Section 430-32(c) (4) shall be permitted to use the abbreviated marking "Z.P."

(b) Locked-Rotor Indicating Code Letters. Code letters marked on motor nameplates to show motor input with locked rotor shall be in accordance with Table 430-7(b).

The code letter indicating motor input with locked rotor shall be in an individual block on the nameplate, properly designated. This code letter shall be used for determining branch-circuit short-circuit and ground-fault protection by reference to Table 430-152, as provided in Section 430-52.

(1) Multispeed motors shall be marked with the code letter designating the locked-rotor kVA per horsepower for the highest speed at which the motor can be started.

Exception: Constant-horsepower multispeed motors shall be marked with the code letter giving the highest locked-rotor kVA per horsepower.

(2) Single-speed motors starting on Y connection and running on delta connections shall be marked with a code letter corresponding to the locked-rotor kVA per horsepower for the Y connection.

(3) Dual-voltage motors that have a different locked-rotor kVA per horsepower on the two voltages shall be marked with the code letter for the voltage giving the highest locked-rotor kVA per horsepower.

(4) Motors with 60- and 50-hertz ratings shall be marked with a code letter designating the locked-rotor kVA per horsepower on 60 hertz.

(5) Part-winding-start motors shall be marked with a code letter designating the locked-rotor kVA per horsepower that is based upon the locked-rotor current for the full winding of the motor.

(c) Torque Motors. Torque motors are rated for operation at standstill and shall be marked in accordance with (a) above.

Exception: Locked-rotor torque shall replace horsepower.

(d) Multimotor and Combination-Load Equipment.

The nameplate marking for the maximum ampere rating of the branch-circuit short-circuit and ground-fault protective device may limit the type of protective device to a fuse by stipulating "fuse" without reference to a circuit breaker. This means that the circuit to the equipment is required to be protected by fuses, such as by a fused disconnect switch. The fused switch may be supplied from a circuit breaker in a panelboard.

(1) Multimotor and combination-load equipment shall be provided with a visible nameplate marked with the maker's name, the rating in volts, frequency, number of phases,

Table 430-7(b). Locked-Rotor Indicating Code Letters

Code Letter	Kilovolt-Amperes per Horsepower with Locked Rotor		
A	0	—	3.14
B	3.15	—	3.54
C	3.55	—	3.99
D	4.0	—	4.49
E	4.5	—	4.99
F	5.0	—	5.59
G	5.6	—	6.29
H	6.3	—	7.09
J	7.1	—	7.99
K	8.0	—	8.99
L	9.0	—	9.99
M	10.0	—	11.19
N	11.2	—	12.49
P	12.5	—	13.99
R	14.0	—	15.99
S	16.0	—	17.99
T	18.0	—	19.99
U	20.0	—	22.39
V	22.4	—	and up

minimum supply circuit conductor ampacity, and the maximum ampere rating of the circuit short-circuit and ground-fault protective device. The conductor ampacity shall be computed in accordance with Section 430-24 and counting all of the motors and other loads that will be operated at the same time. The short-circuit and ground-fault protective device rating shall not exceed the value computed in accordance with Section 430-53. Multimotor equipment for use on two or more circuits shall be marked with the above information for each circuit.

(2) Where the equipment is not factory-wired and the individual nameplates of motors and other loads are visible after assembly of the equipment, the individual nameplates shall be permitted to serve as the required marking.

430-8. **Marking on Controllers.** A controller shall be marked with the maker's name or identification, the voltage, the current or horsepower rating, and such other necessary data to properly indicate the motors for which it is suitable. A controller that includes motor overload protection suitable for group motor application shall be marked with the motor overload protection and the maximum branch-circuit short-circuit and ground-fault protection for such applications.

Combination controllers employing adjustable instantaneous trip circuit breakers shall be clearly marked to indicate the ampere settings of the adjustable trip element.

Where a controller is built-in as an integral part of a motor or of a motor-generator set, individual marking of the controller shall not be required if the necessary data are on the nameplate. For controllers that are an integral part of equipment approved as a unit, the above marking shall be permitted on the equipment nameplate.

430-9. **Terminals.**

(a) **Markings.** Terminals of motors and controllers shall be suitably marked or colored where necessary to indicate the proper connections.

(b) **Conductors.** Motor controllers and terminals of control circuit devices shall be connected with copper conductors unless identified for use with a different conductor.

Terminals for motor controllers are tested, designed, and listed using copper conductors, unless marked for other conductors. This section highlights this limitation while permitting other conductors to be used if they are determined to be suitable and are identified as such.

(c) **Torque Requirements.** Control circuit devices with screw-type pressure terminals used with No. 14 or smaller copper conductors shall be torqued to a minimum of 7 pound-inches (0.79 N-m) unless identified for a different torque value.

Proper torque is essential for safe and reliable connections. This section enhances safety by providing a minimum torque value for screw-type pressure terminals.

430-10. **Wiring Space in Enclosures.**

(a) **General.** Enclosures for motor controllers and disconnecting means shall not be used as junction boxes, auxiliary gutters, or raceways for conductors feeding through or tapping off to the other apparatus unless designs are employed that provide adequate space for this purpose.

During the planning stages of a motor(s) installation, consideration should be given to location and proper working spaces (as required by Sections 110-16 and 110-34) for motor controllers and disconnects, including provisions for the use of auxiliary gutters or junction boxes to ensure space for conductors feeding through or tapping off to other apparatus. For switch and overcurrent device enclosures, see Section 373-8.

(FPN): See Section 373-8 for switch and overcurrent-device enclosures.

(b) Wire Bending Space in Enclosures. Minimum wire bending space within the enclosures for motor controllers shall be in accordance with Table 430-10(b) where measured in a straight line from the end of the lug or wire connector (in the direction the wire leaves the terminal) to the wall or barrier. Where alternate wire termination means is substituted for that supplied by the manufacturer of the controller, it shall be of a type identified by the manufacturer for use with the controller and shall not reduce the minimum wire bending space.

Table 430-10(b). **Minimum Wire-Bending Space at the Terminals of Enclosed Motor Controllers (in inches)**

Size of Wire AWG or kcmil	Wires per Terminal*	
	1	2
14-10	Not specified	—
8-6	1 1/2	—
4-3	2	—
2	2 1/2	—
1	3	—
1/0	5	5
2/0	6	6
3/0-4/0	7	7
250	8	8
300	10	10
350-500	12	12
600-700	14	16
750-900	18	19

* Where provision for 3 or more wires per terminal exists, the minimum wire-bending space shall be in accordance with the requirements of Article 373.

Figure 430-1. *Wire bending space in enclosures for motor controllers.*

Enclosure

Minimum wire bending space

In accordance with Section 430-10(b) for one or two wires per terminal

In accordance with Section 373-6 (b) for three or more wires per terminal

Motor controller

See Figure 430-1 for illustration of measurement in accordance with Section 430-10(b).

430-11. **Protection Against Liquids.** Suitable guards or enclosures shall be provided to protect exposed current-carrying parts of motors and the insulation of motor leads where installed directly under equipment, or in other locations where dripping or spraying oil, water, or other injurious liquid may occur, unless the motor is designed for the existing conditions.

Exposed current-carrying parts and insulated leads of motors should be suitably protected from liquids (dripping or sprayed oil or other lubricants, water, or excessive moisture) whose presence may cause deterioration and insulation breakdown.

430-12. **Motor Terminal Housings.**

(a) Material. Where motors are provided with terminal housings, the housings shall be of metal and of substantial construction.

Exception: In other than hazardous (classified) locations, substantial, nonmetallic, nonburning housings shall be permitted provided an internal grounding means between the motor frame and the equipment grounding connection is incorporated within the housing.

Nonmetallic terminal housings are permitted on motors of any size provided the housing material has been determined to be nonburning; for example, a flammability rating of at least 94-5V in accordance with UL 746C, Polymeric Materials — Use in Electrical Equipment Evaluations.

(b) Dimensions and Space — Wire-to-Wire Connections. Where these terminal housings enclose wire-to-wire connections, they shall have minimum dimensions and usable volumes in accordance with Table 430-12(b).

Table 430-12(b). Terminal Housings — Wire-to-Wire Connections Motors 11 inches in Diameter or Less

HP	Cover Opening, Minimum Dimension, Inches	Usable Volume, Minimum, Cubic Inches
1 and smaller*	$1^5/_8$	$7^1/_2$
$1^1/_2$, 2, and 3†	$1^3/_4$	12
5 and $7^1/_2$	2	16
10 and 15	$2^1/_2$	26

For SI units: one inch = 25.4 millimeters.

*For motors rated 1 horsepower and smaller and with the terminal housing partially or wholly integral with the frame or end shield, the volume of the terminal housing shall be not less than 0.8 cubic inch per wire-to-wire connection. The minimum cover opening dimension is not specified.

†For motors rated $1^1/2$, 2, and 3 horsepower and with the terminal housing partially or wholly integral with the frame or end shield, the volume of the terminal housing shall not be less than 1.0 cubic inch per wire-to-wire connection. The minimum cover opening dimension is not specified.

Motors Over 11 inches in Diameter Alternating-Current Motors

Max. Full-load Current for Three-phase Motors with Max. of Twelve Leads Amperes	Terminal Box Minimum Dimension Inches	Usable Volume Minimum Cubic Inches	Typical Maximum Horsepower Three Phase	
			230 Volt	460 Volt
45	2.5	26	15	30
70	3.3	55	25	50
110	4.0	100	40	75
160	5.0	180	60	125
250	6.0	330	100	200
400	7.0	600	150	300
600	8.0	1100	250	500

For SI units: one inch = 25.4 millimeters.

Direct-Current Motors

Maximum Full-Load Current for Motors with Maximum of Six Leads Amperes	Terminal Box Minimum Dimensions Inches	Usable Volume, Minimum Cubic Inches
68	2.5	26
105	3.3	55
165	4.0	100
240	5.0	180
375	6.0	330
600	7.0	600
900	8.0	1100

For SI units: one inch = 25.4 millimeters.

Auxiliary leads for such items as brakes, thermostats, space heaters, exciting fields, etc., shall be permitted to be neglected if their current-carrying area does not exceed 25 percent of the current-carrying area of the machine power leads.

(c) Dimensions and Space — Fixed Terminal Connections. Where these terminal housings enclose rigidly mounted motor terminals, the terminal housing shall be of sufficient size to provide minimum terminal spacings and usable volumes in accordance with Table 430-12(c)(1) and Table 430-12(c)(2).

Table 430-12(c)(1). Terminal Spacings — Fixed Terminals

Nominal Volts	Minimum Spacing, Inches	
	Between Line Terminals	Between Line Terminals and Other Uninsulated Metal Parts
240 or less	$1/_4$	$1/_4$
Over 250 through 600	$3/_8$	$3/_8$

For SI units: one inch = 25.4 millimeters.

Table 430-12(c)(2). Usable Volumes — Fixed Terminals

Power-Supply Conductor Size, AWG	Minimum Usable Volume per Power-Supply Conductor, Cubic Inches
14	1.0
12 and 10	$1^1/_4$
8 and 6	$2^1/_4$

For SI units: one inch = 25.4 millimeters.

(d) Large Wire or Factory Connections. For motors with larger ratings, greater number of leads, or larger wire sizes, or where motors are installed as a part of factory-wired equipment, without additional connection being required at the motor terminal housing during equipment installation, the terminal housing shall be of ample size to make connections, but the foregoing provisions for the volumes of terminal housings shall not be considered applicable.

(e) Equipment Grounding Connections. A means for attachment of an equipment grounding conductor termination in accordance with Section 250-113 shall be provided at motor terminal housings for wire-to-wire connections or fixed terminal connections. The means for such connections shall be permitted to be located either inside or outside the motor terminal housing.

Exception: Where a motor is installed as a part of factory-wired equipment that is required to be grounded and without additional connection being required at the motor terminal housing during equipment installation, a separate means for motor grounding at the motor terminal housing shall not be required.

430-13. **Bushing.** Where wires pass through an opening in an enclosure, conduit box, or barrier, a bushing shall be used to protect the conductors from the edges of openings having sharp edges. The bushing shall have smooth, well-rounded surfaces where it may be in contact with the conductors. If used where oils, greases, or other contaminants may be present, the bushing shall be made of material not deleteriously affected.

(FPN): For conductors exposed to deteriorating agents, see Section 310-9.

430-14. **Location of Motors.**

(a) Ventilation and Maintenance. Motors shall be located so that adequate ventilation is provided and so that maintenance, such as lubrication of bearings and replacing of brushes, can be readily accomplished.

(b) Open Motors. Open motors having commutators or collector rings shall be located or protected so that sparks cannot reach adjacent combustible material, but this shall not prohibit the installation of these motors on wooden floors or supports.

430-16. **Exposure to Dust Accumulations.** In locations where dust or flying material will collect on or in motors in such

quantities as to seriously interfere with the ventilation or cooling of motors and thereby cause dangerous temperatures, suitable types of enclosed motors that will not overheat under the prevailing conditions shall be used.

(FPN): Especially severe conditions may require the use of enclosed pipe-ventilated motors, or enclosure in separate dusttight rooms, properly ventilated from a source of clean air.

For motors exposed to combustible dust or readily ignitible flying material, see the requirements of Sections 502-8 and 502-9 (Class II, Divisions 1 and 2) and Sections 503-6 and 503-7 (Class III, Divisions 1 and 2). For classification of locations, see Sections 500-6 (Class II locations) and 500-7 (Class III locations).

430-17. **Highest Rated or Smallest Rated Motor.** In determining compliance with Sections 430-24, 430-53(b), and 430-53(c), the highest rated or smallest rated motor shall be based on the rated full-load current as selected from Tables 430-147, 430-148, 430-149, and 430-150.

430-18. **Nominal Voltage of Rectifier Systems.** The nominal value of the ac voltage being rectified shall be used to determine the voltage of a rectifier derived system.

Exception: The nominal dc voltage of the rectifier shall be used if it exceeds the peak value of the ac voltage being rectified.

B. Motor Circuit Conductors

430-21. **General.** Part B specifies sizes of conductors capable of carrying the motor current without overheating under the conditions specified.

Exception: The provisions of Section 430-124 shall apply over 600 volts, nominal.

The provisions of Articles 250, 300, and 310 shall not apply to conductors that form an integral part of approved equipment, or to integral conductors of motors, motor controllers, and the like.

(FPN No. 1): See Sections 300-1(b) and 310-1 for similar requirements.

(FPN No. 2): See Section 430-9(b) for equipment device terminal requirements.

430-22. Single Motor.

(a) General. Branch-circuit conductors supplying a single motor shall have an ampacity not less than 125 percent of the motor full-load current rating.

For a multispeed motor, the selection of branch-circuit conductors on the line side of the controller shall be based on the highest of the full-load current ratings shown on the motor nameplate; the selection of branch-circuit conductors between the controller and the motor shall be based on the current rating of the winding(s) that the conductors energize.

(FPN): See Chapter 9, Example No. 8 and Diagram 430-1.

Exception No. 1: Conductors for a motor used for short-time, intermittent, periodic, or varying duty shall have an ampacity not less than the percentage of the motor nameplate current rating shown in Table 430-22(a), Exception unless the authority having jurisdiction grants special permission for conductors of smaller size.

Exception No. 2: For direct-current motors operating from a rectified single-phase power supply, the conductors between the controller and the motor shall have an ampacity of not less than the following percent of the motor full-load current rating:

a. Where a rectifier bridge of the single-phase half-wave type is used, 190 percent.

b. Where a rectifier bridge of the single-phase full-wave type is used, 150 percent.

The provision for a conductor with an ampacity of at least 125 percent of the motor full-load current rating does not constitute a conductor derating. It is based on the need to provide for a sustained running current greater than the rated full-load current and for protection of the conductors by the motor overload protective device set above the motor full-load current rating.

The ampacity of the motor branch-circuit conductors is based on the full-load current rating values provided in Tables 430-147 through 430-150.

(b) Separate Terminal Enclosure. The conductors between a stationary motor rated 1 horsepower or less and the separate terminal enclosure permitted in Section 430-145(b) shall be permitted to be smaller than No. 14 but not smaller than No. 18, provided they have an ampacity as specified in (a) above.

Table 430-22(a), Exception.   Duty-Cycle Service

| Classification of Service | Percentages of Nameplate Current Rating | | | |
	5-Minute Rated Motor	15-Minute Rated Motor	30 & 60 Minute Rated Motor	Continuous Rated Motor
Short-Time Duty Operating valves, raising or lowering rolls, etc.	110	120	150	—
Intermittent Duty Freight and passenger elevators, tool heads, pumps, drawbridges, turn-tables, etc. For arc welders, see Section 630-21	85	85	90	140
Periodic Duty Rolls, ore- and coal-handling machines, etc.	85	90	95	140
Varying Duty	110	120	150	200

Any motor application shall be considered as continuous duty unless the nature of the apparatus it drives is such that the motor will not operate continuously with load under any condition of use.

Section 240-40 requires a disconnecting means on the supply side of cartridge fuses to disconnect the fuses from the source of electrical energy.

Figure 430-2 illustrates each motor on an individual branch circuit with branch-circuit short-circuit and ground-fault protective devices located at a distribution panel and disconnecting means, controllers, and overload protection at the motor locations.

Figure 430-3 also illustrates each motor on an individual branch circuit, but, unlike Figure 430-2, the branch circuits are tapped from a feeder at a convenient location such as a junction box, wireway, or from open wiring. The tap conductors are required to terminate in a branch-circuit protective device located not more than 25 feet from where the taps are connected to the feeder in accordance with Section 430-28. Also see Section 430-28, Exception, which permits a 100-foot tap under some conditions.

Where motors or motor-operated appliances are connected to a 15- or 20-A branch circuit that also supplies lighting or other appliance loads, as illustrated in Figure 430-4,

Figure 430-2. Each motor shown is supplied by an individual branch circuit from a distribution center. (*branch-circuit, short-circuit, and ground-fault protective devices)

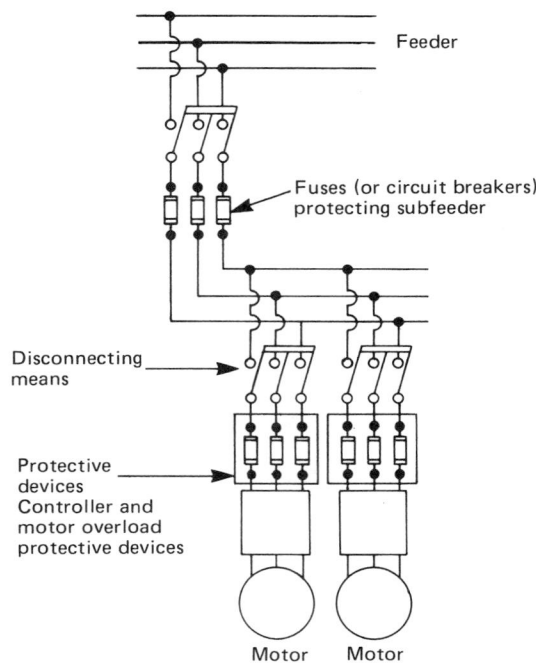

Figure 430-3. A feeder supplying individual branch circuits to each motor.

the provisions of Articles 210 and 430 apply. Motors rated less than 1 horsepower may be connected to these circuits and are required to be provided with overload protective devices unless the motors are not permanently installed, are started manually, and are within sight from the controller location. For additional information for the installation of motors (1 horsepower or less), see Sections 430-32(b) and (c), and 430-53(a).

Figure 430-5 illustrates the essential parts of a motor branch circuit: (1) the branch-circuit conductors, (2) the disconnecting means, (3) the branch-circuit short-circuit and ground-fault protective devices, and (4) the motor overload protective devices. The branch-circuit short-circuit and ground-fault protective device may be fuses or a circuit breaker and is required to be capable of carrying the starting current of the motor without opening the circuit. See Table 430-152.

In general, it is required that every motor be provided with overload protective devices intended to protect the motor windings, motor-control apparatus, and motor branch-circuit conductors against excessive heating due to

motor overloads and failure to start. Overload in equipment is defined as operation in excess of normal full-load rating, which, when it persists for a sufficient length of time, will cause damage or dangerous overheating. Overload in a motor includes stalled rotor, but does not include fault currents due to short circuits or ground faults. See Section 430-44 for conditions where providing automatic opening of a motor circuit due to overload may be objectionable.

A motor is considered to be used for continuous duty unless the nature of the apparatus it drives is such that the motor cannot operate continuously with load under any condition of use. Conductors for a motor used for short-time, intermittent, periodic, or varying duty are required to have an ampacity in accordance with Table 430-22(a), Exception. Branch-circuit conductors for a motor with a rated horsepower used for 5-minute short-time duty service are permitted to be sized smaller than for the same motor with a 60-minute rating, due to the cooling intervals between operating periods.

Figure 430-4. *A 20-ampere branch circuit supplying small motors, lighting, and appliances.*

Figure 430-5. *A motor branch circuit showing the three essential parts: the branch-circuit conductors, branch-circuit overcurrent protection, and motor overload protection.*

When selecting the smallest permissible size branch-circuit conductors for elevator motors, which are generally considered intermittent duty motors, it is safest to be guided

by the recommendations of the manufacturer of the equipment. This also applies to feeders of two or more elevator motors or other types of similar equipment.

430-23. Wound-Rotor Secondary.

(a) **Continuous Duty.** For continuous duty, the conductors connecting the secondary of a wound-rotor alternating-current motor to its controller shall have an ampacity not less than 125 percent of the full-load secondary current of the motor.

(b) **Other than Continuous Duty.** For other than continuous duty, these conductors shall have an ampacity, in percent of full-load secondary current, not less than that specified in Table 430-22(a), Exception.

(c) **Resistor Separate from Controller.** Where the secondary resistor is separate from the controller, the ampacity of the conductors between controller and resistor shall not be less than that shown in Table 430-23(c).

Table 430-23(c). **Secondary Conductor**

Resistor Duty Classification	Ampacity of Conductor in Percent of Full-Load Secondary Current
Light starting duty	35
Heavy starting duty	45
Extra-heavy starting duty	55
Light intermittent duty	65
Medium intermittent duty	75
Heavy intermittent duty	85
Continuous duty	110

Wound-rotor ac motors are generally used where speed control is desired, where high starting torque for a rapid smooth acceleration to full load is required, for frequent starting, and for low starting current. These motors are also known as slip-ring motors because three slip rings are mounted on the shaft, and brushes that are in contact with the slip rings are connected to field-installed external resistance units and a controller. See Figure 430-6. The resistors are a part of the rotor circuit, and the full value of the external resistance is in the circuit when starting the motor. This value is gradually reduced until the motor attains the desired speed.

The selection of a controller used for speed regulation, usually a dial-type or a drum-type switch, is basically for two types of loads, constant-torque (machine loads) and variable-torque (fan loads).

Disconnecting and starting switch with running overcurrent devices

Drum controller

Separately mounted accelerating and speed regulating resistors

Sliprings

Figure 430-6. A branch circuit to a wound-rotor induction motor showing a drum controller and separate bank of resistors for motor starting and speed regulation.

The ampacities of the conductors between the controller and the resistor units are the allowable percentages of Table 430-23(c) for the resistor classification of duty.

430-24. Several Motors or a Motor(s) and Other Load(s). Conductors supplying several motors, or a motor(s) and other load(s), shall have an ampacity at least equal to the sum of the full-load current rating of all the motors, plus 25 percent of the highest rated motor in the group, plus the ampere rating of other loads determined in accordance with Article 220 and other applicable sections.

Exception No. 1: Where one or more of the motors of the group are used for short-time, intermittent, periodic, or varying duty, the ampere rating of such motors to be used in the summation shall be determined in accordance with Section 430-22(a), Exception No. 1. For the highest rated motor, the greater of either the ampere rating from 430-22(a), Exception No. 1 or the largest continuous duty motor full-load current multiplied by 1.25 shall be used in the summation.

Exception No. 2: The ampacity of conductors supplying motor-operated fixed electric space heating equipment shall conform with Section 424-3(b).

Exception No. 3: Where the circuitry is interlocked so as to prevent operation of selected motors or other loads at the same time, the conductor ampacity shall be permitted to be based on the summation of the currents of the motors and other loads to be operated at the same time that results in the highest total current.

(FPN): See Chapter 9, Example No. 8.

Where the conductors are feeders, the highest rating or setting of the feeder short-circuit and ground-fault protective devices for the minimum size feeder conductor permitted by this section is specified in Section 430-62.

The size of the feeder conductors is required to be increased accordingly where the selection of a feeder protective device of higher rating or setting is based on the simultaneous starting of two or more motors.

These requirements, and those of Section 430-62 for the short-circuit and ground-fault protection of power feeders, are based on the principle that a power feeder should be of such size that it will have an ampacity equal to 125 percent of the full-load current of the largest motor, plus the full-load currents of all other motors supplied by the feeder.

Except where two or more motors may be started simultaneously, the heaviest load that a power feeder will ever be required to carry occurs when the largest motor is started at a time when all the other motors supplied by the same feeder are running and delivering their full-rated horsepower.

Where the conductors are branch-circuit conductors to multimotor equipment, Section 430-53 specifies the maximum rating of the branch-circuit short-circuit and ground-fault protective device. Section 430-7(d)(1) requires the maximum ampere rating of the short-circuit and ground-fault protective device to be marked on the equipment.

430-25. Multimotor and Combination-Load Equipment.
The ampacity of the conductors supplying multimotor and combination-load equipment shall be not less than the minimum circuit ampacity marked on the equipment in accordance with Section 430-7(d). Where the equipment is not factory-wired and the individual nameplates are visible in accordance with Section 430-7(d)(2), the conductor ampacity shall be determined in accordance with Section 430-24.

To compute the load for the minimum allowable conductor size for a combination lighting (or lighting and appliance) load and motor load, the capacity for the lighting load is determined in accordance with Article 220 (and other applicable sections, Article 422, etc.) plus the sum of the motor load, determined in accordance with Section 430-22 (single motor) or Section 430-24 (two or more motors).

430-26. Feeder Demand Factor.
Where reduced heating of the conductors results from motors operating on duty-cycle, intermittently, or from all motors not operating at one time, the authority having jurisdiction shall be permitted to grant permission for feeder conductors to have an ampacity less than specified in Section 430-24, provided the conductors have sufficient ampacity for the maximum load determined in accordance with the sizes and number of motors supplied and the character of their loads and duties.

The authority having jurisdiction may grant permission to allow a demand factor of less than 100 percent where operational procedures, production demands, or the nature of the work is such that all the motors are not running at one time.

430-27. Capacitors with Motors.
Where capacitors are installed in motor circuits, conductors shall comply with Sections 460-8 and 460-9.

430-28. Feeder Taps.
Feeder tap conductors shall have an ampacity not less than that required by Part B, shall terminate in a branch-circuit protective device and, in addition, shall meet one of the following requirements: (1) be enclosed by either an enclosed controller or by a raceway, be not more than 10 feet (3.05 m) in length, and, for field installation, be protected by an overcurrent device on the line side of the tap conductor, the rating or setting of which shall not exceed 1000 percent of the tap conductor ampacity; or (2) have an ampacity of at least one-third that of the feeder conductors, be protected from physical damage and be not more than 25 feet (7.62 m) in length; or (3) have the same ampacity as the feeder conductors.

The requirements for protecting motor feeder taps are very similar to those in Section 240-21. The basic rule requires the conductors to be protected at the point where they receive their supply. However, the short-circuit ground-fault protection may be located up to 10 feet away under specified conditions; for example, where the 10-foot tap conductors are sized in accordance with Part B and are enclosed by a controller or raceway and protected by a feeder overcurrent device not exceeding 10 times (1000 percent) the tap conductor ampacity.

The tap conductors are permitted to be up to 25 feet long provided they have an ampacity equal to that of the feeders or have an ampacity at least one third that of the feeders and are protected from physical damage (raceway not required).

In high-bay manufacturing building, feeder taps up to 100 feet long are conditionally permitted under Section 430-28, Exception.

Tap conductors are required to terminate in a branch-circuit short-circuit and ground-fault protective device. Conductors from this point to the motor-running protective device and to the motor are required to have an ampacity that is 125 percent of the full-load motor current, as specified in Section 430-22.

Example: A 15-hp, 230-V, 3-phase motor with autotransformer starter is to be supplied by a tap made to a 250 kcmil feeder. Assuming that there are three conductors in an individual raceway, all to be Type THW copper, and that there is no ambient correction factor, the feeder

Branch–circuit
protective device

Figure 430-7. Protective devices (branch-circuit, short-circuit, and ground-fault) for a branch circuit located not more than 25 feet from the point where the conductors are tapped to the main feeder.

Mains

Disconnecting means

Controller
with motor–
overload
protective device

has an ampacity of 255 A (see Table 310-16). Where the tap conductors are not over 25 feet long (see Figure 430-7), No. 4 conductors with an ampacity of 85 A are permitted (¹/₃ × 255 A = 85 A).

The full-load current of the motor is 42 A and, according to Part D of Article 430, assuming that the motor is not marked with a code letter, the branch-circuit fuses or circuit breakers are required to be rated at 80 A (nontime-delay fuse) or less, in accordance with Table 430-152 and Section 430-52, Exception No. 1. The next higher size is permitted if the 80-A fuse is not adequate to allow the motor to start. With the motor overload protection set at 50 A, the tap conductors are well protected from overload.

Tap conductors connected to feeders are not permitted to be sized smaller than the ampacity of branch-circuit conductors required by Section 430-22.

Exception: Feeder Taps Over 25 Feet (7.62 m) Long. In high-bay manufacturing buildings [over 35 feet (10.67 m) high at walls] conductors tapped to a feeder shall be permitted to be not over 25 feet (7.62 m) long horizontally and not over 100 feet (30.5) total length where all of the following conditions are met:

a. The ampacity of the tap conductors is not less than one-third that of the feeder conductors.

b. The tap conductors terminate with a single circuit breaker or a single set of fuses conforming with (1) Part D if the tap is a branch circuit or (2) Part E if the tap is a feeder.

c. The tap conductors are suitably protected from physical damage and are installed in raceways.

d. The tap conductors are continuous from end-to-end and contain no splices.

e. The tap conductors shall be No. 6 copper or No. 4 aluminum or larger.

f. The tap conductors shall not penetrate walls, floors, or ceilings.

g. The tap shall not be made less than 30 feet (9.14 m) from the floor.

430-29. **Constant Voltage DC Motors — Power Resistors.** Conductors connecting the motor controller to separately mounted power accelerating and dynamic braking resistors in the armature circuit shall have an ampacity not less than the value calculated from Table 430-29 using motor full-load current. If an armature shunt resistor is used, the power accelerating resistor conductor ampacity shall be calculated using the total of motor full-load current and armature shunt resistor current.

Armature shunt resistor conductors shall have an ampacity of not less than that calculated from Table 430-29 using rated shunt resistor current as full-load current.

Table 430-29. Conductor Rating Factors for Power Resistors

Time in Seconds On	Off	Ampacity of Conductor in Percent of Full-Load Current
5	75	35
10	70	45
15	75	55
15	45	65
15	30	75
15	15	85
Continuous Duty		110

C. Motor and Branch-Circuit Overload Protection

430-31. **General.** Part C specifies overload devices intended to protect motors, motor-control apparatus, and motor branch-circuit conductors against excessive heating due to motor overloads and failure to start.

Overload in electrical apparatus is an operating overcurrent that, when it persists for a sufficient length of time, would cause damage or dangerous overheating of the apparatus. It does not include short circuits or ground faults.

These provisions shall not be interpreted as requiring overload protection where it might introduce additional or increased hazards, as in the case of fire pumps.

(FPN): See Installation of Centrifugal Fire Pumps, NFPA 20-1990 (ANSI).

See the commentary following Section 230-90(a), Exception No. 4 on centrifugal fire pumps.

The provisions of Part C shall not apply to motor circuits rated over 600 volts, nominal. See Part J.

(FPN): See Chapter 9, Example No. 8.

NFPA 20-1990, *Standard for the Installation of Centrifugal Fire Pumps*, contains, in general, the minimum requirements for the selection and installation of centrifugal fire pumps.

Table 430-152 lists the allowable percentages of full-load current for the selection of the maximum rating or setting of motor branch-circuit short-circuit and ground-fault protective devices. The motor branch-circuit short-circuit and ground-fault protective devices are required to be capable of carrying the starting current of the motor without opening the circuit; therefore, the protective device cannot provide overload protection for the motor.

NFPA 20, *Standard for Centrifugal Fire Pumps*, requires the fire pump branch-circuit to be protected by circuit breakers and allows much larger short-circuit and ground-fault protection than for other motors. This concept recognizes that the pump should be allowed to operate to failure rather than be removed from the line under adverse fire conditions. A manually operated fuseless isolating switch is required to be connected ahead (supply side) of the circuit breaker.

For squirrel-cage induction motors, which are generally used, the circuit breaker is required to be of the time-delay type and have a time delay of not over 20 seconds at locked-rotor current (approximately 600 percent of the rated full-load motor current) and is required to be calibrated up to and set at 300 percent of the motor full-load current.

Combined overload protection (special-type fuses), as described in Section 430-55, is permitted as a single protective device. In most cases where motor overload protection is provided, however, the motor controller consists of a switch or contactor to control the circuit to the motor, and the motor-overload protective device is an overload relay with a heater coil selected to match the motor.

430-32. **Continuous-Duty Motors.**

(a) **More than 1 Horsepower.** Each continuous-duty motor rated more than 1 horsepower shall be protected against overload by one of the following means:

(1) A separate overload device that is responsive to motor current. This device shall be selected to trip or rated at no more than the following percent of the motor nameplate full-load current rating.

Motors with a marked service factor not less than 1.15	125%
Motors with a marked temperature rise not over 40° C	125%
All other motors	115%

Modification of this value shall be permitted as provided in Section 430-34.

For a multispeed motor, each winding connection shall be considered separately.

Where a separate motor overload device is so connected that it does not carry the total current designated on the motor nameplate, such as for wye-delta starting, the proper percentage of nameplate current applying to the selection or setting of the overload device shall be clearly designated on the equipment, or the manufacturer's selection table shall take this into account.

(2) A thermal protector integral with the motor, approved for use with the motor it protects on the basis that it will prevent dangerous overheating of the motor due to overload and failure to start. The ultimate trip current of a thermally protected motor shall not exceed the following percentage of motor full-load current given in Tables 430-148, 430-149, and 430-150.

Motor full-load current not exceeding 9 amperes	170%
Motor full-load current 9.1 to and including 20 amperes	156%
Motor full-load current greater than 20 amperes	140%

Figure 430-8. Line-voltage magnetic starter. (Square D Co.)

If the motor current-interrupting device is separate from the motor and its control circuit is operated by a protective device integral with the motor, it shall be so arranged that the opening of the control circuit will result in interruption of current to the motor.

Figure 430-9. A Type S nonrenewable plug fuse and adapter.

(3) A protective device integral with a motor that will protect the motor against damage due to failure to start shall be permitted if the motor is part of an approved assembly that does not normally subject the motor to overloads.

(4) For motors larger than 1500 horsepower, a protective device having embedded temperature detectors that cause current to the motor to be interrupted when the motor attains a temperature rise greater than marked on the nameplate in an ambient of 40°C.

(b) One Horsepower or Less, Nonautomatically Started.

(1) Each continuous-duty motor rated at 1 horsepower or less that is not permanently installed, is nonautomatically started, and is within sight from the controller location shall be permitted to be protected against overload by the branch-circuit short-circuit and ground-fault protective device. This branch-circuit protective device shall not be larger than that specified in Part D of Article 430.

Exception: Any such motor shall be permitted on a nominal 120-volt branch circuit protected at not over 20 amperes.

(2) Any such motor that is not in sight from the controller location shall be protected as specified in Section 430-32(c). Any motor rated at 1 horsepower or less that is permanently installed shall be protected in accordance with Section 430-32(c).

(c) One Horsepower or Less, Automatically Started. Any motor of 1 horsepower or less that is started automatically shall be protected against overload by one of the following means:

(1) A separate overload device that is responsive to motor current. This device shall be selected to trip or rated at no more than the following percentage of the motor nameplate full-load current rating.

Motors with a marked service factor not less than 1.15	125%
Motors with a marked temperature rise not over 40°C	125%
All other motors	115%

For a multispeed motor, each winding connection shall be considered separately. Modification of this value shall be permitted as provided in Section 430-34.

(2) A thermal protector integral with the motor, approved for use with the motor that it protects on the basis that it will prevent dangerous overheating of the motor due to overload and failure to start. Where the motor current-interrupting device is separate from the motor and its control circuit is operated by a protective device integral with the motor, it shall be so arranged that the opening of the control circuit will result in interruption of current to the motor.

(3) A protective device integral with a motor that will protect the motor against damage due to failure to start shall be permitted (1) if the motor is part of an approved assembly that does not subject the motor to overloads, or (2) if the assembly is also equipped with other safety controls (such as the safety combustion controls on a domestic oil burner) that protect the motor against damage due to failure to start. Where the assembly has safety controls that protect the motor, it shall be so indicated on the nameplate of the assembly where it will be visible after installation.

(4) In case the impedance of the motor windings is sufficient to prevent overheating due to failure to start, the motor shall be permitted to be protected as specified in Section 430-32(b)(1) for manually started motors if the motor is part of an approved assembly in which the motor will limit itself so that it will not be dangerously overheated.

(FPN): Many alternating-current motors of less than $1/20$ horsepower, such as clock motors, series motors, etc., and also some larger motors such as torque motors, come within this classification. It does not include split-phase motors having automatic switches that disconnect the starting windings.

(d) Wound-Rotor Secondaries. The secondary circuits of wound-rotor alternating-current motors, including conductors, controllers, resistors, etc., shall be permitted to be protected against overload by the motor-overload device.

Operation of a motor in excess of its normal full-load rating for a prolonged period of time causes damage or dangerous overheating that may start a fire. Overload protection is intended to protect the motor and the system components from damaging overload currents.

A continuous-duty motor with a marked service factor not less than 1.15 or with a marked temperature rise not over 40°C can carry a 25 percent overload for an extended period of time without damage to the motor. Other such types of motors are those with a service factor less than 1.15 or those with a marked temperature rise greater than 40°C that are incapable of withstanding a prolonged overload, where the motor-overload protective device opens the circuit if the motor continues to draw 115 percent of its rated full-load current.

A thermal protector located inside the motor housing is connected in series with the motor winding. This protective device commonly consists of a set of normally closed contacts attached to a bimetallic disk through which the circuit is normally closed. The thermal protector heating coil (in series with the motor winding) causes the disk to heat rapidly and the heat-actuated disk snaps the contacts open to protect the motor windings from overheating due to failure to start, a sudden heavy overload, or dangerous overheating due to a prolonged overload.

After opening the circuit and after the motor has cooled to a normal temperature, the contacts will automatically close and restart the motor. In some cases this may not be desirable. For such applications the protective device is so designed that it must be returned to the closed position by a manually controlled reset as required by Section 430-43. See Figures 430-10 and 430-11. For larger motors (usually over 1 horsepower), a similar device is used. This device, upon abnormal overload, acts as a control circuit switch and operates the control circuit of a motor current-interrupting device, usually a motor contactor or starter, located separately from the motor. A thermal protector and circuit-interrupting device should be approved for use with the motor it protects and is required to open the circuit on an overcurrent as specified in Section 430-32(a)(2).

Figure 430-10. *A thermal protector for a motor. A heat-sensitive, snap-action disk opens contacts and protects the motor against dangerous overheating. (Texas Instruments, Inc.)*

430-33. **Intermittent and Similar Duty.** A motor used for a condition of service that is inherently short-time, intermittent,

Figure 430-11. *Integral mounting of the thermal protective device (Figure 430-10) in a motor housing.*

periodic, or varying duty, as illustrated by Table 430-22(a), Exception shall be permitted to be protected against overload by the branch-circuit short-circuit and ground-fault protective device, provided the protective device rating or setting does not exceed that specified in Table 430-152.

Where a motor is selected for duty-cycle service (intermittent, short-time, periodic, or varying), it can be assumed that the motor will not operate continuously due to the nature of the apparatus or machinery it drives. Therefore, prolonged overloads are not likely to occur unless mechanical failure in the driven apparatus stalls the motor; however, in this case the branch-circuit protective device would open the circuit. The omission of overload protective devices for such motors is based on the type of duty and not on the time rating of the motor.

Any motor application shall be considered to be for continuous duty unless the nature of the apparatus it drives is such that the motor cannot operate continuously with load under any condition of use.

430-34. **Selection of Overload Relay.** Where the overload relay selected in accordance with Section 430-32(a)(1) and (c)(1) is not sufficient to start the motor or to carry the load, the next higher size overload relay shall be permitted to be used, provided the trip current of the overload relay does not exceed the following percentage of motor full-load current rating.

Motors with marked service factor not less than 1.15	140%
Motors with a marked temperature rise not over 40°C	140%
All other motors	130%

If not shunted during the starting period of the motor as provided in Section 430-35, the overload device shall have sufficient time delay to permit the motor to start and accelerate its load.

(FPN): A Class 20 or 30 overload relay will provide a longer motor acceleration time than a Class 10 or 20, respectively. Use of a higher class overload relay may preclude the need for selection of a higher trip current.

430-35. Shunting During Starting Period.

(a) Nonautomatically Started. For a nonautomatically started motor, the overload protection shall be permitted to be shunted or cut out of the circuit during the starting period of the motor if the device by which the overload protection is shunted or cut out cannot be left in the starting position and if fuses or inverse time circuit breakers rated or set at not over 400 percent of the full-load current of the motor are so located in the circuit as to be operative during the starting period of the motor.

(b) Automatically Started. The motor overload protection shall not be shunted or cut out during the starting period if the motor is automatically started.

If not shunted during the starting period of the motor, the overload device is required to have sufficient time delay to start and accelerate its load; whereas, if shunting is employed, the overload protection is cut out of the circuit during the starting period of the motor. See Figure 430-12.

Where fuses are used as overload protection, they may be shunted or cut out of the circuit during the starting period by a device (in this case a double-throw switch designed so that it cannot be left in the starting position). Therefore, during the starting period, the motor is protected only by the branch-circuit fuses that are always rated within the limits of this section. If there are no branch-circuit fuses, as permitted by Section 430-53, then a starter (shunting) device is not allowed during the starting period unless the feeder protection is within the limits of this section (not over 400 percent of the full-load motor current).

Figure 430-12. Arrangement for across-the-line starting of a motor. When the switch is thrown momentarily in one direction to start the motor, the overload protective fuses are shunted or cut out of the circuit. The switch is then thrown in the opposite direction (running position) and is required to be so designed that it cannot be left in the starting position.

Exception: The motor overload protection shall be permitted to be shunted or cut out during the starting period on an automatically started motor where:

(1) The motor starting period exceeds the time delay of available motor overload protective devices, and

(2) Listed means are provided to:

a. Sense motor rotation and to automatically prevent the shunting or cutout in the event that the motor fails to start, and

b. Limit the time of overload protection shunting or cutout to less than the locked rotor time rating of the protected motor, and

c. Provide for shutdown and manual restart if motor running condition is not reached.

430-36. Fuses — In Which Conductor.
Where fuses are used for motor overload protection, a fuse shall be inserted in each ungrounded conductor and also in the grounded conductor if the supply system is 3-wire, 3-phase ac with one conductor grounded.

430-37. Devices Other than Fuses — In Which Conductor.
Where devices other than fuses are used for motor overload protection, Table 430-37 shall govern the minimum allowable number and location of overload units such as trip coils or relays.

Table 430-37.   Overload Units

Kind of Motor	Supply System	Number and Location of Overload Units, such as trip coils or relays
1-phase ac or dc	2-wire, 1-phase ac or dc ungrounded	1 in either conductor
1-phase ac or dc	2 wire, 1-phase ac or dc, one conductor grounded	1 in an ungrounded conductor
1-phase ac or dc	3-wire, 1-phase ac or dc, grounded neutral	1 in either ungrounded conductor
1-phase ac	Any 3-phase	1 in an ungrounded conductor
2-phase ac	3-wire, 2-phase ac, ungrounded	2, one in each phase
2-phase ac	3-wire, 2-phase ac, one conductor grounded	2 in ungrounded conductors
2-phase ac	4-wire, 2-phase ac, grounded or ungrounded	2, one per phase in ungrounded conductors
2-phase ac	5-wire, 2-phase ac, grounded neutral or ungrounded	2, one per phase in any ungrounded phase wire
3-phase ac	Any 3-phase	3, one in each phase*

* Exception: Where protected by other approved means.

All 3-phase motors are required to be provided with three overload units, one in each phase. The exceptions are those protected by other approved means. Specially designed or integral-type detectors, with or without supplementary external protective devices, are some exceptions.

430-38.   **Number of Conductors Opened by Overload Device.** Motor overload devices other than fuses or thermal protectors shall simulta- neously open a sufficient number of ungrounded conductors to interrupt current flow to the motor.

430-39.   **Motor Controller as Overload Protection.** A motor controller shall also be permitted to serve as an overload device if the number of overload units complies with Table 430-37 and if these units are operative in both the starting and running position in the case of a direct-current motor, and in the running position in the case of an alternating-current motor.

For the purpose of this article, a controller may be a switch, a circuit breaker, a contactor, or other device to start and stop a motor by making and breaking the motor circuit current. It is required to be capable of interrupting the stalled-rotor current of the motor and have a horsepower rating not lower than the horsepower rating of the motor.

Dual-element fuses can be sized to provide motor overload protection. See Section 430-36. Automatically operated contactors or circuit breakers (with trip units) are governed by the requirements of Sections 430-37 and 430-38.

430-40.   **Overload Relays.** Overload relays and other devices for motor overload protection that are not capable of opening short circuits shall be protected by fuses or circuit breakers with ratings or settings in accordance with Section 430-52 or by a motor short-circuit protector in accordance with Section 430-52.

Exception No. 1: Where approved for group installation and marked to indicate the maximum size of fuse or inverse time circuit breaker by which they must be protected.

Exception No. 2: The fuse or circuit breaker ampere rating shall be permitted to be marked on the nameplate of approved equipment in which overload relay is used.

(FPN):   For instantaneous trip circuit breakers or motor short-circuit protectors, see Section 430-52.

430-42.   **Motors on General-Purpose Branch Circuits.** Overload protection for motors used on general-purpose branch circuits as permitted in Article 210 shall be provided as specified in (a), (b), (c), or (d) below.

   (a) Not Over 1 Horsepower. One or more motors without individual overload protection shall be permitted to be connected to a general-purpose branch circuit only where the installation complies with the limiting conditions specified in Sections 430-32(b) and (c) and Sections 430-53(a)(1) and (a)(2).

   (b) Over 1 Horsepower. Motors of larger ratings than specified in Section 430-53(a) shall be permitted to be connected to general-purpose branch circuits only where each motor is protected by overload protection selected to protect the motor as specified in Section 430-32. Both the controller and the motor overload device shall be approved for group installation with the short-circuit and ground-fault protective device selected in accordance with Section 430-53.

(c) Cord- and Plug-Connected. Where a motor is connected to a branch circuit by means of an attachment plug and receptacle and individual overload protection is omitted as provided in (a) above, the rating of the attachment plug and receptacle shall not exceed 15 amperes at 125 volts, or 10 amperes at 250 volts. Where individual overload protection is required as provided in (b) above for a motor or motor-operated appliance that is attached to the branch circuit through an attachment plug and receptacle, the overload device shall be an integral part of the motor or of the appliance. The rating of the attachment plug and receptacle shall determine the rating of the circuit to which the motor may be connected, as provided in Article 210.

(d) Time Delay. The branch-circuit short-circuit and ground-fault protective device protecting a circuit to which a motor or motor-operated appliance is connected shall have sufficient time delay to permit the motor to start and accelerate its load.

430-43. **Automatic Restarting.** A motor overload device that can restart a motor automatically after overload tripping shall not be installed unless approved for use with the motor it protects. A motor that can restart automatically after shutdown shall not be installed if its automatic restarting can result in injury to persons.

An integral motor overload protective device may be of the type that, after tripping and sufficiently cooling, will automatically restart the motor, or it may be of the type that, after tripping, is closed by use of a manually operated reset button. See commentary following Section 430-32.

430-44. **Orderly Shutdown.** If immediate automatic shutdown of a motor by a motor overload protective device(s) would introduce additional or increased hazard(s) to a person(s) and continued motor operation is necessary for safe shutdown of equipment or process, a motor overload sensing device(s) conforming with the provisions of Part C of this article shall be permitted to be connected to a supervised alarm instead of causing immediate interruption of the motor circuit, so that corrective action or an orderly shutdown can be initiated.

D. Motor Branch-Circuit Short-Circuit and Ground-Fault Protection

430-51. **General.** Part D specifies devices intended to protect the motor branch-circuit conductors, the motor control apparatus, and the motors against overcurrent due to short circuits or grounds. They add to or amend the provisions of Article 240. The devices specified in Part D do not include the types of devices required by Sections 210-8, 230-95, and 305-6.

The provisions of Part D do not apply to motor circuits rated over 600 volts, nominal. See Part J.

(FPN): See Chapter 9, Example No. 8.

430-52. **Rating or Setting for Individual Motor Circuit.** The motor branch-circuit short-circuit and ground-fault protective device shall be capable of carrying the starting current of the motor.

(a) General Motor Applications. Other than as specified for torque motors in (b) below, a protective device having a rating or setting not exceeding the value calculated according to the values given in Table 430-152 shall be used.

Exception No. 1: Where the values for branch-circuit short-circuit and ground-fault protective devices determined by Table 430-152 do not correspond to the standard sizes or ratings of fuses, nonadjustable circuit breakers, thermal protective devices, or possible settings of adjustable circuit breakers, and the next lower standard size, rating, or possible setting is not adequate to carry the load, the next higher standard size, rating, or possible setting shall be permitted.

Exception No. 2: Where the rating specified in Table 430-152 is not sufficient for the starting current of the motor:

a. The rating of a nontime-delay fuse not exceeding 600 amperes shall be permitted to be increased but shall in no case exceed 400 percent of the full-load current.

b. The rating of a time-delay (dual-element) fuse shall be permitted to be increased but shall in no case exceed 225 percent of the full-load current.

c. The rating of an inverse time circuit breaker shall be permitted to be increased but shall in no case exceed (1) 400 percent for full-load currents of 100 amperes or less or (2) 300 percent for full-load currents greater than 100 amperes.

d. The rating of a fuse of 601-6000 ampere classification shall be permitted to be increased but shall in no case exceed 300 percent of the full-load current.

(FPN): See Section 240-6 for standard ratings of fuses and circuit breakers.

An instantaneous trip circuit breaker shall be used only if adjustable, and if part of a listed combination controller having coordinated motor overload and short-circuit and ground-fault protection in each conductor, and if it will operate at not more than 1300 percent of full-load motor current. A motor short-circuit protector shall be permitted in lieu of devices listed in Table 430-152 if the motor short-circuit protector is part of a listed combination controller having coordinated motor overload protection and short-circuit and ground-fault protection in each conductor and if it will operate at not more than 1300 percent of full-load motor current.

(FPN): For the purpose of this article, instantaneous-trip circuit breakers may include a damping means to accomodate a transient motor inrush current without nuisance tripping of the circuit breaker.

Exception: Where the setting specified in Table 430-152 is not sufficient for the starting current of the motor, the setting of an instantaneous trip circuit breaker shall be permitted to be increased but shall in no case exceed 1300 percent of the motor full-load current. Trip settings above 700 percent shall be permitted where the need has been demonstrated by engineering evaluation. In such cases, it shall not be necessary to first apply an instantaneous trip circuit breaker at 700 percent.

For a multispeed motor, a single short-circuit and ground-fault protective device shall be permitted for two or more windings of the motor, provided the rating of the protective device does not exceed the above applicable percentage of the nameplate rating of the smallest winding protected.

Exception: For a multispeed motor, a single short-circuit and ground-fault protective device shall be permitted to be used and sized according to the full-load current of the highest current winding, provided that each winding is equipped with individual overload protection sized according to its full-load current and that the branch-circuit conductors feeding each winding are sized according to the full-load current of the highest full-load current winding.

Where maximum branch-circuit short-circuit and ground-fault protective device ratings are shown in the manufacturer's overload relay table for use with a motor controller or are otherwise marked on the equipment, they shall not be exceeded even if higher values are allowed as shown above.

(FPN): See Chapter 9, Example No. 8 and Diagram 430-1.

Suitable fuses shall be permitted in lieu of devices listed in Table 430-152 for an adjustable speed drive system or a solid state motor controller system provided that the marking for replacement fuses is provided adjacent to the fuses.

This section defines the maximum allowable ratings or settings of devices (fuses or circuit breakers) acceptable for motor branch-circuit short-circuit and ground-fault protection and states that these devices are expected to carry the starting currents of the motor and to provide short-circuit and ground-fault protection.

For certain exceptions to the maximum rating or setting of these motor branch-circuit protective devices as specified in Table 430-152, see Sections 430-52, 430-53, and 430-54. See Figure 430-2.

Section 430-6 requires that where the current rating of a motor is used to determine the ampacity of conductors or ampere ratings of switches, branch-circuit overcurrent devices, etc., the values given in Tables 430-147 through 430-150 (including notes) are required to be used instead of the actual motor nameplate current rating. Separate motor overload protection is required to be based on the motor nameplate current rating.

Figure 430-5 illustrates a typical motor circuit where the branch-circuit short-circuit and ground-fault protective fuses or circuit breaker rating must carry the starting current and may be sized 150 to 300 percent of the motor full-load current (depending on the type of motor). It should be noted that it is not necessary to size the branch-circuit conductors to the percentages (150 to 300) permitted for the branch-circuit short-circuit and ground-fault protective devices.

The rules for short-circuit and ground-fault protection are specific for particular situations. A short circuit is a fault between two conductors or between phases. A ground fault is a fault to ground. During a short-circuit or phase-to-ground condition, the extreme excess current would cause the protective fuses or circuit breakers to open the circuit. Excess current flow caused by an overload condition must pass through the overload protective device at the motor controller, thereby causing this device to open the circuit. Branch-circuit conductors with an ampacity of 125 percent (Note: not 150 to 300 percent) of the motor full-load current are reasonably protected by motor-protective devices set to operate at nearly the same current as the ampacity of the conductors.

Branch-circuit short-circuit and ground-fault protective devices will open the circuit under short-circuit conditions and thereby provide short-circuit and ground-fault protection for both the motor and overload protective device; however, the overload protective device is not intended to open short circuits or ground faults.

Section 430-7 provides information that is required to be marked on motor nameplates. AC motors rated ½ horsepower or more are required to be marked with code letters, in accordance with Table 430-7(b), that are used to determine the correct rating of the branch-circuit protective devices. For motors smaller than ½ horsepower, or for the many motors still in use without code letters, the provisions of Table 430-152 apply.

The rating or setting of the branch-circuit short-circuit and ground-fault protective device should be selected as low as possible for maximum protection; however, where the rating or setting specified in Table 430-152 or permitted by Exception No. 1 is not sufficient for the starting current of the motor, such as in the case of severe starting conditions where the motor and its driven machinery require an extended period of time to reach their desired speed, it is allowable to use a higher rating or setting as permitted in Exception No. 2 to Section 430-52.

Two or more small motors, each not over 1 horsepower and not over 6 amperes, may be connected to 120-V, 20-A, or to 208 through 600-V, 15-A branch circuits, if each motor has overload protection and the rating of the branch-circuit protective device does not exceed the rating specified on the motor controller (for the overload relay heater coil). See Section 430-53(a). Also, if the branch-circuit short-circuit and ground-fault protective device can be selected for the smallest motor in the group, two or more motors may be connected to the same branch circuit. This may be feasible where two motors are nearly the same size and cannot start simultaneously. See Section 430-53(b).

For other than the conditions specified in Sections 430-53(a) and (b) as described above, the equipment or controllers and protective devices are required to be listed (See Article 100). Where listed multimotor equipment is installed, it is required to be marked with the maximum rating of the branch-circuit short-circuit and ground-fault protective device in accordance with Section 430-7(d)(1), and the protective device is not permitted to exceed this marked rating. Where the short-circuit and ground-fault

protective device, the controller, and the overload protective device are field installed, they are required to be listed for such use and provided with instructions for use with each other. See Section 430-53(c).

(b) Torque Motors. Torque motor branch circuits shall be protected at the motor nameplate current rating in accordance with Section 240-3(b).

430-53. Several Motors or Loads on One Branch Circuit.
Two or more motors or one or more motors and other loads shall be permitted to be connected to the same branch circuit under the conditions specified in (a), (b), or (c) below.

(a) Not Over 1 Horsepower. Several motors, each not exceeding 1 horsepower in rating, shall be permitted on a nominal 120-volt branch circuit protected at not over 20 amperes or a branch circuit of 600 volts, nominal, or less, protected at not over 15 amperes, if all of the following conditions are met:

(1) The full-load rating of each motor does not exceed 6 amperes.

(2) The rating of the branch-circuit short-circuit and ground-fault protective device marked on any of the controllers is not exceeded.

(3) Individual overload protection conforms to Section 430-32.

Two or more motors, or one or more motors and other loads, may be connected to the same 120-V, 15- or 20-A single-phase lighting circuit. The provision is that each motor is to be rated not more than 1 horsepower, the full-load rating of each motor is not to exceed 6 amperes, and the rating of the branch-circuit protective device is not permitted to be exceeded.

Motors with ratings larger than 1 horsepower or 6 amperes may be connected to general-purpose branch circuits only if the motor is protected against overload as required by Section 430-32.

It should be understood that the requirements for overload protection, as provided in Section 430-32, are required to be applied in all cases, regardless of the number (one or more) of motors or the type of branch circuit.

(b) If Smallest Rated Motor Protected. If the branch-circuit short-circuit and ground-fault protective device is selected not to exceed that allowed by Section 430-52 for the smallest rated motor, two or more motors or one or more motors and other load(s), with each motor having individual overload protection, shall be permitted to be connected to a branch circuit where it can be determined that the branch-circuit short-circuit and ground-fault protective device will not open under the most severe normal conditions of service that might be encountered.

(c) Other Group Installations. Two or more motors of any rating or one or more motors and other load(s), with each motor having individual overload protection, shall be permitted to be connected to one branch circuit where the motor controller(s) and overload device(s) are (1) installed as a listed factory assembly and the motor branch-circuit short-circuit and ground-fault protective device is either provided as part of the assembly or is specified by a marking on the assembly, or (2) the motor branch-circuit short-circuit and ground-fault protective device, the motor controller(s), and overload device(s) are field-installed as separate assemblies listed for such use and provided with manufacturers' instructions for use with each other, and (3) all of the following conditions are complied with:

(1) Each motor overload device is listed for group installation with a specified maximum rating of fuse or inverse time circuit breaker, or both.

(2) Each motor controller is listed for group installation with a specified maximum rating of fuse or circuit breaker, or both.

(3) Each circuit breaker is one of the inverse time type and listed for group installation.

(4) The branch circuit shall be protected by fuses or inverse time circuit breakers having a rating not exceeding that specified in Section 430-52 for the highest rated motor connected to the branch circuit plus an amount equal to the sum of the full-load current ratings of all other motors and the ratings of other loads connected to the circuit. Where this calculation results in a rating less than the ampacity of the supply conductors, it shall be permitted to increase the maximum rating of the fuses or circuit breaker to a value not exceeding that permitted by Section 240-3(b).

(5) The branch-circuit fuses or inverse time circuit breakers are not larger than allowed by Section 430-40 for the overload relay protecting the smallest rated motor of the group.

(FPN): See Section 110-10 for circuit impedance and other characteristics.

Section 110-10 addresses characteristics of components such as impedance and short-circuit withstand ratings. It should be noted that devices with the same ampere rating may have significantly different short-circuit withstand ratings. A proper selection of components includes consideration of the characteristics of all components so that the occurrence of a fault will not cause unacceptable damage.

(d) Single Motor Taps. For group installations described above, the conductors of any tap supplying a single motor shall not be required to have an individual branch-circuit short-circuit and ground-fault protective device, provided they comply with either of the following: (1) no conductor to the motor shall have an ampacity less than that of the branch-circuit conductors, or (2) no conductor to the motor shall have an ampacity less than one-third that of the branch-circuit conductors, with a minimum in accordance with Section 430-22; the conductors to the motor overload device being not more than 25 feet (7.62 m) long and being protected from physical damage.

The following two examples describe installations permitting the omission of individual motor branch-circuit short-circuit and ground-fault protective devices. See Figures 430-13 and 430-14.

Figure 430-13 illustrates main branch-circuit conductors supplying a motor that is part of a group installation. The tap conductors have an ampacity equal to the ampacity of the main branch-circuit conductors; therefore, branch-circuit short-circuit and ground-fault protective devices, fuses, or circuit breakers for the conductors in the tap are not required at the point of connection of the tap conductors to the main conductors, provided that the motor controller and motor overload protective device are listed for group installation with the size of main branch-circuit short-circuit and ground-fault protective device used.

Figure 430-14 illustrates main branch-circuit conductors supplying a motor that is part of a group installation. The tap conductors have an ampacity at least $\frac{1}{3}$ the ampacity of the main branch-circuit conductors, are not more than 25 feet in length, and are suitably protected from physical damage. The motor controller and motor overload protective device are required to be listed for group installation with the size of main branch-circuit short-circuit and ground-fault protective device used.

In both examples, the main branch-circuit fuses or circuit breakers would operate in the event of a short circuit, and the overload protective device would operate to protect the motor and the tap conductors under overload conditions.

It should be noted that the tap conductors should never be of a smaller size and ampacity than the branch-circuit conductors required by Section 430-22; that is, a tap conductor (25 feet or less) may be ⅓ the ampacity of the main branch-circuit conductor to which it is connected. However, this ampacity is required to be equal to or larger than 125 percent of the motor full-load current rating. See Section 430-22. For example, a feeder sized at No. ²⁄₀ copper THW typically has an ampacity of 175 amperes (see Table 310-16) and a tap conductor (25 feet or less) would normally be permitted to be sized at No. 6 copper THW (65 amperes). However, if a 25-hp, 230-V, 3-phase, squirrel-cage motor is to be supplied from this feeder, a No. 6 tap conductor would not meet the requirements of Section 430-22; that is, 125 percent of the full-load current of the motor is 85 amperes [1.25 × 68 A = 85 A (Table 430-150)]. Therefore, the branch-circuit tap conductors are not permitted to be smaller than a No. 4 copper THW with a normal ampacity of 85 amperes. See Table 310-16. Note that the ampacities in Table 310-16 are reduced for ambient temperatures above 30°C and for more than three conductors in the raceway or cable.

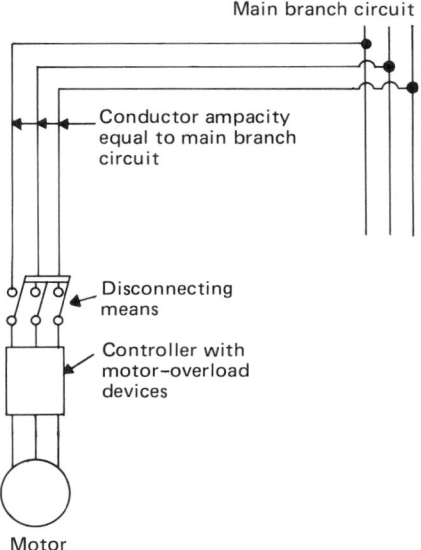

Figure 430-13. Motor branch-circuit protective devices can be omitted for tap conductors that have the same ampacity as the main branch-circuit conductors.

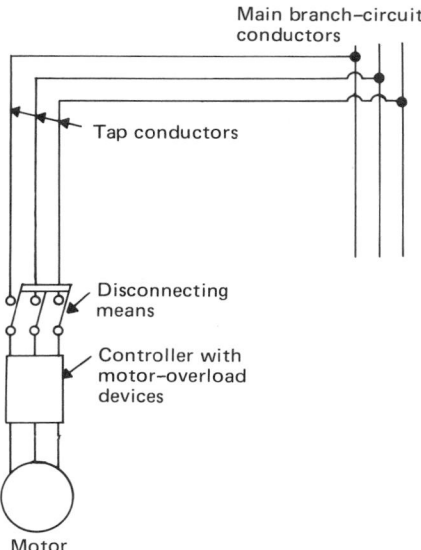

Figure 430-14. Motor branch-circuit protective devices can be omitted where the tap conductors have at least ⅓ the ampacity of the main conductors, are not over 25 feet long, and are protected from physical damage.

430-54. **Multimotor and Combination-Load Equipment.** The rating of the branch-circuit short-circuit and ground-fault protective device for multimotor and combination-load equipment shall not exceed the rating marked on the equipment in accordance with Section 430-7(d).

430-55. **Combined Overcurrent Protection.** Motor branch-circuit short-circuit and ground-fault protection and motor overload protection shall be permitted to be combined in a single protective device where the rating or setting of the device provides the overload protection specified in Section 430-32.

Either a circuit breaker with inverse time characteristics or a dual-element (time-delay) fuse may serve as both motor overload protection and also as the branch-circuit short-circuit and ground-fault protection. Figures 430-9, 430-15, and 430-16 are examples of dual-element fuses that are able to withstand the normal motor starting current where sized at or near the motor full-load rating, but open when subjected to prolonged overload or blow quickly during a short circuit or ground fault.

Figure 430-9 illustrates a dual-element Type S fuse and adapter that is available with up to a 30-A rating and is designed to prevent oversize fusing. See Sections 240-51 through 240-54.

Figures 430-15 and 430-16 illustrate time-delay, cartridge-type dual-element fuses. The dual-element characteristics, similar to those of the Type S fuse shown in Figure 430-9, are the thermal cutout element that permits harmless high-inrush currents to flow for short periods (but that would open the circuit during a prolonged period), and the fuse link element, which has current-limiting ability for short-circuit currents (and which would blow quickly). Dual-element fuses may be used in larger sizes to provide only short-circuit and ground-fault protection.

Figure 430-15. A Fusetron cartridge-type fuse. (Bussmann Mfg. Co.)

Figure 430-16. Class R dual-element fuse with physical rejection feature to prevent interchangeability. (International Association of Electrical Inspectors)

430-56. **Branch-Circuit Protective Devices — In Which Conductor.** Branch-circuit protective devices shall comply with the provisions of Section 240-20.

430-57. **Size of Fuseholder.** Where fuses are used for motor branch-circuit short-circuit and ground-fault protection, the fuseholders shall not be of a smaller size than required to accommodate the fuses specified by Table 430-152.

Exception: Where fuses having time delay appropriate for the starting characteristics of the motor are used, fuseholders of smaller size than specified in Table 430-152 shall be permitted.

Use of dual-element (time-delay) fuses makes it possible to use smaller sizes of fuses, thereby providing better protection because of the lower ratings. This also permits a considerable saving in installation cost by using smaller-size switches and panels and allows for easier arrangement of equipment where space is at a premium at motor control centers.

430-58. **Rating of Circuit Breaker.** A circuit breaker for motor branch-circuit short-circuit and ground-fault protection shall have a current rating in accordance with Sections 430-52 and 430-110.

An instantaneous trip circuit breaker has no intentional time-delay and opens only in response to currents in excess of its trip setting. Combination motor controller assemblies (see Section 430-52) are available with either interchangeable or noninterchangeable instantaneous trip units. In such a combination controller, the motor overload protective device in each conductor is relied on to protect against excessive heating due to motor overloads and failure to start.

E. Motor Feeder Short-Circuit and Ground-Fault Protection

430-61. **General.** Part E specifies protective devices intended to protect feeder conductors supplying motors against overcurrents due to short circuits or grounds.

(FPN): See Chapter 9, Example No. 8.

430-62. **Rating or Setting — Motor Load.**

(a) **Specific Load.** A feeder supplying a specific fixed motor load(s) and consisting of conductor sizes based on Section 430-24 shall be provided with a protective device having a rating or setting not greater than the largest rating or setting of the branch-circuit short-circuit and ground-fault protective device for any motor of the group (based on the maximum permitted value for the specific type of a protective device shown in Table 430-152, or Section 440-22(a) for hermetic refrigerant motor-compressors), plus the sum of the full-load currents of the other motors of the group.

This section recognizes the lower setting for motor overload devices required for hermetic refrigerant motor-compressors.

Where the same rating or setting of the branch-circuit short-circuit and ground-fault protective device is used on two or more of the branch circuits of the group, one of the protective devices shall be considered the largest for the above calculations.

Exception: Where one or more instantaneous trip circuit breakers or motor short-circuit protectors are used for motor branch-circuit short-circuit and ground-fault protection as permitted in Section 430-52(a), the procedure provided above for determining the maximum rating of the feeder protective device shall apply with the following provision. For the purpose of the calculation, each instantaneous trip circuit breaker or motor short-circuit protector shall be assumed to have a rating not exceeding the maximum percentage of motor full-load current permitted by Table 430-152 for the type of feeder protective device employed.

(FPN): See Chapter 9, Example No. 8.

(b) Future Additions. For large-capacity installations, where heavy-capacity feeders are installed to provide for future additions or changes, the rating or setting of the feeder protective devices shall be permitted to be based on the ampacity of the feeder conductors.

430-63. **Rating or Setting — Power and Light Loads.** Where a feeder supplies a motor load and, in addition, a lighting or a lighting and appliance load, the feeder protective device shall be permitted to have a rating or setting sufficient to carry the lighting or the lighting and appliance load as determined in accordance with Articles 210 and 220 plus, for a single motor, the rating permitted by Section 430-52, and, for two or more motors, the rating permitted by Section 430-62.

F. Motor Control Circuits

430-71. **General.** Part F contains modifications of the general requirements and applies to the particular conditions of motor control circuits.

(FPN): See Section 430-9(b) for equipment device terminal requirements.

Definition of Motor Control Circuit: The circuit of a control apparatus or system that carries the electric signals directing the performance of the controller, but does not carry the main power current.

430-72. **Overcurrent Protection.**

(a) General. A motor control circuit tapped from the load side of a motor branch-circuit short-circuit and ground-fault protective device(s) and functioning to control the motor(s) connected to that branch circuit shall be protected against overcurrent in accordance with Section 430-72. Such a tapped control circuit shall not be considered to be a branch circuit and shall be permitted to be protected by either a supplementary or branch-circuit overcurrent protective device(s). A motor control circuit other than such a tapped control circuit shall be protected against overcurrent in accordance with Section 725-12 or 725-35, as applicable.

(b) Conductor Protection. The overcurrent protection for conductors shall not exceed the values specified in Column A of Table 430-72(b).

Exception No. 1: Conductors that do not extend beyond the motor control equipment enclosure shall require only short-circuit and ground-fault protection and shall be permitted to be protected by the motor branch-circuit short-circuit and ground-fault protective device(s) where the rating of the protective device(s) is not over the value specified in Column B of Table 430-72(b).

Exception No. 2: Conductors that extend beyond the motor control equipment enclosure shall require only short-circuit and ground-fault protection and shall be permitted to be protected by the motor branch-circuit short-circuit and ground-fault protective device(s) where the rating of the protective device(s) is not over the value specified in Column C of Table 430-72(b).

Exception No. 3: Conductors supplied by the secondary side of a single-phase transformer having only a two-wire (single-voltage) secondary shall be permitted to be protected by overcurrent protection provided on the primary (supply) side of the transformer, provided this protection does not exceed the value determined by multiplying the appropriate maximum rating of the overcurrent device for the secondary conductor from Table 430-72(b) by the secondary-to-primary voltage ratio. Transformer secondary conductors (other than two-wire) are not considered to be protected by the primary overcurrent protection.

Exception No. 4: Conductors of control circuits shall require only short-circuit and ground-fault protection and shall be permitted to be protected by the motor branch-circuit short-circuit and ground-fault protective device(s) where the opening of the control circuit would create a hazard as, for example, the control circuit of a fire pump motor, and the like.

Table 430-72(b). Maximum Rating of Overcurrent Protective Device-Amperes

Control Circuit-Conductor Size, AWG	Column A Basic Rule		Column B Exception No. 1		Column C Exception No. 2	
	Copper	Alum. or Copper-Clad Alum.	Copper	Alum. or Copper-Clad Alum.	Copper	Alum. or Copper-Clad Alum.
18	7	—	25	—	7	—
16	10	—	40	—	10	—
14	Note 1	—	100	—	45	—
12	Note 1	Note 1	120	100	60	45
10	Note 1	Note 1	160	140	90	75
larger than 10	Note 1	Note 1	Note 2	Note 2	Note 3	Note 3

Note 1: Value specified in Section 310-15 as applicable.
Note 2: 400 percent of value specified in Table 310-17 for 60°C conductors.
Note 3: 300 percent of value specified in Table 310-16 for 60°C conductors.

(c) Control Circuit Transformer. Where a motor control circuit transformer is provided, the transformer shall be protected in accordance with Article 450.

Exception No. 1: Control circuit transformers rated less than 50 VA and that are an integral part of the motor controller and located within the motor controller enclosure shall be permitted to be protected by primary overcurrent devices, impedance limiting means, or other inherent protective means.

Exception No. 2: Where the control circuit transformer rated primary current is less than 2 amperes, an overcurrent device rated or set at not more than 500 percent of the rated primary current shall be permitted in the primary circuit.

Exception No. 3: Where the transformer supplies a Class 1 power-limited circuit [see Section 725-11(a)], Class 2, or Class 3 remote-control circuit conforming with the requirements of Article 725. See Article 725, Part C.

Exception No. 4: Where protection is provided by other approved means.

Exception No. 5: Overcurrent protection shall be omitted where the opening of the control circuit would create a hazard, as, for example, the control circuit of a fire pump motor and the like.

430-73. **Mechanical Protection of Conductor.** Where damage to a motor control circuit would constitute a hazard, all conductors of such a remote motor control circuit that are outside the control device itself shall be installed in a raceway or be otherwise suitably protected from physical damage.

Where one side of the motor control circuit is grounded, the motor control circuit shall be so arranged that an accidental ground in the remote-control devices will (1) not start the motor, and (2) not bypass manually operated shutdown devices or automatic safety shutdown devices.

Where damage to the motor control circuit conductors would constitute a fire or accident hazard, physical protection of the motor control circuit conductors is extremely important. Conductors are required to be installed in raceways in locations where damage to the control circuit conductors could result in an accidental ground-fault or short-circuit, causing the device to operate or render the device inoperative. Either condition could constitute a hazard to persons or property. Where boilers or furnaces are equipped with an automatic safety control device, damage to the conductors of the low-voltage (Article 725, Class 2) control circuit (thermostat, etc.) is not considered to constitute a hazard.

The second paragraph of Section 430-73 requires that if one side of the motor control circuit is grounded the circuit be arranged so that an accidental ground in the remote-control devices will not start the motor. For example, if the control circuit is a 120-V, single-phase circuit derived from a 208-V, 3-phase wye system supplying the motor, one side of the control circuit will be the grounded neutral. If the start button of the motor control circuit is in the grounded neutral, a ground fault on the coil side of the start button can short-circuit the start circuit and start the motor. The same condition will exist if the ground fault is in the wiring rather than the control device itself. By locating the start button in the ungrounded side of the control circuit, this hazardous condition is avoided. See Figure 430-17.

Combinations of ground faults in motor and motor-control circuits can produce the same problem. If the circuit is ungrounded, the first fault may go undetected. One solution is to use double-pole control devices, one pole in each of the two control lines.

430-74. Disconnection.

(a) General. Motor control circuits shall be so arranged that they will be disconnected from all sources of supply when the disconnecting means is in the open position. The disconnecting means shall be permitted to consist of two or more separate devices, one of which disconnects the motor and the controller from the source(s) of power supply for the motor, and the other(s), the motor control circuit(s) from its power supply. Where separate devices are used, they shall be located immediately adjacent one to each other.

Exception No. 1: Where more than twelve motor control circuit conductors are required to be disconnected, the disconnecting means shall be permitted to be located other than immediately adjacent one to each other where all of the following conditions are complied with:

a. Access to energized parts is limited to qualified persons in accordance with Part K of this article.

b. A warning sign is permanently located on the outside of each equipment enclosure door or cover permitting access to the live parts in the motor control circuit(s), warning that motor control circuit disconnecting means are remotely located and specifying the location and identification of each disconnect. Where energized parts are not in an equipment enclosure as permitted by Sections 430-132 and 430-133, an additional warning sign(s) shall be located where visible to persons who may be working in the area of the energized parts.

Exception No. 2: Where the opening of one or more motor control circuit disconnect means may result in potentially unsafe conditions for personnel or property and the conditions of items a and b of Exception No. 1 above are complied with.

(b) Control Transformer in Controller Enclosure. Where a transformer or other device is used to obtain a reduced voltage for the motor control circuit and is located in the controller

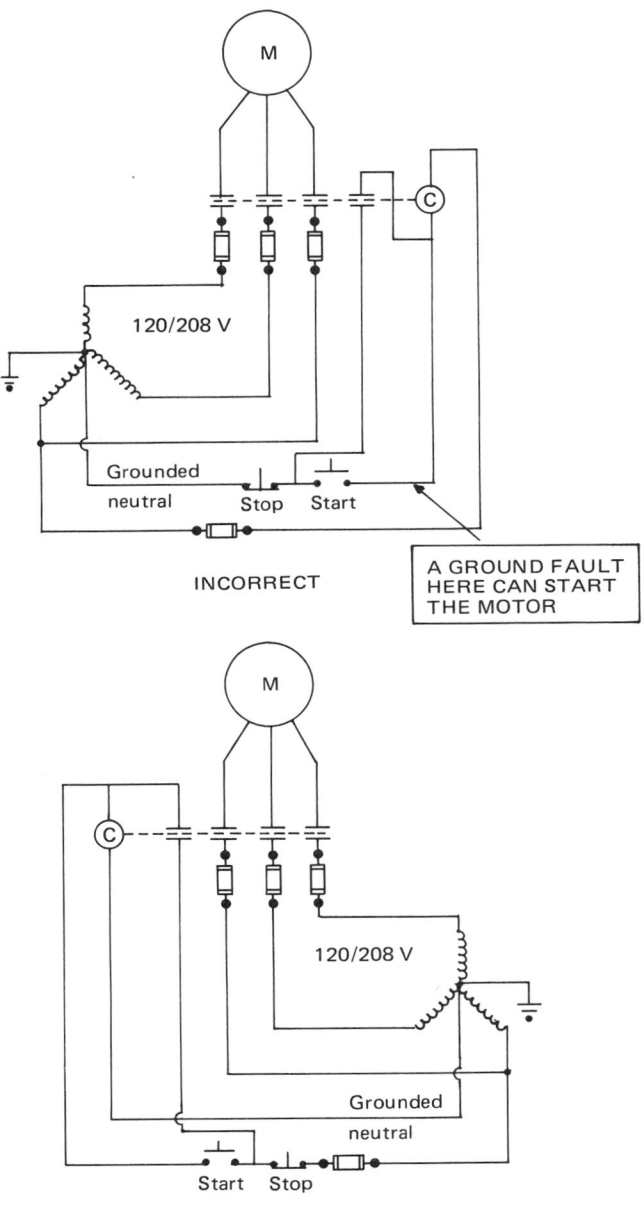

Figure 430-17. Control wiring in violation of Paragraph 2, Section 430-73 (top) and in compliance with Paragraph 2, Section 430-73 (bottom). (To simplify the illustration, motor overload elements and disconnecting means are not shown.) 120/208V Source.

enclosure, such transformer or other device shall be connected to the load side of the disconnecting means for the motor control circuit.

Figure 430-18. An example of control wiring utilizing a transformer. 480 V Source. The lower control circuit is not in compliance with the second paragraph of Section 430-17.

CORRECT

INCORRECT

G. Motor Controllers

430-81. **General.** Part G is intended to require suitable controllers for all motors.

(a) Definition. For definition of "Controller," see Article 100. For the purpose of this article, a controller is any switch or device normally used to start and stop a motor by making and breaking the motor circuit current.

(b) Stationary Motor of ⅛ Horsepower or Less. For a stationary motor rated at ⅛ horsepower or less that is normally left running and is so constructed that it cannot be damaged by overload or failure to start, such as clock motors and the like, the branch-circuit protective device shall be permitted to serve as the controller.

(c) Portable Motor of ⅓ Horsepower or Less. For a portable motor rated at ⅓ horsepower or less, the controller shall be permitted to be an attachment plug and receptacle.

430-82. Controller Design.

(a) Starting and Stopping. Each controller shall be capable of starting and stopping the motor it controls and shall be capable of interrupting the locked-rotor current of the motor.

(b) Autotransformer. An autotransformer starter shall provide an "off" position, a running position, and at least one starting position. It shall be so designed that it cannot rest in the starting position or in any position that will render the overload device in the circuit inoperative.

(c) Rheostats. Rheostats shall be in compliance with the following:

(1) Motor-starting rheostats shall be so designed that the contact arm cannot be left on intermediate segments. The point or plate on which the arm rests when in the starting position shall have no electrical connection with the resistor.

(2) Motor-starting rheostats for direct-current motors operated from a constant voltage supply shall be equipped with automatic devices that will interrupt the supply before the speed of the motor has fallen to less than one-third its normal rate.

430-83. Ratings.

(a) Horsepower Rating at the Application Voltage. The controller shall have a horsepower rating at the application voltage not lower than the horsepower rating of the motor.

Exception No. 1: For a stationary motor rated at 2 horsepower or less, and 300 volts or less, the controller shall be permitted to be a general-use switch having an ampere rating not less than twice the full-load current rating of the motor.

On ac circuits, general-use snap switches suitable only for use on ac (not general-use ac-dc snap switches) shall be permitted to control a motor rated at 2 horsepower or less, and 300 volts or less, having a full-load current rating not more than 80 percent of the ampere rating of the switch.

Exception No. 2: A branch-circuit inverse time circuit breaker rated in amperes only shall be permitted as a controller. Where

this circuit breaker is also used for overload protection, it shall conform to the appropriate provisions of this article governing overload protection.

Exception No. 3: The motor controller for a torque motor shall have a continuous-duty, full-load current rating not less than the nameplate current rating of the motor. For a motor controller rated in horsepower but not marked with the foregoing current rating, the equivalent current rating shall be determined from the horsepower rating by using Table 430-147, 430-148, 430-149, or 430-150.

A controller, as defined in Section 430-81(a), includes any switch or device normally used to start and stop a motor by making and breaking the motor circuit current. Circuit breakers are suitable for this use; however, circuit breakers used for branch-circuit short-circuit and ground-fault protection are not well adapted for motor overload protective devices.

(b) Voltage Rating. A controller with a straight voltage rating, e.g., 240V or 480V, shall be permitted to be applied in a circuit in which the nominal voltage between any two conductors does not exceed the controller's voltage rating. A controller with a slash rating, e.g., 120/240V or 480/277V, shall only be applied in a circuit in which the nominal voltage to ground from any conductor does not exceed the lower of the two values of the controller's voltage rating and the nominal voltage between any two conductors does not exceed the higher value of the controller's voltage rating.

A new section 430-83(b) has been added to the 1993 *Code*. It requires that controllers identified with slash voltage ratings, such as 240/120 V and 480/277 V grounded systems, are allowed to be used ONLY on electrical systems in which the voltage to ground does not exceed the lower voltage rating of the controllers and the nominal voltage between any two phases of the electrical system is not greater than the higher value of the controller voltage rating.

430-84. Need Not Open All Conductors. The controller shall
not be required to open all conductors to the motor.

Exception: Where the controller serves also as a disconnecting means, it shall open all ungrounded conductors to the motor as provided in Section 430-111.

A controller that does not also serve as a disconnecting means is required to open only as many motor-circuit conductors as may be necessary to stop the motor. That is, one conductor for a dc or single-phase motor circuit, two conductors for a 3-phase motor circuit, and three conductors for a 2-phase motor circuit.

430-85. **In Grounded Conductors.** One pole of the controller shall be permitted to be placed in a permanently grounded conductor, provided the controller is so designed that the pole in the grounded conductor cannot be opened without simultaneously opening all conductors of the circuit.

Generally, one conductor of a 120-V circuit is grounded and a single-pole device is required to be connected in the ungrounded conductor to serve as a controller. A 2-pole controller is permitted for such a circuit where both conductors (grounded and ungrounded) are opened simultaneously. The same requirement can be applied to other circuits, such as 240-V, 3-wire circuits with one conductor grounded.

430-87. **Number of Motors Served by Each Controller.** Each motor shall be provided with an individual controller.

Exception: For motors rated 600 volts or less, a single controller rated at not less than the sum of the horsepower ratings of all of the motors of the group shall be permitted to serve the group of motors under any one of the following conditions:

a. Where a number of motors drive several parts of a single machine or piece of apparatus, such as metal and woodworking machines, cranes, hoists, and similar apparatus.

b. Where a group of motors is under the protection of one overcurrent device as permitted in Section 430-53(a).

c. Where a group of motors is located in a single room within sight from the controller location.

These requirements for an individual controller are the same as those specified in Section 430-112 permitting the use of a single disconnecting means for a group of motors.

430-88. **Adjustable-Speed Motors.** Adjustable-speed motors that are controlled by means of field regulation shall be so equipped and connected that they cannot be started under weakened field.

Exception: Where the motor is designed for such starting.

The torque and speed of a motor depend on the amount of current passing through the armature. This current is a function of shunt field strength and RPM of the armature. A reduction of the shunt field magnetic flux causes a reduction of the counter emf in the armature, resulting in an increase in armature current, thereby increasing torque, thus increasing speed.

Because of excessive armature starting currents, this type of motor is not permitted to be started under a weakened field condition, unless some means is provided to limit the speed to within safe limits.

430-89. **Speed Limitation.** Machines of the following types shall be provided with speed limiting devices or other speed limiting means:

(a) Separately Excited DC Motors. Separately excited direct-current motors.

(b) Series Motors. Series motors.

(c) Motor-Generators and Converters. Motor-generators and converters that can be driven at excessive speed from the direct-current end, as by a reversal of current or decrease in load.

Exception No. 1: Where the inherent characteristics of the machines, the system, or the load and the mechanical connection thereto are such as to safely limit the speed.

Exception No. 2: Where the machine is always under the manual control of a qualified operator.

It is common for dc motors to be used where speed control is essential, such as in the case of electric railways and elevators, where a smooth start, controlled acceleration, and a smooth stop are necessary.

If the load is removed from a series motor when it is running, the speed of the motor will increase until it is dangerously high. To produce the necessary counterelectromotive force with a weakened field, the armature must turn faster correspondingly. Series motors are commonly used as gear-drive traction motors of electric locomotives and, thus, are continuously loaded.

The Ward Leonard speed control system is widely used to control a separately excited dc motor for the operation of electric elevators or hoists. Figure 430-18 is a simplified diagram of the speed control system where the armatures of two generators (G_1 and G_2) are mounted on a shaft that is driven by a motor (not shown). M is the motor drive for the elevator. The fields of G_1 and M are excited by G_1. By varying the rheostat R position, the voltage generated by G_2 is also varied, and this in turn controls the speed of M. If the field circuit of M were to be accidently opened during a light load, the motor would reach an excessive speed; however, no speed-limiting device is required, as the motor is always loaded.

Separately excited dc motors, series motors, motor (compound-wound dc) generators, and (synchronous) converters are required to be provided with speed-limiting devices (note exceptions) such as a centrifugal device on the shaft of the machine or a remotely located overspeed device, which may be set at a predetermined speed to operate a set of contacts and thereby trip a circuit breaker and deenergize the machine.

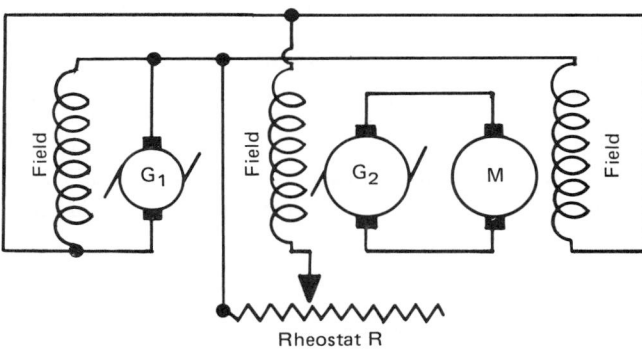

Figure 430-19. *A schematic diagram of the Ward Leonard speed control system.*

430-90. **Combination Fuseholder and Switch as Controller.** The rating of a combination fuseholder and switch used as a motor controller shall be such that the fuseholder will accommodate the size of the fuse specified in Part C of this article for motor overload protection.

Exception: Where fuses having time delay appropriate for the starting characteristics of the motor are used, fuseholders of smaller size than specified in Part C of this article shall be permitted.

Time-delay (dual element) fuses can commonly be used for both motor overload and branch-circuit short-circuit and ground-fault protection and can be sized in accordance with Section 430-32. See also Sections 430-36, 430-55, and 430-57.

430-91. **Motor Controller Enclosure Types.** Table 430-91 provides the basis for selecting enclosures for use in specific nonhazardous locations. The enclosures are not intended to protect against conditions such as condensation, icing, corrosion, or contamination that may occur within the enclosure or enter via the conduit or unsealed openings. These internal conditions require special consideration by the installer and user.

Table 430-91.   Motor Controller Enclosure Selection Table

Provides a Degree of Protection Against the Following Environmental Conditions	For Outdoor Use Enclosure Type Number †						
	3	3R	3S	4	4X	6	6P
Incidental contact with the enclosed equipment	X	X	X	X	X	X	X
Rain, snow, and sleet	X	X	X	X	X	X	X
Sleet*	—	—	X	—	—	—	—
Windblown dust	X	—	X	X	X	X	X
Hosedown	—	—	—	X	X	X	X
Corrosive agents	—	—	—	—	X	—	X
Occasional temporary submersion	—	—	—	—	—	X	X
Occasional prolonged submersion	—	—	—	—	—	—	X

† Enclosure type number shall be marked on the motor controller enclosure.
* Mechanism shall be operable when ice covered.

Provides a Degree of Protection Against the Following Environmental Conditions	For Indoor Use Enclosure Type Number †									
	1	2	4	4X	5	6	6P	12	12K	13
Incidental contact with the enclosed equipment	X	X	X	X	X	X	X	X	X	X
Falling dirt	X	X	X	X	X	X	X	X	X	X
Falling liquids and light splashing	—	X	X	X	X	X	X	X	X	X
Circulating dust, lint, fibers, and flyings	—	—	X	X	—	X	X	X	X	X
Settling airborne dust, lint, fibers, and flyings	—	—	X	X	X	X	X	X	X	X
Hosedown and splashing water	—	—	X	X	—	X	X	—	—	—
Oil and coolant seepage	—	—	—	—	—	—	—	X	X	X
Oil or coolant spraying and splashing	—	—	—	—	—	—	—	—	—	X
Corrosive agents	—	—	—	X	—	—	X	—	—	—
Occasional temporary submersion	—	—	—	—	—	X	X	—	—	—
Occasional prolonged submersion	—	—	—	—	—	—	X	—	—	—

† Enclosure type number shall be marked on the motor controller enclosure.

Enclosure-type numbers are described in greater detail in industry standards such as ANSI/NEMA ICS6-1988, NEMA Pub. 250-179, UL 508, and controller manufacturers' literature. For other than general-use Type No. 1 enclosures, the type number is required to be marked on the motor controller enclosure.

H. Motor Control Centers

430-92. General. Part H covers motor control centers installed for the control of motors, lighting, and power circuits.

A motor control center is an assembly of one or more enclosed sections having a common power bus and principally containing motor control units.

430-94. Overcurrent Protection. Motor control centers shall be provided with overcurrent protection in accordance with Article 240 based on the rating of the common power bus. This protection shall be provided by either (1) an upstream overcurrent-protective device or (2) a main overcurrent-protective device located within the motor control center.

430-95. Service-Entrance Equipment. Where used as service equipment, each motor control center shall be provided with a single main disconnecting means to disconnect all ungrounded service conductors.

Exception: A second service disconnect shall be permitted to supply additional equipment.

Where a grounded (neutral) conductor is provided, the motor control center shall be provided with a main bonding jumper, sized in accordance with Section 250-79(d), within one of the sections for connecting the grounded (neutral) conductor, on its supply side, to the motor control center equipment ground bus.

430-96. Grounding. Multisection motor control centers shall be bonded together with an equipment grounding conductor or an equivalent grounding bus sized in accordance with Table 250-95. Equipment grounding conductors shall terminate on this grounding bus or to a grounding termination point provided in a single-section motor control center.

430-97. Busbars and Conductors.

(a) Support and Arrangement. Busbars shall be protected from physical damage and be held firmly in place. Other than

for required interconnections and control wiring, only those conductors that are intended for termination in a vertical section shall be located in that section.

Exception: Conductors shall be permitted to travel horizontally through vertical sections where such conductors are isolated from the busbars by a barrier.

(b) Phase Arrangement. The phase arrangement on 3-phase buses shall be A, B, C from front to back, top to bottom, or left to right, as viewed from the front of the motor control center.

Exception: Rear-mounted units connected to a vertical bus that is common to front-mounted units shall be permitted to have a C, B, A phase arrangement where properly identified.

(c) Minimum Wire Bending Space. The minimum wire bending space at the motor control center terminals and minimum gutter space shall be as required in Article 373.

(d) Spacings. Spacings between motor control center bus terminals and other bare metal parts shall not be less than specified in Table 430-97.

Table 430-97. Minimum Spacing Between Bare Metal Parts

	Opposite Polarity Where Mounted on the Same Surface	Opposite Polarity Where Held Free in Air	Live Parts to Ground
Not over 125 volts, nominal	3/4 inch	1/2 inch	1/2 inch
Not over 250 volts, nominal	1 1/4 inch	3/4 inch	1/2 inch
Not over 600 volts, nominal	2 inches	1 inch	1 inch

For SI units: one inch = 25.4 millimeters.

(e) Barriers. Barriers shall be placed in all service-entrance motor control centers to isolate service busbars and terminals from the remainder of the motor control center.

430-98. Marking.

(a) Motor Control Centers. Motor control centers shall be marked according to Section 110-21, and such marking shall be plainly visible after installation. Marking shall also include common power bus current rating and motor control center short-circuit rating.

(b) Motor Control Units. Motor control units in a motor control center shall comply with Section 430-8.

Article 430, Part H, in previous editions of the *Code*, provided requirements for motor and controller disconnecting means. These requirements have been relocated to a new Part I. Part H now provides the requirements for the installation of motor control centers. Section 430-1, Exception No. 1, states that the *installation* requirements for motor control centers are covered in Section 384-4.

Motor control centers are made up of a number of motor starters, controls, and disconnect switches assembled in one large enclosure. Motor control centers are allowed to be used as service equipment where provided with a single main disconnecting means. However, a second service disconnecting means is permitted in the motor control center where it is provided to serve other loads.

Access and working space clearances in Section 110-16 and dedicated space requirements of Section 384-4 are applicable to motor control centers.

I. Disconnecting Means

430-101. **General.** Part I is intended to require disconnecting means capable of disconnecting motors and controllers from the circuit.

(FPN No. 1): See Diagram 430-1.

(FPN No. 2): See Section 110-22 for identification of disconnecting means.

430-102. **Location.**

(a) Controller. A disconnecting means shall be located in sight from the controller location and shall disconnect the controller.

Exception No. 1: For motor circuits over 600 volts, nominal, a controller disconnecting means capable of being locked in the open position shall be permitted to be out of sight of the controller, provided the controller is marked with a warning label giving the location of the disconnecting means.

Exception No. 2: A single disconnecting means shall be permitted to be located adjacent to a group of coordinated controllers mounted adjacent one to each other on a multimotor continuous process machine.

(b) Motor. A disconnecting means shall be located in sight from the motor location and the driven machinery location.

Exception: Where the disconnecting means provided in accordance with Section 430-102(a) is capable of being locked in the open position.

The rule requires that the disconnecting means be in sight from the controller, the motor location, and the driven machinery location. For motors over 600 V, the controller disconnecting means may be out of sight of the controller, provided that the controller has a warning label indicating the location and identification of the disconnecting means, which must be capable of being locked in the open position. See Figure 430-20.

The disconnecting means may be out of sight of the motor if the disconnecting means complying with Section 430-102(a) is capable of being locked in the open position. See Figure 430-21.

A group of coordinated controllers for a multimotor continuous process machine may use a single disconnecting means where the motors are mounted adjacent to one another on the machine. See Figure 430-22.

Figure 430-20. A motor controller (for motors over 600 V) that is out of sight from the disconnecting means must be marked with a label indicating the location of the disconnecting means. The controller must be capable of being locked in the open position.

Figure 430-21. *A controller disconnecting means that is not in sight from the motor must be designed so that it can be locked in the open position.*

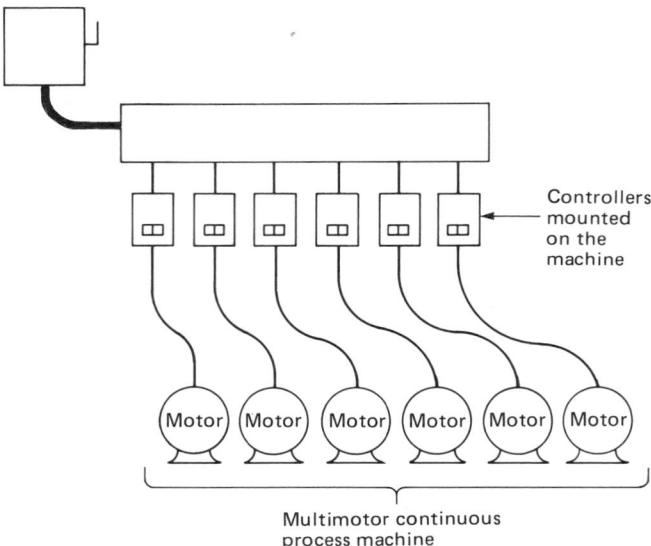

Figure 430-22. *A single disconnecting means located adjacent to a group of coordinated controllers mounted on a multimotor continuous process machine.*

430-103. Operation. The disconnecting means shall open all ungrounded supply conductors and shall be so designed that no pole can be operated independently. The disconnecting means shall be permitted in the same enclosure with the controller.

(FPN): See Section 430-113 for equipment receiving energy from more than one source.

The *Code* requires that a switch, circuit breaker, or other device serve as a disconnecting means for both the controller and the motor, thereby providing safety during maintenance and inspection shutdown periods. The disconnecting means also disconnects the controller; therefore, it cannot be a part of the controller. However, separate disconnects and controllers may be mounted on the same panel or contained in the same enclosure, such as combination fused-switch, magnetic-starter units.

Depending on the size of the motor and other conditions, the type of disconnecting means required may be a motor-circuit switch, a circuit breaker, a general-use switch, an isolating switch, an attachment plug and receptacle, or a branch-circuit short-circuit and ground-fault protective device. See Section 430-109.

If a motor is stalled or under heavy overload, and the motor controller fails to properly open the circuit, the disconnecting means, which is required to be rated to interrupt locked-rotor current, can be used to open the circuit. For motors larger than 100 horsepower ac or 40 horsepower dc, the disconnecting means is permitted to be a general-use or isolating switch where plainly marked "Do not operate under load." See Section 430-109, Exception No. 4.

430-104. To Be Indicating. The disconnecting means shall plainly indicate whether it is in the open ("off") or closed ("on") position.

430-105. Grounded Conductors. One pole of the disconnecting means shall be permitted to disconnect a permanently grounded conductor, provided the disconnecting means is so designed that the pole in the grounded conductor cannot be opened without simultaneously disconnecting all conductors of the circuit.

430-106. Service Switch as Disconnecting Means. Where an installation consists of a single motor, the service switch shall be permitted to serve as the disconnecting means if it complies with this article and is within sight from the controller location.

430-107. Readily Accessible. One of the disconnecting means shall be readily accessible.

Figure 430-23. Heavy-duty safety switches UL-listed for use on systems up to 200,000 A, fault current rms symmetrical with Class J or Class R fuses installed. (Square D Co.)

430-108. **Every Switch.** Every disconnecting means in the motor branch circuit between the point of attachment to the feeder and the point of connection to the motor shall comply with the requirements of Sections 430-109 and 430-110.

430-109. **Type.** The disconnecting means shall be one of the following types: a motor-circuit switch rated in horsepower, a circuit breaker, or a molded-case switch, and shall be a listed device.

Exception No. 1: For stationary motors of ⅛ horsepower or less, the branch-circuit overcurrent device shall be permitted to serve as the disconnecting means.

Exception No. 2: For stationary motors rated at 2 horsepower or less and 300 volts or less, the disconnecting means shall be permitted to be a general-use switch having an ampere rating not less than twice the full-load current rating of the motor.

On ac circuits, general-use snap switches suitable only for use on ac (not general-use ac-dc snap switches) shall be permitted to disconnect a motor rated 2 horsepower or less and 300 volts or less having a full-load current rating not more than 80 percent of the ampere rating of the switch.

Exception No. 3: For motors of over 2 horsepower to and including 100 horsepower, the separate disconnecting means required for a motor with an autotransformer-type controller shall be permitted to be a general-use switch where all of the following provisions are met:

a. The motor drives a generator that is provided with overload protection.

b. The controller (1) is capable of interrupting the locked-rotor current of the motor; (2) is provided with a no-voltage release; and (3) is provided with running overload protection not exceeding 125 percent of the motor full-load current rating.

c. Separate fuses or an inverse time circuit breaker rated or set at not more than 150 percent of the motor full-load current are provided in the motor branch circuit.

Exception No. 4: For stationary motors rated at more than 40 horsepower direct current or 100 horsepower alternating current, the disconnecting means shall be permitted to be a general-use or isolating switch where plainly marked "Do not operate under load."

Exception No. 5: For a cord- and plug-connected motor, a horsepower-rated attachment plug and receptacle having ratings no less than the motor ratings shall be permitted to serve as the disconnecting means. A horsepower-rated attachment plug and receptacle shall not be required for a cord- and plug-connected appliance in accordance with Section 422-22, a room air conditioner in accordance with Section 440-63, or a portable motor rated ⅓ horsepower or less.

Exception No. 6: For torque motors, the disconnecting means shall be permitted to be a general-use switch.

Section 430-108 requires every disconnecting means in the motor circuit to comply with Sections 430-109 and 430-110.

The disconnecting means is required to be a circuit breaker, a motor-circuit switch, or a molded case switch (nonautomatic circuit interrupter). A motor-circuit switch is a horsepower-rated switch capable of interrupting the

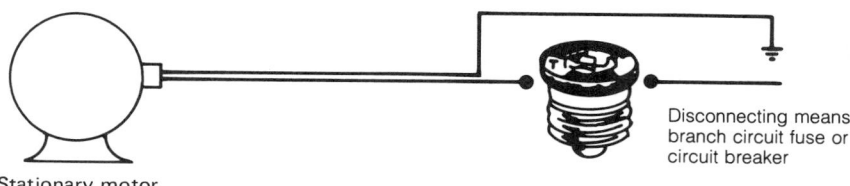

Figure 430-24. *Exception No. 1: The branch-circuit overcurrent device may serve as the disconnecting means for stationary motors of ⅛ horsepower or less.*

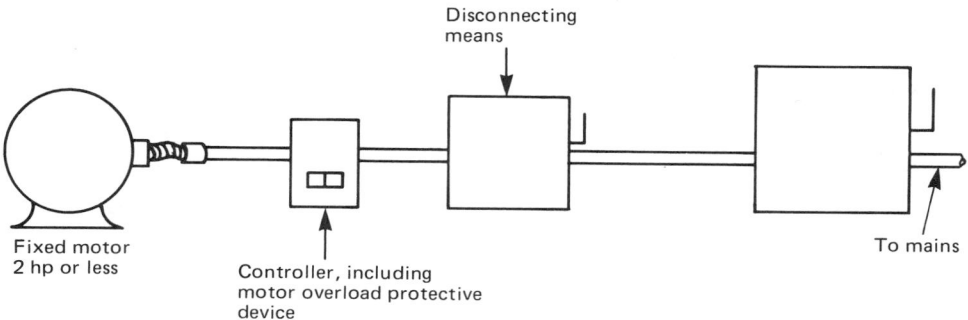

Figure 430-25. *Exception No. 2: A general-use switch having an ampere rating not less than twice the motor full-load rating may serve as the disconnecting means for motors rated 2 horsepower or less and operating at 300 V or less.*

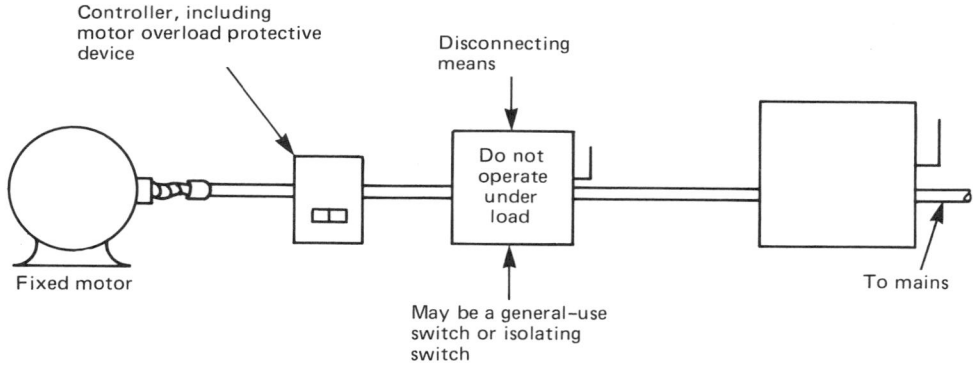

Figure 430-26. *Exception No. 4: A general-use switch or isolation switch may serve as the disconnecting means for stationary motors rated more than 40 horsepower dc or 100 horsepower ac if marked "Do not operate under load."*

maximum overload current of a motor. See definition, Article 100. A molded case switch (nonautomatic circuit interrupter) is a circuit breaker-like device without the overcurrent element and automatic trip mechanism. It is rated in amperes and is suitable for use as a motor circuit disconnect based on its ampere rating, as is a circuit breaker. The disconnecting means is required to be listed.

Figures 430-23 through 430-26 illustrate the exceptions to this general requirement.

Where horsepower-rated fused switches are required, it is to be noted that marking within the enclosure usually permits a dual horsepower rating. The standard horsepower rating is based on the largest nontime-delay (nondual-element) fuse rating that can be used in the switch and that

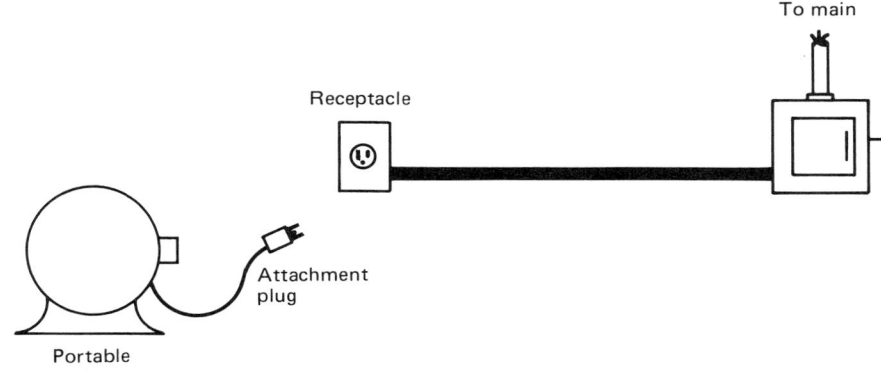

Figure 430-27. *Exception No. 5: An attachment plug and receptacle of the proper rating may serve as the disconnecting means for cord- and plug-connected motors.*

will permit the motor to start. The maximum horsepower rating is based on the largest rated time-delay (dual-element) fuse that can be used in the switch and that will permit the motor to start. Thus, where time-delay fuses are used, smaller sized switches and fuseholders can be used. See Section 430-57, Exception.

Exception No. 7: An instantaneous trip circuit breaker that is part of a listed combination motor controller shall be permitted to serve as a disconnecting means.

430-110. Ampere Rating and Interrupting Capacity.

(a) General. The disconnecting means for motor circuits rated 600 volts, nominal, or less, shall have an ampere rating of at least 115 percent of the full-load current rating of the motor.

(b) For Torque Motors. Disconnecting means for a torque motor shall have an ampere rating of at least 115 percent of the motor nameplate current.

(c) For Combination Loads. Where two or more motors are used together or where one or more motors are used in combination with other loads, such as resistance heaters, and where the combined load may be simultaneous on a single disconnecting means, the ampere and horsepower ratings of the combined load shall be determined as follows:

(1) The rating of the disconnecting means shall be determined from the summation of all currents, including resistance loads, at the full-load condition and also at the locked-rotor condition. The combined full-load current and the combined locked-rotor current so obtained shall be considered as a single motor for the purpose of this requirement as follows:

The full-load current equivalent to the horsepower rating of each motor shall be selected from Table 430-148, 430-149, or 430-150. These full-load currents shall be added to the rating in amperes of other loads to obtain an equivalent full-load current for the combined load.

The locked-rotor current equivalent to the horsepower rating of each motor shall be selected from Table 430-151. The locked-rotor currents shall be added to the rating in amperes of other loads to obtain an equivalent locked-rotor current for the combined load. Where two or more motors or other loads cannot be started simultaneously, appropriate combinations of locked-rotor and full-load current shall be permitted to be used to determine the equivalent locked-rotor current for the simultaneous combined loads.

Exception: Where part of the concurrent load is resistance load, and where the disconnecting means is a switch rated in horsepower and amperes, the switch used shall be permitted to have a horsepower rating not less than the combined load of the motor(s), if the ampere rating of the switch is not less than the locked-rotor current of the motor(s) plus the resistance load.

(2) The ampere rating of the disconnecting means shall not be less than 115 percent of the summation of all currents at the full-load condition determined in accordance with (c)(1) above.

(3) For small motors not covered by Tables 430-147, 430-148, 430-149, or 430-150, the locked-rotor current shall be assumed to be six times the full-load current.

A general-use switch, fuse, circuit breaker, molded case switch (nonautomatic circuit interrupter), or attachment plug and receptacle used as a disconnecting means is required to have an ampere rating of not less than 115 percent of the motor full-load current.

Following is an example of how to determine the size of a disconnect for a combination load. Assume the load consists of one 5-hp, one 3-hp, and two ½-hp motors, plus a 10-kW heater, all rated 240 V, 3-phase.

Calculation of Equivalent Full-Load Current Rating:

5-hp motor (Table 430-150)	15.2 A
3-hp motor (Table 430-150)	9.6 A
½-hp motor (Table 430-150)	2.0 A
½-hp motor (Table 430-150)	2.0 A
10-kW heater $\dfrac{10 \times 1000}{140 \times 1.73}$	24.1 A
Total	52.9 A

Calculation of Equivalent Locked-Rotor Current Rating:

5-hp motor (Table 430-151)	91 A
3-hp motor (Table 430-151)	58 A
½-hp motor (Table 430-151)	12 A
½-hp motor (Table 430-151)	12 A
10-kW heater $\dfrac{10 \times 1000}{140 \times 1.73}$	24.1 A
Total	197.1 A

From Table 430-151, a 15-horsepower switch has adequate locked rotor capability (252 A) but has a full-load capability of only 42 A (from Table 430-150), insufficient for the 52.9-A equivalent full-load current rating. The 15-horsepower switch could be used if it also had an ampere rating of at least 52.9 A. See Section 430-110(c)(1), Exception.

If the nonmotor load had *not* been a heater or other resistance load, the 15-horsepower switch would have to have an ampere rating of at least 52.9 A × 1.15 = 60.8 A.

A 20-horsepower switch could be used, since the locked-rotor current for a 20-horsepower, 3-phase, 240-V motor is 324 A (over the needed 197.1 A) and the full-load current is 54 A (over the equivalent full-load rating of 52.9 A).

A 70-A circuit breaker or molded-case switch could also be used, since such devices are tested to control motors with full-load ratings up to 80 percent of their ampere rating (0.8 × 70 A = 56 A, more than the 52.9 A equivalent full-load rating.). Also, 1.15 × 52.9 A = 60.8 A, less than the 70-A rating of the circuit breaker.

430-111. **Switch or Circuit Breaker as Both Controller and Disconnecting Means.** A switch or circuit breaker complying with Section 430-83 shall be permitted to serve as both controller and disconnecting means if it opens all ungrounded conductors to the motor, if it is protected by an overcurrent device (which shall be permitted to be the branch-circuit fuses) that opens all ungrounded conductors to the switch or circuit breaker, and if it is of one of the types specified in (a), (b), or (c) below:

(a) Air-Break Switch. An air-break switch, operable directly by applying the hand to a lever or handle.

(b) Inverse Time Circuit Breaker. An inverse time circuit breaker operable directly by applying the hand to a lever or handle.

(c) Oil Switch. An oil switch used on a circuit whose rating does not exceed 600 volts or 100 amperes, or by special permission on a circuit exceeding this capacity where under expert supervision.

The oil switch or circuit breaker specified above shall be permitted to be both power and manually operable.

The overcurrent device protecting the controller shall be permitted to be part of the controller assembly or shall be permitted to be separate.

An autotransformer-type controller shall be provided with a separate disconnecting means.

Where the controller consists of a manually operable air-break switch, an inverse time circuit breaker, or a 100-A maximum oil switch (higher rating by special permission), the controller is considered to be a satisfactory disconnecting means. It is the intent of this section to permit omission of an additional device to serve as a disconnecting means. See Figure 430-27.

It should be noted that a separate disconnecting means is required to be provided if the controller is of the autotransformer or compensator type (this switch may be combined in the same enclosure with a motor overload protective device).

Where used as a controller, the switch or circuit breaker is required to meet all of the requirements for controllers and be protected by branch-circuit short-circuit and ground-fault protective devices (fuses or a circuit breaker), which ensure that all ungrounded conductors will be opened.

430-112. Motors Served by Single Disconnecting Means.
Each motor shall be provided with an individual disconnecting means.

Exception: A single disconnecting means shall be permitted to serve a group of motors under any one of the conditions of a, b, and c below. The single disconnecting means shall be rated in accordance with Section 430-110(c):

a. Where a number of motors drive several parts of a single machine or piece of apparatus, such as metal and woodworking machines, cranes, and hoists.

b. Where a group of motors is under the protection of one set of branch-circuit protective devices as permitted by Section 430-53(a).

c. Where a group of motors is in a single room within sight from the location of the disconnecting means.

The exception permits a single disconnecting means to serve a group of motors. The disconnecting means is required to have a rating equal to the sum of the horsepower or current of each motor in the group. If the sum is over 2 horsepower, a motor-circuit switch (horsepower-rated) is required to be used; thus, for five 2-horsepower motors, the disconnecting means should be a motor-circuit switch rated at not less than 10 horsepower.

Exception a. A single disconnecting means may be used where a number of motors drive several parts of a single machine such as cranes (see Sections 610-31 and 610-32), metal or woodworking machines, steel rolling mill machinery, etc. The single disconnecting means for multimotor machinery provides a positive means of simultaneously deenergizing all motor branch circuits, including remote-control circuits, interlocking circuits, limit-switch circuits, and operator control stations.

Exception b. Section 430-53(a) permits a group of motors under the protection of the same branch-circuit device, provided the device is rated not more than 20 A at 125 V or 15 A at more than 125 V but not more than 600 V. The motors are required to be rated 1 horsepower or less, and the full-load current for each motor is not permitted to

exceed 6 A. A single disconnecting means is both practical and economical for a group of such small motors.

Exception c. Many times, a group of motors is located in one room, such as a pump room, compressor room, mixer room, etc. It is therefore possible to design the layout of a single disconnecting means with an unobstructed view (not more than 50 feet) from each motor.

These conditions are similar to the requirements in Section 430-87, which permit the use of a single controller for a group of motors.

430-113. Energy from More than One Source.
Motor and motor-operated equipment receiving electrical energy from more than one source shall be provided with disconnecting means from each source of electrical energy immediately adjacent to the equipment served. Each source shall be permitted to have a separate disconnecting means.

Exception No. 1: Where a motor receives electrical energy from more than one source, the disconnecting means for the main power supply to the motor shall not be required to be immediately adjacent to the motor, provided the controller disconnecting means is capable of being locked in the open position.

Exception No. 2: A separate disconnecting means shall not be required for a Class 2 remote-control circuit conforming with Article 725, rated not more than 30 volts, and that is isolated and ungrounded.

Exception No. 1 applies to large synchronous motors that receive electrical energy from more than one source. Exception No. 2 applies to low-voltage control circuits, such as thermostat circuits used with heating and air-conditioning equipment.

J. Over 600 Volts, Nominal

430-121. General.
Part J recognizes the additional hazard due to the use of higher voltages. It adds to or amends the other provisions of this article. Other requirements for circuits and equipment operating at over 600 volts, nominal, are in Article 710.

430-122. Marking on Controllers.
In addition to the marking required by Section 430-8, a controller shall be marked with the control voltage.

Overcurrent protection that
opens all ungrounded conductors

Switch
(hand operable)

or

Oilbreak switch
not over 600 V
not over 100 A
except by
permission*

Oil

Motor

or

Circuit
breaker*

Mains

*Figure 430-28.   Three alternative arrangements where a switch, or circuit breaker, or oilbreak switch can serve satisfactorily as both the controller and disconnecting means. (*Oilbreak switch or circuit breaker may be hand operated or power operated.)*

430-123. **Conductor Enclosures Adjacent to Motors.** Flexible metal conduit or liquidtight flexible metal conduit not exceeding 6 feet (1.83 m) in length shall be permitted to be employed for raceway connection to a motor terminal enclosure.

430-124. **Size of Conductors.** Conductors supplying motors shall have an ampacity not less than the current at which the motor overload protective device(s) is selected to trip.

430-125. **Motor Circuit Overcurrent Protection.**

(a) General. Each motor circuit shall include coordinated protection to automatically interrupt overload and fault currents in the motor, the motor circuit conductors, and the motor control apparatus.

Exception: Where a motor is vital to operation of the plant and the motor should operate to failure if necessary to prevent a greater hazard to persons, the sensing device(s) is permitted to be connected to a supervised annunciator or alarm instead of interrupting the motor circuit.

(b) Overload Protection.

(1) Each motor shall be protected against dangerous heating due to motor overloads and failure to start by a thermal

protector integral with the motor or external current-sensing devices, or both.

(2) The secondary circuits of wound-rotor alternating-current motors including conductors, controllers, and resistors rated for the application shall be considered as protected against overcurrent by the motor overload protection means.

(3) Operation of the overload interrupting device shall simultaneously disconnect all ungrounded conductors.

(4) Overload sensing devices shall not automatically reset after trip unless resetting of the overload sensing device does not cause automatic restarting of the motor or there is no hazard to persons created by automatic restarting of the motor and its connected machinery.

(c) Fault-Current Protection.

(1) Fault-current protection shall be provided in each motor circuit by one of the following means:

a. A circuit breaker of suitable type and rating so arranged that it can be serviced without hazard. The circuit breaker shall simultaneously disconnect all ungrounded conductors. The circuit breaker shall be permitted to sense the fault current by means of integral or external sensing elements.

b. Fuses of a suitable type and rating placed in each ungrounded conductor.

Fuses shall be used with suitable disconnecting means or they shall be of a type that can also serve as the disconnecting means. They shall be so arranged that they cannot be serviced while they are energized.

(2) Fault-current interrupting devices shall not reclose the circuit automatically.

Exception: Where circuits are exposed to transient faults and where automatic reclosing of the circuit does not create a hazard to persons.

(3) Overload protection and fault-current protection shall be permitted to be provided by the same device.

430-126. **Rating of Motor Control Apparatus.** Motor controllers and motor branch-circuit disconnecting means shall have a continuous ampere rating not less than the current at which the overload protective device(s) is selected to trip.

430-127. **Disconnecting Means.** The controller disconnecting means shall be capable of being locked in the open position.

K. Protection of Live Parts — All Voltages

430-131. **General.** Part K specifies that live parts shall be protected in a manner judged adequate for the hazard involved.

430-132. **Where Required.** Exposed live parts of motors and controllers operating at 50 volts or more between terminals shall be guarded against accidental contact by enclosure or by location as follows:

(a) In a Room or Enclosure. By installation in a room or enclosure that is accessible only to qualified persons.

(b) On a Suitable Balcony. By installation on a suitable balcony, gallery, or platform, so elevated and arranged as to exclude unqualified persons.

(c) Elevation. By elevation 8 feet (2.44 m) or more above the floor.

Exception: Stationary motors having commutators, collectors, and brush rigging located inside of motor-end brackets and not

conductively connected to supply circuits operating at more than 150 volts to ground.

430-133. **Guards for Attendants.** Where live parts of motors or controllers operating at over 150 volts to ground are guarded against accidental contact only by location as specified in Section 430-132, and where adjustment or other attendance may be necessary during the operation of the apparatus, suitable insulating mats or platforms shall be provided so that the attendant cannot readily touch live parts unless standing on the mats or platforms.

(FPN): For working space, see Sections 110-16 and 110-34.

L. Grounding — All Voltages

430-141. **General.** Part L specifies the grounding of exposed noncurrent-carrying metal parts, likely to become energized, of motor and controller frames to prevent a voltage above ground in the event of accidental contact between energized parts and frames. Insulation, isolation, or guarding are suitable alternatives to grounding of motors under certain conditions.

430-142. **Stationary Motors.** The frames of stationary motors shall be grounded under any of the following conditions: (1) where supplied by metal-enclosed wiring; (2) where in a wet location and not isolated or guarded; (3) if in a hazardous (classified) location as covered in Articles 500 through 517; (4) if the motor operates with any terminal at over 150 volts to ground.

Where the frame of the motor is not grounded, it shall be permanently and effectively insulated from the ground.

Any motor in a wet location and subject to contact by personnel constitutes a serious hazard and, unless it is isolated, elevated, or guarded from reach, is required to be grounded.

Stationary motors are usually supplied by wiring enclosed in metal raceways, flexible metal conduit, or cables with metal sheaths. When effectively attached to the motor junction box or frame, the metal raceway or cable armor serves as the equipment grounding conductor. See Section 250-91(b).

430-143. **Portable Motors.** The frames of portable motors that operate at over 150 volts to ground shall be guarded or grounded.

(FPN No. 1): See Section 250-45(d) for grounding of portable appliances in other than residential occupancies.

(FPN No. 2): See Section 250-59(b) for color of grounding conductor.

430-144. Controllers. Controller enclosures shall be grounded regardless of voltage. Controller enclosures shall have means for attachment of an equipment grounding conductor termination in accordance with Section 250-113.

Exception No. 1: Enclosures attached to ungrounded portable equipment.

Exception No. 2: Lined covers of snap switches.

430-145. Method of Grounding. Where required, grounding shall be done in the manner specified in Article 250.

(a) Grounding through Terminal Housings. Where the wiring to fixed motors is metal-enclosed cable or in metal raceways, junction boxes to house motor terminals shall be provided, and the armor of the cable or the metal raceways shall be connected to them in the manner specified in Article 250.

(FPN): See Section 430-12(e) for grounding connection means required at motor terminal housings.

(b) Separation of Junction Box from Motor. The junction box required by (a) above shall be permitted to be separated from the motor by not more than 6 feet (1.83 m), provided the leads to the motor are Type AC cable or armored cord or are stranded leads enclosed in liquidtight flexible metal conduit, flexible metal conduit, intermediate metal conduit, rigid metal conduit, or electrical metallic tubing not smaller than ³/₈-inch electrical trade size, the armor or raceway being connected both to the motor and to the box. Where stranded leads are used, protected as specified above, they shall not be larger than No. 10 and shall comply with other requirements of this Code for conductors to be used in raceways.

Liquidtight flexible nonmetallic conduit and rigid nonmetallic conduit shall be permitted to enclose the leads to the motor provided the required grounding conductor is connected to both the motor and to the box.

(c) Grounding of Controller Mounted Devices. Instrument transformer secondaries and exposed noncurrent-carrying metal or other conductive parts or cases of instrument transformers, meters, instruments, and relays shall be grounded as specified in Sections 250-121 through 250-125.

Most motors are subject to vibration, and good wiring practice requires that, in nearly all cases, the wiring to motors that are fixed be installed with a short section of liquidtight flexible metal or nonmetallic conduit, or flexible metal conduit, to the motor terminal housing. Such use of flexible conduit requires an equipment grounding conductor.

M. Tables

Table 430-147. Full-Load Current in Amperes, Direct-Current Motors

The following values of full-load currents* are for motors running at base speed.

HP	Armature Voltage Rating*					
	90V	120V	180V	240V	500V	550V
¹/₄	4.0	3.1	2.0	1.6		
¹/₃	5.2	4.1	2.6	2.0		
¹/₂	6.8	5.4	3.4	2.7		
³/₄	9.6	7.6	4.8	3.8		
1	12.2	9.5	6.1	4.7		
1 ¹/₂		13.2	8.3	6.6		
2		17	10.8	8.5		
3		25	16	12.2		
5		40	27	20		
7 ¹/₂		58		29	13.6	12.2
10		76		38	18	16
15				55	27	24
20				72	34	31
25				89	43	38
30				106	51	46
40				140	67	61
50				173	83	75
60				206	99	90
75				255	123	111
100				341	164	148
125				425	205	185
150				506	246	222
200				675	330	294

* These are average direct-current quantities.

Table 430-148. **Full-Load Currents in Amperes Single-Phase Alternating-Current Motors**

The following values of full-load currents are for motors running at usual speeds and motors with normal torque characteristics. Motors built for especially low speeds or high torques may have higher full-load currents, and multispeed motors will have full-load current varying with speed, in which case the nameplate current ratings shall be used.

The voltages listed are rated motor voltages. The currents listed shall be permitted for system voltage ranges of 110 to 120 and 220 to 240.

HP	115V	200V	208V	230V
$1/6$	4.4	2.5	2.4	2.2
$1/4$	5.8	3.3	3.2	2.9
$1/3$	7.2	4.1	4.0	3.6
$1/2$	9.8	5.6	5.4	4.9
$3/4$	13.8	7.9	7.6	6.9
1	16	9.2	8.8	8
$1\,1/2$	20	11.5	11	10
2	24	13.8	13.2	12
3	34	19.6	18.7	17
5	56	32.2	30.8	28
$7\,1/2$	80	46	44	40
10	100	57.5	55	50

Table 430-149. **Full-Load Current Two-Phase Alternating-Current Motors (4-Wire)**

The following values of full-load current are for motors running at speeds usual for belted motors and motors with normal torque characteristics. Motors built for especially low speeds or high torques may require more running current, and multispeed motors will have full-load current varying with speed, in which case the nameplate current rating shall be used. Current in the common conductor of a 2-phase, 3-wire system will be 1.41 times the value given.

The voltages listed are rated motor voltages. The currents listed shall be permitted for system voltage ranges of 110 to 120, 220 to 240, 440 to 480, and 550-600 volts.

	Induction Type Squirrel-Cage and Wound-Rotor Amperes				
HP	115V	230V	460V	575V	2300V
$1/2$	4	2	1	.8	
$3/4$	4.8	2.4	1.2	1.0	
1	6.4	3.2	1.6	1.3	
$1\,1/2$	9	4.5	2.3	1.8	
2	11.8	5.9	3	2.4	
3		8.3	4.2	3.3	
5		13.2	6.6	5.3	
$7\,1/2$		19	9	8	
10		24	12	10	
15		36	18	14	
20		47	23	19	
25		59	29	24	
30		69	35	28	
40		90	45	36	
50		113	56	45	
60		133	67	53	14
75		166	83	66	18
100		218	109	87	23
125		270	135	108	28
150		312	156	125	32
200		416	208	167	43

Table 430-150. Full-Load Current*
Three-Phase Alternating-Current Motors

HP	Induction Type Squirrel-Cage and Wound-Rotor Amperes							Synchronous Type Unity Power Factor† Amperes			
	115V	200V	208V	230V	460V	575V	2300V	230V	460V	575V	2300V
$^1/_2$	4	2.3	2.2	2	1	.8					
$^3/_4$	5.6	3.2	3.1	2.8	1.4	1.1					
1	7.2	4.1	4.0	3.6	1.8	1.4					
$1^1/_2$	10.4	6.0	5.7	5.2	2.6	2.1					
2	13.6	7.8	7.5	6.8	3.4	2.7					
3		11.0	10.6	9.6	4.8	3.9					
5		17.5	16.7	15.2	7.6	6.1					
$7^1/_2$		25.3	24.2	22	11	9					
10		32.2	30.8	28	14	11					
15		48.3	46.2	42	21	17					
20		62.1	59.4	54	27	22					
25		78.2	74.8	68	34	27		53	26	21	
30		92	88	80	40	32		63	32	26	
40		119.6	114.4	104	52	41		83	41	33	
50		149.5	143.0	130	65	52		104	52	42	
60		177.1	169.4	154	77	62	16	123	61	49	12
75		220.8	211.2	192	96	77	20	155	78	62	15
100		285.2	272.8	248	124	99	26	202	101	81	20
125		358.8	343.2	312	156	125	31	253	126	101	25
150		414	396.0	360	180	144	37	302	151	121	30
200		552	528.0	480	240	192	49	400	201	161	40

* These values of full-load current are for motors running at speeds usual for belted motors and motors with normal torque characteristics. Motors built for especially low speeds or high torques may require more runnning current, and multispeed motors will have full-load current varying with speed, in which case the nameplate current rating shall be used.

† For 90 and 80 percent power factor, the above figures shall be multipled by 1.1 and 1.25 respectively.

The voltages listed are rated motor voltages. The currents listed shall be permitted for system voltage ranges of 110 to 120, 220 to 240, 440 to 480, and 550 to 600 volts.

Table 430-151. Conversion Table of Locked-Rotor Currents for Selection of Disconnecting Means and Controllers as Determined from Horsepower and Voltage Rating

For use only with Sections 430-110, 440-12, 440-41, and 455-8(c).

Motor Locked-Rotor Current Amperes*							
Single Phase		Two or Three Phase					Max. HP Rating
115V	230V	115V	200V	230V	460V	575V	
58.8	29.4	24	18.8	12	6	4.8	$^1/_2$
82.8	41.4	33.6	19.3	16.8	8.4	6.6	$^3/_4$
96	48	43.2	24.8	21.6	10.8	8.4	1
120	60	62	35.9	31.2	15.6	12.6	$1^1/_2$
144	72	81	46.9	40.8	20.4	16.2	2
204	102	—	66	58	26.8	23.4	3
336	168	—	105	91	45.6	36.6	5
480	240	—	152	132	66	54	$7^1/_2$
600	300	—	193	168	84	66	10
—	—	—	290	252	126	102	15
—	—	—	373	324	162	132	20
—	—	—	469	408	204	162	25
—	—	—	552	480	240	192	30
—	—	—	718	624	312	246	40
—	—	—	897	780	390	312	50
—	—	—	1063	924	462	372	60
—	—	—	1325	1152	576	462	75
—	—	—	1711	1488	744	594	100
—	—	—	2153	1872	936	750	125
—	—	—	2484	2160	1080	864	150
—	—	—	3312	2880	1440	1152	200

* These values of motor locked-rotor current are approximately six times the full-load current values given in Tables 430-148 and 430-150.

Table 430-150 through Article 440 – Contents

430-152. Maximum Rating or Setting of Motor Branch-Circuit Short-Circuit and Ground-Fault Protective Devices

Type of Motor	Percent of Full-Load Current			
	Nontime Delay Fuse	Dual Element (Time-Delay) Fuse	Instan-taneous Trip Breaker	Inverse Time Breaker*
Single-phase, all types				
No code letter	300	175	700	250
All ac single-phase and polyphase squirrel-cage and synchronous motors† with full-voltage, resistor or reactor starting:				
No code letter	300	175	700	250
Code letters F to V	300	175	700	250
Code letters B to E	250	175	700	200
Code letter A	150	150	700	150
All ac squirrel-cage and synchronous motors† with autotransformer starting:				
Not more than 30 amps				
No code letter	250	175	700	200
More than 30 amps				
No code letter	200	175	700	200
Code letters F to V	250	175	700	200
Code letters B to E	200	175	700	200
Code letter A	150	150	700	150
High reactance squirrel-cage				
Not more than 30 amps				
No code letter	250	175	700	250
More than 30 amps				
No code letter	200	175	700	200
Wound-rotor —				
No code letter	150	150	700	150
Direct-current (constant voltage)				
No more than 50 hp				
No code letter	150	150	250	150
More than 50 hp				
No code letter	150	150	175	150

For explanation of code letter marking, see Table 430-7(b).
For certain exceptions to the values specified, see Sections 430-52 through 430-54.
* The values given in the last column also cover the ratings of nonadjustable inverse time types of circuit breakers that may be modified as in Section 430-52.
† Synchronous motors of the low-torque, low-speed type (usually 450 rpm or lower), such as are used to drive reciprocating compressors, pumps, etc., that start unloaded, do not require a fuse rating or circuit-breaker setting in excess of 200 percent of full-load current.

ARTICLE 440 Air-Conditioning and Refrigerating Equipment

Contents

A. General

A. General

440-1. Scope. The provisions of this article apply to electric motor-driven air-conditioning and refrigerating equipment, and to the branch circuits and controllers for such equipment. It provides for the special considerations necessary for circuits supplying hermetic refrigerant motor-compressors and for any air-conditioning or refrigerating equipment that is supplied from an individual branch circuit that supplies a hermetic refrigerant motor-compressor.

440-2. Definitions.

Branch-Circuit Selection Current: Branch-circuit selection current is the value in amperes to be used instead of the rated-load current in determining the ratings of motor branch-circuit conductors, disconnecting means, controllers, and branch-circuit short-circuit and ground-fault protective devices wherever the running overload protective device permits a sustained current greater than the specified percentage of the rated-load current. The value of branch-circuit selection current will always be equal to or greater than the marked rated-load current.

Hermetic Refrigerant Motor-Compressor: A combination consisting of a compressor and motor, both of which are enclosed in the same housing, with no external shaft or shaft seals, the motor operating in the refrigerant.

Rated-Load Current: The rated-load current for a hermetic refrigerant motor-compressor is the current resulting when the motor-compressor is operated at the rated load, rated voltage, and rated frequency of the equipment it serves.

440-3. Other Articles.

(a) **Article 430.** These provisions are in addition to, or amendatory of, the provisions of Article 430 and other articles in this Code, which apply except as modified in this article.

(b) **Article 422, 424, or 430.** The rules of Article 422, 424, or 430, as applicable, shall apply to air-conditioning and refrigerating equipment that does not incorporate a hermetic refrigerant motor-compressor. Examples of such equipment are devices that employ refrigeration compressors driven by conventional motors, furnaces with air-conditioning evaporator coils installed, fan-coil units, remote forced air-cooled condensers, remote commercial refrigerators, etc.

(c) Article 422. Devices such as room air conditioners, household refrigerators and freezers, drinking water coolers, and beverage dispensers shall be considered appliances, and the provisions of Article 422 shall also apply.

(d) Other Applicable Articles. Hermetic refrigerant motor-compressors, circuits, controllers, and equipment shall also comply with the applicable provisions of the following:

Capacitors	Section 460-9
Garages, Aircraft Hangars, Gasoline Dispensing and Service Stations, Bulk Storage Plants, Spray Application, Dipping, and Coating Processes, and Inhalation Anesthetizing Locations	Articles 511, 513, 514, 515, 516, and 517, Part D
Hazardous (Classified) Locations	Articles 500 through 503
Motion Picture and Television Studios and Similar Locations	Article 530
Resistors and Reactors	Artice 470

Article 440 provides for special considerations necessary for circuits supplying HERMETIC refrigerant motor-compressors and is in addition to, or amendatory of, the provisions of Article 430 and other applicable articles. However, many requirements, such as disconnecting means, controllers, single or group installations, and sizing of conductors, are the same as, or very similar to, those applied in Article 430.

Article 440 does not apply unless a hermetic refrigerant motor-compressor is supplied. Article 440 must be applied in conjunction with Article 430.

Note the terms "rated-load current," and "branch-circuit selection current," defined in Section 440-2.

When a branch-circuit selection current is marked on a nameplate, it is required to be used INSTEAD of the rated-load current in order to determine the size of the disconnecting means, the controller, the motor branch-circuit conductors, and the overcurrent protective devices for the branch-circuit conductors and the motor. The value of branch-circuit selection current will always be greater than the marked rated-load current.

440-4. **Marking on Hermetic Refrigerant Motor-Compressors and Equipment.**

(a) Hermetic Refrigerant Motor-Compressor Nameplate. A hermetic refrigerant motor-compressor shall be provided with a nameplate that shall indicate the manufacturer's name, trademark, or symbol; identifying designation; phase; voltage; and frequency. The rated-load current in amperes of the motor-compressor shall be marked by the equipment manufacturer on either or both the motor-compressor nameplate and the nameplate of the equipment in which the motor-compressor is used. The locked-rotor current of each single-phase motor-compressor having a rated-load current of more than 9 amperes at 115 volts, or more than 4.5 amperes at 230 volts, and each polyphase motor-compressor shall be marked on the motor-compressor nameplate. Where a thermal protector complying with Sections 440-52(a)(2) and (b)(2) is used, the motor-compressor nameplate or the equipment nameplate shall be marked with the words "thermally protected." Where a protective system complying with Sections 440-52(a)(4) and (b)(4) is used and is furnished with the equipment, the equipment nameplate shall be marked with the words, "thermally protected system." Where a protective system complying with Sections 440-52(a)(4) and (b)(4) is specified, the equipment nameplate shall be appropriately marked.

(b) Multimotor and Combination-Load Equipment. Multimotor and combination-load equipment shall be provided with a visible nameplate marked with the maker's name, the rating in volts, frequency and number of phases, minimum supply circuit conductor ampacity, and the maximum rating of the branch-circuit short-circuit and ground-fault protective device. The ampacity shall be calculated by using Part D and counting all the motors and other loads that will be operated at the same time. The branch-circuit short-circuit and ground-fault protective device rating shall not exceed the value calculated by using Part C. Multimotor or combination-load equipment for use on two or more circuits shall be marked with the above information for each circuit.

Exception No. 1: Multimotor and combination-load equipment that is suitable under the provisions of this article for connection to a single 15- or 20-ampere, 120-volt, or a 15-ampere, 208- or 240-volt, single-phase branch circuit shall be permitted to be marked as a single load.

Exception No. 2: Room air conditioners as provided in Part G of Article 440.

(c) Branch-Circuit Selection Current. A hermetic refrigerant motor-compressor, or equipment containing such a compressor, having a protection system that is approved for use with the motor-compressor that it protects and that permits continuous current in excess of the specified percentage of nameplate rated-load current given in Section 440-52(b)(2) or (b)(4), shall also be marked with a branch-circuit selection current that complies with Section 440-52(b)(2) or (b)(4). This marking shall be provided by the equipment manufacturer and shall be on the nameplate(s) where the rated-load current(s) appears.

440-5. **Marking on Controllers.** A controller shall be marked with the maker's name, trademark, or symbol; identifying designation; the voltage; phase; full-load and locked-rotor current (or horsepower) rating; and such other data as may be needed to properly indicate the motor-compressor for which it is suitable.

440-6. **Ampacity and Rating.** The size of conductors for equipment covered by this article shall be selected from Tables 310-16 through 310-19 or calculated in accordance with Section 310-15 as applicable. The required ampacity of conductors and rating of equipment shall be determined as follows.

(a) Hermetic Refrigerant Motor-Compressor. For a hermetic refrigerant motor-compressor, the rated-load current marked on the nameplate of the equipment in which the motor-compressor is employed shall be used in determining the rating or ampacity of the disconnecting means, the branch-circuit conductors, the controller, the branch-circuit short-circuit and ground-fault protection, and the separate motor overload protection. Where no rated-load current is shown on the equipment nameplate, the rated-load current shown on the compressor nameplate shall be used. For disconnecting means and controllers, see also Sections 440-12 and 440-41.

Exception No. 1: Where so marked, the branch-circuit selection current shall be used instead of the rated-load current to determine the rating or ampacity of the disconnecting means, the branch-circuit conductors, the controller, and the branch-circuit short-circuit and ground-fault protection.

Exception No. 2: As permitted in Section 440-22(b) for branch-circuit short-circuit and ground-fault protection of cord- and plug-connected equipment.

(b) Multimotor Equipment. For multimotor equipment employing a shaded-pole or permanent split-capacitor-type fan or blower motor, the full-load current for such motor marked on the nameplate of the equipment in which the fan or blower motor is employed shall be used instead of the horsepower rating to determine the ampacity or rating of the disconnecting means, the branch-circuit conductors, the controller, the branch-circuit short-circuit and ground-fault protection, and the separate overload protection. This marking on the equipment nameplate shall not be less than the current marked on the fan or blower motor nameplate.

440-7. **Highest Rated (Largest) Motor.** In determining compliance with this article and with Sections 430-24, 430-53(b) and (c), and 430-62(a), the highest rated (largest) motor shall be considered to be the motor that has the highest rated-load current. Where two or more motors have the same rated-load current, only one of them shall be considered as the highest rated (largest) motor. For other than hermetic refrigerant motor-compressors, and fan or blower motors as covered in Section 440-6(b), the full-load current used to determine the highest rated motor shall be the equivalent value corresponding to the motor horsepower rating selected from Table 430-148, 430-149, or 430-150.

Exception: Where so marked, the branch-circuit selection current shall be used instead of the rated-load current in determining the highest rated (largest) motor-compressor.

440-8. **Single Machine.** An air-conditioning or refrigerating system shall be considered to be a single machine under the provisions of Section 430-87, Exception and Section 430-112, Exception. The motors shall be permitted to be located remotely from each other.

B. Disconnecting Means

440-11. **General.** The provisions of Part B are intended to require disconnecting means capable of disconnecting air-conditioning and refrigerating equipment including motor-compressors, and controllers, from the circuit feeder. See Diagram 430-1.

440-12. **Rating and Interrupting Capacity.**

(a) Hermetic Refrigerant Motor-Compressor. A disconnecting means serving a hermetic refrigerant motor-compressor shall be selected on the basis of the nameplate rated-load current or branch-circuit selection current, whichever is greater, and locked-rotor current, respectively, of the motor-compressor as follows:

(1) The ampere rating shall be at least 115 percent of the nameplate rated-load current or branch-circuit selection current, whichever is greater.

(2) To determine the equivalent horsepower in complying with the requirements of Section 430-109, the horsepower rating shall be selected from Table 430-148, 430-149, or 430-150 corresponding to the rated-load current or branch-circuit selection current, whichever is greater, and also the horsepower rating from Table 430-151 corresponding to the locked-rotor current. In case the nameplate rated-load current or branch-circuit selection current and locked-rotor current do not correspond to the currents shown in Table 430-148, 430-149, 430-150, or 430-151, the horsepower rating corresponding to the next higher value shall be selected. In case different horsepower ratings are obtained when applying these tables, a horsepower rating at least equal to the larger of the values obtained shall be selected.

(b) **Combination Loads.** Where one or more hermetic refrigerant motor-compressors are used together or are used in combination with other motors or loads, and where the combined load may be simultaneous on a single disconnecting means, the rating for the combined load shall be determined as follows:

(1) The horsepower rating of the disconnecting means shall be determined from the summation of all currents, including resistance loads, at the rated-load condition and also at the locked-rotor condition. The combined rated-load current and the combined locked-rotor current so obtained shall be considered as a single motor for the purpose of this requirement as follows:

a. The full-load current equivalent to the horsepower rating of each motor, other than a hermetic refrigerant motor-compressor, and fan or blower motors as covered in Section 440-6(b) shall be selected from Table 430-148, 430-149, or 430-150. These full-load currents shall be added to the motor-compressor rated-load current(s) or branch-circuit selection current(s), whichever is greater, and to the rating in amperes of other loads to obtain an equivalent full-load current for the combined load.

b. The locked-rotor current equivalent to the horsepower rating of each motor, other than a hermetic refrigerant motor-compressor, shall be selected from Table 430-151,

and, for fan and blower motors of the shaded-pole or permanent split-capacitor type marked with the locked-rotor current, the marked value shall be used. The locked-rotor currents shall be added to the motor-compressor locked-rotor current(s) and to the rating in amperes of other loads to obtain an equivalent locked-rotor current for the combined load. Where two or more motors or other loads such as resistance heaters, or both, cannot be started simultaneously, appropriate combinations of locked-rotor and rated-load current or branch-circuit selection current, whichever is greater, shall be an acceptable means of determining the equivalent locked-rotor current for the simultaneous combined load.

Exception: Where part of the concurrent load is a resistance load and the disconnecting means is a switch rated in horsepower and amperes, the switch used shall be permitted to have a horsepower rating not less than the combined load to the motor-compressor(s) and other motor(s) at the locked-rotor condition, if the ampere rating of the switch is not less than this locked-rotor load plus the resistance load.

(2) The ampere rating of the disconnecting means shall be at least 115 percent of the summation of all currents at the rated-load condition determined in accordance with Section 440-12(b)(1).

(c) **Small Motor-Compressors.** For small motor-compressors not having the locked-rotor current marked on the nameplate, or for small motors not covered by Table 430-147, 430-148, 430-149, or 430-150, the locked-rotor current shall be assumed to be six times the rated-load current. See Section 440-3(a).

(d) **Every Switch.** Every disconnecting means in the refrigerant motor-compressor circuit between the point of attachment to the feeder and the point of connection to the refrigerant motor-compressor shall comply with the requirements of Section 440-12.

(e) **Disconnecting Means Rated in Excess of 100 Horsepower.** Where the rated-load or locked-rotor current as determined above would indicate a disconnecting means rated in excess of 100 horsepower, the provisions of Section 430-109, Exception No. 4 shall apply.

440-13. **Cord-Connected Equipment.** For cord-connected equipment such as room air conditioners, household refrigerators and freezers, drinking water coolers, and beverage dispensers, a separable connector or an attachment plug and receptacle shall be permitted to serve as the disconnecting means. See also Section 440-63.

440-14. **Location.** Disconnecting means shall be located within sight from and readily accessible from the air-conditioning or refrigerating equipment. The disconnecting means shall be permitted to be installed on or within the air-conditioning or refrigerating equipment.

Exception: Cord- and plug-connected appliances.

(FPN): See Parts G and I of Article 430 for additional requirements.

The reference to Parts G and I of Article 430 in the fine print note is intended to call attention to the additional disconnect location requirements in Sections 430-102, 430-107, and 430-113. Since Section 440-3(a) makes the requirements in Article 440 in addition or amendatory to the provisions of Article 430, the requirement of Section 440-14 mandates equipment disconnecting means within sight from and readily accessible from the equipment, even if there is also a remote disconnect capable of being locked in the open position under the provision of Section 430-102(b), Exception. This special requirement for air-conditioning and refrigeration equipment covered by Article 440 is more stringent than the provisions in Article 430 in order to provide protection for service personnel working on equipment located in attics, on roofs, or outside in a remote location where it is difficult to gain access to a remote lockable disconnect.

C. Branch-Circuit Short-Circuit and Ground-Fault Protection

440-21. **General.** The provisions of Part C specify devices intended to protect the branch-circuit conductors, control apparatus, and motors in circuits supplying hermetic refrigerant motor-compressors against overcurrent due to short circuits and grounds. They are in addition to or amendatory of the provisions of Article 240.

Where an air conditioner is listed by a qualified electrical testing laboratory with a nameplate that reads "maximum fuse size," the listing restricts the use of this unit to fuse protection only and does not cover its use with circuit breakers. If the air conditioner has been evaluated for both fuses and ordinary circuit breakers, or both fuses and

HACR-Type circuit breakers, it may be so marked. UL-listed circuit breakers that have been found suitable for use with heating, air-conditioning, and refrigeration equipment comprising multimotor or combination loads are marked "Listed HACR Type." It is the intent of Section 110-3(b) to have any restriction of listing applied to the installation of the equipment in order to comply with the *Code.*

The UL Electrical Appliance and Utilization Equipment Directory states the following under "Air-Conditioners, Central Cooling": "This marked protective device rating is the maximum for which the equipment has been investigated and found acceptable. Where the marking specifies fuses, or HACR-type circuit breakers, the circuit is intended to be protected only by the type of protective device specified." See Figure 440-1.

UL 1995 indicates that the short-circuit test values to which HVAC equipment is subjected is 3,500 amperes through 40 ampere units, and 5,000 amperes for units above 40 amperes. Available fault current at the line terminals of such equipment should not exceed these levels. Current-limiting overcurrent devices can be installed in the branch-circuit supplying the equipment that can reduce the amount of fault current to which the equipment will be subjected. See Section 240-11 for definition of current-limiting device and commentary explaining short-circuit damage. This is important particularly for the larger commercial and industrial installations. See also Sections 110-3(b) and 110-10.

440-22. **Application and Selection.**

(a) Rating or Setting for Individual Motor-Compressor. The motor-compressor branch-circuit short-circuit and ground-fault protective device shall be capable of carrying the starting current of the motor. A protective device having a rating or setting not exceeding 175 percent of the motor-compressor rated-load current or branch-circuit selection current, whichever is greater, shall be permitted, provided that, where the protection specified is not sufficient for the starting current of the motor, the rating or setting shall be permitted to be increased, but shall not exceed 225 percent of the motor rated-load current or branch-circuit selection current, whichever is greater.

Exception: The rating of the branch-circuit short-circuit and ground-fault protective device shall not be required to be less than 15 amperes.

Figure 440-1. *Three correct alternate wiring configurations satisfying a nameplate that specifies fuses. The equipment is intended to be protected by fuses ONLY.*

(b) Rating or Setting for Equipment. The equipment branch-circuit short-circuit and ground-fault protective device shall be capable of carrying the starting current of the equipment. Where the hermetic refrigerant motor-compressor is the only load on the circuit, the protection shall conform with Section 440-22(a). Where the equipment incorporates more than one hermetic refrigerant motor-compressor or a hermetic refrigerant motor-compressor and other motors or other loads, the equipment short-circuit and ground-fault protection shall conform with Section 430-53 and the following:

(1) Where a hermetic refrigerant motor-compressor is the largest load connected to the circuit, the rating or setting of the branch-circuit short-circuit and ground-fault protective device shall not exceed the value specified in Section 440-22(a) for the largest motor-compressor plus the sum of the rated-load current or branch-circuit selection current, whichever is greater, of the other motor-compressor(s) and the ratings of the other loads supplied.

(2) Where a hermetic refrigerant motor-compressor is not the largest load connected to the circuit, the rating or setting of the branch-circuit short-circuit and ground-fault protective device shall not exceed a value equal to the sum of the rated-load current or branch-circuit selection current, whichever is greater, rating(s) for the motor-compressor(s) plus the value specified in Section 430-53(c)(4) where other motor loads are supplied, or the value specified in Section 240-3 where only nonmotor loads are supplied in addition to the motor-compressor(s).

Exception No. 1: Equipment that will start and operate on a 15- or 20-ampere 120-volt, or 15-ampere 208- or 240-volt single-phase branch circuit, shall be permitted to be protected by the 15- or 20-ampere overcurrent device protecting the branch circuit, but if the maximum branch-circuit short-circuit and ground-fault protective device rating marked on the equipment is less than these values, the circuit protective device shall not exceed the value marked on the equipment nameplate.

Exception No. 2: The nameplate marking of cord- and plug-connected equipment rated not greater than 250 volts, single-phase, such as household refrigerators and freezers, drinking water coolers, and beverage dispensers, shall be used in determining the branch-circuit requirements, and each unit shall be considered as a single motor unless the nameplate is marked otherwise.

(c) Protective Device Rating Not to Exceed the Manufacturer's Values. Where maximum protective device ratings shown on a manufacturer's heater table for use with a motor controller are less than the rating or setting selected in accordance with Sections 440-22(a) and (b), the protective device rating shall not exceed the manufacturer's values marked on the equipment.

D. Branch-Circuit Conductors

440-31. **General.** The provisions of Part D and Articles 300 and 310 specify sizes of conductors required to carry the motor current without overheating under the conditions specified, except as modified in Section 440-6(a), Exception No. 1.

The provisions of these articles shall not apply to integral conductors of motors, motor controllers and the like, or to conductors that form an integral part of approved equipment.

(FPN):   See Sections 300-1(b) and 310-1 for similar requirements.

440-32. **Single Motor-Compressor.** Branch-circuit conductors supplying a single motor-compressor shall have an ampacity not less than 125 percent of either the motor-compressor rated-load current or the branch-circuit selection current, whichever is greater.

440-33. **Motor-Compressor(s) with or without Additional Motor Loads.** Conductors supplying one or more motor-compressor(s) with or without additional load(s) shall have an ampacity not less than the sum of the rated-load or branch-circuit selection current ratings, whichever is larger, of all the motor-compressor(s) plus the full-load currents of the other motor(s), plus 25 percent of the highest motor or motor-compressor rating in the group.

Exception No. 1: Where the circuitry is so interlocked as to prevent the starting and running of a second motor-compressor or group of motor-compressors, the conductor size shall be determined from the largest motor-compressor or group of motor-compressors that is to be operated at a given time.

Exception No. 2: Room air conditioners as provided in Part G of Article 440.

440-34. **Combination Load.** Conductors supplying a motor-compressor load in addition to a lighting or appliance load as computed from Article 220 and other applicable articles shall have an ampacity sufficient for the lighting or appliance load plus the required ampacity for the motor-compressor load determined in accordance with Section 440-33, or, for a single motor-compressor, in accordance with Section 440-32.

Exception: Where the circuitry is so interlocked as to prevent simultaneous operation of the motor-compressor(s) and all other loads connected, the conductor size shall be determined from the largest size required for the motor-compressor(s) and other loads to be operated at a given time.

440-35. **Multimotor and Combination-Load Equipment.** The ampacity of the conductors supplying multimotor and combination-load equipment shall not be less than the minimum circuit ampacity marked on the equipment in accordance with Section 440-4(b).

E. Controllers for Motor-Compressors

440-41. **Rating.**

(a) Motor-Compressor Controller. A motor-compressor controller shall have both a continuous-duty full-load current rating, and a locked-rotor current rating, not less than the nameplate rated-load current or branch-circuit selection current, whichever is greater, and locked-rotor current, respectively (see Sections 440-6 and 440-7) of the compressor. In case the motor controller is rated in horsepower, but is without one or both of the foregoing current ratings, equivalent currents shall be determined from the ratings as follows: use Table 430-148, 430-149, or 430-150 to determine the equivalent full-load current rating. Use Table 430-151 to determine the equivalent locked-rotor current ratings.

(b) Controller Serving More than One Load. A controller, serving more than one motor-compressor or a motor-compressor and other loads, shall have a continuous-duty full-load current rating, and a locked-rotor current rating not less than the combined load as determined in accordance with Section 440-12(b).

F. Motor-Compressor and Branch-Circuit Overload Protection

440-51. **General.** The provisions of Part F specify devices intended to protect the motor-compressor, the motor-control apparatus, and the branch-circuit conductors against excessive heating due to motor overload and failure to start. See Sections 240-3(e) through (h).

(FPN):   Note: Overload in electrically driven apparatus is an operating overcurrent that, when it persists for a sufficient length of time, would cause damage or dangerous overheating. It does not include short circuits or ground faults.

440-52. **Application and Selection.**

(a) Protection of Motor-Compressor. Each motor-compressor shall be protected against overload and failure to start by one of the following means:

(1) A separate overload relay that is responsive to motor-compressor current. This device shall be selected to trip at not more than 140 percent of the motor-compressor rated-load current.

(2) A thermal protector integral with the motor-compressor, approved for use with the motor-compressor that it protects on the basis that it will prevent dangerous overheating of the motor-compressor due to overload and failure to start. If the current-interrupting device is separate from the motor-compressor and its control circuit is operated by a protective device integral with the motor-compressor, it shall be so arranged that the opening of the control circuit will result in interruption of current to the motor-compressor.

(3) A fuse or inverse time circuit breaker responsive to motor current, which shall also be permitted to serve as the branch-circuit short-circuit and ground-fault protective device. This device shall be rated at not more than 125 percent of the motor-compressor rated-load current. It shall have sufficient time delay to permit the motor-compressor to start and accelerate its load. The equipment or the motor-compressor shall be marked with this maximum branch-circuit fuse or inverse time circuit breaker rating.

(4) A protective system, furnished or specified and approved for use with the motor-compressor that it protects on the basis that it will prevent dangerous overheating of the motor-compressor due to overload and failure to start. If the current interrupting device is separate from the motor-compressor and its control circuit is operated by a protective device that is not integral with the current-interrupting device, it shall be so arranged that the opening of the control circuit will result in interruption of current to the motor-compressor.

(b) Protection of Motor-Compressor Control Apparatus and Branch-Circuit Conductors. The motor-compressor controller(s), the disconnecting means, and branch-circuit conductors shall be protected against overcurrent due to motor overload and failure to start by one of the following means, which shall be permitted to be the same device or system protecting the motor-compressor in accordance with Section 440-52(a).

Exception: For motor-compressors and equipment on 15- or 20-ampere single-phase branch circuits as provided in Sections 440-54 and 440-55.

(1) An overload relay selected in accordance with Section 440-52(a)(1).

(2) A thermal protector applied in accordance with Section 440-52(a)(2) and that will not permit a continuous current in excess of 156 percent of the marked rated-load current or branch-circuit selection current.

(3) A fuse or inverse time circuit breaker selected in accordance with Section 440-52(a)(3).

(4) A protective system in accordance with Section 440-52(a)(4) and that will not permit a continuous current in excess of 156 percent of the marked rated-load current or branch-circuit selection current.

440-53. **Overload Relays.** Overload relays and other devices for motor overload protection, that are not capable of opening short circuits, shall be protected by fuses or inverse time circuit breakers with ratings or settings in accordance with Part C unless approved for group installation or for part-winding motors and marked to indicate the maximum size of fuse or inverse time circuit breaker by which they shall be protected.

Exception: The fuse or inverse time circuit breaker size marking shall be permitted on the nameplate of approved equipment in which the overload relay or other overload device is used.

440-54. **Motor-Compressors and Equipment on 15- or 20-Ampere Branch Circuits — Not Cord- and Attachment Plug-Connected.** Overload protection for motor-compressors and equipment used on 15- or 20-ampere 120-volt, or 15-ampere 208- or 240-volt single-phase branch circuits as permitted in Article 210 shall be permitted as indicated in (a) and (b) below.

(a) Overload Protection. The motor-compressor shall be provided with overload protection selected as specified in Section 440-52(a). Both the controller and motor overload protective device shall be approved for installation with the short-circuit and ground-fault protective device for the branch circuit to which the equipment is connected.

(b) Time Delay. The short-circuit and ground-fault protective device protecting the branch circuit shall have sufficient time delay to permit the motor-compressor and other motors to start and accelerate their loads.

440-55. **Cord- and Attachment Plug-Connected Motor-Compressors and Equipment on 15- or 20-Ampere Branch Circuits.** Overload protection for motor-compressors and equipment that are cord- and attachment plug-connected and used on 15- or 20-ampere 120-volt, or 15-ampere 208- or 240-volt single-phase branch circuits as permitted in Article 210 shall be permitted as indicated in (a), (b), and (c) below.

(a) Overload Protection. The motor-compressor shall be provided with overload protection as specified in Section 440-52(a). Both the controller and the motor overload protective device shall be approved for installation with the short-circuit and ground-fault protective device for the branch circuit to which the equipment is connected.

(b) Attachment Plug and Receptacle Rating. The rating of the attachment plug and receptacle shall not exceed 20 amperes at 125 volts or 15 amperes at 250 volts.

(c) Time Delay. The short-circuit and ground-fault protective device protecting the branch circuit shall have sufficient time delay to permit the motor-compressor and other motors to start and accelerate their loads.

G. Provisions for Room Air Conditioners

440-60. **General.** The provisions of Part G shall apply to electrically energized room air conditioners that control temperature and humidity. For the purpose of Part G, a room air conditioner (with or without provisions for heating) shall be considered as an alternating-current appliance of the air-cooled window, console, or in-wall type that is installed in the conditioned room and that incorporates a hermetic refrigerant motor-compressor(s). The provisions of Part G cover equipment rated not over 250 volts, single phase, and such equipment shall be permitted to be cord- and attachment plug-connected.

A room air conditioner that is rated three phase or rated over 250 volts shall be directly connected to a wiring method recognized in Chapter 3, and provisions of Part G shall not apply.

440-61. **Grounding.** Room air conditioners shall be grounded in accordance with Sections 250-42, 250-43, and 250-45.

440-62. **Branch-Circuit Requirements.**

(a) Room Air Conditioner as a Single Motor Unit. A room air conditioner shall be considered as a single motor unit in determining its branch-circuit requirements where all the following conditions are met:

(1) It is cord- and attachment plug-connected.

(2) Its rating is not more than 40 amperes and 250 volts, single phase.

(3) Total rated-load current is shown on the room air-conditioner nameplate rather than individual motor currents, and

(4) The rating of the branch-circuit short-circuit and ground-fault protective device does not exceed the ampacity of the branch-circuit conductors or the rating of the receptacle, whichever is less.

(b) Where No Other Loads Are Supplied. The total marked rating of a cord- and attachment plug-connected room air conditioner shall not exceed 80 percent of the rating of a branch circuit where no other loads are supplied.

(c) Where Lighting Units or Other Appliances Are also Supplied. The total marked rating of a cord-and attachment plug-connected room air conditioner shall not exceed 50 percent of the rating of a branch circuit where lighting units or other appliances are also supplied.

440-63. **Disconnecting Means.** An attachment plug and receptacle shall be permitted to serve as the disconnecting means for a single-phase room air conditioner rated 250 volts or less if (1) the manual controls on the room air conditioner are readily accessible and located within 6 feet (1.83 m) of the floor or (2) an approved manually operable switch is installed in a readily accessible location within sight from the room air conditioner.

440-64. **Supply Cords.** Where a flexible cord is used to supply a room air conditioner, the length of such cord shall not exceed (1) 10 feet (3.05 m) for a nominal, 120-volt rating or (2) 6 feet (1.83 m) for a nominal, 208- or 240-volt rating.

ARTICLE 445   Generators

Contents

445-1. **General.** Generators and their associated wiring and equipment shall also comply with the applicable provisions of Articles 230, 250, 700, 701, 702, and 705.

445-2. **Location.** Generators shall be of a type suitable for the locations in which they are installed. They shall also meet the requirements for motors in Section 430-14. Generators installed in hazardous (classified) locations as described in Articles 500 through 503, or in other locations as described in Articles 510 through 517, and in Articles 520, 530, and 665 shall also comply with the applicable provisions of those articles.

445-3. **Marking.** Each generator shall be provided with a nameplate giving the maker's name, the rated frequency, power factor, number of phases if of alternating current, the rating in kilowatts or kilovolt amperes, the normal volts and amperes corresponding to the rating, rated revolutions per minute, insulation system class and rated ambient temperature or rated temperature rise, and time rating.

445-4. **Overcurrent Protection.**

(a) **Constant-Voltage Generators.** Constant-voltage generators, except alternating-current generator exciters, shall be protected from overloads by inherent design, circuit breakers, fuses, or other acceptable overcurrent protective means suitable for the conditions of use.

(b) **Two-Wire Generators.** Two-wire, direct-current generators shall be permitted to have overcurrent protection in one conductor only if the overcurrent device is actuated by the entire current generated other than the current in the shunt field. The overcurrent device shall not open the shunt field.

(c) **65 Volts or Less.** Generators operating at 65 volts or less and driven by individual motors shall be considered as protected by the overcurrent device protecting the motor if these devices will operate when the generators are delivering not more than 150 percent of their full-load rated current.

(d) **Balancer Sets.** Two-wire, direct-current generators used in conjunction with balancer sets to obtain neutrals for 3-wire systems shall be equipped with overcurrent devices that will disconnect the 3-wire system in case of excessive unbalancing of voltages or currents.

(e) **Three-Wire, Direct-Current Generators.** Three-wire, direct-current generators, whether compound or shunt wound, shall be equipped with overcurrent devices, one in each armature lead, and so connected as to be actuated by the entire

current from the armature. Such overcurrent devices shall consist either of a double-pole, double-coil circuit breaker, or of a 4-pole circuit breaker connected in the main and equalizer leads and tripped by two overcurrent devices, one in each armature lead. Such protective devices shall be so interlocked that no one pole can be opened without simultaneously disconnecting both leads of the armature from the system.

Exception to (a) through (e): Where deemed by the authority having jurisdiction, a generator is vital to the operation of an electrical system and the generator should operate to failure to prevent a greater hazard to persons, the overload sensing device(s) shall be permitted to be connected to an annunciator or alarm supervised by authorized personnel instead of interrupting the generator circuit.

Alternating-current generators can be designed so that during short periods of time, when the generator may carry an excessive overload, the voltage will fall off sufficiently to limit the current and power output to values that will not damage the generator.

The connection of a 2-wire generator, protected by a single-pole circuit breaker, is illustrated in Figure 445-1. Where two or more dc generators are operated in parallel or multiple, an equalizer conductor lead is connected to the positive terminal of each generator and, in effect, connects the series fields in parallel so as to maintain equal output voltage for each generator. The current could divide at the positive terminal, some flowing through the series field and positive lead and some flowing through the equalizer lead. The entire current generated flows through the negative lead; therefore, the fuse or circuit breaker (or at least the operating coil of the circuit breaker) must be placed in the negative lead. Overcurrent devices are required to be connected so as to be actuated by the entire armature output current.

An overcurrent device should not be placed in the shunt-field circuit because, if the circuit were to open when the field is at full strength, an extremely high voltage would be induced that could damage the field-winding insulation and damage the generator.

Section 445-4(c) indicates that generators operating at 65 V or less are to be thought of as protected by the overcurrent devices that also protect the drive motor, provided these devices will operate when the generator delivers 150 percent of its rated full-load current.

Figure 445-2 illustrates a double-pole circuit breaker with one pole connected in each lead of the main generator and with the operating coil properly designed to be connected in the neutral lead from the balancer, and so arranged as to be operated by either one of the "A" coils or by the "B" coil. Each of the two generators used as a balancer set carries approximately one half of the unbalanced load and, thus, is always smaller than the main generator. During an excessive imbalance of the load, the balancer set would be overloaded with no overload on the main generator; hence, a double-pole circuit breaker is connected (as noted) to guard against this condition.

It should be noted that the authority having jurisdiction may judge that having the generator operate to failure is preferable to providing automatic means to shut it down, which, in many cases, could present a greater hazard to personnel. An overload sensing device(s) would be permitted to be connected to an annunciator or an alarm (instead of interrupting the generator) and allow operating personnel to shut down load-side equipment in a safe and orderly fashion.

Figure 445-2. A double-pole circuit breaker (one pole connected in each lead of the main generator) with the opening coil arranged to be connected in the neutral of the balancer set.

tral conductors in accordance with Section 220-22. Conductors that must carry ground-fault currents shall not be smaller than required by Section 250-23(b).

Exception No. 1: Where the design and operation of the generator prevent overloading, the ampacity of the conductors shall not be less than 100 percent of the nameplate current rating of the generator.

Exception No. 2: Where the generator manufacturer's leads are connected directly to an overcurrent device that is an integral part of the generator set assembly.

445-6. **Protection of Live Parts.** Live parts of generators operated at more than 50 volts to ground shall not be exposed to accidental contact where accessible to unqualified persons.

445-7. **Guards for Attendants.** Where necessary for the safety of attendants, the requirements of Section 430-133 shall apply.

445-8. **Bushings.** Where wires pass through an opening in an enclosure, conduit box, or barrier, a bushing shall be used to protect the conductors from the edges of an opening having sharp edges. The bushing shall have smooth, well-rounded surfaces where it may be in contact with the conductors. If used where oils, grease, or other contaminants may be present, the bushing shall be made of a material not deleteriously affected.

Figure 445-1. A 2-wire dc generator protected by a single-pole circuit breaker.

445-5. **Ampacity of Conductors.** The ampacity of the phase conductors from the generator terminals to the first overcurrent device shall not be less than 115 percent of the nameplate current rating of the generator. It shall be permitted to size the neu-

ARTICLE 450 Transformers and Transformer Vaults

(Including Secondary Ties)

Contents

450-1. Scope. This article covers the installation of all transformers.

Exception No. 1: Current transformers.

Exception No. 2: Dry-type transformers that constitute a component part of other apparatus and comply with the requirements for such apparatus.

Exception No. 3: Transformers that are an integral part of an X-ray, high-frequency, or electrostatic-coating apparatus.

Exception No. 4: Transformers used with Class 2 and Class 3 circuits that comply with Article 725.

Exception No. 5: Transformers for sign and outline lighting that comply with Article 600.

Exception No. 6: Transformers for electric-discharge lighting that comply with Article 410.

Exception No. 7: Transformers used for power-limited fire protective signaling circuits that comply with Part C of Article 760.

Exception No. 8: Transformers used for research, development, or testing, where effective arrangements are provided to safeguard persons from contacting energized parts.

Exception No. 8 permits an exemption for transformers used for research, development, or testing because they are usually energized only when tests are being made. It is intended that measures such as guarding and interlocking be utilized to protect personnel against accidental contact.

This article also covers the installation of transformers in hazardous (classified) locations as modified by Articles 501 through 504.

A. General Provisions

450-2. **Definitions.** For the purpose of this article:

Transformer: The word transformer is intended to mean an individual transformer, single- or polyphase, identified by a single nameplate, unless otherwise indicated in this article.

450-3. **Overcurrent Protection.** Overcurrent protection of transformers shall comply with (a), (b), (c), or (d) below. The secondary overcurrent device shall be permitted to consist of not more than six circuit breakers or six sets of fuses grouped in one location. Where multiple overcurrent devices are utilized, the total of all the device ratings shall not exceed the allowed value of a single overcurrent device. If both breakers and fuses are utilized as the overcurrent device, the total of the device ratings shall not exceed that allowed for fuses. As used in this section, the word "transformer" shall mean a transformer or polyphase bank of two or more single-phase transformers operating as a unit.

(FPN No. 1): See Sections 240-3, 240-21, and 240-100 for overcurrent protection of conductors.

(FPN No. 2): Nonlinear currents caused by loads such as electric-discharge lighting, electronic computer/data processing, or similar equipment can increase heat in a transformer without operating its overcurrent protective device.

The requirements for protection of transformer secondaries in Article 450 apply only to protection of transformers, not to protection of conductors. Article 240 applies only to protection of conductors, not to protection of transformers. Both sets of rules are applicable. It is possible that the overcurrent protection required by Article 450 will satisfy the requirements in Article 240, and vice versa, but it is also possible that they will not. See Sections 240-3 and 240-21.

If the transformer is rated over 600 volts, nominal, Section 450-3(a) requires secondary protection for the transformer. The secondary protection may consist of a single set of fuses or a circuit breaker. The 1993 *Code* now permits this protection to consist of a maximum of six sets of fuses or six circuit breakers grouped in one location. Where multiple overcurrent protective devices are used, the sum of all the device ratings is not permitted to exceed the rating required for a single device to protect the transformer secondary. The ratings are selected based on Table 450-3(a)(1) or 450-3(a)(2)(b).

If the transformer is rated 600 volts or less, secondary protection may not be required. However, if it is provided, it may consist of up to six circuit breakers or six sets of fuses. The sum of all of the devices is not permitted to exceed the rating required for a single device, as specified in Section 450-3(b).

(a) Transformers Over 600 Volts, Nominal.

(1) Primary and Secondary. Each transformer over 600 volts, nominal, shall have primary and secondary protective devices rated or set to open at no more than the values of transformer rated currents as noted in Table 450-3(a)(1) Electronically-actuated fuses that may be set to open at a specific current shall be set in accordance with settings for circuit breakers.

Exception No. 1: Where the required fuse rating or circuit breaker setting does not correspond to a standard rating or setting, the next higher standard rating or setting shall be permitted.

Exception No. 2: As provided in (a)(2) below.

(2) Supervised Installations. Where conditions of maintenance and supervision assure that only qualified persons will monitor and service the transformer installation, overcurrent protection as provided in (a)(2)a. shall be permitted.

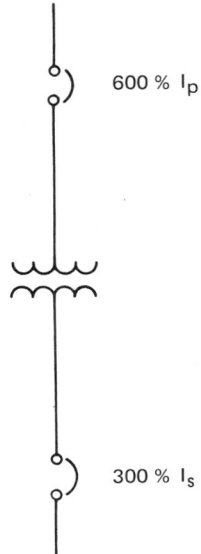

Figure 450-1(a). *A transformer rated over 600 volts with a secondary rated over 600 volts protected by a single circuit breaker on the secondary.*

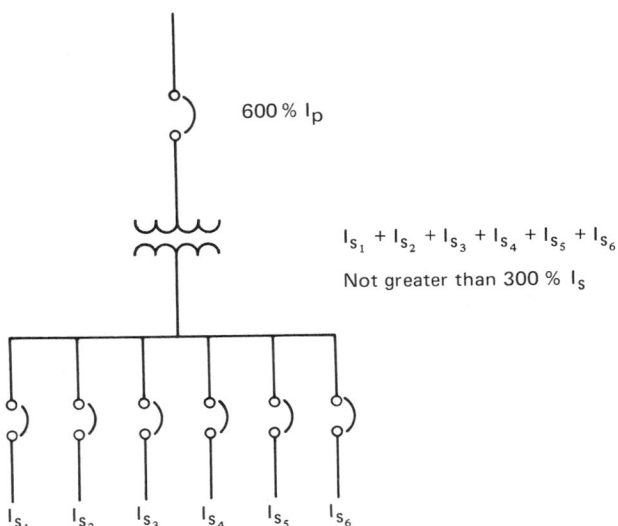

Figure 450-1(b). *A transformer rated over 600 volts with a secondary rated over 600 volts with six circuit breakers protecting the secondary of the transformer. The sum of the ratings of the circuit breakers is not permitted to exceed 300 percent of the rated secondary current.*

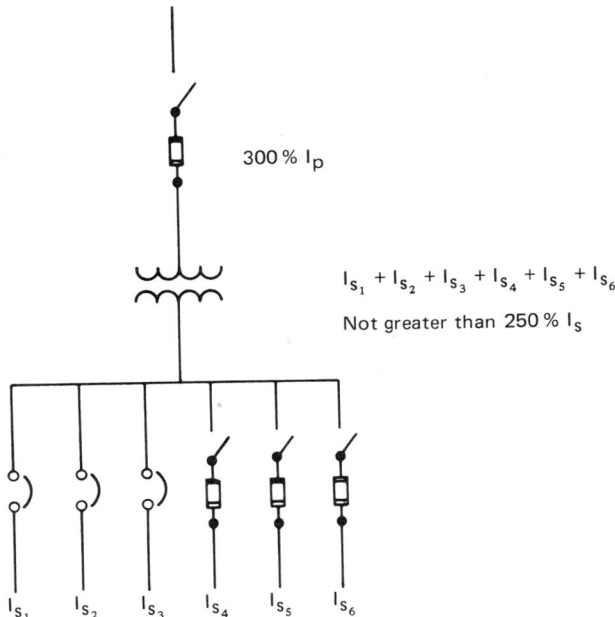

Figure 450-1(c). *A transformer rated over 600 volts with a secondary rated over 600 volts. Secondary protection consists of fuses and circuit breakers. The sum of the ratings of all of the overcurrent devices protecting the secondary of the transformer is not permitted to exceed the rating permitted for fuses.*

Exception No. 2 permits the use of a fuse or circuit breaker set at 250 percent where certain conditions of monitoring and maintenance are met.

a. Primary. Each transformer over 600 volts, nominal, shall be protected by an individual overcurrent device on the primary side. Where fuses are used, their continuous current rating shall not exceed 250 percent of the rated primary current of the transformer. Where circuit breakers or electronically-actuated fuses are used, they shall be set at not more than 300 percent of the rated primary current of the transformer.

Exception No. 1: Where the required fuse rating or circuit breaker setting does not correspond to a standard rating or setting, the next higher standard rating or setting shall be permitted.

Exception No. 2: An individual overcurrent device shall not be required where the primary circuit overcurrent device provides the protection specified in this section.

Exception No. 3: As provided in (a)(2)b below:

Table 450-3(a)(1). Transformers Over 600 Volts

	Maximum Rating or Setting for Overcurrent Device					
	Primary			Secondary		
	Over 600 Volts			Over 600 Volts		600 Volts or Below
Transformer Rated Impedance	Circuit Breaker Setting	Fuse Rating		Circuit Breaker Setting	Fuse Rating	Circuit Breaker Setting or Fuse Rating
Not more than 6%	600%	300%		300%	250%	125%
More than 6% and not more than 10%	400%	300%		250%	225%	125%

Table 450-3(a)(2)b. Transformers Over 600 Volts in Supervised Locations

	Maximum Rating or Setting for Overcurrent Device					
	Primary			Secondary		
	Over 600 Volts			Over 600 Volts		600 Volts or Below
Transformer Rated Impedance	Circuit Breaker Setting	Fuse Rating		Circuit Breaker Setting	Fuse Rating	Circuit Breaker Setting or Fuse Rating
Not more than 6%	600%	300%		300%	250%	250%
More than 6% and not more than 10%	400%	300%		250%	225%	250%

b. Primary and Secondary. A transformer over 600 volts, nominal, having an overcurrent device on the secondary side rated or set to open at not more than the values noted in Table 450-3(a)(2)b, or a transformer equipped with a coordinated thermal overload protection by the manufacturer, shall not be required to have an individual overcurrent device in the primary connection, provided the primary feeder overcurrent device is rated or set to open at not more than the values noted in Table 450-3(a)(2)b.

(b) Transformers 600 Volts, Nominal, or Less. Overcurrent protection of transformers rated 600 volts, nominal, or less, shall comply with (1) or (2) below.

(1) Primary. Each transformer 600 volts, nominal, or less, shall be protected by an individual overcurrent device on the primary side, rated or set at not more than 125 percent of the rated primary current of the transformer.

Exception No. 1: Where the rated primary current of a transformer is 9 amperes or more and 125 percent of this current does not correspond to a standard rating of a fuse or nonadjustable circuit breaker, the next higher standard rating described in Section 240-6 shall be permitted. Where the rated primary current is less than 9 amperes, an overcurrent device rated or set at not more than 167 percent of the primary current shall be permitted.

Where the rated primary current is less than 2 amperes, an overcurrent device rated or set at not more than 300 percent shall be permitted.

Exception No. 2: An individual overcurrent device shall not be required where the primary circuit overcurrent device provides the protection specified in this section.

Exception No. 3: As provided in (b)(2) below.

(2) Primary and Secondary. A transformer 600 volts, nominal, or less, having an overcurrent device on the secondary side rated or set at not more than 125 percent of the rated secondary current of the transformer shall not be required to have an individual overcurrent device on the primary side if the primary feeder overcurrent device is rated or set at a current value not more than 250 percent of the rated primary current of the transformer.

A transformer 600 volts, nominal, or less, equipped with coordinated thermal overload protection by the manufacturer and arranged to interrupt the primary current, shall not be required to have an individual overcurrent device on the primary side if the primary feeder overcurrent device is rated or set at a current value not more than six times the rated current of the transformer for transformers having not more than 6 percent impedance, and not more than four times the rated current of the transformer for transformers having more than 6 percent but not more than 10 percent impedance.

Exception: Where the rated secondary current of a transformer is 9 amperes or more and 125 percent of this current does not correspond to a standard rating of a fuse or nonadjustable circuit breaker, the next higher standard rating described in Section 240-6 shall be permitted.

Where the rated secondary current is less than 9 amperes, an overcurrent device rated or set at not more than 167 percent of the rated secondary current shall be permitted.

(c) Voltage Transformers. Voltage transformers installed indoors or enclosed shall be protected with primary fuses.

Questions frequently arise as to whether the overcurrent protection required for transformers, as specified in Section 450-3, will provide satisfactory protection for the primary and secondary conductors. Where polyphase transformers are involved, primary and secondary conductors will usually not be properly protected. The rules in Section 450-3 are intended to protect the transformer alone. The primary overcurrent device provides short-circuit protection for the primary conductors and a degree of overload protection for the transformer, and secondary overcurrent devices prevent the transformer and secondary conductors from being overloaded. The transformer is considered the point of supply, and the conductors that it supplies are required to be protected in accordance with their ampacity.

Exceptions to this rule are permitted under special conditions outlined in Sections 230-207 and 240-21. See Figures 230-22 and 240-8. See also commentary following Section 450-3, FPN No. 2.

Single-phase transformers having a 2-wire (single voltage) secondary are not required to have a secondary conductor overcurrent protective device if the primary transformer overcurrent protection is provided in accordance with this section, and its rating does not exceed the value determined by multiplying the secondary conductor ampacity by the secondary-to-primary voltage ratio. See commentary following Section 240-3(i). Single-phase transformers with a 3-wire secondary are not included in Section 240-3(i) because of the possibility of a severe unbalanced load that the primary transformer protection would not recognize.

In those cases in which the primary feeder to the transformer incorporates overcurrent protective devices that are rated (or set) at a level not to exceed those prescribed herein, it is not necessary to duplicate them at the transformer.

(FPN): For protection of instrument circuits including voltage transformers, see Section 384-32.

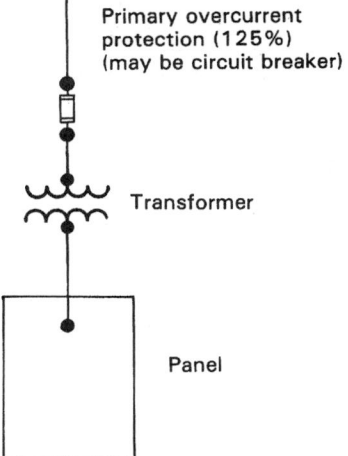

Primary overcurrent protection (125%) (may be circuit breaker)

Transformer

Panel

Figure 450-2. Transformers of 600 V or less are required to be protected by an individual overcurrent device on the primary side. Exceptions to the basic rule are given in Section 450-3(b)(1).

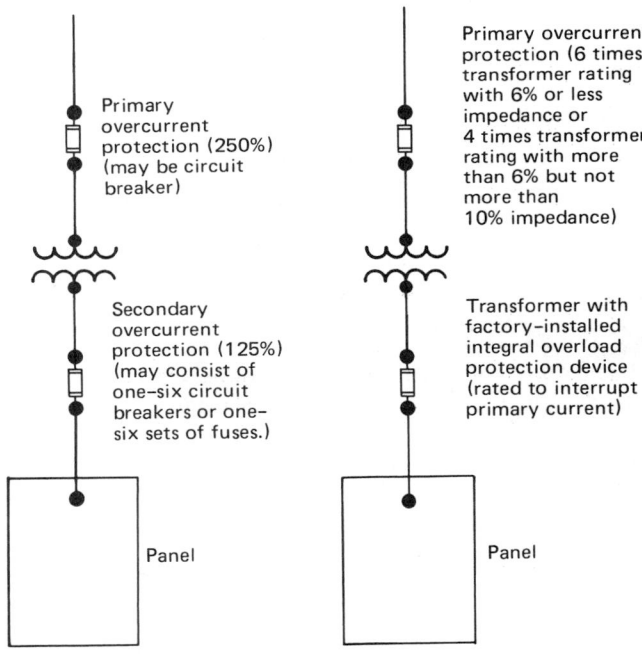

Primary overcurrent protection (250%) (may be circuit breaker)

Secondary overcurrent protection (125%) (may consist of one–six circuit breakers or one–six sets of fuses.)

Panel

Primary overcurrent protection (6 times transformer rating with 6% or less impedance or 4 times transformer rating with more than 6% but not more than 10% impedance)

Transformer with factory–installed integral overload protection device (rated to interrupt primary current)

Panel

Figure 450-3. Overcurrent protection on the primary and secondary sides of transformers rated 600 V or less. Exceptions to the basic rule are given in Section 450-3(b)(2).

(d) Fire Pump Installations. Where the transformer is dedicated to supplying power to a fire pump installation, it shall not require secondary overcurrent protection. Primary overcurrent protection shall be provided in accordance with Section 450-3(a) or 450-3(b). The primary rating or setting shall be sufficient to carry the equivalent of the transformer secondary current sum of the locked-rotor currents of the fire pump motor(s) and associated fire pump accessory equipment indefinitely.

Figure 450-4. *The overcurrent protective device for a transformer supplying a fire pump installation is required to be sized to carry indefinitely the locked rotor current of the fire pump motors and associated fire pump accessory equipment. This may require the transformer to be increased in size.*

450-4. Autotransformers 600 Volts, Nominal, or Less.

(a) **Overcurrent Protection.** Each autotransformer 600 volts, nominal, or less, shall be protected by an individual overcurrent device installed in series with each ungrounded input conductor. Such overcurrent device shall be rated or set at not more than 125 percent of the rated full-load input current of the autotransformer. An overcurrent device shall not be installed in series with the shunt winding (the winding common to both the input and the output circuits) of the autotransformer between Points A and B as shown in Diagram 450-4.

Because of the voltage feed-back problem that may occur, an overcurrent device is not permitted between Points A and B in Diagram 450-4, even though use of an overcurrent device in this part of the circuit would provide closer protection of the transformer windings.

Refer to Figure 450-5, which shows a two-winding, single-phase transformer connected to boost a 208-V supply to 240 V. It is provided with single-pole overcurrent devices in the supply. If an overcurrent device were located between points A and B (OC-2), and this overcurrent device opened, the full 208-V supply voltage would be applied across the 32-V secondary winding in series with the load. Under these conditions, a higher than normal voltage would appear across the primary winding. If the load impedance were very low, this voltage could approach $208/32 \times 208 = 1352$ V.

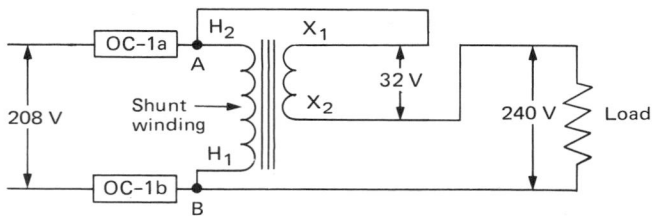

Figure 450-5. *An overcurrent device in series with shunt winding of autotransformer is not permitted by Section 450-4(a).*

Diagram 450-4

Exception: Where the rated input current of an autotransformer is 9 amperes or more and 125 percent of this current does not correspond to a standard rating of a fuse or nonadjustable circuit breaker, the next higher standard rating described in Section 240-6 shall be permitted. Where the rated input current is less than 9 amperes, an overcurrent device rated or set at not more than 167 percent of the input current shall be permitted.

(b) Transformer Field-Connected as an Autotransformer. A transformer field-connected as an autotransformer shall be identified for use at elevated voltage.

This requirement is necessary because of the dielectric voltage withstand test requirements applied to transformers. The test is conducted at 2,500 volts for windings rated 250 V or less, and 4,000 V for higher rated windings. A transformer intended for buck or boost operation would require that the test for the low-voltage winding be based on the sum of the primary and secondary voltage ratings.

(FPN): For information on permitted uses of autotransformers, see Section 210-9.

450-5. Grounding Autotransformers. Grounding autotransformers covered in this section are zig-zag or T-connected transformers connected to 3-phase, 3-wire ungrounded systems for the purpose of creating a 3-phase, 4-wire distribution system or to provide a neutral reference for grounding purposes. Such transformers shall have a continuous per phase current rating and a continuous neutral current rating.

(FPN): The phase current in a grounding autotransformer is one-third the neutral current.

(a) Three-Phase, 4-Wire System. A grounding autotransformer used to create a 3-phase, 4-wire distribution system from a 3-phase, 3-wire ungrounded system shall conform to the following:

(1) **Connections.** The transformer shall be directly connected to the ungrounded phase conductors and shall not be switched or provided with overcurrent protection that is independent of the main switch and common-trip overcurrent protection for the 3-phase, 4-wire system.

(2) **Overcurrent Protection.** An overcurrent sensing device shall be provided that will cause the main switch or common-trip overcurrent protection referred to in (a)(1) above to open if the load on the autotransformer reaches or exceeds 125 percent of its continuous current per phase or neutral rating. Delayed tripping for temporary overcurrents sensed at the autotransformer overcurrent device shall be permitted for

the purpose of allowing proper operation of branch or feeder protective devices on the 4-wire system.

(3) **Transformer Fault Sensing.** A fault sensing system that will cause the opening of a main switch or common-trip overcurrent device for the 3-phase, 4-wire system shall be provided to guard against single-phasing or internal faults.

(FPN): This can be accomplished by the use of two subtractive-connected donut-type current transformers installed to sense and signal when an unbalance occurs in the line current to the autotransformer of 50 percent or more of rated current.

(4) **Rating.** The autotransformer shall have a continuous neutral current rating sufficient to handle the maximum possible neutral unbalanced load current of the 4-wire system.

The donut-type current transformers shown as CT-1, CT-2, and CT-3 in Figure 450-5 are intended to trip the main breaker if the current in any phase or the neutral conductor exceeds 125 percent of the rated current. See Section 450-5(a)(2). The current transformers CT-2 and CT-3 are also differentially connected to protect against an internal failure of the autotransformer. See Section 450-5(a)(3).

Figure 450-5 shows the proper method of protecting a grounding autotransformer where used to provide a neutral for a 3-phase system where necessary to supply a group of single-phase, line-to-neutral loads. Separate overcurrent protection is not provided for the autotransformer because there will be no control of the system line-to-neutral voltages if it becomes disconnected. Consequently, simultaneous interruption of the power supply to all the line-to-neutral loads is necessary whenever the grounding autotransformer is switched off.

CT-1 is connected to an overload relay responsive to excess neutral current being supplied. See Section 450-5(a)(2).

CT-2 and CT-3 are connected to differential-type fault-current sensing relays responsive to an unbalance of neutral current among the three phases of the grounding autotransformer (indicating an internal fault). See Section 450-5(a)(3).

All three relays are required to be arranged to trip the circuit breaker located upstream of both the autotransformer and the line-to-neutral connected loads to satisfy the requirements of Section 450-5(a)(1).

Figure 450-6. A zig-zag autotransformer used to create a 3-phase, 4-wire distribution system or to provide a neutral reference for grounding purposes.

Figure 450-7. Zig-zag autotransformer for establishing a neutral connection for a 480Y/277-V, 3-phase ungrounded system to supply single-phase, line-to-neutral loads. See Section 450-5(a).

The overcurrent protective device is to have a rating (or setting) not in excess of 125 percent of the rated-phase current of the autotransformer (42 percent of the neutral current rating) and not more than 42 percent of the continuous-current rating of the neutral grounding resistor or other current-carrying device in the neutral connection. See Section 450-5(b)(2).

(b) Ground Reference for Fault Protection Devices. A grounding autotransformer used to make available a specified

Figure 450-8. Zig-zag autotransformer for establishing a reference ground-fault current for fault-protective device operation or for damping transitory overvoltage surges. See Section 450-5(b) and (c).

magnitude of ground-fault current for operation of a ground responsive protective device on a 3-phase, 3-wire ungrounded system shall conform to the following requirements:

(1) Rating. The autotransformer shall have a continuous neutral current rating sufficient for the specified ground-fault current.

(2) Overcurrent Protection. An overcurrent protective device of adequate short-circuit rating that will open simultaneously all ungrounded conductors when it operates shall be applied in the grounding autotransformer branch circuit and rated or set at a current not exceeding 125 percent of the autotransformer continuous per phase current rating or 42 percent of the continuous current rating of any series connected devices in the autotransformer neutral connection. Delayed tripping for temporary overcurrents to permit the proper operation of ground responsive tripping devices on the main system shall be permitted, but shall not exceed values that would be more than the short-time current rating of the grounding autotransformer or any series connected devices in the neutral connection thereto.

(c) Ground Reference for Damping Transitory Overvoltages. A grounding autotransformer used to limit transitory overvoltages shall be of suitable rating and connected in accordance with (a)(1) above.

For installations involving a high-resistance grounding package, the functional performance of the installation parallels that described in Section 450-5(b), differing only in that the magnitude of available ground-fault current would likely be a lower value. It would be appropriate to employ the connections displayed in Figure 450-6, and conform with the overcurrent protection requirements prescribed in Section 450-5(b)(2).

With any of the grounding autotransformer applications covered by Sections 450-5(a), (b), or (c), it is important to emphasize the use of a ganged, 3-pole switching interrupter for connecting and disconnecting the autotransformer in order to accomplish simultaneous connection (and disconnection) of the three line terminals. If, at any time, one or two of the line connections to the autotransformer should open, which could occur if the protective devices were single-pole, the grounding autotransformer would cease to function in the desired fashion and would act as a high-inductive-reactance connection between the electrical system and ground. The latter connection is prone to create high-value transitory overvoltages, line-to-ground.

450-6. **Secondary Ties.** A secondary tie is a circuit operating at 600 volts, nominal, or less, between phases that connects two power sources or power supply points, such as the secondaries of two transformers. The tie shall be permitted to consist of one or more conductors per phase.

As used in this section, the word "transformer" means a transformer or a bank of transformers operating as a unit.

(a) Tie Circuits. Tie circuits shall be provided with overcurrent protection at each end as required in Article 240.

Exception: Under the conditions described in (a)(1) and (a)(2) below, the overcurrent protection shall be permitted to be in accordance with (a)(3) below.

(1) Loads at Transformer Supply Points Only. Where all loads are connected at the transformer supply points at each end of the tie and overcurrent protection is not provided in accordance with Article 240, the rated ampacity of the tie shall not be less than 67 percent of the rated secondary current of the largest transformer connected to the secondary tie system.

(2) Loads Connected Between Transformer Supply Points. Where load is connected to the tie at any point between transformer supply points and overcurrent protection is not provided in accordance with Article 240, the rated ampacity of the tie shall not be less than 100 percent of the rated secondary current of the largest transformer connected to the secondary tie system.

Exception: As otherwise provided in (a)(4) below.

(3) Tie Circuit Protection. Under the conditions described in (a)(1) and (a)(2) above, both ends of each tie conductor shall be equipped with a protective device that will open at a predetermined temperature of the tie conductor under short-circuit conditions. This protection shall consist of one of the following: (1) a fusible link cable connector, terminal, or lug, commonly known as a limiter, each being of a size corresponding with that of the conductor and of construction and characteristics according to the operating voltage and the type of insulation on the tie conductors or (2) automatic circuit breakers actuated by devices having comparable current-time characteristics.

(4) Interconnection of Phase Conductors Between Transformer Supply Points. Where the tie consists of more than one conductor per phase, the conductors of each phase shall be interconnected in order to establish a load supply point, and the protection specified in (a)(3) above shall be provided in each tie conductor at this point.

Exception: Loads shall be permitted to be connected to the individual conductors of a paralleled conductor tie without interconnecting the conductors of each phase and without the protection specified in (a)(3) above at load connection points, provided the tie conductors of each phase have a combined capacity of not less than 133 percent of the rated secondary current of the largest transformer connected to the secondary tie system; the total load of such taps does not exceed the rated secondary current of the largest transformer; and the loads are equally divided on each phase and on the individual conductors of each phase as far as practicable.

(5) Tie Circuit Control. Where the operating voltage exceeds 150 volts to ground, secondary ties provided with limiters shall have a switch at each end that, when open, will deenergize the associated tie conductors and limiters. The current rating of the switch shall not be less than the rated current of the conductors connected to the switch. It shall be capable of opening its rated current, and it shall be constructed so that it will not open under the magnetic forces resulting from short-circuit current.

(b) Overcurrent Protection for Secondary Connections. Where secondary ties are used, an overcurrent device rated or set at not more than 250 percent of the rated secondary current of the transformers shall be provided in the secondary connections of each transformer. In addition, an automatic circuit breaker actuated by a reverse-current relay set to open the circuit at not more than the rated secondary current of the transformer shall be provided in the secondary connection of each transformer.

The requirements of Section 450-6 apply specifically to network systems for power distribution that are commonly employed where the load density is high and reliability of service is important. Such a system is illustrated in Figure 450-9. This type of distribution system introduces a variety of problems not encountered in the more common radial-type distribution system and must be designed by experienced electrical engineers. The sketch shows a typical 3-phase network system for an industrial plant fed by two primary feeders, preferably from separate substations, that are energized at any standard voltage up to 34,500 V. Each of the transformers is supplied by the two primary feeders that are arranged by means of a double-throw switch at the transformer so that it may be supplied by either feeder.

Each of the network transformers is rated in the range of 300 kVA to 1,000 kVA and is required to be protected as illustrated in Figure 450-10. The primary and secondary protection is in accordance with Section 450-3, but an additional protective device is also required to be provided on the secondary side. This protective device is known as a network protector, consisting of a circuit breaker and a reverse-power relay. This operates on reverse current to prevent power from being fed back into the transformer through the secondary ties should a fault occur in the transformer or in a primary feeder. The reverse-power relay is set to trip the circuit breaker at a current value not more than the rated secondary current of the transformer. The relay is not designed to trip the circuit breaker in the event of an overload on the secondary of the transformer.

The secondary ties shown in Figure 450-9 are required to be protected at each end with an overcurrent device, in accordance with Section 450-6(a)(3). The overcurrent device most commonly provided for this purpose is a special type of fuse known as a current limiter. See Figure 450-11. This is a high-interrupting capacity device designed to provide short-circuit protection only for the secondary ties and will open safely before temperatures damaging to the cable insulation are reached. See Section 240-11 for definition of

"Current-Limiting Overcurrent Protective Device." See also commentary following Section 240-11. The secondary ties form a closed loop that is equipped with switching devices, so that any part of the loop may be isolated when repairs are needed or a current limiter must be replaced.

450-7. **Parallel Operation.** Transformers shall be permitted to be operated in parallel and switched as a unit provided that the overcurrent protection for each transformer meets the requirements of Section 450-3 (a)(1) or (b)(2).

450-8. **Guarding.** Transformers shall be guarded as specified in (a) through (d) below.

(a) **Mechanical Protection.** Appropriate provisions shall be made to minimize the possibility of damage to transformers from external causes where the transformers are exposed to physical damage.

One way of providing mechanical protection is to use 3-inch to 4-inch inside diameter vertical steel pipes embedded in the ground and filled with concrete. This method can be used where transformers may otherwise be subjected to damage by vehicles.

(b) **Case or Enclosure.** Dry-type transformers shall be provided with a noncombustible moisture-resistant case or enclosure that will provide reasonable protection against the accidental insertion of foreign objects.

(c) **Exposed Energized Parts.** Switches or other equipment operating at 600 volts, nominal, or less, and serving only equipment within a transformer enclosure shall be permitted to be installed in the transformer enclosure if accessible to qualified persons only. All energized parts shall be guarded in accordance with Sections 110-17 and 110-34.

(d) **Voltage Warning.** The operating voltage of exposed live parts of transformer installations shall be indicated by signs or visible markings on the equipment or structures.

450-9. **Ventilation.** The ventilation shall be adequate to dispose of the transformer full-load losses without creating temperature rise that is in excess of the transformer rating.

This section is intended to clarify that transformers are not permitted to be installed directly against walls or other obstructions that block openings for ventilation. See Section 450-11.

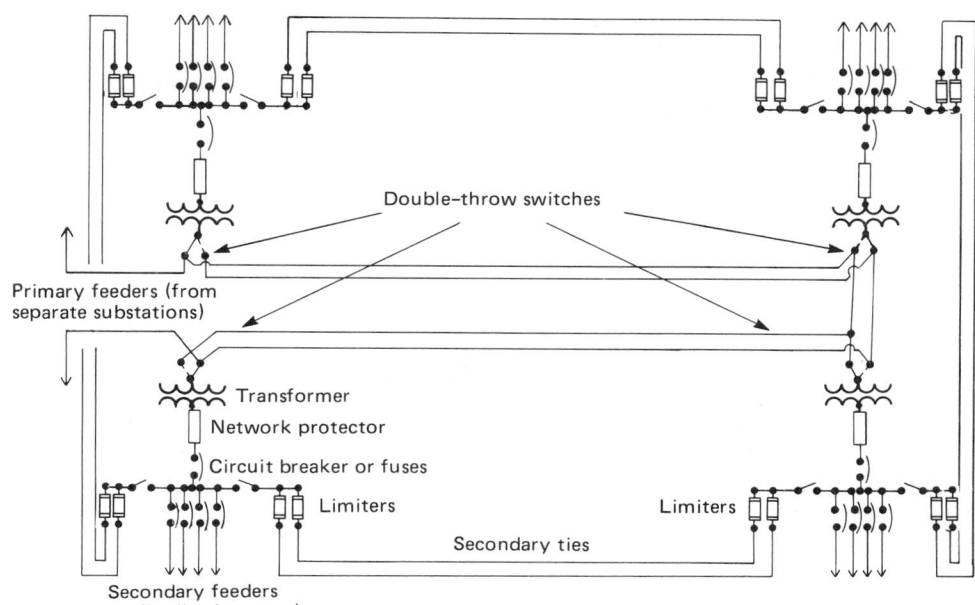

Figure 450-9. *A typical 3-phase network system for an industrial plant fed by two primary feeders.*

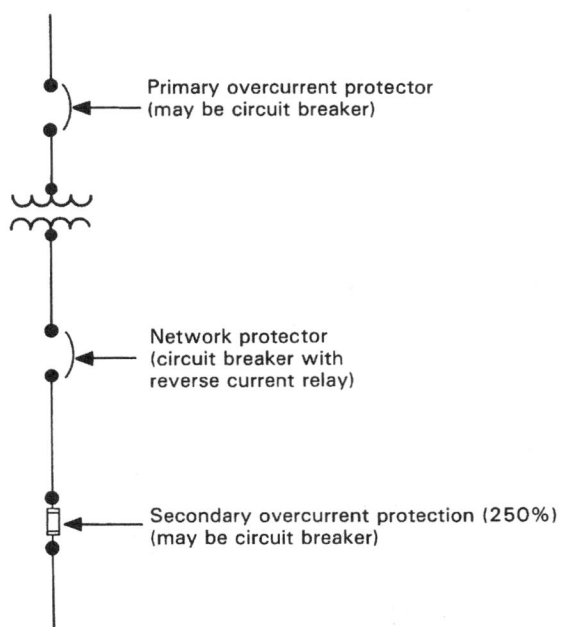

Figure 450-10. *Primary and secondary overcurrent protection for a transformer in a network system showing a network protector (an automatic circuit breaker actuated by a reverse-current relay).*

Figure 450-11. *A current-limiter is a special type of high-interrupting capacity fuse.*

(FPN): See General Requirements for Liquid-Immersed Distribution, Power, and Regulating Transformers, ANSI/IEEE C57.12.00-1987, and General Requirements for Dry-Type Distribution and Power Transformers, ANSI/IEEE C57.12.01-1979.

Transformers with ventilating openings shall be installed so that the ventilating openings are not blocked by walls or other obstructions. The required clearances shall be clearly marked on the transformer.

450-10. **Grounding.** Exposed noncurrent-carrying metal parts of transformer installations, including fences, guards, etc., shall be grounded where required under the conditions and in the manner specified for electric equipment and other exposed metal parts in Article 250.

450-11. **Marking.** Each transformer shall be provided with a nameplate giving the name of the manufacturer; rated kilovolt-amperes; frequency; primary and secondary voltage; impedance of transformers 25 kVA and larger; required clearances for transformers with ventilating openings; and the amount and kind of insulating liquid where used. In addition, the nameplate of each dry-type transformer shall include the temperature class for the insulation system.

The information given on a transformer nameplate is necessary for determining whether the transformer is capable of carrying the load it is supplying as calculated in accordance with Article 220.

450-12. **Terminal Wiring Space.** The minimum wire bending space at fixed, 600 volts and below terminals of transformer line and load connections shall be as required in Section 373-6. Wiring space for pigtail connections shall conform to Table 370-16(b).

This rule is to ensure adequate wire bending space at fixed terminals of transformer line and load connections, rated 600 V or less, as this is a point of maximum mechanical and electrical stress on the conductor insulation. See commentary following Section 370-16.

450-13. **Location.** Transformers and transformer vaults shall be readily accessible to qualified personnel for inspection and maintenance.

Exception No. 1: Dry-type transformers 600 volts, nominal, or less, located in the open on walls, columns, or structures, shall not be required to be readily accessible.

Exception No. 2: Dry-type transformers not exceeding 600 volts, nominal, and 50 kVA shall be permitted in fire-resistant hollow spaces of buildings not permanently closed in by structure and provided they meet the ventilation requirements of Section 450-9.

Unless specified otherwise in this article, the term "fire-resistant" means a construction having a minimum fire rating of 1 hour.

(FPN No. 1): See Method for Fire Tests of Building Construction and Materials, ANSI/ASTM E119-83, and Methods of Fire Tests of Building Construction and Materials, NFPA 251-1990.

(FPN No. 2): The location of different types of transformers is covered in Part B of Article 450. The location of transformer vaults is covered in Section 450-41.

B. Specific Provisions Applicable to Different Types of Transformers

450-21. **Dry-type Transformers Installed Indoors.**

(a) Not Over 112½ kVA. Dry-type transformers installed indoors and rated 112½ kVA or less shall have a separation of at least 12 inches (305 mm) from combustible material.

Exception No. 1: Where separated from the combustible material by a fire-resistant, heat-insulating barrier.

Exception No. 2: Transformers 600 volts, nominal, or less completely enclosed, with or without ventilating openings.

(b) Over 112½ kVA. Individual dry-type transformers of more than 112½ kVA rating shall be installed in a transformer room of fire-resistant construction.

Exception No. 1: Transformers with 80°C rise or higher ratings and separated from combustible material by a fire-resistant, heat-insulating barrier or by not less than 6 feet (1.83 m) horizontally and 12 feet (3.66 m) vertically.

Dry-type transformers with 80°C rise or higher ratings are not required to be installed in transformer rooms or vaults if space separation or a fire-resistant heat insulating barrier is provided. Although these units are designed for higher operating temperatures, the need for a transformer vault is mitigated by the fire-resistant characteristics of high temperature insulations.

Exception No. 2: Transformers with 80°C rise or higher ratings and completely enclosed except for ventilating openings.

(c) Over 35,000 Volts. Dry-type transformers rated over 35,000 volts shall be installed in a vault complying with Part C of this article.

Dry-type transformers depend on the surrounding air for adequate ventilation and where rated 112½ kVA or less are not required to be installed in a fire-resistive transformer room. See Section 450-9.

Transformers of the dry type, or gas-filled or less-flammable liquid-insulated transformers (see Section 450-23), installed indoors with a primary voltage of not more than 35,000 volts are commonly used because a transformer vault is not required.

For the same reason, askarel-filled transformers have been extensively used indoors in the past. Askarel, which contains a polychlorinated biphenyl (PCB), is no longer being manufactured, but acceptable substitutes that comply with Section 450-23 are available. See Figure 450-14.

Figure 450-10 shows a 1,500 kVA, gas-filled, dry-type transformer available in ratings through 5,000 kVA, 34½ kV for use indoors or outdoors. These units are built using the conventional ventilated dry-type core and coils, but sealed in a heavy welded steel tank and filled with fluorocarbon gas for dielectric strength as well as cooling. Since the transformers are completely hermetically sealed in a heavy-gauge steel tank, they are considered safe indoors and outdoors, and there is little likelihood of flames or gases escaping in the event of a short circuit or transformer failure. See Sections 501-2, 502-2, and 503-2 for requirements for transformers in hazardous (classified) locations.

Figure 450-12 shows a dry-type transformer with the outside casing in place and with the latest core and coil design for a typical dry-type power transformer rated at 1,000 kVA, 13,800-V to 480-V, 3-phase, 60 Hz. This transformer has a high-voltage and low-voltage flange for connection to switchgear and a high-voltage, 2-position (double-throw), 3-pole load break-air switch that may be attached to the case and arranged as a selector switch for the connection of the transformer primary to either of two feeder sources.

Dry-type transformers rated 112½ kVA or less require 12 inches of separation from combustible material or separation by fire-resistive barriers. Transformers rated less than 600 V and completely enclosed, except for ventilating openings, are exempt from this requirement unless the manufacturer's installation instructions specify clearance distances.

Noncombustible insulations used in transformers, such as mica, porcelain, and glass, which can withstand high temperatures, have permitted the application of larger dry-type transformers. However, combustible materials, such as varnishes, are used with those insulations, and, under short-circuit conditions, flames can escape from the transformer enclosure. Those transformers rated over 112½ kVA are required to be located in fire-resistive transformer rooms or vaults.

Figure 450-12. 1,500-kVA, gas-filled, dry-type transformer available in ratings through 5,000 kVA, 34½ kVA for use indoors or outdoors. (Westinghouse Electric Corp.)

450-22 . Dry-type Transformers Installed Outdoors. Dry-type transformers installed outdoors shall have a weatherproof enclosure.

Transformers exceeding 112½ kVA shall not be located within 12 inches (305 mm) of combustible materials of buildings.

Exception: Transformers with 80°C rise or higher ratings and completely enclosed except for ventilating openings.

450-23 . Less-Flammable Liquid-Insulated Transformers. Transformers insulated with listed less-flammable liquids shall

Figure 450-13. *A dry-type transformer with a core and coil design rated at 1,000 kVA, 13,800 V to 480 V, 3-phase, 60 Hz. (Westinghouse Electric Corp.)*

be permitted to be installed without a vault in Type I and Type II buildings in areas in which no combustible materials are stored, provided there is a liquid confinement area, the liquid has a fire point of not less than 300°C, and the installation complies with all restrictions provided for in the listing of the liquid. Such indoor transformer installations not meeting the restrictions of the liquid listing, or installed in other than Type I or Type II buildings, or in areas where combustible materials are stored, shall (1) be provided with an automatic fire extinguishing system and a liquid confinement area or (2) be installed in a vault complying with Part C of this article.

Transformers installed indoors and rated over 35,000 volts shall be installed in a vault.

Less-flammable liquid-insulated transformers shall be permitted to be installed outdoors attached to, adjacent to, or on the roof of Type I or Type II buildings.

Such installations attached to, adjacent to, or on the roof of other than Type I or Type II buildings, adjacent to combustible material, fire escapes, or door and window openings, shall be provided with one or more safeguards according to the degree of hazard. Fire barriers, space separation, and compliance with all of the requirements provided for in the listing of the liquid are recognized safeguards.

(FPN No. 1): As used in this section, "noncombustible" refers to Type I and Type II building construction and noncombustible materials as defined in Types of Building Construction, NFPA 220-1992 (ANSI).

NFPA 220 defines Type I building construction as "that type in which the structural members, including walls, columns, beams, floors, and roofs, are of approved noncombustible or limited-combustible materials and have fire resistance ratings not less than those set forth in Table 3."

Type II building construction is defined as "that type not qualifying as Type I construction in which the structural members including walls, columns, beams, floors, and roofs are of approved noncombustible or limited-combustible materials and have fire resistance ratings not less than those set forth in Table 3."

(FPN No. 2): See definition of "Listed" in Article 100.

Two listing agencies, Factory Mutual Research Corp. and Underwriters Laboratories Inc., list less-flammable liquids for transformers. These liquids have a fire point of at least 300°C. This type of transformer may be installed indoors without a vault in buildings of Types I and II construction in areas where no combustible materials are stored provided they are not rated over 35,000 V, there is a liquid confinement area, and the installation complies with all of the limitations provided for in the listing. They are also permitted to be installed outdoors or on the roofs of buildings of Type I or Type II construction. They may be attached to or adjacent to the building. However, all of the provisions of the listing must be complied with. The listing may restrict attachment to the structure or proximity to the structure. See Section 110-3(b).

The Factory Mutual listing is based on a test in which the burning characteristics of the fluid are measured. These characteristics, the radiative and convective heat, may be found in the Factory Mutual Approval Guide. The radiative heat release is the heat exposure to the walls. See Figure 450-14. The convective heat release is the exposure to the ceiling. See Figure 450-15. Application of the heat release criteria is based on the size of the liquid confinement area, the building construction, the ceiling height, and the distance from the confinement area to the walls. Further information on application may be found in the Factory Mutual Loss Prevention Data Sheet 5-4/14-8.

The Underwriters Laboratories Inc. listing is based on UL requirements that no tank rupture or noted fluid leakage occurs during low- and high-current arcing fault tests. Further information may be obtained from the Underwriters Laboratories Inc. Gas and Oil Equipment Directory under Dielectric Mediums (EQUV) or the manufacturer. See also commentary following Section 450-27.

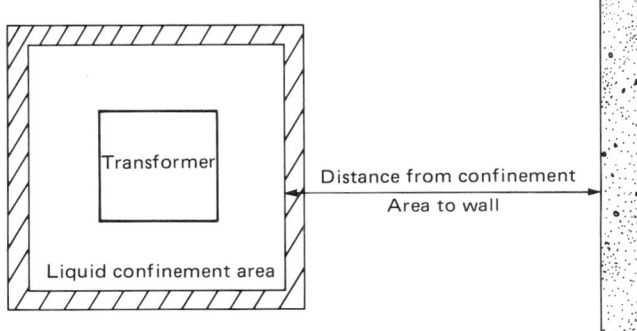

Figure 450-14. The Factory Mutual Research Corp. listing restricts the distance from the liquid confinement area to the wall in which a given fluid may be used based on the radiative heat release rate of the fluid. Radiative heat release is considered as a fire exposure to the wall. See also Figure 450-15.

Figure 450-15. The Factory Mutual Research Corp. listing restricts the minimum ceiling height above the floor of the confinement area in which a given fluid may be used based on its convective heat release rate. Convective heat release is considered as a fire exposure to the ceiling. See also Figure 450-14.

Figure 450-16. A liquid-insulated transformer filled with a listed, less-flammable liquid with a fire point of at least 300°C. (Square D Co.)

450-24. Nonflammable Fluid-Insulated Transformers. Transformers insulated with a dielectric fluid identified as nonflammable shall be permitted to be installed indoors or outdoors. Such transformers installed indoors and rated over 35,000 volts shall be installed in a vault. Such transformers installed indoors shall be furnished with a liquid confinement area and a pressure relief vent. The transformers shall be furnished with a means for absorbing any gases generated by arcing inside the tank, or the pressure relief vent shall be connected to a chimney or flue that will carry such gases to an environmentally safe area.

(FPN): Safety will be increased if fire hazard analyses are performed for such transformer installations.

This section was revised for the 1990 *Code* to require a liquid confinement area and a pressure relief vent. If a means for absorbing gases generated by arcing within the transformer is not provided, the pressure relief vent must be connected to a chimney or flue that vents to an environmentally safe area.

The liquid confinement area is intended to limit the extent of a spill if the tank leaks or ruptures.

The need for a gas absorption system or a chimney or flue that vents to an environmentally safe area is required due to concerns about products generated during arcing. The high arc temperatures may cause the insulating medium to break down resulting in the evolution of toxic or corrosive compounds.

For the purposes of this section, a nonflammable dielectric fluid is one that does not have a flash point or fire point, and is not flammable in air.

450-25. **Askarel-Insulated Transformers Installed Indoors.** Askarel-insulated transformers installed indoors and rated over 25 kVA shall be furnished with a pressure-relief vent. Where installed in a poorly ventilated place, they shall be furnished with a means for absorbing any gases generated by arcing inside the case, or the pressure-relief vent shall be connected to a chimney or flue that will carry such gases outside the building. Askarel-insulated transformers rated over 35,000 volts shall be installed in a vault.

450-26. **Oil-Insulated Transformers Installed Indoors.** Oil-insulated transformers installed indoors shall be installed in a vault constructed as specified in Part C of this article.

Exception No. 1: Where the total capacity does not exceed 112½ kVA, the vault specified in Part C of this article shall be permitted to be constructed of reinforced concrete not less than 4 inches (102 mm) thick.

Exception No. 2: Where the nominal voltage does not exceed 600, a vault shall not be required if suitable arrangements are made to prevent a transformer oil fire from igniting other materials, and the total capacity in one location does not exceed 10 kVA in a section of the building classified as combustible, or 75 kVA where the surrounding structure is classified as fire-resistant construction.

Exception No. 3: Electric furnace transformers having a total rating not exceeding 75 kVA shall be permitted to be installed without a vault in a building or room of fire-resistant construction, provided suitable arrangements are made to prevent a transformer oil fire from spreading to other combustible material.

Exception No. 4: Transformers shall be permitted to be installed in a detached building that does not comply with Part C of this article if neither the building nor its contents presents a fire

hazard to any other building or property, and if the building is used only in supplying electric service and the interior is accessible only to qualified persons.

Exception No. 5: Oil-insulated transformers shall be permitted to be used without a vault in portable and mobile surface mining equipment (such as electric excavators) if each of the following conditions is met:

a. Provision is made for draining leaking fluid to the ground.

b. Safe egress is provided for personnel.

c. A minimum ¼-inch (6.35-mm) steel barrier is provided for personnel protection.

450-27. **Oil-Insulated Transformers Installed Outdoors.** Combustible material, combustible buildings, and parts of buildings, fire escapes, and door and window openings shall be safeguarded from fires originating in oil-insulated transformers installed on roofs, attached to, or adjacent to a building or combustible material.

Space separations, fire-resistant barriers, automatic water spray systems, and enclosures that confine the oil of a ruptured transformer tank are recognized safeguards. One or more of these safeguards shall be applied according to the degree of hazard involved in cases where the transformer installation presents a fire hazard.

Oil enclosures shall be permitted to consist of fire-resistant dikes, curbed areas or basins, or trenches filled with coarse, crushed stone. Oil enclosures shall be provided with trapped drains where the exposure and the quantity of oil involved are such that removal of oil is important.

(FPN): For additional information on transformers installed on poles or structures or underground, see National Electrical Safety Code, ANSI C2-1990.

450-28. **Modification of Transformers.** When modifications are made to a transformer in an existing installation that change the type of the transformer with respect to Part B of this article, such transformer shall be marked to show the type of insulating liquid installed, and the modified transformer installation shall comply with the applicable requirements for that type of transformer.

Many askarel-insulated transformers are being modified by replacing the askarel with either oil or a less-flammable liquid. Where such a modification takes place, the completed media and the size of the transformer. Transformers insulated with mineral oil have the greatest need for passive protection to prevent the spread of burning oil to other combustible materials.

This section was revised for the 1990 *Code* to prohibit the use of studs and wallboard construction, even though it is possible to construct a 3-hour fire wall of these materials. It is believed that such a wall would not have adequate structural integrity during a burning oil fire.

There is less of a need for a vault around a dry-type transformer of less than 35,000 V. If the transformer has adequate clearance from combustible construction and storage, a fire would be confined to the transformer. See Section 450-21.

Askarel-insulated transformers of less than 35,000 V do not require vaults since askarel is considered a noncombustible fluid. Transformers with a listed less-flammable liquid insulation may be installed without a vault where they are in compliance with all of the restrictions of the listing. See commentary following Section 450-23.

(FPN No. 1):   For additional information, see Method for Fire Tests of Building Construction and Materials, ANSI/ASTM E119-83, and Methods of Fire Tests of Building Construction and Materials, NFPA 251-1990.

(FPN No. 2):   Six-inch (152-mm) thick reinforced concrete is a typical 3-hour construction.

Exception: Where transformers are protected with automatic sprinkler, water spray, carbon dioxide, or halon, construction of 1-hour rating shall be permitted.

450-43. Doorways. Vault doorways shall be protected as follows:

(a) **Type of Door.** Each doorway leading into a vault from the building interior shall be provided with a tight-fitting door having a minimum fire rating of 3 hours. The authority having jurisdiction shall be permitted to require such a door for an exterior wall opening where conditions warrant.

Exception: Where transformers are protected with automatic sprinkler, water spray, carbon dioxide, or halon, construction of 1-hour rating shall be permitted.

(FPN):   For additional information, see Fire Doors and Fire Windows, NFPA 80-1992 (ANSI).

Formal Interpretation 81-2
Reference: Sections 450-23 and 450-27

Question 1: Is it the intent of the 1981 *National Electrical Code* to consider a high fire point liquid as described in Section 450-23 a substitute for any of the fire safeguards described in Section 450-27?

Answer: No.

Question 2: Is it the intent of the 1981 *National Electrical Code* that a high fire point liquid-insulated transformer have one or more of the fire safeguards described in Section 450-27 if the installation (i.e. location) of the transformer presents a fire hazard?

Answer: Yes.

Issue Edition: 1981
Date: June 1981 ∎

---

installation is required to have the same degree of safety as a new installation. For example, replacement of askarel with oil in an indoor installation without a vault may not be acceptable. See Section 450-26 and exceptions. If the replacement liquid is a less-flammable liquid, see Section 450-23.

C. Transformer Vaults

450-41. Location. Vaults shall be located where they can be ventilated to the outside air without using flues or ducts wherever such an arrangement is practicable.

450-42. Walls, Roof, and Floor. The walls and roofs of vaults shall be constructed of materials that have adequate structural strength for the conditions with a minimum fire resistance of 3 hours. The floors of vaults in contact with the earth shall be of concrete not less than 4 inches (102 mm) thick, but where the vault is constructed with a vacant space or other stories below it, the floor shall have adequate structural strength for the load imposed thereon and a minimum fire resistance of 3 hours. For the purposes of this section, studs and wall board construction shall not be acceptable.

Vaults are intended primarily as passive fire protection. The need is dictated by the combustibility of the dielectric

(b) Sills. A door sill or curb of sufficient height to confine within the vault the oil from the largest transformer shall be provided, and in no case shall the height be less than 4 inches (102 mm).

(c) Locks. Doors shall be equipped with locks, and doors shall be kept locked, access being allowed only to qualified persons. Personnel doors shall swing out and be equipped with panic bars, pressure plates, or other devices that are normally latched but open under simple pressure.

This section was revised for the 1990 *Code* to prohibit the use of conventional rotation-type door knobs on transformer vault doors. It is believed that an injured worker attempting to escape from a transformer vault may not be able to operate a rotating-type door knob but would be able to operate panic-type door hardware.

450-45. **Ventilation Openings.** Where required by Section 450-9, openings for ventilation shall be provided in accordance with (a) through (f) below.

(a) Location. Ventilation openings shall be located as far away as possible from doors, windows, fire escapes, and combustible material.

(b) Arrangement. A vault ventilated by natural circulation of air shall be permitted to have roughly half of the total area of openings required for ventilation in one or more openings near the floor and the remainder in one or more openings in the roof or in the sidewalls near the roof, or all of the area required for ventilation shall be permitted in one or more openings in or near the roof.

(c) Size. For a vault ventilated by natural circulation of air to an outdoor area, the combined net area of all ventilating openings, after deducting the area occupied by screens, gratings, or louvers, shall not be less than 3 square inches (1936 sq mm) per kVA of transformer capacity in service, and in no case shall the net area be less than 1 square foot (0.093 sq m) for any capacity under 50 kVA.

(d) Covering. Ventilation openings shall be covered with durable gratings, screens, or louvers, according to the treatment required in order to avoid unsafe conditions.

(e) Dampers. All ventilation openings to the indoors shall be provided with automatic closing fire dampers that operate in response to a vault fire. Such dampers shall possess a standard fire rating of not less than 1½ hours.

(FPN): See Standard for Fire Dampers, ANSI/UL 555-1972.

(f) Ducts. Ventilating ducts shall be constructed of fire-resistant material.

450-46. **Drainage.** Where practicable, vaults containing more than 100 kVA transformer capacity shall be provided with a drain or other means that will carry off any accumulation of oil or water in the vault unless local conditions make this impracticable. The floor shall be pitched to the drain where provided.

450-47. **Water Pipes and Accessories.** Any pipe or duct system foreign to the electrical installation shall not enter or pass through a transformer vault. Piping or other facilities provided for vault fire protection, or for transformer cooling, shall not be considered foreign to the electrical installation.

This section permits automatic sprinkler protection for transformer vaults. Piping or ductwork for cooling of the transformer is also permitted to be installed in a transformer vault. No other piping or ductwork is permitted to enter or pass through a transformer vault.

450-48. **Storage in Vaults.** Materials shall not be stored in transformer vaults.

ARTICLE 455   Phase Converters

Contents

A. General

B. Specific Provisions Applicable to Different Types of Phase Converters.

455-20. Disconnecting Means.
455-21. Start-Up.
455-22. Power Interruption.
455-23. Capacitors.

A. General

455-1. **Scope.** This article covers the installation and use of phase converters.

Requirements for phase converters have been relocated from Article 430 to Article 455 for the 1993 *Code*. A phase converter is an electrical device that converts single-phase electrical power to three-phase for the operation of equipment that normally operates from a three-phase electrical supply. Phase converters are of two types: (1) static with no moving parts, and (2) rotary with an internal rotor that is required to be rotating before load is applied. See Section 430-19 for the definition. See also commentary following Section 430-86.

Phase converters are most commonly used to supply three-phase motor loads in locations where only single-phase power is available from the local utility. Electrical installations on farms and in other rural areas are examples of such locations. Although the most common loads for phase converters are motors, they are being used increasingly to supply such loads as cellular telephone transmitter sites.

455-2. **Definition.** A phase converter is an electrical device that converts single-phase power to 3-phase electrical power. Phase converters are of two types: static and rotary.

(FPN): Phase converters have characteristics that modify the starting torque and locked-rotor current of motors served, and consideration is required in selecting a phase converter for a specific load.

455-3. **Other Articles.** All requirements of this Code shall apply to phase converters except as amended by this article.

455-4. **Marking.** Each phase converter shall be provided with a permanent nameplate indicating (1) manufacturer's name; (2) rated input and output voltages; (3) frequency; (4) rated single-phase input full-load amperes; (5) rated minimum and maximum single load in kVA or horsepower; and (6) maximum total load in kVA or horsepower.

455-5. **Equipment Grounding Connection.** A means for attachment of an equipment grounding conductor termination in accordance with Section 250-113 shall be provided.

455-6. **Conductor Ampacity.** The ampacity of the single-phase supply conductors shall not be less than 125 percent of the phase converter nameplate single-phase input full-load amperes.

Exception: Where the phase converter supplies specific fixed loads, the conductors shall have an ampacity not less than 250 percent of the sum of the full-load, 3-phase current rating of the motors and other loads served where the input and output voltages of the phase converter are identical.

Where the input and output voltages of the phase converter are different, the current as determined by this section shall be multiplied by the ratio of output to input voltage.

(FPN): Single-phase conductors sized to prevent a voltage drop not exceding 3 percent from the source of supply to the phase converter will help ensure proper starting and operation of motor loads.

455-7. **Overcurrent Protection.** The single-phase supply conductor and phase converter shall be protected from overcurrent at not more than 125 percent of the phase converter nameplate single-phase input full-load amperes.

Exception No. 1: Where the phase converter supplies specific fixed loads, the overcurrent protection shall have a rating not greater than 250 percent of the sum of the full-load, 3-phase current rating of the motors and other loads served where the input and output voltages of the phase converter are identical.

Where the input and output voltages of the phase converter are different, the current as determined by this section shall be multiplied by the ratio of output to input voltage.

Exception No. 2: Where the required fuse rating or circuit breaker setting does not correspond to a standard rating or setting, the next higher standard rating or setting shall be permitted.

455-8. **Disconnecting Means.** Means shall be provided to disconnect simultaneously all ungrounded single-phase supply conductors to the phase converter.

(a) Location. The disconnecting means shall be readily accessible and located in sight from the phase converter.

(b) Type. The disconnecting means shall be a switch rated in horsepower, a circuit breaker, or a molded-case switch.

Exception: Where only nonmotor loads are served, an ampere-rated switch shall be permitted.

(c) Rating. The ampere rating of the disconnecting means shall not be less than 115 percent of the rated maximum single-phase input full-load amperes.

Exception No. 1: Where the phase converter supplies specific fixed loads, and the input and output voltages of the phase converter are identical, the disconnecting means shall be permitted to be a circuit breaker or molded-case switch with an ampere rating not less than 250 percent of the sum of the following:

a. Full-load 3-phase current ratings of the motors, and
b. Other loads served.

Where the input and output voltages of the phase converter are different, the current shall be multiplied by the ratio of the output to input voltage.

Exception No. 2: Where the phase converter supplies specific fixed loads, and the input and output voltages of the phase converter are identical, the disconnecting means shall be permitted to be a switch with a horsepower rating. The horsepower rating shall be equivalent to 200 percent of the sum of the following:

a. Nonmotor loads,
b. The 3-phase locked-rotor current of the largest motor as determined from Table 430-151, and
c. The full-load current of all other 3-phase motors operating at the same time.

Where the input and output voltages of the phase converter are different, the current shall be multiplied by the ratio of the output to input voltage.

455-9. **Connection of Single-Phase Loads.** Where single-phase loads are connected on the load side of a phase converter, they shall not be connected to the derived phase.

455-10. **Terminal Housings.** A terminal housing shall be provided on a phase converter, and the terminal housing shall be in accordance with the provisions of Section 430-12.

B. Specific Provisions Applicable to Different Types of Phase Converters

455-20. **Disconnecting Means.** The single-phase disconnecting means for the input of a static phase converter shall be permitted to serve as the disconnecting means for the phase converter and a single load if the load is within sight of the disconnecting means.

455-21. **Start-Up.** Power to the utilization equipment shall not be supplied until the rotary phase converter has been started.

455-22. **Power Interruption.** Utilization equipment supplied by a rotary phase converter shall be controlled in such a manner that power to the equipment will be disconnected in the event of a power interruption.

(FPN): Magnetic motor starters, magnetic contactors, and similar devices, with manual or time delay restarting for the load, will provide restarting after power interruption.

455-23. **Capacitors.** Capacitors that are not an integral part of the rotary phase conversion system but are installed for a motor load shall be connected to the line side of that motor overload protective device.

ARTICLE 460 Capacitors

Contents

460-9. Rating or Setting of Motor Overload Device.

460-10. Grounding.

460-12. Marking.

B. Over 600 Volts, Nominal

460-24. Switching.

  (a) Load Current.

  (b) Isolation.

  (c) Additional Requirements for Series Capacitors.

460-25. Overcurrent Protection.

  (a) Provided to Detect and Interrupt Fault Current.

  (b) Single-Phase or Multiphase Devices.

  (c) Protected Individually or in Groups.

  (d) Protective Devices Rated or Adjusted.

460-26. Identification.

460-27. Grounding.

460-28. Means for Discharge.

  (a) Means to Reduce the Residual Voltage.

  (b) Connection to Terminals.

460-1. **Scope.** This article covers the installation of capacitors on electric circuits.

Surge capacitors or capacitors included as a component part of other apparatus and conforming with the requirements of such apparatus are excluded from these requirements.

This article also covers the installation of capacitors in hazardous (classified) locations as modified by Articles 501 through 503.

460-2. **Enclosing and Guarding.**

  (a) Containing More than 3 Gallons (11.36 L) of Flammable Liquid. Capacitors containing more than 3 gallons (11.36 L) of flammable liquid shall be enclosed in vaults or outdoor fenced enclosures complying with Article 710. This limit shall apply to any single unit in an installation of capacitors.

This section was revised for the 1993 *Code* to clarify that the three-gallon limitation applies to any single unit in an installation.

  (b) Accidental Contact. Capacitors shall be enclosed, located, or guarded so that persons cannot come into accidental contact or bring conducting materials into accidental contact with exposed energized parts, terminals, or buses associated with them.

Figure 460-1. *Power factor correction capacitors with discharge resistors. (Square D Co.)*

Means are required to drain off the stored charge in a capacitor after the supply circuit has been opened. Otherwise, a person servicing the equipment could receive a severe shock or damage may occur to the equipment.

Figure 460-2, parts (a) and (b), shows the method in which capacitors are connected in a motor circuit so that they may be switched with the motor. In either arrangement, the stored charge will drain off through the windings when the circuit is opened. Figure 460-2, part (c), shows a third arrangement where the capacitor is connected to the line side of the motor starter contacts. An automatic discharge device and a separate disconnecting means are required.

Capacitors are often equipped with built-in resistors to drain off the stored charge, although this type is not needed where connected as shown in Figure 460-2, parts (a) and (b).

Exception: No additional guarding is required for enclosures accessible only to authorized and qualified persons.

A. 600 Volts, Nominal, and Under

460-6. **Discharge of Stored Energy.** Capacitors shall be provided with a means of discharging stored energy.

Figure 460-2. Methods of connecting capacitors in induction motor circuit for power factor correction.

(a) Time of Discharge. The residual voltage of a capacitor shall be reduced to 50 volts, nominal, or less, within 1 minute after the capacitor is disconnected from the source of supply.

(b) Means of Discharge. The discharge circuit shall be either permanently connected to the terminals of the capacitor or capacitor bank, or provided with automatic means of connecting it to the terminals of the capacitor bank on removal of voltage from the line. Manual means of switching or connecting the discharge circuit shall not be used.

460-8. Conductors.

(a) Ampacity. The ampacity of capacitor circuit conductors shall not be less than 135 percent of the rated current of the capacitor. The ampacity of conductors that connect a capacitor to the terminals of a motor or to motor circuit conductors shall not be less than one third the ampacity of the motor circuit conductors and in no case less than 135 percent of the rated current of the capacitor.

(b) Overcurrent Protection.

(1) An overcurrent device shall be provided in each ungrounded conductor for each capacitor bank.

Except as permitted in the following exception, it is intended that the overcurrent device be separate from the overcurrent device protecting any other equipment or conductor. See Figure 460-2(a) and (b).

Exception: A separate overcurrent device shall not be required for a capacitor connected on the load side of a motor overload protective device.

(2) The rating or setting of the overcurrent device shall be as low as practicable.

(c) Disconnecting Means.

(1) A disconnecting means shall be provided in each ungrounded conductor for each capacitor bank.

Except as permitted in the following exception, it is intended that the disconnecting means be separate from the disconnecting means for any other equipment. See Figure 460-2(a) and (b).

Exception: Where a capacitor is connected on the load side of a motor overload protective device.

(2) The disconnecting means shall open all ungrounded conductors simultaneously.

(3) The disconnecting means shall be permitted to disconnect the capacitor from the line as a regular operating procedure.

(4) The rating of the disconnecting means shall not be less than 135 percent of the rated current of the capacitor.

Capacitors are rated in kilovars, which is abbreviated "kvar" and stands for reactive kilovolt-amperes. The kvar rating shows how many reactive kilovolt-amperes the capacitor will supply in order to cancel out the reactive kilovolt-amperes caused by inductance. For example, a 20-kvar capacitor will cancel out 20 kVA of inductive reactive kilovolt-amperes.

The basic unit is 3-phase and delta-connected internally, but single-phase and 2-phase units are also available. They are constructed with built-in fuses for short-circuit protection and discharge resistors that reduce the voltage to 50-V crest or less when disconnected from the power supply. This will occur within one minute on 600-V units and within 5 minutes for 2,400- and 4,160-V units.

The capacitor circuit conductors and disconnecting means are required to have an ampacity not less than 135 percent of the rated current of the capacitor. This is because all capacitors are manufactured with a tolerance of zero percent to +15 percent, so that a 100-kvar capacitor may actually draw a current equivalent to a 115-kvar capacitor. In addition, the current drawn by a capacitor varies directly with the line voltage, and any variation in the line voltage from a pure sine wave form causes the capacitor to draw an increased current. Considering these several factors, the increased current can amount to 135 percent of the rated current of the capacitor.

The current corresponding to the kvar rating of a 3-phase capacitor is computed from the formula

$$Ic = \frac{\text{kVAr} \times 1,000}{1.73 \times \text{volts}}.$$

The ampacity of the conductors and the switching device is then determined by multiplying Ic × 1.35. The most effective power factor correction is obtained where the individual capacitors are connected directly to the terminals of the motors, transformers, and other inductive machinery.

Where connected together and operated as a unit, no complicated calculations are needed to determine the proper size capacitor to use. Capacitor manufacturers publish tables in which the required capacitor value is indicated by referring to the speed and horsepower of the motor. These values will improve the motor power factor to approximately 95 percent. To improve a plant power factor, capacitor manufacturers also publish tables to assist in calculating the total kvar rating of capacitors required to improve the power factor to any desired value.

460-9. Rating or Setting of Motor Overload Device. Where a motor installation includes a capacitor connected on the load side of the motor overload device, the rating or setting of the motor overload device shall be based on the improved power factor of the motor circuit.

The effect of the capacitor shall be disregarded in determining the motor circuit conductor rating in accordance with Section 430-22.

Where a capacitor is connected on the load side of the overload relays, as shown in Figure 460-2(a), consideration is required to be given to the reduction in line current due to the improved power factor when selecting the rating or setting of the motor running overcurrent device. A value lower than indicated in Section 430-32 should be used for proper protection of the motor.

460-10. Grounding. Capacitor cases shall be grounded in accordance with Article 250.

Exception: Where the capacitor units are supported on a structure that is designed to operate at other than ground potential.

460-12. Marking. Each capacitor shall be provided with a nameplate giving the name of the manufacturer, rated voltage, frequency, kilovar or amperes, number of phases, and, if filled with a combustible liquid, the amount of liquid in gallons. Where filled with a nonflammable liquid, the nameplate shall so state. The nameplate shall also indicate if a capacitor has a discharge device inside the case.

B. Over 600 Volts, Nominal

460-24. Switching.

(a) Load Current. Group-operated switches shall be used for capacitor switching and shall be capable of (1) carrying continuously not less than 135 percent of the rated current of the capacitor installation; (2) interrupting the maximum continuous load current of each capacitor, capacitor bank, or capacitor installation that will be switched as a unit; (3) withstanding the maximum inrush current, including contributions from adjacent capacitor installations; (4) carrying currents due to faults on capacitor side of switch.

(b) Isolation.

(1) A means shall be installed to isolate from all sources of voltage each capacitor, capacitor bank, or capacitor installation that will be removed from service as a unit.

(2) The isolating means shall provide a visible gap in the electrical circuit adequate for the operating voltage.

(3) Isolating or disconnecting switches (with no interrupting rating) shall be interlocked with the load-interrupting device or shall be provided with prominently displayed caution signs in accordance with Section 710-22 to prevent switching load current.

(c) Additional Requirements for Series Capacitors. The proper switching sequence shall be assured by use of one of the following: (1) mechanically sequenced isolating and bypass switches; (2) interlocks; or (3) switching procedure prominently displayed at the switching location.

460-25. Overcurrent Protection.

(a) Provided to Detect and Interrupt Fault Current. A means shall be provided to detect and interrupt fault current likely to cause dangerous pressure within an individual capacitor.

(b) Single-Phase or Multiphase Devices. Single-phase or multiphase devices shall be permitted for this purpose.

(c) Protected Individually or in Groups. Capacitors shall be permitted to be protected individually or in groups.

(d) Protective Devices Rated or Adjusted. Protective devices for capacitors or capacitor equipment shall be rated or adjusted to operate within the limits of the safe zone for individual capacitors.

Exception: If the protective devices are rated or adjusted to operate within the limits for Zone 1 or Zone 2, the capacitors shall be enclosed or isolated.

In no event shall the rating or adjustment of the protective devices exceed the maximum limit of Zone 2.

(FPN): For definitions of the Safe Zone, Zone 1, and Zone 2, see Shunt Power Capacitors, ANSI/IEEE 18-1980.

The reference to Zones 1 and 2 of ANSI/IEEE 18-1980 pertains to the performance of the capacitors under fault conditions. If a fault current exceeds the limit established for Zone 2, the capacitor tank may burst.

460-26. Identification.
Each capacitor shall be provided with a permanent nameplate giving the maker's name, rated voltage, frequency, kilovar or amperes, number of phases, and the amount of liquid in gallons identified as flammable, if such is the case.

460-27. Grounding.
Capacitor neutrals and cases, if grounded, shall be grounded in accordance with Article 250.

Exception: Where the capacitor units are supported on a structure that is designed to operate at other than ground potential.

460-28. Means for Discharge.

(a) Means to Reduce the Residual Voltage. A means shall be provided to reduce the residual voltage of a capacitor to 50 volts or less within 5 minutes after the capacitor is disconnected from the source of supply.

(b) Connection to Terminals. A discharge circuit shall be either permanently connected to the terminals of the capacitor or provided with automatic means of connecting it to the terminals of the capacitor bank after disconnection of the capacitor from the source of supply. The windings of motors, or transformers, or of other equipment directly connected to capacitors without a switch or overcurrent device interposed shall meet the requirements of (a) above.

ARTICLE 470   Resistors and Reactors

For Rheostats, see Section 430-82.

Contents

A. 600 Volts, Nominal, and Under

470-1. Scope.
470-2. Location.
470-3. Space Separation.
470-4. Conductor Insulation.

B. Over 600 Volts, Nominal

470-18. General.
  (a) Protected Against Physical Damage.
  (b) Isolated by Enclosure or Elevation.
  (c) Combustible Materials.
  (d) Clearances.
  (e) Temperature Rise from Induced Circulating Currents.
470-19. Grounding.
470-20. Oil-Filled Reactors.

A. 600 Volts, Nominal, and Under

470-1. Scope.
This article covers the installation of separate resistors and reactors on electric circuits.

Exception: Resistors and reactors that are component parts of other apparatus.

This article also covers the installation of resistors and reactors in hazardous (classified) locations as modified by Articles 501 through 504.

470-2. Location.
Resistors and reactors shall not be placed where exposed to physical damage.

470-3. Space Separation. A thermal barrier shall be required if the space between the resistors and reactors and any combustible material is less than 12 inches (305 mm).

470-4. Conductor Insulation. Insulated conductors used for connections between resistance elements and controllers shall be suitable for an operating temperature of not less than 90°C (194°F).

Exception: Other conductor insulations shall be permitted for motor starting service.

Resistors are made in many different sizes and shapes and for different purposes. They may be wire or ribbon wound, form wound, edgewise wound, cast grid, punched steel grid, or box resistors. They may be mounted in the open or in ventilated metal boxes or cabinets depending on their use and location. Since they give off heat, they are required to be guarded and located at safe distances from combustible materials. Where mounted on switchboards or installed in control panels, they are not required to have additional guards.

Reactors are installed in a circuit to introduce inductance for motor starting, controlling the current, and paralleling of transformers. Current-limiting reactors are installed to limit the amount of current that can flow in a circuit when a short circuit occurs. Reactors can be divided into two classes, those with iron cores and those that use no magnetic materials in the windings. Both types may be air cooled or oil immersed.

Mechanical stresses exist between air-core reactors due to their external fields, and the manufacturer's recommendations should be followed in spacing and bracing between units and fastening of supporting insulators.

Saturable reactors are used for theater dimming. See Section 520-25 and commentary. These have, in addition to the ac winding, an auxiliary winding connected line-to-line or line-to-ground in order to neutralize charging current and prevent a voltage rise. Those used on high-voltage systems are usually oil immersed.

B. Over 600 Volts, Nominal

470-18. General.

(a) Protected Against Physical Damage. Resistors and reactors shall be protected against physical damage.

(b) Isolated by Enclosure or Elevation. Resistors and reactors shall be isolated by enclosure or elevation to protect personnel from accidental contact with energized parts.

(c) Combustible Materials. Resistors and reactors shall not be installed in close enough proximity to combustible materials to constitute a fire hazard and shall have a clearance of not less than 1 foot (305 mm) from combustible materials.

(d) Clearances. Clearances from resistors and reactors to grounded surfaces shall be adequate for the voltage involved.

(FPN):   See Article 710.

(e) Temperature Rise from Induced Circulating Currents. Metallic enclosures of reactors and adjacent metal parts shall be installed so that the temperature rise from induced circulating currents will not be hazardous to personnel or constitute a fire hazard.

470-19. Grounding. Resistor and reactor cases or enclosures shall be grounded in accordance with Article 250.

470-20. Oil-Filled Reactors. Installation of oil-filled reactors, in addition to the above requirements, shall comply with applicable requirements of Article 450.

ARTICLE 480   Storage Batteries

Contents

(b) Live Parts.
480-9. Vents.
  (a) Vented Cells.
  (b) Sealed Cells.

480-1. **Scope.** The provisions of this article shall apply to all stationary installations of storage batteries.

There are two general types of storage cells, the lead-acid type and the alkali type. Basically, a lead-acid cell consists of a positive plate, usually lead peroxide (a semi-solid compound) mounted on a framework or grid for support, and a negative plate made of sponge lead mounted on a grid. Grids are generally made of a lead-antimony alloy and the electrolyte is usually sulfuric acid and distilled water.

In the alkali-type cell (or Edison cell), the positive plate material is nickel oxide and the negative plate material is iron oxide. The electrolyte is a solution consisting mostly of potassium hydroxide (an alkaline).

Another common alkali-type cell is the nickel-cadmium-alkaline battery, usually referred to as the nickel-cadmium battery. The principal active material in the positive plate is nickelous hydroxide; in the negative plate, it is cadmium hydroxide. The electrolyte is potassium hydroxide.

Nickel-cadmium cells may be of the vented or hermetically sealed type. Under certain charging conditions, the vented type will liberate gases, hydrogen at the negative plate, and oxygen at the positive plate.

480-2. **Definitions.**

Storage Battery: A battery comprised of one or more rechargeable cells of the lead-acid, nickel-cadmium, or other rechargeable electrochemical types.

Sealed Cell or Battery: A sealed cell or battery is one that has no provision for the addition of water or electrolyte or for external measurement of electrolyte specific gravity. The individual cells shall be permitted to contain a venting arrangement as described in Section 480-9(b).

Nominal Battery Voltage: The voltage computed on the basis of 2.0 volts per cell for the lead-acid type and 1.2 volts per cell for the alkali type.

480-3. **Wiring and Equipment Supplied from Batteries.** Wiring and equipment supplied from storage batteries shall be subject to the requirements of this Code applying to wiring and equipment operating at the same voltage.

Exception: As otherwise provided for communication systems in Article 800.

480-4. **Grounding.** The requirements of Article 250 shall apply.

480-5. **Insulation of Batteries of Not Over 250 Volts.** This section shall apply to storage batteries having cells so connected as to operate at a nominal battery voltage of not over 250 volts.

(a) Vented Lead-Acid Batteries. Cells and multicompartment batteries with covers sealed to containers of nonconductive, heat-resistant material shall not require additional insulating support.

(b) Vented Alkaline-type Batteries. Cells with covers sealed to jars of nonconductive, heat-resistant material shall require no additional insulation support. Cells in jars of conductive material shall be installed in trays of nonconductive material with not more than 20 cells (24 volts, nominal) in the series circuit in any one tray.

(c) Rubber Jars. Cells in rubber or composition containers shall require no additional insulating support where the total nominal voltage of all cells in series does not exceed 150 volts. Where the total voltage exceeds 150 volts, batteries shall be sectionalized into groups of 150 volts or less, and each group shall have the individual cells installed in trays or on racks.

(d) Sealed Cells or Batteries. Sealed cells and multicompartment sealed batteries constructed of nonconductive, heat-resistant material shall not require additional insulating support. Batteries constructed of a conducting container shall have insulating support if a voltage is present between the container and ground.

480-6. **Insulation of Batteries of Over 250 Volts.** The provisions of Section 480-5 shall apply to storage batteries having the cells so connected as to operate at a nominal voltage exceeding 250 volts, and, in addition, the provisions of this section shall also apply to such batteries. Cells shall be installed in groups having a total nominal voltage of not over 250 volts. Insulation, which can be air, shall be provided between groups and shall have a minimum separation between live battery parts of opposite polarity of 2 inches (50.8 mm) for battery voltages not exceeding 600 volts.

480-7. Racks and Trays. Racks and trays shall comply with (a) and (b) below.

(a) Racks. Racks, as required in this article, are rigid frames designed to support cells or trays. They shall be substantial and made of:

(1) Metal, so treated as to be resistant to deteriorating action by the electrolyte and provided with nonconducting members directly supporting the cells or with continuous insulating material other than paint or conducting members; or

(2) Other construction such as fiberglass or other suitable nonconductive materials.

(b) Trays. Trays are frames, such as crates or shallow boxes usually of wood or other nonconductive material, so constructed or treated as to be resistant to deteriorating action by the electrolyte.

480-8. Battery Locations. Battery locations shall conform to (a) and (b) below.

(a) Ventilation. Provisions shall be made for sufficient diffusion and ventilation of the gases from the battery to prevent the accumulation of an explosive mixture.

Compliance with this section is necessary to prevent classification of a battery location as a hazardous (classified) location in accordance with Article 500.

It is not the intent of Section 480-8(a) to mandate mechanical ventilation. Hydrogen disperses rapidly and requires very little air movement to prevent accumulation. Unrestricted natural air movement in the vicinity of the battery, together with normal air changes for occupied spaces or heat removal, will normally be sufficient. If the space is confined, mechanical ventilation may be required in the vicinity of the battery.

Hydrogen is lighter than air and will tend to concentrate at ceiling level, so some form of ventilation should be provided at the upper portion of the structure. Ventilation can be a fan, roof ridge vent, or louvered areas.

(b) Live Parts. Guarding of live parts shall comply with Section 110-17.

Batteries are required to be located in a clean, dry room and arranged to provide sufficient work space for inspection and maintenance. Provision is required to be made for adequate ventilation to prevent an accumulation of an explosive mixture of the gases from the batteries.

The fumes given off by storage batteries are very corrosive; therefore, wiring and its insulation is required to be of a type that will withstand corrosive action. See Section 310-9. Special precautions are necessary to ensure that all metalwork (metal raceways, metal racks, etc.) is designed or treated so as to be corrosion resistant. Manufacturers suggest that aluminum conduit be used to withstand the corrosive battery fumes, or, if steel conduits are used, it is recommended that they be zinc-coated and corrosion protected with a coating of an asphaltum-type paint. See Section 300-6.

Overcharging heats a battery and causes gassing and loss of water. A battery should not be allowed to reach temperatures over 110°F (43.3°C) because heat causes a shedding of active materials from the plates that will eventually form a sediment buildup in the bottom of the case and short-circuit the plates and the cell. Because mixtures of oxygen and hydrogen are highly explosive, flame or sparks should never be allowed near a cell, especially if the filler cap is removed.

480-9. Vents.

(a) Vented Cells. Each vented cell shall be equipped with a flame arrestor designed to prevent destruction of the cell due to ignition of gases within the cell by an external spark or flame under normal operating conditions.

(b) Sealed Cells. Sealed battery/cells shall be equipped with a pressure-release vent to prevent excessive accumulation of gas pressure, or the battery/cell shall be designed to prevent scatter of cell parts in event of a cell explosion.

5
Special Occupancies

Contents

500-1. Scope — **Articles 500 through 504.** Articles 500 through 504 cover the requirements for electrical equipment and wiring for all voltages in locations where fire or explosion hazards may exist due to flammable gases or vapors, flammable liquids, combustible dust, or ignitible fibers or flyings.

The *National Electrical Code* does not classify areas for the manufacture, transportation, storage, and use of explosive materials such as ammunition, dynamite, and blasting powder. Areas where such materials are present are not considered hazardous (classified) locations in accordance with Article 500. However, many organizations responsible for the safety of such areas require equipment and wiring methods suitable for hazardous locations as part of many safety precautions, even though the equipment and wiring have not been investigated for such locations. The logic is that use of hazardous location equipment and wiring methods is safer than ordinary location equipment and wiring methods.

Further information on these locations can be found in NFPA 495-1992, *Explosive Materials Code*.

For information on hazardous locations in general, including background on the classification of areas, equipment protection systems, ignition sources, static electricity and lightning, and requirements that apply outside of the United States, see *Electrical Installations in Hazardous Locations* by Peter J. Schram and Mark W. Earley. This book is available from NFPA.

500-2. Location and General Requirements. Locations shall be classified depending on the properties of the flammable vapors, liquids or gases, or combustible dusts or fibers that may be present and the likelihood that a flammable or combustible concentration or quantity is present. Where pyrophoric materials are the only materials used or handled, these locations shall not be classified.

Pyrophoric materials ignite spontaneously upon contact with the air. The use of electrical equipment suitable for a hazardous (classified) location will not prevent ignition of the material. The process containment system should be designed to prevent contact between the pyrophoric material and the air.

Each room, section, or area shall be considered individually in determining its classification.

Exception: Except as modified in Articles 500 through 504, all other applicable rules contained in this Code shall apply to electric equipment and wiring installed in hazardous (classified) locations.

(FPN No. 1): For definitions of "approved" and "explosionproof" as used in these articles, see Article 100; "dust-ignition-proof" is defined in Section 502-1.

Intrinsically safe apparatus and wiring shall be permitted in any hazardous (classified) location for which it is approved, and the provisions of Articles 501 through 503 and 510 through 516 shall not be considered applicable to such installations except as required by Article 504.

For the construction and performance requirements for intrinsically safe equipment, see ANSI/UL 913-1988, *Standard for Intrinsically Safe Apparatus and Associated Apparatus for Use in Class I, II, and III, Division 1 Hazardous (Classified) Locations*.

ANSI/UL 913 applies not only to apparatus or parts of apparatus in a hazardous (classified) location, but also to any parts, such as power supplies and recorders, located outside of a hazardous (classified) location where the intrinsic safety of electrical circuits in a hazardous (classified) location may be influenced by the design and construction of such parts. The detailed requirements apply only to apparatus for use in, or associated with, a location made hazardous by the presence of flammable gas or vapor, combustible dust, or easily ignitible fibers or flyings in air under normal atmospheric conditions. If an oxygen-enriched atmosphere exists, equipment approved as intrinsically safe may not be intrinsically safe.

In evaluating safety, all interconnected apparatus and circuits are required to be considered, even if located in a Division 2 hazardous (classified) location or a nonhazardous location, or protected by other means, such as an explosionproof or purged enclosure. They are required to be examined to ensure that, under normal or fault conditions, they cannot provide a source of ignition-capable energy to the apparatus in the Division 1 hazardous (classified) location. Associated apparatus and circuits are required to conform to the requirements of the location in which the apparatus and circuits are installed.

An intrinsically safe circuit is one in which any spark or thermal effect produced either normally or under specified fault conditions is, under the test conditions prescribed in ANSI/UL 913, incapable of causing ignition of a specified mixture of gas or vapor in air in its most easily ignited concentration. Intrinsically safe circuits are required to be identified as intrinsically safe. See Section 504-80.

Wiring of intrinsically safe circuits shall be physically separated from wiring of all other circuits that are not intrinsically safe. Means shall be provided to minimize the passage of gases and vapors.

The requirement that means be provided to minimize the passage of gases and vapors will necessitate, in Class I locations, some type of sealing or ventilation for raceways and cables capable of transmitting gases or vapors, if these cables or raceways provide communication between a Division 1 and a Division 2 or a nonhazardous location, or between a Division 2 and a nonhazardous location. Raceways and some cables can act to transmit gases. See also Section 504-70.

Installation of intrinsically safe apparatus and wiring shall be in accordance with the requirements of Article 504.

Article 504 was new in the 1990 *NEC*. See commentary with Article 504.

(FPN No. 2): Through the exercise of ingenuity in the layout of electrical installations for hazardous (classified) locations, it is frequently possible to locate much of the equipment in less hazardous or in nonhazardous locations and, thus, to reduce the amount of special equipment required. In some cases, hazards may be reduced or hazardous (classified) locations limited or eliminated by adequate positive-pressure ventilation from a source of clean air in conjunction with effective safeguards against ventilation failure. For further information, see Purged and Pressurized Enclosures for Electrical Equipment, NFPA 496-1989 (ANSI), Flammable and Combustible Liquids Code, NFPA 30-1990 (ANSI), Section 5-3.3, and American Petroleum Institute, API RP 500-1991, Recommended Practice for Classification of Locations for Electrical Installations at Petroleum Facilities, Section 4.6.

NFPA 496 covers purged and pressurized enclosures for electrical equipment in Class I hazardous (classified) locations and pressurized enclosures for electrical equipment in Class II hazardous (classified) locations.

Class I Hazardous (Classified) Locations: The object of NFPA 496 for Class I hazardous (classified) locations is to provide information on purged enclosures to eliminate or reduce within the enclosure a Class I hazardous (classified) location classification, as defined in Article 500 of the *Code*. By use of purged enclosures, equipment that is not otherwise acceptable for hazardous (classified) locations maybe utilized for these locations in accordance with the *Code*.

Purging is defined as the process of supplying an enclosure with a protective gas, at a sufficient flow and positive pressure to reduce the concentration of any flammable gas or vapor initially present to an acceptable level.

Type X purging reduces the classification within a protected enclosure from Division 1 to nonclassified.

Type Y purging reduces the classification within a protected enclosure from Division 1 to Division 2.

Type Z purging reduces the classification within a protected enclosure from Division 2 to nonclassified.

Class II Hazardous (Classified) Locations: The object of NFPA 496 for Class II locations is to provide information on pressurized enclosures, which prevent the entrance of dusts into an enclosure. By use of pressurized enclosures, equipment that is not otherwise acceptable for hazardous (classified) locations may be utilized for these locations in accordance with the *Code*. Pressurization, for the purposes of NFPA 496, may be defined as the process of supplying an enclosure with a protective gas, with or without continuous flow at sufficient pressure to prevent the entrance of a flammable gas or vapor, a combustible dust, or an ignitable fiber.

It should be noted that an atmosphere made hazardous by combustible dust inside an enclosure cannot be reduced to a safe level by supplying a flow of protective gas in the same manner as gases or vapors. The enclosure must be opened and the dust removed. Visual inspection can determine if the dust has been removed. Positive pressure will prevent entrance of dust into a clean enclosure.

Field installed devices and equipment such as pushbutton controls and pilot lights are permitted in purged or pressurized enclosures provided the conductor terminals are within the purged or pressurized atmosphere.

Section 5-3.3 of NFPA 30 and Section 4.6 of API RP500 provide guidelines on ventilation.

(FPN No. 3): It is important that the authority having jurisdiction be familiar with such recorded industrial experience as well as with such standards of the National Fire Protection Association as may be of use in the classification of various areas with respect to hazard.

(FPN No. 4): For further information, see Flammable and Combustible Liquids Code, NFPA 30-1990; Drycleaning Plants, NFPA 32-1990; Manufacture of Organic Coatings, NFPA 35-1987 (ANSI); Solvent Extraction Plants, NFPA 36-1988 (ANSI); Storage and Handling of Liquefied Petroleum Gases, NFPA 58-1992; Storage and Handling of Liquefied Petroleum Gases at Utility Gas Plants, NFPA 59-1992; Classification of Class I Hazardous (Classified) Locations for Electrical Installations in Chemical Process Areas, NFPA 497A-1992 (ANSI); and Fire Protection in Wastewater Treatment and Collection Facilities, NFPA 820-1992 (ANSI).

(FPN No. 5): For protection against static electricity hazards, see Recommended Practice on Static Electricity, NFPA 77-1988 (ANSI).

(FPN No. 6): For electrical classification of laboratory areas, see Fire Protection for Laboratories Using Chemicals, NFPA 45-1991.

All conduit referred to herein shall be threaded with an NPT standard conduit cutting die that provides ³/₄-inch taper per foot. Such conduit shall be made up wrenchtight to minimize sparking when fault current flows through the conduit system. Where it is impractical to make a threaded joint tight, a bonding jumper shall be utilized.

Ground continuity, without arcing or sparking, is critical in hazardous locations.

500-3. **Special Precaution.** Articles 500 through 504 require equipment construction and installation that will ensure safe performance under conditions of proper use and maintenance.

(FPN No. 1): It is important that inspection authorities and users exercise more than ordinary care with regard to installation and maintenance.

(FPN No. 2): Low ambient conditions require special consideration. Explosionproof or dust-ignitionproof equipment may not be suitable for use at temperatures lower than -25°C (-13°F) unless they are approved for low-temperature service. However, at low ambient temperatures, flammable concentrations of vapors may not exist in a location classified Class I, Division 1 at normal ambient temperature.

At low ambient temperatures, such as those encountered in the arctic, the strengths of materials change. This is particularly true for some sealing materials. In addition, explosion pressures increase at very low temperatures. However, the extent of the hazardous (classified) location may also change under low ambient conditions, depending on the flash point and autoignition temperature of the material involved.

For purposes of testing, approval, and area classification, various air mixtures (not oxygen-enriched) shall be grouped in accordance with Sections 500-3(a) and 500-3(b).

Exception: Equipment approved for a specific gas, vapor, or dust.

Determining the proper group classification for flammable gases and vapors involves a determination of explosion pressures and maximum safe clearance between parts of a clamped joint under several conditions, and comparison of the values obtained with those obtained for presently classified materials under the same test conditions. Although some work has been done on the classification of flammable materials on the basis of chemical structure, the method is not sufficiently refined or accurate to ensure proper classification of all flammable materials.

For additional information on the rationale for classification, reference may be made to the following: (1) "Rationale for Classification of Combustible Gases, Vapors, and Dusts with Reference to the National Electrical Code," Publication NMAB 353-6, 1982, a report of the Committee on Evaluation of Industrial Hazards, The National Materials Advisory Board, Commission on Engineering and Technical Systems, National Research Council. This publication is available from the National Technical Information Service (NTIS), Springfield, VA 22151; (2) "An Investigation of Fifteen Flammable Gases or Vapors with Respect to Explosion-Proof Electrical Equipment," Bulletin of Research No. 58 by Underwriters Laboratories Inc., August 1969 (also Bulletin of Research Nos. 58A and 58B, which supplement No. 58). These are available from Underwriters Laboratories Inc., Publications Stock, 333 Pfingsten Rd., Northbrook, IL 60062; (3) *Electrical Installations in Hazardous Locations*, Peter J. Schram and Mark W. Earley, Chapter 2. This book is available from NFPA.

(FPN): This grouping is based on the characteristics of the materials. Facilities have been made available for testing and approving equipment for use in the various atmospheric groups.

The intent of the exception at the end of Section 500-3 and before the Fine Print Note is to permit qualified testing laboratories to test and list (certify, classify, etc.) equipment acceptable for one or some, but not all, materials in a particular group.

(a) Class I Group Classifications. Class I groups shall be as follows:

(1) Group A: Atmospheres containing acetylene.

(2) Group B: Atmospheres containing hydrogen, fuel and combustible process gases containing more than 30 percent hydrogen by volume, or gases or vapors of equivalent hazard such as butadiene, ethylene oxide, propylene oxide, and acrolein.

Exception No. 1: Group D equipment shall be permitted to be used for atmospheres containing butadiene if such equipment is isolated in accordance with Section 501-5(a) by sealing all conduit ¹/₂-inch size or larger.

Exception No. 2: Group C equipment shall be permitted to be used for atmospheres containing ethylene oxide, propylene oxide, and acrolein if such equipment is isolated in accordance with Section 501-5(a) by sealing all conduit ½-inch size or larger.

The materials identified in Exception No. 1 and Exception No. 2 produce high pressures as a result of pressure piling strong unsealed conduits. However, if all conduits are sealed, this problem is eliminated.

(3) Group C: Atmospheres such as ethyl ether, ethylene, or gases or vapors of equivalent hazard.

(4) Group D: Atmospheres such as acetone, ammonia, benzene, butane, cyclopropane, ethanol, gasoline, hexane, methanol, methane, natural gas, naphtha, propane, or gases or vapors of equivalent hazard.

Exception: For atmospheres containing ammonia, the authority having jurisdiction for enforcement of this Code shall be permitted to reclassify the location to a less hazardous location or a nonhazardous location.

See FPN No. 4 and Notes to Table 273 of NFPA 497M-1991.

(FPN No. 1): For additional information on the properties and group classification of Class I materials, see Classification of Gases, Vapors, and Dusts for Electrical Equipment in Hazardous (Classified) Locations, NFPA 497M-1991, and Fire Hazard Properties of Flammable Liquids, Gases, and Volatile Solids, NFPA 325M-1991.

The table that follows is Table 2-3 from NFPA 497M-1991. Additional tables in NFPA 497M cover materials with flash points 37.8°C (100°F) and higher.

Group Classification and Autoignition Temperature (AIT) of Selected Flammable Gases and Vapors of Liquids Having Flash Points below 100°F (37.8°C).

Material	Group	AIT °F	AIT °C
Acetaldehyde	C*	347	175
Acetone	D*	869	465
Acetonitrile	D	975	524
Acetylene	A*	581	305
Acrolein (inhibited)	B (C)*1	455	235
Acrylonitrile	D*	898	481
Allyl Alcohol	C*	713	378
Allyl Chloride	D	905	485
Ammonia	D*2	928	498
n-Amyl Acetate	D	680	360
sec-Amyl Acetate	D	—	—
Benzene	D*	928	498
1,3-Butadiene	B (D)*1	788	420
Butane	D*	550	288
1-Butanol	D*	650	343
2-Butanol	D*	761	405
n-Butyl Acetate	D*	790	421
iso-Butyl Acetate	D*	790	421
sec-Butyl Acetate	D	—	—

Group Classification and Autoignition Temperature (AIT), continued

Material	Group	AIT °F	AIT °C
Butylamine	D	594	312
Butylene	D	725	385
Butyl Mercaptan	C	—	—
n-Butyraldehyde	C*	425	218
Carbon Disulfide	-*3	194	90
Carbon Monoxide	C*	1128	609
Chlorobenzene	D	1099	593
Chloroprene	D	—	—
Crotonaldehyde	C*	450	232
Cumene	D	795	424
Cyclohexane	D	473	245
Cyclohexene	D	471	244
Cyclopropane	D*	938	503
1,1-Dichloroethane	D	820	438
1,2-Dichloroethylene	D	860	460
1,3-Dichloropropene	D	—	—
Dicyclopentadiene	C	937	503
Diethyl Ether	C*	320	160
Diethylamine	C*	594	312
Di-isobutylene	D*	736	391

Group Classification and Autoignition Temperature (AIT), continued

Material	Group	AIT °F	AIT °C
Di-isopropylamine	C	600	316
Dimethylamine	C	752	400
1,4-Dioxane	C	356	180
Di-n-propylamine	C	570	299
Epichlorohydrin	C*	772	411
Ethane	D*	882	472
Ethanol	D*	685	363
Ethyl Acetate	D*	800	427
Ethyl Acrylate (inhibited)	D*	702	372
Ethylamine	D*	725	385
Ethyl Benzene	D	810	432
Ethyl Chloride	D	966	519
Ethylene	C*	842	450
Ethylenediamine	D*	725	385
Ethylene Dichloride	D*	775	413
Ethylenimine	C*	608	320
Ethylene Oxide	B (C)*1	804	429
Ethyl Formate	D	851	455
Ethyl Mercaptan	C*	572	300
n-Ethyl Morpholine	C	—	—
Formaldehyde (Gas)	B	795	429
Gasoline	D*	536-880	280-471
Heptane	D*	399	204
Heptene	D	500	260
Hexane	D*	437	225
2-Hexanone	D	795	424
Hexenes	D	473	245
Hydrogen	B*	968	520
Hydrogen Cyanide	C*	1000	538
Hydrogen Selenide	C	—	—
Hydrogen Sulfide	C*	500	260
Isoamyl Acetate	D	680	360
Isobutyl Acrylate	D	800	427
Isobutyraldehyde	C	385	196
Isoprene	D*	428	220
Isopropyl Acetate	D	860	460
Isopropylamine	D	756	402
Isopropyl Ether	D*	830	443

Group Classification and Autoignition Temperature (AIT), continued

Material	Group	AIT °F	AIT °C
Isopropyl Glycidyl Ether	C	—	—
Liquefied Petroleum Gas	D	761-842	405-450
Manufactured Gas (containing more than 30% H_2 by volume)	B*	—	—
Mesityl Oxide	D*	652	344
Methane	D*	999	537
Methanol	D*	725	385
Methyl Acetate	D	850	454
Methylacetylene	C*	—	—
Methylacetylene-Propadiene (stabilized)	C	—	—
Methyl Acrylate	D	875	468
Methylamine	D	806	430
Methylcyclohexane	D	482	250
Methyl Ether	C*	662	350
Methyl Ethyl Ketone	D*	759	404
Methyl Formal	C*	460	238
Methyl Formate	D	840	449
Methyl Isobutyl Ketone	D*	840	449
Methyl Isocyanate	D	994	534
Methyl Mercaptan	C	—	—
Methyl Methacrylate	D	792	422
2-Methyl-l-Propanol	D*	780	416
2-Methyl-2-Propanol	D*	892	478
Monomethyl Hydrazine	C	382	194
Naphtha (Petroleum)	D*4	550	288
Nitroethane	C	778	414
Nitromethane	C	785	418
1-Nitropropane	C	789	421
2-Nitropropane	C*	802	428
Nonane	D	401	205
Nonene	D	—	—
Octane	D*	403	206
Octene	D	446	230
Pentane	D*	470	243

Group Classification and Autoignition Temperature (AIT), continued

Material	Group	AIT °F	AIT °C
1-Pentanol	D*	572	300
2-Pentanone	D	846	452
1-Pentene	D	527	275
Propane	D*	842	450
1-Propanol	D*	775	413
2-Propanol	D*	750	399
Propionaldehyde	C	405	207
n-Propyl Acetate	D	842	450
Propylene	D*	851	455
Propylene Dichloride	D	1035	557
Propylene Oxide	B (C)*1	840	449
n-Propyl Ether	C*	419	215
Propyl Nitrate	B*	347	175
Pyridine	D*	900	482
Styrene	D*	914	490
Tetrahydrofuran	C*	610	321
Toluene	D*	896	480
Triethylamine	C*	—	—
Turpentine	D	488	253
Unsymmetrical Dimethyl Hydrazine (UDMH)	C*	480	249
Valeraldehyde	C	432	222
Vinyl Acetate	D*	756	402
Vinyl Chloride	D*	882	472
Vinylidene Chloride	D	1058	570
Xylenes	D*	867-984	464-529

*Material has been classified by test.

**Fuel and process gas mixtures found by test not to present hazards similar to those of hydrogen may be grouped based on the test results.

1If equipment is isolated by sealing all conduit 1/2 inch or larger, in accordance with Section 501-5(a) of NFPA 70, *National Electrical Code*, equipment for the group classification shown in parentheses is permitted.

2For classification of areas involving ammonia, see *Safety Code for Mechanical Refrigeration*, ANSI/ASHRAE 15, and *Safety Requirements for the Storage and Handling of Anhydrous Ammonia*, ANSI/CGA G2.1.

3Certain chemicals may have characteristics that require safeguards beyond those required for any of the above groups. Carbon disulfide is one of these chemicals because of its low autoignition temperature and the small joint clearance to arrest its flame propagation.

Notes continued next column

(FPN No. 2): The explosion characteristics of air mixtures of gases or vapors vary with the specific material involved. For Class I locations, Groups A, B, C, and D, the classification involves determinations of maximum explosion pressure and maximum safe clearance between parts of a clamped joint in an enclosure. It is necessary, therefore, that equipment be approved not only for class but also for the specific group of the gas or vapor that will be present.

(FPN No. 3): Certain chemical atmospheres may have characteristics that require safeguards beyond those required for any of the above groups. Carbon disulfide is one of these chemicals because of its low ignition temperature [100°C (212°F)] and the small joint clearance permitted to arrest its flame.

(FPN No. 4): For classification of areas involving ammonia atmosphere, see Safety Code for Mechanical Refrigeration, ANSI/ASHRAE 15-1978, and Safety Requirements for the Storage and Handling of Anhydrous Ammonia, ANSI/CGA G2.1-1981.

(b) Class II Group Classifications. Class II groups shall be as follows:

(1)x **Group E:** Atmospheres containing combustible metal dusts, including aluminum, magnesium, and their commercial alloys, or other combustible dusts whose particle size, abrasiveness, and conductivity present similar hazards in the use of electrical equipment.

(FPN): Certain metal dusts may have characteristics that require safeguards beyond those required for atmospheres containing the dusts of aluminum, magnesium, and their commercial alloys. For example, zirconium, thorium, and uranium dusts have extremely low ignition temperatures [as low as 20°C (68°F)] and minimum ignition energies lower than any material classified in any of the Class I or Class II Groups.

(2)x **Group F:** Atmospheres containing combustible carbonaceous dusts, including carbon black, charcoal, coal, or coke dusts that have more than 8 percent total entrapped voltatiles, or dusts that have been sensitized by other materials so that they present an explosion hazard.

(FPN): See ASTM D 3175-89, *Standard Test Method for Volatile Material in the Analysis Sample for Coal and Coke.*

4Petroleum Naphtha is a saturated hydrocarbon mixture whose boiling range is 20° to 135°C. It is also known as benzine, ligroin, petroleum ether, and naphtha.

References: Autoignition temperatures listed above are the lowest value for each material as listed in NFPA 325M-1991, *Fire Hazard Properties of Flammable Liquids, Gases, and Volatile Solids*, or as reported in an article by Hilado, C. J. and Clark, S. W., in *Chemical Engineering*, September 4, 1972.

The following table is a list of selected dusts classified as Group F.

Selected Carbonaceous Dusts Classified as Group F — Ignition Sensitivity Equal to or Greater than 0.2; Explosion Severity Equal to or Greater than 0.5.

Material	Minimum Cloud or Layer Ignition Temp.[1]		
	°F		°C
Asphalt, (Blown Petroleum Resin)	950	CI	
Charcoal	356		180
Coal, Kentucky Bituminous	356		180
Coal, Pittsburgh Experimental	338		170
Coal, Wyoming	—		—
Gilsonite	932		500
Lignite, California	356		180
Pitch, Coal Tar	1310	NL	710
Pitch, Petroleum	1166	NL	630
Shale, Oil	—		—

[1]Normally, the minimum ignition temperature of a layer of a specific dust is lower than the minimum ignition temperature of a cloud of that dust. Since this is not universally true, the lower of the two minimum ignition temperatures is listed. If no symbol appears between the two temperature columns, then the layer ignition temperature is shown. "CI" means the cloud ignition temperature is shown. "NL" means that no layer ignition temperature is available, and the cloud ignition temperature is shown.

See also commentary following Section 500-3(d).

(3) Group G: Atmospheres containing combustible dusts not included in Group E or F, including flour, grain, wood, plastic, and chemicals.

(FPN No. 1):   For additional information on group classification of Class II materials, see Classification of Gases, Vapors, and Dusts for Electrical Equipment in Hazardous (Classified) Locations, NFPA 497M-1991.

The following table is part of Table 3-6 in NFPA 497M-1991.

Selected Nonconductive Dusts Classified as Group G — Ignition Sensitivity Equal to or Greater than 0.2; Explosion Severity Equal to or Greater than 0.5.

Material	Minimum Cloud or Layer Ignition Temp.[1]		
	°F		°C
AGRICULTURAL DUSTS			
Alfalfa Meal	392		200
Almond Shell	392		200
Apricot Pit	446		230
Cellulose	500		260
Cherry Pit	428		220
Cinnamon	446		230
Citrus Peel	518		270
Cocoa Bean Shell	698		370
Cocoa, natural, 19% fat	464		240
Coconut Shell	428		220
Corn	482		250
Corncob Grit	464		240
Corn Dextrine	698		370
Cornstarch, commerical	626		330
Cornstarch, modified	392		200
Cork	410		210
Cottonseed Meal	392		200
Cube Root, South Amer.	446		230
Flax Shive	446		230
Garlic, dehydrated	680	NL	360
Guar Seed	932	NL	500
Gum, Arabic	500		260
Gum, Karaya	464		240
Gum, Manila (copal)	680	Cl	360
Gum, Tragacanth	500		260
Hemp Hurd	428		220
Lycopodium	590		310
Malt Barley	482		250
Milk, Skimmed	392		200
Pea Flour	500		260
Peach Pit Shell	410		210
Peanut Hull	410		210
Peat, Sphagnum	464		240
Pecan Nut Shell	410		210

Selected Nonconductive Dusts Classified as Group G, continued

Material	Minimum Cloud or Layer Ignition Temp.[1]		
	°F		°C
Pectin	392		200
Potato Starch, Dextrinated	824	NL	440
Pyrethrum	410		210
Rauwolfia Vomitoria Root	446		230
Rice	428		220
Rice Bran	914	NL	490
Rice Hull	428		220
Safflower Meal	410		210
Soy Flour	374		190
Soy Protein	500		260
Sucrose	662	Cl	350
Sugar, Powdered	698	Cl	370
Tung, Kernels, Oil-free	464		240
Walnut Shell, Black	428		220
Wheat	428		220
Wheat Flour	680		360
Wheat Gluten, gum	968	NL	520
Wheat Starch	716	NL	380
Wheat Straw	428		220
Woodbark, Ground	482		250
Wood Flour	500		260
Yeast, Torula	500		260
CHEMICALS			
Acetoacetanilide	824	M	440
Acetoacet-p-phenetidide	1040	NL	560
Adipic Acid	1022	M	550
Anthranilic Acid	1076	M	580
Aryl-nitrosomethylamide	914	NL	490
Azelaic Acid	1130	M	610
2,2-Azo-bis-butyronitrile	662		350
Benzoic Acid	824	M	440
Benzotriazole	824	M	440
Bisphenol-A	1058	M	570
Chloroacetoacetanilide	1184	M	640
Diallyl Phthalate	896	M	480

Selected Nonconductive Dusts Classified as Group G, continued

Material	Minimum Cloud or Layer Ignition Temp.[1]		
	°F		°C
Dicumyl Peroxide (suspended on CaCO$_3$), 40-60	356		180
Dicyclopentadiene Dioxide	788	NL	420
Dihydroacetic Acid	806	NL	430
Dimethyl Isophthalate	1076	M	580
Dimethyl Terephthalate	1058	M	570
3,5-Dinitrobenzoic Acid	860	NL	460
Dinitrotoluamide	932	NL	500
Diphenyl	1166	M	630
Ditertiary Butyl Paracresol	878	NL	470
Ethyl Hydroxyethyl Cellulose	734	NL	390
Fumaric Acid	968	M	520
Hexamethylene Tetramine	770	S	410
Hydroxyethyl Cellulose	770	NL	410
Isotoic Anhydride	1292	NL	700
Methionine	680		360
Nitrosoamine	518	NL	270
Para-oxy-benzaldehyde	716	Cl	380
Paraphenylene Diamine	1148	M	620
Paratertiary Butyl Benzoic Acid	1040	M	560
Pentaerythritol	752	M	400
Phenylbetanaph-thylamine	1256	NL	680
Phthalic Anhydride	1202	M	650
Phthalimide	1166	M	630
Salicylanilide	1130	M	610
Sorbic Acid	860		460
Stearic Acid, Aluminum Salt	572		300
Stearic Acid, Zinc Salt	950	M	510
Sulfur	428		220
Terephthalic Acid	1256	NL	680
DRUGS			
2-Acetylamino-5-nitrothiazole	842		450

Selected Nonconductive Dusts Classified as Group G, continued

Material	Minimum Cloud or Layer Ignition Temp.[1] °F		°C
2-Amino-5-nitrothiazole	860		460
Aspirin	1220	M	660
Gulasonic Acid, Diacetone	788	NL	420
Mannitol	860	M	460
Nitropyridone	806	M	430
l-Sorbose	698	M	370
Vitamin B1, mononitrate	680	NL	360
Vitamin C (Ascorbic Acid)	536		280
DYES, PIGMENTS, INTERMEDIATES			
Beta-napthalene-azo-Dimethylaniline	347		175
Green Base Harmon Dye	347		175
Red Dye Intermediate	347		175
Violet 200 Dye	347		175
PESTICIDES			
Benzethonium Chloride	716	CI	380
Bis (2-Hydroxy-5-chlorophenyl) methane	1058	NL	570
Crag No. 974	590	C1	310
Dieldrin (20%)	1022	NL	550
2,6-Ditertiary-butyl-paracresol	788	NL	420
Dithane	356		180
Ferbam	302		150
Manganese Vancide	248		120
Sevin	284		140
α, α-Trithiobis (N, N-Dimethylthioformamide)	446		230
THERMOPLASTIC RESINS AND MOLDING COMPOUNDS			
Acetal Resins			
Acetal, Linear (Poly-formaldehyde)	824	NL	440

Selected Nonconductive Dusts Classified as Group G, continued

Material	Minimum Cloud or Layer Ignition Temp.[1] °F		°C
Acrylic Resins			
Acrylamide Polymer	464		240
Acrylonitrile Polymer	860		460
Acrylonitrile-Vinyl Pyridine Copolymer	464		240
Acrylonitrile-Vinyl Chloride-Vinylidene Chloride Copolymer (70-20-10)	410		210
Methyl Methacrylate Polymer	824	NL	440
Methyl Methacrylate-Ethyl Acrylate Copolymer	896	NL	480
Methyl Methacrylate-Ethyl Acrylate-Styrene Copolymer	824	NL	440
Methyl Methacrylate-Styrene-Butadiene-Acrylonitrile Copolymer	896	NL	480
Methacrylic Acid Polymer	554		290
Cellulosic Resins			
Cellulose Acetate	644		340
Cellulose Triacetate	806	NL	430
Cellulose Acetate Butyrate	698	NL	370
Cellulose Propionate	860	NL	460
Ethyl Cellulose	608	C1	320
Methyl Cellulose	644		340
Carboxymethyl Cellulose	554		290
Hydroxyethyl Cellulose	644		340
Chlorinated Polyether Resins			
Chlorinated Polyether Alcohol	860		460
Nylon (Polyamide) Resins			
Nylon Polymer (Polyhexa-methylene Adipamide)	806		430
Polycarbonate Resins			
Polycarbonate	1310	NL	710
Polyethylene Resins			
Polyethylene, High Pressure Process	716		380
Polyethylene, Low Pressure Process	788	NL	420
Polyethylene Wax	752	NL	400
Polymethylene Resins			
Carboxypolymethylene	968	NL	520

Selected Nonconductive Dusts Classified as Group G, continued

Material	Minimum Cloud or Layer Ignition Temp.[1]		
	°F		°C
Polypropylene Resins			
Polypropylene (No Antioxidant)	788	NL	420
Rayon Resins			
Rayon (Viscose) Flock	482		250
Styrene Resins			
Polystyrene Molding Compound	1040	NL	560
Polystyrene Latex	932		500
Styrene-Acrylonitrile (70-30)	932	NL	500
Styrene-Butadiene Latex (>75% Styrene; Alum Coagulated)	824	NL	440
Vinyl Resins			
Polyvinyl Acetate	1022	NL	550
Polyvinyl Acetate/ Alcohol	824		440
Polyvinyl Butyral	734	NL	390
Vinyl Chloride-Acrylonitrile Copolymer	878		470
Polyvinyl Chloride-Dioctyl Phthalate Mixture	608	NL	320
Vinyl Toluene-Acrylonitrile Butadiene Copolymer	936	NL	530
THERMOSETTING RESINS AND MOLDING COMPOUNDS			
Allyl Resins			
Allyl Alcohol Derivative (CR-39)	932	NL	500
Amino Resins			
Urea Formaldehyde Molding Compound	860	NL	460
Urea Formaldehyde-Phenol Formaldehyde Molding Compound (Wood Flour Filler)	464		240

Selected Nonconductive Dusts Classified as Group G, continued

Material	Minimum Cloud or Layer Ignition Temp.[1]		
	°F		°C
Epoxy Resins			
Epoxy	1004	NL	540
Epoxy-Bisphenol A	950	NL	510
Phenol Furfural	590		310
Phenolic Resins			
Phenol Formaldehyde	1076	NL	580
Phenol Formaldehyde Molding Compound (Wood Flour Filler)	932	NL	500
Phenol Formaldehyde, Polyalkylene-Polyamine Modified	554		290
Polyester Resins			
Polyethylene Terephthalate	932	NL	500
Styrene Modified Polyester-Glass Fiber Mixture	680		360
Polyurethane Resins			
Polyurethane Foam, No Fire Retardant	824		440
Polyurethane Foam, Fire Retardant	734		390
SPECIAL RESINS AND MOLDING COMPOUNDS			
Alkyl Ketone Dimer Sizing Compound	320		160
Cashew Oil, Phenolic, Hard	356		180
Chlorinated Phenol	1058	NL	570
Coumarone-Indene, Hard	968	NL	520
Ethylene Oxide Polymer	662	NL	350
Ethylene-Maleic Anhydride Copolymer	1004	NL	540
Lignin, Hydrolized, Wood-Type, Fines	842	NL	450
Petin Acrylate Monomer	428	NL	220
Petroleum Resin (Blown Asphalt)	932		500

Selected Nonconductive Dusts Classified as Group G, continued

Material	Minimum Cloud or Layer Ignition Temp.[1]		
	°F		°C
Rosin, DK	734	NL	390
Rubber, Crude, Hard	662	NL	350
Rubber, Synthetic, Hard (33% S)	608	NL	320
Shellac	752	NL	400
Sodium Resinate	428		220
Styrene-Maleic Anhydride Copolymer	878	CI	470

[1]Normally, the minimum ignition temperature of a layer of a specific dust is lower than the minimum ignition temperature of a cloud of that dust. Since this is not universally true, the lower of the two minimum ignition temperatures is listed. If no symbol appears between the two temperature columns, then the layer ignition temperature is shown. "CI" means the cloud ignition temperature is shown. "NL" means that no layer ignition temperature is available and the cloud ignition temperature is shown. "M" signifies that the dust layer melts before it ignites; the cloud ignition temperature is shown. "S" signifies that the dust layer sublimes before it ignites; the cloud ignition temperature is shown.

(FPN No. 2): The explosion characteristics of air mixtures of dust vary with the materials involved. For Class II locations, Groups E, F, and G, the classification involves the tightness of the joints of assembly and shaft openings to prevent the entrance of dust in the dust-ignitionproof enclosure, the blanketing effect of layers of dust on the equipment that may cause overheating, and the ignition temperature of the dust. It is necessary, therefore, that equipment be approved not only for the class, but also for the specific group of dust that will be present.

(FPN No. 3): Certain dusts may require additional precautions due to chemical phenomena that can result in the generation of ignitible gases. See National Electrical Safety Code, ANSI C2-1990, Section 127A-Coal Handling Areas.

Publication NMAB 353-4, "Classifications of Dusts Relative to Electrical Equipment in Class II Hazardous Locations," published in 1982 by the Committee on Evaluation of Industrial Hazards, National Materials Advisory Board, Commission on Engineering and Technical Systems, National Research Council, National Academy of Sciences, includes a description of test methods to determine the ignition temperatures and electrical resistivity of combustible dusts. The publication is available from the National Technical Information Service (NTIS), Springfield, VA 22151.

(c) **Approval for Class and Properties.** Equipment shall be approved not only for the class of location but also for the explosive, combustible, or ignitible properties of the specific gas, vapor, dust, fiber, or flyings that will be present. In addition, Class I equipment shall not have any exposed surface that operates at a temperature in excess of the ignition temperature of the specific gas or vapor. Class II equipment shall not have an external temperature higher than that specified in Section 500-3(f). Class III equipment shall not exceed the maximum surface temperatures specified in Section 503-1.

Equipment that has been approved for a Division 1 location shall be permitted in a Division 2 location of the same class and group.

Where specifically permitted in Articles 501 through 503, general-purpose equipment or equipment in general-purpose enclosures shall be permitted to be installed in Division 2 locations if the equipment does not constitute a source of ignition under normal operating conditions.

Unless otherwise specified, normal operating conditions for motors shall be assumed to be rated full-load steady conditions.

It is not intended that locked-rotor or other motor overload conditions, such as single phasing, be considered when evaluating motor operating temperatures (internal and external) in Class I, Division 2 locations. However, such abnormal load conditions *are* considered when evaluating external temperatures of explosionproof motors for Class I, Division 1 locations and motors for Class II, Division 1 locations, such as dust-ignitionproof motors.

Where flammable gases or combustible dusts are or may be present at the same time, the simultaneous presence of both shall be considered when determining the safe operating temperature of the electrical equipment.

A coal-handling facility is an example of a location where methane gas and coal dust may be present at the same time.

(FPN): The characteristics of various atmospheric mixtures of gases, vapors, and dusts depend on the specific material involved.

(d) **Marking.** Approved equipment shall be marked to show the Class, Group, and operating temperature or temperature range referenced to a 40°C ambient.

The marked operating temperature or temperature range is referenced to a 40°C (104°F) ambient. Unless the equipment is provided with thermally actuated sensors that limit the temperature to that marked on the equipment, operation in ambient temperatures higher than 40°C (104°F) will increase the operating temperature of the equipment. Many explosionproof and dust-ignitionproof motors are equipped with thermal protectors. In a like manner, operation in ambient temperatures lower than 40°C (104°F) will usually reduce the operating temperature.

The temperature range, if provided, shall be indicated in identification numbers, as shown in Table 500-3(d).

Identification numbers marked on equipment nameplates shall be in accordance with Table 500-3(d).

Equipment that is approved for Class I and Class II shall be marked with the maximum safe operating temperature, as determined by simultaneous exposure to the combinations of Class I and Class II conditions.

Exception No. 1: Equipment of the nonheat-producing type, such as junction boxes, conduit, and fittings and equipment of the heat-producing type having a maximum temperature not more than 100°C (212°F) shall not be required to have a marked operating temperature or temperature range.

Exception No. 2: Fixed lighting fixtures marked for use in Class I, Division 2 or Class II, Division 2 locations only shall not be required to be marked to indicate the group.

Exception No. 3: Fixed general-purpose equipment in Class I locations, other than fixed lighting fixtures, that is acceptable for use in Class I, Division 2 locations shall not be required to be marked with the Class, Group, Division, or operating temperature.

An example of such equipment is a squirrel-cage induction motor without brushes, switching mechanisms, or similar arc-producing devices. See the second paragraph of Section 501-8(b).

Exception No. 4: Fixed dusttight equipment other than fixed lighting fixtures that are acceptable for use in Class II, Division 2 and Class III locations shall not be required to be marked with the Class, Group, Division, or operating temperature.

(e) Class I Temperature. The temperature marking specified in (d) above shall not exceed the ignition temperature of the specific gas or vapor to be encountered.

Table 500-3(d). Identification Numbers

Maximum Temperature Degrees C	Degrees F	Identification Number
450	842	T1
300	572	T2
280	536	T2A
260	500	T2B
230	446	T2C
215	419	T2D
200	392	T3
180	356	T3A
165	329	T3B
160	320	T3C
135	275	T4
120	248	T4A
100	212	T5
85	185	T6

(FPN): Since there is no consistent relationship between explosion properties and ignition temperature, the two are independent requirements.

The ignition temperature of a solid, liquid, or gaseous substance is the minimum temperature required to initiate or cause self-sustained combustion independent of the heating or heated element. The ignition temperature and the flash point are unrelated properties, except that the flash point is always lower than the ignition temperature.

(FPN): For information regarding ignition temperatures of gases and vapors, see Classification of Gases, Vapors, and Dusts for Electrical Equipment in Hazardous (Classified) Locations, NFPA 497M-1991, and Fire Hazard Properties of Flammable Liquids, Gases, and Volatile Solids, NFPA 325M-1991.

Formerly, the temperature limit of each group was assumed to be the lowest ignition temperature of any material in the group, i.e., 280°C (536°F) for Group D and 180°C (356°F) for Group C.

(FPN): To avoid revising this limit as new gases are added (see hexane in Group D and acetaldehyde in Group C), temperature will be specified in future markings.

The ignition temperature for which equipment was approved prior to this requirement shall be assumed to be as follows:

Group A – 280°C (536°F)	Group C – 180°C (356°F)
Group B – 280°C (536°F)	Group D – 280°C (536°F)

The preceding information on ignition for Class I materials was added as a Tentative Interim Amendment to the 1968 edition of the *NEC* and has been part of the *Code* since the 1971 edition. Listed or labeled heat-producing equipment, such as lighting fixtures and motors, manufactured before circa 1975 may not be marked with the operating temperature or temperature range. Unless the actual operating temperatures are marked on the equipment or are otherwise known, the intent is that the operating temperatures noted above be assumed. For multiple rated equipment (e.g., Class I, Groups C and D), the lowest operating temperature (180°C [356°F]) may be assumed.

Flammable gases or vapors are separated into four different atmospheric groups: Groups A, B, C, and D. The *Code* requirements for Class I locations do not vary for different kinds of gas or vapor contained in the atmosphere except in those cases where seals may be used in all conduits to change the group classification. See Exception Nos. 1 and 2 to Section 500-3(a)(2) on materials such as butadiene and ethylene oxide. It is necessary to select equipment that is designed for use in the particular group involved. The reason for designating the groups in this way is that explosive mixtures have different explosion pressures and maximum safe clearances between parts of a joint in an enclosure.

Underwriters Laboratories Inc. and Factory Mutual Research Corp. list or approve electrical equipment suitable for use in all groups of Class I locations and further information is available from the UL Hazardous Locations Equipment Directory and FM Approval Guide. It should be noted (from the UL Directory) that "only those products bearing the appropriate Listing Mark and the company's name, trade name, trademark, or other recognized identification should be considered as covered by UL's Listing and Follow-Up Service." Other testing laboratories may also list equipment for hazardous locations for use in the United States. The acceptance of the listing agency is the responsibility of the authority having jurisdiction.

There are several testing laboratories outside of the United States that also provide "listing," "approval," or "certification" of equipment for use in hazardous locations. However, they may not be testing and investigating the equipment for use in hazardous locations as defined in the *NEC*.

(f) Class II Temperature. The temperature marking specified in (d) above shall be less than the ignition temperature of the specific dust to be encountered. For organic dusts that may dehydrate or carbonize, the temperature marking shall not exceed the lower of either the ignition temperature or 165°C (329°F). See Classification of Gases, Vapors, and Dusts for Electrical Equipment in Hazardous (Classified) Locations, NFPA 497M-1991, for minimum ignition temperatures of specific dusts.

The ignition temperature for which equipment was approved prior to this requirement shall be assumed to be as shown in Table 500-3(f).

Table 500-3(f)

Equipment that is Not Subject to Overloading		Equipment (such as Motors or Power Transformers) that May Be Overloaded			
		Normal Operation		Abnormal Operation	
Class II Group	Degrees C	Degrees F	Degrees C	Degrees F	Degrees C	Degrees F
E	200	392	200	392	200	392
F	200	392	150	302	200	392
G	165	329	120	248	165	329

As in Class I locations, equipment must be approved not only for the class but also for the specific group. It is important that, in addition to the proper selection of equipment, high standards of installation be maintained for subsequent additions or alterations.

The NFPA and ANSI standards referenced in Articles 500 through 517 are essential for proper application of these articles.

The following NFPA standards and recommended practices include information on hazardous (classified) locations and the extent of hazardous (classified) locations in specific occupancies or industries.

NFPA No.	Title of Standard
30	Flammable and Combustible Liquids Code
30A	Automotive and Marine Service Station Code
32	Drycleaning Plants
33	Spray Application Using Flammable and Combustible Materials
34	Dipping and Coating Processes Using Flammable or Combustible Liquids
35	Manufacture of Organic Coatings

NFPA No.	Title of Standard
36	Solvent Extraction Plants
45	Fire Protection for Laboratories Using Chemicals
50A	Gaseous Hydrogen Systems at Consumer Sites
50B	Liquefied Hydrogen Systems at Consumer Sites
51	Design and Installation of Oxygen-Fuel Gas Systems for Welding, Cutting, and Allied Processes
51A	Acetylene Cylinder Charging Plants
52	Compressed Natural Gas (CNG) Vehicular Fuel Systems
54	Natural Fuel Gas Code
58	Storage and Handling of Liquefied Petroleum Gases
59	Storage and Handling of Liquefied Petroleum Gases at Utility Gas Plants
59A	Production, Storage, and Handling of Liquefied Natural Gas (LNG)
61A	Prevention of Fire and Dust Explosions in Facilities Manufacturing and Handling Starch
61B	Prevention of Fires and Explosions in Grain Elevators and Facilities Handling Bulk Raw Agricultural Commodities
61C	Prevention of Fire and Dust Explosions in Feed Mills
61D	Prevention of Fire and Dust Explosions in Milling of Agricultural Commodities for Human Consumption
65	Processing and Finishing of Aluminum
81	Fur Storage, Fumigation, and Cleaning
85C	Prevention of Furnace Explosions/Implosions in Multiple Burner Boiler-Furnaces
85H	Prevention of Combustion Hazards of Atmospheric Fluidized Bed Combustion System Boilers
88A	Parking Structures
88B	Repair Garages
99	Health Care Facilities
407	Aircraft Fuel Servicing
409	Aircraft Hangars
480	Storage, Handling and Processing of Magnesium
481	Production, Processing, Handling, and Storage of Titanium
495	Explosive Materials Code
496	Purged and Pressurized Enclosures for Electrical Equipment
497A	Classification of Class I Hazardous (Classified) Locations for Electrical Installations in Chemical Process Areas
651	Manufacture of Aluminum or Magnesium Powder
654	Prevention of Fire and Dust Explosions in the Chemical, Dye, Pharmaceutical, and Plastics Industries
655	Prevention of Sulfur Fires and Explosions
8503	Pulverized Fuel Systems
8505	Stoker Operations

500-4. **Specific Occupancies.** Articles 510 through 517 cover garages, aircraft hangars, gasoline dispensing and service stations, bulk storage plants, spray application, dipping and coating processes, and health care facilities.

500-5. **Class I Locations.** Class I locations are those in which flammable gases or vapors are or may be present in the air in quantities sufficient to produce explosive or ignitible mixtures. Class I locations shall include those specified in (a) and (b) below.

(a) **Class I, Division 1.** A Class I, Division 1 location is a location (1) in which ignitible concentrations of flammable gases or vapors can exist under normal operating conditions; or (2) in which ignitible concentrations of such gases or vapors may exist frequently because of repair or maintenance operations or because of leakage; or (3) in which breakdown or faulty operation of equipment or processes might release ignitible concentrations of flammable gases or vapors, and might also cause simultaneous failure of electric equipment.

(FPN): This classification usually includes locations where volatile flammable liquids or liquefied flammable gases are transferred from one container to another; interiors of spray booths and areas in the vicinity of spraying and painting operations where volatile flammable solvents are used; locations containing open tanks or vats of volatile flammable liquids; drying rooms or compartments for the evaporation of flammable solvents; locations containing fat and oil extraction equipment using volatile flammable solvents; portions of cleaning and dyeing plants where flammable liquids are used; gas generator rooms and other portions of gas manufacturing plants where flammable gas may escape; inadequately ventilated pump rooms for flammable gas or for volatile flammable liquids; the interiors of refrigerators and freezers in which volatile flammable materials are stored in open, lightly stoppered, or easily ruptured containers; and all other locations where ignitible concentrations of flammable vapors or gases are likely to occur in the course of normal operations.

(b) **Class I, Division 2.** A Class I, Division 2 location is a location (1) in which volatile flammable liquids or flammable gases are handled, processed, or used, but in which the liquids, vapors, or gases will normally be confined within closed containers or closed systems from which they can escape only in case of accidental rupture or breakdown of such containers or systems, or in case of abnormal operation of equipment; or (2) in which ignitible concentrations of gases or vapors are normally prevented by positive mechanical ventilation, and which might become hazardous through failure or abnormal operation of the ventilating equipment; or (3) that is adjacent to a Class I, Division 1 location, and to which ignitible concentrations of gases or vapors might occasionally be communicated unless such communication is prevented by adequate positive-pressure ventilation from a source of clean air, and effective safeguards against ventilation failure are provided.

(FPN No. 1): This classification usually includes locations where volatile flammable liquids or flammable gases or vapors are used but that, in the judgment of the authority having jurisdiction, would become hazardous only in case of an accident or of some unusual operating condition. The quantity of flammable material that might escape in case of accident, the adequacy of ventilating equipment, the total area involved, and the record of the industry or business with respect to explosions or fires are all factors that merit consideration in determining the classification and extent of each location.

(FPN No. 2): Piping without valves, checks, meters, and similar devices would not ordinarily introduce a hazardous condition even though used for flammable liquids or gases. Locations used for the storage of flammable liquids or of liquefied or compressed gases in sealed containers would not normally be considered hazardous unless subject to other hazardous conditions also.

Electrical conduits and their associated enclosures separated from process fluids by a single seal or barrier shall be classed as a Division 2 location if the outside of the conduit and enclosures is an unclassified location.

500-6. **Class II Locations.** Class II locations are those that are hazardous because of the presence of combustible dust. Class II locations shall include those specified in (a) and (b) below.

(a) Class II, Division 1. A Class II, Division 1 location is a location (1) in which combustible dust is in the air under normal operating conditions in quantities sufficient to produce explosive or ignitible mixtures; or (2) where mechanical failure or abnormal operation of machinery or equipment might cause such explosive or ignitible mixtures to be produced, and might also provide a source of ignition through simultaneous failure of electric equipment, operation of protection devices, or from other causes; or (3) in which combustible dusts of an electrically conductive nature may be present in hazardous quantities.

(FPN): Combustible dusts that are electrically nonconductive include dusts produced in the handling and processing of grain and grain products, pulverized sugar and cocoa, dried egg and milk powders, pulverized spices, starch and pastes, potato and woodflour, oil meal from beans and seed, dried hay, and other organic materials that may produce combustible dusts when processed or handled. Only Group E dusts are considered to be electrically conductive for classification purposes. Dusts containing magnesium or aluminum are particularly hazardous, and the use of extreme precaution will be necessary to avoid ignition and explosion.

(b) Class II, Division 2. A Class II, Division 2 location is a location where combustible dust is not normally in the air in quantities sufficient to produce explosive or ignitible mixtures, and dust accumulations are normally insufficient to interfere with the normal operation of electrical equipment or other apparatus, but combustible dust may be in suspension in the air as a result of infrequent malfunctioning of handling or processing equipment and where combustible dust accumulations on, in, or in the vicinity of the electrical equipment may be sufficient to interfere with the safe dissipation of heat from electrical equipment or may be ignitible by abnormal operation or failure of electrical equipment.

(FPN No. 1): The quantity of combustible dust that may be present and the adequacy of dust removal systems are factors that merit consideration in determining the classification and may result in an unclassified area.

(FPN No. 2): Where products such as seed are handled in a manner that produces low quantities of dust, the amount of dust deposited may not warrant classification.

500-7. **Class III Locations.** Class III locations are those that are hazardous because of the presence of easily ignitible fibers or flyings, but in which such fibers or flyings are not likely to be in suspension in the air in quantities sufficient to produce ignitible mixtures. Class III locations shall include those specified in (a) and (b) below.

(a) Class III, Division 1. A Class III, Division 1 location is a location in which easily ignitible fibers or materials producing combustible flyings are handled, manufactured, or used.

(FPN No. 1): Such locations usually include some parts of rayon, cotton, and other textile mills; combustible fiber manufacturing and processing plants; cotton gins and cotton-seed mills; flax-processing plants; clothing manufacturing plants; woodworking plants; and establishments and industries involving similar hazardous processes or conditions.

(FPN No. 2): Easily ignitible fibers and flyings include rayon, cotton (including cotton linters and cotton waste), sisal or henequen, istle, jute, hemp, tow, cocoa fiber, oakum, baled waste kapok, Spanish moss, excelsior, and other materials of similar nature.

(b) Class III, Division 2. A Class III, Division 2 location is a location in which easily ignitible fibers are stored or handled.

Exception: In process of manufacture.

Sections 500-5, 500-6, and 500-7 recognize three classes of hazardous (classified) locations, based on the type of material involved. Within each class there are varying degrees of hazard, so each class is subdivided into two divisions. The classification by division is based on the likelihood the material will be present. The requirements for Division 1 of each class are more stringent than those for Division 2.

The materials in the three classes are defined as follows: Class I, flammable gases or vapors; Class II, combustible dust; and Class III, combustible fibers or flyings.

Where a given location is classified as hazardous, it should not be difficult to determine in which of the three classes it belongs. Common sense and good judgment must prevail in classifying an area that is likely to become hazardous and in determining those portions of the premises to be classed Division 1 or Division 2.

ARTICLE 501   Class I Locations

Contents

501-1. **General.** The general rules of this Code shall apply to the electric wiring and equipment in locations classified as Class I in Section 500-5.

Exception: As modified by this article.

The most common Class I locations are those areas involved in the handling or processing of volatile flammable liquids such as gasoline, naphtha, benzene, diethyl ether, and acetone, or flammable gases such as hydrogen, methane, and propane.

Where ignitible concentrations (concentrations within the flammable or explosive limits) of flammable gases or vapors are present, atmospheres exist that are explosive when ignited by an arc, a spark, or high temperature. NFPA 325M-1991, *Fire Hazard Properties of Flammable Liquids, Gases, and Volatile Solids*, includes information on the explosive limits of flammable liquids, gases, and volatile solids. All electrical equipment that may cause ignition-capable arcs or sparks should be kept out of Class I locations where practicable. If this is not practicable, such apparatus must be approved for the purpose and installed properly. The arc produced at the contacts of listed or labeled intrinsically safe equipment is not ignition-capable because the energy available is insufficient to cause ignition.

Hermetic sealing of all electrical equipment is impractical because equipment such as motors, conventional switches, and circuit breakers have movable parts that must be operated through the enclosing case; that is, the lever of a switch or the shaft of a motor must have sufficient clearance to operate freely.

In addition, in many cases it is necessary to have access to the inside of enclosures for installation, servicing, or alterations.

It is practically impossible to make threaded conduit joints gastight. The conduit system and apparatus enclosure "breathe" due to temperature changes, and any flammable gases or vapors in the room may slowly enter the conduit or enclosure creating an explosive mixture. Should an arc occur, an explosion could take place.

When an explosion occurs within the enclosure or conduit system, the burning mixture, or hot gases, must be sufficiently confined within the system to prevent ignition of any explosive mixture that might be present in the room. An apparatus enclosure must be designed with sufficient strength to withstand the maximum pressure that can be generated by an internal explosion in order to prevent rupture and the release of burning or hot gases. Enclosures have been designed to withstand such internal explosions. Such enclosures are by definition "explosionproof."

It has been found that during an explosion within an enclosure, gases will escape through any paths or openings that exist, but the gases will be sufficiently cooled where carried out through an opening that is long in proportion to its width; that is, the spiral path of at least five fully engaged threads of a screwed-on junction box cover, as illustrated in Figure 501-1. This principle is also applied in the design of explosionproof enclosures for apparatus where a wide machined flange on the body of the enclosure and a similar machined flange on the cover are provided. These machined flanges are so ground that, when the cover is seated in place, the clearance between the two surfaces will at no point exceed, for example, 0.0015 inches. If an explosion occurs within the enclosure, escaping gas travels a considerable distance through a very small opening. It is, therefore, sufficiently cooled when it enters and mixes with the surrounding atmosphere that ignition of the external explosive mixture cannot occur.

The clearance between flat surfaces may increase somewhat under explosion conditions because the internal pressures created by the explosion tend to force the surfaces apart. The amount of increase in the joint clearance depends on the "stiffness" of the enclosure parts, the size, strength, and spacing of the bolts, and the explosion pressure. See Figure 501-3. Simply measuring the joint width and clearance when there are no internal pressures will not indicate what the actual clearances will be under the dynamic conditions of an explosion.

Explosion tests are usually needed to demonstrate the acceptability of the design.

Figure 501-1. *Hot gases are cooled as they pass through the threads of a screw-type cover of an explosionproof junction box.*

Figure 501-2. *Hot gases are cooled as they pass across a machined-flanged joint. The clearance between the machined surfaces is kept very small.*

Normal clearance

Clearance during explosion

Figure 501-3. Effect of internal explosion on cover-to-body joint clearance in explosionproof enclosure. (Underwriters Laboratories Inc.)

501-2. Transformers and Capacitors.

(a) Class I, Division 1. In Class I, Division 1 locations, transformers and capacitors shall comply with the following:

(1) Containing Liquid that Will Burn. Transformers and capacitors containing a liquid that will burn shall be installed only in approved vaults that comply with Sections 450-41 through 450-48, and, in addition, (1) there shall be no door or other communicating opening between the vault and the Division 1 location; and (2) ample ventilation shall be provided for the continuous removal of flammable gases or vapors; and (3) vent openings or ducts shall lead to a safe location outside of buildings; and (4) vent ducts and openings shall be of sufficient area to relieve explosion pressures within the vault, and all portions of vent ducts within the buildings shall be of reinforced concrete construction.

(2) Not Containing Liquid that Will Burn. Transformers and capacitors that do not contain a liquid that will burn shall (1) be installed in vaults complying with (a)(1) above or (2) be approved for Class I locations.

(b) Class I, Division 2. In Class I, Division 2 locations, transformers and capacitors shall comply with Sections 450-21 through 450-27.

501-3. Meters, Instruments, and Relays.

(a) Class I, Division 1. In Class I, Division 1 locations, meters, instruments, and relays, including kilowatt-hour meters, instrument transformers, resistors, rectifiers, and thermionic tubes, shall be provided with enclosures approved for Class I, Division 1 locations.

See the comments on purged and pressurized enclosures for electrical equipment in hazardous (classified) locations following Section 500-2, FPN No. 2, and the comments on explosionproof enclosures following the exception to Section 501-1.

Enclosures approved for Class I, Division 1 locations include (1) explosionproof enclosures and (2) purged and pressurized enclosures.

(FPN): See Purged and Pressurized Enclosures for Electrical Equipment, NFPA 496-1989 (ANSI).

(b) Class I, Division 2. In Class I, Division 2 locations, meters, instruments, and relays shall comply with the following:

(1) Contacts. Switches, circuit breakers, and make-and-break contacts of pushbuttons, relays, alarm bells, and horns shall have enclosures approved for Class I, Division 1 locations in accordance with (a) above.

Exception: General-purpose enclosures shall be permitted, if current-interrupting contacts are:

a. Immersed in oil; or

b. Enclosed within a chamber hermetically sealed against the entrance of gases or vapors; or

There are several types of hermetic seals, including fusion seals such as the glass-to-metal seals in mercury tube switches and some reed switches, welded seals, soldered seals, and seals made with gaskets. Seals of the glass-to-metal fusion type are usually the most reliable. Soft solder seals can be relatively porous, and their effectiveness is highly dependent on workmanship. Although gasketed seals can be very effective, depending on the gasket material used, gasket materials can be damaged and can deteriorate rapidly where exposed to atmospheres containing solvent vapors.

c. In nonincendive circuits that under normal conditions do not release sufficient energy to ignite a specific ignitible atmospheric mixture.

The word "nonincendive" as used here originated in publications of the Instrument Society of America (ISA), such as ISA Monogram No. 1110. It first appeared in this section and Section 501-14(b)(1) in the 1975 edition of the

Code. It means that, under the conditions specified, there is insufficient energy available to cause ignition. "Nonincendive" is similar to "intrinsically safe," which is defined in Article 504 and ANSI/UL 913, but does not include consideration of faults and all of the abnormal conditions inherent in the definition of intrinsically safe. A circuit may be nonincendive in a Group D atmosphere, but not in a Group C atmosphere, as the minimum ignition energies for the various flammable materials differ. Also see the definition of "Nonincendive Circuit" in Article 100.

(2) Resistors and Similar Equipment. Resistors, resistance devices, thermionic tubes, rectifiers, and similar equipment that are used in or in connection with meters, instruments, and relays shall comply with (a) above.

Exception: General-purpose-type enclosures shall be permitted if such equipment is without make-and-break or sliding contacts [other than as provided in (b)(1) above] and if the maximum operating temperature of any exposed surface will not exceed 80 percent of the ignition temperature in degrees Celsius of the gas or vapor involved or has been tested and found incapable of igniting the gas or vapor.

The intent of "or has been tested and found incapable of igniting the gas or vapor" is to permit listed equipment with operating temperatures higher than 80 percent of the ignition temperature. If the equipment has been tested, the safety factor inherent in this 80 percent rule is not needed. The system of temperature measurement must be specified, as 80 percent of a temperature in degrees Celsius is not the same temperature as 80 percent of that temperature in degrees Fahrenheit.

(3) Without Make-or-Break Contacts. Transformer windings, impedance coils, solenoids, and other windings that do not incorporate sliding or make-or-break contacts shall be provided with enclosures. General-purpose-type enclosures shall be permitted.

(4) General-Purpose Assemblies. Where an assembly is made up of components for which general-purpose enclosures are acceptable as provided in (b)(1), (b)(2), and (b)(3) above, a single general-purpose enclosure shall be acceptable for the assembly. Where such an assembly includes any of the equipment described in (b)(2) above, the maximum obtainable surface temperature of any component of the

assembly shall be clearly and permanently indicated on the outside of the enclosure. Alternatively, approved equipment shall be permitted to be marked to indicate the temperature range for which it is suitable, using the identification numbers of Table 500-3(d).

(5) Fuses. Where general-purpose enclosures are permitted in (b)(1), (b)(2), (b)(3), and (b)(4) above, fuses for overcurrent protection of instrument circuits not subject to overloading in normal use shall be permitted to be mounted in general-purpose enclosures if each such fuse is preceded by a switch complying with (b)(1) above.

(6) Connections. To facilitate replacements, process control instruments shall be permitted to be connected through flexible cord, attachment plug, and receptacle, provided (1) a switch complying with (b)(1) above is provided so that the attachment plug is not depended on to interrupt current; and (2) the current does not exceed 3 amperes at 120 volts, nominal; and (3) the power-supply cord does not exceed 3 feet (914 mm), is of a type approved for extra-hard usage or for hard usage if protected by location, and is supplied through an attachment plug and receptacle of the locking and grounding type; and (4) only necessary receptacles are provided; and (5) the receptacle carries a label warning against unplugging under load.

501-4. **Wiring Methods.** Wiring methods shall comply with (a) and (b) below.

(a) Class I, Division 1. In Class I, Division 1 locations, threaded rigid metal conduit, threaded steel intermediate metal conduit, or Type MI cable with termination fittings approved for the location shall be the wiring method employed. All boxes, fittings, and joints shall be threaded for connection to conduit or cable terminations and shall be explosionproof. Threaded joints shall be made up with at least five threads fully engaged. Type MI cable shall be installed and supported in a manner to avoid tensile stress at the termination fittings. Where necessary to employ flexible connections, as at motor terminals, flexible fittings approved for Class I locations shall be used.

Exception: As provided in Section 501-11.

This section indicates that termination fittings used with Type MI cable are required to be approved for the specific purpose. It is intended that Type MI cable fittings approved and marked [see Section 500-3(d)] for the hazardous (classified) location class and group be used.

Type MI cable fittings have a clamp-type joint that must be investigated to determine that it is explosionproof. Type MI cable fittings suitable for nonhazardous locations may not be suitable for Class I, Division 1 hazardous (classified) locations. See Figure 501-4. Rigid metal conduit and intermediate metal conduit are required to be threaded with a (NPT) standard conduit cutting die that provides ¾-inch taper per foot, and five full threads must be engaged. Each joint is required to be made up tight at couplings and unions, and threaded hubs of junction boxes, device boxes, and conduit bodies, etc.

Figure 501-5 shows an explosionproof junction box having three hubs and a threaded opening for the screw-type cover. Unused openings must be effectively closed by inserting threaded metal plugs engaging at least five full threads and affording protection equivalent to that of the wall of the box. Figure 501-6 shows a larger type explosionproof junction box with a bolted flanged cover.

Figure 501-7 shows a flexible fitting, which is available in lengths up to 3 feet, for use in Class I, Division 1 locations. The fitting consists of a deeply corrugated bronze tube with an internal nonmetallic tubular protective liner and an outer cover of braided fine bronze wires. A threaded fitting is securely attached to each end of the flexible tube. The flexible fitting is commonly used at motor connections, can withstand continuous vibration for long periods of time, is explosionproof, and affords maximum protection to any enclosed conductors.

Figure 501-4. Type MI cable and fitting. The flat joint between the gland body and the compression ring, and between the compression ring and the gland nut, must be explosionproof. Also, the threaded connections must be explosionproof. Type MI cable fittings not investigated for use in hazardous locations may not be explosionproof.

Figure 501-5. An explosionproof junction box with a screw-type cover. (Crouse-Hinds)

Figure 501-6. Cutaway view of explosionproof junction box and bolted flanged cover. (Appleton Electric Co.)

Figure 501-7. A flexible explosionproof fitting. (Crouse-Hinds)

(b) Class I, Division 2. In Class I, Division 2 locations, threaded rigid metal conduit, threaded steel intermediate metal conduit, enclosed gasketed busways, enclosed gasketed wireways, or Type PLTC cable in accordance with the provisions of Article 725, Type MI, MC, MV, TC, or SNM cable with approved termination fittings shall be the wiring method employed. Type PLTC, MI, MC, MV, TC, or SNM cable shall be permitted to be installed in cable tray systems and shall be installed in a manner to avoid tensile stress at the termination fittings. Boxes, fittings, and joints shall not be required to be explosionproof except as required by Sections 501-3(b)(1), 501-6(b)(1), and 501-14(b)(1). Where provision must be made for limited flexibility, as at motor terminals, flexible metal fittings, flexible metal conduit with approved fittings, liquidtight flexible metal conduit with approved fittings, liquidtight flexible nonmetallic conduit with approved fittings, or flexible cord approved for extra-hard usage and provided with approved bushed fittings shall be used. An additional conductor for grounding shall be included in the flexible cord.

In Class I, Division 2 locations, boxes, fittings, and joints are not required to be explosionproof at lighting outlets or at enclosures containing no arcing devices. Where general-purpose enclosures are permitted by this section, rigid or intermediate metal conduit may be used with locknuts and bushings; however, a bonding jumper with proper fittings is required to be used between the enclosure and the raceway to ensure adequate bonding from the hazardous area to the point of grounding for the service equipment. See Section 501-16(a).

Where limited flexibility is necessary and approved fittings are required for use with flexible metal conduit, liquidtight flexible conduit, and extra-hard usage flexible cord, the fittings are not required to be specifically approved for Class I locations. Also, where flexible conduit or liquidtight flexible conduit is used, internal or external bonding jumpers with proper fittings are required to be provided in accordance with Section 501-16(b) and the exception to this section.

This section also permits a variety of cables, cable tray systems in accordance with Section 318-3(d), enclosed gasketed wireways, and enclosed gasketed busways. The cable and cable fittings, cable trays, wireways, and busways are not required to be specifically listed or labeled for Class I locations. For example, if Type MC cable is used, neither the cable nor the fittings need to be listed for use in hazardous (classified) locations. Type AC cable is not a permitted wiring method in Section 501-4(b). This is due to concern about arcing between convolutions during ground fault conditions. This prohibition is new in the 1993 Code.

Any wiring method suitable for ordinary locations may be used in a nonincendive circuit. See Section 501-4(b), Exception.

(FPN): See Section 501-16(b) for grounding requirements where flexible conduit is used.

Exception: Wiring in nonincendive circuits shall be permitted using any of the methods suitable for wiring in ordinary locations.

This exception is intended to permit what have been termed "nonincendive field circuits." See comments on "nonincendive" following Item c of the exception to Section 501-3(b)(1) and the definition of "Nonincendive Circuit" in Article 100. Many low-voltage, low-energy circuits are of this type. However, a Class 2 circuit as defined in Article 725 is not necessarily nonincendive. There is considerable equipment listed by such testing laboratories as Factory Mutual Research Corp. and Underwriters Laboratories Inc. that have nonincendive circuits intended for field wiring in the various groups in Class I, Division 2 locations. Some common telephone circuits and thermocouple circuits are also nonincendive.

501-5. **Sealing and Drainage.** Seals in conduit and cable systems shall comply with (a) through (f) below. Sealing compound shall be of a type approved for the conditions and use. Sealing compound shall be used in Type MI cable termination fittings to exclude moisture and other fluids from the cable insulation.

See Figures 501-9, 501-10, and 501-11. Also see commentary following Section 501-5(f)(3).

(FPN No. 1): Seals are provided in conduit and cable systems to minimize the passage of gases and vapors and prevent the passage of flames from one portion of the electrical installation to another through the conduit. Such communication through Type MI cable is inherently prevented by construction of the cable. Unless specifically designed and tested for the purpose, conduit and cable seals are not intended to prevent the passage of liquids, gases, or vapors at a continuous pressure differential across the seal. Even at differences in pressure across the seal equivalent to a few inches of water, there may be a slow passage of gas or vapor through a seal, and through conductors passing through the seal. See Section 501-5(e)(2). Temperature extremes and highly corrosive liquids and vapors can affect the ability of seals to perform their intended function. See Section 501-5(c)(2).

(FPN No. 2): Gas or vapor leakage and propagation of flames may occur through the interstices between the strands of standard stranded conductors larger than No. 2. Special conductor constructions, e.g., compacted strands or sealing of the individual strands, are means of reducing leakage and preventing the propagation of flames.

The sealing compound used in conduit seal fittings is somewhat porous, so that gases, particularly those under slight pressure and gases with small molecules such as hydrogen, can pass slowly through the sealing compound. Also, the seal is around the insulation on the conductor, and gases can be transmitted slowly through the air spaces (the interstices) between strands of stranded conductors. See Section 501-5(e)(2), FPN No. 2. However, experience has shown that under normal conditions for the smaller conductors, and with only normal atmospheric pressure differentials across the seal, the passage of gas through a seal is not sufficient to result in a hazard. However, for larger conductors, see FPN No. 2. Sealing fittings should only be used with the sealing compound or compounds recommended by the fitting manufacturer. Sealing compounds have different rates of expansion and contraction that may affect their function within a given fitting.

The use of teflon tapes or joint compounds on conduit threads may weaken the seal fitting and interrupt the equipment grounding path. Cracks have occurred during hydrostatic testing of fittings where these materials have been used.

(a) Conduit Seals, Class I, Division 1. In Class I, Division 1 locations, conduit seals shall be located as follows:

(1) In each conduit run entering an enclosure for switches, circuit breakers, fuses, relays, resistors, or other apparatus that may produce arcs, sparks, or high temperatures. Seals shall be installed within 18 inches (457 mm) from such enclosures. Explosionproof unions, couplings, reducers, elbows, capped elbows, and conduit bodies similar to "L," "T," and "Cross" types shall be the only enclosures or fittings permitted between the sealing fitting and the enclosure. The conduit bodies shall not be larger than the largest trade size of the conduits.

Exception: Conduit 1½ inches and smaller entering an explosionproof enclosure for switches, circuit breakers, fuses, relays, or other apparatus that may produce arcs or sparks shall not be required to be sealed if the current-interrupting contacts are:

a. Enclosed within a chamber hermetically sealed against the entrance of gases or vapors, or

b. Immersed in oil in accordance with Section 501-6(b)(1)(2).

(2) In each conduit of 2-inch size or larger entering the enclosure or fitting housing terminals, splices, or taps and within 18 inches (457 mm) of such enclosure or fitting.

(FPN): See Section 500-3(c)(2).

(3) Where two or more enclosures for which seals are required under (a)(1) and (a)(2) above are connected by nipples or by runs of conduit not more than 36 inches (914 mm) long, a single seal in each such nipple connection or run of conduit shall be considered sufficient if located not more than 18 inches (457 mm) from either enclosure.

See Figure 501-8.

Figure 501-8. *Two seals are required here so that the run of conduit between Enclosure No. 1 and Enclosure No. 2 is sealed. Even if Enclosure No. 3 were not required to be sealed, the seal in the vertical run of conduit to Enclosure No. 3 would be required to be sealed within 18 inches of Enclosure No. 1 because the vertical conduit run to the "T" fitting is a conduit run to Enclosure No. 1.*

(4) In each conduit run leaving the Class I, Division 1 location. The sealing fitting shall be permitted on either side of the boundary of such location but shall be so designed and installed to minimize the amount of gas or vapor that may have entered the conduit system within the Division 1 location from being communicated to the conduit beyond the seal. There shall be no union, coupling, box, or fitting in the conduit between the sealing fitting and the point at which the conduit leaves the Division 1 location.

Exception: Metal conduit containing no unions, couplings, boxes, or fittings that passes completely through a Class I, Division 1 location with no fittings less than 12 inches (305 mm) beyond each boundary shall not be required to be sealed if the termination points of the unbroken conduit are in unclassified locations.

(b) Conduit Seals, Class I, Division 2. In Class I, Division 2 locations, conduit seals shall be located as follows:

(1) For connections to explosionproof enclosures that are required to be approved for Class I locations, seals shall be provided in accordance with (a)(1), (a)(2), and (a)(3) above. All portions of the conduit run or nipple between the seal and such enclosure shall comply with Section 501-4(a).

(2) In each conduit run passing from a Class I, Division 2 location into an unclassified location. The sealing fitting shall be permitted on either side of the boundary of such location but shall be so designed and installed to minimize the amount of gas or vapor that may have entered the conduit system within the Division 2 location from being communicated to the conduit beyond the seal. Rigid metal conduit or threaded steel intermediate metal conduit shall be used between the sealing fitting and the point at which the conduit leaves the Division 2 location, and a threaded connection shall be used at the sealing fitting. There shall be no union, coupling, box, or fitting in the conduit between the sealing fitting and the point at which the conduit leaves the Division 2 location.

Exception No. 1: Metal conduit containing no unions, couplings, boxes, or fittings that passes completely through a Class I, Division 2 location with no fittings less than 12 inches (305 mm) beyond each boundary shall not be required to be sealed if the termination points of the unbroken conduit are in unclassified locations.

Exception No. 2: Conduit systems terminating at an outdoor unclassified location where a wiring method transition is made to cable tray, cablebus, ventilated busway, Type MI cable, or open wiring shall not be required to be sealed where passing from the Class I, Division 2 location into the unclassified area. The conduits shall not terminate at an enclosure containing an ignition source.

(c) Class I, Divisions 1 and 2. Where required, seals in Class I, Division 1 and 2 locations shall comply with the following:

(1) Fittings. Enclosures for connections or equipment shall be provided with an approved integral means for sealing, or sealing fittings approved for Class I locations shall be used. Sealing fittings shall be accessible.

(2) Compound. Sealing compound shall be approved and shall provide a seal against passage of gas or vapors through the seal fitting, shall not be affected by the surrounding atmosphere or liquids, and shall not have a melting point of less than 93°C (200°F).

(3) Thickness of Compounds. In a completed seal, the minimum thickness of the sealing compound shall not be less than the trade size of the conduit and, in no case, less than ⅝ inch (16 mm).

(4) Splices and Taps. Splices and taps shall not be made in fittings intended only for sealing with compound, nor shall other fittings in which splices or taps are made be filled with compound.

(5) Assemblies. In an assembly where equipment that may produce arcs, sparks, or high temperatures is located in a compartment separate from the compartment containing splices or taps, and an integral seal is provided where conductors pass from one compartment to the other, the entire assembly shall be approved for Class I locations. Seals in conduit connections to the compartment containing splices or taps shall be provided in Class I, Division 1 locations where required by (a)(2) above.

(d) Cable Seals, Class I, Division 1. In Class I, Division 1 locations, each multiconductor cable in conduit shall be considered as a single conductor if the cable is incapable of transmitting gases or vapors through the cable core. These cables shall be sealed in accordance with (a) above.

Cables with a gas/vapor-tight continuous sheath capable of transmitting gases or vapors through the cable core shall be sealed in the Division 1 location after removing the jacket and any other coverings so that the sealing compound will surround each individual insulated conductor and the outer jacket.

Exception: Multiconductor cables with a gas/vapor-tight continuous sheath capable of transmitting gases or vapors through the cable core shall be permitted to be considered as a single conductor by sealing the cable in the conduit within 18 inches (457 mm) of the enclosure and the cable end within the enclosure by an approved means to prevent the entrance of gases or vapors or propagation of flame into the cable core, or by other approved methods.

The intent of the exception is to permit flat computer cables, coaxial cables, and twisted pairs to be treated as single conductor cables, since separating the individual conductors or removing the outer jacket (of a coaxial cable, for example) is impractical and can destroy the electrical properties of the cable. In addition to the cable seal, the end of the cable within the enclosure must also be sealed.

(e) Cable Seals, Class I, Division 2. In Class I, Division 2 locations, cable seals shall be located as follows:

(1) Cables entering enclosures that are required to be approved for Class I locations shall be sealed at the point of entrance. The sealing fitting shall comply with (b)(1) above. Multiconductor cables with a gas/vapor-tight continuous sheath capable of transmitting gases or vapors through the cable core shall be sealed in an approved fitting in the Division 2 location after removing the jacket and any other coverings so that the sealing compound will surround each individual insulated conductor in such a manner as to minimize the passage of gases and vapors. Multiconductor cables in conduit shall be sealed as described in (d) above.

(2) Cables with a gas/vapor-tight continuous sheath and that will not transmit gases or vapors through the cable core in excess of the quantity permitted for seal fittings shall not be required to be sealed except as required in (e)(1) above. The minimum length of such cable run shall not be less than that length that limits gas or vapor flow through the cable core to the rate permitted for seal fittings [0.007 cubic feet per hour (198 cubic centimeters per hour) of air at a pressure of 6 inches of water (1493 pascals)].

The ability of a cable to transmit gases or vapors through the core (primarily between insulated conductors) depends not only on how tightly packed the conductors are within the outer sheaths, and the location and composition of fillers, but also on how the cable has been handled and the geometry of the cable run. If there is any question as to whether or not the cable run is capable of transmitting gases or vapors through the core, sealing is suggested. See Section 501-5, FPN No. 2.

(FPN No. 1): See Outlet Boxes and Fittings for Use in Hazardous Locations, ANSI/UL 886-1985.

(FPN No. 2): The cable core does not include the interstices of the conductor strands.

The intent is that the conductors themselves be individually sealed, such as by dipping the ends in wax, before measuring the rate of flow. However, if this is done, the wax should be removed before making electrical connections or putting the system into service.

(3) Cables with a gas/vapor-tight continuous sheath capable of transmitting gases or vapors through the cable core shall not be required to be sealed except as required in (e)(1) above, unless the cable is attached to process equipment or devices that may cause a pressure in excess of 6 inches (1493 pascals) of water to be exerted at a cable end, in which case a seal, barrier, or other means shall be provided to prevent migration of flammables into an unclassified area.

Exception: Cables with an unbroken gas/vapor-tight continuous sheath shall be permitted to pass through a Class I, Division 2 location without seals.

(4) Cables that do not have gas/vapor-tight continuous sheath shall be sealed at the boundary of the Division 2 and unclassified location in such a manner as to minimize the passage of gases or vapors into an unclassified location.

(FPN): The sheath mentioned in (d) and (e) above may be either metal or a nonmetallic material.

(f) Drainage.

(1) Control Equipment. Where there is a probability that liquid or other condensed vapor may be trapped within enclosures for control equipment or at any point in the raceway system, approved means shall be provided to prevent accumulation or to permit periodic draining of such liquid or condensed vapor.

See Figure 501-12.

(2) Motors and Generators. Where the authority having jurisdiction judges that there is a probability that liquid or condensed vapor may accumulate within motors or generators, joints and conduit systems shall be arranged to minimize entrance of liquid. If means to prevent accumulation or to permit periodic draining are judged necessary, such means shall be provided at the time of manufacture and shall be considered an integral part of the machine.

(3) Canned Pumps, Process or Service Connections, Etc. For canned pumps, process or service connections for flow, pressure, or analysis measurement, etc., that depend upon a single compression seal, diaphragm, or tube to prevent flammable or combustible fluids from entering the electrical conduit system, an additional approved seal, barrier, or other means shall be provided to prevent the flammable or combustible fluid from entering the conduit system beyond the additional devices or means, if the primary seal fails.

The additional approved seal or barrier and the interconnecting enclosure shall meet the temperature and pressure conditions to which they will be subjected upon failure of the primary seal, unless other approved means are provided to accomplish the purpose above.

Drains, vents, or other devices shall be provided so that primary seal leakage will be obvious.

Other means of preventing flammable or combustible fluid from entering the conduit system employed by the liquefied natural gas industry is the use of a vented enclosure containing busbars or specifically designed process connected instrumentation. The conduit from the canned pump terminates at the enclosure, and the conductors are connected to one end of the solid busbars. The circuit continues through the short busbar section to another set of conductors and a sealed conduit.

(FPN): See also the last paragraph of Section 500-5(b) and Fine Print Notes to Section 501-5.

Seals in conduits are used to prevent an explosion from traveling through the conduit to another enclosure, and to minimize the passage of gases or vapors from a hazardous (classified) location to a nonhazardous location. Sealing compound must be used as soon as possible on Type MI cable terminations to exclude moisture from cable insulation.

Where the conduit enters an enclosure containing arcing or high-temperature equipment, a sealing fitting is required to be placed within 18 inches of the enclosure it isolates; conduit bodies ("L," "T," etc.), couplings, unions, and elbows are the only enclosures or fittings permitted between the seal and the enclosure. See Figure 501-13 for an approved type of union. If two enclosures are spaced not more than 36 inches apart, a single seal may be placed between two connecting nipples if the seal is located not more than 18 inches from either enclosure.

In each 2-inch or larger conduit, a sealing fitting is required to be placed within 18 inches of the entrance to an explosionproof enclosure that houses terminals, splices, or taps.

A sealing fitting is required where the conduit leaves a Division 1 location or passes from a Division 2 location to a nonhazardous location. The sealing fitting is permitted on either side of the boundary, and there is to be no union, coupling, box, etc., between the seal and the boundary. It is preferable to locate the fitting on the nonhazardous location side. This sealing fitting serves two purposes: It completes the explosionproof wiring and the enclosure system. Note that a $1/2$-inch conduit connected to an explosionproof box containing only splices, even in a Division 1 location, is not required to be sealed within 18 inches of the box. The seal at the boundary of the Division 1 location serves to complete the explosionproof system. The sealing fitting at the boundary also prevents the conduit system from serving as a pipe to transmit flammable mixtures from a Division 1 or Division 2 location to a nonhazardous location.

In Class I, Division 2 locations, a seal is required in each conduit entering an enclosure that is required to be explosionproof in order to complete the explosionproof enclosure.

Figure 501-9 illustrates the proper sealing of a fitting. A dam must be provided to prevent the sealing material from running out of the fitting while it is still in the liquid state. All conductors must be separated to permit the sealing material to run between them. The sealing compound is required to have a minimum thickness of not less than the trade size of the conduit and in no case less than $5/8$ inch. Conduit fittings for sealing are for use only with sealing compound supplied with the fitting and specified by the manufacturer in instructions furnished with the fitting.

Unless the additional seal or barrier, described in Section 501-5(f)(3), and interconnecting enclosures meet the performance requirements of the primary seal, the application of pressure or exposure to extreme temperatures must be prevented at the additional seal or barrier, so that the process fluid will not enter the conduit system if the primary seal fails. If the process fluid is a gas or can become a gas under ordinary atmospheric conditions (liquefied natural gas, for example), the drain mentioned in Section 501-5(f)(3) should be a vent. See commentary following Section 501-5(f)(3).

The necessary sealing may be accomplished by a sealing fitting and compound. To eliminate the time-consuming task of field-poured seals, a factory-sealed device with the seal designed into the device is permissible. A wide selection of factory-sealed devices is available for a variety of installations in hazardous (classified) locations. Factory-sealed devices are usually marked as such. Explosionproof motors are normally factory sealed, and no other seal is required. Where a conduit terminates in a motor, however, and if the conduit is 2 inches or larger, a seal is required to be placed within 18 inches of the motor terminal housing.

Figure 501-11 shows a sealing fitting designed for use in a vertical run of conduit to provide drainage for any condensation of moisture trapped by the seal above an enclosure. Any accumulation of water runs down over the surface of the sealing compound, flowing through an explosionproof drain. Figure 501-10 illustrates a sealing fitting designed for either a horizontal or vertical conduit run. Figure 501-12 shows a combination drain and breather fitting. These fittings are specially designed to serve as a water drain and an air vent while providing positive explosionproof protection. The fitting permits the escape of accumulated water through its drain, and the breather allows the continuous circulation of air, preventing condensation of any moisture that may be present. Individual drain or breather fittings are also available. It is good practice to consider the installation of drain, breather, or combination fittings in order to guard against water accumulation, which can cause future insulation failures, even though prevalent conditions may not indicate a need.

Figure 501-14 illustrates a Class I, Division 1 location using threaded rigid metal conduit or threaded intermediate metal conduit and explosionproof fittings and equipment including motors, motor controllers, pushbutton stations,

lighting outlets, and junction boxes. The enclosures for the disconnecting means and motor controller for the motor (right portion of the drawing) are placed in a nonhazardous location and are thus not required to be explosionproof.

Each of the three conduits is sealed on the nonhazardous side before passing into the hazardous (classified) location. The pigtail leads of both motors are factory sealed at the motor-terminal housing, and, unless the size of the flexible fitting entering the motor-terminal housing is 2 inch trade size or larger, no other seals are needed at this point. Because the pushbutton control station and the motor controller and disconnect (left portion of the drawing) are considered arc-producing devices, conduits are sealed within 18 inches of the entrance to these enclosures. Seals are required even though the contacts may be immersed in oil.

A seal is provided within 18 inches of the lighting switch. The design of the lighting fixture, as required by ANSI/UL 844, is such that the explosionproof chamber for the wiring must be separated or sealed from the lamp compartment; hence a separate seal is not required adjacent to lighting fixtures complying with ANSI/UL 844. The lighting fixture is suspended on a conduit stem threaded into the cover of an explosionproof ceiling box. See Section 501-9.

Figure 501-10. A sealing fitting for a horizontal or vertical conduit run with a removable screw-type fitting for draining purposes. (Appleton Electric Co.)

Figure 501-9. A sealing fitting placed in a run of conduit to minimize the passage of gases from one portion of the electrical installation to another. (Crouse-Hinds)

Figure 501-11. *A sealing fitting with an automatic drain plug. (Appleton Electric Co.)*

Figure 501-12. *A combination breather-drainage fitting. (Appleton Electric Co.)*

Figure 501-13. *An explosionproof union. (Appleton Electric Co.)*

501-6. **Switches, Circuit Breakers, Motor Controllers, and Fuses.**

(a) Class I, Division 1. In Class I, Division 1 locations, switches, circuit breakers, motor controllers, and fuses, including pushbuttons, relays, and similar devices, shall be provided with enclosures, and the enclosure in each case, together with the enclosed apparatus, shall be approved as a complete assembly for use in Class I locations.

(b) Class I, Division 2. Switches, circuit breakers, motor controllers, and fuses in Class I, Division 2 locations shall comply with the following:

(1) Type Required. Circuit breakers, motor controllers, and switches intended to interrupt current in the normal performance of the function for which they are installed shall be provided with enclosures approved for Class I, Division 1 locations in accordance with Section 501-3(a), unless general-purpose enclosures are provided and (1) the interruption of current occurs within a chamber hermetically sealed against the entrance of gases and vapors, or (2) the current make-and-break contacts are oil-immersed and of the general-purpose type having a 2-inch (50.8-mm) minimum immersion for power contacts and a 1-inch (25.4-mm) minimum immersion for control contacts, or (3)

Figure 501-14. *A Class I, Division 1 location where threaded metal conduits, sealing fittings, explosionproof fittings, and equipment for power and lights are used.*

the interruption of current occurs within a factory-sealed explosionproof chamber approved for the location.

(2) Isolating Switches. Fused or unfused disconnect and isolating switches for transformers or capacitor banks that are not intended to interrupt current in the normal performance of the function for which they are installed shall be permitted to be installed in general-purpose enclosures.

(3) Fuses. For the protection of motors, appliances, and lamps, other than as provided in (b)(4) below, standard plug or cartridge fuses shall be permitted, provided they are placed within enclosures approved for the location; or fuses shall be permitted if they are within general-purpose enclosures, and if they are of a type in which the operating element is immersed in oil or other approved liquid, or the operating element is enclosed within a chamber hermetically sealed against the entrance of gases and vapors.

(4) Fuses or Circuit Breakers for Overcurrent Protection. Where not more than ten sets of approved enclosed fuses or not more than ten circuit breakers that are not intended to be used as switches for the interruption of current are installed for branch-circuit or feeder protection in any one room, area, or section of the Class I, Division 2 location, general-purpose-type enclosures for such fuses or circuit breakers shall be permitted if the fuses or circuit breakers are for the protection of circuits or feeders supplying lamps in fixed positions only.

(FPN): A set of fuses is all the fuses required to protect all the ungrounded conductors of a circuit. For example, a group of three fuses protecting an ungrounded 3-phase circuit and a single fuse protecting the ungrounded conductor of an identified 2-wire, single-phase circuit is a set of fuses in each instance.

Fuses complying with (b)(3) above shall not be required to be included in counting the ten sets of fuses permitted in general-purpose enclosures.

(5) Fuses Internal to Lighting Fixtures. Approved cartridge fuses shall be permitted as supplementary protection within lighting fixtures.

Figure 501-15 shows an explosionproof panelboard consisting of an assembly of branch-circuit devices enclosed in a cast-metal explosionproof housing. These panelboards are provided with bolted access covers and threaded conduit-entry hubs designed to withstand the force of an internal explosion.

Figure 501-16 shows an open and closed view of a cylindrical-type ("spin-top") combination motor controller, a motor control starter, and circuit breaker in an explosionproof enclosure. The top and bottom covers are threaded on for quick removal for installation and servicing. Figure 501-17 shows the same type of equipment in a rectangular enclosure with a hinged, bolted-on cover. These types of housings are designed to accommodate a wide range of manually or magnetically operated across-the-line types of motor starters in a variety of ratings.

Figure 501-18 illustrates a standard toggle switch in an explosionproof enclosure.

Figure 501-15. *An explosionproof panelboard with provisions for 12 circuits. (Appleton Electric Co.)*

In Class I, Division 2 locations, it is assumed that fuses or circuit breakers will seldom open the circuit where used to protect feeders or branch circuits supplying lamps in fixed positions only. Division 2 locations are not normally hazardous but may become so [see Section 500-5(b)], and since it is unlikely that the fuse or circuit breaker in such a circuit will operate simultaneously with the occurrence of an explosive mixture inside the enclosure, general-purpose enclosures are permitted for such overcurrent devices.

Section 501-6(b)(5) permits fuses, often used for ballast protection in high-intensity-discharge and outdoor fluorescent fixtures.

Figure 501-16. *An explosionproof enclosure for a motor control starter and circuit breaker (open and closed views). (Appleton Electric Co.)*

Figure 501-17. *A magnetic motor starter for use in a Class I, Group D location. Note the number of securing bolts and the width of the flange. (General Electric Co.)*

Single–pole single–throw toggle switch

Figure 501-18. *A standard toggle switch in an explosionproof enclosure.*

501-7. **Control Transformers and Resistors.** Transformers, impedance coils, and resistors used as, or in conjunction with, control equipment for motors, generators, and appliances shall comply with (a) and (b) below.

(a) **Class I, Division 1.** In Class I, Division 1 locations, transformers, impedance coils, and resistors, together with any switching mechanism associated with them, shall be provided with enclosures approved for Class I, Division 1 locations in accordance with Section 501-3(a).

(b) **Class I, Division 2.** In Class I, Division 2 locations, control transformers and resistors shall comply with the following:

(1) **Switching Mechanisms.** Switching mechanisms used in conjunction with transformers, impedance coils, and resistors shall comply with Section 501-6(b).

(2) **Coils and Windings.** Enclosures for windings of transformers, solenoids, or impedance coils shall be permitted to be of the general-purpose type.

(3) **Resistors.** Resistors shall be provided with enclosures; and the assembly shall be approved for Class I locations, unless resistance is nonvariable and maximum operating temperature, in degrees Celsius, will not exceed 80 percent of the ignition temperature of the gas or vapor involved, or has been tested and found incapable of igniting the gas or vapor.

501-8. Motors and Generators.

(a) Class I, Division 1. In Class I, Division 1 locations, motors, generators, and other rotating electric machinery shall be (1) approved for Class I, Division 1 locations; or (2) of the totally enclosed type supplied with positive-pressure ventilation from a source of clean air with discharge to a safe area, so arranged to prevent energizing of the machine until ventilation has been established and the enclosure has been purged with at least 10 volumes of air, and also arranged to automatically deenergize the equipment when the air supply fails; or (3) of the totally enclosed inert gas-filled type supplied with a suitable reliable source of inert gas for pressuring the enclosure, with devices provided to ensure a positive pressure in the enclosure and arranged to automatically deenergize the equipment when the gas supply fails; or (4) of a type designed to be submerged in a liquid that is flammable only when vaporized and mixed with air, or in a gas or vapor at a pressure greater than atmospheric and that is flammable only when mixed with air; and the machine is so arranged to prevent energizing it until it has been purged with the liquid or gas to exclude air, and also arranged to automatically deenergize the equipment when the supply of liquid or gas or vapor fails or the pressure is reduced to atmospheric.

Totally enclosed motors of Types (2) or (3) shall have no external surface with an operating temperature in degrees Celsius in excess of 80 percent of the ignition temperature of the gas or vapor involved. Appropriate devices shall be provided to detect and automatically deenergize the motor or provide an adequate alarm if there is any increase in temperature of the motor beyond designed limits. Auxiliary equipment shall be of a type approved for the location in which it is installed.

(FPN): See ASTM Test Procedure (Designation D 2155-69).

The intent of Section 501-8(a), item (4) is to permit nonexplosionproof motors submerged in liquefied natural gas (LNG), liquefied petroleum gas (LPG), etc. It does not permit nonexplosionproof motors under water, such as in wet pits, unless the motors are provided with some other system of explosion protection, e.g., purged per NFPA 496-1989, *Standard for Purged and Pressurized Enclosures for Electrical Equipment.*

The ASTM test procedure is used to determine the ignition temperature of some flammable and combustible liquids.

(b) Class I, Division 2. In Class I, Division 2 locations, motors, generators, and other rotating electric machinery in which are employed sliding contacts, centrifugal or other types of switching mechanism (including motor overcurrent, overloading, and overtemperature devices), or integral resistance devices, either while starting or while running, shall be approved for Class I, Division 1 locations, unless such sliding contacts, switching mechanisms, and resistance devices are provided with enclosures approved for Class I, Division 2 locations in accordance with Section 501-3(b). The exposed surface of space heaters used to prevent condensation of moisture during shutdown periods shall not exceed 80 percent of the ignition temperature in degrees Celsius of the gas or vapor involved when operated at rated voltage, and the maximum surface temperature [based upon a 40°C (104°F) ambient] shall be permanently marked on a visible nameplate mounted on the motor. Otherwise, space heaters shall be approved for Class I, Division 2 locations.

Many motor heaters are deenergized automatically when the motor is running. However, the heater ratings are usually low when compared to the normal heat generated during motor operation. Unless otherwise indicated on the motor wiring diagram or in instructions provided with the motor, there is no need to deenergize the heater except to save energy. Note the requirement (new in the 1993 *Code*) for marking the heater temperature on the motor or the use of heaters approved for the location.

In Class I, Division 2 locations, the installation of open or nonexplosionproof enclosed motors, such as squirrel-cage induction motors without brushes, switching mechanisms, or similar arc-producing devices, shall be permitted.

(FPN No. 1): It is important to consider the temperature of internal and external surfaces that may be exposed to the flammable atmosphere.

(FPN No. 2): It is important to consider the risk of ignition due to currents arcing across discontinuities and overheating of parts in multisection enclosures of large motors and generators. Such motors and generators may require equipotential bonding jumpers across joints in the enclosures and from enclosure to ground and clean-air purging immediately prior to and during start-up periods.

Large induction motors may produce ignition-capable arcs and heating at discontinuities in the enclosure under starting conditions. For more information, see "Risks of Ignition Due to Transient Currents in Large Induction Motors."

It is intended that the phrase "other rotating electric machinery" include electric brakes. Listed and labeled electric brakes are available for Class I, Division 1, Group C and D locations.

Figures 501-19 and 501-20 show closed and opened views of a totally enclosed fan-cooled motor approved for use in explosive atmospheres. The main frame and end-bells are designed with sufficient strength to withstand an internal explosion, and flames or hot gases are cooled while escaping because of the wide metal-to-metal joints between the frame and the end-bells and the long, close-tolerance clearance provided for the free-turn of the shaft. Air circulation outside the motor is maintained by a nonsparking (aluminum, bronze, or a nonstatic-generating-type plastic) fan on the end opposite the shaft end of the motor. A sheet metal housing surrounds this fan to reduce the likelihood of an individual or object coming into contact with the moving blades and to direct the flow of air. Internal fans on the shaft circulate air around the windings.

Motors that have arcing or sparking devices, such as commutators, internal switches, or other control devices, must be explosionproof. General-purpose squirrel-cage induction motors may be used in Division 2 locations.

Since some open-type motors are permitted in Class I, Division 2 locations, care should be exercised in selecting the motor types where flammable gases or vapors with very low ignition temperatures may be present. Modern motors with high-temperature insulation systems, such as Class H (180°C [356°F]), may operate close to or above the ignition temperature of the flammable mixture.

Figure 501-19. Terminal housing of a motor approved for use in specific hazardous locations. Note integral sealing of the motor. (General Electric Co.)

501-9. **Lighting Fixtures.** Lighting fixtures shall comply with (a) or (b) below.

(a) Class I, Division 1. In Class I, Division 1 locations, lighting fixtures shall comply with the following:

(1) **Approved Fixtures.** Each fixture shall be approved as a complete assembly for the Class I, Division 1 location and shall be clearly marked to indicate the maximum wattage of lamps for which it is approved. Fixtures intended for portable use shall be specifically approved as a complete assembly for that use.

(2) **Physical Damage.** Each fixture shall be protected against physical damage by a suitable guard or by location.

(3) **Pendant Fixtures.** Pendant fixtures shall be suspended by and supplied through threaded rigid metal conduit stems or threaded steel intermediate conduit stems, and threaded joints shall be provided with set-screws or other effective means to prevent loosening. For stems longer than 12 inches (305 mm), permanent and effective bracing against lateral displacement shall be provided at a level not more than 12 inches (305 mm) above the lower end of the stem, or

flexibility in the form of a fitting or flexible connector approved for the Class I, Division 1 location shall be provided not more than 12 inches (305 mm) from the point of attachment to the supporting box or fitting.

(4) **Supports.** Boxes, box assemblies, or fittings used for the support of lighting fixtures shall be approved for Class I locations.

(b) Class I, Division 2. In Class I, Division 2 locations, lighting fixtures shall comply with the following:

(1) **Portable Lighting Equipment.** Portable lighting equipment shall comply with (a)(1) above.

Exception: Where portable lighting equipment are mounted on movable stands and are connected by flexible cords, as covered in Section 501-11, they shall be permitted, where mounted in any position, provided that they conform to Section 501-9(b)(2) below.

(2) **Fixed Lighting.** Lighting fixtures for fixed lighting shall be protected from physical damage by suitable guards or by location. Where there is danger that falling sparks or hot metal

from lamps or fixtures might ignite localized concentrations of flammable vapors or gases, suitable enclosures or other effective protective means shall be provided. Where lamps are of a size or type that may, under normal operating conditions, reach surface temperatures exceeding 80 percent of the ignition temperature in degrees Celsius of the gas or vapor involved, fixtures shall comply with (a)(1) above or shall be of a type that has been tested in order to determine the marked operating temperature or temperature range.

(3) Pendant Fixtures. Pendant fixtures shall be suspended by threaded rigid metal conduit stems, threaded steel intermediate metal conduit stems, or by other approved means. For rigid stems longer than 12 inches (305 mm), permanent and effective bracing against lateral displacement shall be provided at a level not more than 12 inches (305 mm) above the lower end of the stem, or flexibility in the form of an approved fitting or flexible connector shall be provided not more than 12 inches (305 mm) from the point of attachment to the supporting box or fitting.

(4) Switches. Switches that are a part of an assembled fixture or of an individual lampholder shall comply with Section 501-6(b)(1).

(5) Starting Equipment. Starting and control equipment for electric-discharge lamps shall comply with Section 501-7(b).

Exception: A thermal protector potted into a thermally protected fluorescent lamp ballast if the lighting fixture is approved for locations of this Class and Division.

Figures 501-21 and 501-22 show typical lighting fixtures for Class I, Group C and D locations and a variety of parts of a complete lighting fixture assembly. The outlet boxes have an internally threaded opening designed to receive the cover. A pendant fixture is attached to the cover by threaded rigid metal conduit or threaded intermediate metal conduit. To prevent loosening from vibration or lamp changing, threaded joints are required to be provided with setscrews. The setscrews should not interrupt the explosionproof joint. Rigid metal conduit or intermediate metal conduit stems longer than 12 inches require effective bracing or a flexible fitting approved for the purpose and placed not more than 12 inches from the point of attachment to the supporting box, cover, or fitting.

A globeholder is threaded onto the body of the fixture housing and supports a heavy glass globe, guard, and reflector. It is available in sizes suitable for lamps from 40 W through 500 W. In designing any hazardous (classified) location lighting system, operating temperatures must be considered. Therefore, if the area is Class I, Division 1, fixtures approved for this location, and properly marked, must be used. Generally, enclosed and gasketed fixtures (previously called vaportight fixtures) without guards, if breakage is unlikely, or fixtures approved for Class I, Division 2 locations, are required in Division 2 locations. Fixtures listed by Underwriters Laboratories Inc. for use in any of the groups under Class I, either Division 1 or 2 locations, or both, are designed to operate without causing ignition of surrounding flammable gas or vapor atmospheres, and are marked with the operating temperature or temperature range code. See Table 500-3(b).

Figure 501-23 shows an explosionproof handlamp. It is required that lamp compartments be sealed from the terminal compartment. Provisions are required to be made for the connection of 3-conductor (one must be a grounding conductor), flexible, extra-hard usage cord. See Section 501-11.

Figure 501-21. A typical lighting fixture for use in Class I, Group C and D locations. (Crouse-Hinds)

Class I, Division 1 – Fixture hanging methods.

GRC GRFC GRJS CPST GRT EFHC

Hub cover Union hub cover GRK Canopy cover Hub cover Hub cover LC couplings

Rigid conduit 12" Maximum length ESD Swivel EXHF Flexible couplings EXGF Flexible couplings

AA51 Pendant fixture

Figure 501-22. Various components used in an explosionproof lighting fixture installation. (Appleton Electric Co.)

Figure 501-23. An explosionproof handlamp for use in Class I locations. (Appleton Electric Co.)

501-10. Utilization Equipment.

(a) Class I, Division 1. In Class I, Division 1 locations, all utilization equipment shall be approved for Class I, Division 1 locations.

(b) Class I, Division 2. In Class I, Division 2 locations, all utilization equipment shall comply with the following:

(1) Heaters. Electrically heated utilization equipment shall conform with either item a or b below.

a. The heater shall not exceed 80 percent of the ignition temperature in degrees Celsius of the gas or vapor involved on any surface that is exposed to the gas or vapor when continuously energized at the maximum rated ambient temperature. If a temperature controller is not provided, these conditions shall apply when the heater is operated at 120 percent of rated voltage.

Exception No. 1: For motor-mounted anticondensation space heaters, see Section 501-8(b).

Exception No. 2: A current-limiting device is applied to the circuit serving the heater that will limit the current in the heater to a value less than that required to raise the heater surface temperature to 80 percent of the ignition temperature.

b. The heater shall be approved for Class I, Division 1 locations.

Exception: Electrical resistance heat tracing approved for Class 1, Division 2 locations.

(2) Motors. Motors of motor-driven utilization equipment shall comply with Section 501-8(b).

(3) Switches, Circuit Breakers, and Fuses. Switches, circuit breakers, and fuses shall comply with Section 501-6(b).

The requirements for utilization equipment in Class I locations are virtually identical for Division 1 and 2 locations, except for heaters. Electric pipe heat tracing systems listed for Class I, Division 2 locations and complying with Section 501-10(b)(1) b, Exception, are available.

501-11. Flexible Cords, Class I, Divisions 1 and 2. A flexible cord shall be permitted only for connection between portable lighting equipment or other portable utilization equipment and the fixed portion of its supply circuit; and, where used, shall (1) be of a type approved for extra-hard usage; (2) contain, in addition to the conductors of the circuit, a grounding conductor complying with Section 400-23; (3) be connected to terminals or to supply conductors in an approved manner; (4) be supported by clamps or by other suitable means in such a manner that there will be no tension on the terminal connections; and (5) be provided with suitable seals where the flexible cord enters boxes, fittings, or enclosures of the explosionproof type.

Exception: As provided in Sections 501-3(b)(6) and 501-4(b).

Electric submersible pumps with means for removal without entering the wet-pit shall be considered portable utilization equipment. The extension of the flexible cord within a suitable raceway between the wet-pit and the power source shall be permitted.

Electric mixers intended for travel into and out of open-type mixing tanks or vats shall be considered portable utilization equipment.

(FPN):   See Section 501-13 for flexible cords exposed to liquids having a deleterious effect on the conductor insulation.

The second paragraph recognizes a wet-pit type of installation that is finding increasing acceptance for use in wastewater systems. This section was revised for the 1993 *Code* to permit a flexible cord to be run in raceway to a junction box outside of the wet-pit.

A new paragraph was also added to the 1993 *Code* to recognize that mixers that travel into and out of open-type mixing tanks are considered portable utilization equipment that may be wired with flexible cord. See commentary following Section 501-8(a).

501-12. Receptacles and Attachment Plugs, Class I, Divisions 1 and 2. Receptacles and attachment plugs shall be of the type providing for connection to the grounding conductor of a flexible cord and shall be approved for the location.

Exception: As provided in Section 501-3(b)(6).

Figure 501-24 shows an explosionproof receptacle and attachment plug with an interlocking switch. The design of this device is such that when the switch is in the "on" position, the plug cannot be removed. Also, the switch cannot be placed in the "on" position when the plug has been removed; that is, the plug cannot be inserted or removed unless the switch is in the "off" position. The receptacle is factory sealed with a provision for threaded-conduit entry to the switch compartment; the plug is to be used with Type S or equivalent extra-hard-service flexible cord having a grounding conductor.

Figure 501-25 shows a 30-A, 4-pole receptacle and attachment plug assembly that is suitable for use without a switch. The design is such that the mating parts of the receptacle and plug are enclosed in a chamber that seals the arc and, by delayed-action construction, prevents complete removal of the plug until the arc or hot metal has cooled. The receptacle is factory sealed and the attachment plug is designed for use with a 4-conductor cord (3-conductor, 3-phase circuit with one grounding conductor) or a 3-conductor cord (two circuit conductors and one grounding conductor).

Figure 501-24.   A receptacle and attachment plug of the explosionproof type with an interlocking switch. The switch must be in the "off" position to remove the attachment plug. (Appleton Electric Co.)

501-13. Conductor Insulation, Class I, Divisions 1 and 2. Where condensed vapors or liquids may collect on, or come in contact with, the insulation on conductors, such insulation shall be of a type approved for use under such conditions; or the insulation shall be protected by a sheath of lead or by other approved means.

Figure 501-25. *A 4-pole (delayed action) explosionproof receptacle and attachment plug suitable for use without a switch. (Appleton Electric Co.)*

Nylon-jacketed conductors, such as Types THWN and TW that are suitable for use where exposed to gasoline, have gained widespread acceptance because of their ease in handling and application, and economics.

An excerpt from Underwriters Laboratories Inc. Electrical Construction Materials Directory states the following under "Wires, Thermoplastic-Insulated":

"Gasoline resistant wire has been tested at 30°C when immersed in gasoline. It is considered inherently resistant to gasoline vapors within the temperature rating of the wire type."

Gasoline Resistant TW — Indicates a TW conductor with a jacket of extruded nylon suitable for use in wet locations, and for exposure to mineral oil, and to liquid gasoline and gasoline vapors at ordinary ambient temperature. It is identified by tag marking and by printing on the insulation or nylon jacket with the designation "Type TW Gasoline and Oil Resistant I."

Also listed for the above use is "Gasoline Resistant THWN" with the designation "Type THWN Gasoline and Oil Resistant I" if suitable for exposure to mineral oil at 60°C, or "Type THWN Gasoline and Oil Resistant II" if the compound is suitable for exposure to mineral oil at 75°C.

It should be noted that other thermoplastic wires may be suitable for exposure to mineral oil; but, with the exception of those marked "Gasoline and Oil Resistant," reference to mineral oil does not include gasoline or similar light-petroleum solvents.

The conductor itself must bear the marking legend designating its use as suitable for gasoline exposure; such designation on the tag alone is not sufficient.

501-14. **Signaling, Alarm, Remote-Control, and Communication Systems.**

(a) **Class I, Division 1.** In Class I, Division 1 locations, all apparatus and equipment of signaling, alarm, remote-control, and communication systems, regardless of voltage, shall be approved for Class I, Division 1 locations, and all wiring shall comply with Sections 501-4(a) and 501-5(a) and (c).

(b) **Class I, Division 2.** In Class I, Division 2 locations, signaling, alarm, remote-control, and communication systems shall comply with the following:

(1) **Contacts.** Switches, circuit breakers, and make-and-break contacts of pushbuttons, relays, alarm bells, and horns shall have enclosures approved for Class I, Division 1 locations in accordance with Section 501-3(a).

Exception: General-purpose enclosures shall be permitted if current-interrupting contacts are:

a. Immersed in oil; or

b. Enclosed within a chamber hermetically sealed against the entrance of gases or vapors; or

c. In nonincendive circuits that under normal conditions do not release sufficient energy to ignite a specific ignitible atmospheric mixture.

See commentary following Item c of Section 501-3(b)(1), Exception.

(2) **Resistors and Similar Equipment.** Resistors, resistance devices, thermionic tubes, rectifiers, and similar equipment shall comply with Section 501-3(b)(2).

(3) **Protectors.** Enclosures shall be provided for lightning protective devices and for fuses. Such enclosures shall be permitted to be of the general-purpose type.

(4) **Wiring and Sealing.** All wiring shall comply with Sections 501-4(b) and 501-5(b) and (c).

Audible signaling devices, such as bells, sirens, and horns, other than the electronic types, usually involve make-and-break contacts that are capable of producing a spark of sufficient energy to cause ignition of a hazardous atmospheric mixture. Therefore, where used in Class I locations, this type of equipment is required to be contained in explosionproof enclosures, wiring methods are required to comply with Section 501-4, and sealing fittings are required to be provided in accordance with Section 501-5. Figure 501-26 shows a signal siren for use in Class I locations.

Explosionproof devices or explosionproof enclosures may prove more practical than oil-immersed contacts because maintaining the condition and level of the oil can be a problem. Hermetically sealed enclosures, such as float-operated mercury-tube switches, are available for some applications. Electronic signal devices without make-and-break contacts will usually not require explosionproof enclosures in Division 2 locations.

Figure 501-26. A signal siren mounted on an explosionproof enclosure for use in hazardous areas. (Crouse-Hinds)

501-15. Live Parts, Class I, Divisions 1 and 2. There shall be no exposed live parts.

Contact with the circuit could produce sparks that could cause an explosion in a hazardous (classified) location.

501-16. Grounding, Class I, Divisions 1 and 2. Wiring and equipment in Class I, Division 1 and 2 locations shall be grounded as specified in Article 250 and with the following additional requirements:

(a) Bonding. The locknut-bushing and double-locknut types of contacts shall not be depended upon for bonding purposes, but bonding jumpers with proper fittings or other approved means of bonding shall be used. Such means of bonding shall apply to all intervening raceways, fittings, boxes, enclosures, etc., between Class I locations and the point of grounding for service equipment or point of grounding of a separately derived system.

Exception: The specific bonding means shall only be required to the point of grounding of a building disconnecting means as specified in Sections 250-24(a), (b), and (c), provided that branch-circuit overcurrent protection is located on the load side of the disconnecting means.

This exception is new in the 1993 *Code*. Where the building in which the hazardous location exists is supplied through a service in another building, it is not necessary to apply the bonding requirement from the hazardous location back to the service. It is only necessary to apply the bonding requirements from the hazardous location back to the building disconnecting means.

(FPN): See Section 250-78 for additional bonding requirements in hazardous (classified) locations.

(b) Types of Equipment Grounding Conductors. Where flexible metal conduit or liquidtight flexible metal conduit is used as permitted in Section 501-4(b) and is to be relied upon to complete a sole equipment grounding path, it shall be installed with internal or external bonding jumpers in parallel with each conduit and complying with Section 250-79.

Special consideration is necessary in the grounding and bonding of exposed noncurrent-carrying metal parts of equipment, such as the frames or metal exteriors of motors, fixed or portable lamps, lighting fixtures, enclosures, and raceways, to ensure permanent and effective mechanical and electrical connections to prevent the possibility of arcs or sparks caused by ineffective or poor grounding methods. To be effective, proper grounding and bonding applies to all interconnected raceways, fittings, enclosures, etc., between hazardous (classified) locations and the point of grounding for service equipment or the point of grounding of building disconnecting means that supplies the branch- circuit overcurrent protection. Where conduit is used in hazardous (classified) locations, it is preferable that threaded connections also be employed in the nonhazardous location.

Exception: In Class I, Division 2 areas, the bonding jumper shall be permitted to be deleted where all the following conditions are met:

a. Approved liquidtight flexible metal conduit 6 feet (1.83 m) or less in length, with approved fittings, is used;

b. Overcurrent protection in the circuit is limited to 10 amperes or less;

c. The load is not a power utilization load.

Figure 501-27. A fitting for the connection of an external bonding jumper used with liquidtight flexible metal conduit.

501-17. Surge Protection.

(a) Class I, Division 1. Surge arresters, including their installation and connection, shall comply with Article 280. The surge arresters and capacitors shall be installed in enclosures approved for Class I, Division 1 locations. Surge-protective capacitors shall be of a type designed for specific duty.

(b) Class I, Division 2. Surge arresters shall be nonarcing, such as metal-oxide varistor (MOV), sealed type, and surge-protective capacitors shall be of a type designed for specific duty. Installation and connection shall comply with Article 280.

Enclosures shall be permitted to be of the general-purpose type. Surge protection of types other than described above shall be installed in enclosures approved for Class I, Division 1 locations.

Some surge arresters, such as the older style lightning arresters, are spark-producing devices. Others, such as solid-state types, are not. Surge arresters should be connected to the service conductors outside the building and be bonded to the service-entrance raceway system. For services less than 1,000 V, the arrester grounding conductor is connected as provided in Section 280-21.

Where the service voltage is less than 600 V, the supply system is a secondary system; therefore, the grounded service conductor should always be bonded to the equipment grounding conductor as required by the provisions of Article 250.

In Class I, Division 1 locations, all surge arresters are required to be installed in explosionproof or purged enclosures. In Class I, Division 2 locations, only the spark-producing types of surge arresters need such protection. They can also be installed in oil-filled enclosures or have the arcing or sparking contacts enclosed in hermetically sealed chambers. The nonsparking type of surge arrester needs no special enclosure in a Class I, Division 2 location.

501-18. Multiwire Branch Circuits. In a Class I, Division 1 location, a separate grounded conductor shall be installed in each single-phase branch circuit that is part of a multiwire branch circuit.

Exception: Where the disconnect device(s) for the circuit opens all ungrounded conductors of the multiwire circuit simultaneously.

ARTICLE 502   Class II Locations

Contents

502-10. Utilization Equipment.
(a) Class II, Division 1.
(b) Class II, Division 2.
502-11. Lighting Fixtures.
(a) Class II, Division 1.
(b) Class II, Division 2.
502-12. Flexible Cords, Class II, Divisions 1 and 2.
502-13. Receptacles and Attachment Plugs.
(a) Class II, Division 1.
(b) Class II, Division 2.
502-14. Signaling, Alarm, Remote-Control, and Communication Systems, Meters, Instruments, and Relays.
(a) Class II, Division 1.
(b) Class II, Division 2.
502-15. Live Parts, Class II, Divisions 1 and 2.
502-16. Grounding, Class II, Divisions 1 and 2.
(a) Bonding.
(b) Types of Equipment Grounding Conductors.
502-17. Surge Protection, Class II, Divisions 1 and 2.
502-18. Multiwire Branch Circuits.

502-1. **General.** The general rules of this Code shall apply to the electric wiring and equipment in locations classified as Class II locations in Section 500-6.

Exception: As modified by this article.

"Dust-ignitionproof," as used in this article, shall mean enclosed in a manner that will exclude dusts and, where installed and protected in accordance with this Code, will not permit arcs, sparks, or heat otherwise generated or liberated inside of the enclosure to cause ignition of exterior accumulations or atmospheric suspensions of a specified dust on or in the vicinity of the enclosure.

(FPN:) For further information on dust-ignitionproof enclosures, see Type 9 enclosure in Enclosures for Electrical Equipment, ANSI/NEMA 250-1985, and Explosionproof and Dust-Ignitionproof Electrical Equipment for Hazardous (Classified) Locations, ANSI/UL 1203-1988.

Equipment installed in Class II locations shall be able to function at full rating without developing surface temperatures high enough to cause excessive dehydration or gradual carbonization of any organic dust deposits that may occur.

(FPN): Dust that is carbonized or excessively dry is highly susceptible to spontaneous ignition.

Equipment and wiring of the type defined in Article 100 as explosionproof shall not be required and shall not be acceptable in Class II locations unless approved for such locations.

See Figure 502-3.

Where Class II, Group E dusts are present in hazardous quantities, there are only Division 1 locations.

Class II, Division 1 and 2 locations are defined in Section 500-6 as hazardous due to the presence of combustible dust. These locations are separated into three groups (see Section 500-3(b)):

It should be noted that equipment suitable for one class and group is not necessarily suitable for any other class and group. To protect against explosions in hazardous (classified) locations, all electrical equipment exposed to the hazardous atmosphere is required to be suitable for such locations. Do not take for granted that equipment suitable for Class I use is also suitable for Class II use. Grain dust, for example, will ignite at a temperature lower than that of most flammable vapors.

Any one, or more, of the following four hazards may be present in a Class II location:

1. An explosive mixture of air and dust;
2. Accumulations of dust that interfere with the safe dissipation of heat from electrical equipment;
3. Accumulation of electrically conductive dust lodging on live parts; and
4. Deposits of dust that could be ignited by arcs or sparks.

In the layout of electrical installations for hazardous (classified) locations, it is preferable to locate service equipment, switchboards, panelboards, and much of the electrical equipment in less hazardous areas, usually in a separate room. The use of pressurized rooms as described in NFPA 496-1989, *Purged and Pressurized Enclosures for Electrical Equipment*, is a common method of protecting panelboards and switchboards in grain elevators and similar locations.

502-2. **Transformers and Capacitors.**

(a) **Class II, Division 1.** In Class II, Division 1 locations, transformers and capacitors shall comply with the following:

(1) **Containing Liquid that Will Burn.** Transformers and capacitors containing a liquid that will burn shall be installed

only in approved vaults complying with Sections 450-41 through 450-48, and, in addition, (1) doors or other openings communicating with the Division 1 location shall have self-closing fire doors on both sides of the wall, and the doors shall be carefully fitted and provided with suitable seals (such as weather stripping) to minimize the entrance of dust into the vault; (2) vent openings and ducts shall communicate only with the outside air; and (3) suitable pressure-relief openings communicating with the outside air shall be provided.

(2) Not Containing Liquid that Will Burn. Transformers and capacitors that do not contain a liquid that will burn shall (1) be installed in vaults complying with Sections 450-41 through 450-48 or (2) be approved as a complete assembly, including terminal connections for Class II locations.

(3) Metal Dusts. No transformer or capacitor shall be installed in a location where dust from magnesium, aluminum, aluminum bronze powders, or other metals of similarly hazardous characteristics may be present.

(b) Class II, Division 2. In Class II, Division 2 locations, transformers and capacitors shall comply with the following:

(1) Containing Liquid that Will Burn. Transformers and capacitors containing a liquid that will burn shall be installed in vaults complying with Sections 450-41 through 450-48.

(2) Containing Askarel. Transformers containing askarel and rated in excess of 25 kVA shall (1) be provided with pressure-relief vents; (2) be provided with a means for absorbing any gases generated by arcing inside the case, or the pressure-relief vents shall be connected to a chimney or flue that will carry such gases outside the building; and (3) have an air space of not less than 6 inches (152 mm) between the transformer cases and any adjacent combustible material.

(3) Dry-type Transformers. Dry-type transformers shall be installed in vaults or shall (1) have their windings and terminal connections enclosed in tight metal housings without ventilating or other openings and (2) operate at not over 600 volts, nominal.

Where it is necessary to install a transformer, it may be possible to construct a small, low-voltage, dusttight (without ventilating openings), dry-type transformer, but transformers having a primary voltage rating of over 600 V are required to be either less-flammable liquid-insulated or installed in a vault. In almost all cases, transformers can be remotely located from dust atmospheres.

Capacitors used for power-factor correction of individual motors are of sealed construction but, if installed in Class II, Division 1 locations, are also required to be approved as a complete assembly including dusttight terminal enclosures. The only special requirement for capacitors in Division 2 locations is that they are not permitted to contain oil or any other liquid that will burn; otherwise they are to be installed in vaults.

Capacitor and transformer oils (such as askarel) that do not burn have, in the past, contained PCBs, and production of such oil has been stopped.

Figure 502-1 illustrates suitable protection for wiring systems in Class II locations supplied from overhead transmission lines. This protection includes surge (lightning) arresters on the primary side of the transformers (within 1,000 feet of the service entrance), surge-protective capacitors connected to the supply side of the main service disconnecting means, and interconnection of all grounds. Arresters should be of the proper voltage rating for the system to which they are connected and, where protecting the primary supply, should be located within 3 feet of the transformers. Surge capacitors are to protect against abrupt increases in voltage and should be provided with automatic means for dissipating any stored charge.

502-4. **Wiring Methods.** Wiring methods shall comply with (a) and (b) below.

(a) Class II, Division 1. In Class II, Division 1 locations, threaded rigid metal conduit, threaded steel intermediate metal conduit, or Type MI cable with termination fittings approved for the location shall be the wiring method employed. Type MI cable shall be installed and supported in a manner to avoid tensile stress at the termination fittings.

(1) Fittings and Boxes. Fittings and boxes shall be provided with threaded bosses for connection to conduit or cable terminations, shall have close-fitting covers, and shall have no openings (such as holes for attachment screws) through which dust might enter or through which sparks or burning material might escape. Fittings and boxes in which taps, joints, or terminal connections are made, or that are used in locations where dusts are of a combustible, electrically conductive nature, shall be approved for Class II locations.

Where boxes or fittings such as conduit L, T, or C fittings are installed in a Class II, Division 1 location and

Figure 502-1. Lightning protection: arrester, interconnected grounding, and surge capacitors.

where splices, taps, or terminations are made within them, they must be of the threaded type with close-fitting covers. There can be no holes in the box or fitting, such as mounting holes that would allow dust to enter or allow sparks or burning material to be ejected from the enclosure. Where used as stated above, the equipment must be approved for Class II locations, usually of the dust-ignitionproof or pressurized type.

Where boxes or fittings of the type described in the preceding paragraph are installed with no splices, taps or terminations made within them, they are required to be dusttight with threaded bosses for connection of conduit or cable connectors.

(2) Flexible Connections. Where necessary to employ flexible connections, dusttight flexible connectors, liquidtight flexible metal conduit with approved fittings, liquidtight flexible nonmetallic conduit with approved fittings, or flexible cord approved for extra-hard usage and provided with bushed fittings shall be used. Where flexible cords are used, they shall comply with Section 502-12. Where flexible connections are subject to oil or other corrosive conditions, the insulation of the conductors shall be of a type approved for the condition or shall be protected by means of a suitable sheath.

(FPN): See Section 502-16(b) for grounding requirements where flexible conduit is used.

(b) Class II, Division 2. In Class II, Division 2 locations, rigid metal conduit, intermediate metal conduit, electrical metallic tubing, dusttight wireways, or Type MC, MI, or SNM cable with approved termination fittings, or Type PLTC in cable trays, or Type MC or TC cable installed in ladder, ventilated trough, or ventilated channel cable trays in a single layer, with a space not less than the larger cable diameter between the two adjacent cables, shall be the wiring method employed.

Exception: Wiring in nonincendive circuits shall be permitted using any of the methods suitable for wiring in ordinary locations.

(1) Wireways, Fittings, and Boxes. Wireways, fittings, and boxes in which taps, joints, or terminal connections are made shall be designed to minimize the entrance of dust and (1) shall be provided with telescoping or close-fitting covers or other effective means to prevent the escape of sparks or burning material and (2) shall have no openings (such as holes for attachment screws) through which, after installation, sparks or burning material might escape or through which adjacent combustible material might be ignited.

(2) Flexible Connections. Where flexible connections are necessary, (a)(2) above shall apply.

Where it is necessary to use flexible connections, liquidtight flexible conduit or extra-hard usage flexible cord is permitted. Another method would be to use a flexible fitting as shown in Figure 501-7. Where liquidtight flexible conduit is used, a bonding jumper (internal or external) is required to be provided around such conduit. See Section 502-16(b). An additional conductor for grounding is required to be provided where flexible cord is used.

In Division 1 locations, boxes containing taps, joints, or terminal connections must be dust-ignitionproof and must be provided with threaded hubs, as shown in Figure 502-2.

To provide adequate bonding in Division 2 locations, use of a threaded hub, as shown in Figure 502-2, is a method of achieving this requirement. Figure 502-2 also shows a close-fitting cover as required for Class II locations. Standard pressed steel boxes are permitted where they do not contain taps, joints, or terminal connections and a bonding jumper is provided around the box.

Figure 502-2. Junction boxes with threaded hubs suitable for use in Class II, Group E hazardous atmospheres. (Appleton Electric Co.)

502-5. Sealing, Class II, Divisions 1 and 2. Where a raceway provides communication between an enclosure that is required to be dust-ignitionproof and one that is not, suitable means shall be provided to prevent the entrance of dust into the dust-ignitionproof enclosure through the raceway. One of the following means shall be permitted: (1) a permanent and effective seal; (2) a horizontal raceway not less than 10 feet (3.05 m) long; or (3) a vertical raceway not less than 5 feet (1.52 m) long and extending downward from the dust-ignitionproof enclosure.

This section provides three suitable ways to prevent dust from entering the dust-ignitionproof enclosure through the raceway where a raceway connects an enclosure that is required to be dust-ignitionproof to one that is not. If sealing fittings are used, any of the fittings designed for use in Class I locations can be used. No sealing method is needed in the special, but not unusual, situation in which no dust can enter the raceway in the hazardous (classified) location. See Figure 502-4.

Where a raceway provides communication between an enclosure that is required to be dust-ignitionproof and an enclosure in an unclassified location, seals shall not be required.

Sealing fittings shall be accessible.

502-6. Switches, Circuit Breakers, Motor Controllers, and Fuses.

(a) **Class II, Division 1.** In Class II, Division 1 locations, switches, circuit breakers, motor controllers, and fuses shall comply with the following:

(1) **Type Required.** Switches, circuit breakers, motor controllers, and fuses, including pushbuttons, relays, and similar devices that are intended to interrupt current during normal operation, or that are installed where combustible dusts of an electrically conductive nature may be present, shall be provided with dust-ignitionproof enclosures, which, together with the enclosed equipment in each case, shall be approved as a complete assembly for Class II locations.

(2) **Isolating Switches.** Disconnecting and isolating switches containing no fuses and not intended to interrupt current and not installed where dusts may be of an electrically conductive nature shall be provided with tight metal enclosures that shall be designed to minimize the entrance of dust and that shall (1) be equipped with telescoping or close-fitting covers or with other effective means to prevent the escape of sparks or burning material and (2) have no openings (such as holes for attachment screws) through which, after installation, sparks or burning material might escape or through which exterior accumulations of dust or adjacent combustible material might be ignited.

(3) **Metal Dusts.** In locations where dust from magnesium, aluminum, aluminum bronze powders, or other metals of similarly hazardous characteristics may be present, fuses, switches, motor controllers, and circuit breakers shall have enclosures specifically approved for such locations.

(b) **Class II, Division 2.** In Class II, Division 2 locations, enclosures for fuses, switches, circuit breakers, and motor controllers, including pushbuttons, relays, and similar devices, shall be dusttight.

The electrical equipment required in Class II locations is slightly different than that for Class I locations. Dust-ignitionproof enclosures for Class II locations are not required to be explosionproof. However, explosionproof equipment is allowed to be used in Class II locations if the equipment is dual rated and identified as suitable for the Class II, division and group. Explosionproof enclosures are not necessarily dust-ignitionproof.

Explosionproof enclosures, where used in a Class II environment, are not required to be sealed within 18 inches of the enclosure to complete the explosionproof assembly as is required in a Class I environment. They must, however, be provided with seals to prevent the entrance of dust into the dust-ignitionproof enclosure, where a raceway provides a means for dust to enter the system, such as in a conduit run between a dust-ignitionproof enclosure and a general-purpose junction box.

Where equipment is located in a Class II, Division 1 location and is likely to produce arcs or sparks during normal operation, it must be installed in a dust-ignitionproof enclosure. In addition, heat-generating equipment, such as control transformers, solenoids, impedance coils, resistors, and any associated overcurrent devices or switching mechanisms, must have dust-ignitionproof enclosures. Use caution where metal dusts such as magnesium, aluminum, or other metals with similar hazardous characteristics may be present; enclosures must be specifically approved for that environment.

Figure 502-3 shows a pushbutton station with pilot light suitable for both Class I and Class II hazardous (classified) locations. Figure 502-5 shows a panelboard suitable for use in Class II locations only. Many, but not all, of the switches or circuit breakers approved for Class I, Division 1 locations are also approved for Class II locations. It is important to always look for the listing and identification of the hazardous (classified) locations for which the listing has been given.

Figure 502-3. *An explosionproof and dusttight pushbutton control station that is suitable for use in Class I, Groups C and D, and Class II, Groups E, F, and G locations. (Appleton Electric Co.)*

502-7. Control Transformers and Resistors.

(a) Class II, Division 1. In Class II, Division 1 locations, control transformers, solenoids, impedance coils, resistors, and any overcurrent devices or switching mechanisms associated with them shall have dust-ignitionproof enclosures approved for Class II locations. No control transformer, impedance coil, or resistor shall be installed in a location where dust from magnesium, aluminum, aluminum bronze powders, or other metals of similarly hazardous characteristics may be present unless provided with an enclosure approved for the specific location.

(b) Class II, Division 2. In Class II, Division 2 locations, transformers and resistors shall comply with the following:

(1) Switching Mechanisms. Switching mechanisms (including overcurrent devices) associated with control transformers, solenoids, impedance coils, and resistors shall be provided with dusttight enclosures.

(2) Coils and Windings. Where not located in the same enclosure with switching mechanisms, control transformers, solenoids, and impedance coils shall be provided with tight metal housings without ventilating openings.

(3) Resistors. Resistors and resistance devices shall have dust-ignition-proof enclosures approved for Class II locations.

Exception: Where the maximum normal operating temperature of the resistor will not exceed 120°C (248°F), nonadjustable resistors or resistors that are part of an automatically timed starting sequence shall be permitted to have enclosures complying with (b)(2) above.

502-8. Motors and Generators.

(a) Class II, Division 1. In Class II, Division 1 locations, motors, generators, and other rotating electrical machinery shall be:

(1) Approved for Class II, Division 1 locations, or

(2) Totally enclosed pipe-ventilated, meeting temperature limitations in Section 502-1.

It is intended that the phrase "other rotating electrical machinery" include electric brakes. Listed and labeled electric brakes are available for Class II, Groups E, F, and G locations.

Although some explosionproof (Class I, Division 1) motors are dust-ignitionproof and approved for both Class I and II locations, this is by no means true of all motors. Always look for the marking to be sure the motor is designed and tested for the Class II location involved. If control wiring to the motor is necessary (see motor installation instruction), be sure the control circuit is properly installed and connected. Most motors for Class II locations require internal thermal protection to comply with the temperature limitations in Section 500-3(f), and integral horsepower Class II motors may require both power and control circuit wiring from the motor controller to the motor.

Figure 502-5. A dust-ignitionproof panelboard for use in Class II, Groups E, F, and G locations. (Crouse-Hinds)

Figure 502-4. Four methods permitted for preventing the entrance of dust into the dust-ignitionproof enclosure through the raceway.

(b) Class II, Division 2. In Class II, Division 2 locations, motors, generators, and other rotating electrical equipment shall be totally enclosed nonventilated, totally enclosed pipe-ventilated, totally enclosed fan-cooled or dust-ignitionproof for which maximum full-load external temperature shall be in accordance with Section 500-3(f) for normal operation when operating in free air (not dust blanketed) and shall have no external openings.

Exception: If the authority having jurisdiction believes accumulations of nonconductive, nonabrasive dust will be moderate and if machines can be easily reached for routine cleaning and maintenance, the following shall be permitted to be installed:

a. Standard open-type machines without sliding contacts, centrifugal or other types of switching mechanism (including motor overcurrent, overloading, and overtemperature devices), or integral resistance devices.

b. Standard open-type machines with such contacts, switching mechanisms, or resistance devices enclosed within dusttight housings without ventilating or other openings.

c. Self-cleaning textile motors of the squirrel-cage type.

Section 502-8(b) permits all types of totally enclosed motors in Class II, Division 2 locations if the external surface temperatures, without a dust blanket, do not exceed the temperatures indicated under maximum full-load (normal operation) conditions in Section 500-3(f). Totally enclosed fan-cooled (TEFC) motors are specifically mentioned. The motor should be examined carefully to be sure there are no external openings, even though the motor may be marked "TEFC."

Figure 502-6 shows a totally enclosed pipe-ventilated motor illustrating intake piping through which cool, clean air is delivered to the motor from a fan or blower. The exhaust opening is connected to a pipe discharging to the outside of the building in order to prevent dust accumulation inside the motor.

Totally enclosed motors that have no special provision for cooling may be used in Class II, Division 2 locations, but to deliver the same horsepower, they must be considerably larger than an open-type, fan-cooled, or pipe-ventilated motor.

Figure 502-6. A pipe-ventilated motor that meets the temperature limitations of Section 502-1. (General Electric Co.)

502-9. **Ventilating Piping.** Ventilating pipes for motors, generators, or other rotating electric machinery, or for enclosures for electric equipment, shall be of metal not less than 0.021 inch (533 micrometers) in thickness, or of equally substantial noncombustible material, and shall comply with the following: (1) lead directly to a source of clean air outside of buildings; (2) be screened at the outer ends to prevent the entrance of small animals or birds; and (3) be protected against physical damage and against rusting or other corrosive influences.

Ventilating pipes shall also comply with (a) and (b).

(a) Class II, Division 1. In Class II, Division 1 locations, ventilating pipes, including their connections to motors or to the dust-ignitionproof enclosures for other equipment, shall be dusttight throughout their length. For metal pipes, seams and joints shall comply with one of the following: (1) be riveted and soldered; (2) be bolted and soldered; (3) be welded; or (4) be rendered dusttight by some other equally effective means.

(b) Class II, Division 2. In Class II, Division 2 locations, ventilating pipes and their connections shall be sufficiently tight to prevent the entrance of appreciable quantities of dust into the ventilated equipment or enclosure and to prevent the escape of sparks, flame, or burning material that might ignite dust accumulations or combustible material in the vicinity. For metal pipes, lock seams and riveted or welded joints shall be permitted; and tight-fitting slip joints shall be permitted where some flexibility is necessary, as at connections to motors.

502-10. **Utilization Equipment.**

(a) Class II, Division 1. In Class II, Division 1 locations, all utilization equipment shall be approved for Class II locations. Where dust from magnesium, aluminum, aluminum bronze powders, or other metals of similarly hazardous characteristics may be present, such equipment shall be approved for the specific location.

(b) Class II, Division 2. In Class II, Division 2 locations, all utilization equipment shall comply with the following:

(1) Heaters. Electrically heated utilization equipment shall be approved for Class II locations.

Exception: Metal-enclosed radiant heating panel equipment shall be dusttight and marked in accordance with Section 500-3(d).

(2) Motors. Motors of motor-driven utilization equipment shall comply with Section 502-8(b).

(3) Switches, Circuit Breakers, and Fuses. Enclosures for switches, circuit breakers, and fuses shall be dusttight.

(4) Transformers, Impedance Coils, and Resistors. Transformers, solenoids, impedance coils, and resistors shall comply with Section 502-7(b).

502-11. **Lighting Fixtures.** Lighting fixtures shall comply with (a) and (b) below.

(a) Class II, Division 1. In Class II, Division 1 locations, lighting fixtures for fixed and portable lighting shall comply with the following:

(1) Approved Fixtures. Each fixture shall be approved for Class II locations and shall be clearly marked to indicate the maximum wattage of the lamp for which it is approved. In locations where dust from magnesium, aluminum, aluminum bronze powders, or other metals of similarly hazardous characteristics may be present, fixtures for fixed or portable lighting and all auxiliary equipment shall be approved for the specific location.

(2) Physical Damage. Each fixture shall be protected against physical damage by a suitable guard or by location.

(3) Pendant Fixtures. Pendant fixtures shall be suspended by threaded rigid metal conduit stems, threaded steel intermediate metal conduit stems, by chains with approved fittings, or by other approved means. For rigid stems longer than 12 inches (305 mm), permanent and effective bracing against lateral displacement shall be provided at a level not more than 12 inches (305 mm) above the lower end of the stem, or flexibility in the form of a fitting or a flexible connector approved for the location shall be provided not more than 12 inches (305 mm) from the point of attachment to the supporting box or fitting. Threaded joints shall be provided with set-screws or other effective means to prevent loosening. Where wiring between an outlet box or fitting and a pendant fixture is not enclosed in conduit, flexible cord approved for hard usage shall be used, and suitable seals shall be provided where the cord enters the fixture and the outlet box or fitting. Flexible cord shall not serve as the supporting means for a fixture.

(4) Supports. Boxes, box assemblies, or fittings used for the support of lighting fixtures shall be approved for Class II locations.

(b) Class II, Division 2. In Class II, Division 2 locations, lighting fixtures shall comply with the following:

(1) Portable Lighting Equipment. Portable lighting equipment shall be approved for Class II locations. They shall be clearly marked to indicate the maximum wattage of lamps for which they are approved.

(2) Fixed Lighting. Lighting fixtures for fixed lighting, where not of a type approved for Class II locations, shall provide enclosures for lamps and lampholders that shall be designed to minimize the deposit of dust on lamps and to prevent the escape of sparks, burning material, or hot metal. Each fixture shall be clearly marked to indicate the maximum wattage of the lamp that shall be permitted without exceeding an exposed surface temperature in accordance with Section 500-3(f) under normal conditions of use.

(3) Physical Damage. Lighting fixtures for fixed lighting shall be protected from physical damage by suitable guards or by location.

(4) Pendant Fixtures. Pendant fixtures shall be suspended by threaded rigid metal conduit stems, threaded steel intermediate metal conduit stems, by chains with approved fittings, or by other approved means. For rigid stems longer than 12 inches (305 mm), permanent and effective bracing against lateral displacement shall be provided at a level not more than 12 inches (305 mm) above the lower end of the stem, or flexibility in the form of an approved fitting or a flexible connector shall be provided not more than 12 inches (305 mm) from the point of attachment to the supporting box or fitting. Where wiring between an outlet box or fitting and a pendant fixture is not enclosed in conduit, flexible cord approved for hard usage shall be used. Flexible cord shall not serve as the supporting means for a fixture.

(5) Electric-Discharge Lamps. Starting and control equipment for electric-discharge lamps shall comply with the requirements of Section 502-7(b).

Figure 502-7 shows a listed fixture suitable for use in Groups E, F, and G of Class II locations. Lighting fixtures, fixed or portable, and auxiliary equipment (such as ballasts) are required to be approved for use in Group E atmospheres where metal dusts are present.

Other than the requirement that the fixture is to be marked to indicate maximum lamp wattage, the only requirements for fixtures in Division 2 locations are that the lamps be enclosed in suitable globes to minimize dust deposits on the lamps and to prevent the escape of sparks or burning material. Guards are required to be provided unless, of course, globe breakage is unlikely.

Flexible cord of the hard-usage type is permitted with approved sealed connections for the wiring of chain-suspended or hook-and-eye suspended fixtures. Flexible cords are not intended to be used as a cord pendant or drop cord.

The portable handlamp shown in Figure 501-23 is approved as a complete assembly for use in Class I locations and also in any Class II, Group F or G location.

Figure 502-7. A typical lighting fixture for use in Class II, Division 1 locations. Where breakage is unlikely, a metal guard is not required.

502-12. **Flexible Cords, Class II, Divisions 1 and 2.** Flexible cords used in Class II locations shall comply with the following: (1) be of a type approved for extra-hard usage; (2) contain, in addition to the conductors of the circuit, a grounding conductor complying with Section 400-23; (3) be connected to terminals or to supply conductors in an approved manner; (4) be supported by clamps or by other suitable means in such a manner that there will be no tension on the terminal connections; and (5) be provided with suitable seals to prevent the entrance of dust where the flexible cord enters boxes or fittings that are required to be dust-ignitionproof.

502-13. **Receptacles and Attachment Plugs.**

(a) Class II, Division 1. In Class II, Division 1 locations, receptacles and attachment plugs shall be of the type providing for connection to the grounding conductor of the flexible cord and shall be approved for Class II locations.

(b) Class II, Division 2. In Class II, Division 2 locations, receptacles and attachment plugs shall be of the type providing for connection to the grounding conductor of the flexible cord and shall be so designed that connection to the supply circuit cannot be made or broken while live parts are exposed.

502-14. **Signaling, Alarm, Remote-Control, and Communication Systems, Meters, Instruments, and Relays.**

(FPN): See Article 800 for rules governing the installation of communication circuits.

(a) Class II, Division 1. In Class II, Division 1 locations, signaling, alarm, remote-control, and communication systems; and meters, instruments, and relays shall comply with the following:

(1) Wiring Methods. The wiring method shall comply with Section 502-4(a).

(2) Contacts. Switches, circuit breakers, relays, contactors, fuses and current-breaking contacts for bells, horns, howlers, sirens, and other devices in which sparks or arcs may be produced shall be provided with enclosures approved for a Class II location.

Exception: Where current-breaking contacts are immersed in oil or where the interruption of current occurs within a chamber sealed against the entrance of dust, enclosures shall be permitted to be of the general-purpose type.

(3) Resistors and Similar Equipment. Resistors, transformers, choke coils, rectifiers, thermionic tubes, and other heat-generating equipment shall be provided with enclosures approved for Class II locations.

Exception: Where resistors or similar equipment are immersed in oil or enclosed in a chamber sealed against the entrance of dust, enclosures shall be permitted to be of the general-purpose type.

(4) Rotating Machinery. Motors, generators, and other rotating electric machinery shall comply with Section 502-8(a).

(5) Combustible, Electrically Conductive Dusts. Where dusts are of a combustible, electrically conductive nature, all wiring and equipment shall be approved for Class II locations.

(6) Metal Dusts. Where dust from magnesium, aluminum, aluminum bronze powders, or other metals of similarly hazardous characteristics may be present, all apparatus and equipment shall be approved for the specific conditions.

(b) Class II, Division 2. In Class II, Division 2 locations, signaling, alarm, remote-control, and communication systems; and meters, instruments, and relays shall comply with the following:

(1) Contacts. Enclosures shall comply with (a)(2) above; or contacts shall have tight metal enclosures designed to minimize the entrance of dust and shall have telescoping or tight-fitting covers and no openings through which, after installation, sparks or burning material might escape.

Exception: In nonincendive circuits that under normal conditions do not release sufficient energy to ignite a dust layer, enclosures shall be permitted to be of the general-purpose type.

(2) Transformers and Similar Equipment. The windings and terminal connections of transformers, choke coils, and similar equipment shall be provided with tight metal enclosures without ventilating openings.

(3) Resistors and Similar Equipment. Resistors, resistance devices, thermionic tubes, rectifiers, and similar equipment shall comply with (a)(3) above.

Exception: Enclosures for thermionic tubes, nonadjustable resistors, or rectifiers for which maximum operating temperature will not exceed 120°C (248°F) shall be permitted to be of the general-purpose type.

(4) Rotating Machinery. Motors, generators, and other rotating electric machinery shall comply with Section 502-8(b).

(5) Wiring Methods. The wiring method shall comply with Section 502-4(b).

502-15. **Live Parts, Class II, Divisions 1 and 2.** Live parts shall not be exposed.

502-16. **Grounding, Class II, Divisions 1 and 2.** Wiring and equipment in Class II, Division 1 and 2 locations shall be grounded as specified in Article 250 and with the following additional requirements:

(a) Bonding. The locknut-bushing and double-locknut types of contact shall not be depended upon for bonding purposes, but bonding jumpers with proper fittings or other approved means of bonding shall be used. Such means of bonding shall apply to all intervening raceways, fittings, boxes, enclosures, etc., between Class II locations and the point of grounding for service equipment or point of grounding of a separately derived system.

Exception: The specified bonding means shall only be required to the point of grounding of a building disconnecting means as specified in Sections 250-24 (a), (b), and (c), provided that branch-circuit protection is located on the load side of the disconnecting means.

(FPN): See Section 250-78 for additional bonding requirements in hazardous (classified) locations.

(b) Types of Equipment Grounding Conductors. Where flexible conduit is used as permitted in Section 502-4, it shall be installed with internal or external bonding jumpers in parallel with each conduit and complying with Section 250-79.

Single locknuts or double locknuts and bushings are not to be depended on for bonding purposes. Bonding jumpers or other approved means with proper fittings are required for the interconnection of all raceways, junction boxes, fittings, enclosures, etc., between the hazardous area and the grounding electrode conductor connection point at the service equipment, the grounding electrode system of the building disconnecting means of separate buildings, or the source of a separately derived system. Where installed outside the raceway or enclosure, the grounding conductor is not to exceed 6 feet and is to be routed with the raceway or enclosure. See Section 250-79.

Exception: In Class II, Division 2 areas, the bonding jumper shall be permitted to be deleted where all the following conditions are met:

a. Approved liquidtight flexible metal conduit 6 feet (1.83 m) or less in length, with approved fittings, is used;
b. Overcurrent protection in the circuit is limited to 10 amperes or less;
c. The load is not a power utilization load.

502-17. **Surge Protection, Class II, Divisions 1 and 2.** Surge arresters, including their installation and connection, shall comply with Article 280. In addition, surge arresters, if installed in a Class II, Division 1 location, shall be in suitable enclosures.

Surge-protective capacitors shall be of a type designed for specific duty.

502-18. **Multiwire Branch Circuits.** In a Class II, Division 1 location, a separate grounded conductor shall be installed in each single-phase branch circuit that is part of a multiwire branch circuit.

Exception: Where the disconnect device(s) for the circuit opens all ungrounded conductors of the multiwire circuit simultaneously.

ARTICLE 503   Class III Locations

Contents

503-1.   **General.** The general rules of this Code shall apply to electric wiring and equipment in locations classified as Class III locations in Section 500-7.

Exception: As modified by this article.

Equipment installed in Class III locations shall be able to function at full rating without developing surface temperatures high enough to cause excessive dehydration or gradual carbonization of accumulated fibers or flyings. Organic material that is carbonized or excessively dry is highly susceptible to spontaneous ignition. The maximum surface temperatures under operating conditions shall not exceed 165°C (329°F) for equipment that is not subject to overloading, and 120°C (248°F) for equipment (such as motors or power transformers) that may be overloaded.

(FPN):   For electric trucks, see Powered Industrial Trucks Including Type Designations, Areas of Use, Maintenance, and Operation, NFPA 505-1992 (ANSI).

Class III locations usually include textile mills (cotton, rayon, etc.) where easily ignitible fibers or combustible flyings are present in the manufacturing process. Sawmills and other woodworking plants, where sawdust, wood shavings, and combustible fibers or flyings are present, may also become hazardous. If wood flour (dust) is present, the location is a Class II, Group G location, not a Class III location.

Fibers or flyings are hazardous not only because they are easily ignited, but also because flames spread through them quickly. Such fires travel with a rapidity approaching an explosion and are commonly called flash fires.

Division 1 of Class III applies to locations where material is handled, manufactured, or used. Division 2 applies to locations where material is stored or handled, but where no manufacturing processes are performed. There are no group designations in Class III locations.

503-2.   **Transformers and Capacitors, Class III, Divisions 1 and 2.** Transformers and capacitors shall comply with Section 502-2(b).

503-3.   **Wiring Methods.** Wiring methods shall comply with (a) and (b) below.

 (a) Class III, Division 1. In Class III, Division 1 locations, the wiring method shall be rigid metal conduit, rigid nonmetallic conduit, intermediate metal conduit, electrical metallic tubing, dusttight wireways, or Type MC, MI, or SNM cable with approved termination fittings.

(1) **Boxes and Fittings.** All boxes and fittings shall be dusttight.

(2) **Flexible Connections.** Where necessary to employ flexible connections, dusttight flexible connectors, liquidtight flexible metal conduit with approved fittings, liquidtight flexible nonmetallic conduit with approved fittings, or flexible cord in conformance with Section 503-10 shall be used.

(FPN): See Section 503-16(b) for grounding requirements where flexible conduit is used.

(b) **Class III, Division 2.** In Class III, Division 2 locations, the wiring method shall comply with (a) above.

Exception: In sections, compartments, or areas used solely for storage and containing no machinery, open wiring on insulators shall be permitted where installed in accordance with Article 320, but only on condition that protection as required by Section 320-14 be provided where conductors are not run in roof spaces and are well out of reach of sources of physical damage.

503-4. **Switches, Circuit Breakers, Motor Controllers, and Fuses, Class III, Divisions 1 and 2.** Switches, circuit breakers, motor controllers, and fuses, including pushbuttons, relays, and similar devices, shall be provided with dusttight enclosures.

See definition of "Dusttight" in Article 100.

503-5. **Control Transformers and Resistors, Class III, Divisions 1 and 2.** Transformers, impedance coils, and resistors used as or in conjunction with control equipment for motors, generators, and appliances shall be provided with dusttight enclosures complying with the temperature limitations in Section 503-1.

See definition of "Dusttight" in Article 100.

503-6. **Motors and Generators, Class III, Divisions 1 and 2.** In Class III, Division 1 and 2 locations, motors, generators, and other rotating machinery shall be totally enclosed nonventilated, totally enclosed pipe-ventilated, or totally enclosed fan-cooled.

Exception: In locations where, in the judgment of the authority having jurisdiction, only moderate accumulations of lint or flyings will be likely to collect on, in, or in the vicinity of a rotating electric machine and where such machine is readily accessible for routine cleaning and maintenance, one of the following shall be permitted:

a. Self-cleaning textile motors of the squirrel-cage types;

b. Standard open-type machines without sliding contacts, centrifugal or other types of switching mechanism, including motor overload devices; or

c. Standard open-type machines having such contacts, switching mechanisms, or resistance devices enclosed within tight housings without ventilating or other openings.

It is intended that the phrase "other rotating machinery" include electric brakes. Listed and labeled electric brakes are available for Class II, Group G locations, and according to Underwriters Laboratories Inc. Hazardous Location Equipment Directory, such brakes are suitable for Class III locations.

503-7. **Ventilating Piping, Class III, Divisions 1 and 2.** Ventilating pipes for motors, generators, or other rotating electric machinery, or for enclosures for electric equipment, shall be of metal not less than 0.021 inch (533 micrometers) in thickness, or of equally substantial noncombustible material, and shall comply with the following: (1) lead directly to a source of clean air outside of buildings; (2) be screened at the outer ends to prevent the entrance of small animals or birds; and (3) be protected against physical damage and against rusting or other corrosive influences.

Ventilating pipes shall be sufficiently tight, including their connections, to prevent the entrance of appreciable quantities of fibers or flyings into the ventilated equipment or enclosure and to prevent the escape of sparks, flame, or burning material that might ignite accumulations of fibers or flyings or combustible material in the vicinity. For metal pipes, lock seams and riveted or welded joints shall be permitted; and tight-fitting slip joints shall be permitted where some flexibility is necessary, as at connections to motors.

503-8. **Utilization Equipment, Class III, Divisions 1 and 2.**

(a) **Heaters.** Electrically heated utilization equipment shall be approved for Class III locations.

(b) **Motors.** Motors of motor-driven utilization equipment shall comply with Section 503-6.

(c) **Switches, Circuit Breakers, Motor Controllers, and Fuses.** Switches, circuit breakers, motor controllers, and fuses shall comply with Section 503-4.

503-9. Lighting Fixtures, Class III, Divisions 1 and 2.

(a) **Fixed Lighting.** Lighting fixtures for fixed lighting shall provide enclosures for lamps and lampholders that are designed to minimize entrance of fibers and flyings and to prevent the escape of sparks, burning material, or hot metal. Each fixture shall be clearly marked to show the maximum wattage of the lamps that shall be permitted without exceeding an exposed surface temperature of 165°C (329°F) under normal conditions of use.

(b) **Physical Damage.** A fixture that may be exposed to physical damage shall be protected by a suitable guard.

(c) **Pendant Fixtures.** Pendant fixtures shall be suspended by stems of threaded rigid metal conduit, threaded intermediate metal conduit, threaded metal tubing of equivalent thickness, or by chains with approved fittings. For stems longer than 12 inches (305 mm), permanent and effective bracing against lateral displacement shall be provided at a level not more than 12 inches (305 mm) above the lower end of the stem, or flexibility in the form of an approved fitting or a flexible connector shall be provided not more than 12 inches (305 mm) from the point of attachment to the supporting box or fitting.

(d) **Portable Lighting Equipment.** Portable lighting equipment shall be equipped with handles and protected with substantial guards. Lampholders shall be of the unswitched type with no provision for receiving attachment plugs. There shall be no exposed current-carrying metal parts, and all exposed noncurrent-carrying metal parts shall be grounded. In all other respects, portable lighting equipment shall comply with (a) above.

503-10. Flexible Cords, Class III, Divisions 1 and 2.
Flexible cords shall comply with the following: (1) be of a type approved for extra-hard usage; (2) contain, in addition to the conductors of the circuit, a grounding conductor complying with Section 400-23; (3) be connected to terminals or to supply conductors in an approved manner; (4) be supported by clamps or other suitable means in such a manner that there will be no tension on the terminal connections; and (5) be provided with suitable means to prevent the entrance of fibers or flyings where the cord enters boxes or fittings.

503-11. Receptacles and Attachment Plugs, Class III, Divisions 1 and 2.
Receptacles and attachment plugs shall be of the grounding type and shall be so designed to minimize the accumulation or the entry of fibers or flyings, and shall prevent the escape of sparks or molten particles.

Exception: In locations where, in the judgment of the authority having jurisdiction, only moderate accumulations of lint or flyings will be likely to collect in the vicinity of a receptacle, and where such receptacle is readily accessible for routine cleaning, general-purpose grounding-type receptacles mounted so as to minimize the entry of fibers or flyings shall be permitted.

503-12. Signaling, Alarm, Remote-Control, and Local Loudspeaker Intercommunication Systems, Class III, Divisions 1 and 2.
Signaling, alarm, remote-control, and local loudspeaker intercommunication systems shall comply with the requirements of Article 503 regarding wiring methods, switches, transformers, resistors, motors, lighting fixtures, and related components.

503-13. Electric Cranes, Hoists, and Similar Equipment, Class III, Divisions 1 and 2.
Where installed for operation over combustible fibers or accumulations of flyings, traveling cranes and hoists for material handling, traveling cleaners for textile machinery, and similar equipment shall comply with (a) through (d) below.

(a) **Power Supply.** Power supply to contact conductors shall be isolated from all other systems and shall be equipped with an acceptable ground detector that will give an alarm and automatically deenergize the contact conductors in case of a fault to ground or will give a visual and audible alarm as long as power is supplied to the contact conductors and the ground fault remains.

(b) **Contact Conductors.** Contact conductors shall be so located or guarded as to be inaccessible to other than authorized persons and shall be protected against accidental contact with foreign objects.

(c) **Current Collectors.** Current collectors shall be so arranged or guarded as to confine normal sparking and prevent escape of sparks or hot particles. To reduce sparking, two or more separate surfaces of contact shall be provided for each contact conductor. Reliable means shall be provided to keep contact conductors and current collectors free of accumulations of lint or flyings.

(d) **Control Equipment.** Control equipment shall comply with Sections 503-4 and 503-5.

In a Class III location, cranes installed over accumulations of fibers or flyings and equipped with rolling or sliding collectors making contact with bare conductors introduce two hazards:

1. Any arcing between a conductor and a collector rail may ignite combustible fibers or lint accumulated on or near the bare conductor. This hazard may be prevented by maintaining the proper alignment of the bare conductor, by using a collector designed so that proper contact is always maintained, and by using guards or shields to confine hot metal particles that may be caused by arcing.

2. If enough moisture is present, fibers and flyings accumulating on the insulating supports of the bare conductors may form a conductive path between the conductors, or from one conductor to ground, thereby permitting enough current to flow to ignite the fibers. Where the system is ungrounded, a current flow to ground is unlikely to start a fire. A suitable recording ground detector will sound an alarm and automatically deenergize contact conductors when the insulation resistance is lowered by an accumulation of fibers on the insulators or in case of a fault to ground. A ground-fault indicator is permitted that will maintain an alarm until the system is deenergized or the ground fault is cleared.

503-14. **Storage-Battery Charging Equipment, Class III, Divisions 1 and 2.** Storage-battery charging equipment shall be located in separate rooms built or lined with substantial noncombustible materials so constructed as to adequately exclude flyings or lint and shall be well ventilated.

503-15. **Live Parts, Class III, Divisions 1 and 2.** Live parts shall not be exposed.

Exception: As provided in Section 503-13.

503-16. **Grounding, Class III, Divisions 1 and 2.** Wiring and equipment in Class III, Divisions 1 and 2 shall be grounded as specified in Article 250 and with the following additional requirements:

(a) Bonding. The locknut-bushing and double-locknut types of contacts shall not be depended upon for bonding purposes, but bonding jumpers with proper fittings or other approved means of bonding shall be used. Such means of bonding shall apply to all intervening raceways, fittings, boxes, enclosures, etc., between Class III locations and the point of grounding for service equipment or point of grounding of a separately derived system.

Exception: The specified bonding means shall only be required to the point of grounding of a building disconnecting means as specified in Sections 250-24(a), (b), and (c), provided that branch-circuit overcurrent protection is located on the load side of the disconnecting means.

(FPN): See Section 250-78 for additional bonding requirements in hazardous (classified) locations.

(b) Types of Equipment Grounding Conductors. Where flexible conduit is used as permitted in Section 503-3, it shall be installed with internal or external bonding jumpers in parallel with each conduit and complying with Section 250-79.

Exception: In Class III, Division 1 and 2 areas, the bonding jumper shall be permitted to be deleted where all the following conditions are met:

a. Approved liquidtight flexible metal 6 feet (1.83 m) or less in length, with approved fittings, is used;

b. Overcurrent protection in the circuit is limited to 10 amperes or less;

c. The load is not a power utilization load.

ARTICLE 504 Intrinsically Safe Systems

Contents

(b) Nonhazardous Locations.

504-70. Sealing.

504-80. Identification.

(a) Terminals.

(b) Wiring.

(c) Color Coding.

504-1. **Scope.** This article covers the installation of intrinsically safe (I.S.) apparatus, wiring, and systems for Class I, II, and III locations.

(FPN): For further information, see Installation of Intrinsically Safe Instrument Systems in Class I Hazardous Locations, ANSI/ISA RP 12.6-1987.

Article 504 was new in the 1990 *NEC*. Previously the installation requirements were in ANSI/ISA RP 12.6-1987 and its earlier 1976 edition.

504-2. **Definitions.** For the purpose of this article:

The standard used in the United States for construction and performance requirements is ANSI/UL 913-1988, *Intrinsically Safe Apparatus and Associated Apparatus for Use in Class I, II, and III, Division 1 Hazardous (Classified) Locations.* This standard is similar to standards in other countries; all standards are based on the IEC (International Electrotechnical Committee) standard. However, since the *National Electrical Code* divides hazardous (classified) locations into 2 divisions (1 and 2), and the installation codes of some other countries use 3 "zones" (0, 1, and 2), ANSI/UL 913 requirements are based on the IEC Zone 0 requirements, which are the most stringent. Equipment certified by a testing laboratory for Zone 1 would not necessarily meet the ANSI/UL 913 requirements for Division 1.

Associated Apparatus: Apparatus in which the circuits are not necessarily intrinsically safe themselves, but that affect the energy in the intrinsically safe circuits and are relied upon to maintain intrinsic safety. Associated apparatus may be either:

1. Electrical apparatus that has an alternative type protection for use in the appropriate hazardous (classified) location, or

2. Electrical apparatus not so protected that shall not be used within a hazardous (classified) location.

(FPN): Associated apparatus has identified intrinsically safe connections for intrinsically safe apparatus and also may have connections for nonintrinsically safe apparatus.

Control Drawing: A drawing or other document provided by the manufacturer of the intrinsically safe or associated apparatus that details the allowed interconnections between the intrinsically safe and associated apparatus.

Different Intrinsically Safe Circuits: Different intrinsically safe circuits are intrinsically safe circuits in which the possible interconnections have not been evaluated and approved as intriniscally safe.

Intrinsically Safe Apparatus: Apparatus in which all the circuits are intrinsically safe.

Intrinsically Safe Circuit: A circuit in which any spark or thermal effect is incapable of causing ignition of a mixture of flammable or combustible material in air under prescribed test conditions.

An intrinsically safe circuit, due to its physical and electrical characteristics, will not develop sufficient electrical energy (millijoules) in an arc or spark or develop sufficient thermal energy due to an overload condition to cause the temperature of the installed circuit to exceed the ignition temperature of a specified gas or vapor under normal or abnormal operating conditions.

An abnormal condition may be due to accidental damage, failure of electrical components, excessive voltage, or improper adjustment or maintenance of the equipment.

(FPN): Test conditions are described in Standard for Safety, Intrinsically Safe Apparatus and Associated Apparatus for Use in Class I, II, and III, Division 1, Hazardous (Classified) Locations, ANSI/UL 913-1988.

Intrinsically Safe System: An assembly of interconnected intrinsically safe apparatus, associated apparatus, and interconnecting cables in that those parts of the system that may be used in hazardous (classified) locations are intrinsically safe circuits.

In installations where low energy devices, such as thermocouples, crystal strain, or pressure transducers are utilized, even though they generate millivolts and currents in the microampere range, they are not intrinsically safe. These devices are normally connected to amplifiers and power supplies connected to 120-volt or higher circuits. Should a fault occur within the amplifier or power supply or a voltage surge occur in the electrical supply systems, high energy arcing, sparking, or overheating of the low energy portion of the circuit could occur.

(FPN): An intrinsically safe system may include more than one intrinsically safe circuit.

504-3. Application of Other Articles. Except as modified by this article, all applicable articles of this Code shall apply.

Because intrinsically safe wiring must be low-energy wiring in order to be intrinsically safe, the wiring itself is most likely to be Class 2 wiring in accordance with Section 725-31 or, if it is used in a fire-protective signaling system, power-limited wiring must be used in accordance with Section 760-21. See Article 725 or 760, as appropriate, for the requirements for such wiring. If the installation falls under the scope of Article 800, that is the applicable article. The intrinsically safe apparatus and associated apparatus, on the other hand, may be supplied by ordinary power circuits, and other *Code* rules may be applicable. It is common for intrinsically safe apparatus or associated apparatus supplied by a power circuit to be located in a hazardous (classified) location, with the apparatus protected by one of the protection systems required by Articles 500 through 503; e.g., explosionproof, dust-ignitionproof, purged, or pressurized. In this case, Articles 500 through 503 are also applicable. Also, intrinsically safe systems are not exempt from the grounding and bonding requirements of Sections 501-16, 502-16, and 503-16.

504-4. Equipment Approval. All intrinsically safe apparatus and associated apparatus shall be approved.

504-10. Equipment Installation.

(a) **Control Drawing.** Intrinsically safe apparatus, associated apparatus, and other equipment shall be installed in accordance with the control drawing(s).

The control drawing may put limitations on cables and separation of circuits within an intrinsically safe system. The control drawing also illustrates what is permitted to be connected in the system. Compliance with all the provisions in the control drawing is essential if intrinsic safety is to be maintained. The investigation of the equipment

by third-party testing laboratories is based on installation in accordance with the control drawing.

(FPN): The control drawing identification is marked on the apparatus.

(b) **Location.** Intrinsically safe and associated apparatus shall be permitted to be installed in any hazardous (classified) location for which it has been approved.

(FPN): Associated apparatus may be installed in hazardous (classified) locations if protected by other means permitted by Articles 501 through 503.

General-purpose enclosures shall be permitted for intrinsically safe apparatus.

504-20. Wiring Methods. Intrinsically safe apparatus and wiring shall be permitted to be installed using any of the wiring methods suitable for unclassified locations. Sealing shall be as provided in Section 504-70, and separation shall be as provided in Section 504-30.

See commentary following Section 504-3.

504-30. Separation of Intrinsically Safe Conductors.

(a) **From Nonintrinsically Safe Circuit Conductors.**

(1) **Open Wiring.** Conductors and cables of intrinsically safe circuits not in raceways or cable trays shall be separated at least 2 inches (50.8 mm) and secured from conductors and cables of any nonintrinsically safe circuits.

Exception: Where either (1) all of the intrinsically safe circuit conductors are in Type MI, MC, or SNM cables or (2) all of the nonintrinsically safe circuit conductors are in raceways or Type MI, MC, or SNM cables where the sheathing or cladding is capable of carrying fault current to ground.

(2) **In Raceways, Cable Trays, and Cables.** Conductors of intrinsically safe circuits shall not be placed in any raceway, cable tray, or cable with conductors of any nonintrinsically safe circuit.

Exception No. 1: Where conductors of intrinsically safe circuits are separated from conductors of nonintrinsically safe circuits by a distance of at least 2 inches (50.8 mm) and secured, or by a grounded metal partition or an approved insulating partition.

(FPN): No. 20 gauge sheet metal partitions 0.0359 inch (912 micrometers) or thicker are generally considered acceptable.

Exception No. 2: Where either (1) all of the intrinsically safe circuit conductors or (2) all of the nonintrinsically safe circuit conductors are in grounded metal-sheathed or metal-clad cables where the sheathing or cladding is capable of carrying fault current to ground.

(FPN): Cables meeting the requirements of Articles 330, 334, and 337 are typical of those considered acceptable.

The cable types mentioned are Type MI, Type MC, and Type SNM. Type MC cable with an interlocked tape-type of outer sheath (as opposed to the smooth or corrugated continuous outer sheath) has not usually been investigated for suitability as an equipment grounding conductor, and may, therefore, not be capable of carrying a fault current to ground as required by Exception No. 2.

(3) Within Enclosures.

a. Conductors of intrinsically safe circuits shall be separated at least 2 inches (50.8 mm) from conductors of any nonintrinsically safe circuits, or as specified in Section 504-30(a)(2).

b. All conductors shall be secured so that any conductor that might come loose from a terminal cannot come in contact with another terminal.

(FPN No. 1): The use of separate wiring compartments for the intrinsically safe and nonintrinsically safe terminals is the preferred method of complying with this requirement.

(FPN No. 2): Physical barriers such as grounded metal partitions or approved insulating partitions or approved restricted access wiring ducts separated from other such ducts by at least ³/₄ in. (19 mm) can be used to help assure the required separation of the wiring.

The intent of Section 504-30(a) is to prevent intrusion of unsafe energy into the intrinsically safe system as a result of a wiring fault. Since low-voltage, low-energy, but nonintrinsically safe circuits are permitted by Articles 725 and 800 to be minimally insulated, and may not be protected by being installed in raceways or cables, particularly in nonhazardous locations, it is essential that nonintrinsically safe circuits and intrinsically safe circuits be physically and electrically separated.

(b) From Different Intrinsically Safe Circuit Conductors. Different intrinsically safe circuits shall be in separate cables or shall be separated from each other by one of the following means:

(1) The conductors of each circuit are within a grounded metal shield;

(2) The conductors of each circuit have insulation with a minimum thickness of 0.01 inches (254 micrometers).

Exception: Unless otherwise approved.

504-50. Grounding.

(a) Intrinsically Safe Apparatus, Associated Apparatus, and Raceways. Intrinsically safe apparatus, associated apparatus, cable shields, enclosures, and raceways, if of metal, shall be grounded.

(FPN): Supplementary bonding to the grounding electrode may be needed for some associated apparatus, e.g., zener diode barriers, if specified in the control drawing. See Installation of Intrinsically Safe Instrument Systems in Class I Hazardous Locations, ANSI/ISA RP 12.6-1987.

It is very important to maintain a low impedance path to ground for zener diode barrier systems, since such systems shunt fault currents to ground.

Figures 504-1 and 504-2 show two common types of zener diode barrier systems. Such barriers may be either unfused or fused. F_1 in Figure 504-1 and R_0 in Figure 504-2 limit the current in Z_1 and Z_2 to the power rating of the zener diodes under fault conditions so that the diodes need not be excessively large. Resistor R_0 has been investigated as a protective component not subject to short-circuit fault. Although the diodes themselves can be considered subject to open-circuit fault, they are redundant components, and either one alone will provide the necessary protection in the event of a first fault, i.e., high voltage across input terminals 1 and 2. Resistor R_2 is the current-limiting resistor and it, too, has been investigated as a protective component not subject to short-circuit fault. Resistor R_1 is used primarily to permit testing to determine that the diodes are intact. Terminals 2 and 4 and the ends of the two diodes are connected to a ground bus that, in turn, is connected to a ground system to which all grounds in the intrinsically safe system are connected. A very low impedance (1 ohm or less is usually recommended) is necessary so that the voltage level on the ground bus will not be raised to an unsafe level under high-current fault conditions.

A shunt diode barrier system is commonly tested with 250 V ac across terminals 1 and 2, which represents a fault in associated apparatus on the nonhazardous location side of the barrier, which imposes a voltage up to 250 V ac on these terminals. Diode Z_1 conducts at its rated voltage, typically 14 or 15 V for a barrier designed for a 12-V (normal operation) system, thus limiting the output voltage of the circuit to 14 or 15 V. The voltage at which this diode conducts is designed to be higher than the rated input voltage (under no fault conditions) at terminals 1 and 2. The fuse in a fused barrier is selected so that it will open before the power rating of Z_1 is exceeded. Diode Z_2 usually conducts within one or two volts of Z_1 and serves as a backup to Z_1 in the event Z_1 fails in an open circuit condition for any reason.

Resistor R_2 limits the current in the intrinsically safe circuit to the required value at the output voltage of Z_1 and Z_2. Therefore, even though up to 250 V ac may be applied to the input of the circuit (terminals 1 and 2) as a result of a fault in the equipment or circuit connected to terminals 1 and 2, the output at terminals 3 and 4 cannot exceed the voltage and current permitted by the diodes and the resistor.

Shunt diode barriers normally have maximum inductance and capacitance ratings on the intrinsically safe side because, even though both the voltage and the current are limited at terminals 3 and 4, too much inductance in the circuit connected to terminals 3 and 4 could result in release of an ignition-capable spark when the circuit is opened. In a like manner, too much capacitance between terminals 3 and 4 could result in release of an ignition-capable spark if there was a short-circuit between wiring connected to terminals 3 and 4 or between wiring connected to terminal 3 and ground.

Wiring always has inductance and capacitance associated with it, depending on the spacing between conductors, size of conductors, length of conductors, etc. Therefore, it is necessary to limit the length of conductors connected to terminals 3 and 4 just as it is necessary to limit the inductance and capacitance of connected equipment. The length limitation is usually in the order of thousands of feet. Manufacturers' instructions provide the information on installation limitations.

By adjusting the values of the components of the barrier, it can be designed for a variety of uses, including different types of instrument systems and thermocouples. Barriers such as described are available commercially from a number of different manufacturers.

Figure 504-1. Fused zener diode barrier.

Figure 504-2. Unfused zener diode barrier.

(b) Connection to Grounding Electrodes. Where connection to a grounding electrode is required, the grounding electrode shall be as specified in Sections 250-81(a), (b), (c), (d) and shall comply with Section 250-26(c). Section 250-83 shall not be used if electrodes specified in Section 250-81 are available.

Electrodes as specified in Section 250-81 are metal underground water pipe, metal frame of building, concrete-encased electrode, and ground ring. These electrodes usually provide lower resistance grounds than electrodes covered in Section 250-83, such as ground rods and plate electrodes.

(c) Shields. Where shielded conductors or cables are used, shields shall be grounded.

Exception: Where a shield is part of an intrinsically safe circuit.

504-60. Bonding.

(a) Hazardous Locations. In hazardous (classified) locations, intrinsically safe apparatus shall be bonded in the hazardous (classified) location in accordance with Section 250-78.

(b) Nonhazardous Locations. In nonhazardous locations, where metal raceways are used for intrinsically safe system wiring in hazardous locations, associated apparatus shall be bonded in accordance with Sections 501-16(a), 502-16(a), or 503-16(a), as applicable.

504-70. Sealing. Conduits and cables that are required to be sealed by Sections 501-5 and 502-5 shall be sealed to minimize the passage of gases, vapors, or dust.

Exception: Seals are not required for enclosures that contain only intrinsically safe apparatus except as required by Section 501-5(f)(3).

(FPN): It is not the intent of this section to require an explosionproof seal.

504-80. Identification. Labels required by this section shall be suitable for the environment where they are installed with consideration given to exposure to chemicals and sunlight.

(a) Terminals. Intrinsically safe circuits shall be identified at terminal and junction locations in a manner that will prevent unintentional interference with the circuits during testing and servicing.

(b) Wiring. Raceways, cable trays, and open wiring for intrinsically safe system wiring shall be identified with permanently affixed labels with the wording "Intrinsic Safety Wiring" or equivalent. The labels shall be so located as to be visible after installation and placed so that they may be readily traced through the entire length of the installation. Spacing between labels shall not be more than 25 feet (7.62 m).

Exception: Circuits run underground shall be permitted to be identified where they become accessible after emergence from the ground.

(FPN No. 1): Wiring methods permitted in nonhazardous locations may be used for intrinsically safe systems in hazardous (classified) locations. Without lables to identify the application of the wiring, enforcement authorities cannot determine that an installation is in compliance with the Code.

(FPN No. 2): In nonhazardous locations, the identification is necessary to assure that nonintrinsically safe wire will not be inadvertently added to existing raceways at a later date.

(c) Color Coding. Color coding shall be permitted to identify intrinsically safe conductors where they are colored light blue and where no other conductors colored light blue are used.

ARTICLE 510 Hazardous (Classified) Locations — Specific

Contents

510-1. Scope. Articles 511 through 517 cover occupancies or parts of occupancies that are or may be hazardous because of atmospheric concentrations of flammable liquids, gases, or vapors, or because of deposits or accumulations of materials that may be readily ignitible.

510-2. General. The general rules of this Code shall apply to electric wiring and equipment in occupancies within the scope of Articles 511 through 517, except as such rules are modified in those articles. Where unusual conditions exist in a specific occupancy, the authority having jurisdiction shall judge with respect to the application of specific rules.

NFPA publishes a number of standards and recommended practices that provide requirements or guidance on the classification of hazardous locations in specific occupancies. Information and copies of standards may be obtained from the National Fire Protection Association (NFPA), 1 Batterymarch Park, P.O. Box 9101, Quincy, MA 02269-9101. If calling to order standards, the number is 1-800-344-3555. For information, call 617-770-3000.

ARTICLE 511 Commercial Garages, Repair and Storage

Contents

(e) Fuel Dispensing Units.

(f) Portable Lighting Equipment.

511-4. Wiring and Equipment in Class I Locations.

511-5. Sealing.

511-6. Wiring in Spaces Above Class I Locations.

(a) Fixed Wiring Above Class I Locations.

(b) Pendants.

(c) Grounded Conductor.

(d) Attachment Plug Receptacles.

511-7. Equipment Above Class I Locations.

(a) Arcing Equipment.

(b) Fixed Lighting.

511-8. Battery Charging Equipment.

511-9. Electric Vehicle Charging.

(a) Connections.

(b) Connector Design and Location.

(c) Plug Connections to Vehicles.

511-10. Ground-Fault Circuit-Interrupter Protection for Personnel.

511-1. **Scope.** These occupancies shall include locations used for service and repair operations in connection with self-propelled vehicles (including passenger automobiles, buses, trucks, tractors, etc.) in which volatile flammable liquids are used for fuel or power.

Article 100 defines a garage as "a building or portion of a building in which one or more self-propelled vehicles carrying volatile flammable liquid for fuel or power are kept for use, sale, storage, rental, repair, exhibition, or demonstrating purposes, and all that portion of a building which is on or below the floor or floors in which such vehicles are kept and which is not separated therefrom by suitable cutoffs."

A mechanical ventilating system capable of continuously providing at least six air changes per hour is required for all enclosed, basement, and underground parking garages.

Operations involving open flame or electric arcs, including fusion gas and electric welding, are required to be restricted to areas specifically provided for such purposes.

Approved suspended unit heaters may be used, provided they are located not less than 8 feet above the floor and are installed in accordance with the conditions of their approval.

511-2. **Locations.** Areas in which flammable fuel is transferred to vehicle fuel tanks shall conform to Article 514. Parking garages

used for parking or storage and where no repair work is done except exchange of parts and routine maintenance requiring no use of electrical equipment, open flame, welding, or the use of volatile flammable liquids are not classified, but they shall be adequately ventilated to carry off the exhaust fumes of the engines.

(FPN): For further information, see Parking Structures, NFPA 88A-1991, and Repair Garages, NFPA 88B-1991.

511-3. **Class I Locations.** Classification under Article 500.

(a) Up to a Level of 18 Inches (457 mm) Above the Floor. For each floor, the entire area up to a level of 18 inches (457 mm) above the floor shall be considered to be a Class I, Division 2 location except where the enforcing agency determines that there is mechanical ventilation providing a minimum of four air changes per hour.

(b) Any Pit or Depression Below Floor Level. Any pit or depression below floor level shall be considered to be a Class I, Division 1 location which shall extend up to said floor level, except that any pit or depression in which six air changes per hour are exhausted at the floor level of the pit shall be permitted to be judged by the enforcing agency to be a Class I, Division 2 location.

Exception: Lubrication and service rooms without dispensing shall be classified in accordance with Table 514-2.

This exception is new in the 1993 *Code*. It provides guidance for determining the classification of facilities primarily offering lubrication-type service, not the dispensing of fuel. The referenced table in Article 514 is extracted from NFPA 30A-1990, *Automotive and Marine Service Station Code*. Any pit or BELOW GRADE WORK SPACE in such a facility that is properly ventilated is an unclassified location.

(c) Areas Adjacent to Defined Locations or with Positive Pressure Ventilation. Areas adjacent to defined locations in which flammable vapors are not likely to be released, such as stock rooms, switchboard rooms, and other similar locations, shall not be classified where mechanically ventilated at a rate of four or more air changes per hour or where effectively cut off by walls or partitions.

(d) Adjacent Areas by Special Permission. Adjacent areas that by reason of ventilation, air pressure differentials, or physical spacing are such that, in the opinion of the authority enforcing this Code, no ignition hazard exists shall be classified as nonhazardous.

(e) Fuel Dispensing Units. Where fuel dispensing units (other than liquid petroleum gas, which is prohibited) are located within buildings, the requirements of Article 514 shall govern.

See Article 514, Figure 1 and Figure 514-1.

Where mechanical ventilation is provided in the dispensing area, the controls shall be interlocked so that the dispenser cannot operate without ventilation as prescribed in Section 500-5(b).

(f) Portable Lighting Equipment. Portable lighting equipment shall be equipped with handle, lampholder, hook, and substantial guard attached to the lampholder or handle. All exterior surfaces that might come in contact with battery terminals, wiring terminals, or other objects shall be of nonconducting material or shall be effectively protected with insulation. Lampholders shall be of unswitched type and shall not provide means for plug-in of attachment plugs. The outer shell shall be of molded composition or other suitable material. Unless the lamp and its cord are supported or arranged in such a manner that they cannot be used in the locations classified in Section 511-3, they shall be of a type approved for Class I, Division 1 locations.

Figure 511-1. This cord, which is part of a portable lamp assembly, is required to be arranged so that the lamp cannot be used in a Class I location; otherwise, the lamp must be of a type approved for Class I, Division 1 hazardous locations (explosion-proof). (Appleton Electric Co.)

Sections 511-3(a) and (b) classify Class I, Divisions 1 and 2 locations of commercial garages. Fuel dispensing units located within the garage are required to be governed by the requirements of Article 514.

The Class I, Division 2 location above grade within a commercial garage extends 18 inches above the floor level unless the authority having jurisdiction determines otherwise because there is mechanical ventilation providing at least four air changes per hour.

The Class I, Division 1 location below grade extends from the floor of the pit or depression to floor level, unless the authority having jurisdiction permits the pit or depression to be classified Class I, Division 2 because ventilation providing at least six air changes per hour exhausts air at the floor level of the pit or depression. Areas suitably cutoff and areas adjacent to nonhazardous ventilated garages are not classified as hazardous.

511-4. **Wiring and Equipment in Class I Locations.** Within Class I locations as defined in Section 511-3, wiring and equipment shall conform to applicable provisions of Article 501. Raceways embedded in a masonry wall or buried beneath a floor shall be considered to be within the Class I location above the floor if any connections or extensions lead into or through such areas.

This section applies to raceways located in walls and below floors of Class I locations in commercial garages. A raceway that is in a masonry wall or buried beneath a floor is not permitted to have any connections or extensions leading into or through a Class I, Division 1 or 2 location if it is to be considered to be located in a nonhazardous location and not subject to the provisions of Article 501. Article 501 applies to the raceway if any part of it is not embedded in the wall, or the wall is not of masonry. Article 501 applies to the raceway if any part of it is not buried beneath the floor. The floor material is not specified.

511-5. **Sealing.** Approved seals conforming to the requirements of Section 501-5 shall be provided, and Section 501-5(b)(2) shall apply to horizontal as well as vertical boundaries of the defined Class I locations.

Seals are required if any part of the raceway is in, or passes through, a Class I, Division 2 location. See commentary on seals in Section 501-5.

Figure 511-2. Classification of locations in commercial garages.

511-6. Wiring in Spaces Above Class I Locations.

(a) Fixed Wiring Above Class I Locations. All fixed wiring above Class I locations shall be in metal raceways, rigid non-metallic conduit, electrical nonmetallic tubing, flexible metal conduit, liquidtight flexible metal conduit, or liquidtight flexible nonmetallic conduit or shall be Type MC, MI, manufactured wiring systems, SNM, or PLTC cable in accordance with Article 725, or TC cable. Cellular metal floor raceways or cellular concrete floor raceways shall be permitted to be used only for supplying ceiling outlets or extensions to the area below the floor, but such raceways shall have no connections leading into or through any Class I location above the floor.

Figure 511-3. Raceways embedded in a masonry wall or buried beneath the floor are not considered to be located in the Class I location only under conditions where there are no extensions into the Class I location.

Several new types of wiring methods have been included in the 1993 *Code* for use in spaces above Class I locations.

(b) Pendants. For pendants, flexible cord suitable for the type of service and approved for hard usage shall be used.

(c) Grounded Conductor. Where a circuit that supplies portables or pendants includes a grounded conductor as provided in Article 200, receptacles, attachment plugs, connectors, and similar devices shall be of polarized type, and the grounded conductor of the flexible cord shall be connected to the screw shell of any lampholder or to the grounded terminal of any utilization equipment supplied.

(d) Attachment Plug Receptacles. Attachment plug receptacles in fixed position shall be located above the level of any defined Class I location or be approved for the location.

511-7. Equipment Above Class I Locations.

(a) Arcing Equipment. Equipment that is less than 12 feet (3.66 m) above the floor level and that may produce arcs, sparks, or particles of hot metal, such as cutouts, switches, charging panels, generators, motors, or other equipment (excluding receptacles, lamps, and lampholders) having make-and-break or sliding contacts, shall be of the totally enclosed type or so constructed as to prevent escape of sparks or hot metal particles.

(b) Fixed Lighting. Lamps and lampholders for fixed lighting that is located over lanes through which vehicles are commonly driven or that may otherwise be exposed to physical damage shall be located not less than 12 feet (3.66 m) above floor level, unless of the totally enclosed type or so constructed as to prevent escape of sparks or hot metal particles.

511-8. **Battery Charging Equipment.** Battery chargers and their control equipment, and batteries being charged, shall not be located within locations classified in Section 511-3.

511-9. **Electric Vehicle Charging.**

(a) Connections. Flexible cords and connectors used for charging shall be suitable for the type of service and approved for extra-hard usage. Their ampacity shall be adequate for the charging current.

(b) Connector Design and Location. Connectors shall be so designed and installed that they will disconnect readily at any position of the charging cable, and live parts shall be guarded from accidental contact. No connector shall be located within a Class I location as defined in Section 511-3.

(c) Plug Connections to Vehicles. Where plugs are provided for direct connection to vehicles, the point of connection shall not be within a Class I location as defined in Section 511-3, and, where the cord is suspended from overhead, it shall be so arranged that the lowest point of sag is at least 6 inches (152 mm) above the floor. Where the vehicle is equipped with an approved plug that will disconnect readily and where an automatic arrangement is provided to pull both cord and plug beyond the range of physical damage, no additional connector shall be required in the cable or at the outlet.

511-10. **Ground-Fault Circuit-Interrupter Protection for Personnel.** All 125-volt single-phase 15- and 20-ampere receptacles installed in areas where electrical diagnostic equipment, electrical hand tools, or portable lighting devices are to be used shall provide ground-fault circuit-interrupter protection for personnel.

Ground-fault circuit-interrupters (GFCIs) intended to protect personnel from shock hazards are designed to trip when a ground fault current of 5 milliamperes (plus or minus 1mA) or greater is detected. Ground-fault protectors intended to protect equipment and prevent fires may trip at a much higher level.

See the definition of ground-fault circuit-interrupter in Article 100 and Figures 210-14 and 210-15.

The GFCI necessary to comply with this requirement may be contained within the receptacle or may be a circuit-breaker type GFCI.

ARTICLE 513   Aircraft Hangars

Contents

513-1. **Definition.** An aircraft hangar is a location used for storage or servicing of aircraft in which gasoline, jet fuels, or other volatile flammable liquids or flammable gases are used. It shall not include locations used exclusively for aircraft that have never contained such liquids or gases, or that have been drained and properly purged.

For further information, see NFPA 409-1990, *Standard on Aircraft Hangars.*

513-2. **Classification of Locations.**

(a) **Below Floor Level.** Any pit or depression below the level of the hangar floor shall be classified as a Class I, Division 1 location that shall extend up to said floor level.

(b) **Areas Not Cut Off or Ventilated.** The entire area of the hangar, including any adjacent and communicating areas not suitably cut off from the hangar, shall be classified as a Class I, Division 2 location up to a level 18 inches (457 mm) above the floor.

(c) **Vicinity of Aircraft.** The area within 5 feet (1.52 m) horizontally from aircraft power plants or aircraft fuel tanks shall be classified as a Class I, Division 2 location that shall extend upward from the floor to a level 5 feet (1.52 m) above the upper surface of wings and of engine enclosures.

In order to properly classify the area in accordance with this section, it is necessary to obtain information on the aircraft parking patterns, the types of aircraft, and the operations to be performed in the hangar. See Figure 513-1.

Consideration of future changes in aircraft types and locations is appropriate to avoid the need for costly wiring and equipment changes as a result of changes in the area classification.

(d) **Areas Suitably Cut Off and Ventilated.** Adjacent areas in which flammable liquids or vapors are not likely to be released, such as stock rooms, electrical control rooms, and other similar locations, shall not be classified where adequately ventilated and where effectively cut off from the hangar itself by walls or partitions.

513-3. **Wiring and Equipment in Class I Locations.** All wiring and equipment that is or may be installed or operated within any of the Class I locations defined in Section 513-2 shall comply with the applicable provisions of Article 501. All wiring installed in or under the hangar floor shall comply with the requirements for Class I, Division 1 locations. Where such wiring is located in vaults, pits, or ducts, adequate drainage shall be provided; and the wiring shall not be placed within the same compartment with any service other than piped compressed air.

Attachment plugs and receptacles in Class I locations shall be approved for Class I locations or shall be so designed that they cannot be energized while the connections are being made or broken.

513-4. **Wiring Not Within Class I Locations.**

(a) **Fixed Wiring.** All fixed wiring in a hangar, but not within a Class I location as defined in Section 513-2, shall be installed in metal raceways or shall be Type MI, TC, SNM, or Type MC cable.

Exception: Wiring in unclassified locations as defined in Section 513-2(d) shall be of a type recognized in Chapter 3.

(b) **Pendants.** For pendants, flexible cord suitable for the type of service and approved for hard usage shall be used. Each such cord shall include a separate equipment grounding conductor.

(c) **Portable Equipment.** For portable utilization equipment and lamps, flexible cord suitable for the type of service and approved for extra-hard usage shall be used. Each such cord shall include a separate equipment grounding conductor.

(d) **Grounded and Grounding Conductors.** Where a circuit supplies portables or pendants and includes a grounded conductor as provided in Article 200, receptacles, attachment plugs, connectors, and similar devices shall be of the grounding type, and the grounded conductor of the flexible cord shall be connected to the screw shell of any lampholder or to the grounded terminal of any utilization equipment supplied. Approved means shall be provided for maintaining continuity of the grounding conductor between the fixed wiring system and the noncurrent-carrying metal portions of pendant fixtures, portable lamps, and portable utilization equipment.

513-5. **Equipment Not within Class I Locations.**

(a) **Arcing Equipment.** In locations other than those described in Section 513-2, equipment that is less than 10 feet (3.05 m) above wings and engine enclosures of aircraft and that may produce arcs, sparks, or particles of hot metal, such as lamps and lampholders for fixed lighting, cutouts, switches, receptacles, charging panels, generators, motors, or other equipment having make-and-break or sliding contacts, shall be of the totally

Figure 513-1. *Area classification in aircraft hangars.*

enclosed type or so constructed as to prevent escape of sparks or hot metal particles.

Exception: Equipment in areas described in Section 513-2(d) shall be permitted to be of the general-purpose type.

(b) Lampholders. Lampholders of metal-shell, fiber-lined types shall not be used for fixed incandescent lighting.

(c) Portable Lighting Equipment. Portable lighting equipment that are used within a hangar shall be approved for the location in which they are used.

(d) Portable Equipment. Portable utilization equipment that is or may be used within a hangar shall be of a type suitable for use in Class I, Division 2 locations.

513-6. **Stanchions, Rostrums, and Docks.**

(a) In Class I Location. Electric wiring, outlets, and equipment (including lamps) on or attached to stanchions, rostrums, or docks that are located or likely to be located in a Class I location as defined in Section 513-2(c) shall comply with the requirements for Class I, Division 2 locations.

(b) Not in Class I Location. Where stanchions, rostrums, or docks are not located or likely to be located in a Class I location as defined in Section 513-2(c), wiring and equipment shall comply with Sections 513-4 and 513-5, except that such wiring and equipment not more than 18 inches (457 mm) above the floor in any position shall comply with (a) above.

Receptacles and attachment plugs shall be of a locking type that will not readily disconnect.

(c) Mobile Type. Mobile stanchions with electric equipment complying with (b) above shall carry at least one permanently affixed warning sign to read: "WARNING — KEEP 5 FEET CLEAR OF AIRCRAFT ENGINES AND FUEL TANK AREAS."

513-7. **Sealing.** Approved seals shall be provided in accordance with Section 501-5. Sealing requirements specified in Sections 501-5(a)(4) and (b)(2) shall apply to horizontal as well as to vertical boundaries of the defined Class I locations. Raceways embedded in a concrete floor or buried beneath a floor shall be considered to be within the Class I location above the floor where any connections or extensions lead into or through such location.

513-8. **Aircraft Electrical Systems.** Aircraft electrical systems shall be deenergized when the aircraft is stored in a hangar, and, whenever possible, while the aircraft is undergoing maintenance.

513-9. **Aircraft Battery — Charging and Equipment.** Aircraft batteries shall not be charged where installed in an aircraft located inside or partially inside a hangar.

Battery chargers and their control equipment shall not be located or operated within any of the Class I locations defined in Section 513-2 and shall preferably be located in a separate building or in an area such as defined in Section 513-2(d). Mobile chargers shall carry at least one permanently affixed warning sign to read: "WARNING — KEEP 5 FEET CLEAR OF AIRCRAFT ENGINES AND FUEL TANK AREAS." Tables, racks, trays, and wiring shall not be located within a Class I location and, in addition, shall comply with Article 480.

513-10. **External Power Sources for Energizing Aircraft.**

(a) Not Less than 18 Inches (457 mm) Above Floor. Aircraft energizers shall be so designed and mounted that all electric equipment and fixed wiring will be at least 18 inches (457 mm) above floor level and shall not be operated in a Class I location as defined in Section 513-2(c).

(b) Marking for Mobile Units. Mobile energizers shall carry at least one permanently affixed warning sign to read: "WARNING — KEEP 5 FEET CLEAR OF AIRCRAFT ENGINES AND FUEL TANK AREAS."

(c) Cords. Flexible cords for aircraft energizers and ground support equipment shall be approved for the type of service and extra-hard usage and shall include an equipment grounding conductor.

513-11. **Mobile Servicing Equipment with Electric Components.**

(a) General. Mobile servicing equipment (such as vacuum cleaners, air compressors, air movers, etc.) having electric wiring and equipment not suitable for Class I, Division 2 locations shall be so designed and mounted that all such fixed wiring and equipment will be at least 18 inches (457 mm) above the floor. Such mobile equipment shall not be operated within the Class I location defined in Section 513-2(c) and shall carry at least one permanently affixed warning sign to read: "WARNING — KEEP 5 FEET CLEAR OF AIRCRAFT ENGINES AND FUEL TANK AREAS."

(b) Cords and Connectors. Flexible cords for mobile equipment shall be suitable for the type of service and approved for extra-hard usage and shall include an equipment grounding conductor. Attachment plugs and receptacles shall be approved for the location in which they are installed and shall provide for connection of the equipment grounding conductor.

(c) Restricted Use. Equipment that is not identified as suitable for Class I, Division 2 locations shall not be operated in locations where maintenance operations likely to release flammable liquids or vapors are in progress.

513-12. **Grounding.** All metal raceways, metal-jacketed cables, and all noncurrent-carrying metal portions of fixed or portable equipment, regardless of voltage, shall be grounded as provided in Article 250.

ARTICLE 514   Gasoline Dispensing and Service Stations

Contents

(b) Attended Self-Service Stations.

(c) Unattended Self-Service Stations.

514-6. Sealing.

(a) At Dispenser.

(b) At Boundary.

514-7. Grounding.

514-8. Underground Wiring.

514-1. **Definition.** A gasoline dispensing and service station is a location where gasoline or other volatile flammable liquids or liquefied flammable gases are transferred to the fuel tanks (including auxiliary fuel tanks) of self-propelled vehicles or approved containers.

The filling of "approved containers" has been included in the scope of Article 514 in the 1993 *Code*. This article now applies to dispensing locations for LPG even if no vehicles are served.

Other areas used as lubritoriums, service rooms, repair rooms, offices, salesrooms, compressor rooms, and similar locations shall comply with Articles 510 and 511 with respect to electric wiring and equipment.

Where the authority having jurisdiction can satisfactorily determine that flammable liquids having a flash point below 38°C (100°F), such as gasoline, will not be handled, such location shall not be required to be classified.

(FPN No. 1): For further information regarding safeguards for gasoline dispensing and service stations, see Automotive and Marine Service Station Code, NFPA 30A-1990.

(FPN No. 2): For information on classified areas pertaining to LP-Gas Systems other than residential or commercial, see Storage and Handling of Liquefied Petroleum Gases, NFPA 58-1992 and Storage and Handling of Liquefied Petroleum Gases at Utility Gas Plants, NFPA 59-1992.

(FPN No. 3): See Section 555-9 for gasoline dispensing stations in marinas and boatyards.

514-2ˣ. **Class I Locations.** Table 514-2 shall be applied where Class I liquids are stored, handled, or dispensed and shall be used to delineate and classify service stations. A Class I location shall not extend beyond an unpierced wall, roof, or other solid partition.

Table 514-2 has been extracted from NFPA 30A-1990, *Automotive and Marine Service Station Code.* See commentary

following Section 511-3(b) Exception regarding the classification of facilities primarily offering lubrication-type service.

514-3. **Wiring and Equipment Within Class I Locations.** All electric equipment and wiring within Class I locations defined in Section 514-2 shall comply with the applicable provisions of Article 501.

Exception: As permitted in Section 514-8.

(FPN): For special requirements for conductor insulation, see Section 501-13.

For gasoline and oil-resistant insulated conductors, see the commentary following Section 501-13.

514-4. **Wiring and Equipment Above Class I Locations.** Wiring and equipment above the Class I locations defined in Section 514-2 shall comply with Sections 511-6 and 511-7.

514-5. **Circuit Disconnects.**

(a) **General.** Each circuit leading to or through dispensing equipment, including equipment for remote pumping systems, shall be provided with a switch or other acceptable means to disconnect simultaneously from the source of supply all conductors of the circuit, including the grounded conductor, if any.

Single-pole breakers utilizing handle ties shall not be permitted.

It is important to note that all conductors of a circuit, including the grounded conductor, that may be present within a dispensing device are required to be provided with a switch or special-type circuit breaker that will simultaneously disconnect all conductors. Handle ties on single-pole circuit breakers are *not* permitted. The intent is that no energized conductors be in the dispenser vicinity during maintenance or alteration. Considering possible accidental reversal of the polarities of conductors at panelboards, the grounded conductor must be able to be switched to the open or "off" position. Grounded conductors may be present in old-style pump motors, or they may pass through a dispenser as part of a circuit for the island lighting.

(b) **Attended Self-Service Stations.ˣ** Emergency controls as specified in (a) above shall be installed at a location acceptable

TOP VIEW

SIDE VIEW

▨ Division 1   ▥ Division 2

Figure 514-1. *Extent of Class I location around overhead gas-oline dispensing units in accordance with Table 514-2*.*

to the authority having jurisdiction, but controls shall not be more than 100 feet (30 m) from dispensers.

(c) **Unattended Self-Service Stations.**[x] Emergency controls as specified in (a) above shall be installed at a location acceptable to the authority having jurisdiction, but the controls shall be more than 20 feet (7 m) but less than 100 feet (30 m) from the dispensers. Additional emergency controls shall

be installed on each group of dispensers or the outdoor equipment used to control the dispensers. Emergency controls shall shut off all power to all dispensing equipment at the station. Controls shall be manually reset only in a manner approved by the authority having jurisdiction.

(FPN): For additional information, see Sections 9-4.5 and 9-5.3 of Automotive and Marine Service Station Code, NFPA 30A-1990.

Since a fire or large gasoline spill at the dispensing island may make it impossible to operate the switches on the dispensing island that shut off the flow of gasoline, Section 4-1.2 of NFPA 30A, *Automotive and Marine Service Station Code*, requires an *easily accessible* and *clearly identified* emergency power cutoff to be provided at a location remote from the dispensing device. Section 514-5(b) and Section 514-5(c) new in the 1993 *Code* are extracted from NFPA 30A and provide the maximum and minimum distances for the location of the Emergency Control for attended and unattended self service stations. The term "clearly identified" means that a sign is to be posted indicating where the cutoff switch is located. This emergency power cutoff should be readily accessible and not blocked by the storage of such things as tires or cases of lubricating oil. All service station operators as well as responding fire fighters should know the location of the emergency power cutoff.

514-6. Sealing.

(a) **At Dispenser.** An approved seal shall be provided in each conduit run entering or leaving a dispenser or any cavities or enclosures in direct communication therewith. The sealing fitting shall be the first fitting after the conduit emerges from the earth or concrete.

(b) **At Boundary.** Additional seals shall be provided in accordance with Section 501-5. Sections 501-5(a)(4) and (b)(2) shall apply to horizontal as well as to vertical boundaries of the defined Class I locations.

Sealing fittings are required in all conduits leaving a Class I location. All conduits passing under the boundaries of the hazardous (classified) locations (20-foot radius from dispenser) or the tank fill-pipe (10-foot radius from a loose-fill connection and 5-foot radius from a tight-fill connection) are considered to be in a Class I, Division 1 location (see Section 514-8), and the seal is to be the first fitting at the

Figure 514-2. A gasoline dispensing installation indicating locations for sealing fittings. Emergency controls are required for self service stations. See Sections 514-5(a) and (b).

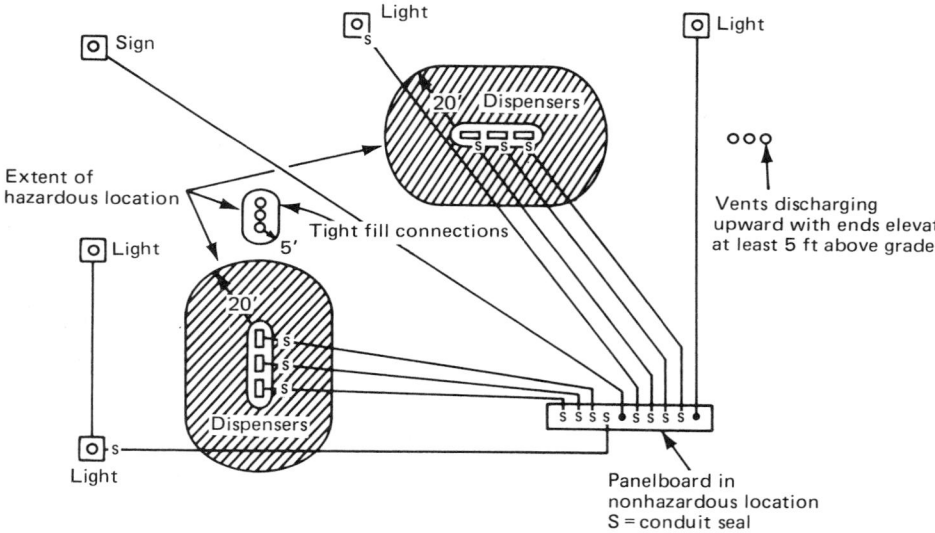

Figure 514-3. Seals are required at points marked "S." Seals are not required at the sign and two of the lights because conduit runs do not pass through a hazardous location.

point of emergence. A seal is required to be provided in each conduit run *entering* or *leaving* a dispenser; therefore, even though a conduit runs from dispenser to dispenser and does not leave the hazardous (classified) location, a seal is necessary where leaving, and again where entering, the dispenser. Panelboards are generally located in a room classified as a nonhazardous location; however, any conduit coming from the dispenser or passing under the hazardous (classified) location boundaries from the dispenser or tank

fill-pipe would require a seal at the panelboard location. Where the panelboard is located in the lube or repair room, all conduits emerging into the 18-inch hazardous (classified) location would require seals. See Figures 514-2 and 514-3.

514-7. Grounding. Metal portions of dispensing pumps, metal raceways, metal-jacketed cables, and all noncurrent-carrying metal parts of electric equipment, regardless of voltage, shall be grounded as provided in Article 250.

Table 514-2.ˣ   Class I Locations — Service Stations

Location	Class I, Group D Division	Extent of Classified Location
Underground Tank Fill Opening	1	Any pit, box, or space below grade level, any part of which is within the Division 1 or 2 classified location.
	2	Up to 18 inches above grade level within a horizontal radius of 10 feet from a loose fill connection and within a horizontal radius of 5 feet from a tight fill connection.
Vent — Discharging Upward	1	Within 3 feet of open end of vent, extending in all directions.
	2	Space between 3 feet and 5 feet of open end of vent, extending in all directions.
Dispensing Device (except overhead type)* Pits	1	Any pit, box, or space below grade level, any part of which is within the Division 1 or 2 classified location.
Dispenser		(FPN): Space classification inside the dispenser enclosure is covered in Power Operated Dispensing Devices for Petroleum Products, ANSI/UL 87-1987.
	2	Within 18 inches horizontally in all directions extending to grade from (1) the dispenser enclosure or (2) that portion of the dispenser enclosure containing liquid handling components.
		(FPN): Space classification inside the dispenser enclosure is covered in Power Operated Dispensing Devices for Petroleum Products, ANSI/UL 87-1987.
Outdoor	2	Up to 18 inches above grade level within 20 feet horizontally of any edge of enclosure.
Indoor with Mechanical Ventilation	2	Up to 18 inches above grade or floor level within 20 feet horizontally of any edge of enclosure.
with Gravity Ventilation	2	Up to 18 inches above grade or floor level within 25 feet horizontally of any edge of enclosure.

Table 514-2, continued

Location	Class I, Group D Division	Extent of Classified Location
Dispensing Device[1] Overhead Type*	1	The space within the dispenser enclosure, and all electrical equipment integral with the dispensing hose or nozzle.
	2	A space extending 18 inches horizontally in all directions beyond the enclosure and extending to grade.
	2	Up to 18 inches above grade level within 20 feet horizontally measured from a point vertically below the edge of any dispenser enclosure.
Remote Pump — Outdoor	1	Any pit, box, or space below grade level if any part is within a horizontal distance of 10 feet from any edge of pump.
	2	Within 3 feet of any edge of pump, extending in all directions. Also up to 18 inches above grade level within 10 feet horizontally from any edge of pump.
Remote Pump — Indoor	1	Entire space within any pit.
	2	Within 5 feet of any edge of pump, extending in all directions. Also up to 3 feet above grade level within 25 feet horizontally from any edge of pump.
Lubrication or Service Room — with Dispensing	1	Any pit within any unventilated space.
	2	Any pit with ventilation.
	2	Space up to 18 inches above floor or grade level and 3 feet horizontally from a lubrication pit.
Dispenser for Class I Liquids	2	Within 3 feet of any fill or dispensing point, extending in all directions.
Lubrication or Service Room — without Dispensing	2	Entire area within any pit used for lubrication or similar services where Class I liquids may be released.
	2	Area up to 18 inches above any such pit, and extending a distance of 3 ft horizontally from any edge of the pit.
	2	Entire unventilated area within any pit, below-grade area, or subfloor area.

Table 514-2, continued

Location	Class I, Group D Division	Extent of Classified Location
Lubrication or Service Room — without Dispensing	2	Area up to 18 inches above any such unventilated pit, below-grade work area, or subfloor work area and extending a distance of 3 feet horizontally from the edge of any such pit, below-grade work area, or subfloor work area.
	Non-classified	Any pit, below-grade work area, or subfloor work area that is ventilated in accordance with 5-1.3.
Special Enclosure Inside Building**	1	(FPN): See Section 5-1.3 of Automotive and Marine Service Station Code, NFPA 30A - 1990, for ventilation requirements. Entire enclosure
Sales, Storage, and Rest Rooms	Non-classified	If there is any opening to these rooms within the extent of a Division 1 location, the entire room shall be classified as Division 1.
Vapor Processing Systems Pits	1	Any pit, box, or space below grade level, any part of which is within a Division 1 or 2 classified location or that houses any equipment used to transport or process vapors.
Vapor Processing Equipment Located within Protective Enclosures	2	Within any protective enclosure housing vapor processing equipment
(FPN): See Automotive and Marine Service Station Code, NFPA 30A-1990, Section 4-5.7		
Vapor Processing Equipment Not within Protective Enclosures (excluding piping and combustion devices)	2	The space within 18 inches in all directions of equipment containing flammable vapor or liquid extending to grade level. Up to 18 inches above grade level within 10 feet horizontally of the vapor processing equipment.
Equipment Enclosures	1	Any space within the enclosure where vapor or liquid is present under normal operating conditions.
Vacuum-Assist Blowers	2	The space within 18 inches in all directions extending to grade level. Up to 18 inches above grade level within 10 feet horizontally.

For SI units: one inch = 2.5 cm; one foot = 0.3048 meter.
¹ Refer to Figure 1 for an illustration of classified location around dispensing devices.
*Ceiling mounted hose reel.
**(FPN): See Automotive and Marine Service Station Code, NFPA 30A-1990, Section 2-2.

Location

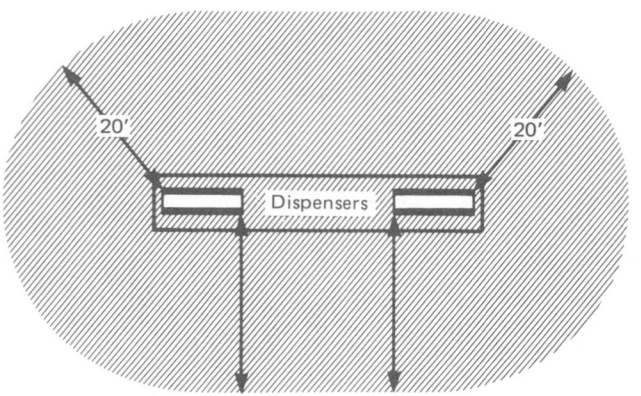

Figure 1. *Classified Locations Adjacent to Dispensers as Detailed in Table 514-2.*

514-8. **Underground Wiring.** Underground wiring shall be installed in threaded rigid metal conduit or threaded steel intermediate metal conduit. Any portion of electrical wiring or equipment that is below the surface of a Class I, Division 1 or Division 2 location (as defined in Table 514-2) shall be considered to be in a Class I, Division 1 location, which shall extend at least to the point of emergence above grade. Refer to Table 300-5.

Experience has shown that the fuel spilled in the vicinity of gasoline pumps in service stations tends to accumulate underground where it can enter electrical conduits and accumulate in voids. Therefore, this section classifies the space below surface areas subject to fuel spills as Class I, Division 1 locations.

Exception No. 1: Type MI cable shall be permitted where it is installed in accordance with Article 330.

Exception No. 2: Rigid nonmetallic conduit complying with Article 347 shall be permitted where buried under not less than 2 feet (610 mm) of earth. Where rigid nonmetallic conduit is used, threaded rigid metal conduit or threaded steel intermediate metal conduit shall be used for the last 2 feet (610 mm) of the underground run to emergence or to the point of connection to the aboveground raceway; an equipment grounding conductor shall be included to provide electrical continuity of the raceway system and for grounding of noncurrent-carrying metal parts.

Exception No. 2 to Section 514-8 makes it clear that if rigid nonmetallic conduit is used for underground wiring, threaded rigid metal conduit or threaded steel intermediate metal conduit must be used for the last 2 feet of the underground run to the point of emergence or to the point of connection to the aboveground raceway. The rigid nonmetallic conduit, including rigid nonmetallic conduit elbows and fittings, is required to be located not less than 2 feet below grade. See Figure 514-4.

If rigid nonmetallic conduit is used, an equipment grounding conductor must be included and bonded to the explosionproof raceway system inside the dispenser. This may be accomplished by terminating the equipment grounding conductor on the ground screw provided in the junction box.

Figure 514-4. Use of rigid nonmetallic conduit in accordance with the exception to Section 514-8.

ARTICLE 515 Bulk Storage Plants

Contents

515-1. **Definition.** A bulk storage plant is that portion of a property where flammable liquids are received by tank vessel, pipelines, tank car, or tank vehicle, and are stored or blended in bulk for the purpose of distributing such liquids by tank vessel, pipeline, tank car, tank vehicle, portable tank, or container.

(FPN): For further information, see Flammable and Combustible Liquids Code, NFPA 30-1990 (ANSI).

515-2ˣ. **Class I Locations.** Table 515-2 shall be applied where Class I liquids are stored, handled, or dispensed and shall be used to delineate and classify bulk storage plants. The Class I location shall not extend beyond a floor, wall, roof, or other solid partition that has no communicating openings.

(FPN): The area classifications listed in Table 515-2 are based on the premise that the installation meets the applicable requirements of Flammable and Combustible Liquids Code, NFPA 30-1990 (ANSI), Chapter 5 in all respects. Should this not be the case, the authority having jurisdiction has the authority to classify the extent of the classified space.

Table 515-2 is essentially the same as Table 5-3.5.3 in NFPA 30-1990, *Flammable and Combustible Liquids Code.* Section 5-3.3.2 of NFPA 30-1990, as referenced in the first two items, column 1, of Table 515-2 is as follows:

"5-3.3.2. Equipment used in a building and the ventilation of the building shall be designed to limit flammable vapor-air mixtures under normal operating conditions to the interior of equipment, and to not more than 5 ft (1.5 m) from equipment that exposes Class I liquids to the air. Examples of such equipment are dispensing stations, open centrifuges, plate and frame filters, open vacuum filters, and surfaces of open equipment."

Article 515 — Bulk Storage Plants

Table 515-2.ˣ   Class I Locations — Bulk Plants

Location	Class I, Division	Extent of Classified Location
Indoor equipment installed in accordance with Flammable and Combustible Liquids Code, NFPA 30-1990 (ANSI), Section 5-3.3.2 where flammable vapor-air mixtures may exist under normal operation.	1	Space within 5 feet of any edge of such equipment, extending in all directions.
	2	Space between 5 feet and 8 feet of any edge of such equipment, extending in all directions. Also, space up to 3 feet above floor or grade level within 5 feet to 25 feet horizontally from any edge of such equipment.*
Outdoor equipment of the type covered in Flammable and Combustible Liquids Code, NFPA 30-1990 (ANSI), Section 5-3.3.2 where flammable vapor-air mixtures may exist under normal operation.	1	Space within 3 feet of any edge of such equipment, extending in all directions.
	2	Space between 3 feet and 8 feet of any edge of such equipment, extending in all directions. Also, space up to 3 feet above floor or grade level within 3 feet to 10 feet horizontally from any edge of such equipment.
Tank — Aboveground**	1	Space inside dike where dike height is greater than the distance from the tank to the dike for more than 50 percent of the tank circumference.
Shell, Ends, or Roof and Dike Space	2	Within 10 feet from shell, ends, or roof of tank. Space inside dikes to level of top of dike.
Vent	1	Within 5 feet of open end of vent, extending in all directions.
	2	Space between 5 feet and 10 feet from open end of vent, extending in all directions.
Floating Roof	1	Space above the roof and within the shell.

* The release of Class I liquids may generate vapors to the extent that the entire building, and possibly a zone surrounding it, should be considered a Class I, Division 2 location.
**For Tanks — Underground, see Section 514-2.

Table 515-2, continued

Location	Class I, Division	Extent of Classified Location
Underground Tank Fill Opening	1	Any pit, box, or space below grade level, if any part is within a Division 1 or 2 classified location.
	2	Up to 18 inches above grade level within a horizontal radius of 10 feet from a loose fill connection, and within a horizontal radius of 5 feet from a tight fill connection.
Vent — Discharging Upward	1	Within 3 feet of open end of vent, extending in all directions.
	2	Space between 3 feet and 5 feet of open end of vent, extending in all directions.
Drum and Container Filling Outdoors, or Indoors with Adequate Ventilation	1	Within 3 feet of vent and fill openings, extending in all directions.
	2	Space between 3 feet and 5 feet from vent or fill opening, extending in all directions. Also, up to 18 inches above floor or grade level within a horizontal radius of 10 feet from vent or fill openings.
Pumps, Bleeders, Withdrawal Fittings, Meters and Similar Devices		
Indoors	2	Within 5 feet of any edge of such devices, extending in all directions. Also up to 3 feet above floor or grade level within 25 feet horizontally from any edge of such devices.
Outdoors	2	Within 3 feet of any edge of such devices, extending in all directions. Also up to 18 inches above grade level within 10 feet horizontally from any edge of such devices.
Pits Without Mechanical Ventilation	1	Entire space within pit if any part is within a Division 1 or 2 classified location.

Table 515-2, continued

Location	Class I, Division	Extent of Classified Location
With Adequate Mechanical Ventilation	2	Entire space within pit if any part is within a Division 1 or 2 classified location.
Containing Valves, Fittings, or Piping, and not within a Division 1 or 2 Classified Location	2	Entire pit.
Drainage Ditches, Separators, Impounding Basins		
Outdoor	2	Space up to 18 inches above ditch, separator, or basin. Also up to 18 inches above grade within 15 feet horizontally from any edge.
Indoor		Same as pits.
Tank Vehicle and Tank Car*		
Loading Through Open Dome	1	Within 3 feet of edge of dome, extending in all directions.
	2	Space between 3 feet and 15 feet from edge of dome, extending in all directions.
Loading through Bottom Connections with Atmospheric Venting	1	Within 3 feet of point of venting to atmosphere, extending in all directions.
	2	Space between 3 feet and 15 feet from point of venting to atmosphere, extending in all directions. Also up to 18 inches above grade within a horizontal radius of 10 feet from point of loading connection.
Office and Rest Rooms	Ordinary	If there is any opening to these rooms within the extent of an indoor classified location, the room shall be classified the same as if the wall, curb, or partition did not exist.

* When classifying extent of space, consideration shall be given to fact that tank cars or tank vehicles may be spotted at varying points. Therefore, the extremities of the loading or unloading positions shall be used.

Table 515-2, continued

Location	Class I, Division	Extent of Classified Location
Loading through Closed Dome with Atmospheric Venting	1	Within 3 feet of open end of vent, extending in all directions.
	2	Space between 3 feet and 15 feet from open end of vent, extending in all directions. Also within 3 feet of edge of dome, extending in all directions.
Loading through Closed Dome with Vapor Control	2	Within 3 feet of point of connection of both fill and vapor lines, extending in all directions.
Bottom Loading with Vapor Control	2	Within 3 feet of point of connections, extending in all directions.
Any Bottom Unloading		Also up to 18 inches above grade within a horizontal radius of 10 feet from point of connections.
Storage and Repair Garage for Tank Vehicles	1	All pits or spaces below floor level.
	2	Space up to 18 inches above floor or grade level for entire storage or repair garage.
Garages for other than Tank Vehicles	Ordinary	If there is any opening to these rooms within the extent of an outdoor classified location, the entire room shall be classified the same as the space classification at the point of the opening.
Outdoor Drum Storage	Ordinary	
Indoor Warehousing Where There is No Flammable Liquid Transfer	Ordinary	If there is any opening to these rooms within the extent of an indoor classified location, the room shall be classified the same as if the wall, curb, or partition did not exist.
Piers and Wharves		See Figure 1.

For SI units: one inch = 25.4 millimeters; one foot = 0.3048 meters.

Figure 1.^X *Marine Terminal Handling Flammable Liquids.*

50'
25'
25'
50'
25'
Deck

Open sump in deck for draining lines and hoses

Operating envelope and stored position of loading arms or hoses

1 Foot = 0.3 meters

50'
2'
25'

Approach
Pier

Shore

Water level

Division 1   Division 2   Nonclassified

Notes:
(1) The "source of vapor" shall be the operating envelope and stored position of the outboard flange connection of the loading arm (or hose).
(2) The berth area adjacent to tanker and barge cargo tanks is to be Division 2 to the following extent:
　　a. 25 ft (7.6 m) horizontally in all directions on the pier side from that portion of the hull containing cargo tanks.
　　b. From the water level to 25 ft (7.6 m) above the cargo tanks at their highest position.
(3) Additional locations may have to be classified as required by the presence of other sources of flammable liquids on the berth, or by Coast Guard or other regulations.

515-3. **Wiring and Equipment Within Class I Locations.** All electric wiring and equipment within the Class I locations defined in Section 515-2 shall comply with the applicable provisions of Article 501.

Exception: As permitted in Section 515-5.

515-4. **Wiring and Equipment Above Class I Locations.** All fixed wiring above Class I locations shall be in metal raceways or PVC schedule 80 rigid nonmetallic conduit, or equivalent, or be Type MI, TC, SNM, or Type MC cable. Fixed equipment that may produce arcs, sparks, or particles of hot metal, such as lamps and lampholders for fixed lighting, cutouts, switches, receptacles, motors, or other equipment having make-and-break or sliding contacts, shall be of the totally enclosed type or be so constructed as to prevent escape of sparks or hot metal particles. Portable lamps or other utilization equipment and their flexible cords shall comply with the provisions of Article 501 for the class of location above which they are connected or used.

515-5. Underground Wiring.

(a) Wiring Method. Underground wiring shall be installed in threaded rigid metal conduit or threaded steel intermediate metal conduit or, where buried under not less than 2 feet (610 mm) of earth, shall be permitted in rigid nonmetallic conduit or an approved cable. Where rigid nonmetallic conduit is used, threaded rigid metal conduit or threaded steel intermediate metal conduit shall be used for the last 2 feet (610 mm) of the conduit run to emergence or to the point of connection to the aboveground raceway. Where cable is used, it shall be enclosed in threaded rigid metal conduit or threaded steel intermediate metal conduit from the point of lowest buried cable level to the point of connection to the aboveground raceway.

See commentary following Section 514-8.

(b) Insulation. Conductor insulation shall comply with Section 501-13.

(c) Nonmetallic Wiring. Where rigid nonmetallic conduit or cable with a nonmetallic sheath is used, an equipment grounding conductor shall be included to provide for electrical continuity of the raceway system and for grounding of noncurrent-carrying metal parts.

515-6. Sealing. Approved seals shall be provided in accordance with Section 501-5. Sealing requirements in Sections 501-5(a)(4) and (b)(2) shall apply to horizontal as well as to vertical boundaries of the defined Class I locations. Buried raceways under defined Class I locations shall be considered to be within a Class I, Division 1 location.

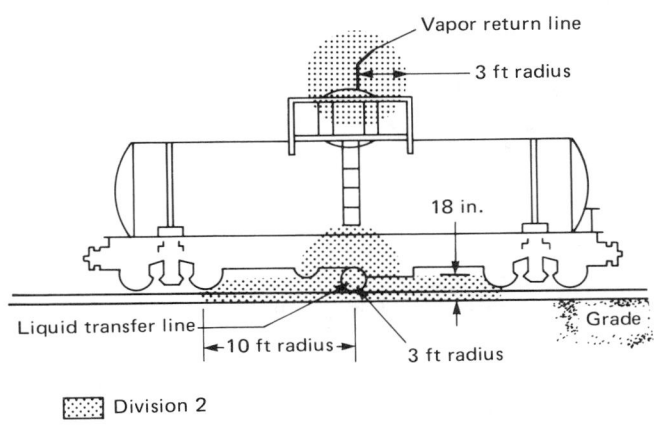

Division 2

Material: Flammable liquid

Figure 515-2. Tank car/tank truck loading and unloading via closed system. Bottom product transfer only.

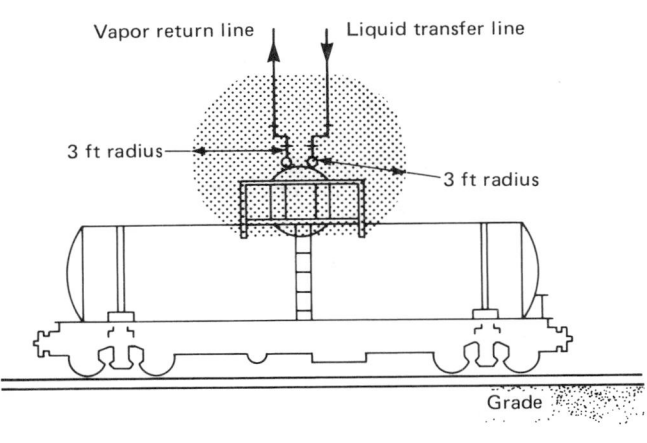

Division 2

Material: Flammable liquid

Figure 515-1. Tank car/tank truck loading and unloading via closed system. Transfer through dome only.

Division 1   Division 2

Material: Flammable liquid

Figure 515-3. Tank car/tank truck loading and unloading via open system. Top or bottom product transfer.

Figure 515-4. *Tank car/tank truck loading and unloading via closed system. Transfer through dome only.*

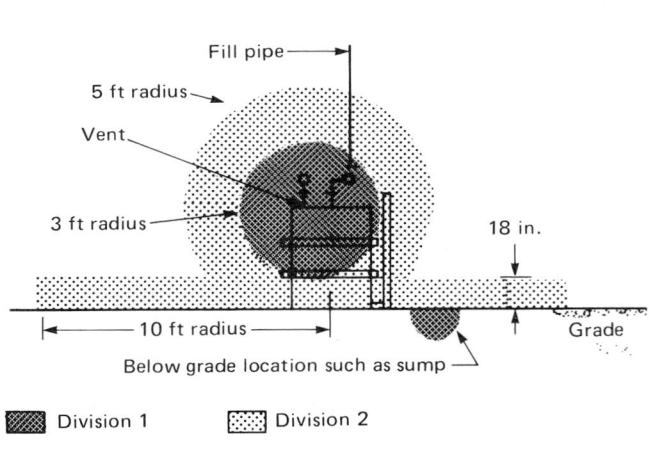

Figure 515-5. *Drum filling station, outdoors or indoors with adequate ventilation.*

Dike height less than the distance from container to dike (H less than X)

Dike height greater than the distance from container to dike (H greater than X)

Figure 515-6. *Storage tanks for cryogenic liquids. [From NFPA 59A-1990, Standard for the Production, Storage, and Handling of Liquefied Natural Gas (LNG)]*

Figure 515-7. Storage tanks, outdoors at grade. (From API Recommended Practice 500A).

515-7. **Gasoline Dispensing.** Where gasoline dispensing is carried on in conjunction with bulk station operations, the applicable provisions of Article 514 shall apply.

515-8. **Grounding.** All metal raceways, metal-jacketed cables, and all noncurrent-carrying metal parts of electric equipment shall be grounded as provided in Article 250. Grounding in Class I areas shall comply with Section 501-16.

(FPN):   For information on grounding for static protection, see Sections 5-4.4.1.2 and 5-4.4.1.7 of Flammable and Combustible Liquids Code, NFPA 30-1990 (ANSI).

ARTICLE 516   Spray Application, Dipping, and Coating Processes

Contents

516-1. **Scope.** This article covers the regular or frequent application of flammable liquids, combustible liquids, and combustible powders by spray operations and the application of flammable liquids, or combustible liquids at temperatures above their flashpoint, by dipping, coating, or other means.

(FPN):   For further information regarding safeguards for these processes, such as fire protection, posting of warning signs, and maintenance, see Spray Application Using Flammable and Combustible Materials, NFPA 33-1989 (ANSI), and Dipping and Coating Processes Using Flammable or Combustible Liquids, NFPA 34-1989 (ANSI). For additional information regarding ventilation, see Blower and Exhaust Systems for Air Conveying of Materials, NFPA 91-1992.

516-2. Classification of Locations.

Classification is based on dangerous quantities of flammable vapors, combustible mists, residues, dusts or deposits.

(a) Class I or Class II, Division 1 Locations. The following spaces shall be considered Class I or Class II, Division 1 locations, as applicable.

(1)^x The interiors of spray booths and rooms except as specifically provided in Section 516-3(d).

(2)^x The interior of exhaust ducts.

(3)^x Any area in the direct path of spray operations.

(4)^x For dipping and coating operations, all space within a 5-foot (1.52-m) radial distance from the vapor sources extending from these surfaces to the floor. The vapor source shall be the liquid exposed in the process and the drainboard, and any dipped or coated object from which it is possible to measure vapor concentrations exceeding 25 percent of the lower flammable limit at a distance of 1 foot (305 mm), in any direction, from the object.

(5)^x Pits within 25 feet (7.62 m) horizontally of the vapor source. If pits extend beyond 25 feet (7.62 m) of the vapor source, a vapor stop shall be provided, or the entire pit shall be classified as Class I, Division 1.

(6)^x The interior of any enclosed coating or dipping process.

(b) Class I or Class II, Division 2 Locations. The following spaces shall be considered Class I or Class II, Division 2 as applicable.

(1)^x For open spraying, all space outside of but within 20 feet (6.10 m) horizontally and 10 feet (3.05 m) vertically of the Class I, Division 1 location as defined in Section 516-2(a), and not separated from it by partitions. See Figure 1^x.

(2)^x For spraying operations conducted within a closed top, open face, or front spray booth or room, the space shown in Figure 2, and the space within 3 feet (914 mm) in all directions from openings other than the open face or front.

The Class I or Class II, Division 2 location shown in Figure 2 shall extend from the open face or front of the spray booth or room in accordance with the following:

a. If the ventilation system is interlocked with the spraying equipment so as to make the spraying equipment inoperable when the ventilation system is not in operation, the space shall extend 5 feet (1.52 m) from the open face or

Top (plan)

Class I or Class II Div. 1

Class I or Class II Div. 2

Roof

10' (3 m)

Spray area

Front (elevation)

For SI units:
one inch = 25.4 millimeters;
one foot = 0.3048 meter.

Figure 1.^x Class I or Class II, Division 2 Location Adjacent to an Unenclosed Spray Operation.

front of the spray booth or room, and as otherwise shown in Figure 2A.

b. If the ventilation system is not interlocked with the spraying equipment so as to make the spraying equipment inoperable when the ventilation system is not in operation, the space shall extend 10 feet (3.05 m) from the open face or front of the spray booth or room, and as otherwise shown in Figure 2B.

(3)^x For spraying operations conducted within an open top spray booth, the space 3 feet (914 mm) vertically above the

For SI units:
one inch = 25.4 millimeters;
one foot = 0.3048 meter.

Figure 2.ˣ *Class I or Class II, Division 2 Locations Adjacent to a Closed Top, Open Face or Open Front Spray Booth or Room.*

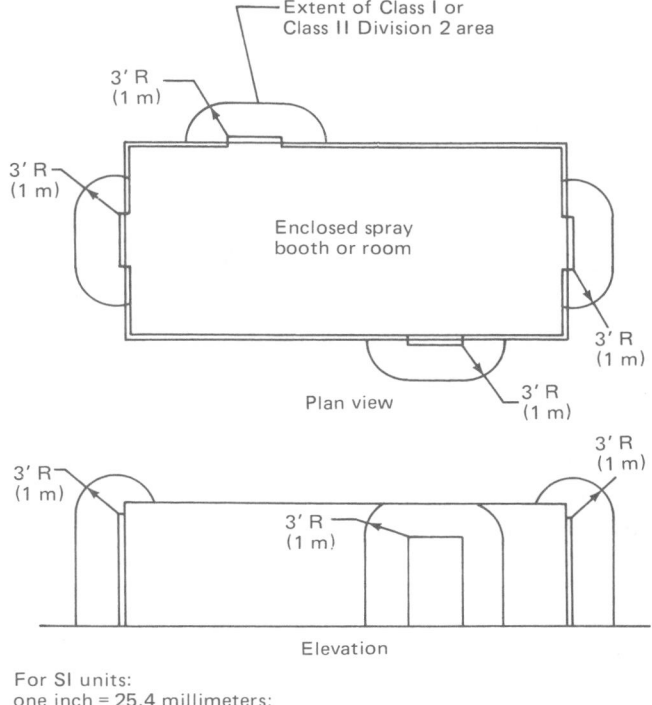

For SI units:
one inch = 25.4 millimeters;
one foot = 0.3048 meter.

Figure 3.ˣ *Class I or Class II, Division 2 Location Adjacent to Openings in an Enclosed Spray Booth or Room*

booth and within 3 feet (914 mm) of other booth openings shall be considered Class I or Class II, Division 2.

(4)ˣ For spraying operations confined to an enclosed spray booth or room, the space within 3 feet (914 mm) in all directions from any openings shall be considered Class I or Class II, Division 2 as shown in Figure 3.

(5)ˣ For dip tanks and drain boards, the 3-foot (914-mm) space surrounding the Class I, Division 1 location as defined in Section 516-2(a)(4) above and as shown in Figure 4.

(6) For dip tanks and drain boards, the space 3 feet (914 mm) above the floor and extending 20 feet (6.1 m) horizontally in all directions from the Class I, Division 1 location.

Exception: This space shall not be required to be considered a hazardous (classified) location where the vapor source area is 5 square feet (0.46 sq m) or less, and where the contents of the open tank, trough, or container do not exceed 5 gallons (18.9 L). In addition, the vapor concentration during operation and shutdown periods shall not exceed 25 percent of the lower flammable limit outside the Class I location specified in Section 516-2(a)(4) above.

(c)ˣ Enclosed Coating and Dipping Operations. The space adjacent to enclosed coating and dipping operations shall be considered nonclassified.

Exception: The space within 3 feet (914 mm) in all directions from any opening in the enclosure shall be classified as Class I, Division 2.

(d) Adjacent Locations. Adjacent locations that are cut off from the defined Class I or Class II locations by tight partitions without communicating openings, and within which hazardous

Figure 4.ˣ   *The Extent of Class I, Division I and Class I, Division 2 Hazardous (Classified) Locations for Open Dipping Processes.*

vapors or combustible powders are not likely to be released, shall be classified as nonhazardous.

(e) Nonhazardous Locations. Locations utilizing drying, curing, or fusion apparatus and provided with positive mechanical ventilation adequate to prevent accumulation of flammable concentrations of vapors, and provided with effective interlocks to deenergize all electric equipment (other than equipment approved for Class I locations) in case the ventilating equipment is inoperative, shall be permitted to be classified as nonhazardous where the authority having jurisdiction so judges.

(FPN):   For further information regarding safeguards, see Ovens and Furnaces, NFPA 86-1990 (ANSI).

516-3. Wiring and Equipment in Class I Locations.

(a) Wiring and Equipment — Vapors. All electric wiring and equipment within the Class I location (containing vapor only —not residues) defined in Section 516-2 shall comply with the applicable provisions of Article 501.

(b)ˣ Wiring and Equipment — Vapors and Residues. Unless specifically listed for locations containing deposits of dangerous quantities of flammable or combustible vapors, mists, residues, dusts or deposits (as applicable), there shall be no electrical equipment in any spray area as herein defined whereon deposits of combustible residue may readily accumulate, except

wiring in rigid metal conduit, intermediate metal conduit, Type MI cable, or in metal boxes or fittings containing no taps, splices or terminal connections.

Only electrical equipment specifically listed for the location is permitted where deposits of combustible residue may accumulate as stated in Section 516-3(b). However, the latter part of the requirement permits wiring in rigid metal conduit, intermediate metal conduit, Type MI cable, or in standard metal boxes without splices or taps.

(c) Illumination. Illumination of readily ignitible areas through panels of glass or other transparent or translucent material shall be permitted only if it complies with the following: (1) fixed lighting units are used as the source of illumination; (2) the panel effectively isolates the Class I location from the area in which the lighting unit is located; (3) the lighting unit is approved for its specific location; (4) the panel is of a material or is so protected that breakage will be unlikely; and (5) the arrangement is such that normal accumulations of hazardous residue on the surface of the panel will not be raised to a dangerous temperature by radiation or conduction from the source of illumination.

Underwriters Laboratories Inc. Hazardous Locations Equipment Directory indicates that UL-listed fixtures suitable for use in hazardous (classified) locations having deposits of readily combustible paint residue are so marked.

(d)ˣ Portable Equipment. Portable electric lamps or other utilization equipment shall not be used in a spray area during spray operations.

Exception No. 1: Where portable electric lamps are required for operations in spaces not readily illuminated by fixed lighting within the spraying area, they shall be of the type approved for Class I, Division 1 locations where readily ignitible residues may be present.

Exception No. 2: Where portable electric drying apparatus are used in automobile refinishing spray booths and the following requirements are met: (1) the apparatus and its electrical connections are not located within the spray enclosure during spray operations; (2) electrical equipment within 18 inches (45.7 cm) of the floor is approved for Class I, Division 2 locations; (3) all metallic parts of the drying apparatus are electrically bonded and grounded; and (4) interlocks are provided to prevent the operation of spray equipment while drying apparatus is within the spray enclosure, to allow for a 3-minute purge of the enclosure before energizing the drying apparatus, and to shut off drying apparatus on failure of ventilation system.

(e) Electrostatic Equipment. Electrostatic spraying or detearing equipment shall be installed and used only as provided in Section 516-4.

(FPN): For further information, see Spray Application Using Flammable and Combustible Materials, NFPA 33-1989 (ANSI).

516-4ˣ. Fixed Electrostatic Equipment. This section shall apply to any equipment using electrostatically charged elements for the atomization, charging, and (or) precipitation of hazardous materials for coatings on articles or for other similar purposes in which the charging or atomizing device is attached to a mechanical support or manipulator. This includes robotic devices. This section shall not apply to devices that are held or manipulated by hand. Where robotic programming procedures involve manual manipulation of the robot arm while spraying with the high voltage on, the provisions of Section 516-5 shall apply. The installation of electrostatic spraying equipment shall comply with (a) through (j) below. Spray equipment shall be listed or approved.

All automatic electrostatic equipment systems shall comply with (a) through (i) below.

(a) Power and Control Equipment. Transformers, high-voltage supplies, control apparatus, and all other electric portions of the equipment shall be installed outside of the Class I location as defined in Section 516-2 or be of a type approved for the location.

Exception: High-voltage grids, electrodes, electrostatic atomizing heads, and their connections shall be permitted within the Class I location.

(b) Electrostatic Equipment. Electrodes and electrostatic atomizing heads shall be adequately supported in permanent locations and shall be effectively insulated from ground. Electrodes and electrostatic atomizing heads that are permanently attached to their bases, supports, reciprocators, or robots shall be deemed to comply with this section.

(c) High-Voltage Leads. High-voltage leads shall be properly insulated and protected from mechanical damage or exposure to destructive chemicals. Any exposed element at high voltage shall be effectively and permanently supported on suitable insulators and shall be effectively guarded against accidental contact or grounding.

(d) Support of Goods. Goods being coated using this process shall be supported on conveyors or hangers. The conveyors or hangers shall be arranged to (1) assure that the parts being coated are electrically connected to ground with a resistance of 1 megohm or less and (2) prevent parts from swinging.

(e) Automatic Controls. Electrostatic apparatus shall be equipped with automatic means that will rapidly deenergize the high-voltage elements under any of the following conditions: (1) stoppage of ventilating fans or failure of ventilating equipment from any cause; (2) stoppage of the conveyor carrying goods through the high-voltage field unless stoppage is required by the spray process; (3) occurrence of excessive current leakage at any point in the high-voltage system; (4) deenergizing the primary voltage input to the power supply.

(f) Grounding. All electrically conductive objects in the spray area, except those objects required by the process to be at high voltage, shall be adequately grounded. This requirement shall apply to paint containers, wash cans, guards, hose connectors, brackets, and any other electrically conductive objects or devices in the area.

(g) Isolation. Safeguards such as adequate booths, fencing, railings, interlocks, or other means shall be placed about the equipment or incorporated therein so that they, either by their location or character, or both, assure that a safe separation of the process is maintained.

(h) Signs. Signs shall be conspicuously posted to (1) designate the process zone as dangerous with regard to fire and accident; (2) identify the grounding requirements for all electrically conductive objects in the spray area; (3) restrict access to qualified personnel only.

(i) Insulators. All insulators shall be kept clean and dry.

(j) Other Than Nonincendive Equipment. Spray equipment that cannot be classified as nonincendive shall comply with (1) and (2) below.

(1) Conveyors or hangers shall be so arranged to maintain a safe distance of at least twice the sparking distance between goods being painted and electrodes, electrostatic atomizing heads, or charged conductors. Warnings defining this safe distance shall be posted.

(2) The equipment shall provide an automatic means of rapidly deenergizing the high-voltage elements in the event the distance between the goods being painted and the eletrodes or electrostatic atomizing heads falls below that specified in item (1) above.

516-5ˣ. Electrostatic Hand-Spraying Equipment. This section shall apply to any equipment using electrostatically charged elements for the atomization, charging, and/or precipitation of materials for coatings on articles, or for other similar purposes in which the atomizing device is hand held or manipulated during the spraying operation. Electrostatic hand-spraying equipment and devices used in connection with paint-spraying operations shall be of approved types and shall comply with (a) through (e) below.

(a) General. The high-voltage circuits shall be designed so as not to produce a spark of sufficient intensity to ignite the most readily ignitible of those vapor-air mixtures likely to be encountered, nor result in appreciable shock hazard upon coming in contact with a grounded object under all normal operating conditions. The electrostatically charged exposed elements of the hand gun shall be capable of being energized only by an actuator that also controls the coating material supply.

(b) Power Equipment. Transformers, power packs, control apparatus, and all other electric portions of the equipment shall be located outside of the Class I location or be approved for the location.

Exception: The hand gun itself and its connections to the power supply shall be permitted within the Class I location.

(c) Handle. The handle of the spraying gun shall be electrically connected to ground by a metallic connection and be so constructed that the operator in normal operating position is in intimate electrical contact with the grounded handle to prevent buildup of a static charge on the operator's body. Signs indicating the necessity for grounding other persons entering the spray area shall be conspicuously posted.

(d) Electrostatic Equipment. All electrically conductive objects in the spraying area shall be adequately grounded. This requirement shall apply to paint containers, wash cans, and any other electrically conductive objects or devices in the area. The equipment shall carry a prominent, permanently installed warning regarding the necessity for this grounding feature.

(e) Support of Objects. Objects being painted shall be maintained in metallic contact with the conveyor or other grounded support. Hooks shall be regularly cleaned to ensure adequate grounding of 1 megohm or less. Areas of contact shall be sharp points or knife edges where possible. Points of support of the object shall be concealed from random spray where feasible; and, where the objects being sprayed are supported from a conveyor, the point of attachment to the conveyor shall be so located as to not collect spray material during normal operation.

516-6ˣ. Powder Coating. This section shall apply to processes in which combustible dry powders are applied. The hazards associated with combustible dusts are present in such a process to a degree, depending upon the chemical composition of the material, particle size, shape, and distribution.

(FPN): The hazards associated with combustible dusts are inherent in this process. Generally speaking, the hazard rating of the powders employed is dependent upon the chemical composition of the material, particle size, shape, and distribution.

(a) Electric Equipment and Sources of Ignition. Electric equipment and other sources of ignition shall comply with the requirements of Article 502. Portable electric lamps and other utilization equipment shall not be used within a Class II location during operation of the finishing processes. When such lamps or utilization equipment are used during cleaning or repairing operations, they shall be of a type approved for Class II, Division 1 locations, and all exposed metal parts shall be effectively grounded.

Exception: Where portable electric lamps are required for operations in spaces not readily illuminated by fixed lighting within the spraying area, they shall be of the type approved for Class II, Division 1 locations where readily ignitible residues may be present.

(b) Fixed Electrostatic Spraying Equipment. The provisions of Sections 516-4 and (a) above shall apply to fixed electrostatic spraying equipment.

(c) Electrostatic Hand-Spraying Equipment. The provisions of Sections 516-5 and (a) above shall apply to electrostatic hand-spraying equipment.

(d) Electrostatic Fluidized Beds. Electrostatic fluidized beds and associated equipment shall be of approved types. The high-voltage circuits shall be so designed that any discharge produced when the charging electrodes of the bed are approached or contacted by a grounded object shall not be of sufficient intensity to ignite any powder-air mixture likely to be encountered nor to result in an appreciable shock hazard.

(1) Transformers, power packs, control apparatus, and all other electric portions of the equipment shall be located outside the powder-coating area or shall otherwise comply with the requirements of (a) above.

Exception: The charging electrodes and their connections to the power supply shall be permitted within the powder-coating area.

(2) All electrically conductive objects within the powder-coating area shall be adequately grounded. The powder-coating equipment shall carry a prominent, permanently installed warning regarding the necessity for grounding these objects.

(3) Objects being coated shall be maintained in electrical contact (less than 1 megohm) with the conveyor or other support in order to ensure proper grounding. Hangers shall be regularly cleaned to ensure effective electrical contact. Areas of electrical contact shall be sharp points or knife edges where possible.

(4) The electric equipment and compressed-air supplies shall be interlocked with a ventilation system so that the equipment cannot be operated unless the ventilating fans are in operation.

516-7. **Wiring and Equipment Above Class I and II Locations.**

(a) Wiring. All fixed wiring above the Class I and II locations shall be in metal raceways, rigid nonmetallic conduit, or electrical nonmetallic tubing, or shall be Type MI, TC, SNM, or Type MC cable. Cellular metal floor raceways shall be permitted only for supplying ceiling outlets or extensions to the area below the floor of a Class I or II location, but such raceways shall have no connections leading into or through the Class I or II location above the floor unless suitable seals are provided.

(b) Equipment. Equipment that may produce arcs, sparks, or particles of hot metal, such as lamps and lampholders for fixed lighting, cutouts, switches, receptacles, motors, or other equipment having make-and-break or sliding contacts, where installed above a Class I or II location or above a location where freshly finished goods are handled, shall be of the totally enclosed type or be so constructed as to prevent escape of sparks or hot metal particles.

516-8. **Grounding.** All metal raceways, metal-jacketed cables, and all noncurrent-carrying metal parts of fixed or portable equipment, regardless of voltage, shall be grounded as provided in Article 250.

NFPA 33-1989, *Standard for Spray Application Using Flammable and Combustible Materials,* covers the spray application of flammable or combustible materials by means of compressed air, "airless" or "hydraulic atomization," or by steam, electrostatic methods, or any other means in continuous or intermittent processes. It also covers the application of combustible powders where applied by powder spray guns, electrostatic powder spray guns, and fluidized beds or electrostatic fluidized beds.

NFPA 33 outlines the requirements for the maintenance of safe conditions.

The proper maintenance and operation of processes and process areas where flammable and combustible materials are handled and applied is critical with respect to the protection of life and property from fire or explosion.

It has been shown that the largest fire losses and frequency of fires have occurred where the proper codes and standards have not been used or properly applied.

Spray Area: Any area in which dangerous quantities of flammable or combustible vapors, mists, residues, dusts, or deposits are present due to the operation of spray processes.

A spray area shall include:

(a) The interior of spray booths and rooms (with certain exceptions).

(b) The interior of ducts exhausting from spraying processes.

(c) Any area in the direct path of spraying operations.

The authority having jurisdiction may, for the purpose of NFPA 33, define the limits of the spray area in any specific case. The spray area in the vicinity of spraying operations will necessarily vary with the design and arrangement of equipment and method of operation. Where spraying operations are strictly confined to predetermined spaces that are provided with adequate and reliable ventilation, such as a properly constructed spray booth, the spray area will ordinarily not extend beyond the booth enclosure. However, where spraying operations are not confined to adequately ventilated spaces, the spray area may extend throughout the entire room containing spraying operations.

Spray Booth: A power-ventilated structure provided to enclose or accommodate a spraying operation; to confine and limit the escape of spray, vapor, and residue; and to safely conduct or direct them to an exhaust system. Spray booths are manufactured in a variety of forms, including automotive refinishing, downdraft, open-face, traveling, tunnel, and updraft booths.

Spray Room: A power-ventilated, fully enclosed room used exclusively for open spraying of flammable or combustible materials. The entire spray room is a spray area. A spray booth is not a spray room.

Waterwash Spray Booth: A spray booth equipped with a water washing system designed to minimize dusts or residues entering exhaust ducts and to permit the recovery of overspray finishing material.

Dry Spray Booth: A spray booth not equipped with a water washing system. A dry spray booth may be equipped with (1) distribution or baffle plates to promote an even flow of air through the booth or cause deposit of overspray before it enters exhaust ducts; (2) overspray dry filters to minimize dusts or residues entering exhaust ducts; (3) overspray dry filter rolls designed to minimize dusts or residues entering exhaust ducts; or (4) where dry powders are being sprayed, powder collection systems so arranged in the exhaust to capture oversprayed material.

Notes on Electrical Installations:
The safety of life and property from fire or explosion as a result of spray applications of flammable and combustible materials such as paints, finishes, and adhesives varies depending on the arrangement and operation of a particular installation.

The principal hazards of spray application operations originate from flammable or combustible liquids or powders and their vapors or mists as well as from highly combustible residues or powders.

Properly constructed spray booths, with adequate mechanical ventilation, may be used to discharge vapors or powder to a safe location and reduce the possibility of an explosion. In like manner, the accumulation of overspray residues, many of which are not only highly combustible but also subject to spontaneous ignition, can be controlled.

The elimination of all sources of ignition in areas where flammable or combustible liquids, vapors, mists, or combustible residues are present, together with constant supervision and maintenance, is essential to the safe operation of spraying.

The human element necessitates careful consideration of the location of the operation and the installation of extinguishing equipment in order to reduce the possibility of fire spreading to other property and minimize the probability of damage to other property.

It is obvious that there should be no open flames or spark-producing equipment in any area where, because of inadequate ventilation, explosive vapor-air mixtures or mists are present. It is equally obvious that no open flames or spark-producing equipment should be located where highly combustible spray residues will be deposited on them. Because some residues may be ignited at very low temperatures, additional consideration must be given to operating temperatures of equipment subject to residue deposits. Many deposits may be ignited at temperatures produced by low-pressure steam pipes or by incandescent light globes, even fixtures of the explosionproof type.

It should be noted that electrical equipment is generally not permitted inside any spray booth, in the exhaust duct from a spray booth, in the entrained air of an exhaust system from a spraying operation, or in the direct path of spray, unless such equipment is specifically listed for both readily ignitible deposits and flammable vapor.

The determination of the extent of hazardous areas involved in spray application requires an understanding of the multiple hazards of flammable vapors, mists, powders, and highly combustible deposits applied at each individual location.

Where electrical equipment is installed in locations not subject to deposits of combustible residues but, due to inadequate ventilation, is subject to explosive concentrations of flammable vapors or mists, only approved explosionproof or other types of equipment approved for Class I, Division 1 locations (for example, purged, pressurized, or intrinsically safe equipment or systems) are permitted.

When spray areas containing dangerous quantities of flammable or combustible vapors, mists, residues, dusts, or deposits under normal operation have been determined, the adjacent unpartitioned areas, which are safe under normal operating conditions but which may become dangerous due to accident or careless operation, should be given consideration. Equipment known to produce sparks or flames under normal operating conditions should not be installed in these adjacent unpartitioned areas.

Where spraying operations are confined to adequately ventilated spray booths or rooms, there should be no deposits of combustible residues or dangerous concentrations of flammable vapors, mists, or dusts outside the spray booth under normal operating conditions.

In the interest of safety, however, it should be noted that unless separated by partitions, an area within a certain distance [see Section 516-2(b)] of the Class I (or Class II), Division 1 spraying area, depending on the arrangement, is classified as Division 2; that is, it should contain no equipment that produces ignition-capable sparks under normal operation. Furthermore, within this distance, electric lamps are required to be enclosed to prevent hot particles from falling on freshly painted stock or other readily ignitible material and, if subject to physical damage, are required to be properly guarded. See Section 516-7(b).

Even though it is contemplated that areas adjacent to spray booths (particularly where coating material stocks are located) will be provided with ventilation sufficient to prevent the presence of flammable vapors or deposits, it is nevertheless advisable that electric lamps be totally enclosed to prevent hot particles from falling in any area where there may be freshly painted stock, accidentally spilled flammable or combustible materials, readily ignitible refuse, or flammable or combustible liquid containers that have been left open accidentally. See Section 516-7(b).

Where electric lamps are in areas subject to atmospheres of flammable vapor, lamps should be replaced while electricity is off; otherwise there may be a spark from this source.

Sufficient lighting for coating operations, booth cleaning, and booth repair work should be provided at the time the equipment is installed in order to avoid the use of temporary or emergency lamps connected to ordinary extension cords in this area. See Section 516-3(d). A satisfactory and practical method of lighting is the use of ¼-inch thick wired or tempered glass panels in the top or sides of the spray booth with electrical light fixtures located outside the booth, avoiding the direct path of the spray. See Section 516-3(c).

In order to prevent sparks from the accumulation of static electricity, all electrically conductive objects, including metal parts of spray booths, exhaust ducts, piping systems conveying flammable or combustible liquids or paint, solvent tanks, and canisters, should be properly grounded. See Section 4-9.1 of NFPA 33.

Automobile undercoating operations in garages, conducted in areas having adequate natural or mechanical ventilation, are exempt from the requirements pertaining to spray-coating operations where (1) undercoating materials not more hazardous than kerosene (as classified by Underwriters Laboratories Inc. with respect to fire hazard rating 30-40) are used, or (2) undercoating materials using only solvents having a flash point in excess of 38°C (100°F) are used, and (3) no open flames are within 20 feet while such operations are conducted.

ARTICLE 517 Health Care Facilities

Contents

A. General

B. Wiring and Protection

A. General

517-1. Scope.

The provisions of this article shall apply to electrical construction and installation criteria in health care facilities.

(FPN No. 1): This article is not intended to apply to veterinary facilities.

(FPN No. 2): For information concerning performance, maintenance, and testing criteria, refer to the appropriate health care facilities documents.

517-2. General.

The requirements in Parts B and C apply not only to single-function buildings, but are also intended to be individually applied to their respective forms of occupancy within a multifunction building (e.g., a doctor's examining room located within a limited care facility would be required to meet the provisions of Section 517-10).

The requirements of this article are intended to apply to all types of health care facilities. The requirements for each type of health care facility are nevertheless intended to be applied in a very specific manner. An example of the application of this article would be a suite of doctors' offices within an office building. The doctor's business office would be treated as an ordinary occupancy and would only be required to meet the applicable portion of other parts of this

Code. However, the examining rooms attached to the doctor's business office would be required to meet the provisions of Part B and Section 517-50 in Article 517.

The scope also includes health care facilities that may be mobile or supply very limited outpatient services. However, the scope does not include animal hospitals.

Other standards referenced in this article are NFPA 99-1990, *Standard for Health Care Facilities*; NFPA 101-1991, *Life Safety Code*; and NFPA 20-1990, *Standard for the Installation of Centrifugal Fire Pumps.*

517-3. Definitions.

Alternate Power Source: One or more generator sets, or battery systems where permitted, intended to provide power during the interruption of the normal electrical services or the public utility electrical service intended to provide power during interruption of service normally provided by the generating facilities on the premises.

Anesthetizing Location: Any area of a health care facility that has been designated to be used for the administration of any flammable or nonflammable inhalation anesthetic agent in the course of examination or treatment, including the use of such agents for relative analgesia.

This definition recognizes that in an emergency it may be necessary to administer an anesthetic almost anywhere in a health care facility; however, only those areas in a health care facility set aside specifically for the induction of anesthetics are required to meet the provisions of Part D of Article 517. This definition and the provisions of Part D are not intended to apply to the administration of analgesic anesthetics such as might be used in a dental office.

Critical Branch: A subsystem of the emergency system consisting of feeders and branch circuits supplying energy to task illumination, special power circuits, and selected receptacles serving areas and functions related to patient care, and which are connected to alternate power sources by one or more transfer switches during interruption of the normal power source.

Electrical Life-Support Equipment: Electrically powered equipment whose continuous operation is necessary to maintain a patient's life.

Emergency System: A system of feeders and branch circuits meeting the requirements of Article 700, and intended to supply alternate power to a limited number of prescribed functions vital to the protection of life and patient safety, with automatic restoration of electrical power within 10 seconds of power interruption.

Equipment System: A system of feeders and branch circuits arranged for delayed, automatic or manual connection to the alternate power source and which serves primarily 3-phase power equipment.

Essential Electrical System: A system comprised of alternate sources of power and all connected distribution systems and ancillary equipment, designed to assure continuity of electrical power to designated areas and functions of a health care facility during disruption of normal power sources, and also designed to minimize disruption within the internal wiring system.

Exposed Conductive Surfaces: Those surfaces which are capable of carrying electric current and which are unprotected, unenclosed, or unguarded, permitting personal contact. Paint, anodizing, and similar coatings are not considered suitable insulation, unless they are listed for use.

Flammable Anesthetics: Gases or vapors, such as fluroxene, cyclopropane, divinyl ether, ethyl chloride, ethyl ether, and ethylene, which may form flammable or explosive mixtures with air, oxygen, or reducing gases such as nitrous oxide.

Flammable Anesthetizing Location: Any area of the facility which has been designated to be used for the administration of any flammable inhalation anesthetic agents in the normal course of examination or treatment.

Hazard Current: For a given set of connections in an isloated power system, the total current that would flow through a low impedance if it were connected between either isolated conductor and ground.

FAULT HAZARD CURRENT: The hazard current of a given isolated system with all devices connected except the line isolation monitor.

MONITOR HAZARD CURRENT: The hazard current of the line isolation monitor alone.

TOTAL HAZARD CURRENT: The hazard current of a given isolated system with all devices, including the line isolation monitor, connected.

Health Care Facilities: Buildings or portions of buildings that contain, but are not limited to, occupancies such as: hospitals; nursing homes; limited care; supervisory care; clinics;

medical and dental offices; and ambulatory care, whether permanent or movable.

Hospital: A building or part thereof used for the medical, psychiatric, obstetrical, or surgical care, on a 24-hour basis, of four or more inpatients. Hospital, wherever used in this Code, shall include general hospitals, mental hospitals, tuberculosis hospitals, children's hospitals, and any such facilites providing inpatient care.

Isolated Power System: A system comprising an isolating transformer or its equivalent, a line isolation monitor, and its ungrounded circuit conductors.

Isolation Transformer: A transformer of the multiple-winding type, with the primary and secondary windings physically separated, which inductively couples its secondary winding to the grounded feeder systems that energize its primary winding.

Life Safety Branch: A subsystem of the emergency system consisting of feeders and branch circuits, meeting the requirements of Article 700 and intended to provide adequate power needs to ensure safety to patients and personnel, and which are automatically connected to alternate power sources during interruption of the normal power source.

Limited Care Facility: A building or part thereof used on a 24-hour basis for the housing of four or more persons who are incapable of self-preservation because of age, physical limitation due to accident or illness, or mental limitations, such as mental retardation/developmental disability, mental illness, or chemical dependency.

Line Isolation Monitor: A test instrument designed to continually check the balanced and unbalanced impedance from each line of an isolated circuit to ground and equipped with a built-in test circuit to exercise the alarm without adding to the leakage current hazard.

(FPN): "Line isolation monitor" was formerly known as "ground contact indicator."

Nursing Home: A building or part thereof used for the lodging, boarding and nursing care, on a 24-hour basis, of four or more persons who, because of mental or physical incapacity, may be unable to provide for their own needs and safety without the assistance of another person. Nursing home, wherever used in this Code, shall include nursing and convalescent homes, skilled nursing facilities, intermediate care facilities, and infirmaries of homes for the aged.

Nurses' Stations: Areas intended to provide a center of nursing activity for a group of nurses serving bed patients, where the patient calls are received, nurses are dispatched, nurses' notes written, inpatient charts prepared, and medications prepared for distribution to patients. Where such activities are carried on in more that one location within a nursing unit, all such separate areas are considered a part of the nurses' station.

Patient Bed Location: The location of an inpatient sleeping bed or the bed or procedure table used in a critical patient care area.

Patient Care Area: Any portion of a health care facility wherein patients are intended to be examined or treated.

(FPN): Business offices, corridors, lounges, day rooms, dining rooms, or similar areas typically are not classified as patient care areas.

Patient Care Areas of a Hospital: Areas of a hospital in which patient care is administered are classified as general care areas, or critical care areas, either of which may be classified as a wet location. The governing body of the facility shall designate these areas in accordance with the type of patient care anticipated and with the following definitions of the area classification.

(1) General care areas are patient bedrooms, examining rooms, treatment rooms, clinics, and similar areas in which it is intended that the patient shall come in contact with ordinary appliances such as a nurse call system, electrical beds, examining lamps, telephone, and entertainment devices. In such areas, it may also be intended that patients be connected to electromedical devices (such as heating pads, electrocardiographs, drainage pumps, monitors, otoscopes, ophthalmoscopes, intravenous lines, etc.).

(2) Critical care areas are those special care units, intensive care units, coronary care units, angiography laboratories, cardiac catheterization laboratories, delivery rooms, operating rooms, and similar areas in which patients are intended to be subjected to invasive procedures and connected to line-operated, electromedical devices.

(3) Wet locations are those patient care areas that are normally subject to wet conditions while patients are present. These include standing fluids on the floor or drenching of the work area, either of which condition is intimate to the patient or staff. Routine housekeeping procedures and incidental spillage of liquids do not define a wet location.

This definition excludes such areas as laundry rooms, boiler rooms, and utility areas, which, although routinely wet, are not patient care areas. The governing body of the health care facility may elect to include such areas as hydrotherapy areas, dialysis laboratories, and certain wet laboratories under this definition. Lavatories or bathrooms within a health care facility are not intended to be classified as wet locations.

Patient Equipment Grounding Point: A jack or terminal bus which serves as the collection point for redundant grounding of electric appliances serving a patient vicinity or for grounding other items in order to eliminate electromagnetic interference problems.

Patient Vicinity: In an area in which patients are normally cared for, the patient vicinity is the space with surfaces likely to be contacted by the patient or an attendant who can touch the patient. Typically in a patient room, this encloses a space within the room not less than 6 feet (1.83 m) beyond the perimeter of the bed in its nominal location, and extending vertically not less than 7½ feet (2.29 m) above the floor.

This area is limited to patient beds in their nominal position; that is, the position of the bed as called for in the architect's plans, rather than the temporary position of the bed subject to movement by housekeeping staff or the convenience of the medical staff.

Definitions for "hospital," "nursing home," and "limited care facility" are identical to the corresponding definitions found in NFPA 101-1991, *Life Safety Code.*

Psychiatric Hospital: A building used exclusively for the psychiatric care, on a 24-hour basis, of four or more inpatients.

Reference Grounding Point: The ground bus of the panelboard or isolated power system panel supplying the patient care area.

Selected Receptacles: A minimum number of electric receptacles to accommodate appliances ordinarily required for local tasks or likely to be used in patient care emergencies.

Task Illumination: Provision for the minimum lighting required to carry out necessary tasks in the described areas, including safe access to supplies and equipment, and access to exits.

Therapeutic High-Frequency Diathermy Equipment: Therapeutic high-frequency diathermy equipment is therapeutic induction and dielectric heating equipment.

X-Ray Installations (Long-Time Rating): A rating based on an operating interval of 5 minutes or longer.

X-Ray Installations (Mobile): X-ray equipment mounted on a permanent base with wheels, casters, or a combination of both to facilitate moving the equipment while completely assembled.

X-Ray Installations (Momentary Rating): A rating based on an operating interval that does not exceed 5 seconds.

X-Ray Installations (Portable): X-ray equipment designed to be hand carried.

X-Ray Installations (Transportable): X-ray equipment to be installed in a vehicle or that may be readily disassembled for transport in a vehicle.

B. Wiring and Protection

517-10. **Applicability.** Part B shall apply to all health care facilities.

Exception No. 1: Part B shall not apply to business offices, corridors, waiting rooms, and the like in clinics, medical and dental offices, and outpatient facilities.

Exception No. 2: Part B shall not apply to patient sleeping areas in nursing homes and residential care facilities wired in accordance with Chapters 1 through 4 of this Code.

This exception recognizes that sleeping rooms in nursing homes are usually not patient care areas.

Exception No. 3ˣ: Part B shall not apply to freestanding buildings used as nursing homes and residential care facilities provided:

a. It maintains admitting and discharge policies that preclude the provision of care for any patient or resident who may need to be sustained by electrical life-support equipment, and

b. Offers no surgical treatment requiring general anesthesia, and

c. Provides an automatic battery-operated system(s) or equipment that shall be effective for at least 1½ hours and is otherwise in accordance with Section 700-12 and that shall be capable of supplying lighting for exit lights, exit corridors, stairways, nursing stations, medical preparation areas, boiler rooms, and communication areas. This system shall also supply power to operate all alarm systems.

(FPN): See Life Safety Code, NFPA 101-1991 (ANSI).

517-11. **General Installation/Construction Criteria.** It is the purpose of this article to specify the installation criteria and wiring methods that will minimize electrical hazards by the maintenance of adequately low-potential differences only between exposed conductive surfaces that are likely to become energized and could be contacted by a patient.

(FPN): In a health care facility, it is difficult to prevent the occurrence of a conductive or capacitive path from the patient's body to some grounded object, because that path may be established accidentally or through instrumentation directly connected to the patient. Other electrically conductive surfaces that may make an additional contact with the patient, or instruments that may be connected to the patient, then become possible sources of electric currents that can traverse the patient's body. The hazard is increased as more apparatus is associated with the patient, and, therefore, more intensive precautions are needed. Control of electric shock hazard requires the limitation of electric current that might flow in an electric circuit involving the patient's body by raising the resistance of the conductive circuit that includes the patient, or by insulating exposed surfaces that might become energized, in addition to reducing the potential difference that can appear between exposed conductive surfaces in the patient vicinity, or by combinations of these methods. A special problem is presented by the patient with an externalized direct conductive path to the heart muscle. The patient may be electrocuted at current levels so low that additional protection in the design of appliances, insulation of the catheter, and control of medical practice are required.

This fine print note recognizes the possibility of increased sensitivity to electric shock by patients whose body resistance may be compromised either accidentally or by a necessary medical procedure. Such diverse situations as incontinence or the insertion of a catheter may render a patient much more vulnerable to the effects of an electric current. For these reasons, it is essential that those responsible for the design, installation, and maintenance of the electrical system in patient care areas be well acquainted with at least the rudiments of the hazard as explained in this note.

Since the original recognition of this hazard in the 1971 *Code*, continued clinical evaluation of the problem has provided a better understanding of the extent of the hazard,

bringing about the changes in both value and wiring methods now found in the *Code*.

The *Code* clearly assigns responsibility for the designation of the types of patient care areas to the governing body of the health care facility. Both the design and inspection of a patient care area must therefore be based on the governing body's designation rather than the superficial appearance of the area.

517-12. **Wiring Methods.** Except as modified in this article, wiring methods shall comply with the applicable requirements of Chapters 1 through 4 of this Code.

One of the major modifications in this article is the requirement for redundant grounding.

517-13. **Grounding of Receptacles and Fixed Electric Equipment.**

(a) Patient Care Area. In an area used for patient care, the grounding terminals of all receptacles and all noncurrent-carrying conductive surfaces of fixed electric equipment likely to become energized that are subject to personal contact, operating at over 100 volts, shall be grounded by an insulated copper conductor. The grounding conductor shall be sized in accordance with Table 250-95 and installed in metal raceways with the branch-circuit conductors supplying these receptacles or fixed equipment.

Exception No. 1: Metal raceways shall not be required where Type MI cable, and Types MC and AC cables where the outer metal jacket is an approved grounding means of a listed cable assembly.

Exception No. 2: Metal faceplates shall be permitted to be grounded by means of a metal mounting screw(s) securing the faceplate to a grounded outlet box or grounded wiring device.

This rule applies to the branch circuits in areas used for patient care and is not limited to patient rooms. Additional areas, such as therapy areas, recreational areas, solaria, and certain patient corridors, are also included. It should be clearly understood that this section requires grounding by means of an insulated copper conductor installed with the branch-circuit conductors. The conductor can be either solid or stranded. A separate insulated equipment grounding conductor is not required to be run to the branch-circuit panelboard with the feeder conductors in a metal raceway.

Exception No. 1 permits approved metal-sheathed cables with an insulated grounding conductor. See commentary below Section 517-13(b).

Exception No. 2 permits metal faceplates to be grounded by means of the metal mounting screws rather than by having a separate equipment grounding conductor run to the metal plate. See also Section 380-12 requiring metal faceplates to be effectively grounded.

(b) Methods. In addition to the requirements of Section 517-13(a), all branch circuits serving patient care areas shall be provided with a ground path for fault current by installation in a metal raceway system or cable assembly. The metal raceway system, or cable armor or sheath assembly, shall qualify as an equipment grounding return path in accordance with Section 250-91(b). Type MC and Type MI cable shall have an outer metal armor or sheath that is identified as an acceptable grounding return path.

It is intended by this section that a redundant ground path through the metal raceway or cable be provided with branch circuits serving patient care areas. This path is in addition to the path through the insulated grounding conductor required in Section 517-13(a).

Patient care areas are not limited to hospitals. They are also found in other health care facilities such as nursing homes, clinics, medical and dental offices, etc. The outer metal jacket of interlocking-tape for Type MC cable does not qualify as an equipment grounding return path in accordance with Section 250-91(b) and would not be accepted for this purpose in the patient care area.

Metal-sheathed cable assemblies are not permitted for EMERGENCY CIRCUITS in the patient vicinity because Section 517-30(c)(3) requires such wiring to be protected by installation in a metal raceway.

517-14. Panelboard Bonding. The equipment grounding terminal busses of the normal and essential branch-circuit panelboards serving the same individual patient vicinity shall be bonded together with an insulated continuous copper conductor not smaller than No. 10. Where more than two (2) panels serve the same location, this conductor shall be continuous from panel to panel, but shall be permitted to be broken in order to terminate on the ground bus in each panel.

Figure 517-1. A battery-operated precision instrument for use on all hospital electrical equipment. This instrument measures and detects line voltage and leakage current between the grounding pole of a receptacle and the exposed conductive surfaces of non-electrical equipment, and/or between the grounding pole and conductive surfaces of fixed or portable electrical equipment. (Neurodyne-Dempsey, Inc.)

517-16. Receptacles with Insulated Grounding Terminals. Receptacles with insulated grounding terminals as permitted in Section 250-74, Exception No. 4 shall be identified; such identification shall be visible after installation.

(FPN): Caution is important in specifying such a system with receptacles having insulated grounding terminals, since the grounding impedance is controlled only by the grounding conductors and does not benefit functionally from any parallel grounding paths.

This section prevents the indiscriminate use of such devices and the risk of compromising the potential difference requirements within critical care areas.

Proper identification may be made by color-coding the receptacle orange or by other approved means.

517-17. Ground-Fault Protection.

(a) Feeders. Where ground-fault protection is provided for operation of the service disconnecting means or feeder disconnecting means as specified by Sections 230-95 or 215-10, an additional step of ground-fault protection shall be provided in the next level of feeder disconnecting means downstream toward the load. Such protection shall consist of overcurrent devices and current transformers or other equivalent protective equipment that shall cause the feeder disconnecting means to open.

(FPN): The additional levels of ground-fault protection required by Section 517-17(a) are not intended:

a. On the load side of an essential electrical system transfer switch, or

b. Between the on-site generating unit(s) described in Section 517-35(b) and the essential electrical system transfer switch(es), or

c. On electrical systems that are not solidly grounded wye systems with greater than 150 volts to ground, but not exceeding 600 volts phase-to-phase.

(b) Selectivity. Ground-fault protection for operation of the service and feeder disconnecting means shall be fully selective such that the feeder device and not the service device shall open on ground faults on the load side of the feeder device. A six-cycle minimum separation between the service and feeder ground-fault tripping bands shall be provided. Operating time of the disconnecting devices shall be considered in selecting the time spread between these two bands to achieve 100 percent selectivity.

(FPN): See Section 230-95, Fine Print Note, for transfer of alternate source where ground-fault protection is applied.

Wherever ground-fault protective (GFP) equipment is applied to the service providing power to a health care facility, whether by design or by reason of the requirements of Section 230-95, an additional level of ground-fault protection is required downstream. Under this rule, ground-fault protection is required to be applied to every feeder, and additional ground-fault protective devices may be applied farther downstream at the option of the governing body of the health care facility. With proper coordination, this additional ground-fault protection is intended to limit a ground fault to a single feeder and thereby prevent a total outage of the entire health care system. Coordination includes consideration of the trip setting, the time setting, and the time required for operation (opening time) of each level of the GFP system.

It is not intended that GFP be installed between the on-site generator and the transfer switch or on the load side of the essential electrical system transfer switch.

However, where a health care installation, such as a doctor's office, is a part of a larger general-use facility (for example, a business office building) that has service ground-fault protection in accordance with Section 230-95, it is not intended that ground-fault protection be required on the health care facility (doctor's office) feeder since no additional protection will be achieved insofar as the doctor's office is concerned.

Section 230-95(b), FPN No. 6 calls attention to problems that may arise when ground-fault protected systems are transferred to another supply system.

(c) Testing. When equipment ground-fault protection is first installed, each level shall be performance tested to ensure compliance with (b) above.

See Section 230-95(c) and its commentary.

517-18. **General Care Areas.**

(a) Patient Bed Location Branch Circuits. Each patient bed location shall be supplied by at least two branch circuits, at least one of which originates in a normal system panelboard; all branch circuits from the normal system shall originate in the same panelboard.

Patient bed locations in general care areas are prohibited from deriving ALL of their branch circuits from the emergency system. At least one branch circuit for each patient bed location is required to originate in a normal system panelboard. This is a reflection of the requirements stated in Section 517-33.

Exception No. 1: Branch circuits serving only special-purpose outlets or receptacles, such as portable X-ray outlets, shall not be required to be served from the same distribution panel or panels.

Exception No. 2: Clinics, medical and dental offices, and outpatient facilities; psychiatric, substance abuse, and rehabilitation hospitals; nursing homes and residential custodial care facilities meeting the requirements of the exceptions to Section 517-10.

(b) Patient Bed Location Receptacles. Each patient bed location shall be provided with a minimum of four receptacles. They shall be permitted to be of the single or duplex types or a combination of both. All receptacles, whether four or more, shall be listed "hospital grade" and so identified. The requirement that the receptacles be listed "hospital grade" and so identified shall become effective January 1, 1993. Each receptacle shall be grounded by means of an insulated copper conductor sized in accordance with Table 250-95.

This was a significant change in the 1990 *Code* because it expanded the requirement for hospital grade receptacles to include general care patient bed locations. See commentary following Section 517-19(b).

Green dot identification

Figure 517-2. *A hospital grade receptacle identified by a green dot on the face of the receptacle.*

Exception No. 1: Psychiatric, substance abuse, and rehabilitation hospitals meeting the requirements of the exceptions to Section 517-10.

Exception No. 2: Psychiatric security rooms shall not be required to have receptacle outlets installed in the room.

(FPN): It is not intended that there be a total, immediate replacement of existing non-"hospital grade" receptacles. It is intended, however, that non-"hospital grade" receptacles be replaced with "hospital grade" receptacles upon modification of use, renovation, or as existing receptacles need replacement.

(c) Pediatric Locations. Fifteen- and 20-ampere, 125-volt receptacles intended to supply patient care areas of pediatric wards, rooms, or areas shall be tamper resistant. For the purpose of this section, a tamper resistant receptacle is a receptacle that, by its construction, limits improper access to its energized contacts.

517-19. Critical Care Areas.

(a) Patient Bed Location Branch Circuits. Each patient bed location shall be supplied by at least two branch circuits, one or more from the emergency system and one or more circuits from the normal system. At least one branch circuit from the emergency system shall supply an outlet(s) only at that bed location. All branch circuits from the normal system shall be from a single panelboard. Emergency system receptacles shall be identified and shall also indicate the panelboard and circuit number supplying them.

Exception: Branch circuits serving only special-purpose receptacles or equipment in critical care areas shall be permitted to be served by other panelboards.

(b) Patient Bed Location Receptacles. Each patient bed location shall be provided with a minimum of six receptacles. They may be of the single or duplex types or a combination of both. All receptacles, whether six or more, shall be listed "hospital grade" and so identified; each receptacle shall be grounded to the reference grounding point by means of an insulated copper equipment grounding conductor.

Section 517-19(a) covers the branch circuit requirements for patient bed locations in critical care areas. Section 517-19(b) covers the receptacle requirements. Each patient bed location is required to be supplied by at least two branch circuits, one from the NORMAL panel and one from the EMERGENCY panel, as shown in Figure 517-3. The normal circuits must be supplied from the same panel (L-1). The emergency circuits are permitted to be supplied from different panels (EML-1 and EML-2). However, the emergency branch circuit to patient bed location "A" cannot supply emergency receptacles for patient bed location "B."

Receptacles may be of the single or duplex type, provided they are listed hospital grade type and are identified as such. A typical method of marking such receptacles is by a green dot on the face of the receptacle. See Figure 517-2. The emergency system receptacles must be marked to indicate the panelboard and circuit number supplying them.

These requirements are intended to ensure that critical care patients will not be without electrical power regardless of whether the equipment, the branch circuits, or the normal system itself is at fault.

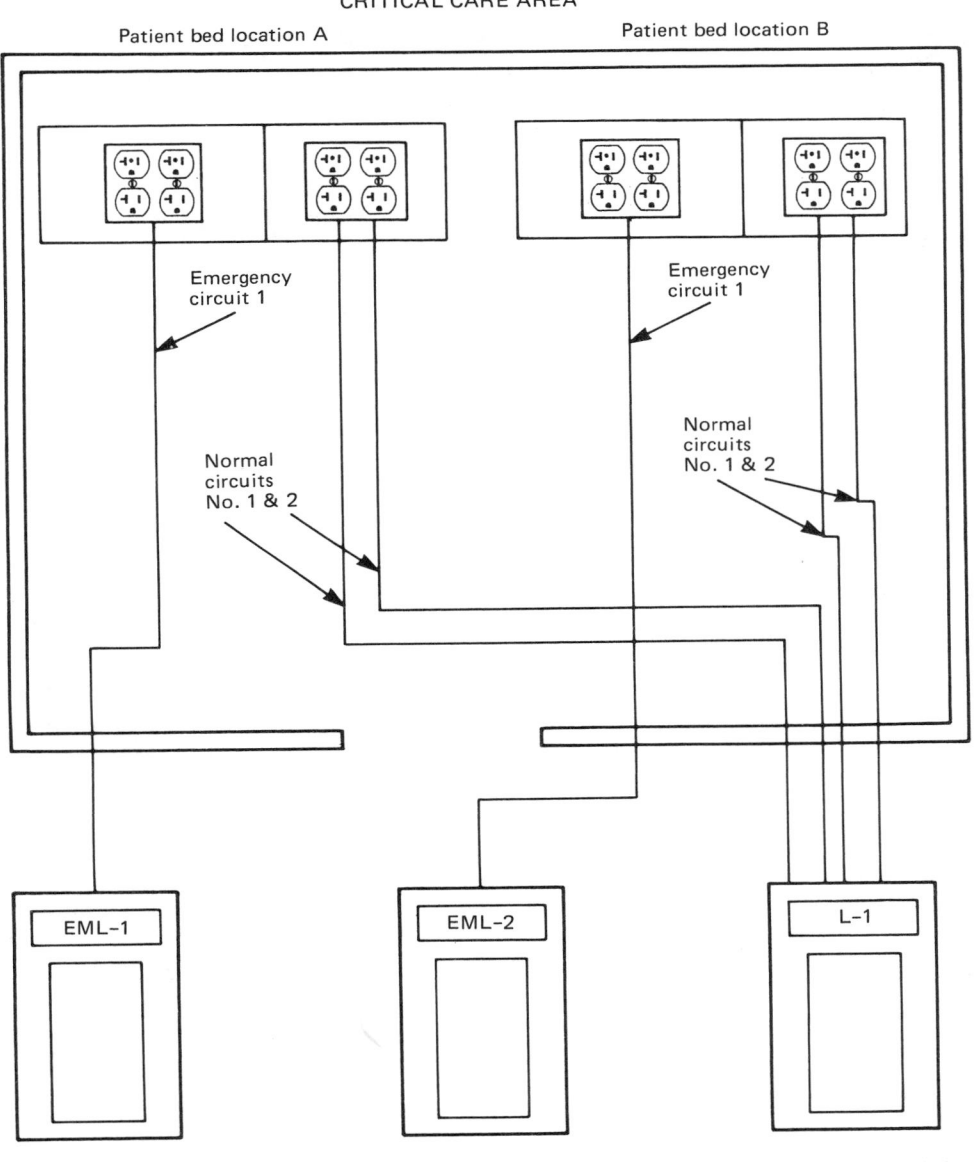

Figure 517-3. *Examples of normal and emergency circuits supplying patient bed locations in a critical care area.*

(c) Patient Vicinity Grounding and Bonding (Optional). A patient vicinity shall be permitted to have a patient equipment grounding point. The patient equipment grounding point, where supplied, shall be permitted to contain one or more jacks listed for the purpose. An equipment bonding jumper, not smaller than No. 10, shall be used to connect the grounding terminal of all grounding-type receptacles to the patient equipment grounding point. The bonding conductor shall be permitted to be arranged centrically or looped as convenient.

(FPN): Where there is no patient equipment grounding point, it is important that the distance between the reference grounding point and the patient vicinity be as short as possible to minimize any potential differences.

(d) Panelboard Grounding. Where a grounded electrical distribution system is used, and metal feeder raceway or Type MC or MI cable is installed, grounding of a panelboard or switchboard shall be assured by one of the following means at each termination or junction point of the raceway or Type MC or MI cable:

(1) A grounding bushing and a continuous copper bonding jumper, sized in accordance with Section 250-95, with the bonding jumper connected to the junction enclosure or the ground bus of the panel.

(2) Connection of feeder raceways or Type MC or MI cable to threaded hubs or bosses on terminating enclosures.

(3) Other approved devices, such as bonding-type locknuts or bushings.

(e) Additional Protective Techniques in Critical Care Areas (Optional). Isolated power systems shall be permitted to be used for critical care areas, and, if used, the isolated power system equipment shall be listed for the purpose and the system so designed and installed that it meets the provisions and is in accordance with Section 517-160.

Exception: The audible and visual indicators of the line isolation monitor shall be permitted to be located at the nursing station for the area being served.

(f) Isolated Power System Grounding. Where an isolated ungrounded power source is used and limits the first-fault current to a low magnitude, the grounding conductor associated with the secondary circuit shall be permitted to be run outside of the enclosure of the power conductors in the same circuit.

(FPN): Although it is permitted to run the grounding conductor outside of the conduit, it is safer to run it with the power conductors to provide better protection in case of a second ground fault.

Running the conductor inside the raceway reduces the impedance of the grounding path.

(g) Special-Purpose Receptacle Grounding. The equipment grounding conductor for special-purpose receptacles such as the operation of mobile X-ray equipment shall be extended to the reference grounding points of branch circuits for all locations likely to be served from such receptacles. Where such a circuit is served from an isolated ungrounded system, the grounding conductor shall not be required to be run with the power conductors; however, the equipment grounding terminal of the special-purpose receptacle shall be connected to the reference grounding point.

517-20 . Wet Locations.

(a) All receptacles and fixed equipment within the area of the wet location shall have ground-fault circuit-interrupter protection for personnel if interruption of power under fault conditions can be tolerated, or be served by an isolated power system if such interruption cannot be tolerated.

Exception: Branch circuits supplying only listed, fixed, therapeutic and diagnostic equipment shall be permitted to be supplied from a normal grounded service, single- or 3-phase system, provided:

a. Wiring for grounded and isolated circuits does not occupy the same raceway, and

b. All conductive surfaces of the equipment are grounded.

In areas designated as patient care wet locations by the governing body of the facility, ground-fault circuit-interrupters are required to be provided for the protection of receptacles and fixed equipment, if a circuit interruption can be tolerated. Otherwise, an isolated power system is required.

(b) Where an isolated power system is utilized, the equipment shall be listed for the purpose and installed so that it meets the provisions of, and is in accordance with, Section 517-160.

(FPN): For requirements for installation of therapeutic pools and tubs, see Part F of Article 680.

C. Essential Electrical System

517-25 . Scope. The essential electrical system for these facilities shall comprise a system capable of supplying a limited amount of lighting and power service which is considered essential for life safety and orderly cessation of procedures during the time normal electrical service is interrupted for any reason. This includes clinics, medical and dental offices, outpatient facilities, nursing homes, limited care facilities, hospitals, and other health care facilities serving patients.

(FPN): For information as to the need for an essential electrical system, see Health Care Facilities, NFPA 99-1990 (ANSI).

517-30. Essential Electrical Systems for Hospitals.

(a) Applicability. The requirements of Part C, Sections 517-30 through 517-35, shall apply to hospitals where an essential electrical system is required.

(FPN No. 1): For performance, maintenance, and testing requirements of essential electrical systems in hospitals, see Health Care Facilities, NFPA 99-1990 (ANSI). For installation of centrifugal fire pumps, see Installation of Centrifugal Fire Pumps, NFPA 20-1990 (ANSI).

(FPN No. 2): For additional information, see Health Care Facilities, NFPA 99-1990 (ANSI).

(b) General.

(1)^x Essential electrical systems for hospitals shall be comprised of two separate systems capable of supplying a limited amount of lighting and power service which is considered essential for life safety and effective hospital operation during the time the normal electrical service is interrupted for any reason. These two systems shall be the emergency system and the equipment system.

(2)^x The emergency system shall be limited to circuits essential to life safety and critical patient care. These are designated the life safety branch and the critical branch.

(3)^x The equipment system shall supply major electric equipment necessary for patient care and basic hospital operation.

(4)^x The number of transfer switches to be used shall be based upon reliability, design, and load considerations. Each branch of the essential electrical system shall be served by one or more transfer switches as shown in Diagrams 517-30(1) and 517-30(2). One transfer switch shall be permitted to serve one or more branches or systems in a facility with a maximum demand on the essential electrical system of 150 kVA as shown in Diagram 517-30(3).

(FPN): See Health Care Facilities, NFPA 99-1990 (ANSI): Section 3-5.1.2.2(a), Transfer Switch Operation Type I; Section 3-4.2.1.4, Automatic Transfer Switch Features; and Section 3-4.2.1.6, Nonautomatic Transfer Device Features.

Diagrams 517-30(1), 517-30(2), and 517-30(3) indicate possible electrical system connections for hospitals. Diagram 517-30(2) illustrates a common situation where the expansion of the facility necessitates the addition of a normal source to that already in place. As shown in the diagram, this would not necessarily require the addition of another alternate source. Provided the alternate source has a capacity for all of the intended load, it may serve multiple services.

For a small electrical system having a maximum demand on the essential electrical system of 150 kVA, see Diagram 517-30(3). A small load can be served by a single transfer switch that can handle the loads associated with both the emergency system and the equipment system. This, of course, is based on the assumption that the transfer switch has sufficient capacity to handle the combined loads, and the alternate source of power is sufficiently large to withstand the impact of the simultaneous transfer of both systems in the event of a normal power loss.

SE	Service entrance
☐	Overcurrent protection
	Automatic switching equipment
	Delayed automatic switching equipment
	Transformer
G	Generator

Diagram 517-30 (1)

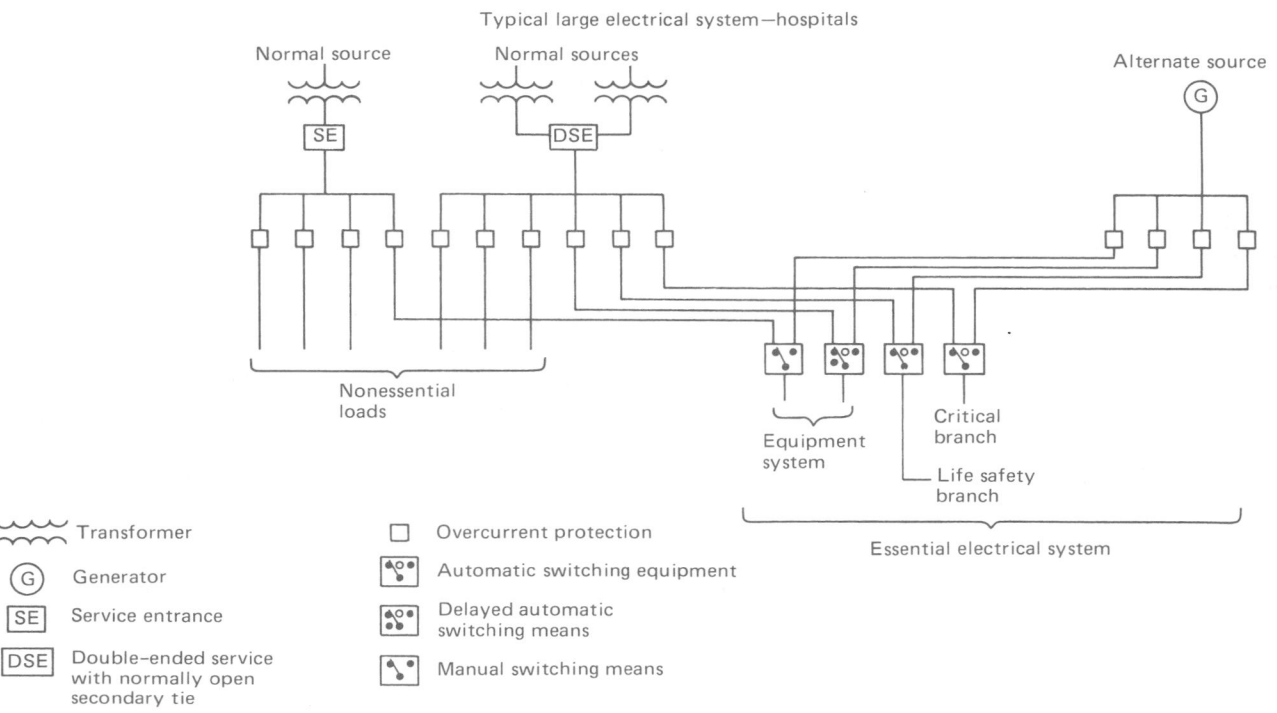

Diagram 517-30 (2)

(c) Wiring Requirements.

(1) Separation from Other Circuits. The life safety branch and critical branch of the emergency system shall be kept entirely independent of all other wiring and equipment and shall not enter the same raceways, boxes, or cabinets with each other or other wiring, except as follows:

    a. In transfer switches,

    b. In exit or emergency lighting fixtures supplied from two sources, or

    c. In a common junction box attached to exit or emergency lighting fixtures supplied from two sources.

The wiring of the equipment system shall be permitted to occupy the same raceways, boxes, or cabinets of other circuits that are not part of the emergency system.

(2) Isolated Power Systems. Where isolated power systems are installed in any of the areas in Sections 517-33(a)(1) and (a)(2), each system shall be supplied by an individual circuit serving no other load.

(3) Mechanical Protection of the Emergency System. The wiring of the emergency system of a hospital shall be mechanically protected by installation in metal raceways.

Exception No. 1: Flexible power cords of appliances, or other utilization equipment, connected to the emergency system shall not be required to be enclosed in raceways.

Exception No. 2: Secondary circuits of transformer-powered communication or signaling systems shall not be required to be enclosed in raceways unless otherwise specified by Chapter 7 or 8.

Exception No. 3: Schedule 80 rigid nonmetallic conduit shall be permitted except for branch circuits serving patient care areas.

Exception No. 2 exempts nurses' call, telephone, and alarm circuits from being run in metal raceways, provided they comply with their applicable articles elsewhere in the *Code*. Although this provides substantial latitude in the wiring method, it should be noted that the restrictions of Section 300-22 (ducts, plenums, and other air-handling spaces)

Small electrical system—hospitals
(single transfer switch)

Normal sources

Alternate sources

SE

Nonessential
loads

Essential electrical system
(150 kVA or less)

SE	Service entrance
☐	Overcurrent protection
	Automatic switching equipment
〜	Transformer
G	Generator

Diagram 517-30 (3)

still apply, unless conductors listed as having adequate fire-resistant and low smoke-producing characteristics are used as required by Sections 725-51(a), 760-51(d), and 800-51(a).

Exception No. 4: Where encased in not less than 2 inches (50.8 mm) of concrete, Schedule 40 PVC shall be permitted except for branch circuits serving patient care areas.

(FPN): See Section 517-13(b) for additional grounding requirements in patient care areas.

(d) Capacity of Systems. The essential electrical system shall have adequate capacity to meet the demand for the operation of all functions and equipment to be served by each system and branch.

517-31ˣ. Emergency System. Those functions of patient care depending on lighting or appliances that are connected to the emergency system shall be divided into two mandatory branches: the life safety branch and the critical branch, described in Sections 517-32 and 517-33.

The branches of the emergency system shall be installed and connected to the alternate power source so that all functions specified herein for the emergency system shall be automatically restored to operation within 10 seconds after interruption of the normal source.

517-32ˣ. Life Safety Branch. No function other than those listed in (a) through (f) shall be connected to the life safety branch. The life safety branch of the emergency system shall supply power for the following lighting, receptacles, and equipment:

(a) Illumination of Means of Egress. Illumination of means of egress, such as lighting required for corridors, passageways, stairways and landings at exit doors, and all necessary ways of approach to exits. Switching arrangements to transfer patient corridor lighting in hospitals from general illumination circuits to night illumination circuits shall be permitted provided only one of two circuits can be selected, and both circuits cannot be extinguished at the same time.

(FPN): See Life Safety Code, NFPA 101-1991 (ANSI), Section 5-10.

(b) Exit Signs. Exit signs and exit directional signs.

(FPN): See Life Safety Code, NFPA 101-1991 (ANSI), Section 5-11.

(c) Alarm and Alerting Systems. Alarm and alerting systems including:

(1) Fire alarms.

(FPN): See Life Safety Code, NFPA 101-1991 (ANSI), Sections 12-1 and 12-2.

(2) Alarms required for systems used for the piping of nonflammable medical gases.

(FPN): See Health Care Facilities, NFPA 99-1990 (ANSI), Section 12-3.4.1.

(d) Communication Systems. Hospital communication systems, where used for issuing instructions during emergency conditions.

(e) Generator Set Location. Task illumination battery charger for emergency battery-powered lighting unit(s) and selected receptacles at the generator set location.

(f) Elevators. Elevator cab lighting, control, communication, and signal systems.

517-33ˣ. Critical Branch.

(a) Task Illumination and Selected Receptacles. The critical branch of the emergency system shall supply power for task illumination, fixed equipment, selected receptacles, and special power circuits serving the following areas and functions related to patient care.

The critical branch is intended to serve a limited number of receptacles and locations to reduce the load and to minimize the chances of a fault condition. Receptacles in general patient care area corridors are permitted on the critical branch, but they are required to be identified in some manner (color coded or labeled) as part of the critical branch, in accordance with Section 3-4.2.2.4(b)(2) of NFPA 99-1990, *Standard for Health Care Facilities.*

(1) Anesthetizing locations — task illumination, all receptacles and fixed equipment.

(2) The isolated power systems in special environments.

(3) Patient care areas — task illumination and selected receptacles in:
  a. Infant nurseries,
  b. Medication preparation areas,
  c. Pharmacy dispensing areas,
  d. Selected acute nursing areas,
  e. Psychiatric bed areas (omit receptacles),
  f. Ward treatment rooms, and
  g. Nurses' stations (unless adequately lighted by corridor luminaires).

(4) Additional specialized patient care task illumination and receptacles, where needed.

(5) Nurse call systems.

(6) Blood, bone, and tissue banks.

(7) Telephone equipment room and closets.

(8) Task illumination, selected receptacles, and selected power circuits for:
  a. General care beds (at least one duplex receptacle per patient bedroom),
  b. Angiographic labs,
  c. Cardiac catheterization labs,
  d. Coronary care units,
  e. Hemodialysis rooms or areas,
  f. Emergency room treatment areas (selected),
  g. Human physiology labs,
  h. Intensive care units, and
  i. Postoperative recovery rooms (selected).

(9) Additional task illumination, receptacles, and selected power circuits needed for effective hospital operation. Single-phase fractional horsepower exhaust fan motors that are interlocked with 3-phase motors on the equipment shall be permitted to be connected to the critical branch.

(b) Subdivision of the Critical Branch. It shall be permitted to subdivide the critical branch into two or more branches.

(FPN): It is important to analyze the consequences of supplying an area with only critical care branch power when failure occurs between the area and the transfer switch. Some proportion of normal and critical power, or critical power from separate transfer switches, may be appropriate.

517-34ˣ. Equipment System Connection to Alternate Power Source.
The equipment system shall be installed and connected to the alternate source, such that the equipment described in Section 517-34(a) is automatically restored to operation at appropriate time-lag intervals following the energizing of the emergency system. Its arrangement shall also provide for the subsequent connection of equipment described in Section 517-34(b).

(a)ˣ Equipment for Delayed Automatic Connection. The following equipment shall be arranged for delayed automatic connection to the alternate power source:

(1) Central suction systems serving medical and surgical functions, including controls. Such suction systems shall be permitted on the critical branch.

(2) Sump pumps and other equipment required to operate for the safety of major apparatus, including associated control systems and alarms.

(3) Compressed air systems serving medical and surgical functions, including controls.

(FPN): The above equipment may be arranged for sequential delayed automatic connection to the alternate power source to prevent overloading the generator where engineering studies indicate it is necessary.

(b)ˣ Equipment for Delayed Automatic or Manual Connection. The following equipment shall be arranged for either delayed automatic or manual connection to the alternate power source:

(1) Heating equipment to provide heating for operating, delivery, labor, recovery, intensive care, coronary care, nurseries, infection/isolation rooms, emergency treatment spaces, and general patient rooms.

Exception: Heating of general patient rooms and infection/isolation rooms during disruption of the normal source shall not be required under any of the following conditions:

a. The outside design temperature is higher than +20°F (-6.7°C), or

b. The outside design temperature is lower than +20°F (-6.7°C) and where a selected room(s) is provided for the needs of all confined patients, then only such room(s) need be heated, or

In some areas of the country, it is common practice to install individual room heating/air conditioners rather than have a central heating/air-conditioning plant. Where these individual units are electrically powered, it may not be practical to apply this high-demand load to the generator. Where the governing body of the nursing home has full-time skilled attendants who can move people to one room(s) that will be heated when this smaller load is picked up by the generator, the intent of the *Code* is satisfied. The provisions for limited heating during emergency conditions are based on consideration of outside design temperature.

c. The facility is served by a dual source of normal power as described in Section 517-35(c), Fine Print Note.

(FPN): The design temperature is based on the 97$^{1}/_{2}$ percent design value as shown in Chapter 24 of the ASHRAE Handbook of Fundamentals (1985).

(2) Elevator(s) selected to provide service to patient, surgical, obstetrical, and ground floors during interruption of normal power.

In instances where interruption of normal power would result in other elevators stopping between floors, throw-over facilities shall be provided to allow the temporary operation of any elevator for the release of patients or other persons who may be confined between floors.

(3) Supply, return, and exhaust ventilating systems for surgical and obstetrical delivery suites, intensive care, coronary care, nurseries, infection/isolation rooms, emergency treatment spaces, and exhaust fans for laboratory fume hoods, nuclear medicine areas where radioactive material is used, ethylene oxide evacuation, and anesthesia evacuation.

(4) Hyperbaric facilities.

(5) Hypobaric facilities.

(6) Automatically operated doors.

(7) Minimal electrically heated autoclaving equipment shall be permitted to be arranged for either automatic or manual connection to the alternate source.

(8) Other selected equipment shall be permitted to be served by the equipment system.

517-35. Sources of Power.

(a)ˣ Two Independent Sources of Power. Essential electrical systems shall have a minimum of two independent sources of power: a normal source generally supplying the entire electrical system, and one or more alternate sources for use when the normal source is interrupted.

(b)ˣ Alternate Source of Power. The alternate source of power shall be a generator(s) driven by some form of prime mover(s), and located on the premises.

Exception: Where the normal source consists of generating units on the premises, the alternate source shall be either another generating set, or an external utility service.

(c) Location of Essential Electrical System Components. Careful consideration shall be given to the location of the spaces housing the components of the essential electrical system to minimize interruptions caused by natural forces common to the area (e.g., storms, floods, earthquakes, or hazards created by adjoining structures or activities). Consideration shall also be given to the possible interruption of normal electrical services resulting from similar causes as well as possible disruption of normal electrical service due to internal wiring and equipment failures.

(FPN): Facilities whose normal source of power is supplied by two or more separate central station-fed services experience greater than normal electrical service reliability than those with only a single feed. Such a dual source of normal power consists of two or more electrical services fed from separate generator sets or a utility distribution network having multiple power input sources and arranged to provide mechanical and electrical separation so that a fault between the facility and the generating sources will not likely cause an interruption of more than one of the facility service feeders.

517-40. Essential Electrical Systems for Nursing Homes and Limited Care Facilities.

(a) Applicability. The requirements of Part C, Sections 517-40(c) through 517-44, shall apply to nursing homes and limited care facilities. Facilities that fulfill Section 517-10, Exception No. 3 shall be exempt from these requirements.

NFPA 99-1990, *Standard for Health Care Facilities*, recognizes two classes of nursing homes or limited care facilities. For the smaller, less complex facility, only a minimum alternate lighting and alarm service need be furnished.

Where treatment of patients is provided, the requirements of Sections 517-41 through 517-44 are required to be applied. The branches of the emergency system for this class of occupancy bear identical titles to their counterparts for hospital-type occupancies.

(b) Inpatient Hospital Care Facilities. Nursing homes and limited care facilities that provide inpatient hospital care shall comply with the requirements of Part C, Sections 517-30 through 517-35.

Regardless of the name given to the facility, the type of electrical system depends on the type of patient care provided. Where such care is clearly inpatient hospital care, a hospital-type electrical system is required to be installed.

(c) Facilities Contiguous with Hospitals. Nursing homes and limited care facilities that are contiguous with a hospital shall be permitted to have their essential electrical systems supplied by that of the hospital.

Where a nursing home or limited care facility shares what is essentially the same building with a hospital, the nursing home is not required to have its own essential electrical system but may derive its supply from the hospital. It should be noted, however, that this rule applies only to the electrical supply and does not permit the sharing of transfer devices and the like.

(FPN): For performance, maintenance, and testing requirements of essential electrical systems in nursing homes and limited care facilities, see Health Care Facilities, NFPA 99-1990 (ANSI).

Section 517-50 and NFPA 99-1990, *Standard for Health Care Facilities*, require an alternate source of power for those types of health care facilities where patients are treated in essentially the same manner as in hospitals, even though the facility may not be called a hospital.

517-41. Essential Electrical Systems.

(a)[x] General. Essential electrical systems for nursing homes and limited care facilities shall be comprised of two separate branches capable of supplying a limited amount of lighting and power service which is considered essential for the protection of life safety and effective operation of the institution during the time normal electrical service is interrupted for any reason. These two separate branches shall be the life safety branch and the critical branch.

(b)[x] Transfer Switches. The number of transfer switches to be used shall be based upon reliability, design, and load considerations. Each branch of the essential electrical system shall be served by one or more transfer switches as shown in Diagrams 517-41(1) and 517-41(2). One transfer switch shall be permitted to serve one or more branches or systems in a facility with a maximum demand on the essential electrical system of 150 kVa as shown in Diagram 517-41(3).

(FPN): See Health Care Facilities, NFPA 99-1990 (ANSI): Section 3-5.1.2.2(b), Transfer Switch Operation Type II; Section 3-4.2.1.4, Automatic Transfer Switch Features; and Section 3-4.2.1.6, Nonautomatic Transfer Device Features.

(c) Capacity of System. The essential electrical system shall have adequate capacity to meet the demand for the operation of all functions and equipment to be served by each branch at one time.

(d) Separation from Other Circuits. The life safety branch shall be kept entirely independent of all other wiring and equipment and shall not enter the same raceways, boxes, or cabinets with other wiring except as follows:

(1) In transfer switches,

(2) In exit or emergency lighting fixtures supplied from two sources, or

(3) In a common junction box attached to exit or emergency lighting fixtures supplied from two sources.

The wiring of the critical branch shall be permitted to occupy the same raceways, boxes, or cabinets of other circuits that are not part of the life safety branch.

517-42ˣ. Automatic Connection to Life Safety Branch. The life safety branch shall be so installed and connected to the alternate source of power that all functions specified herein shall be automatically restored to operation within 10 seconds after the interruption of the normal source. No function other than those listed in (a) through (g) shall be connected to the life safety branch. The life safety branch shall supply power for the following lighting, receptacles, and equipment:

(FPN): The life safety branch is called the emergency system in Health Care Facilities, NFPA 99-1990 (ANSI).

(a) Illumination of Means of Egress. Illumination of means of egress as is necessary for corridors, passageways, stairways, landings, and exit doors and all ways of approach to exits. Switching arrangement to transfer patient corridor lighting from general illumination circuits shall be permitted providing only one of two circuits can be selected, and both circuits cannot be extinguished at the same time.

(FPN): See Life Safety Code, NFPA 101-1991 (ANSI), Section 5-10.

(b) Exit Signs. Exit signs and exit directional signs.

(FPN): See Life Safety Code, NFPA 101-1991 (ANSI), Section 5-11.

(c) Alarm and Alerting Systems. Alarm and alerting systems, including:

(1) Fire alarms.

(FPN): See Life Safety Code, NFPA 101-1991 (ANSI), Sections 7-6, 12-3.4, and 12-3.5.

(2) Alarms required for systems used for the piping of nonflammable medical gases.

(FPN): See Health Care Facilities, NFPA 99-1990 (ANSI), Section 16-3.4.1.

(d) Communications Systems. Communications systems, where used for issuing instructions during emergency conditions.

(e) Dining and Recreation Areas. Sufficient lighting in dining and recreation areas to provide illumination to exit ways.

(f) Generator Set Location. Task illumination and selected receptacles in the generator set location.

(g) Elevators. Elevator cab lighting, control, communication, and signal systems.

Small electrical system—Nursing homes and residential custodial care facilities

Diagram 517-41(1)

517-43ˣ. Connection to Critical Branch. The critical branch shall be so installed and connected to the alternate power source that the equipment listed in Section 517-43(a) shall be automatically restored to operation at appropriate time-lag intervals following the restoration of the life safety branch to operation. Its arrangement shall also provide for the additional connection of equipment listed in Section 517-43(b) by either delayed automatic or manual operation.

(a) Delayed Automatic Connection. The following equipment shall be connected to the critical branch and shall be arranged for delayed automatic connection to the alternate power source:

(1) Patient care areas — task illumination and selected receptacles in:

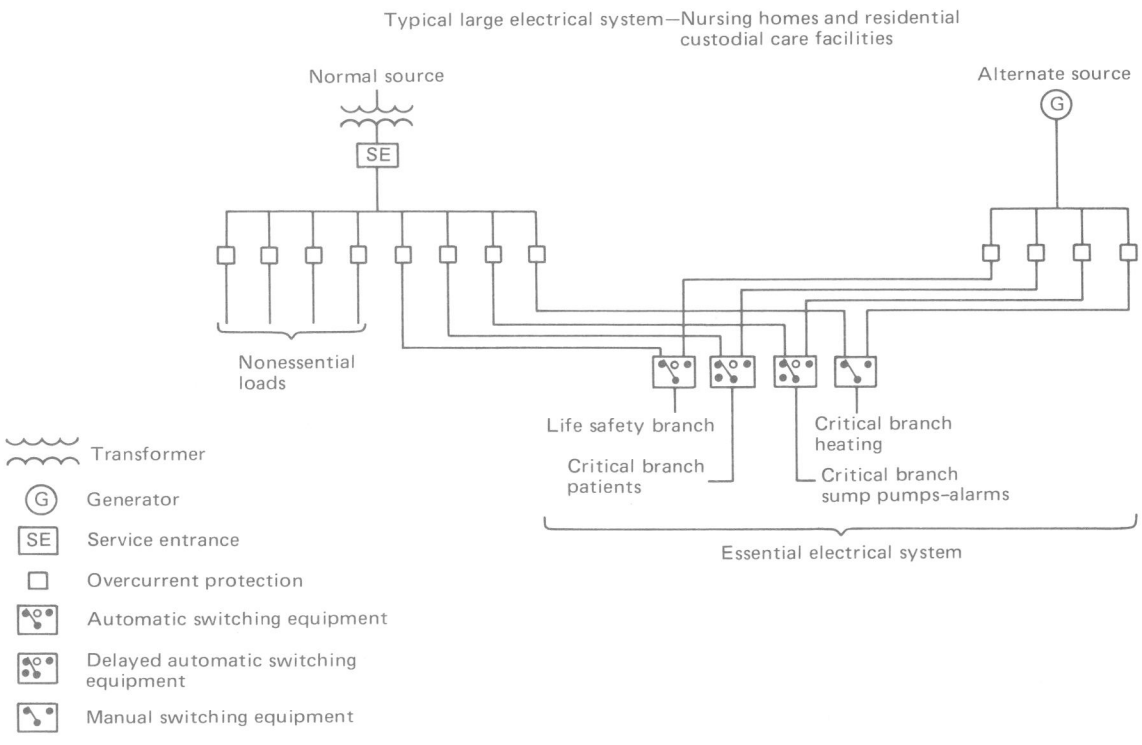

Typical large electrical system—Nursing homes and residential custodial care facilities

Normal source

Alternate source

SE

Nonessential loads

Life safety branch

Critical branch patients

Critical branch heating

Critical branch sump pumps–alarms

Essential electrical system

〜〜〜 Transformer

Ⓖ Generator

SE Service entrance

☐ Overcurrent protection

Automatic switching equipment

Delayed automatic switching equipment

Manual switching equipment

Diagram 517-41(2)

a. Medication preparation areas.

b. Pharmacy dispensing areas.

c. Nurses' stations (unless adequately lighted by corridor luminaires).

(2) Sump pumps and other equipment required to operate for the safety of major apparatus and associated control systems and alarms.

(b) Delayed Automatic or Manual Connection. The following equipment shall be connected to the critical branch and shall be arranged for either delayed automatic or manual connection to the alternate power source:

(1) Heating equipment to provide heating for patient rooms.

Exception: Heating of general patient rooms during disruption of the normal source shall not be required under any of the following conditions:

a. The outside design temperature is higher than +20°F (-6.7°C), or

b. The outside design temperature is lower than +20°F (-6.7°C) and where a selected room(s) is provided for the needs of all confined patients, then only such room(s) need be heated, or

c. The facility is served by a dual source of normal power as described in Section 517-44(c), Fine Print Note.

(FPN): The outside design temperature is based on the 97½ percent design values as shown in Chapter 24 of the ASHRAE Handbook of Fundamentals (1985).

(2) Elevator Service. In instances where disruption of power would result in elevators stopping between floors, throwover facilities shall be provided to allow the temporary operation of any elevator for the release of passengers. For elevator cab lighting, control, and signal system requirements, see Section 517-42(g).

(3) Additional illumination, receptacles, and equipment shall be permitted to be connected only to the critical branch.

Small electrical system—Nursing homes
and residential custodial
care facilities
(single transfer switch)

Normal sources   Alternate source

Nonessential
loads

Essential electrical system
(150 kVa or less)

 Automatic switching
equipment

 Transformer

G   Generator

 Overcurrent
protection

SE   Service entrance

Diagram 517-41(3)

517-44. Sources of Power.

(a)ˣ Two Independent Sources of Power. Essential electrical systems shall have a minimum of two independent sources of power: a normal source generally supplying the entire electrical system, and one or more alternate sources for use when the normal source is interrupted.

(b)ˣ Alternate Source of Power. The alternate source of power shall be a generator(s) driven by some form of prime mover(s), and located on the premises.

Exception No. 1: Where the normal source consists of generating units on the premises, the alternate source shall be either another generator set, or an external utility service.

Exception No. 2: Nursing homes or residential custodial care facilities meeting the requirements of Section 517-10, Exception No. 3 shall be permitted to use a battery system or self-contained battery integral with the equipment.

(c) Location of Essential Electrical System Components. Careful consideration shall be given to the location of the spaces housing the components of the essential electrical system to minimize interruptions caused by natural forces common to the area (e.g., storms, floods, earthquakes, or hazards created by adjoining structures or activities). Consideration shall also be given to the possible interruption of normal electrical services resulting from similar causes as well as possible disruption of normal electrical service due to internal wiring and equipment failures.

(FPN): Facilities whose normal source of power is supplied by two or more separate central station-fed services experience greater than normal electrical service reliability than those with only a single feed. Such a dual source of normal power consists of two or more electrical services fed from separate generator sets or a utility distribution network having multiple power input sources and arranged to provide mechanical and electrical separation so that a fault between the facility and the generating sources will not likely cause an interruption of more than one of the facility service feeders.

517-50. Essential Electrical Systems for Clinics, Medical and Dental Offices, Outpatient Facilities, and Other Health Care Facilities Not Covered in Sections 517-30 and 517-40.

(a)ˣ Applicability. The requirements of this section shall apply to those health care facilities described in Section 517-50, and in which:

(1) Inhalation anesthetics are administered in any concentration to patients, or

(2) Patients require electrical life-support equipment.

(b)ˣ Connections. The essential electrical system shall supply power for:

(1) Task illumination which is related to the safety of life and which is necessary for the safe cessation of procedures in progress.

(2) All anesthesia and resuscitative equipment used in areas where inhalation anesthetics are administered to patients, including alarm and alerting devices.

(FPN): See Health Care Facilities, NFPA 99-1990 (ANSI), Sections 13-3.4.1, 14-3.4.1, and 15-3.4.1.

(3) All electrical life-support equipment in areas where procedures are performed that require such equipment for the support of the patient's life.

(c) Alternate Source of Power.

(1)ˣ Power Source. The alternate source of power for the system shall be specifically designed for this purpose and shall be either a generator, battery system, or self-contained battery integral with the equipment.

(2)ˣ System Capacity. The alternate source of power shall be separate and independent of the normal source and shall have a capacity to sustain its connected loads for a minimum of 1½ hours after loss of the normal source.

(3)ˣ System Operation. The system shall be so arranged that, in the event of a failure of the normal power source, the alternate source of power shall be automatically connected to the load within 10 seconds.

(FPN): See Health Care Facilities, NFPA 99-1990 (ANSI), Sections 3-5.1.2.2(c), Transfer Switch Operation for Type III with Generator Sets, and 3-5.1.2.2(d), Transfer Switch Operation for Type III with Battery Systems.

D. Inhalation Anesthetizing Locations

(FPN): For further information regarding safeguards for anesthetizing locations, see Health Care Facilities, NFPA 99-1990 (ANSI).

517-60. Anesthetizing Location Classification.

(FPN): If either of the following anesthetizing locations is designated a wet location, refer to Section 517-20.

(a) Hazardous (Classified) Location.

(1)ˣ In a location where flammable anesthetics are employed, the entire area shall be considered to be a Class I, Division 1 location which shall extend upward to a level 5 feet (1.52 m) above the floor. The remaining volume up to the structural ceiling is considered to be above a hazardous (classified) location.

(2) Any room or location in which flammable anesthetics or volatile flammable disinfecting agents are stored shall be considered to be a Class I, Division 1 location from floor to ceiling.

(b) Other-than-Hazardous (Classified) Location. Any inhalation anesthetizing location designated for the exclusive use of nonflammable anesthetizing agents shall be considered to be an other-than-hazardous (classified) location.

This section divides anesthetizing locations into either a hazardous (classified) location, where flammable or nonflammable anesthetics may be interchangeably employed, or an other-than-hazardous location, where only nonflammable anesthetics are used. In the case of the flammable anesthetizing location, the entire volume of the room extending upward from a level 5 feet above the floor to the surface of the structural ceiling of the room, and including the space between a drop ceiling and the structural ceiling, is considered to be above a hazardous (classified) location.

517-61. Wiring and Equipment.

(a) Within Hazardous Anesthetizing Locations.

(1)ˣ Except as permitted in Section 517-160, each power circuit within, or partially within, a flammable anesthetizing location as referred to in Section 517-60 shall be isolated from any distribution system by the use of an isolated power system.

(2) Isolated power system equipment shall be listed for the purpose and the system so designed and installed that it meets the provisions and is in accordance with Part G.

(3)ˣ In hazardous (classified) location(s) referred to in Section 517-60, all fixed wiring and equipment, and all portable equipment, including lamps and other utilization equipment, operating at more than 10 volts between conductors shall comply with the requirements of Sections 501-1 through 501-15 and Sections 501-16(a) and (b) for Class I, Division 1 locations. All such equipment shall be specifically approved for the hazardous atmospheres involved.

(4) Where a box, fitting, or enclosure is partially, but not entirely, within a hazardous (classified) location(s), the hazardous (classified) location(s) shall be considered to be extended to include the entire box, fitting, or enclosure.

(5) Receptacles and attachment plugs in hazardous (classified) location(s) shall be listed for use in Class I, Group C hazardous (classified) locations and shall have provision for the connection of a grounding conductor.

(6) Flexible cords used in hazardous areas for connection to portable utilization equipment, including lamps operating at more than 8 volts between conductors, shall be of a type approved for extra-hard usage in accordance with Table 400-4 and shall include an additional conductor for grounding.

(7) A storage device for the flexible cord shall be provided and shall not subject the cord to bending at a radius of less than 3 inches (76 mm).

(b) Above Hazardous Anesthetizing Locations.

(1) Wiring above a hazardous area referred to in Section 517-60 shall be installed in rigid metal conduit, electrical metallic tubing, intermediate metal conduit, Type MI cable, or Type MC cable that employs a continuous, gas/vapor-tight metal sheath.

(2) Installed equipment that may produce arcs, sparks, or particles of hot metal, such as lamps and lampholders for fixed lighting, cutouts, switches, generators, motors, or other equipment having make-and-break or sliding contacts, shall be of the totally enclosed type or so constructed as to prevent escape of sparks or hot metal particles.

Exception: Wall-mounted receptacles installed above the hazardous area in flammable anesthetizing locations shall not be required to be totally enclosed or have openings guarded or screened to prevent dispersion of particles.

(3) Surgical and other lighting fixtures shall conform to Section 501-9(b).

Exception No. 1: The surface temperature limitations set forth in Section 501-9(b)(2) shall not apply.

Exception No. 2: Integral or pendant switches that are located above and cannot be lowered into the hazardous (classified) location(s) shall not be required to be explosionproof.

(4) Approved seals shall be provided in conformance with Section 501-5, and Section 501-5(a)(4) shall apply to horizontal as well as to vertical boundaries of the defined hazardous (classified) locations.

(5) Receptacles and attachment plugs located above hazardous anesthetizing locations shall be listed for hospital use for services of prescribed voltage, frequency, rating, and number of conductors with provision for the connection of the grounding conductor. This requirement shall apply to attachment plugs and receptacles of the 2-pole, 3-wire grounding type for single-phase 120-volt, nominal, ac service.

See commentary following Section 517-19(b) regarding receptacles listed for hospital use.

(6) Plugs and receptacles rated 250-volt, for connection of 50-ampere, and 60-ampere ac medical equipment for use above hazardous (classified) locations shall be so arranged that the 60-ampere receptacle will accept either the 50-ampere or the 60-ampere plug. Fifty-ampere receptacles shall be designed so as not to accept the 60-ampere attachment plug. The plugs shall be of the 2-pole, 3-wire design with a third contact connecting to the insulated (green or green with yellow stripe) equipment grounding conductor of the electrical system.

(c) Other-than-Hazardous Anesthetizing Locations.

(1) Wiring serving other-than-hazardous (classified) locations, as defined in Section 517-60, shall be installed in a metal raceway system or cable assembly. The metal raceway system, or cable armor or sheath assembly, shall qualify as an equipment grounding return path in accordance with Section 250-91(b). Type MC and Type MI cable shall have an outer metal armor or sheath that is identified as an acceptable grounding return path.

Exception: Pendant receptacle constructions employing at least Type SJO or equivalent flexible cords suspended not less than 6 feet (1.83 m) from the floor.

(2) Receptacles and attachment plugs installed and used in other-than-hazardous (classified) locations shall be listed for hospital use for services of prescribed voltage, frequency, rating, and number of conductors with provision for connection of the grounding conductor. This requirement shall apply to 2-pole, 3-wire grounding type for single-phase 120-, 208-, or 240-volt, nominal, ac service.

See commentary following Section 517-19(b) regarding receptacles listed for hospital use.

(3) Plugs and receptacles rated 250-volt, for connection of 50-ampere, and 60-ampere ac medical equipment for use in other-than-hazardous (classified) locations shall be so arranged that the 60-ampere receptacle will accept either the 50-ampere or the 60-ampere plug. Fifty-ampere receptacles shall be designed so as not to accept the 60-ampere attachment plug. The plugs shall be of the 2-pole, 3-wire design with a third contact connecting to the insulated (green or green with yellow stripe) equipment grounding conductor of the electrical system.

517-62. **Grounding.** In any anesthetizing area, all metal raceways and metal-sheathed cables, and all noncurrent-carrying conductive portions of fixed electric equipment, shall be grounded.

Exception: Equipment operating at not more than 10 volts between conductors shall not be required to be grounded.

It should be noted that the grounding requirements for anesthetizing locations apply only to metal raceways and electric equipment. Carts, tables, and other nonelectrical items are not required to be grounded. However, in flammable anesthetizing locations, portable carts and tables usually have a resistance to ground of not over 1,000,000 ohms, through use of conductive tires and wheels and conductive flooring, to avoid the buildup of static electrical charges. Such requirements will be found in NFPA 99-1990, *Standard for Health Care Facilities*, Chapter 3.

517-63. **Grounded Power Systems in Anesthetizing Locations.**

(a) **General-Purpose Lighting Circuit.** A general-purpose lighting circuit connected to the normal grounded service shall be installed in each operating room.

Exception: Where connected to any alternate source permitted in Section 700-12 that is separate from the source serving the emergency system.

The failure of the emergency circuit feeder that supplies the operating room will ordinarily plunge the room into darkness. Requiring a general-purpose lighting circuit supplied by a normal source feeder will minimize the effect of this kind of failure.

(b) **Branch-Circuit Wiring.** Branch circuits supplying only listed, fixed, therapeutic and diagnostic equipment, permanently installed above the hazardous (classified) location and in other-than-hazardous (classified) locations, shall be permitted to be supplied from a normal grounded service, single- or three-phase system, provided:

(1) Wiring for grounded and isolated circuits does not occupy the same raceway,

(2) All conductive surfaces of the equipment are grounded,

(3) Equipment (except enclosed X-ray tubes and the leads to the tubes) are located at least 8 feet (2.44 m) above the floor or outside the anesthetizing location, and

(4) Switches for the grounded branch circuit are located outside the hazardous (classified) location.

Exception: Sections 517-63 (b)(3) and (b)(4) shall not apply in other-than-hazardous (classified) locations.

(c) **Fixed Lighting Branch Circuits.** Branch circuits supplying only fixed lighting shall be permitted to be supplied by a normal grounded service, provided:

(1) Such fixtures are located at least 8 feet (2.44 m) above the floor,

(2) All conductive surfaces of fixtures are grounded,

(3) Wiring for circuits supplying power to fixtures does not occupy the same raceway for circuits supplying isolated power, and

(4) Switches are wall-mounted and located above hazardous (classified) locations.

(d) **Remote-Control Stations.** Wall-mounted remote-control stations for remote-control switches operating at 24 volts or less shall be permitted to be installed in any anesthetizing location.

(e) **Location of Isolated Power Systems.** An isolated power center listed for the purpose and its grounded primary feeder shall be permitted to be located in an anesthetizing location, provided it is installed above a hazardous (classified) location or in an other-than-hazardous (classified) location.

(f) **Circuits in Anesthetizing Locations.** Except as permitted above, each power circuit within, or partially within, a flammable anesthetizing location as referred to in Section 517-60 shall be isolated from any distribution system supplying other-than-anesthetizing locations.

517-64ˣ. **Low-Voltage Equipment and Instruments.**

(a) **Equipment Requirements.** Low-voltage equipment that is frequently in contact with the bodies of persons or has exposed current-carrying elements shall:

(1) Operate on an electrical potential of 10 volts or less, or

(2) Be approved as intrinsically safe or double-insulated equipment.

(3) Be moisture-resistant.

(b) **Power Supplies.** Power shall be supplied to low-voltage equipment from:

(1) An individual portable isolating transformer (autotransformers shall not be used) connected to an isolated power circuit receptacle by means of an appropriate cord and attachment plug, or

(2) A common low-voltage isolating transformer installed in a nonhazardous location, or

(3) Individual dry-cell batteries, or

(4) Common batteries made up of storage cells located in a nonhazardous location.

(c) Isolated Circuits. Isolating-type transformers for supplying low-voltage circuits shall:

(1) Have approved means for insulating the secondary circuit from the primary circuit, and

(2) Have the core and case grounded.

(d) Controls. Resistance or impedance devices shall be permitted to control low-voltage equipment but shall not be used to limit the maximum available voltage to the equipment.

(e) Battery-Powered Appliances. Battery-powered appliances shall not be capable of being charged while in operation unless their charging circuitry incorporates an integral isolating-type transformer.

(f) Receptacles or Attachment Plugs. Any receptacle or attachment plug used on low-voltage circuits shall be of a type that does not permit interchangeable connection with circuits of higher voltage.

(FPN): Any interruption of the circuit, even circuits as low as 10 volts, either by any switch, or loose or defective connections anywhere in the circuit, may produce a spark sufficient to ignite flammable anesthetic agents. See Section 7-5.1.2.3 of Health Care Facilities, NFPA 99-1990 (ANSI).

E. X-Ray Installations

Nothing in this part shall be construed as specifying safeguards against the useful beam or stray X-ray radiation.

(FPN No. 1): Radiation safety and performance requirements of several classes of X-ray equipment are regulated under Public Law 90-602 and are enforced by the Department of Health and Human Services.

(FPN No. 2): In addition, information on radiation protection by the National Council on Radiation Protection and Measurements is published as Reports of the National Council on Radiation Protection and Measurement. These reports are obtainable from NCRP Publications, P.O. Box 30175, Washington, D.C. 20014.

517-71. Connection to Supply Circuit.

(a) Fixed and Stationary Equipment. Fixed and stationary X-ray equipment shall be connected to the power supply by means of a wiring method meeting the general requirements of this Code.

Exception: Equipment properly supplied by a branch circuit rated at not over 30 amperes shall be permitted to be supplied through a suitable attachment plug and hard-service cable or cord.

(b) Portable, Mobile, and Transportable Equipment. Individual branch circuits shall not be required for portable, mobile, and transportable medical X-ray equipment requiring a capacity of not over 60 amperes.

(c) Over 600-Volt Supply. Circuits and equipment operated on a supply circuit of over 600 volts shall comply with Article 710.

517-72. Disconnecting Means.

(a) Capacity. A disconnecting means of adequate capacity for at least 50 percent of the input required for the momentary rating or 100 percent of the input required for the long-time rating of the X-ray equipment, whichever is greater, shall be provided in the supply circuit.

(b) Location. The disconnecting means shall be operable from a location readily accessible from the X-ray control.

(c) Portable Equipment. For equipment connected to a 120-volt branch circuit of 30 amperes or less, a grounding-type attachment plug and receptacle of proper rating shall be permitted to serve as a disconnecting means.

517-73. Rating of Supply Conductors and Overcurrent Protection.

(a) Diagnostic Equipment.

(1) The ampacity of supply branch-circuit conductors and the current rating of overcurrent protective devices shall not be less than 50 percent of the momentary rating or 100 percent of the long-time rating, whichever is greater.

(2) The ampacity of supply feeders and the current rating of overcurrent protective devices supplying two or more branch circuits supplying X-ray units shall not be less than 50 percent of the momentary demand rating of the largest unit plus 25 percent of the momentary demand rating of the next largest unit plus 10 percent of the momentary demand rating of each additional unit. Where simultaneous biplane examinations are undertaken with the X-ray units, the supply conductors and overcurrent protective devices shall be 100 percent of the momentary demand rating of each X-ray unit.

(FPN): The minimum conductor size for branch and feeder circuits is also governed by voltage regulation requirements. For a specific installation, the manufacturer usually specifies minimum distribution transformer and conductor sizes, rating of disconnecting means, and overcurrent protection.

(b) Therapeutic Equipment. The ampacity of conductors and rating of overcurrent protective devices shall not be less than 100 percent of the current rating of medical X-ray therapy equipment.

(FPN): The ampacity of the branch-circuit conductors and the ratings of disconnecting means and overcurrent protection for X-ray equipment are usually designated by the manufacturer for the specific installation.

517-74. Control Circuit Conductors.

(a) Number of Conductors in Raceway. The number of control circuit conductors installed in a raceway shall be determined in accordance with Section 300-17.

(b) Minimum Size of Conductors. Size No. 18 or No. 16 fixture wires as specified in Section 725-16 and flexible cords shall be permitted for the control and operating circuits of X-ray and auxiliary equipment where protected by not larger than 20-ampere overcurrent devices.

517-75. Equipment Installations.
All equipment for new X-ray installations and all used or reconditioned X-ray equipment moved to and reinstalled at a new location shall be of an approved type.

517-76. Transformers and Capacitors.
Transformers and capacitors that are part of an X-ray equipment shall not be required to comply with Articles 450 and 460.

Capacitors shall be mounted within enclosures of insulating material or grounded metal.

517-77. Installation of High Tension X-Ray Cables.
Cables with grounded shields connecting X-ray tubes and image intensifiers shall be permitted to be installed in cable trays or cable troughs along with X-ray equipment control and power supply conductors without the need for barriers to separate the wiring.

517-78. Guarding and Grounding.

(a) High-Voltage Parts. All high-voltage parts, including X-ray tubes, shall be mounted within grounded enclosures. Air, oil, gas, or other suitable insulating media shall be used to insulate the high-voltage from the grounded enclosure. The connection from the high-voltage equipment to X-ray tubes and other high-voltage components shall be made with high-voltage shielded cables.

(b) Low-Voltage Cables. Low-voltage cables connecting to oil-filled units that are not completely sealed, such as transformers, condensers, oil coolers, and high-voltage switches, shall have insulation of the oil-resistant type.

(c) Noncurrent-Carrying Metal Parts. Noncurrent-carrying metal parts of X-ray and associated equipment (controls, tables, X-ray tube supports, transformer tanks, shielded cables, X-ray tube heads, etc.) shall be grounded in the manner specified in Article 250, as modified by Sections 517-13(a) and (b).

Exception: Battery-operated equipment.

F. Communications, Signaling Systems, Data Systems, Fire Protective Signaling Systems, and Systems Less than 120 Volts, Nominal

517-80. Patient Care Areas.
Equivalent insulation and isolation to that required for the electrical distribution systems in patient care areas shall be provided for communications, signaling systems, data system circuits, fire protective signaling systems, and systems less than 120 volts, nominal.

(FPN): An acceptable alternate means of providing isolation for patient/nurse call systems is by the use of nonelectrified signaling, communication, or control devices held by the patient or within reach of the patient.

517-81. Other-than-Patient-Care Areas.
In other than patient care areas, installations shall be in accordance with the appropriate provisions of Articles 725, 760, and 800.

517-82. Signal Transmission Between Appliances.

(a) General. Permanently installed signal cabling from an appliance in a patient location to remote appliances shall employ a signal transmission system that prevents hazardous grounding interconnection of the appliances.

(FPN):   See Sections 517-13(b) and 517-15.

(b) Common Signal Grounding Wire. Common signal grounding wires (i.e., the chassis ground for single-ended transmission) shall be permitted to be used between appliances all located within the patient vicinity, provided the appliances are served from the same reference grounding point.

G. Isolated Power Systems

517-160. Isolated Power Systems.

(a) Installations.

(1) Each isolated power circuit shall be controlled by a switch having a disconnecting pole in each isolated circuit conductor to simultaneously disconnect all power. Such isolation shall be accomplished by means of one or more transformers having no electrical connection between primary and secondary windings, by means of motor generator sets, or by means of suitably isolated batteries.

(2)ˣ Circuits supplying primaries of isolating transformers shall operate at not more than 600 volts between conductors and shall be provided with proper overcurrent protection. The secondary voltage of such transformers shall not exceed 600 volts between conductors of each circuit. All circuits supplied from such secondaries shall be ungrounded, and shall have an approved overcurrent device of proper ratings in each conductor. Circuits supplied directly from batteries or from motor generator sets shall be ungrounded, and shall be protected against overcurrent in the same manner as transformer-fed secondary circuits. If an electrostatic shield is present, it shall be connected to the reference grounding point.

(3) The isolating transformers, motor generator sets, batteries and battery chargers, and associated primary or secondary overcurrent devices shall not be installed in hazardous (classified) locations. The isolated secondary circuit wiring extending into a hazardous anesthetizing location shall be installed in accordance with Section 501-4.

(4) An isolated branch circuit supplying an anesthetizing location shall supply no other location.

(5) The isolated circuit conductors shall be identified as follows:

   Isolated Conductor No. 1 — Orange
   Isolated Conductor No. 2 — Brown

For 3-phase systems, the third conductor shall be identified as yellow.

(6) Wire-pulling compounds that increase the dielectric constant shall not be used on the secondary conductors of the isolated power supply.

(FPN No. 1):   It is desirable to limit the size of the isolation transformer to 10 kVA or less and to use conductor insulation with low leakage to meet impedance requirements.

(FPN No. 2):   Minimizing the length of branch-circuit conductors and utilizing conductor insulations with a dielectric constant less than 3.5 and insulation resistance constant greater than 6100 megohm-meters (20,000 megohm-feet) at 60°F (16°C) reduces leakage from line to ground reducing the monitor hazard current.

(b)ˣ Line Isolation Monitor.

(1) In addition to the usual control and overcurrent protective devices, each isolated power system shall be provided with a continually operating line isolation monitor that indicates possible leakage or fault currents from either isolated conductor to ground. The monitor shall be designed so that a green signal lamp, conspicuously visible to persons in the anesthetizing location, remains lighted when the system is adequately isolated from ground; an adjacent red signal lamp and an audible warning signal (remote if desired) shall be energized when the total hazard current (consisting of possible resistive and capacitive leakage currents) from either isolated conductor to ground reaches a threshold value of 5 milliamperes under nominal line voltage conditions. The line monitor shall not alarm for a fault hazard of less than 3.7 milliamperes or for a total hazard current of less than 5.0 milliamperes.

Exception: A system shall be permitted to be designed to operate at a lower threshold value of total hazard current. A line isolation monitor for such a system shall be permitted to be approved with the provision that the fault hazard current shall be permitted to be reduced but not to less than 35 percent of the corresponding threshold value of the total hazard current, and the monitor hazard current is to be correspondingly reduced to no more than 50 percent of the alarm threshold value of the total hazard current.

(2) The line isolation monitor shall be designed to have sufficient internal impedance such that, when properly connected

to the isolated system, the maximum internal current that can flow through the line isolation monitor, when any point of the isolated system is grounded, shall be 1 milliampere.

Exception: The line isolation monitor shall be permitted to be of the low-impedance type such that the current through the line isolation monitor, when any point of the isolated system is grounded, will not exceed twice the alarm threshold value for a period not exceeding 5 milliseconds.

(FPN): Reduction of the monitor hazard current, provided this reduction results in an increased "not alarm" threshold value for the fault hazard current, will increase circuit capacity.

(3) An ammeter calibrated in the total hazard current of the system (contribution of the fault hazard current plus monitor hazard current) shall be mounted in a plainly visible place on the line isolation monitor with the "alarm on" zone at approximately the center of the scale.

Exception: The line isolation monitor may be a composite unit, with a sensing section cabled to a separate display panel section on which the alarm or test functions are located.

See Figure 517-4.

(FPN): It is desirable to locate the ammeter so that it is conspicuously visible to persons in the anesthetizing location.

ARTICLE 518   Places of Assembly

Contents

518-1. **Scope.** This article covers all buildings or portions of buildings or structures designed or intended for the assembly of 100 or more persons.

Figure 517-4.   Line isolation monitor (top) for use with isolated power systems, remote indicator alarm (middle), and multiple annunciator panel (bottom), which can monitor several operating rooms from a central location such as a nurses' station. (Square D Co.)

518-2. **General Classifications.** Places of assembly shall include, but are not limited to:

Assembly Halls	Exhibition Halls
Armories	Dining Facilities
Restaurants	Church Chapels
Dance Halls	Mortuary Chapels
Museums	Skating Rinks
Gymnasiums	Multipurpose Rooms
Bowling Lanes	Pool Rooms
Club Rooms	Places of Awaiting Transportation
Court Rooms	Auditoriums
Conference Rooms	
Auditoriums within:	
Schools	
Mercantile Establishments	
Business Establishments	
Other Occupancies	

Occupancy of any room or space for assembly purposes by less than 100 persons in a building of other occupancy, and incidental to such other occupancy, shall be classed as part of the other occupancy and subject to the provisions applicable thereto.

Where any such building structure, or portion thereof, contains a projection booth or stage platform or area for the presentation of theatrical or musical productions, either fixed or portable, the wiring for that area and all equipment that is used in the referenced area, and portable equipment and wiring for use in the production that will not be connected to permanently installed wiring, shall comply with Article 520.

See commentary following Section 520-1.

(FPN): For methods of determining population capacity, see local building code or in its absence Life Safety Code, NFPA 101-1991 (ANSI).

This article applies to places of assembly designed or intended for the assembly of 100 or more persons. It would apply, for example, to a church chapel or auditorium for occupancy of 100 or more persons, its capacity determined by the methods for occupancy population capacity in accordance with NFPA 101-1991, *Life Safety Code*. This article does not apply to a supermarket, even though it may contain 100 or more persons, because a supermarket is not specifically designed or intended for the assembly of persons; nor is it considered to be an auditorium. Article 518 does not apply to an office building or a school building, even though such buildings, as a rule, are designed for occupancy by 100 or more persons. Article 518 does, however, apply to assembly halls, restaurants, etc. within office or school buildings if these parts of the building are designed or intended for assembly of 100 or more persons.

The following information for determining occupancy capacity is contained in NFPA 101-1991, *Life Safety Code.*

8-1.7 Occupant Load

8-1.7.1 The occupant load permitted in any assembly building, structure, or portion thereof shall be determined on the basis of the following occupant load factors:

(a) An assembly area of concentrated use without fixed seats, such as an auditorium, place of worship, dance floor, discotheque, or lodge hall — one person per 7 net square feet (.65 net square meter).

(b) An assembly area of less concentrated use, such as a conference room, dining room, drinking establishment,

exhibit room, gymnasium, or lounge — one person per 15 net square feet (1.4 net square meter).

(c) Bleachers, pews, and similar bench-type seating — one person per 18 linear inches (45.7 linear centimeters).

(d) Fixed seating. The occupant load of an area having fixed seats shall be determined by the number of fixed seats installed. Required aisle space serving the fixed seats shall not be used to increase the occupant load.

(e) Kitchens. One person per 100 gross square feet (9.3 square meters).

(f) Libraries. In stack areas — one person per 100 square feet (9.3 square meters); in reading rooms — one person per 50 net square feet (4.6 net square meters).

8-1.7.2 The occupant load permitted in a building or portion thereof may be increased above that specified in 8-1.7.1 if the necessary aisles and exits are provided. To increase the occupant load, a diagram indicating placement of equipment, aisles, exits, and seating shall be provided to and approved by the authority having jurisdiction prior to any increase in occupant load. In areas not greater than 10,000 square feet (930 square meters), the occupant load shall not exceed one person in 5 square feet (.46 square meter); in areas greater than 10,000 square feet (930 square meters), the occupant load shall not exceed one person in 7 square feet (.65 square meter).

518-3. Other Articles.

(a) **Hazardous (Classified) Areas.** Hazardous (classified) areas located in any assemblage occupancy shall be installed in accordance with Article 500, Hazardous (Classified) Locations.

(b) **Temporary Wiring.** In exhibition halls used for display booths, as in trade shows, the temporary wiring shall be installed in accordance with Article 305, Temporary Wiring, except that approved flexible cables and cords shall be permitted to be laid on floors where protected from contact by the general public.

See Figure 518-1.

(c) **Emergency Systems.** Control of emergency systems shall comply with Article 700, Emergency Systems.

518-4. Wiring Methods. The fixed wiring methods shall be metal raceways, nonmetallic raceways encased in not less than 2 inches (50.8 mm) of concrete, Type MI cable, or Type MC cable.

Figure 518-1. A treadle, such as this one, can be used to protect cords from abuse where they are laid across pedestrian ways; for instance, as part of a temporary wiring scheme such as may be used in exhibition halls. (Daniel Woodhead Co.)

Exception No. 1: Nonmetallic-sheathed cable, type AC cable, electrical nonmetallic tubing, and rigid nonmetallic conduit shall be permitted to be installed in those buildings or portions thereof that are not required to be fire-rated construction by the applicable building code.

Exception No. 2: As provided in Article 640, Sound-Recording and Similar Equipment, in Article 800, Communication Circuits, and in

Article 725 for Class 2 and Class 3 remote-control and signaling circuits, and in Article 760 for fire protective signaling circuits.

(FPN): Fire-rated construction is the fire-resistive classification used in building codes.

Refer to Figure 518-2. The washrooms and office area of this single-story facility are not places of assembly as defined in Section 518-2 and therefore require no special wiring methods. Ordinary wiring methods can be used on the inside surface of the storage area walls and on or in the partitions between storage areas, as these also are not places of assembly. However, inside any hollow spaces of the *fire-rated* storage area walls, the main requirements of Section 518-4 and Exception No. 2 are applicable, since the serving corridors are part of the places of assembly as a result of this particular building design.

Figure 518-2. The double lines represent walls required by the local building code to be of fire-rated construction. See the commentary text for discussion. The single lines represent walls not required by the local building code to be of fire-rated construction.

In a like manner, wiring in ceilings or floors, required to be of fire-rated construction in a place of assembly as defined in Section 518-2, is also required to comply with the main rule of Section 518-4, except as noted in Exception No. 2.

Although the partitions between the places of assembly and the central serving corridors, the partitions between the reception area and adjacent place of assembly, and the partitions between the food preparation area and the adjacent places of assembly are not required to be fire-rated by the local building code (in this case), they are part of the *place of assembly*. The wiring in or on these partitions is still subject to the main rule of Section 518-4; and Exception No. 1 is not applicable.

The intent is that, within a place of assembly as defined in Section 518-2, the main rule of Section 518-4 and Exception No. 2 apply to any wall, floor, or ceiling. Exception No. 1 applies to those portions of the building and those places of assembly not required to be fire-rated.

518-5. **Supply.** Portable switchboards and portable power distribution equipment shall be supplied only from listed power outlets of sufficient voltage and ampere rating. Such power outlets shall be protected by overcurrent devices. Such overcurrent devices and power outlets shall not be accessible to the general public. Provisions for connection of an equipment grounding conductor shall be provided. The neutral of feeders supplying solid-state, 3-phase, 4-wire dimmer systems shall be considered a current-carrying conductor.

A new section 518-5 has been added to the 1993 *Code*. It requires portable switchboards and portable power distribution equipment to be supplied only from listed power outlets that are rated for the voltage and current they are used for. The overcurrent devices and power outlets used to supply such equipment must be located so as not to be accessible to the general public.

ARTICLE 520 Theaters, Audience Areas of Motion Picture and Television Studios, and Similar Locations

Contents

A. General

520-47. Lamps in Scene Docks.

520-48. Curtain Machines.

520-49. Flue Damper Control.

D. Portable Switchboards on Stage

520-50. Road-Show Connection Panel (A Type of Patch Panel).

  (a) Load Circuits.

  (b) Circuit Transfer.

  (c) Overcurrent Protection.

  (d) Enclosure.

520-51. Supply.

520-52. Overcurrent Protection.

520-53. Construction and Feeders.

  (a) Enclosure.

  (b) Energized Parts.

  (c) Switches and Circuit Breakers.

  (d) Circuit Protection.

  (e) Dimmers.

  (f) Interior Conductors.

  (g) Pilot Light.

  (h) Supply Conductors.

  (i) Cable Arrangement.

  (j) Number of Supply Interconnections.

  (k) Single-Pole Separable Connectors.

  (l) Protection of Supply Conductors and Connectors.

  (m) Flanged Surface Inlets.

  (n) Terminals.

  (o) Supply Neutral Terminal.

  (p) Qualified Personnel.

E. Stage Equipment — Portable

520-61. Arc Lamp Fixtures.

520-62. Portable Plugging Boxes.

  (a) Enclosure.

  (b) Receptacles and Overcurrent Protection.

  (c) Busbars and Terminals.

  (d) Flanged Surface Inlets.

  (e) Cable Arrangement.

520-63. Bracket Fixture Wiring.

  (a) Bracket Wiring.

  (b) Mounting.

520-64. Portable Strips.

520-65. Festoons.

520-66. Special Effects.

520-67. Cable Connectors.

520-68. Conductors for Portables.

  (a) Conductor Type.

  (b) Conductor Ampacity.

520-69. Adapters.

  (a) No Reduction in Current Rating.

  (b) Connectors.

F. Dressing Rooms

520-71. Pendant Lampholders.

520-72. Lamp Guards.

520-73. Switches Required.

G. Grounding

520-81. Grounding.

A. General

520-1. Scope. This article covers all buildings or that part of a building or structure designed or used for presentation, dramatic, musical, motion picture projection, or similar purposes and to specific audience seating areas within motion picture or television studios.

These special requirements apply only to that part of a building used as a theater, or for a similar purpose, and do not necessarily apply to the entire building. For example, they would apply to an auditorium in a school building used for dramatic or other performances. The special requirements of this chapter would be applicable to the stage, auditorium, dressing rooms, and main corridors leading to the auditorium, but not to other parts of the building that are not involved in the use of the auditorium for performances or entertainment.

520-2. Motion Picture Projectors. Motion picture equipment and its installation and use shall comply with Article 540.

520-3. Sound Reproduction. Sound-reproducing equipment and its installation shall comply with Article 640.

520-4. Wiring Methods. The fixed wiring method shall be metal raceways, nonmetallic raceways encased in at least 2 inches (50.8 mm) of concrete, Type MI cable, or Type MC cable.

Exception No. 1: The wiring for portable switchboards, stage set lighting, stage effects, and other wiring not fixed as to location shall be permitted with approved flexible cords and cables as provided elsewhere in Article 520. Fastening such cables and cords by uninsulated staples or nailing shall not be permitted.

Exception No. 2: As provided in Article 640 for sound recording, in Article 800 for communication circuits, in Article 725 for Class 2 and Class 3 remote-control and signaling circuits, and in Article 760 for fire protective signaling circuits.

Theaters and similar buildings are usually required to be of fire-rated construction as determined by applicable building codes; therefore, per Section 518-4, the fixed wiring methods are limited to metal raceways such as rigid metal conduit, intermediate metal conduit, electrical metallic tubing, nonmetallic raceways encased in 2 inches of concrete, or Type MI or MC cable.

Exceptions to the wiring rules for metal- (or concrete-) enclosed wiring are permitted for the installation of communication circuits, Class 2 and Class 3 remote-control and signaling circuits, sound-reproduction wiring, and fire-protective signaling circuits. See Section 518-4, Exception No. 2. Where portability, flexibility, and adjustments are necessary for portable switchboards, stage lighting, and special effects, suitable cords and cables are permitted. Exception No. 3 permits buildings or portions of buildings that are not required to be of fire-rated construction to be wired with Type NM cable, Type AC cable, ENT or RNC.

Exception No. 3: Nonmetallic-sheathed cable, Type AC cable, electrical nonmetallic tubing, and rigid nonmetallic conduit shall be permitted to be installed in those buildings or portions thereof that are not required to be of fire-rated construction by the applicable building code.

520-5 . **Number of Conductors in Raceway.** The number of conductors permitted in any metal conduit, rigid nonmetallic conduit as permitted in this article, or electrical metallic tubing for border or stage pocket circuits or for remote-control conductors shall not exceed the percentage fill shown in Table 1 of Chapter 9. Where contained within an auxiliary gutter or a wireway, the sum of the cross-sectional areas of all contained conductors at any cross section shall not exceed 20 percent of the interior cross-sectional area of the auxiliary gutter or wireway. The thirty-conductor limitation of Sections 362-5 and 374-5 shall not apply.

520-6 . **Enclosing and Guarding Live Parts.** Live parts shall be enclosed or guarded to prevent accidental contact by persons and objects. All switches shall be of the externally operable type. Dimmers, including rheostats, shall be placed in cases or cabinets that enclose all live parts.

Figure 520-1. *An electronic computer lighting console for controlling dimmers. (Electronic Theatre Controls, Inc.)*

520-7 . **Emergency Systems.** Control of emergency systems shall comply with Article 700, Emergency Systems.

520-8 . **Branch Circuits.** A branch circuit of any size supplying one or more receptacles shall be permitted to supply stage set lighting. The voltage rating of the receptacles shall not be less than the circuit voltage. Receptacle ampere ratings and branch-circuit conductor ampacity shall not be less than the branch-circuit overcurrent device ampere rating. Table 210-21(b)(2) shall not apply.

A new Section 520-8 has been added to the 1993 *Code.* Branch-circuits that supply one or more receptacles for stage set lighting are permitted to be of any size, provided the ampere rating of the receptacle(s) and the ampacity of the conductors is not less than the rating of the overcurrent device.

B. Fixed Stage Switchboard

520-21 . **Dead Front.** Stage switchboards shall be of the dead-front type and shall comply with Part C of Article 384 unless approved based on suitability as a stage switchboard as determined by a qualified testing laboratory and recognized test standards and principles.

520-22. Guarding Back of Switchboard. Stage switchboards having exposed live parts on the back of such boards shall be enclosed by the building walls, wire mesh grills, or by other approved methods. The entrance to this enclosure shall be by means of a self-closing door.

520-23. Control and Overcurrent Protection of Receptacle Circuits. Means shall be provided at a stage lighting switchboard to which load circuits are connected for overcurrent protection of stage lighting branch circuits, including branch circuits supplying stage and auditorium receptacles used for cord- and plug-connected stage equipment. Where the stage switchboard contains dimmers to control nonstage lighting, the locating of the overcurrent protective devices for these branch circuits at the stage switchboard shall be permitted.

520-24. Metal Hood. A stage switchboard that is not completely enclosed dead-front and dead-rear or recessed into a wall shall be provided with a metal hood extending the full length of the board to protect all equipment on the board from falling objects.

Because stages are usually crowded and a great deal of flammable material is often present, a stage switchboard is not permitted to have exposed live parts on its front. Moreover, the space at the rear of a stage switchboard is required to be guarded in order to prevent entrance or contact by unqualified and unauthorized persons. One accepted method of accomplishing this is by enclosing the space between the rear of the switchboard and the wall in a sheet-steel housing with a door at one end.

Major stage switchboards are usually of the remote-control type. Pilot switches on the stage switchboard control the operation of remote contactors, which are installed in a convenient location such as below the stage. In turn, these contactors control the lighting circuits.

The front view of a small stage switchboard of the partial remote-control type is shown in Figure 520-2. Dimmers for individual circuits are operated by the egg-shaped handles. The usual location of a stage switchboard is in a recess in the proscenium wall. After passing through switches and dimmers, many of the main circuits are required to be subdivided into branch circuits so that no branch circuit will be loaded to more than 20 amperes. See Section 520-41. In a switchboard of the remote-control type, the branch-circuit fuses are located on the same panel as the contactors.

In a direct-control-type switchboard, and sometimes in a remote-control-type switchboard, branch-circuit fuses are located on special panelboards called magazine panels that are placed in the space behind the switchboard, usually in the location of the junction box.

Figure 520-2. A digital SCR dimmer switchboard. (Electronic Theatre Controls, Inc.)

520-25. Dimmers. Dimmers shall comply with (a) through (d) below.

(a) Disconnection and Overcurrent Protection. Where dimmers are installed in ungrounded conductors, each dimmer shall have overcurrent protection not greater than 125 percent of the dimmer rating, and shall be disconnected from all ungrounded conductors when the master or individual switch or circuit breaker supplying such dimmer is in the open position.

(b) Resistance- or Reactor-type Dimmers. Resistance- or series reactor-type dimmers shall be permitted to be placed in either the grounded or the ungrounded conductor of the circuit. Where designed to open either the supply circuit to the dimmer or the circuit controlled by it, the dimmer shall then comply with Section 380-1. Resistance- or reactor-type dimmers placed in the grounded neutral conductor of the circuit shall not open the circuit.

(c) Autotransformer-type Dimmers. The circuit supplying an autotransformer-type dimmer shall not exceed 150 volts between conductors. The grounded conductor shall be common to the input and output circuits.

(d) Solid-State-type Dimmers. The circuit supplying a solid-state dimmer shall not exceed 150 volts between conductors unless the dimmer is specifically approved for higher voltage operation. Where a grounded conductor supplies a dimmer, it shall be common to the input and output circuits. Dimmer chassis shall be connected to the equipment grounding conductor.

(FPN):   See Section 210-9 for circuits derived from autotransformers.

Figure 520-3 illustrates three branch circuits arranged to be controlled by a single switch and a single dimmer plate. A single-pole switch on the stage switchboard feeds a short bus on the magazine panel. The magazine panel is like an ordinary panelboard, but branch circuits are directly

connected to the bus (without switches) and the circuits are divided into several sections that contain separate feeder-buses. One side of the variable resistor or dimmer plate is connected to the neutral bus at the switchboard, and the other side is connected to the neutral bus in the magazine panel. In order to avoid shunting of the dimmer, causing it to lose its control of the brightness of the lamps, the neutral bus in the magazine is required to be effectively insulated from ground and to be separate from other neutral buses in the panel.

The dimmer is permanently connected to the neutral of the wiring system, which is required to be effectively grounded; therefore, the dimmer is essentially at ground potential.

Circuits supplying autotransformer-type dimmers are not permitted to exceed 150 V between conductors. Any desired voltage may be applied to the lamps from full-line voltage to voltage so low that the lamps provide no illumination by means of a movable contact. See Figure 520-4. This type of dimmer produces very little heat, operates at a high efficiency, and, within its maximum rating, its dimming effect is independent of the wattage of the load. See commentary under Section 470-4, which discusses saturable reactors that are used for dimmers on stage switchboards.

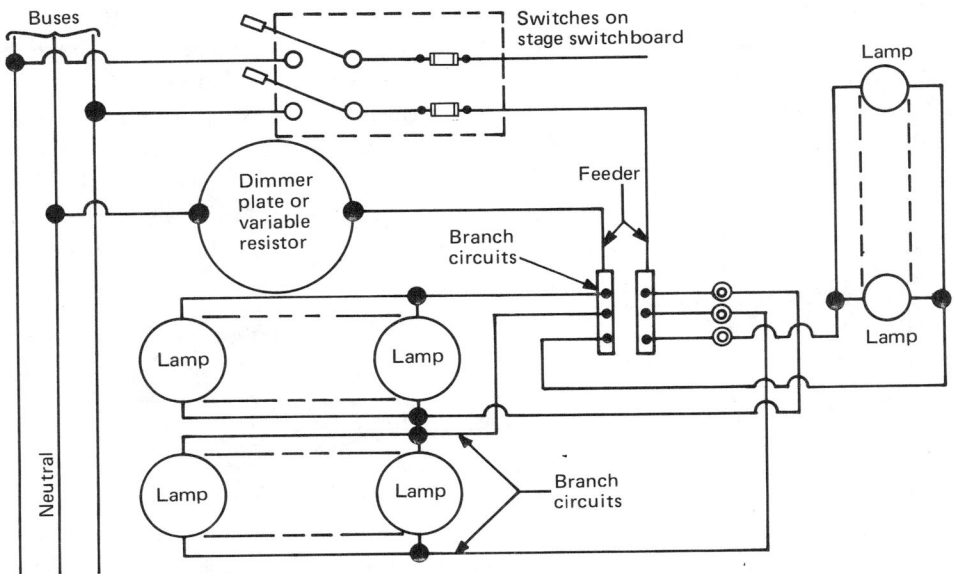

Figure 520-3. *A schematic diagram of a typical stage switchboard illustrating connections for control switches, dimmer plate, and one section of a magazine panel showing feeder and branch-circuit connections for control of three lighting circuits.*

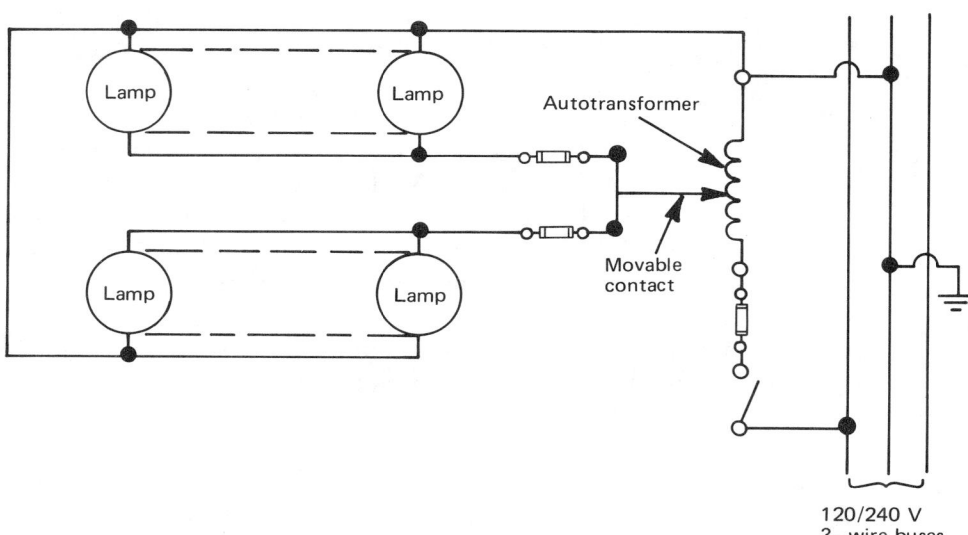

Figure 520-4. Typical connections for an autotransformer-type dimmer.

120/240 V
3—wire buses

520-26. **Type of Switchboard.** Stage switchboard shall be either one or a combination of the following types:

(a) **Manual.** Dimmers and switches are operated by handles mechanically linked to the control devices.

(b) **Remotely Controlled.** Devices are operated electrically from a pilot-type control console or panel. Pilot control panels shall either be part of the switchboard or shall be permitted to be at another location.

(c) **Intermediate.** A stage switchboard with circuit interconnections is a secondary switchboard (patch panel) or panelboard remote to the primary stage switchboard. It shall contain overcurrent protection. Where the required branch circuit overcurrent protection is provided in the dimmer panel, it shall be permitted to be omitted from the intermediate switchboard.

520-27. **Stage Switchboard Feeders.** Feeders supplying stage switchboards shall be one of the following:

(a) **Single Feeder.** A single feeder disconnected by a single disconnect device. The neutral of feeders supplying solid-state, 3-phase, 4-wire dimming systems shall be considered a current-carrying conductor.

(b) **Multiple Feeders to Intermediate Stage Switchboard (Patch Panel).** Multiple feeders of unlimited quantity shall be permitted, provided that all multiple feeders are part of a single system. Where combined, neutral conductors in a given

raceway shall be of sufficient ampacity to carry the maximum unbalanced current supplied by multiple feeder conductors in the same raceway, but need not be greater than the ampacity of the neutral supplying the primary stage switchboard. Parallel neutral conductors shall comply with Section 310-4. The neutral of feeders supplying solid-state, 3-phase, 4-wire dimming systems shall be considered a current-carrying conductor.

The feeders to this device are often dimmer-controlled circuits at 100 amperes or less, single phase, so they can be distributed to different combinations of the same size or smaller branch circuits. Many installations use a common neutral. Therefore, the neutral must be capable of carrying the maximum unbalanced current supplied by multiple feeder conductors in the same raceway. The neutral of feeders supplying solid-state, 3-phase, 4-wire dimming systems will carry third harmonic currents that are present even under balanced load conditions.

(c) **Separate Feeders to Single Primary Stage Switchboard (Dimmer Bank).** Installations with separate feeders to a single primary stage switchboard shall have a disconnecting means for each feeder. The primary stage switchboard shall have a permanent and obvious label stating the number and location of disconnecting means. If the disconnecting means are located in more than one distribution switchboard, the primary stage switchboard shall be provided with barriers to correspond with these multiple locations. The neutral of feeders supplying solid-state, 3-phase, 4-wire dimming systems shall be considered a current-carrying conductor.

This section permits several separate feeders to a stage switchboard rather than one very large feeder.

For purposes of computing supply capacity to switchboards, it shall be permissible to consider the maximum load that the switchboard is intended to control in a given installation, provided that all feeders supplying the switchboard shall be protected by an overcurrent device with a rating not greater than the ampacity of the feeder, and that the opening of the overcurrent device does not have any effect on the egress or emergency lighting systems.

A new second paragraph has been added to section 520-27(c) for the purpose of calculating the feeder size for single, primary switchboards rather than in accordance with the rating of the switchboard. The feeder(s) is sized in accordance with the maximum load the switchboard is intended to control for a specific installation. The feeder(s) is required to be protected by an overcurrent device that has a rating not greater than the feeder ampacity. Operation of the overcurrent device is not allowed to have any effect on egress or emergency lighting systems.

The neutral of feeders supplying solid-state, 3-phase, 4-wire dimming systems will carry third harmonic currents that are present even under balanced load conditions.

(FPN): For computation of stage switchboard feeder loads, see Section 220-10.

C. Stage Equipment—Fixed

520-41. **Circuit Loads.** Footlights, border lights, and proscenium side lights shall be so arranged that no branch circuit supplying such equipment will carry a load exceeding 20 amperes.

Exception: Where heavy-duty lampholders only are used, such circuits shall be permitted to comply with Article 210 for circuits supplying heavy-duty lampholders.

Sections 210-23(b) and (c) permit 30-A, 40-A, or 50-A branch circuits if heavy-duty lampholders, such as admedium- or mogul-base Edison screw-shell types, are used for fixed lighting.

520-42. **Conductor Insulation.** Foot, border, proscenium, or portable strip light fixtures and connector strips shall be wired with

conductors having insulation suitable for the temperature at which the conductors will be operated, but not less than 125°C (257°F). The ampacity of the 125°C (257°F) conductors shall be that of 60°C (140°F) conductors. All drops from connector strips shall be 90°C (194°F) wire with no more than 6 inches (152 mm) of conductor extending into the connector strip. Article 310, Note 8(a), Notes to Ampacity Tables of 0 to 2000 Volts, shall not apply.

The 125°C (257°F) minimum temperature rating is based on the heat from the lamps raising the ambient temperature in which the wiring is located. Drops from connector strips are usually flexible cord. The cord is not located in the high ambient. The derating factors of Note 8 are judged unnecessary because the conductors are not all energized at one time and are not continuously energized.

(FPN): See Table 310-13 for conductor types.

520-43. **Footlights.**

(a) Metal Trough Construction. Where metal trough construction is employed for footlights, the trough containing the circuit conductors shall be made of sheet metal not lighter than No. 20 MSG treated to prevent oxidation. Lampholder terminals shall be kept at least ½ inch (12.7 mm) from the metal of the trough. The circuit conductors shall be soldered to the lampholder terminals.

(b) Other-than-Metal-Trough Construction. Where the metal trough construction specified in Section 520-43(a) is not used, footlights shall consist of individual outlets with lampholders wired with rigid metal conduit, intermediate metal conduit, or flexible metal conduit, Type MC cable, or mineral-insulated, metal-sheathed cable. The circuit conductors shall be soldered to the lampholder terminals.

Metal troughs are commonly employed for footlights because the installation costs are less than those for individual outlets. Figure 520-5 illustrates a view of footlights in a typical installation.

Disappearing footlights are arranged so as to automatically disconnect the current supply when the footlights are in the closed position, thereby preventing heat-entrapment that could cause a fire.

(c) Disappearing Footlights. Disappearing footlights shall be so arranged that the current supply will be automatically disconnected when the footlights are replaced in the storage recesses designed for them.

Figure 520-5. *To prevent heat entrapment, disappearing footlights are arranged to automatically disconnect the current supply when in the closed position.*

520-44. Borders and Proscenium Sidelights.

(a) General. Borders and proscenium sidelights shall be (1) constructed as specified in Section 520-43; (2) suitably stayed and supported; and (3) so designed that the flanges of the reflectors or other adequate guards will protect the lamps from mechanical damage and from accidental contact with scenery or other combustible material.

(b) Cables for Border Lights. Cables for supply to border lights shall be listed for extra-hard usage. The cables shall be suitably supported. Such cables shall be employed only where flexible conductors are necessary. Ampacity of the conductors shall be as provided in Section 400-5.

Section 520-44(b) of the 1993 *Code* has been expanded to include a new exception that permits extra-hard usage cords that are not in direct contact with heat-producing equipment to have their ampacity determined by new Table 520-44 instead of Section 400-5. Table 520-44 permits the cords to have a higher ampacity rating than allowed in Table 400-5(2).

Figure 520-6 shows a border light installed over a stage. Figure 520-7 is a cross-sectional view that illustrates construction details. This particular border light is designed for 200-W lamps. Each lamp is provided with its own reflector to obtain the highest illumination efficiency. Fitted to each reflector is a glass roundel available in any color.

Commonly, red, white, and blue are used for 3-color equipment, and red, white, blue, and amber for 4-color equipment. A splice box is provided on top of the housing for enclosing connections between the cable supplying the border light and the border light's internal wiring, which consists of wiring from the splice box to the lamp sockets in a trough extending the length of the border.

To facilitate height adjustment for cleaning and lamp replacement, border lights are usually supported by steel cables. Therefore, the circuit conductors supplying the border lights are required to be carried to the border in a flexible cable. The size of the individual conductor of the cable may be No. 14, although No. 12 is more commonly used.

Figure 520-6. *A suspended border-light assembly for installation over a stage. (Kliegl Bros.)*

Figure 520-7. A cross-sectional view of a typical light in the border assembly shown in Figure 520-6. (Kliegl Bros.)

Exception: Listed multiconductor extra-hard usage type cords not in direct contact with equipment containing heat-producing elements shall be permitted to have their ampacity determined by Table 520-44. Maximum load current in any conductor shall not exceed the values in Table 520-44.

520-45. **Receptacles.** Receptacles for electrical equipment or fixtures on stages shall be rated in amperes.

Conductors supplying receptacles shall be in accordance with Articles 310 and 400.

520-46. **Connector Strips, Drop Boxes, and Stage Pockets.** Receptacles for the connection of portable stage lighting equipment shall be pendant or mounted in suitable pockets or enclosures and comply with Section 520-45. Supply cables for connector strips and drop boxes shall be as specified in Section 520-44(b).

Table 520-44. **Allowable Ampacity of Listed Extra-Hard Usage Cords with Temperature Ratings of 75°C (167°F) and 90°C (194°F)*** [Based on Ambient Temperature of 30°C (86°F)]

Size AWG	Temperature Rating of Cord		Maximum Rating of Over- current Device
	75° (167°F)	90°C (194°F)	
14	24	28	15
12	32	35	20
10	41	47	25
8	57	65	35
6	77	87	45
4	101	114	60
2	133	152	80

* Ampacity shown is the allowable ampacity for multiconductor cords where only three copper conductors are current-carrying. If the number of current-carrying conductors in a cord exceeds three and the load diversity factor is a minimum of 50 percent, the allowable ampacity of each conductor shall be reduced as shown in the following table.

Number of Conductors	Percent of Allowable Ampacity
4 thru 6	80
7 thru 24	70
25 thru 42	60
43 and above	50

Note: Ultimate Insulation Temperature. In no case shall conductors be associated together in such a way with respect to the kind of circuit, the wiring method used, or the number of conductors such that the temperature limit of the conductors will be exceeded.

Figure 520-8. A 3-gang, 3-receptacle pin-plug outlet box designed for flush mounting. (Electronic Theatre Controls, Inc.)

520-47. **Lamps in Scene Docks.** Lamps installed in scene docks shall be so located and guarded as to be free from physical damage and shall provide an air space of not less than 2 inches (50.8 mm) between such lamps and any combustible material.

520-48. **Curtain Machines.** Curtain machines shall be listed.

520-49. **Flue Damper Control.** Where stage flue dampers are released by an electrical device, the circuit operating the device shall be normally closed and shall be controlled by at least two externally operable switches, one switch being placed on stage at either the electrician's or stage manager's station and the other where designated by the authority having jurisdiction. The device shall be designed for the full voltage of the circuit to which it is connected, no resistance being inserted. The device shall be located in the loft above the scenery and shall be enclosed in a suitable metal box having a tight, self-closing door.

In addition to the flue dampers being controlled from two externally operable switches at different locations, the design of a normally closed circuit ensures that the flue dampers will operate when the circuit opens for any reason, such as a circuit breaker tripping or a fuse blowing.

D. Portable Switchboards on Stage

520-50. **Road-Show Connection Panel (A Type of Patch Panel).** A panel designed to allow for road-show connection of portable stage switchboards to fixed lighting outlets by means of permanently installed supplementary circuits. The panel, supplementary circuits, and outlets shall comply with (a) through (d) below.

(a) **Load Circuits.** Circuits shall terminate in grounded polarized inlets of current and voltage rating that match the fixed load receptacle.

(b) **Circuit Transfer.** Circuits that are transferred between fixed and portable switchboards shall have both the line and neutral transferred simultaneously.

(c) **Overcurrent Protection.** The supply devices of these supplementary circuits shall be protected by branch-circuit overcurrent protective devices. The individual supplementary circuit, within the road-show connection panel and theater, shall be protected by branch-circuit overcurrent protective devices of suitable ampacity installed within the road-show connection panel.

(d) **Enclosure.** Panel construction shall be in accordance with Article 384.

Road-show connection panels facilitate the connection of portable switchboards to permanently installed wiring. The requirements in Section 520-50(c) are intended to prevent damage to the permanently installed wiring from overloads occurring in the portable switchboards.

520-51. **Supply.** Portable switchboards shall be supplied only from power outlets of sufficient voltage and ampere rating. Such power outlets shall include only externally operable, enclosed fused switches or circuit breakers mounted on stage or at the permanent switchboard in locations readily accessible from the stage floor. Provisions for connection of an equipment grounding conductor shall be provided. The neutral of feeders supplying solid-state, 3-phase, 4-wire dimmer systems shall be considered a current-carrying conductor.

520-52. **Overcurrent Protection.** Circuits from portable switchboards directly supplying equipment containing incandescent lamps of not over 300 watts shall be protected by overcurrent protective devices having a rating or setting of not over 20 amperes. Circuits for lampholders over 300 watts shall be permitted where overcurrent protection complies with Article 210.

520-53. **Construction and Feeders.** Portable switchboards and feeders for use on stages shall comply with (a) through (p) below.

(a) **Enclosure.** Portable switchboards shall be placed within an enclosure of substantial construction, which shall be permitted to be so arranged that the enclosure is open during operation. Enclosures of wood shall be completely lined with sheet metal of not less than No. 24 MSG and shall be well-galvanized, enameled, or otherwise properly coated to prevent corrosion or be of a corrosion-resistant material.

(b) **Energized Parts.** There shall not be exposed energized parts within the enclosure.

Exception: For dimmer faceplates as provided in (e) below.

(c) **Switches and Circuit Breakers.** All switches and circuit breakers shall be of the externally operable, enclosed type.

(d) **Circuit Protection.** Overcurrent devices shall be provided in each ungrounded conductor of every circuit supplied through the switchboard. Enclosures shall be provided for all overcurrent devices in addition to the switchboard enclosure.

(e) Dimmers. The terminals of dimmers shall be provided with enclosures, and dimmer faceplates shall be so arranged that accidental contact cannot be readily made with the faceplate contacts.

(f) Interior Conductors. All conductors other than busbars within the switchboard enclosure shall be stranded. Conductors shall be approved for an operating temperature at least equal to the approved operating temperature of the dimming devices used in the switchboard and in no case less than the following: (1) resistance-type dimmers, 200°C (392°F); or (2) reactor-type, autotransformer, and solid-state dimmers, 125°C (257°F). All control wiring shall comply with Article 725.

Each conductor shall have an ampacity not less than the rating of the circuit breaker, switch, or fuse that it supplies. Circuit interrupting and bus bracing shall be in accordance with Sections 110-9 and 110-10. Switchboards with inadequate short-circuit withstand rating shall be protected on the line side by current-limiting devices. The short-circuit withstand rating shall be marked on the switchboard.

Exception: Conductors for pilot light circuits having overcurrent protection of not over 20 amperes.

Conductors shall be enclosed in metal wireways or be securely fastened in position and shall be bushed where they pass through metal.

(g) Pilot Light. A pilot light shall be provided within the enclosure and shall be so connected to the circuit supplying the board that the opening of the master switch will not cut off the supply to the lamp. This lamp shall be on an individual branch circuit having overcurrent protection rated or set at not over 15 amperes.

(h) Supply Conductors. The supply to a portable switchboard shall be by means of listed extra-hard usage cords or cables. The supply cords or cable shall terminate within the switchboard enclosure, in an externally operable fused master switch or circuit breaker, or in a connector assembly identified for the purpose. The supply cords or cable (and connector assembly) shall have sufficient ampacity to carry the total load connected to the switchboard and shall be protected by overcurrent devices.

Single-conductor portable supply cable sets shall not be smaller than No. 2 conductors. The equipment grounding conductor shall not be smaller than No. 6 conductor. The single-conductor cables for a supply shall be of the same length, type, size, and be grouped together, but not bundled. The equipment grounding conductor shall be permitted to be of a different type, provided it meets the other requirements of this section, and it shall be permitted to be reduced in size as permitted by Section 250-95. Grounded (neutral) and equipment grounding conductors shall be identified in accordance with Sections 200-6, 250-57(b), and 310-12. Grounded conductors shall be permitted to be identified by marking at least the first 6 inches (152.4 mm) from both ends of each length of conductor with white or natural gray. Equipment grounding conductors shall be permitted to be identified by marking at least the first 6 inches (152.4 mm) from both ends of each length of conductor with green or green with yellow stripes. Where more than one nominal voltage exists within the same premises, each ungrounded system conductor shall be identified by system.

Exception No. 1: Supply Conductors Not Over 10 Feet (3.05 m) Long. In cases where supply conductors do not exceed 10 feet (3.05 m) in length between supply and switchboard or supply and a subsequent overcurrent device, the ampacity of the supply conductors shall be at least one-quarter of the ampacity of the supply overcurrent protection device where all of the following conditions are met:

a. The supply conductors shall terminate in a single overcurrent protection device that will limit the load to the ampacity of the supply conductors. This single overcurrent device shall be permitted to supply additional overcurrent devices on its load side.

b. The supply conductors shall not penetrate walls, floors, or ceilings or be run through doors or traffic areas. The supply conductors shall be adequately protected from physical damage.

c. The supply conductors shall be suitably terminated in an approved manner.

d. Conductors shall be continuous without splices or connectors.

e. Conductors shall not be bundled.

f. Conductors shall be supported above the floor in an approved manner.

Exception No. 2: Supply Conductors Not Over 20 Feet (6.1 m) Long. In cases where supply conductors do not exceed 20 feet (6.1 m) in length between supply and switchboard or supply and a subsequent overcurrent protection device, the ampacity of the supply conductors shall be at least one-half the rating of the supply overcurrent protection device where all of the following conditions are met:

a. The supply conductors shall terminate in a single overcurrent protection device that will limit the load to the ampacity of the supply conductors. This single overcurrent device shall be permitted to supply additional overcurrent devices on its load side.

b. The supply conductors shall not penetrate walls, floors, or ceilings or be run through doors or traffic areas. The supply conductors shall be adequately protected from physical damage.

c. The supply conductors shall be suitably terminated in an approved manner.

d. The supply conductors shall be supported in an approved manner at least 7 feet (2.13 m) above the floor except at terminations.

e. The supply conductors shall not be bundled.

f. Tap conductors shall be in unbroken lengths.

Loads of 144 kVA and greater are not uncommon, even on portable switchboard equipment. Installations in the field include lighting for theatrical-type productions with large numbers of lighting fixtures. However, only a fraction of the many fixtures installed are used at any one time. The intent of the exceptions is that the supply conductors are required to be sized according to their overcurrent protection, and not by the total connected load. These exceptions are similar to the requirements for taps found in Section 240-21.

(i) Cable Arrangement. Cables shall be protected by bushings where they pass through enclosures and shall be so arranged that tension on the cable will not be transmitted to the connections. Where power conductors pass through metal, the requirements of Section 300-20 shall apply.

(j) Number of Supply Interconnections. Where connectors are used in a supply conductor, there shall be a maximum number of three interconnections (mated connector pairs) where the total length from supply to switchboard does not exceed 100 feet (30.5 m). In cases where the total length from supply to switchboard exceeds 100 feet (30.5 m), one additional interconnection shall be permitted for each additional 100 feet (30.5 m) of supply conductor.

Addition of excessive numbers of interconnects could jeopardize the mechanical and electrical integrity of the supply conductors.

(k) Single-Pole Separable Connectors. Where single-pole portable cable connectors are used, they shall be listed and of the locking type. The use of such connectors shall comply with at least one of the following conditions:

(1) Connection and disconnection of connectors are only possible where the supply connectors are interlocked to the source and it is not possible to connect or disconnect connectors when the supply is energized.

(2) Line connectors are of the listed sequential-interlocking type so that load connectors shall be connected in the following sequence:

    a. Equipment grounding conductor connection.

    b. Grounded circuit conductor connection, if provided.

    c. Ungrounded conductor connection, and that disconnection shall be in the reverse order.

(3) A caution notice shall be provided adjacent to the line connectors indicating that plug connection shall be in the following order:

    a. Equipment grounding conductor connectors.

    b. Grounded circuit conductor connectors, if provided.

    c. Ungrounded conductor connectors, and that disconnection shall be in the reverse order.

Section 520-53(k) of the 1993 *Code* has been expanded to require single-pole portable cable connectors to be listed and be of the interlocking type. The connectors must be interlocked in such a manner as to prevent plugging in the grounded conductor and phase conductors before the equipment grounding connection has been achieved. In addition, the connectors must be interlocked so that the equipment ground is the last to be unplugged.

(l) Protection of Supply Conductors and Connectors. All supply conductors and connectors shall be protected against physical damage by an approved means. This protection shall not be required to be raceways.

(m) Flanged Surface Inlets. Flanged surface inlets (recessed plugs) that are used to accept the power shall be rated in amperes.

(n) Terminals. Terminals to which stage cables are connected shall be so located as to permit convenient access to the terminals.

In a worst case situation, the neutral current that can occur in a 3-phase solid-state switchboard due to SCR phase control is 26 percent above the maximum load current. A neutral conductor of a convertible switchboard will usually be rated at least 50 percent larger than the largest ungrounded supply conductor.

(o) Supply Neutral Terminal. In portable switchboard equipment designed for use with 3-phase, 4-wire with ground supply, the supply neutral terminal, its associated busbar, or equivalent wiring, or both, shall have an ampacity equal to twice the ampacity of the largest ungrounded supply terminal. The power supply lines for portable switchboards shall be sized considering the neutral as a current-carrying conductor. Where single-conductor feeder cables, not installed in raceways, are used on multiphase circuits, the grounded neutral conductor shall have an ampacity of 130 percent of the ungrounded circuit conductors feeding the portable switchboard.

Exception: Where portable switchboard equipment is specifically constructed and identified to be internally converted in the field, in an approved manner, from use with a balanced 3-phase, 4-wire with ground supply to a balanced single-phase, 3-wire with ground supply, the supply neutral terminal and its associated busbar, equivalent wiring, or both, shall have an ampacity equal to that of the largest ungrounded single-phase supply terminal.

(p) Qualified Personnel. The routing of portable supply conductors, the making and breaking of supply connectors and other supply connections, and the energization and deenergization of supply services shall be performed by qualified personnel, and portable switchboards shall be so marked, indicating this requirement in a permanent and conspicuous manner.

Exception: Connection of a portable switchboard to a permanently installed supply receptacle outlet, that supply receptacle outlet being protected for its rated ampacity by an overcurrent device of not greater than 150 amps, and where the receptacle outlet, interconnection, and switchboard further:

a. Employ listed multipole connectors suitable for the purpose for every supply interconnection, and

b. Prevent access to all supply connections by the general public, and

c. Employ listed extra-hard usage multiconductor cords or cables with an ampacity suitable for the type of load and not less than the ampere rating of the connectors.

E. Stage Equipment — Portable

520-61. **Arc Lamp Fixtures.** Arc lamp fixtures, including enclosed arc lamp fixtures and associated ballasts, shall be listed. Interconnecting cord sets and interconnecting cords and cables shall be extra-hard usage type and listed.

520-62. **Portable Plugging Boxes.** Portable plugging boxes shall comply with (a) through (e) below.

(a) Enclosure. The construction shall be such that no current-carrying part will be exposed.

(b) Receptacles and Overcurrent Protection. Receptacles shall comply with Section 520-45 and shall have branch-circuit overcurrent protection in the box. Fuses and circuit breakers shall be protected against physical damage. Cords or cables supplying pendant receptacles shall be listed for extra-hard usage.

(c) Busbars and Terminals. Busbars shall have an ampacity equal to the sum of the ampere ratings of all the circuits connected to the busbar. Lugs shall be provided for the connection of the master cable.

(d) Flanged Surface Inlets. Flanged surface inlets (recessed plugs) that are used to accept the power shall be rated in amperes.

(e) Cable Arrangement. Cables shall be adequately protected where they pass through enclosures and be so arranged that tension on the cable will not be transmitted to the terminations.

520-63. **Bracket Fixture Wiring.**

(a) Bracket Wiring. Brackets for use on scenery shall be wired internally, and the fixture stem shall be carried through to the back of the scenery where a bushing shall be placed on the end of the stem.

Exception: Externally wired brackets or other fixtures shall be permitted where wired with cords designed for hard usage that extend through scenery and without joint or splice in canopy of fixture back and terminate in an approved-type stage connector located, where practical, within 18 inches (457 mm) of the fixture.

(b) Mounting. Fixtures shall be securely fastened in place.

520-64. **Portable Strips.** Portable strips shall be constructed in accordance with the requirements for border lights and proscenium side lights in Section 520-44(a). The supply cable shall be protected by bushings where it passes through metal and shall be so arranged that tension on the cable will not be transmitted to the connections.

(FPN No. 1): See Section 520-42 for wiring of portable strips.

(FPN No. 2): See Section 520-68(a), Exception No. 2 for insulation types required on single conductors.

520-65. **Festoons.** Joints in festoon wiring shall be staggered. Lamps enclosed in lanterns or similar devices of combustible material shall be equipped with guards.

Festoon wiring is a string of lights that is suspended between two points more than 15 feet apart. Joints in festoon wiring are required to be staggered and properly insulated. This ensures that connections will not be opposite one another, which could cause sparking due to improper insulation or unraveling of insulation, which, in turn, could ignite lanterns or other combustible material enclosing lamps. Where lampholders have terminals of a type that puncture the conductor insulation and make contact with the conductors, stranded-type conductors should be used.

520-66. **Special Effects.** Electrical devices used for simulating lightning, waterfalls, and the like shall be so constructed and located that flames, sparks, or hot particles cannot come in contact with combustible material.

520-67. **Cable Connectors.** Cable connectors, male and female, for flexible conductors shall be constructed so that tension on the cord or cable will not be transmitted to the connections. The female half shall be attached to the load end of the power supply cord or cable. The connector shall be rated in amperes and designed so that differently rated devices cannot be connected together. AC multipole connectors shall be polarized and comply with Section 410-56(f) and Section 410-58.

(FPN):   See Section 400-10 for pull at terminals.

520-68. **Conductors for Portables.**

(a) **Conductor Type.** Flexible conductors, including cable extensions, used to supply portable stage equipment shall be listed, extra-hard usage cords or cables.

Exception No. 1: Reinforced cord shall be permitted to supply stand lamps where the cord is not subject to severe physical damage and is protected by an overcurrent device rated at not over 20 amperes.

Exception No. 2: A special assembly of conductors in sleeving no longer than 3.3 feet (1.0 m) shall be permitted to be employed in lieu of flexible cord if the individual wires are stranded and rated not less than 125°C (257°F) and the outer sleeve is glass fiber with a wall thickness of at least 0.025 inches (635 micrometers).

Exception No. 3: Portable stage equipment requiring flexible supply conductors with a higher temperature rating where one end is permanently attached to the equipment shall be permitted to employ alternate, suitable conductors as determined by a qualified testing laboratory and recognized test standards.

(b) **Conductor Ampacity.** The ampacity of conductors shall be as given in Section 400-5, except multiconductor listed extra-hard usage portable cords, that are not in direct contact with equipment containing heat-producing elements, shall be permitted to have their ampacity determined by Table 520-44. Maximum load current in any conductor shall not exceed the values in Table 520-44.

Exception: Where alternate conductors are allowed in Exception Nos. 2 and 3 of Section 520-68(a), their ampacity shall be as given in the appropriate table in this Code for the types of conductors employed.

520-69. **Adapters.** Adapters, two-fers, and other single and multiple circuit outlet devices shall comply with (a) and (b) below.

See Figure 520-9.

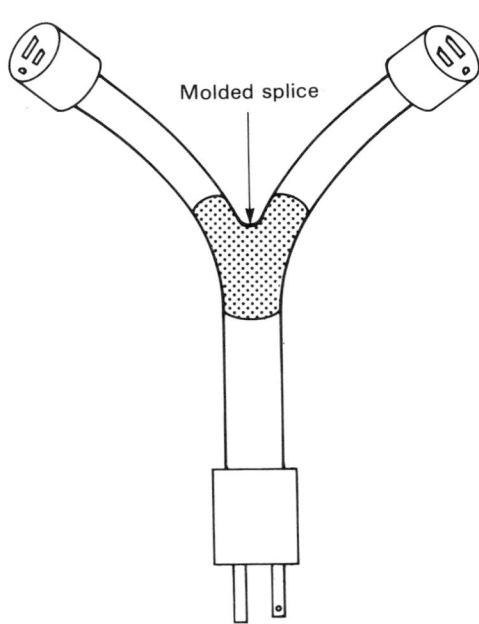

Molded splice

Figure 520-9. A two-fer consists of two cord connectors on separate cords connected to a single supply cord.

(a) No Reduction in Current Rating. Each receptacle and its corresponding cable shall have the same current and voltage rating as the plug supplying it. It shall not be utilized in a stage circuit with a greater current rating.

(b) Connectors. All connectors shall be wired in accordance with Sections 520-67 and 520-68(a).

Adapters are available that would permit the use of under-sized cords on portable switchboards for connection to larger-sized receptacles. For example, a No. 12 conductor with an ampacity of 20 amperes could be connected to a 100-ampere circuit. An overload could result in a fire since the circuit breaker or fuse would not provide adequate protection.

F. Dressing Rooms

520-71. Pendant Lampholders. Pendant lampholders shall not be installed in dressing rooms.

520-72. Lamp Guards. All exposed incandescent lamps in dressing rooms, where less than 8 feet (2.44 m) from the floor, shall be equipped with open-end guards riveted to the outlet box cover or otherwise sealed or locked in place.

Because of the many different types of flammable materials present in dressing rooms, such as costumes and wigs, pendant lampholders are not permitted. Lamps are required to be provided with suitable open-end (to permit relamping) guards that are not easily removed. This makes it difficult to circumvent their intended purpose of preventing contact between the lamps and flammable material.

520-73. Switches Required. All lights and receptacles in dressing rooms shall be controlled by wall switches installed in the dressing rooms. Each switch controlling receptacles shall be provided with a pilot light to indicate when the receptacles are energized.

G. Grounding

520-81. Grounding. All metal raceways and metal-sheathed cables shall be grounded. The metal frames and enclosures of all equipment, including border lights and portable lighting fixtures, shall be grounded. Grounding, where used, shall be in accordance with Article 250.

ARTICLE 530 Motion Picture and Television Studios and Similar Locations

Contents

A. General

D. Viewing, Cutting, and Patching Tables

530-41. Lamps at Tables.

E. Cellulose Nitrate Film Storage Vaults

530-51. Lamps in Cellulose Nitrate Film Storage Vaults.

530-52. Motors and Other Equipment in Cellulose Nitrate Film Storage Vaults.

F. Substations

530-61. Substations.

530-62. Low-Voltage Switchboards.

530-63. Overcurrent Protection of DC Generators.

530-64. Working Space and Guarding.

530-65. Portable Substations.

530-66. Grounding at Substations.

A. General

530-1. **Scope.** The requirements of this article shall apply to television studios and motion picture studios using either film or electronic cameras, except as provided in Section 520-1, and exchanges, factories, laboratories, stages, or a portion of the building in which film or tape more than ⅞ inch (22 mm) in width is exposed, developed, printed, cut, edited, rewound, repaired, or stored.

(FPN): For methods of protecting against cellulose nitrate film hazards, see Storage and Handling of Cellulose Nitrate Motion Picture Film, NFPA 40-1988 (ANSI).

The requirements for motion picture studios and television studios are virtually the same and are intended to apply only to those locations presenting special hazards. Otherwise, the conditions are similar to theater stages; therefore, the applicable provisions of Article 520 should be observed, such as those for stages and dressing rooms.

The special hazards are temporary structures constructed of wood or other combustible material.

530-2. **Definitions.**

Portable Equipment: Equipment intended to be moved from one place to another.

Plugging Box: A dc device consisting of one or more 2-pole, 2-wire, nonpolarized, ungrounded receptacles intended to be used on dc circuits only.

AC Power Distribution Box (AC Plugging Box, Scatter Box): An ac distribution center or box that contains one or more grounded, polarized receptacles, that may contain overcurrent protection devices.

B. Stage or Set

530-11. **Permanent Wiring.** The permanent wiring shall be Type MC cable, Type MI cable, or in approved raceways.

Exception: Communications circuits, sound-recording and reproducing circuits, Class 2 and Class 3 remote-control or signaling circuits and power-limited fire protective signaling circuits shall be permitted to be wired in accordance with Articles 640, 725, 760, and 800.

530-12. **Portable Wiring.** The wiring for stage set lighting, stage effects, electric equipment used as stage properties, and other wiring not fixed as to location shall be done with approved flexible cords and cables. Splices or taps shall be permitted in flexible cords used to supply stage properties where such are made with approved devices and the circuit is protected at not more than 20 amperes. Such cables and cords shall not be fastened by staples or nailing.

530-13. **Stage Lighting and Effects Control.** Switches used for studio stage set lighting and effects (on the stages and lots and on location) shall be of the externally operable type. Where contactors are used as the disconnecting means for fuses, an individual externally operable switch, such as a tumbler switch, for the control of each contactor shall be located at a distance of not more than 6 feet (1.83 m) from the contactor, in addition to remote-control switches.

Exception: A single externally operable switch shall be permitted to simultaneously disconnect all the contactors on any one location board, where located at a distance of not more than 6 feet (1.83 m) from the location board.

530-14. **Plugging Boxes.** Each receptacle of dc plugging boxes shall be rated at not less than 30 amperes.

530-15. Enclosing and Guarding Live Parts.

(a) Live Parts. Live parts shall be enclosed or guarded to prevent accidental contact by persons and objects.

(b) Switches. All switches shall be of the externally operable type.

(c) Rheostats. Rheostats shall be placed in approved cases or cabinets that enclose all live parts, having only the operating handles exposed.

(d) Current-Carrying Parts. Current-carrying parts of bull-switches, location boards, spiders, and plugging boxes shall be so enclosed, guarded, or located that persons cannot accidentally come into contact with them or bring conductive material into contact with them.

530-16. Portable Lamps.
Portable lamps and work lights shall be equipped with flexible cords, composition or metal-sheathed porcelain sockets, and substantial guards.

Exception: Portable lamps used as properties in a motion picture set or television stage set, on a studio stage or lot, or on location.

530-17. Portable Arc Lamp Fixtures.

(a) Portable Carbon Arc Lamps. Portable carbon arc lamps shall be substantially constructed. The arc shall be provided with an enclosure designed to retain sparks and carbons and to prevent persons or materials from coming into contact with the arc or bare live parts. The enclosures shall be ventilated. All switches shall be of the externally-operable type.

(b) Portable Noncarbon Arc Electric-Discharge Lamp Fixtures. Portable noncarbon arc lamp fixtures, including enclosed arc lamp fixtures, and associated ballasts shall be listed. Interconnecting cord sets, and interconnecting cords and cables, shall be extra-hard usage type and listed.

530-18. Overcurrent Protection — Short-Time Rating.*

General. Automatic overcurrent protective devices (circuit breakers or fuses) for motion picture studio stage set lighting and the stage cables for such stage set lighting shall be as given in (a) through (f) below.

(FPN): Note: * Special consideration is given to motion picture studios and similar locations, because filming periods are of short duration of 20 minutes.

(a) Stage Cables. Stage cables for stage set lighting shall be protected by means of overcurrent devices set at not more than 400 percent of the ampacity given in applicable tables of Articles 310 and 400.

(b) Feeders. In buildings used primarily for motion picture production, the feeders from the substations to the stages shall be protected by means of overcurrent devices (generally located in the substation) having suitable ampere rating. The overcurrent devices shall be permitted to be multipole or single-pole gang-operated. No pole or overcurrent device shall be required in the neutral conductor. The overcurrent device setting for each feeder shall not exceed 400 percent of the ampacity of the feeder, as given in applicable tables of Article 310. Short-term ratings shall not be permitted when equipment is operated for periods in excess of 20 minutes.

An overcurrent device setting of up to 400 percent is permissible where the loads are of short duration. This section permits the use of short-term ratings where the equipment operates for 20 minutes or less. A longer period of operation may pose a fire hazard.

(c) Location Boards. Overcurrent protection (fuses or circuit breakers) shall be provided at the "location boards." Fuses in the "location boards" shall have an ampere rating of not over 400 percent of the ampacity of the cables between the "location boards" and the plugging boxes.

(d) Plugging Boxes. Cables and cords supplied through plugging boxes shall be of copper. Cables and cords smaller than No. 8 shall be attached to the plugging box by means of a plug containing two cartridge fuses or a 2-pole circuit breaker. The rating of the fuses or the setting of the circuit breaker shall not be over 400 percent of the rated ampacity of the cables or cords as given in applicable tables of Articles 310 and 400. Plugging boxes shall not be permitted on ac systems.

(e) AC Power Distribution Boxes. AC power distribution boxes used on sound stages and shooting locations shall contain connection receptacles of a polarized, grounding type.

(f) Lighting. Work lights, stand lamps, and fixtures, where connected to dc plugging boxes, shall be by means of plugs containing two cartridge fuses not larger than 20 amperes, or they shall be permitted to be connected to special outlets on circuits protected by fuses or circuit breakers rated at not over 20 amperes. Plug fuses shall not be used unless they are on the load side of the fuse or circuit breakers on the "location boards."

530-19. Sizing of Feeder Conductors for Television Studio Sets.

(a) **General.** It shall be permissible to apply the demand factors listed in Table 530-19(a) to that portion of the maximum possible connected load for studio or stage set lighting for all permanently installed feeders between substations and stages and to all permanently installed feeders between the main stage switchboard and stage distribution centers or location boards.

Table 530-19(a). Demand Factors for Stage Set Lighting

Portion of Stage Set Lighting Load to Which Demand Factor Applied (volt-amperes)	Feeder Demand Factor
First 50,000 or less at	100%
From 50,001 to 100,000 at	75%
From 100,001 to 200,000 at	60%
Remaining over 200,000 at	50%

(b) **Portable Feeders.** A demand factor of 50 percent of maximum possible connected load shall be permitted for all portable feeders.

530-20. Grounding.
Type MC cable, Type MI cable, metal raceways, and all noncurrent-carrying metal parts of appliances, devices, and equipment shall be grounded as specified in Article 250. This shall not apply to pendant and portable lamps, to stage lighting and stage sound equipment, nor to other portable and special stage equipment operating at not over 150 volts dc to ground.

530-21. Single-Pole Separable Connectors.
Where single-pole portable cable connectors are used, they shall be listed and of the locking type. The use of such connectors shall comply with at least one of the following conditions:

(1) Connection and disconnection of connectors are only possible where the supply connectors are interlocked to the source and it is not possible to connect or disconnect connectors when the supply is energized.

(2) Line connectors are of the listed sequential-interlocking type so that load connectors shall be connected in the following sequence:

    a. Equipment grounding conductor connection.

    b. Grounded circuit conductor connection, if provided.

    c. Ungrounded conductor connection, and that disconnection shall be in the reverse order.

(3) A caution notice shall be provided adjacent to the line connectors indicating that plug connection shall be in the following order:

    a. Equipment grounding conductor connectors.

    b. Grounded circuit conductor connectors, if provided.

    c. Ungrounded conductor connectors, and that disconnection shall be in the reverse order.

530-22. Branch Circuits.
A branch circuit of any size supplying one or more receptacles shall be permitted to supply stage set lighting loads.

C. Dressing Rooms

530-31. Dressing Rooms.
Fixed wiring in dressing rooms shall be installed in accordance with wiring methods covered in Chapter 3. Wiring for portable dressing rooms shall be approved.

D. Viewing, Cutting, and Patching Tables

530-41. Lamps at Tables.
Only composition or metal-sheathed, porcelain, keyless lampholders equipped with suitable means to guard lamps from physical damage and from film and film scrap shall be used at patching, viewing, and cutting tables.

E. Cellulose Nitrate Film Storage Vaults

530-51. Lamps in Cellulose Nitrate Film Storage Vaults.
Lamps in cellulose nitrate film storage vaults shall be installed in rigid fixtures of the glass enclosed and gasketed type. Lamps shall be controlled by a switch having a pole in each ungrounded conductor. This switch shall be located outside of the vault and provided with a pilot light to indicate whether the switch is on or off. This switch shall disconnect from all sources of supply all ungrounded conductors terminating in any outlet in the vault.

530-52. Motors and Other Equipment in Cellulose Nitrate Film Storage Vaults.
Except as permitted in Section 530-51, no receptacles, outlets, electric motors, heaters, portable lights, or other portable electric equipment shall be located in cellulose nitrate film storage vaults.

F. Substations

530-61. **Substations.** Wiring and equipment of over 600 volts, nominal, shall comply with Article 710.

530-62. **Low-Voltage Switchboards.** On 600 volts, nominal, or less, switchboards shall comply with Article 384.

530-63. **Overcurrent Protection of DC Generators.** Three-wire dc generators shall have protection consisting of overcurrent devices having an ampere rating or setting in accordance with the generator ampere rating. Single-pole or double-pole overcurrent devices shall be permitted, and no pole or overcurrent coil shall be required in the neutral lead (whether it is grounded or ungrounded).

530-64. **Working Space and Guarding.** Working space and guarding in permanent fixed substations shall comply with Sections 110-16 and 110-17.

(FPN): For guarding of live parts on motors and generators, see Sections 430-11 and 430-14.

Exception: Switchboards of not over 250 volts dc between conductors, where located in substations or switchboard rooms accessible to qualified persons only, shall not be required to be dead-front.

530-65. **Portable Substations.** Wiring and equipment in portable substations shall conform to the sections applying to installations in permanently fixed substations, but, due to the limited space available, the working spaces shall be permitted to be reduced, provided that the equipment shall be so arranged that the operator can work safely and so that other persons in the vicinity cannot accidentally come into contact with current-carrying parts or bring conducting objects into contact with them while they are energized.

530-66. **Grounding at Substations.** Noncurrent-carrying metal parts shall be grounded in accordance with Article 250.

Exception: Frames of dc circuit breakers installed on switchboards.

ARTICLE 540 Motion Picture Projectors

Contents

A. General

540-1. Scope.

B. Definitions

540-2. Professional Projector.
540-3. Nonprofessional Projector.

C. Equipment and Projectors of the Professional Type

540-10. Motion Picture Projection Room Required.
540-11. Location of Associated Electrical Equipment.
  (a) Motor Generator Sets, Transformers, Rectifiers, Rheostats, and Similar Equipment.
  (b) Switches, Overcurrent Devices, or Other Equipment.
  (c) Emergency Systems.
540-12. Work Space.
540-13. Conductor Size.
540-14. Conductors on Lamps and Hot Equipment.
540-15. Flexible Cords.
540-20. Approval.
540-21. Marking.

D. Nonprofessional Projectors

540-31. Motion Picture Projection Room Not Required.
540-32. Approval.

E. Sound Recording and Reproduction

540-50. Sound Recording and Reproduction.

A. General

540-1. **Scope.** The provisions of this article apply to motion picture projection rooms, motion picture projectors, and associated equipment of the professional and nonprofessional types using incandescent, carbon arc, xenon, or other light source equipment that develops hazardous gases, dust, or radiation.

(FPN): For further information, see Storage and Handling of Cellulose Nitrate Motion Picture Film, NFPA 40-1988 (ANSI).

The definitions of hazardous (classified) locations in Article 500 do not include a motion picture projection room as a hazardous (classified) location, even though some of the older types of film such as cellulose nitrate film, rarely used now, are highly flammable. In comparison, cellulose acetate film, called "safety film," a much safer film, is in wide use today. Since film is not volatile at ordinary temperatures and no flammable gases are present, the wiring installation is not required to be suitable for hazardous (classified) locations as defined in Article 500, but should be installed with special care to protect against the hazards of fire.

B. Definitions

540-2. **Professional Projector:** The professional projector is a type using 35-or 70-millimeter film that has a minimum width of 1⅜ inches (35 mm) and has on each edge 5.4 perforations per inch, or a type using carbon arc, xenon, or other light source equipment that develops hazardous gases, dust, or radiation.

540-3. **Nonprofessional Projector:** Nonprofessional projectors are those types other than described in Section 540-2.

C. Equipment and Projectors of the Professional Type

540-10. **Motion Picture Projection Room Required.** Every professional-type projector shall be located within a projection room. Every projection room shall be of permanent construction, approved for the type of building in which the projection room is located. All projection ports, spotlight ports, viewing ports, and similar openings shall be provided with glass or other approved material so as to completely close the opening. Such rooms shall not be considered as hazardous (classified) locations as defined in Article 500.

(FPN): For further information on protecting openings in projection rooms handling cellulose nitrate motion picture film, see Life Safety Code, NFPA 101-1991 (ANSI).

540-11. **Location of Associated Electrical Equipment.**

(a) Motor Generator Sets, Transformers, Rectifiers, Rheostats, and Similar Equipment. Motor generator sets, transformers, rectifiers, rheostats, and similar equipment for the supply or control of current to projection or spotlight equipment shall, if practicable, be located in a separate room. Where placed in the projection room, they shall be so located or guarded that arcs or sparks cannot come in contact with film, and motor generator sets shall have the commutator end or ends protected as provided in Section 520-48.

(b) Switches, Overcurrent Devices, or Other Equipment. Switches, overcurrent devices, or other equipment not normally required or used for projectors, sound reproduction, flood or other special effect lamps, or other equipment shall not be installed in projection rooms.

Exception No. 1: In projection rooms approved for use only with cellulose acetate (safety) film, the installation of appurtenant electrical equipment used in conjunction with the operation of the projection equipment and the control of lights, curtains, and audio equipment, etc., shall be permitted. In such projection rooms, a sign reading "Safety Film Only Permitted in This Room" shall be posted on the outside of each projection room door and within the projection room itself in a conspicuous location.

Exception No. 2: Remote-control switches for the control of auditorium lights or switches for the control of motors operating curtains and masking of the motion picture screen.

(c) Emergency Systems. Control of emergency systems shall comply with Article 700, Emergency Systems.

The plan of a projection room of a motion picture theater is illustrated in Figure 540-1. This plan shows one stereopticon or "effect machine" (L), two spot machines (S), and three motion picture projectors (P).

A dc arc lamp is the light source in each of the six machines. The dc supply is furnished by two motor generator sets that are usually installed in soundproof areas so as not to interfere with the sound-reproducing equipment and are controlled from the generator panel in the projection room or booth. Two 500 kcmil feeder cables are run from each generator to the dc panelboard.

A branch circuit consisting of two No. 2/0 cables runs from the dc panelboard to each projector (P) and to each spot machine (S). One of the two branch-circuit conductors runs directly to projector (P); the other passes through an auxiliary gutter to the bank of resistors in the rheostat room and then to the projector. The resistors are equipped with short-circuiting switches so that the total resistance in series with each arc may be preset to a desired value.

Figure 540-1. A typical layout of a projection room including associated generator equipment. Modern projectors contain rectifiers as an integral part of their equipment, thereby eliminating generators and other associated equipment.

Since the stereopticon or effect machine (L) contains two arc lamps, two circuits with No. 1 conductors are routed to this machine.

Section 540-13 requires that the conductors supplying outlets for arc and xenon projectors of the professional type are not to be smaller than No. 8 and are required to be of sufficient size for the projector employed. Therefore, in each case, the maximum current drawn by the lamps should be determined. In this example, when the arc lamps are adjusted for a large picture, the arc in each projector draws nearly 150 amperes. Four outlets, in addition to the main outlet for supplying the arc, are located at each projector for the following auxiliary circuits:

(1) Foot switches operating the shutters in front of the lenses for changing from one projector to another are supplied by Outlets F.

(2) Outlets G are for the No. 8 equipment grounding conductor, which is connected to the projector frames and to a metal water pipe.

(3) Outlets C supply a small incandescent lamp inside the lamphouse and a lamp illuminating the turntable.

(4) Motors used to operate the projectors are supplied from Outlets M.

Two exhaust fans and two duct systems, one exhausting from the ceiling of the projection room and one connected to the arc-lamp housing of each machine, provide ventilation.

540-12. **Work Space.** Each motion picture projector, floodlight, spotlight, or similar equipment shall have clear working space not less than 30 inches (762 mm) wide on each side and at the rear thereof.

Exception: One such space shall be permitted between adjacent pieces of equipment.

540-13. **Conductor Size.** Conductors supplying outlets for arc and xenon projectors of the professional type shall not be smaller than No. 8 and shall be of sufficient size for the projector employed. Conductors for incandescent-type projectors shall conform to normal wiring standards as provided in Section 210-24.

540-14. Conductors on Lamps and Hot Equipment. Insulated conductors having a rated operating temperature of not less than 200°C (392°F) shall be used on all lamps or other equipment where the ambient temperature at the conductors as installed will exceed 50°C (122°F).

540-15. Flexible Cords. Cords approved for hard usage as provided in Table 400-4 shall be used on portable equipment.

540-20. Approval. Projectors and enclosures for arc, xenon and incandescent lamps and rectifiers, transformers, rheostats, and similar equipment shall be listed.

540-21. Marking. Projectors and other equipment shall be marked with the maker's name or trademark and with the voltage and current for which they are designed in accordance with Section 110-21.

D. Nonprofessional Projectors

540-31. Motion Picture Projection Room Not Required. Projectors of the nonprofessional or miniature type, where employing cellulose acetate (safety) film, shall be permitted to be operated without a projection room.

540-32. Approval. Projection equipment shall be listed.

E. Sound Recording and Reproduction

540-50. Sound Recording and Reproduction. Sound-recording and reproduction equipment shall be installed as provided in Article 640.

ARTICLE 545   Manufactured Building

Contents

A. General

A. General

545-1. Scope. This article covers requirements for a manufactured building and building components as herein defined.

545-2. Other Articles. Wherever the requirements of other articles of this Code and Article 545 differ, the requirements of Article 545 shall apply.

545-3. Definitions.

Manufactured Building: "Manufactured Building" means any building that is of closed construction and is made or assembled in manufacturing facilities on or off the building site for installation, or assembly and installation on the building site, other than mobile homes or recreational vehicles.

Building Component: "Building Component" means any subsystem, subassembly, or other system designed for use in or integral with or as part of a structure, which can include structural, electrical, mechanical, plumbing, and fire protection systems, and other systems affecting health and safety.

Building System: "Building System" means plans, specifications, and documentation for a system of manufactured building or for a type or a system of building components, which can include structural, electrical, mechanical, plumbing, and fire protection systems, and other systems affecting health and safety, and including such variations thereof as are specifically permitted by regulation, and which variations are submitted as part of the building system or amendment thereto.

Closed Construction: "Closed Construction" means any building, building component, assembly, or system manufactured in such a manner that all concealed parts of processes of manufacture cannot be inspected before installation at the building site without disassembly, damage, or destruction.

545-4. **Wiring Methods.**

(a) **Methods Permitted.** All raceway and cable wiring methods included in this Code and such other wiring systems specifically intended and listed for use in manufactured buildings shall be permitted with listed fittings and with fittings listed and identified for manufactured buildings.

(b) **Securing Cables.** In closed construction, cables shall be permitted to be secured only at cabinets, boxes, or fittings where No. 10 or smaller conductors are used and protection against physical damage is provided as required by Section 300-4.

545-5. **Service-Entrance Conductors.** Service-entrance conductors shall meet the requirements of Article 230. Provisions shall be made to route the service-entrance conductors from the service equipment to the point of attachment of the service.

(FPN): See Section 310-10 for temperature limitation of conductors.

545-6. **Installation of Service-Entrance Conductors.** Service-entrance conductors shall be installed after erection at the building site.

Exception: Where point of attachment is known prior to manufacture.

545-7. **Service Equipment Location.** Service equipment shall be installed in accordance with Section 230-70(a).

545-8. **Protection of Conductors and Equipment.** Protection shall be provided for exposed conductors and equipment during processes of manufacturing, packaging, in transit, and erection at the building site.

545-9. **Boxes.**

(a) **Other Dimensions.** Boxes of dimensions other than those required in Table 370-16(a) shall be permitted to be installed when tested, identified, and listed to applicable standards.

(b) **Not Over 100 Cubic Inches.** Any box not over 100 cubic inches in size, intended for mounting in closed construction, shall

be affixed with anchors or clamps so as to provide a rigid and secure installation.

545-10. **Receptacle or Switch with Integral Enclosure.** A receptacle or switch with integral enclosure and mounting means, when tested, identified, and listed to applicable standards, shall be permitted to be installed.

See Figure 545-1 and the commentary following Section 300-15(b), Exception No. 5.

Figure 545-1. A special type of tool that is used to connect nonmetallic-sheathed cable to an approved boxless switch or receptacle. (Amp Inc.)

545-11. **Bonding and Grounding.** Prewired panels and building components shall provide for the bonding, or bonding and grounding, of all exposed metals likely to become energized, in accordance with Article 250, Parts E, F, and G.

545-12. **Grounding Electrode Conductor.** The grounding electrode conductor shall meet the requirements of Article 250, Part J. Provisions shall be made to route the grounding electrode conductor from the service equipment to the point of attachment to the grounding electrode.

545-13. **Component Interconnections.** Fittings and connectors that are intended to be concealed at the time of on-site assembly, when tested, identified, and listed to applicable standards, shall be permitted for on-site interconnection of modules or other building components. Such fittings and connectors shall be equal to the wiring method employed in insulation, temperature rise, and fault-current withstand and shall be capable of enduring the vibration and minor relative motions occurring in the components of manufactured building.

Structural components or modules are usually constructed in manufacturing facilities and then transported over the road to a building site for complete assembly of a structure such as a dwelling unit, a motel, or an office building. At the on-site location, approved wiring methods are employed to interconnect two or more modules. Figures 545-2 and 545-3 show types of nonmetallic-sheathed cable connectors permitted for such interconnections.

Figure 545-3. *The nonmetallic-sheathed cable connector shown in Figure 545-2 after being joined together. (Amp Inc.)*

Figure 545-2. *A type of nonmetallic-sheathed cable connector used for interconnecting modules in a manufacturing building. The parts are shown before mating together. (Amp Inc.)*

ARTICLE 547   Agricultural Buildings

Contents

547-1. **Scope.** The provisions of this article shall apply to the following agricultural buildings or that part of a building or adjacent area as specified in (a) and (b) below.

(a) Excessive Dust and Dust with Water. Agricultural buildings where excessive dust and dust with water may accumulate, including all areas of poultry, livestock, and fish confinement systems, where litter dust, or feed dust, including mineral feed particles, may accumulate, and adjacent areas of similar or like nature.

(b) Corrosive Atmosphere. Agricultural buildings where a corrosive atmosphere exists. Such buildings include areas where (1) poultry and animal excrement may cause corrosive vapors; (2) corrosive particles may combine with water; (3) the area is damp and wet by reason of periodic washing for cleaning and sanitizing with water and cleansing agents; (4) similar conditions exist.

The revised Section 547-1 in the 1993 *Code* greatly increases the scope of the article.

547-2. **Other Articles.** For agricultural buildings not having conditions as specified in Section 547-1, the electrical installations shall be made in accordance with the applicable articles in this Code.

547-3. **Surface Temperatures.** Electrical equipment or devices installed in accordance with the provisions of this article shall be installed in a manner such that they will function at full rating without developing surface temperatures in excess of the specified normal safe operating range of the equipment or device.

547-4. **Wiring Methods.** In agricultural buildings as described in Sections 547-1(a) and (b), Types UF, NMC, SNM, copper SE, or other cables or raceways suitable for the location, with approved termination fittings, shall be the wiring methods employed. Article 320 and Article 502 wiring methods shall be permitted for Section 547-1(a). Article 347 and Article 351, Part B wiring methods shall be permitted. All cables shall be secured within 8 inches (203 mm) of each cabinet, box, or fitting. The ¼-inch (6.35-mm) air space required for nonmetallic boxes, fittings, conduit, and cables in Section 300-6(c) shall not be required in buildings covered by this article.

Where cables are installed in agricultural buildings, they are required to be secured within 8 inches of cabinets, boxes, or fittings. This distance is less than that required for cables in other types of occupancies. The requirement for a ¼-inch air space in Section 300-6(c) is judged unnecessary in agricultural buildings provided that nonmetallic

wiring methods are used. Locating the wiring methods directly on the surface of the interior building surface allows a sealant to be placed along the wiring method to facilitate cleaning. Also, the spacing results in a potential mechanical damage problem on farms. See also the Exception to Section 300-6(c).

(FPN): See Sections 300-7 and 347-9 for installation of raceway systems exposed to widely different temperatures.

(a) Boxes, Fittings, and Wiring Devices. All boxes and fittings shall comply with Section 547-5.

(b) Flexible Connections. Where necessary to employ flexible connections, dusttight flexible connectors, liquidtight flexible conduit, or flexible cord listed and identified for hard usage shall be used. All shall be used with listed and identified fittings.

547-5. **Switches, Circuit Breakers, Controllers, and Fuses.** Switches, circuit breakers, controllers, and fuses, including pushbuttons, relays, and similar devices, used in buildings described in Sections 547-1(a) and (b), shall be provided with enclosures as specified in (a) and (b) below.

(a) Excessive Dust and Dust with Water. Buildings described in Section 547-1(a) shall utilize dustproof and weatherproof enclosures.

(b) Corrosive Atmosphere. Buildings described in Section 547-1(b) shall utilize watertight, corrosion-resistant enclosures.

(FPN): Cast aluminum and magnetic steels will corrode in agricultural environments.

547-6. **Motors.** Motors and other rotating electrical machinery shall be totally enclosed or so designed as to minimize the entrance of dust, moisture, or corrosive particles.

547-7. **Lighting Fixtures.** Lighting fixtures installed in agricultural buildings described in Section 547-1 shall comply with the following:

(a) Minimize the Entrance of Dust. Lighting fixtures shall be installed to minimize the entrance of dust, foreign matter, moisture, and corrosive material.

(b) Exposed to Physical Damage. Any lighting fixture that may be exposed to physical damage shall be protected by a suitable guard.

(c) **Exposed to Water.** A fixture that may be exposed to water from condensation, building cleansing water, or solution shall be watertight.

547-8. Grounding, Bonding, and Equipotential Plane.

(a) **Grounding and Bonding.** Grounding and bonding shall comply with Article 250.

(FPN):   See Section 250-21 for objectionable current over grounding conductors.

Neutral-to-earth potentials can be increased [see commentary following Sections 547-8(b) and 547-8(c)] where services (to more than one farm, for example) are supplied from a common transformer on the utility distribution system. Where neutral-to-earth potentials are a problem, separation of the service supplying the building where the problem exists from other services may be part of the solution. The utility may also provide a primary-to-secondary neutral isolator at or near its power transformer to isolate the farm services from those supplying other utilities customers.

Exception No. 1: The main bonding jumper shall not be required at the distribution panelboard in or on buildings housing livestock or poultry where all the following conditions are met:

a. All buildings and premises wiring are under the same ownership.

b. An equipment grounding conductor is run with the supply conductors and is of the same size as the largest supply conductor, if of the same material, or is adjusted in size in accordance with the equivalent size columns of Table 250-95 if of different materials.

c. Service disconnecting means is provided at the distribution point for supply to those buildings.

d. The equipment grounding conductor is bonded to the grounded circuit conductor at the service equipment or the source of a separately derived system.

e. A grounding electrode is provided and connected to the equipment grounding conductor in the distribution panelboard.

Exception No. 2: A metal interior water piping system or other interior metal or metallic piping system of an agricultural building to which electrical equipment requiring grounding is not attached or in electrical contact shall be permitted to be bonded to the service equipment enclosure, the grounded conductor at the service, or to the equipment grounding terminal bar in a panelboard that serves the building by means of an impedance device listed for the purpose, provided that all the following conditions are complied with:

a. The device shall have the short-circuit withstand rating identified where other than the minimum of 10,000 amperes.

b. The bonding conductor shall be an insulated copper conductor not smaller than No. 8 and shall be installed without splice other than where connected to the impedance device.

c. The bonding conductor shall be installed in a raceway suitable for the conditions.

d. The bonding conductor shall be connected to the metal piping system or other metal by means of a listed pressure connector suitable for the conditions or by exothermic welding.

Interactions of primary and secondary neutral currents can impose low levels of neutral-to-earth voltage on the grounded equipment in livestock buildings that may result in loss of production. See commentary following Section 547-8(b). This exception permits a listed high-impedance device between interior metal piping to which electrical equipment is not attached or in electrical contact and the grounding terminal in the panelboard or service. Such devices have been shown to help in reducing low-level voltages on exposed metal parts that can be contacted by animals (dairy cows, for example). If electrical equipment requiring grounding is attached to this piping (an electric water heater, for example), the exception is not applicable.

(b) **Concrete Embedded Elements.** Wire mesh or other conductive elements where provided in the concrete floor of animal confinement areas to provide an equipotential plane shall be bonded to the building grounding electrode system. The bonding conductor shall be copper, insulated, covered or bare, and not smaller than No. 8. The means of bonding to wire mesh or conductive elements shall be by pressure connectors or clamps of brass, copper, copper alloy, or an equally substantial approved means.

Equipotential Plane: An equipotential plane is an area where a wire mesh or other conductive elements are embedded in concrete, bonded to all adjacent conductive equipment, structures, or surfaces, and connected to the electrical grounding system to prevent a difference in voltage from developing within the plane.

(FPN):   If a wire mesh or other conductive grid is embedded in a concrete floor or platform, and, if this grid is bonded to the electrical system grounding bus, livestock making contact between the concrete floor or platform and the equipment or metal structure will be less likely to be exposed to a level of voltage that may alter animal behavior or productivity.

The requirements in the exceptions to Section 547-8(a) and in Section 547-8(b) address the so-called "stray voltage" problem resulting from the neutral-to-earth potentials common in electrical systems. In most occupancies this neutral-to-earth potential does not result in a problem because, under normal conditions, it involves only a fraction of a volt up to just a few volts, steady-state. However, livestock (dairy cows in particular) are very sensitive to voltage differences, and a potential difference of only ½ volt or so may affect their behavior and milk production. Dairy cows may be exposed to these neutral-to-earth potentials where they are standing on wet concrete and come into contact with a metal water pipe or feeder trough, for example. The concrete is at approximately earth potential, and the metal trough may be connected to the building service neutral by the equipment grounding conductor for the water-pump motor or feeder motor.

The neutral-to-earth potential on any system is a function of the neutral circuit impedances, the ground resistances of the many grounding electrodes in the typical system where transformer primary and secondary neutral conductors are connected together, the current in the primary and secondary neutral conductors, and other variables. The neutral-to-earth potential usually increases momentarily when 120-volt motors start because of the larger current, and therefore there is a larger voltage drop in the branch-circuit and feeder neutral conductors.

Exception No. 1 to Section 547-8(a) maintains the low-impedance path in the grounding conductor circuit needed to rapidly clear ground faults. However, since it permits separation of the grounded (neutral) and equipment grounding conductors at the livestock building disconnect, the voltage drop on the feeder neutral does not appear as a voltage differential on grounded equipment in the building. See Figure 547-1. See also commentary following Exception No. 2 to Section 547-8(a).

Where the equipment grounding conductor with the supply (feeder) conductors to the livestock or poultry building is run underground, it is required to be a copper conductor that is insulated or covered. See Sections 250-24 and 547-7(c).

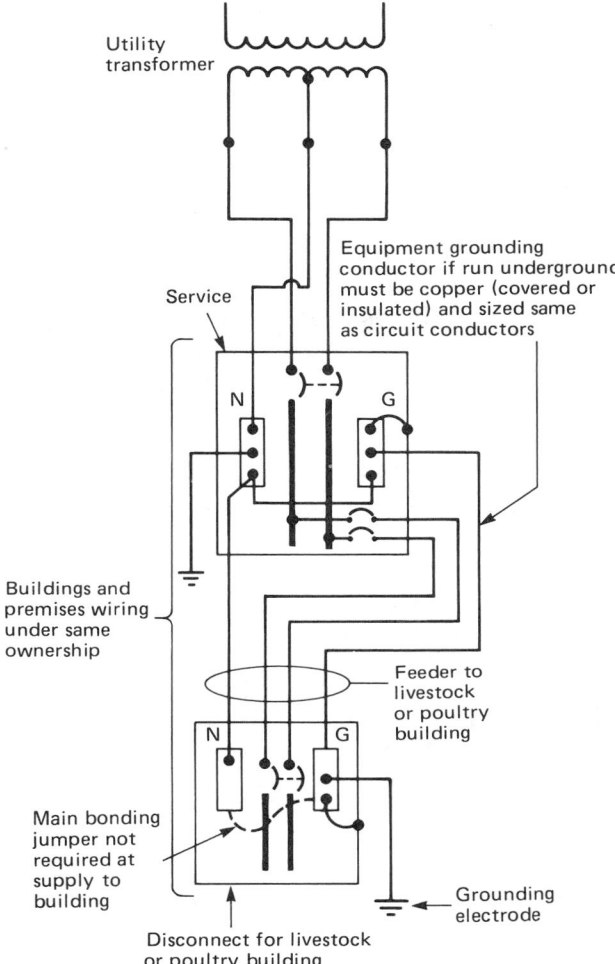

Figure 547-1. A main bonding jumper is not required at livestock or poultry buildings in accordance with Section 547-8(a), Exception No. 1 if the provisions of this section are met. Overcurrent devices for other circuits are not shown in order to simplify the drawing. Note that there may be distribution points (panelboards) between the service and the livestock or poultry building.

(c) **Separate Equipment Grounding Conductor.** In agricultural buildings as described in Sections 547-1(a) and (b), noncurrent-carrying metal parts of equipment, raceways, and other enclosures, where required to be grounded, shall be grounded by a copper equipment grounding conductor installed between the equipment and the building disconnecting means. If installed underground, the equipment grounding conductor shall be insulated or covered.

The intent of Section 547-8(c) is to improve the longevity of equipment grounding conductors in the highly corrosive locations typical of many farm buildings.

(FPN): Grounding electrode system resistances lower than required by Article 250, Part H, may reduce potential differences in livestock facilities.

The minimum system grounding requirements achieved by the grounding electrode systems covered in Article 250, Part H are adequate for electrical safety, but may not be adequate where neutral-to-earth potentials are a problem. See commentary following Section 547-8(b). Ground resistances on the order of 0.5 to 4 ohms may be needed.

(d) Water Pumps and Metal Well Casings. The frame of the motor of any water pump shall be grounded as required for Section 430-142. Where a submersible pump is used in metal well casing, the well casing shall be bonded to the pump circuit equipment grounding conductor, or to the equipment grounding bus of the panelboard supplying the submersible pump.

This requirement was new in the 1990 *NEC*. It is intended to help reduce the stray voltage problem discussed in the commentary following Section 547-8(b).

ARTICLE 550 Mobile Homes and Mobile Home Parks

Contents

A. General

550-11. Grounding.
  (a) Insulated Neutral.
  (b) Equipment Grounding Means.
  (c) Bonding of Noncurrent-Carrying Metal Parts.
550-12. Testing.
  (a) Dielectric Strength Test.
  (b) Continuity and Operational Tests and Polarity Checks.
550-13. Calculations.
  (a) Lighting and Small Appliance Load.
  (b) Total Load for Determining Power Supply.
  (c) Optional Method of Calculation for Lighting and Appliance Load.
550-14. Interconnection of Multiple Section Mobile Home Units.
  (a) Fixed-type Wiring.
  (b) Disconnecting Means.
550-15. Outdoor Outlets, Fixtures, Air-Cooling Equipment, Etc.
  (a) Listed for Outdoor Use.
  (b) Outside Heating Equipment, Air-Conditioning Equipment, or Both.

C. Services and Feeders

550-21. Distribution System.
550-22. Minimum Allowable Demand Factors.
550-23. Mobile Home Service Equipment.
  (a) Service Equipment.
  (b) Rating.
  (c) Additional Outside Electrical Equipment.
  (d) Additional Receptacles.
  (e) Mounting Height.
  (f) Grounded.
  (g) Marking.
550-24. Feeder.
  (a) Feeder Conductors.
  (b) Adequate Feeder Capacity.

A. General

550-1. **Scope.** The provisions of this article cover the electrical conductors and equipment installed within or on mobile homes, the conductors that connect mobile homes to a supply of electricity, and the installation of electrical wiring, fixtures, equipment, and appurtenances related to electrical installations within a mobile home park up to the mobile home service-entrance conductors or, if none, the mobile home service equipment.

The Federal Mobile Home Construction and Safety Standard, issued by the Federal Housing and Urban Development Administration (HUD), has incorporated many of the provisions of Article 550 of the *NEC*. The federal standard contains the requirements for electrical systems, conductors, and equipment installed within or on mobile homes and the conductors that connect mobile homes to a supply of electricity. Mobile homes are defined as "manufactured homes" in the HUD Regulations.

The regulations pertaining to electrical systems are located in the Code of Federal Regulations, Title 24, Sections 3280.801 through 3280.816. It is required that new mobile homes comply with the federal standard. In some cases, HUD has delegated the enforcement of this standard to state and private inspection agencies and to qualified testing laboratories.

See Article 545 for the requirements for manufactured buildings.

550-2. **Definitions.**

Appliance, Fixed: An appliance that is fastened or otherwise secured at a specific location.

Appliance, Portable: An appliance that is actually moved or can easily be moved from one place to another in normal use.

(FPN): For the purpose of this article, the following major appliances, other than built-in, are considered portable if cord-connected: refrigerators, gas range equipment, clothes washers, dishwashers without booster heaters, or other similar appliances.

Appliance, Stationary: An appliance that is not easily moved from one place to another in normal use.

Distribution Panelboard: See definition of panelboard in Article 100.

Feeder Assembly: The overhead or under-chassis feeder conductors, including the grounding conductor, together with the necessary fittings and equipment or a power-supply cord listed for mobile home use, designed for the purpose of delivering energy from the source of electrical supply to the distribution panelboard within the mobile home.

Laundry Area: An area containing or designed to contain a laundry tray, clothes washer, or a clothes dryer.

Mobile Home: A factory-assembled structure or structures transportable in one or more sections, that is built on a permanent chassis and designed to be used as a dwelling without a permanent foundation where connected to the required utilities, and includes the plumbing, heating, air-conditioning, and electric systems contained therein.

Unless otherwise indicated, the term "mobile home" includes manufactured homes that are similar structure(s) designed to be used with a permanent foundation.

(FPN): The phrase "with a permanent foundation" indicates that the home is permanently attached to a permanent foundation acceptable to the authority having jurisdiction, such that moving the structure is not likely to occur.

The definition of "mobile home" was changed in the 1993 *Code*. Manufactured *homes* (not to be confused with manufactured *buildings* covered in Article 545) are now covered by Article 550.

It is intended that a mobile home (or manufactured home) constructed under the requirements of Article 550 (or under the HUD regulations) be installed in accordance with the requirements of Article 550, including the requirements of Part C, even though the mobile home (manufactured home) may be installed on a permanent foundation.

Section 550-23 of Part C, which prohibits the service equipment from being mounted on the mobile home, has an exception permitting the service equipment to be installed in or on a manufactured home under the specified conditions. Also Section 550-5(a) concerning feeders includes new Exception No. 2 for manufactured homes.

Mobile Home Accessory Building or Structure: Any awning, cabana, ramada, storage cabinet, carport, fence, windbreak, or porch established for the use of the occupant of the mobile home upon a mobile home lot.

Mobile Home Lot: A designated portion of a mobile home park designed for the accommodation of one mobile home and its accessory buildings or structures for the exclusive use of its occupants.

Mobile Home Park: A contiguous parcel of land that is used for the accommodation of occupied mobile homes.

Mobile Home Service Equipment: The equipment containing the disconnecting means, overcurrent protective devices, and receptacles or other means for connecting a mobile home feeder assembly.

Park Electrical Wiring Systems: All of the electrical wiring, fixtures, equipment, and appurtenances related to electrical installations within a mobile home park, including the mobile home service equipment.

550-3. **Other Articles.** Wherever the requirements of other articles of this Code and Article 550 differ, the requirements of Article 550 shall apply.

550-4. **General Requirements.**

(a) **Mobile Home Not Intended as a Dwelling Unit.** A mobile home not intended as a dwelling unit, as for example equipped for sleeping purposes only, contractor's on-site offices, construction job dormitories, mobile studio dressing rooms, banks, clinics, mobile stores, or intended for the display or demonstration of merchandise or machinery, shall not be required to meet the provisions of this article pertaining to the number or capacity of circuits required. It shall, however, meet all other applicable requirements of this article if provided with an electrical installation intended to be energized from a 120-volt or 120/240-volt ac power supply system. Where different voltage is required by either design or available power supply system, adjustment shall be made in accordance with other articles and sections for the voltage used.

(b) **In Other than Mobile Home Parks.** Mobile homes installed in other than mobile home parks shall comply with the provisions of this article.

(c) **Connection to Wiring System.** The provisions of this article apply to mobile homes intended for connection to a wiring system rated 120/240 volts, nominal, 3-wire ac, with grounded neutral.

(d) **Listed or Labeled.** All electrical materials, devices, appliances, fittings, and other equipment shall be listed or labeled by a qualified testing agency and shall be connected in an approved manner when installed.

B. Mobile Homes

550-5. **Power Supply.**

(a) **Feeder.** The power supply to the mobile home shall be a feeder assembly consisting of not more than one listed

50-ampere mobile home power-supply cord with integral molded cap, or a permanently installed feeder.

Exception No. 1: A mobile home that is factory-equipped with gas or oil-fired central heating equipment and cooking appliances shall be permitted to be provided with a listed mobile home power-supply cord rated 40 amperes.

Exception No. 2: Manufactured homes constructed in accordance with Section 550-23(a), Exception No. 2.

Exception No. 2 of Section 550-23(a) permits the service equipment to be installed in or on a manufactured home provided it is installed by the manufacturer. Power supply cords would not be necessary for such installations.

(b) Power-Supply Cord. If the mobile home has a power-supply cord, it shall be permanently attached to the distribution panelboard or to a junction box permanently connected to the distribution panelboard, with the free end terminating in an attachment plug cap.

Cords with adapters and pigtail ends, extension cords, and similar items shall not be attached to, or shipped with, a mobile home.

A suitable clamp or the equivalent shall be provided at the distribution panelboard knockout to afford strain relief for the cord to prevent strain from being transmitted to the terminals when the power-supply cord is handled in its intended manner.

The cord shall be a listed type with four conductors, one of which shall be identified by a continuous green color or a continuous green color with one or more yellow stripes for use as the grounding conductor.

(c) Attachment Plug Cap. The attachment plug cap shall be a 3-pole, 4-wire, grounding type, rated 50 amperes, 125/250 volts with a configuration as shown in Figure 550-5(c) and intended for use with the 50-ampere, 125/250 receptacle configuration shown in Figure 550-5(c). It shall be molded of butyl rubber, neoprene, or other materials that have been found suitable for the purpose and shall be molded to the flexible cord so that it adheres tightly to the cord at the point where the cord enters the attachment plug cap. If a right-angle cap is used, the configuration shall be so oriented that the grounding member is farthest from the cord.

(FPN): Complete details of the 50-ampere plug and receptacle shown in Figure 550-5(c) can be found in ANSI Standard Dimensions of Caps, Plugs and Receptacles, C73.17-1972.

Receptacle   Cap

125/250-volt, 50-amp,
3-pole, 4-wire, grounding type

Figure 550-5(c). 50-ampere, 125/250-Volt Receptacle and Attachment-plug-cap Configurations, 3-pole, 4-wire, Grounding-types, Used for Mobile Homes Supply Cords and Mobile Home Parks.

(d) Overall Length of a Power-Supply Cord. The overall length of a power-supply cord, measured from the end of the cord, including bared leads, to the face of the attachment plug cap shall not be less than 21 feet (6.4 m) and shall not exceed 36½ feet (11.13 m). The length of the cord from the face of the attachment plug cap to the point where the cord enters the mobile home shall not be less than 20 feet (6.1 m).

(e) Marking. The power-supply cord shall bear the following marking: "For use with mobile homes — 40 amperes" or "For use with mobile homes — 50 amperes."

(f) Point of Entrance. The point of entrance of the feeder assembly to the mobile home shall be in the exterior wall, floor, or roof.

(FPN No. 1): For location of distribution panelboard, see Section 550-6(a).

(FPN No. 2): For location of attachment of feeder assembly, see Section 550-23(e).

(g) Protected. Where the cord passes through walls or floors, it shall be protected by means of conduits and bushings or equivalent. The cord shall be permitted to be installed within the mobile home walls, provided a continuous raceway having a maximum size of 1¼ inches (31.8 mm) is installed from the branch-circuit panelboard to the underside of the mobile home floor.

(h) Protection Against Corrosion and Mechanical Damage. Permanent provisions shall be made for the protection of the attachment plug cap of the power-supply cord and any connector cord assembly or receptacle against corrosion and mechanical damage if such devices are in an exterior location while the mobile home is in transit.

(i) Mast Weatherhead or Raceway. Where the calculated load exceeds 50 amperes or where a permanent feeder is used, the supply shall be by means of:

(1) One mast weatherhead installation, installed in accordance with Article 230, containing four continuous, insulated, color-coded feeder conductors, one of which shall be an equipment grounding conductor; or

(2) A metal raceway or rigid nonmetallic conduit from the disconnecting means in the mobile home to the underside of the mobile home, with provisions for the attachment to a suitable junction box or fitting to the raceway on the underside of the mobile home (with or without conductors as in Section 550-5(i)(1)).

In some localities, mobile homes are permanently connected, as permitted in Sections 550-5(i) and 550-24. In this regard, local requirements must be checked for the approved method of installing overhead and underground feeder assemblies.

A raceway is required from the distribution panelboard in the mobile home to the underside of the mobile home. Whether the feeder conductors in this raceway are pulled in by the mobile home manufacturer or by installers in the field is optional. Regardless of who installs the conductors, they should comprise four continuous, insulated, color-coded conductors, as indicated in Sections 550-5(i)(1) and 550-24.

550-6. **Disconnecting Means and Branch-Circuit Protective Equipment.** The branch-circuit equipment shall be permitted to be combined with the disconnecting means as a single assembly. Such a combination shall be permitted to be designated as a distribution panelboard. If a fused distribution panelboard is used, the maximum fuse size for the mains shall be plainly marked, with lettering at least $\frac{1}{4}$ inch (6.4 mm) high and visible when fuses are changed.

Where plug fuses and fuseholders are used, they shall be tamper-resistant Type S, enclosed in dead-front fuse panelboards. Electrical distribution panelboards containing circuit breakers shall also be dead-front type.

(FPN): See Section 110-22 concerning identification of each disconnecting means and each service, feeder, or branch circuit at the point where it originated and the type marking needed.

(a) Disconnecting Means. A single disconnecting means shall be provided in each mobile home consisting of a circuit breaker, or a switch and fuses and its accessories installed in a readily accessible location near the point of entrance of the supply cord or conductors into the mobile home. The main circuit breakers or fuses shall be plainly marked "Main." This equipment shall contain a solderless type of grounding connector or bar for the purposes of grounding, with sufficient terminals for all grounding conductors. The neutral bar termination of the grounded circuit conductors shall be insulated in accordance with Section 550-11(a). The disconnecting equipment shall have a rating suitable for the connected load. The distribution equipment, either circuit breaker or fused type, shall be located a minimum of 24 inches (610 mm) from the bottom of such equipment to the floor level of the mobile home.

(FPN): See Section 550-15(b) for information on disconnecting means for branch circuits designed to energize heating or air-conditioning equipment, or both, located outside the mobile home, other than room air conditioners.

A distribution panelboard shall be rated not less than 50 amperes and employ a 2-pole circuit breaker rated 40 amperes for a 40-ampere supply cord, or 50 amperes for a 50-ampere supply cord. A distribution panelboard employing a disconnect switch and fuses shall be rated 60 amperes and shall employ a single 2-pole, 60-ampere fuseholder with 40- or 50-ampere main fuses for 40- or 50-ampere supply cords, respectively. The outside of the distribution panelboard shall be plainly marked with the fuse size.

The distribution panelboard shall be located in an accessible location but shall not be located in a bathroom or a clothes closet. A clear working space at least 30 inches (762 mm) wide and 30 inches (762 mm) in front of the distribution panelboard shall be provided. This space shall extend from floor to the top of the distribution panelboard.

(b) Branch-Circuit Protective Equipment. Branch-circuit distribution equipment shall be installed in each mobile home and shall include overcurrent protection for each branch circuit consisting of either circuit breakers or fuses.

The branch-circuit overcurrent devices shall be rated (1) not more than the circuit conductors; and (2) not more than 150 percent of the rating of a single appliance rated 13.3 amperes or more that is supplied by an individual branch circuit; but (3) not more than the overcurrent protection size and of the type marked on the air conditioner or other motor-operated appliance.

A 15-ampere multiple receptacle shall be permitted where connected to a 20-ampere laundry circuit.

(c) Two-Pole Circuit Breakers. Where circuit breakers are provided for branch-circuit protection, 240-volt circuits shall be protected by a 2-pole common or companion trip, or handle-tied paired circuit breakers.

(d) Electrical Nameplates. A metal nameplate on the outside adjacent to the feeder assembly entrance shall read: "This Connection for 120/240-Volt, 3-Pole, 4-Wire, 60 Hertz, . . . Ampere Supply." The correct ampere rating shall be marked in the blank space.

550-7. Branch Circuits. The number of branch circuits required shall be determined in accordance with (a) through (c) below.

(a) Lighting. Based on 3 volt-amperes per square foot 32.26 VA/sq m) times outside dimensions of the mobile home (coupler excluded) divided by 120 volts to determine the number of 15- or 20-ampere lighting area circuits, e.g.,

$$\frac{3 \times \text{Length} \times \text{Width}}{120 \times 15 \text{ (or 20)}} = \text{No. of 15- (or 20-) ampere circuits}$$

The lighting circuits shall be permitted to serve built-in gas ovens with electric service only for lights, clocks or timers, or listed cord-connected garbage disposal units.

(b) Small Appliances. Small appliance branch circuits shall be installed in accordance with Section 210-52(b).

(c) General Appliances. (Including furnace, water heater, range, and central or room air conditioner, etc.) There shall be one or more circuits of adequate rating in accordance with the following:

(1) Ampere rating of fixed appliances not over 50 percent of circuit rating if lighting outlets (receptacles, other than kitchen, dining area, and laundry, considered as lighting outlets) are on the same circuit;

(2) For fixed appliances on a circuit without lighting outlets, the sum of rated amperes shall not exceed the branch-circuit rating. Motor loads or other continuous duty loads shall not exceed 80 percent of the branch-circuit rating;

(3) The rating of a single cord- and plug-connected appliance on a circuit having no other outlets shall not exceed 80 percent of the circuit rating;

(4) The rating of a range branch circuit shall be based on the range demand as specified for ranges in Section 550-13(b)(5).

(FPN No. 1): For the laundry branch circuit, see Section 220-4(c).

(FPN No. 2): For central air conditioning, see Article 440.

550-8. Receptacle Outlets.

(a) Grounding-type Receptacle Outlets. All receptacle outlets (1) shall be of grounding type; (2) shall be installed according to Section 210-7; and (3), except where supplying specific appliances, receptacles shall be 15- or 20-ampere, 125-volt, either single or duplex, and shall accept parallel-blade attachment plugs.

(b) Ground-Fault Circuit-Interrupters. All 120-volt, single-phase, 15- and 20-ampere receptacle outlets installed outdoors and in bathrooms, including receptacles in light fixtures, shall have ground-fault circuit-interrupter protection for personnel. Ground-fault circuit-interrupter protection for personnel shall be provided for receptacle outlets located within 6 feet (1.83 m) of any lavatory or sink.

Exception: Receptacles installed for appliances in dedicated spaces, such as for dishwashers, disposals, refrigerators, freezers, and laundry equipment.

No receptacle shall be required in the area occupied by a toilet, shower, tub, or any combination thereof. If a receptacle is installed in such an area, it shall have ground-fault circuit-interrupter protection for personnel.

Feeders supplying branch circuits shall be permitted to be protected by a ground-fault circuit-interrupter in lieu of the provision for such interrupters specified herein.

(c) Cord-Connected Fixed Appliance. A grounding-type receptacle outlet shall be provided for each cord-connected fixed appliance installed.

(d) Required Receptacle Outlets. Receptacle outlets shall be provided in all rooms other than the bath, closet, and hall areas, and shall be installed so that no point along the floor line is more than 6 feet (1.83 m) measured horizontally from an outlet in that space. Counter tops shall have receptacles located every 6 feet (1.83 m). The contiguous measurement of counter top and floor line shall be permitted where measured from the required receptacle in rooms requiring small appliance circuits. Receptacle outlets on small appliance circuits shall not be included in determining the spacing for receptacle outlets of other circuits.

Exception No. 1: Where the measured distance is interrupted by an interior doorway, sink, refrigerator, range, oven, or cooktop, an additional receptacle outlet shall be provided where the interrupted space is at least 2 feet (610 mm) wide at the floor line and at least 12 inches (305 mm) wide at the counter top.

Exception No. 2: Receptacles rendered not readily accessible by stationary appliances shall not be considered as the required outlets.

Exception No. 3: The distance along a floor line occupied by a door opened fully against that space shall not be required to be included in establishing the horizontal measurement if the door swing is limited to 90 degrees nominal by that wall space.

Exception No. 4: Receptacle requirements for bar-type counters and for fixed room dividers shall be permitted to be provided by a receptacle outlet in the wall at the nearest point where the counter or room divider attaches to the wall provided:

a. The divider does not exceed 8 feet (2.44 m) in length; and

b. The divider does not exceed 4 feet (1.22 m) in height; and

c. The divider is attached to a wall at one end only.

(e) Outdoor Receptacle Outlets. At least one receptacle outlet shall be installed outdoors. A receptacle outlet located in a compartment accessible from the outside of the mobile home shall be considered an outdoor receptacle. Outdoor receptacle outlets shall be protected as required in Section 550-8(b).

(f) Receptacle Outlets Not Permitted.

(1) Shower or Bathtub Space. Receptacle outlets shall not be installed in or within reach [30 inches (762 mm)] of a shower or bathtub space.

(2) Face-Up Position. A receptacle shall not be installed in a face-up position in any counter top.

(g) Heat Tape Outlet. A heat tape outlet, if installed, and if located on the underside of the mobile home at least 3 feet (914 mm) from the outside edge, shall not be considered an outdoor receptacle outlet. A heat tape outlet, if installed, shall be located within 2 feet (610 mm) of the cold water inlet.

550-9. Fixtures and Appliances.

(a) Fasten Appliances in Transit. Means shall be provided to securely fasten appliances when the mobile home is in transit. (See Section 550-11 for provisions on grounding.)

(b) Accessibility. Every appliance shall be accessible for inspection, service, repair, or replacement without removal of permanent construction.

(c) Pendants. Pendant-type fixtures or pendant cords shall be listed and identified for the interconnection of building components.

(d) Bathtub and Shower Fixtures. Where a lighting fixture is installed over a bathtub or in a shower stall, it shall be of the enclosed and gasketed type listed for wet locations.

(e) Location of Switches. The switch for shower lighting fixtures and exhaust fans located over a tub or in a shower stall shall be located outside the tub or shower space.

550-10. Wiring Methods and Materials.
Except as specifically limited in this section, the wiring methods and materials included in this Code shall be used in mobile homes.

(a) Nonmetallic Boxes. Nonmetallic boxes shall be permitted only with nonmetallic cable or nonmetallic raceways.

(b) Nonmetallic Cable Protection. Nonmetallic cable located 15 inches (381 mm) or less above the floor, if exposed, shall be protected from physical damage by covering boards, guard strips, or raceways. Cable likely to be damaged by stowage shall be so protected in all cases.

(c) Metal-Covered and Nonmetallic Cable Protection. Metal-covered and nonmetallic cables shall be permitted to pass through the centers of the wide side of 2-inch by 4-inch studs. However, they shall be protected where they pass through 2-inch by 2-inch studs or at other studs or frames where the cable or armor would be less than 1½ inches (38 mm) from the inside or outside surface of the studs where the wall covering materials are in contact with the studs. Steel plates on each side of the cable, or a tube, with not less than No. 16 MSG wall thickness shall be required to protect the cable. These plates or tubes shall be securely held in place.

(d) Metal Faceplates. Where metal faceplates are used, they shall be effectively grounded.

(e) Installation Requirements. If a range, clothes dryer, or similar appliance is connected by metal-covered cable or flexible metal conduit, a length of not less than 3 feet (914 mm) of free cable or conduit shall be provided to permit moving the appliance. The cable or flexible metal conduit shall be secured to the wall. Type NM or Type SE cable shall not be used to connect a range or dryer. This shall not prohibit the use of Type NM or

Type SE cable between the branch-circuit overcurrent-protective device and a junction box or range or dryer receptacle.

(f) Raceways. Where rigid metal conduit or intermediate metal conduit is terminated at an enclosure with a locknut and bushing connection, two locknuts shall be provided, one inside and one outside of the enclosure. Rigid nonmetallic conduit or electrical nonmetallic tubing shall be permitted. All cut ends of conduit and tubing shall be reamed or otherwise finished to remove rough edges.

(g) Switches. Switches shall be rated as follows:

(1) For lighting circuits, switches shall be rated not less than 10 amperes, 120-125 volts, and in no case less than the connected load.

(2) For motors or other loads, switches shall have ampere or horsepower ratings, or both, adequate for loads controlled. (An "ac general-use" snap switch shall be permitted to control a motor 2 horsepower or less with full-load current not over 80 percent of the switch ampere rating.)

(h) Free Conductor at Each Box. At least 4 inches (102 mm) of free conductor shall be left at each box except where conductors are intended to loop without joints.

(i) Under-Chassis Wiring. (Exposed to weather.)

(1) Where outdoor or under-chassis line-voltage (120 volts, nominal, or higher) wiring is exposed to moisture or physical damage, it shall be protected by rigid metal conduit or intermediate metal conduit. The conductors shall be suitable for wet locations.

Exception: Electrical metallic tubing or rigid nonmetallic conduit shall be permitted where closely routed against frames and equipment enclosures.

(2) The cables or conductors shall be Type NMC, TW, or equivalent.

(j) Boxes, Fittings, and Cabinets. Boxes, fittings, and cabinets shall be securely fastened in place and shall be supported from a structural member of the home, either directly or by using a substantial brace.

Exception: Snap-in type boxes. Boxes provided with special wall or ceiling brackets and wiring devices with integral enclosures, that securely fasten to walls or ceilings and are identified for the use, shall be permitted without support from a structural member or brace. The testing and approval shall include the wall and

ceiling construction systems for which the boxes and devices are intended to be used.

(k) Appliance Terminal Connections. Appliances having branch-circuit terminal connections that operate at temperatures higher than 60°C (140°F) shall have circuit conductors as described in (1) or (2) below.

(1) Branch-circuit conductors having an insulation suitable for the temperature encountered shall be permitted to be run directly to the appliance.

(2) Conductors having an insulation suitable for the temperature encountered shall be run from the appliance terminal connection to a readily accessible outlet box placed at least 1 foot (305 mm) from the appliance. These conductors shall be in a suitable raceway that shall extend for at least 4 feet (1.22 m).

(l) Component Interconnections. Fittings and connectors that are intended to be concealed at the time of assembly shall be listed and identified for the interconnection of building components. Such fittings and connectors shall be equal to the wiring method employed in insulation, temperature rise, and fault-current withstanding and shall be capable of enduring the vibration and shock occurring in mobile home transportation.

550-11. **Grounding.** Grounding of both electrical and non-electrical metal parts in a mobile home shall be through connection to a grounding bus in the mobile home distribution panelboard. The grounding bus shall be grounded through the green-colored insulated conductor in the supply cord or the feeder wiring to the service ground in the service-entrance equipment located adjacent to the mobile home location. Neither the frame of the mobile home nor the frame of any appliance shall be connected to the grounded circuit conductor (neutral) in the mobile home.

(a) Insulated Neutral.

(1) The grounded circuit conductor (neutral) shall be insulated from the grounding conductors and from equipment enclosures and other grounded parts. The grounded (neutral) circuit terminals in the distribution panelboard and in ranges, clothes dryers, counter-mounted cooking units, and wall-mounted ovens shall be insulated from the equipment enclosure. Bonding screws, straps, or buses in the distribution panelboard or in appliances shall be removed and discarded.

(2) Connections of ranges and clothes dryers with 120/240-volt, 3-wire ratings shall be made with 4-conductor cord and 3-pole, 4-wire, grounding-type plugs or by Type AC cable, Type MC cable, or conductors enclosed in flexible metal conduit.

The provisions of Section 550-24(a) require that the feeder assembly for a mobile home consist of a listed cord or four color-coded insulated conductors, one of which is the grounded conductor (white) and one of which is used for grounding purposes (green). Thus, the "grounded" and "grounding" conductors are kept independent of each other and are connected only at the service equipment (at the point of connection of the grounding electrode conductor). Grounding of both electrical and nonelectrical metal parts, including the frame of the mobile home or the frame of any appliance, is accomplished by connection to the equipment grounding bus [never to the grounded conductor (neutral bus)].

Bonding screws, straps, or buses, which bond the grounded (neutral) circuit conductors to the noncurrent-carrying metal parts in the mobile home panelboard or in appliances (ranges, clothes dryers, etc.), are required to be removed and discarded.

(b) Equipment Grounding Means.

(1) The green-colored insulated grounding wire in the supply cord or permanent feeder wiring shall be connected to the grounding bus in the distribution panelboard or disconnecting means.

(2) In the electrical system, all exposed metal parts, enclosures, frames, lamp fixture canopies, etc., shall be effectively bonded to the grounding terminal or enclosure of the distribution panelboard.

(3) Cord-connected appliances, such as washing machines, clothes dryers, refrigerators, and the electrical system of gas ranges, etc., shall be grounded by means of a cord with grounding conductor and grounding-type attachment plug.

(c) Bonding of Noncurrent-Carrying Metal Parts.

(1) All exposed noncurrent-carrying metal parts that may become energized shall be effectively bonded to the grounding terminal or enclosure of the distribution panelboard. A bonding conductor shall be connected between the distribution panelboard and accessible terminal on the chassis.

(2) Grounding terminals shall be of the solderless type and listed as pressure-terminal connectors recognized for the wire size used. The bonding conductor shall be solid or stranded, insulated or bare, and shall be No. 8 copper minimum, or equal. The bonding conductor shall be routed so as not to be exposed to physical damage.

(3) Metallic gas, water, and waste pipes and metallic air-circulating ducts shall be considered bonded if they are connected to the terminal on the chassis [see Section 550-11(c)(1)] by clamps, solderless connectors, or by suitable grounding-type straps.

(4) Any metallic roof and exterior covering shall be considered bonded if (a) the metal panels overlap one another and are securely attached to the wood or metal frame parts by metallic fasteners and (b) if the lower panel of the metallic exterior covering is secured by metallic fasteners at a cross member of the chassis by two metal straps per mobile home unit or section at opposite ends.

The bonding strap material shall be a minimum of 4 inches (102 mm) in width of material equivalent to the skin or a material of equal or better electrical conductivity. The straps shall be fastened with paint-penetrating fittings, such as screws and starwashers or equivalent.

550-12. Testing.

(a) Dielectric Strength Test. The wiring of each mobile home shall be subjected to a 1-minute, 900-volt, dielectric strength test (with all switches closed) between live parts (including neutral) and the mobile home ground. Alternatively, the test shall be permitted to be performed at 1,080 volts for 1 second. This test shall be performed after branch circuits are complete and after fixtures or appliances are installed.

Exception: Listed fixtures or appliances shall not be required to withstand the dielectric strength test.

(b) Continuity and Operational Tests and Polarity Checks. Each mobile home shall be subjected to:

(1) An electrical continuity test to ensure that all exposed electrically conductive parts are properly bonded;

(2) An electrical operational test to demonstrate that all equipment, except water heaters and electric furnaces, is connected and in working order; and

(3) Electrical polarity checks of permanently wired equipment and receptacle outlets to determine that connections have been properly made.

550-13. **Calculations.** The following method shall be employed in computing the supply-cord and distribution-panelboard load for each feeder assembly for each mobile home in lieu of the procedure shown in Article 220 and shall be based on a 3-wire, 120/240-volt supply with 120-volt loads balanced between the two legs of the 3-wire system.

(a) Lighting and Small Appliance Load.

Lighting Volt-Amperes: Length times width of mobile home floor (outside dimensions) times 3 volt-amperes per square foot; e.g.,

Length × width × 3 = ...lighting volt-amperes.

Small Appliance Volt-Amperes: Number of circuits times 1,500 volt-amperes for each 20-ampere appliance receptacle circuit (see definition of "Appliance, Portable" with note) including 1,500 volt-amperes for laundry circuit; e.g.,

Number of circuits × 1,500 = ...small appliance volt-amperes.

Total: Lighting volt-amperes plus small appliance = ...total volt-amperes.
First 3,000 total volt-amperes at 100 percent plus remainder at 35 percent = ...volt-amperes to be divided by 240 volts to obtain current (amperes) per leg.

(b) Total Load for Determining Power Supply. Total load for determining power supply is the summation of:

(1) Lighting and small appliance load as calculated in Section 550-13(a).

(2) Nameplate amperes for motors and heater loads (exhaust fans, air conditioners, electric, gas, or oil heating).

Omit smaller of the heating and cooling loads, except include blower motor if used as air-conditioner evaporator motor. Where an air conditioner is not installed and a 40-ampere power-supply cord is provided, allow 15 amperes per leg for air conditioning.

(3) 25 percent of current of largest motor in (2).

(4) Total of nameplate amperes for: disposal, dishwasher, water heater, clothes dryer, wall-mounted oven, cooking units.

Where number of these appliances exceeds three, use 75 percent of total.

(5) Derive amperes for freestanding range (as distinguished from separate ovens and cooking units) by dividing the following values by 240 volts.

The values referred to in the Code text are shown at the top of the next column.

(6) If outlets or circuits are provided for other than factory-installed appliances, include the anticipated load.

Nameplate Rating	Use
0 thru 10,000 watts	80 percent of rating
Over 10,000 thru 12,500 watts	8,000 volt-amperes
Over 12,500 thru 13,500 watts	8,400 volt-amperes
Over 13,500 thru 14,500 watta	8,800 volt-amperes
Over 14,500 thru 15,500 watts	9,200 volt-amperes
Over 15,500 thru 16,500 watts	9,600 volt-amperes
Over 16,500 thru 17,500 watts	10,000 volt-amperes

See following Example for illustration of application of this calculation.

Example

A mobile home floor is 70 feet × 10 feet and has two small appliance circuits, a 1000-volt-ampere, 240-volt heater, a 200-volt-ampere, 120-volt exhaust fan, a 400-volt-ampere, 120-volt dishwasher, and a 7000-volt-ampere electric range.

Lighting and small appliance load

Lighting 70 × 10 × 3 VA/sq ft =	2100 volt-amperes
Small appliance 1500 × 2 =	3000 volt-amperes
Laundry 1500 × 1=	1500 volt-amperes
	6600 volt-amperes
1st 3000 volt-amperes at 100 percent	3000 volt-amperes
Remainder (6600 - 3000) at 35 percent	1260 volt-amperes
	4260 volt-amperes

$$\frac{4260 \text{ volt-amperes}}{240 \text{ volts}} = 17.75 \text{ amperes per leg}$$

	Amperes per leg	
	A	B
Lighting and appliances	17.75	17.75
Heater, 1000 VA † 240 volt =	4.2	4.2
Fan, 200 VA † 120 volt =	1.7	
Dishwasher, 400VA † 120 =		3.3
Range, 7000 VA × .8 † 240 =	23.3	23.3
Totals	46.95	48.55

Based on the higher current calculated for either leg, a minimum 50-ampere supply cord is required.

For SI units: one square foot = 0.093 square meter; one foot = 0.3048 meter.

(c) Optional Method of Calculation for Lighting and Appliance Load. For mobile homes, the optional method for calculating lighting and appliance load shown in Section 220-30 and Table 220-30 shall be permitted.

550-14. Interconnection of Multiple Section Mobile Home Units.

(a) **Fixed-type Wiring.** Approved and listed fixed-type wiring methods shall be used to join portions of a circuit that must be electrically joined that are located in adjacent sections of mobile homes after the home is installed on its support foundation. The circuit's junction shall be accessible for disassembly when the home is prepared for relocation.

(b) **Disconnecting Means.** Multiple section mobile homes not having permanently installed feeders, and that are to be moved from one location to another, shall be permitted to have disconnecting means with branch-circuit protective equipment in each unit where so located that, after assembly or joining together of units, they shall not be interconnected on either the line side or the load side, except that the grounding means shall be electrically interconnected.

(FPN): Subsection (b) above applies to connection of previously constructed mobile homes where multiple feeder assemblies were allowed. The present Code does not permit more than one cord or feeder to a mobile home.

550-15. Outdoor Outlets, Fixtures, Air-Cooling Equipment, Etc.

(a) **Listed for Outdoor Use.** Outdoor fixtures and equipment shall be listed for outdoor use. Outdoor receptacle or convenience outlets shall be of a gasketed-cover type for use in wet locations.

(b) **Outside Heating Equipment, Air-Conditioning Equipment, or Both.** A mobile home provided with a branch circuit designed to energize outside heating equipment or air-conditioning equipment, or both, located outside the mobile home, other than room air conditioners, shall have such branch-circuit conductors terminate in a listed outlet box, or disconnecting means, located on the outside of the mobile home. A label shall be permanently affixed adjacent to the outlet box and contain the following information:

> This connection is for heating and/or air-conditioning equipment. The branch circuit is rated at not more than _____ amperes, at _____ volts, 60-Hertz, _____ conductor ampacity. A disconnecting means shall be located within sight of the equipment.

The correct voltage and ampere rating shall be given. The tag shall be not less than 0.020-inch (508-micrometer) thick etched brass, stainless steel, anodized or alclad aluminum, or equivalent. The tag shall not be less than 3 inches (76 mm) by 1¾ inches (44.5 mm) minimum size.

C. Services and Feeders

550-21. **Distribution System.** The mobile home park secondary electrical distribution system to mobile home lots shall be single-phase, 120/240 volts, nominal. For the purpose of Part C, where the park service exceeds 240 volts, nominal, transformers and secondary distribution panelboards shall be treated as services.

(FPN No. 1): See Table 550-22 for calculation of load.

(FPN No. 2): See Section 550-4(b) for mobile homes not located in mobile home parks.

Mobile homes are intended for connection to a wiring system nominally rated 120/240 V, 3-wire ac, with a grounded neutral; therefore, distribution systems at mobile home parks must supply 120/240 V to the mobile home lot. Because appliances and other equipment are usually installed during the manufacturing process of mobile homes and are rated 120/240 V, a 120/208-V supply derived from a 4-wire, 120/208-V wye system is unsuitable.

Section 550-22 requires park electrical wiring systems to be calculated on the basis of the larger of (1) not less than 16,000 VA (at 120/240 V) for each mobile home lot, or (2) the calculated load of the largest typical mobile home the lot will accommodate. However, the ampacity of the feeder circuit conductors to each mobile home lot is not to be less than 100 A (at 120/240 V) according to Section 550-24(b).

550-22. **Minimum Allowable Demand Factors.** Park electrical wiring systems shall be calculated (at 120/240 volts) on the larger of (1) 16,000 volt-amperes for each mobile home lot or (2) the load calculated in accordance with Section 550-13 for the largest typical mobile home that each lot will accept. It shall be permissible to compute the feeder or service load in accordance with Table 550-22. No demand factor shall be allowed for any other load, except as provided in this Code.

Service and feeder conductors to a mobile home in compliance with Article 310, Note 3 of Notes to Ampacity Tables of 0 to 2000 Volts shall be permitted.

See commentary following Section 550-21.

Table 550-22. Demand Factors for Feeders and Service-Entrance Conductors

Number of Mobile Homes	Demand Factor (percent)
1	100
2	55
3	44
4	39
5	33
6	29
7-9	28
10-12	27
13-15	26
16-21	25
22-40	24
41-60	23
61 and over	22

550-23. Mobile Home Service Equipment.

(a) Service Equipment. The mobile home service equipment shall be located adjacent to the mobile home and not mounted in or on the mobile home. The service equipment shall be located in sight from and not more than 30 feet (9.14 m) from the exterior wall of the mobile home it serves.

Exception No. 1: The service equipment shall be permitted to be located elsewhere on the premises, provided that all of the following conditions are met:

a. A disconnecting means suitable for service equipment is located in sight from and not more than 30 feet (9.14 m) from the exterior wall of the mobile home it serves.

b. Grounding at the disconnecting means shall be in accordance with Section 250-24.

Exception No. 2: Service equipment shall be permitted to be installed in or on a manufactured home, provided that all of the following conditions are met:

a. The service equipment is completely installed by the manufacturer of the structure.

b. The installation of the service equipment complies with Article 230.

c. Means are provided for the connection of a grounding electrode conductor to the service equipment and routing it outside the structure.

(b) Rating. Mobile home service equipment shall be rated at not less than 100 amperes, and provision shall be made for

connecting a mobile home feeder assembly by a permanent wiring method. Power outlets used as mobile home service equipment shall also be permitted to contain receptacles rated up to 50 amperes with appropriate overcurrent protection. Fifty-ampere receptacles shall conform to the configuration shown in Figure 550-5(c).

(FPN): Complete details on the 50-ampere attachment plug cap configuration can be found in American National Standard Dimensions of Caps, Plugs and Receptacles, ANSI C73.17-1972.

(c) Additional Outside Electrical Equipment. Mobile home service equipment shall also contain a means for connecting a mobile home accessory building or structure or additional electrical equipment located outside a mobile home by a fixed wiring method.

(d) Additional Receptacles. Additional receptacles shall be permitted for connection of electrical equipment located outside the mobile home, and all such 125-volt, single-phase, 15- and 20-ampere receptacles shall be protected by a listed ground-fault circuit-interrupter protection.

(e) Mounting Height. Outdoor mobile home disconnecting means shall be installed so the bottom of the enclosure containing the disconnecting means is not less than 2 feet (610 mm) above finished grade or working platform. The disconnecting means shall be so installed that the center of the grip of the operating handle, when in its highest position, will not be more than 6½ feet (1.98 m) above the finished grade or working platform.

Mobile home service equipment is required to be located in sight from the mobile home, but the equipment can be up to 30 feet from any point on the exterior wall of the mobile home. This recognizes use of feeder raceways external to the mobile home. Service equipment may be located more than 30 feet from the mobile home if an additional disconnecting means is located 30 feet from the mobile home and proper grounding and bonding measures are taken. See Section 550-23(a).

Exception No. 2 was added for the 1993 *Code*. It permits the service equipment to be installed in or on a manufactured home by the manufacturer of the structure. Means must be provided for routing of the grounding electrode conductor from the service equipment to the grounding electrode.

(f) Grounded. Each mobile home service equipment shall be grounded in accordance with Article 250 for service equipment.

Figure 550-1. *Mobile home service equipment and power outlet assembly showing metering, disconnecting means, overcurrent protective devices, and receptacle. (Midwest)*

(g) Marking. Where a 125/250-volt receptacle is used in mobile home service equipment, the service equipment shall be marked as follows:

"Turn disconnecting switch or circuit breaker off before inserting or removing plug. Plug must be fully inserted or removed."

The marking shall be located on the service equipment adjacent to the receptacle outlet.

550-24. Feeder.

(a) Feeder Conductors. Mobile home feeder conductors shall consist of either a listed cord, factory-installed in accordance with Section 550-5(b), or a permanently installed feeder consisting of four, insulated, color-coded conductors that shall be identified by the factory or field marking of the conductors in compliance with Section 310-12. Equipment grounding conductors shall not be identified by stripping the insulation.

Exception: A mobile home feeder located between service equipment and a mobile home disconnecting means as covered in Section 550-23(a), Exception No. 1 shall be permitted to omit the equipment grounding conductor where the grounded circuit conductor is grounded at the disconnecting means as permitted in Section 250-24(a).

(b) Adequate Feeder Capacity. Mobile home lot feeder circuit conductors shall have adequate capacity for the loads supplied and shall be rated at not less than 100 amperes at 120/240 volts.

ARTICLE 551 Recreational Vehicles and Recreational Vehicle Parks

Contents

A. General

B. Low-Voltage Systems

C. Combination Electrical Systems

A. General

551-1. Scope. The provisions of this article cover the electrical conductors and equipment installed within or on recreational vehicles, the conductors that connect recreational vehicles to a supply of electricity, and the installation of equipment and devices related to electrical installations within a recreational vehicle park.

(FPN): For requirements on the installation of plumbing and heating systems in recreational vehicles, refer to the Standard on Recreational Vehicles, NFPA 501C-1990 (ANSI).

Laws in many states require a factory inspection by state electrical inspectors. The requirements of such laws follow closely the requirements of NFPA 501C, *Standard on Recreational Vehicles*. Section 1-5 in NFPA 501C specifies that electrical installations in recreational vehicles shall comply with Part A of Article 551 and other applicable sections of the *Code*. This reference to Part A of Article 551 is based on the 1984 edition of the *NEC*. Parts B through F in the 1993 *NEC* were formerly Part A.

551-2. Definitions. (See Article 100 for other definitions.)

Air-Conditioning or Comfort-Cooling Equipment: All of that equipment intended or installed for the purpose of processing the treatment of air so as to control simultaneously its temperature, humidity, cleanliness, and distribution to meet the requirements of the conditioned space.

Appliance, Fixed: An appliance that is fastened or otherwise secured at a specific location.

Appliance, Portable: An appliance that is actually moved or can easily be moved from one place to another in normal use.

(FPN): For the purpose of this article, the following major appliances, other than built-in, are considered portable if cord-connected: refrigerators, gas range equipment, clothes washers, dishwashers without booster heaters, or other similar appliances.

Appliance, Stationary: An appliance that is not easily moved from one place to another in normal use.

Camping Trailer: A vehicular portable unit mounted on wheels and constructed with collapsible partial side walls that fold for towing by another vehicle and unfold at the campsite to provide temporary living quarters for recreational, camping, or travel use. (See "Recreational Vehicle.")

Converter: A device that changes electrical energy from one form to another, as from alternating current to direct current.

Dead Front: (As applied to switches, circuit breakers, switchboards, and distribution panelboards.) So designed, constructed, and installed that no current-carrying parts are normally exposed on the front.

Disconnecting Means: The necessary equipment usually consisting of a circuit breaker or switch and fuses, and their accessories, located near the point of entrance of supply conductors in a recreational vehicle and intended to constitute the means of cutoff for the supply to that recreational vehicle.

Distribution Panelboard: A single panel or group of panel units designed for assembly in the form of a single panel; including buses, and with or without switches and/or automatic overcurrent-protective devices for the control of light, heat, or power circuits of small individual as well as aggregate capacity; designed to be placed in a cabinet or cutout box placed in or against a wall or partition and accessible only from the front.

Frame: Chassis rail and any welded addition thereto of metal thickness of 16 MSG or greater.

Low Voltage: An electromotive force rated 24 volts, nominal, or less, supplied from a transformer, converter, or battery.

Motor Home: A vehicular unit designed to provide temporary living quarters for recreational, camping, or travel use built on or permanently attached to a self-propelled motor vehicle chassis or on a chassis cab or van that is an integral part of the completed vehicle. (See "Recreational Vehicle.")

Power-Supply Assembly: The conductors, including ungrounded, grounded, and equipment grounding conductors, the connectors, attachment plug caps, and all other fittings, grommets, or devices installed for the purpose of delivering energy from the source of electrical supply to the distribution panel within the recreational vehicle.

Recreational Vehicle: A vehicular-type unit primarily designed as temporary living quarters for recreational, camping, or travel use, which either has its own motive power or is mounted on or drawn by another vehicle. The basic entities are: travel trailer, camping trailer, truck camper, and motor home.

Recreational Vehicle Park. A plot of land upon which two or more recreational vehicle sites are located, established, or maintained for occupancy by recreational vehicles of the general public as temporary living quarters for recreation or vacation purposes.

Recreational Vehicle Site. A plot of ground within a recreational vehicle park intended for the accommodation of either a recreational vehicle, tent, or other individual camping unit on a temporary basis.

Recreational Vehicle Site Feeder Circuit Conductors. The conductors from the park service equipment to the recreational vehicle site supply equipment.

Recreational Vehicle Site Supply Equipment. The necessary equipment, usually a power outlet, consisting of a circuit breaker or switch and fuse and their accessories, located near the point of entrance of supply conductors to a recreational vehicle site and intended to constitute the disconnecting means for the supply to that site.

Recreational Vehicle Stand. That area of a recreational vehicle site intended for the placement of a recreational vehicle.

Transformer: A device that, when used, will raise or lower the voltage of alternating current of the original source.

Travel Trailer: A vehicular unit mounted on wheels, designed to provide temporary living quarters for recreational, camping, or travel use, of such size or weight as not to require special highway movement permits when towed by a motorized vehicle, and of gross trailer area less than 320 square feet (29.77 sq m). (See "Recreational Vehicle.")

Truck Camper: A portable unit constructed to provide temporary living quarters for recreational, travel, or camping use, consisting of a roof, floor, and sides, designed to be loaded onto and unloaded from the bed of a pick-up truck. (See "Recreational Vehicle.")

551-3. **Other Articles.** Wherever the requirements of other articles of this Code and Article 551 differ, the requirements of Article 551 shall apply.

551-4. **General Requirements.**

(a) Not Covered. A recreational vehicle not used for the purposes as defined in Section 551-2 shall not be required to meet the provisions of Part A pertaining to the number or capacity of circuits required. It shall, however, meet all other applicable requirements of this article if the recreational vehicle is provided with an electrical installation intended to be energized from a 120- or 120/240-volt, nominal, ac power-supply system.

(b) Systems. This article covers battery and direct-current power (24-volts or less) systems, combination electrical systems, generator installations, and 120- or 120/240-volt, nominal, systems.

B. Low-Voltage Systems

551-10. **Low-Voltage Systems.**

(a) Low-Voltage Circuits. Low-voltage circuits furnished and installed by the recreational vehicle manufacturer, other than those related to braking and cranking/ignition, are subject to this Code. Circuits supplying lights subject to federal or state regulations shall comply with applicable government regulations and this Code.

(b) Low-Voltage Wiring.

(1) Copper conductors shall be used for low-voltage circuits.

It is not the intent of this section to permit the sidewalls or the roof to serve as the ground return path. See definition of "Frame" in Section 551-2.

Exception: Metal chassis or frame shall be permitted as the return path to the source of supply. Connections to the chassis or frame shall be made (1) in an accessible location, (2) by means of copper conductors and copper or copper alloy terminals of the

solderless type identified for the size of wire used, and (3) mechanically secure.

(2) Conductors shall conform to the requirements for Type HDT, SGT, SGR, or Type SXL or shall have insulation in accordance with Table 310-13 or the equivalent. Conductor sizes No. 6 through 18 or SAE shall be listed.

(FPN): See SAE Standard J1128-1975 for Types HDT and SXL and SAE Standard J1127-1980 for Types SGT and SGR.

(3) Single-wire, low-voltage conductors shall be of the stranded type.

(4) All insulated low-voltage conductors shall be surface marked at intervals no greater than 4 feet (1.22 m) as follows:

a. Listed conductors shall be marked as required by the listing agency.

b. SAE conductors shall be marked with the name or logo of the manufacturer, specification designation, and wire gage.

c. Other conductors shall be marked with the name or logo of the manufacturer, temperature rating, wire gage, conductor material, and insulation thickness.

(c) Low-Voltage Wiring Methods.

(1) Conductors shall be protected against physical damage and shall be secured. Where insulated conductors are clamped to the structure, the conductor insulation shall be supplemented by an additional wrap or layer of equivalent material, except that jacketed cables need not be so protected. Wiring shall be routed away from sharp edges, moving parts, or heat sources.

(2) Conductors shall be spliced or joined with splicing devices that provide a secure connection or by brazing, welding, or soldering with a fusible metal or alloy. Soldered splices shall first be so spliced or joined as to be mechanically and electrically secure without solder and then soldered. All splices, joints, and free ends of conductors shall be covered with an insulation equivalent to that on the conductors.

(3) Battery and direct-current circuits shall be physically separated by at least a ½-inch (12.7-mm) gap or other approved means from circuits of a different power source. Acceptable methods shall be by clamping, routing, or equivalent means that ensure permanent total separation. Where circuits of different power sources cross, the external jacket of the nonmetallic-sheathed cables shall be deemed adequate separation.

(4) Ground terminals shall be accessible for service. The surface on which ground terminals make contact shall be cleaned and free from oxide or paint, or shall be electrically connected through use of a cadmium, tin, or zinc-plated internal-external toothed lockwasher or lockring terminals. Ground terminal attaching screws, rivets or bolts, nuts, and lockwashers shall be cadmium, tin, or zinc-plated, except rivets shall be permitted to be unanodized aluminum when attaching to aluminum structures.

(5) The chassis-grounding terminal of the battery shall be bonded to the vehicle chassis with a minimum No. 8 copper conductor or equivalent. In the event the power lead from the battery exceeds No. 8, then the bonding conductor shall be of an equal size.

Section 551-10(c)(5) requires that the chassis-grounding terminal of the battery be bonded to the vehicle chassis with a minimum No. 8 copper conductor or equivalent. This minimizes the possibility of low-voltage, circuit-fault currents passing through the ac panelboard bonding conductor and the equipment grounding conductor of the combination ac/dc appliance and subsequently passing through the negative dc conductor feeding the appliance that also may be bonded to the external metal cover of the appliance. The ac equipment grounding conductor of the appliance may not have sufficient ampacity to safely conduct the dc fault current. This will necessitate installation of the battery bonding conductor. Some recreational vehicles already have one side of the battery circuit bonded to the frame by a No. 8 or larger copper conductor.

(d) Battery Installations. Storage batteries subject to the provisions of this Code shall be securely attached to the vehicle and installed in an area vapor-tight to the interior and ventilated directly to the exterior of the vehicle. Where batteries are installed in a compartment, the compartment shall be ventilated with openings having a minimum area of 1.7 square inches (1100 sq mm) at both the top and at the bottom. Where compartment doors are equipped for ventilation, the openings shall be within 1 inch (25.4 mm) of the top and bottom. Batteries shall not be installed in a compartment containing spark- or flame-producing equipment, except that they shall be permitted to be installed in the engine generator compartment if the only charging source is from the engine generator.

(e) Overcurrent Protection.

(1) Low-voltage circuit wiring shall be protected by overcurrent-protective devices rated not in excess of the ampacity of copper conductors, as follows:

Wire Size	Ampacity	Wire Type
18	6	Stranded only
16	8	Stranded only
14	15	Stranded or Solid
12	20	Stranded or Solid
10	30	Stranded or Solid

(2) Circuit breakers or fuses shall be of an approved type, including automotive types. Fuseholders shall be clearly marked with maximum fuse size and shall be protected against shorting and physical damage by a cover or equivalent means.

The requirement for protection of fuseholders by a cover or equivalent means is intended to reduce the possibility of the low-voltage system shorting to ground.

(FPN): For further information, see Society of Automotive Engineers (SAE) Standard for Electric Fuses (Cartridge Type), ANSI/SAE J554(b)-1981; Standard for Blade Type Electric Fuses, SAE J1284; and Underwriters Laboratories Inc. Standard for Automotive Glass Tube Fuses, UL 275-1986.

(3) Higher current-consuming, direct-current appliances such as pumps, compressors, heater blowers, and similar motor-driven appliances shall be installed in accordance with themanufacturer's instructions.

Motors that are controlled by automatic switching or by latching-type manual switches shall be protected in accordance with Section 430-32(c).

(4) The overcurrent-protective device shall be installed in an accessible location on the vehicle within 18 inches (457 mm) of the point where the power supply connects to the vehicle circuits. If located outside the recreational vehicle, the device shall be protected against weather and physical damage.

Exception: External low-voltage supply shall be permitted to be fused within 18 inches (457 mm) after entering the vehicle or after leaving a metal raceway.

(f) Switches. Switches shall have a direct-current rating not less than the connected load.

(g) Lighting Fixtures. All low-voltage interior lighting fixtures shall be listed.

Exception: Fixtures rated 4 watts or less, employing lamps rated 1.2 watts or less.

(h) Cigarette Lighter Receptacles. Twelve-volt receptacles that will accept and energize cigarette lighters shall be installed in a noncombustible outlet box, or the assembly shall be identified by the manufacturer of the product as thermally protected.

Twelve-volt systems for running and signal lights, similar to those in a conventional automobile, are covered in Sections 551-10, 551-20, and 551-30. In many recreational vehicles, 12-V systems are also used for interior lighting and other small loads. The 12-V system is often supplied from an onboard battery or through a transfer switch from a 120/12-V transformer in conjunction with a full-wave rectifier.

C. Combination Electrical Systems

551-20. **Combination Electrical Systems.**

(a) General. Vehicle wiring suitable for connection to a battery or direct-current supply source shall be permitted to be connected to a 120-volt source, provided that the entire wiring system and equipment are rated and installed in full conformity with Parts A, C, D, E, and F requirements covering 120-volt electrical systems. Circuits fed from alternating-current transformers shall not supply direct-current appliances.

(b) Voltage Converters (120-Volt Alternating Current to Low-Voltage Direct Current). The 120-volt alternating current side of the voltage converter shall be wired in full conformity with Parts A, C, D, E, and F requirements for 120-volt electrical systems.

Exception: Converters supplied as an integral part of a listed appliance shall not be subject to the above.

All converters and transformers shall be listed for use in recreation vehicles and designed or equipped to provide over-temperature protection. To determine the converter rating, the following formula shall be applied to the total connected load, including average battery charging rate, of all 12-volt equipment:

The first 20 amperes of load at 100 percent; plus
The second 20 amperes of load at 50 percent; plus

All load above 40 amperes at 25 percent.

Exception: A low-voltage appliance that is controlled by a momentary switch (normally "open") that has no means for holding in the "closed" position shall not be considered as a "connected load" when determining the required converter rating. Momentarily energized appliances shall be limited to those used to prepare the vehicle for occupancy or travel.

(c) Bonding Voltage Converter Enclosures. The noncurrent-carrying metal enclosure of the voltage converter shall be bonded to the frame of the vehicle with a No. 8 copper conductor minimum or equivalent. The grounding conductor for the battery and the metal enclosure shall be permitted to be the same conductor.

The intent of this section is to reduce the possibility of damage to the power-supply cord by large dc fault currents that may find their way back to the vehicle frame or the battery through the ac grounding conductor of the converter. Metal enclosures of UL-listed converters are provided with an external pressure terminal connector for this purpose. See commentary following Section 551-10(c)(5).

(d) Dual-Voltage Fixtures or Appliances. Fixtures or appliances having both 120-volt and low-voltage connections shall be listed for dual voltage.

In such fixtures, barriers are used to separate the 120-V and the 12-V wiring connections.

(e) Autotransformers. Autotransformers shall not be used.

(f) Receptacles and Plug Caps. Where a recreational vehicle is equipped with a 120-volt or 120/240-volt alternating-current system, a low-voltage system, or both, receptacles and plug caps of the low-voltage system shall differ in configuration from those of the 120- or 120/240-volt system. Where a vehicle equipped with a battery or direct-current system has an external connection for low-voltage power, the connector shall have a configuration that will not accept 120-volt power.

D. Other Power Sources

551-30. **Generator Installations.**

(a) Mounting. Generators shall be mounted in such a manner as to be effectively bonded to the recreational vehicle chassis.

(b) Generator Protection. Equipment shall be installed to ensure that the current-carrying conductors from the engine generator and from an outside source are not connected to a vehicle circuit at the same time.

Receptacles used as disconnecting means shall be accessible (as applied to wiring methods) and capable of interrupting their rated current without hazard to the operator.

(c) Installation of Storage Batteries and Generators. Storage batteries and internal-combustion-driven generator units (subject to the provisions of this Code) shall be secured in place to avoid displacement from vibration and road shock.

(d) Ventilation of Generator Compartments. Compartments accommodating internal-combustion-driven generator units shall be provided with ventilation in accordance with instructions provided by the manufacturer of the generator unit.

(FPN): For generator compartment construction requirements, see the Standard on Recreational Vehicles, NFPA 501C-1990.

(e) Supply Conductors. The supply conductors from the engine generator to the first termination on the vehicle shall be of the stranded type and be installed in listed flexible conduit. The point of first termination shall be in a (1) panelboard, (2) junction box with a blank cover, (3) junction box with a receptacle, (4) enclosed transfer switch, or (5) receptacle assembly listed in conjunction with the generator.

The panelboard or junction box with a receptacle shall be installed within the vehicle's interior and within 18 inches (457 mm) of the compartment wall but not inside the compartment. A junction box with a blank cover shall be mounted on the compartment wall and shall be permitted inside or outside the compartment. A receptacle assembly listed in conjunction with the generator shall be mounted in accordance with its listing. Overcurrent protection in accordance with Section 240-3 shall be provided for supply conductors as an integral part of a listed generator or shall be located within 18 inches (457 mm) of their point of entry into the vehicle.

551-31. **Multiple Supply Source.**

(a) Multiple Supply Sources. Where a multiple supply system consisting of an alternate power source and a power-supply cord is installed, the feeder from the alternate power source shall be protected by an overcurrent-protective device. Installation shall be in accordance with Sections 551-30(a) and (b) and 551-40.

(b) Calculation of Loads. Calculation of loads shall be in accordance with Section 551-42.

(c) Multiple Supply Sources Capacity. The multiple supply sources shall not be required to be of the same capacity.

(d) Alternate Power Sources Exceeding 30 Amperes. If an alternate power source exceeds 30 amperes, 120 volts, nominal, it shall be permissible to wire it as a 120-volt, nominal, system or a 120/240-volt, nominal, system, provided an overcurrent-protective device of the proper rating is installed in the feeder.

(e) Power-Supply Assembly Not Less than 30 Amperes. The external power-supply assembly shall be permitted to be less than the calculated load but not less than 30 amperes and shall have overcurrent protection not greater than the capacity of the external power-supply assembly.

551-32. **Other Sources.** Other sources of ac power such as inverters or motor generators shall be listed for use in recreational vehicles and shall be installed in accordance with the terms of the listing. Other sources of ac power shall be wired in full conformity with the requirements in Parts A, C, D, E, and F of this article covering 120-volt electrical systems.

551-33. **Alternate Source Restriction.** Transfer equipment, if not integral with the listed power source, shall be installed to ensure that the current-carrying conductors from other sources of ac power and from an outside source are not connected to the vehicle circuit at the same time.

E. Nominal 120- or 120/240-Volt Systems

551-40. **120- or 120/240-Volt, Nominal, Systems.**

(a) General Requirements. The electrical equipment and material of recreational vehicles indicated for connection to a wiring system rated 120 volts, nominal, 2-wire with ground, or a wiring system rated 120/240 volts, nominal, 3-wire with ground, shall be listed and installed in accordance with the requirements of Parts A, C, D, E, and F.

(b) Materials and Equipment. Electrical materials, devices, appliances, fittings, and other equipment installed, intended for use in, or attached to the recreational vehicle shall be listed. All products shall be used only in the manner in which they have been tested and found suitable for the intended use.

(c) Ground-Fault Circuit-Interrupter Protection. The internal wiring of a recreational vehicle having only one 15- or 20-ampere branch circuit as permitted in Sections 551-42(a) and (b) shall have ground-fault circuit-interrupter protection for personnel. The ground-fault circuit-interrupter shall be installed at the point where the power supply assembly terminates within the recreational vehicle. Where a separable cord set is not employed, the ground-fault circuit-interrupter shall be permitted to be an integral part of the attachment plug of the power supply assembly. The ground-fault circuit-interrupter shall provide protection also under the conditions of an open grounded circuit conductor, interchanged circuit conductors, or both.

551-41. Receptacle Outlets Required.

(a) Spacing. Receptacle outlets shall be installed at wall spaces 2 feet (610 mm) wide or more so that no point along the floor line is more than 6 feet (1.83 m), measured horizontally, from an outlet in that space.

Exception No. 1: Bath and hall areas.

Exception No. 2: Wall spaces occupied by kitchen cabinets, wardrobe cabinets, built-in furniture, behind doors that may open fully against a wall surface, or similar facilities.

(b) Location. Receptacle outlets shall be installed:

(1) Adjacent to counter tops in the kitchen [at least one on each side of the sink if counter tops are on each side and are 12 inches (305 mm) or over in width].

(2) Adjacent to the refrigerator and gas range space, except where a gas-fired refrigerator or cooking appliance, requiring no external electrical connection, is factory-installed.

(3) Adjacent to counter top spaces of 12 inches (305 mm) or more in width that cannot be reached from a receptacle required in Section 551-41(b)(1) by a cord of 6 feet (1.83 m) without crossing a traffic area, cooking appliance, or sink.

(c) Ground-Fault Circuit-Interrupter Protection. Where provided, each 120-volt, single-phase, 15- or 20-ampere receptacle outlet shall have ground-fault circuit-interrupter protection for personnel in the following locations:

(1) Adjacent to a bathroom lavatory. [The receptacle outlet shall be a minimum of 24 inches (610 mm) from the compartment floor.]

This section permits mounting of a bathroom receptacle in the side of a lavatory cabinet where installation of a receptacle is not possible in a thin wall.

(2) Within 6 feet (1.83 m) of any lavatory or sink.

Exception: Receptacles installed for appliances in dedicated spaces, such as for dishwashers, disposals, refrigerators, freezers, and laundry equipment.

(3) In the area occupied by a toilet, shower, tub, or any combination thereof.

(4) On the exterior of the vehicle.

Exception: Receptacles that are located inside of an access panel that is installed on the exterior of the vehicle to supply power for an installed appliance shall not be required to have ground-fault circuit-interrupter protection.

The receptacle outlet shall be permitted in a listed lighting fixture. A receptacle outlet shall not be installed in a tub or combination tub-shower compartment.

Exception: Where ground-fault circuit-interrupter protection is provided in accordance with Section 551-40(c).

(d) Face-Up Position. A receptacle shall not be installed in a face-up position in any counter top or similar horizontal surfaces within the living area.

551-42. Branch Circuits Required.
Each recreational vehicle containing a 120-volt electrical system shall contain one of the following:

(a) One 15-Ampere Circuit. One 15-ampere circuit to supply lights, receptacle outlets, and fixed appliances. Such recreational vehicles shall be equipped with one 15-ampere switch and fuse or 15-ampere circuit breaker.

(b) One 20-Ampere Circuit. One 20-ampere circuit to supply lights, receptacle outlets, and fixed appliances. Such recreational vehicles shall be equipped with one 20-ampere switch and fuse or 20-ampere circuit breaker.

(c) Two or More 15- or 20-Ampere Circuits. Two or more 15- or 20-ampere circuits to supply lights, receptacle outlets, and fixed appliances. Such recreational vehicles shall be equipped with a 30-ampere rated main power supply assembly.

(FPN): See Section 210-23(a) for permissible loads. See Section 551-45(c) for main disconnect and overcurrent protection requirements.

(d) Power-Supply Assembly. A 40- or 50-ampere power-supply assembly that shall be calculated in accordance with the following method:

(1) Lighting. If electric lighting is provided either directly or indirectly (through a voltage converter) by the 120-volt or 120/240-volt system, calculate lighting wattage at 3 volt-amperes per square foot using exterior dimensions (exclusive of hitch and cab) as follows:

Length (feet) × width (feet) × 3 = _____ lighting volt-amperes.

(2) Small Appliance. Number of circuits times 1,500 volt-amperes for each 20-ampere appliance receptacle circuit, e.g.,

Number of Circuits × 1,500 = _____ small appliance volt-amperes.

(3) Total. Lighting volt-amperes plus small appliance volt-amperes = _____ total volt-amperes.

(4) First 3,000 total volt-amperes at 100 percent plus remainder at 35 percent = _____ volt-amperes to be divided by voltage to obtain current (amperes) per leg.

	Amperes per Leg	
	A	B
Lighting and small appliance current (amperes) per leg [from (d) above] =	_____	

(5) Add nameplate amperes for motors and heater loads (exhaust fans, air conditioners,* electric, gas, or oil heating*). Also include anticipated loads in above categories where prewired outlets or circuits are installed for other than factory-installed major appliances. _____

*Omit smaller of heating or air-conditioning load, except include any motor common to both functions.

(6) Add 25 percent of amperes of largest motor in E = _____

(7) Add nameplate amperes of the following appliances. Include anticipated loads where prewired outlets or circuits are installed for other than factory-installed major appliances. Where the number of appliances is four or more, use 75 percent of total.

Disposal	_____	_____	
Water Heater	_____	_____	
Wall-Mounted Ovens	_____	_____	
Cooking Units	_____	_____	
TOTAL	_____	_____	= _____

(8) Add amperes for freestanding range as distinguished from separate ovens and cooking units. Derive from following table by dividing volt-amperes by 240 volts.

Range	Nameplate Rating (watts)	Use (volt-amperes)
(Freestanding range as distinguished from separate oven and cooking units)	0 thru 10,000	80 percent of rating
	Over 10,000 thru 12,500	8,000
	Over 12,500 thru 13,500	8,400
	Over 13,500 thru 14,500	8,800
	Over 14,500 thru 15,500	9,200
	Over 15,500 thru 16,500	9,600
	Over 16,500 thru 17,500	10,000

551-43. Branch-Circuit Protection.

(a) Rating. The branch-circuit overcurrent devices shall be rated:

(1) Not more than the circuit conductors; and

(2) Not more than 150 percent of the rating of a single appliance rated 13.3 amperes or more and supplied by an individual branch circuit; but

(3) Not more than the overcurrent protection size marked on an air conditioner or other motor-operated appliances.

(b) Protection for Smaller Conductors. A 20-ampere fuse or circuit breaker shall be permitted for protection for fixture leads, cords, or small appliances, and No. 14 tap conductors, not over 6 feet (1.83 m) long for recessed lighting fixtures.

(c) 15-Ampere Receptacle Considered Protected by 20 Amperes. If more than one outlet or load is on a branch circuit, a 15-ampere receptacle shall be permitted to be protected by a 20-ampere fuse or circuit breaker.

551-44. Power-Supply Assembly.

(a) 15-Ampere Main Power-Supply Assembly. Recreational vehicles wired in accordance with Section 551-42(a) shall use a listed 15-ampere, or larger, main power-supply assembly.

(b) 20-Ampere Main Power-Supply Assembly. Recreational vehicles wired in accordance with Section 551-42(b) shall use a listed 20-ampere, or larger, main power-supply assembly.

(c) 30-Ampere Main Power-Supply Assembly. Recreational vehicles wired in accordance with Section 551-42(c) shall use a listed 30-ampere, or larger, main power-supply assembly.

(d) 40- or 50-Ampere Power-Supply Assembly. In accordance with Section 551-42(d), any recreational vehicle with a rating in excess of 30 amperes, 120 volts, shall use a listed 40-ampere or 50-ampere, 120/240-volt power-supply assembly.

Exception No. 1: Where the calculated load of the recreational vehicle exceeds 30 amperes, 120 volts, a second power-supply cord shall be permitted. Where a two-cord supply system is installed, they shall not be interconnected on either the line side or the load side. The grounding circuits and grounding means shall be electrically interconnected.

Exception No. 2: For a dual-supply source consisting of a generator and a power-supply cord, see Section 551-31.

551-45. Distribution Panelboard.

(a) Listed and Appropriately Rated. A listed and appropriately rated distribution panelboard or other equipment specifically listed for the purpose shall be used. The grounded conductor termination bar shall be insulated from the enclosure as provided in Section 551-54(c). An equipment grounding terminal bar shall be attached inside the metal enclosure of the panelboard.

(b) Location. The distribution panelboard shall be installed in a readily accessible location. Working clearance for the panelboard shall be no less than 24 inches (610 mm) wide and 30 inches (762 mm) deep.

Exception No. 1: Where the panelboard cover is exposed to the inside aisle space, then one of the working clearance dimensions shall be permitted to be reduced to a minimum of 22 inches (559 mm). A panelboard is considered exposed where the panelboard cover is within 2 inches (50.8 mm) of the aisle's finished surface.

Exception No. 2: Compartment doors used for access to a generator shall be permitted to be equipped with a locking system.

(c) Dead-Front Type. The distribution panelboard shall be of the dead-front type and shall consist of one or more circuit breakers or Type S fuseholders. A main disconnecting means shall be provided where fuses are used or where more than two circuit breakers are employed. A main overcurrent protective device not exceeding the power-supply assembly rating shall be provided where more than two branch circuits are employed.

551-46. Means for Connecting to Power Supply.

(a) Assembly. The power-supply assembly or assemblies shall be factory-supplied or factory-installed and be of one of the types as specified herein:

(1) Separable. Where a separable power-supply assembly consisting of a cord with a female connector and molded attachment plug cap is provided, the vehicle shall be equipped with a permanently mounted, flanged surface inlet (male, recessed-type motor-base attachment plug) wired directly to the distribution panelboard by an approved wiring method. The attachment plug cap shall be of a listed type.

(2) Permanently Connected. Each power-supply assembly shall be connected directly to the terminals of the distribution panelboard or conductors within a junction box and provided with means to prevent strain from being transmitted to the terminals. The ampacity of the conductors between each junction box and the terminals of each distribution panelboard shall be at least equal to the ampacity of the power-supply cord. The supply end of the assembly shall be equipped with an attachment plug of the type described in Section 551-46(c). Where the cord passes through the walls or floors, it shall be protected by means of conduit and bushings or equivalent. The cord assembly shall have permanent provisions for protection against corrosion and mechanical damage while the vehicle is in transit.

(b) Cord. The cord exposed usable length shall be measured from the point of entrance to the recreational vehicle or the face of the flanged surface inlet (motor-base attachment plug) to the face of the attachment plug at the supply end.

The cord exposed usable length, measured to the point of entry on the vehicle exterior, shall be a minimum of 23 feet (7.0 m) where the point of entrance is at the side of the vehicle, or shall be a minimum 28 feet (8.5 m) where the point of entrance is at the rear of the vehicle.

Where the cord entrance into the vehicle is more than 3 feet (0.9 m) above the ground, the minimum cord lengths above shall be increased by the vertical distance of the cord entrance heights above 3 feet (0.9 m).

(FPN): See Section 551-46(e).

(c) Attachment Plugs.

(1) Recreational vehicles having only one 15-ampere branch circuit as permitted by Section 551-42(a) shall have an attachment plug that shall be 2-pole, 3-wire, grounding type, rated 15 amperes, 125 volts, conforming to the configuration shown in Figure 551-46(c).

(FPN): Complete details of this configuration can be found in American National Standard ANSI C73.11-1972.

(2) Recreational vehicles having only one 20-ampere branch circuit as permitted in Section 551-42(b) shall have an attachment plug that shall be 2-pole, 3-wire, grounding type, rated 20 amperes, 125 volts, conforming to the configuration shown in Figure 551-46(c).

(FPN): Complete details of this configuration can be found in American National Standard ANSI C73.12-1972.

(3) Recreational vehicles wired in accordance with Section 551-42(c) shall have an attachment plug that shall be 2-pole, 3-wire, grounding type, rated 30 amperes, 125 volts, conforming to the configuration shown in Figure 551-46(c) intended for use with units rated at 30 amperes, 125 volts.

(FPN): Complete details of this configuration can be found in American National Standard Dimensions of Caps, Plugs and Receptacles, ANSI C73.13-1972.

(4) Recreational vehicles having a power-supply assembly rated 40 amperes or 50 amperes as permitted by Section 551-42(d) shall have a 3-pole, 4-wire, grounding-type attachment plug rated 50 amperes, 125/250 volts, conforming to the configuration shown in Figure 551-46(c).

(FPN): Complete details of this configuration can be found in American National Standard Dimensions of Caps, Plugs and Receptacles, ANSI C73.17-1972.

The 20- and 50-ampere receptacle and plug configurations used for recreational vehicles appear in Figure 210-7 (NEMA configuration chart); however, the 30-ampere plug and receptacle are special for recreational vehicles and are described in UL 498.

(d) Labeling at Electrical Entrance. Each recreational vehicle shall have permanently affixed to the exterior skin, at or near the point of entrance of the power-supply cord(s), a label 3 inches (76 mm) by 1¾ inches (44.5 mm) minimum size, made of etched, metal-stamped or embossed brass, stainless steel, or anodized or alclad aluminum not less than 0.020 inch (508 micrometers) thick, or other suitable material [e.g., 0.005-inch (127-micrometer) thick plastic laminate], that reads, as appropriate, either:

Figure 551-46(c). *Configurations for Grounding-type Receptacles and Attachment Plug Caps Used for Recreational Vehicle Supply Cords and Recreatonal Vehicle Lots.*

"This connection is for 110-125 volt ac, 60 Hz ampere supply," or

"This connection is for 120/240 volt ac, 3-pole, 4-wire 60 Hz ____ ampere supply."

The correct ampere rating shall be marked in the blank space.

(e) Location. The point of entrance of a power-supply assembly shall be located within 15 feet (4.57 m) of the rear, on the left (road) side or at the rear, left of the longitudinal center of the vehicle, within 18 inches (457 mm) of the outside wall.

Exception No. 1: A recreational vehicle equipped with only a listed flexible drain system or a side-vent drain system shall be permitted to have the electrical point of entrance located on either side, provided the drain(s) for the plumbing system is (are) located on the same side.

Exception No. 2: A recreational vehicle shall be permitted to have the electrical point of entrance located more than 15 feet (4.57 m) from the rear. Where this occurs, the distance beyond the 15-foot (4.57-m) dimension shall be added to the cord's minimum length as specified in 551-46(b).

551-47. Wiring Methods.

(a) Wiring Systems. Rigid metal conduit, intermediate metal conduit, electrical metallic tubing, rigid nonmetallic conduit, flexible metal conduit, Type MC cable, Type MI cable, Type AC cable, and nonmetallic-sheathed cable shall be permitted. An equipment grounding means shall be provided in accordance with Section 250-91.

See commentary following Section 350-5.

(b) Conduit and Tubing. Where rigid metal conduit or intermediate metal conduit is terminated at an enclosure with a locknut and bushing connection, two locknuts shall be provided, one inside and one outside of the enclosure. All cut ends of conduit and tubing shall be reamed or otherwise finished to remove rough edges.

See commentary following Sections 348-11 and 373-6(c).

(c) Nonmetallic Boxes. Nonmetallic boxes shall be acceptable only with nonmetallic-sheathed cable or rigid nonmetallic conduit.

(d) Boxes. In walls and ceilings constructed of wood or other combustible material, boxes and fittings shall be flush with the finished surface or project therefrom.

(e) Mounting. Wall and ceiling boxes shall be mounted in accordance with Article 370.

Exception No. 1: Snap-in type boxes or boxes provided with special wall or ceiling brackets that securely fasten boxes in walls or ceilings shall be permitted.

Exception No. 2: A wooden plate providing a 1½-inch (38-mm) minimum width backing around the box and of a thickness of ½ inch (12.7 mm) or greater (actual) glued to the wall panel shall be considered as approved means for mounting outlet boxes.

This exception permits mounting of outlet boxes by screws to a wooden plate secured by adhesive to the back of the wall panel. This wooden plate is required to be not less than ½-inch thick and is required to extend at least 1½ inches around the box. This recognizes the special construction of recreational vehicle walls, which often makes it quite difficult or impossible to attach an outlet box to a structural member as required by Section 370-23(b).

(f) Sheath Armor. The sheath of nonmetallic-sheathed cable, metal-clad cable, and Type AC cable shall be continuous between outlet boxes and other enclosures.

(g) Protected. Metal-clad, Type AC, or nonmetallic-sheathed cables shall be permitted to pass through the centers of the wide side of 2-inch by 4-inch wood studs. However, they shall be protected where they pass through 2-inch by 2-inch wood studs or at other wood studs or frames where the cable would be less than 1½ inches (38 mm) from the inside or outside surface. Steel plates on each side of the cable, or a steel tube, with not less than No. 16 MSG wall thickness, shall be installed to protect the cable. These plates or tubes shall be securely held in place. Where nonmetallic-sheathed cables pass through punched, cut, or drilled slots or holes in metal members, the cable shall be protected by bushings or grommets securely fastened in the opening prior to installation of the cable.

(h) Bends. No bend shall have a radius of less than five times the cable diameter.

(i) Cable Supports. Where connected with cable connectors or clamps, cables shall be supported within 12 inches (305 mm) of outlet boxes, distribution panelboards, and splice boxes on appliances. Supports shall be provided every 4½ feet (1.37 m) at other places.

(j) Nonmetallic Box without Cable Clamps. Nonmetallic-sheathed cables shall be supported within 8 inches (203 mm) of a nonmetallic outlet box without cable clamps.

Exception: Where wiring devices with integral enclosures are employed with a loop of extra cable to permit future replacement of the device, the cable loop shall be considered as an integral portion of the device.

(k) Physical Damage. Where subject to physical damage, exposed nonmetallic cable shall be protected by covering boards, guard strips, raceways, or other means.

(l) Metal Faceplates. Metal faceplates shall be of ferrous metal not less than 0.030 inch (762 micrometers) in thickness or of nonferrous metal not less than 0.040 inch (1.02 mm) in thickness. Nonmetallic faceplates shall be listed.

(m) Metal Faceplates Effectively Grounded. Where metal faceplates are used, they shall be effectively grounded.

(n) Moisture or Physical Damage. Where outdoor or underchassis wiring is 120 volts, nominal, or over and is exposed to moisture or physical damage, the wiring shall be protected by rigid metal conduit, intermediate metal conduit, or by electrical metallic tubing or rigid nonmetallic conduit that is closely routed against frames and equipment enclosures or other raceway or cable identified for the application.

(o) Component Interconnections. Fittings and connectors that are intended to be concealed at the time of assembly shall be listed and identified for the interconnection of building components. Such fittings and connectors shall be equal to the wiring method employed in insulation, temperature rise, fault-current withstanding, and shall be capable of enduring the vibration and shock occurring in recreational vehicles.

(p) Method of Connecting Expandable Units.

(1) That portion of a branch circuit that is installed in an expandable unit shall be permitted to be connected to the portion of the branch circuit in the main body of the vehicle by means of an attachment plug and cord listed for hard usage. The cord and its connections shall conform to all provisions of Article 400 and shall be considered as a permitted use under Section 400-7.

Exception: Where the attachment plug and cord are located within the vehicle's interior, use of plastic thermoset or elastomer parallel cord Type SPT-3, SP-3, or SPE shall be permitted.

(2) If the receptacle provided for connection of the cord to the main circuit is located on the outside of the vehicle, it shall be protected with a ground-fault circuit-interrupter for personnel and be listed for wet locations. A cord located on the outside of a vehicle shall be identified for outdoor use.

(3) Unless removable or stored within the vehicle interior, the cord assembly shall have permanent provisions for protection against corrosion and mechanical damage while the vehicle is in transit.

(4) The cord shall be installed so as not to permit exposed live attachment plug pins.

(q) Prewiring for Air Conditioning Installation. Prewiring installed for the purpose of facilitating future air-conditioning installation shall conform to the following and other applicable portions of this article. The circuit shall serve no other purpose.

(1) An overcurrent-protective device with a rating compatible with the circuit conductors shall be installed in the distribution panelboard and wiring connections completed.

(2) The load end of the circuit shall terminate in a junction box with a blank cover or a device listed for the purpose. Where a junction box with a blank cover is used, the free ends of the conductors shall be adequately capped or taped.

(3) A label conforming to Section 551-46(d) shall be placed on or adjacent to the junction box and shall read:

AIR-CONDITIONING CIRCUIT. THIS
CONNECTION IS FOR AIR CONDITIONERS
RATED 110-125 VOLT AC, 60 HZ _____
AMPERES MAXIMUM. DO NOT EXCEED
CIRCUIT RATING.

An ampere rating, not to exceed 80 percent of the circuit rating, shall be legibly marked in the blank space.

(r) Prewiring for Generator Installation. Prewiring installed for the purpose of facilitating future generator installation shall conform to the following and other applicable portions of this article.

(1) Circuit conductors shall be appropriately sized in relation to the anticipated load and shall be protected by an overcurrent device in accordance with their ampacities.

(2) Where junction boxes are utilized at either of the circuit originating or terminus points, free ends of the conductors shall be adequately capped or taped.

(3) Where devices such as receptacle outlet, transfer switch, etc., are installed, the installation shall be complete, including circuit conductor connections. All devices shall be listed and appropriately rated.

(4) A label conforming to Section 551-46(d) shall be placed on the cover of each junction box containing incomplete circuitry and shall read, as appropriate, either:

GENERATOR CIRCUIT. THIS CONNECTION
IS FOR GENERATORS RATED 110-125 VOLT
AC, 60 HZ _____ AMPERES MAXIMUM.
OR
GENERATOR CIRCUIT. THIS CONNECTION
IS FOR GENERATORS RATED 120/240 VOLT
AC, 60 HZ _____ AMPERES MAXIMUM.

The correct ampere rating shall be legibly marked in the blank space.

551-48. Conductors and Boxes.

(a) Maximum Number of Conductors. The maximum number of conductors permitted in boxes shall be in accordance with Section 370-16.

(b) Free Conductor at Each Box. At least 4 inches (102 mm) of free conductor shall be left at each box except where conductors are intended to loop without joints.

551-49. **Grounded Conductors.** The identification of grounded conductors shall be in accordance with Section 200-6.

551-50. **Connection of Terminals and Splices.** Conductor splices and connections at terminals shall be in accordance with Section 110-14. If splices of the equipment grounding conductor in nonmetallic-sheathed cable are made in boxes containing devices, the splices shall be insulated.

551-51. **Switches.** Switches shall be rated as follows:

(a) Lighting Circuits. For lighting circuits, switches shall be rated not less than 10 amperes, 120-125 volts and in no case less than the connected load.

(b) Motors or Other Loads. For motors or other loads, switches shall have ampere or horsepower ratings, or both, adequate for loads controlled. (An ac general-use snap switch shall be permitted to control a motor 2 horsepower or less with full-load current not over 80 percent of the switch ampere rating.)

551-52. **Receptacles.** All receptacle outlets shall be (1) of the grounding type and (2) installed in accordance with Sections 210-7 and 210-21.

551-53. **Lighting Fixtures.**

(a) General. Any combustible wall or ceiling finish exposed between the edge of a fixture canopy, or pan and the outlet box, shall be covered with noncombustible material or a material identified for the purpose.

(b) Shower Fixtures. If a lighting fixture is provided over a bathtub or in a shower stall, it shall be of the enclosed and gasketed type and listed for the type of installation, and it shall be ground-fault circuit-interrupter protected if rated at 120 volts, nominal.

Many shower lights have a metal base and due to low ceilings in recreational vehicles may be easily reached by most persons under a shower or standing in a bathtub. This section will permit lighting fixtures listed for a wet location to be installed above a tub or shower enclosure if shock-hazard protection is provided by a ground-fault circuit-interrupter.

The switch for shower lighting fixtures and exhaust fans, located over a tub or in a shower stall, shall be located outside the tub or shower space.

(c) Outdoor Outlets, Fixtures, Air-Cooling Equipment, Etc. Outdoor fixtures and other equipment shall be listed for outdoor use.

551-54. **Grounding.** (See also Section 551-56 on bonding of noncurrent-carrying metal parts.)

(a) Power-Supply Grounding. The grounding conductor in the supply cord or feeder shall be connected to the grounding bus or other approved grounding means in the distribution panelboard.

(b) Distribution Panelboard. The distribution panelboard shall have a grounding bus with sufficient terminals for all grounding conductors or other approved grounding means.

(c) Insulated Neutral.

(1) The grounded circuit conductor (neutral) shall be insulated from the equipment grounding conductors and from equipment enclosures and other grounded parts. The grounded (neutral) circuit terminals in the distribution panelboard and in ranges, clothes dryers, counter-mounted cooking units, and wall-mounted ovens shall be insulated from the equipment enclosure. Bonding screws, straps, or buses in the distribution panelboard or in appliances shall be removed and discarded.

(2) Connection of electric ranges and electric clothes dryers utilizing a grounded (neutral) conductor, if cord-connected, shall be made with 4-conductor cord and 3-pole, 4-wire, grounding-type plug caps and receptacles.

551-55. **Interior Equipment Grounding.**

(a) Exposed Metal Parts. In the electrical system, all exposed metal parts, enclosures, frames, lighting fixture canopies, etc., shall be effectively bonded to the grounding terminals or enclosure of the distribution panelboard.

(b) Equipment Grounding Conductors. Bare wires, green-colored wires, or green wires with yellow stripe(s) shall be used for equipment grounding conductors only.

(c) Grounding of Electrical Equipment. Where grounding of electrical equipment is specified, it shall be permitted as follows:

(1) Connection of metal raceway (conduit or electrical metallic tubing), the sheath of Type MC and Type MI cable where the sheath is identified for grounding, or the armor of Type AC cable to metal enclosures.

(2) A connection between the one or more equipment grounding conductors and a metal box by means of a grounding screw, which shall be used for no other purpose, or a listed grounding device.

(3) The equipment grounding conductor in nonmetallic-sheathed cable shall be permitted to be secured under a screw threaded into the fixture canopy other than a mounting screw or cover screw, or attached to a listed grounding means (plate) in a nonmetallic outlet box for fixture mounting (grounding means shall also be permitted for fixture attachment screws).

(d) Grounding Connection in Nonmetallic Box. A connection between the one or more grounding conductors brought into a nonmetallic outlet box shall be so arranged that a connection can be made to any fitting or device in that box that requires grounding.

(e) Grounding Continuity. Where more than one equipment grounding conductor of a branch circuit enters a box, all such conductors shall be in good electrical contact with each other, and the arrangement shall be such that the disconnection or removal of a receptacle, fixture, or other device fed from the box will not interfere with or interrupt the grounding continuity.

(f) Cord-Connected Appliances. Cord-connected appliances, such as washing machines, clothes dryers, refrigerators, and the electrical system of gas ranges, etc., shall be grounded by means of an approved cord with equipment grounding conductor and grounding-type attachment plug.

551-56. Bonding of Noncurrent-Carrying Metal Parts.

(a) Required Bonding. All exposed noncurrent-carrying metal parts that may become energized shall be effectively bonded to the grounding terminal or enclosure of the distribution panelboard.

(b) Bonding Chassis. A bonding conductor shall be connected between any distribution panelboard and an accessible terminal on the chassis. Aluminum or copper-clad aluminum conductors shall not be used for bonding if such conductors or their terminals are exposed to corrosive elements.

Exception: Any recreational vehicle that employs a unitized metal chassis-frame construction to which the distribution panelboard is securely fastened with a bolt(s) and nut(s) or by welding or riveting shall be considered to be bonded.

(c) Bonding Conductor Requirements. Grounding terminals shall be of the solderless type and listed as pressure terminal connectors recognized for the wire size used. The bonding conductor shall be solid or stranded, insulated or bare, and shall be No. 8 copper minimum, or equal.

(d) Metallic Roof and Exterior Bonding. The metal roof and exterior covering shall be considered bonded where:

(1) The metal panels overlap one another and are securely attached to the wood or metal frame parts by metal fasteners, and

(2) The lower panel of the metal exterior covering is secured by metal fasteners at each cross member of the chassis, or the lower panel is bonded to the chassis by a metal strap.

(e) Gas, Water, and Waste Pipe Bonding. The gas, water, and waste pipes shall be considered grounded if they are bonded to the chassis.

(FPN): See Section 551-56(b) for chassis bonding.

(f) Furnace and Metal Air Duct Bonding. Furnace and metal circulating air ducts shall be bonded.

551-57. Appliance Accessibility and Fastening. Every appliance shall be accessible for inspection, service, repair, and replacement without removal of permanent construction. Means shall be provided to securely fasten appliances in place when the recreational vehicle is in transit.

F. Factory Tests

551-60. Factory Tests (Electrical). Each recreational vehicle shall be subjected to the following tests:

(a) Circuits of 120 Volts or 120/240 Volts. Each recreational vehicle designed with a 120-volt or a 120/240-volt electrical system shall withstand the applied potential without electrical breakdown of a 1-minute, 900-volt dielectric strength test, or a 1-second, 1080-volt dielectric strength test, with all switches closed, between ungrounded and grounded conductors and the recreational vehicle ground. During the test, all switches and other controls shall be in the "on" position. Fixtures and permanently installed appliances shall not be required to withstand this test.

Each recreational vehicle shall be subjected to (1) a continuity test to assure that all metal parts are properly bonded; (2) operational tests to demonstrate that all equipment is properly connected and in working order; and (3) polarity checks to determine that connections have been properly made.

(b) Low-Voltage Circuits. Low-voltage circuit conductors in each recreational vehicle shall withstand the applied potential without electrical breakdown of a 1-minute, 500-volt or a 1-second, 600-volt dielectric strength test. The potential shall be applied between ungrounded and grounded conductors.

The test shall be permitted on running light circuits before the lights are installed provided the vehicle's outer covering and interior cabinetry has been secured. The braking circuit shall be permitted to be tested before being connected to the brakes, provided the wiring has been completely secured.

G. Recreational Vehicle Parks

551-71. **Type Receptacles Provided.** Every recreational vehicle site with electrical supply shall be equipped with at least one 20-ampere, 125-volt receptacle. A minimum of 75 percent of all recreational vehicle sites with electrical supply shall each be equipped with a 30-ampere, 125-volt receptacle conforming to Figure 551-46(c). This supply shall be permitted to include additional receptacle configurations conforming to Section 551-81. The remainder of all recreational vehicle sites with electrical supply shall be equipped with one or more of the receptacle configurations conforming to Section 551-81. All 20-ampere, 125-volt receptacles shall have listed ground-fault circuit-interrupter protection for personnel.

This section requires at least one 20-ampere, 125-volt receptacle at each recreational vehicle campsite. Existing recreational vehicle campgrounds may have some sites that are equipped with 30-ampere receptacles only. Adapter plugs or "cheater" cords are often used to connect a recreational vehicle with a 20-ampere supply cord to a 30-ampere receptacle outlet. This practice does not provide adequate overload protection for the cord or the connected load. This section will help ensure the availability of the proper receptacle.

Additional receptacles shall be permitted for the connection of electrical equipment outside the recreational vehicle within the recreational vehicle park. All such 125-volt, single-phase, 15- and 20-ampere receptacles shall have ground-fault circuit-interrupter protection for personnel.

551-72. **Distribution System.** The recreational vehicle park secondary electrical distribution system to recreational vehicle sites shall be derived from a single-phase 120/240-volt, 3-wire system.

See Section 551-73(b). The reason for requiring single-phase, 120/240-V, 3-wire systems to the recreational vehicle site is because the recreational vehicles are designed for connection to such systems. If the recreational vehicle park supplies another type of system to the recreational vehicle site (two-phase conductors and a neutral of a 3-phase, 4-wire, 208Y/120-V system, for example), a hazard could result due to a supply of less than 240V, nominal, to motors, for example, or attempts to adapt the recreational vehicle to a different supply system than the one for which it was designed.

(FPN): On a 120/240-volt, 3-wire, single-phase service or feeder, the neutral cannot be reduced in size (below the size of the ungrounded conductors) if there are no 240-volt loads, because, under the most severe conditions of unbalance, the neutral will carry the same current as the ungrounded conductor supplying the load.

551-73. **Calculated Load.**

(a) Basis of Calculations. Electrical service and feeders shall be calculated on the basis of not less than 9,600 volt-amperes per site equipped with 50-ampere 120/240-volt supply facilities, 3,600 volt-amperes per site equipped with both 20-ampere and 30-ampere supply facilities, and 2,400 volt-amperes per site equipped with only 20-ampere supply facilities. The demand factors set forth in Table 551-73 shall be the minimum allowable demand factors that shall be permitted in calculating load for service and feeders.

Loads for other amenities such as, but not limited to, service buildings, recreational buildings, and swimming pools shall be sized separately and then be added to the value calculated for the recreational vehicle sites where they are all supplied by one service.

Table 551-73. Demand Factors for Site Feeders and Service-Entrance Conductors for Park Sites

Number of Recreational Vehicle Sites	Demand Factor (percent)	Number of Recreational Vehicle Sites	Demand Factor (percent)
1	100	10-12	50
2	90	13-15	48
3	80	16-18	47
4	75	19-21	45
5	65	22-24	43
6	60	25-35	42
7-9	55	36 plus	41

(b) Transformers and Secondary Distribution Panelboards. For the purpose of this Code, where the park service exceeds 240 volts, transformers and secondary distribution panelboards shall be treated as services.

(c) Demand Factors. The demand factor for a given number of sites shall apply to all sites indicated. For example: twenty sites calculated at 42 percent of 3,600 volt-amperes result in a permissible demand of 1512 volt-amperes per site or a total of 30,240 volt-amperes for twenty sites.

(FPN): These demand factors may be inadequate in areas of extreme hot or cold temperature with loaded circuits for heating or air conditioning.

(d) Feeder Circuit Capacity. Recreational vehicle site feeder circuit conductors shall have adequate ampacity for the loads supplied and shall be rated at not less than 30 amperes. The grounded conductors shall have the same ampacity as the ungrounded conductors.

See FPN below Section 551-72.

(FPN): Due to the long circuit lengths typical in most recreational vehicle parks, feeder conductor sizes found in ampacity tables of Article 310 may be inadequate to maintain the voltage regulation suggested in the Fine Print Note to Section 210-19. Total circuit voltage drop is a summation of the voltage drops of each serial circuit segment, where the load for each segment is calculated using the load that segment sees and the demand factors of Section 551-73(a).

551-74. **Overcurrent Protection.** Overcurrent protection shall be provided in accordance with Article 240.

551-75. **Grounding.** All electrical equipment and installations in recreational vehicle parks shall be grounded as required by Article 250.

551-76. **Recreational Vehicle Site Supply Equipment.**

(a) Location. Where provided, the recreational vehicle site electrical supply equipment shall be located on the left (road) side of the parked vehicle, on a line that is 9 feet (2.74 m), + 1 foot (0.3 m), from the longitudinal centerline of the stand and shall be located at any point on this line from the rear of the stand to 15 feet (4.57 m) forward of the rear of the stand.

Exception: For pull-through sites, it shall be permitted to locate the electrical supply equipment at any point along the line from

16 feet (4.88 m) forward of the rear of the stand to 32 feet (9.75 m) forward of the rear of the stand.

This exception is new in the 1993 *Code.* It is intended to accommodate vehicles towing boats, etc. The location of the site supply equipment permitted for pull-through sites will reduce the use of extension cords.

(b) Disconnecting Means. A disconnecting switch or circuit breaker shall be provided in the site supply equipment for disconnecting the power supply to the recreational vehicle.

(c) Access. All site supply equipment shall be accessible by an unobstructed entrance or passageway not less than 2 feet (610 mm) wide and 6½ feet (1.98 m) high.

(d) Mounting Height. Site supply equipment shall be located not less than 2 feet (610 mm) nor more than 6½ feet (1.98 m) above the ground.

(e) Working Space. Sufficient space shall be provided and maintained about all electric equipment to permit ready and safe operation, in accordance with Section 110-16.

551-77. **Grounding, Recreational Vehicle Site Supply Equipment.**

(a) Exposed Noncurrent-Carrying Metal Parts. Exposed noncurrent-carrying metal parts of fixed equipment, metal boxes, cabinets, and fittings, that are not electrically connected to grounded equipment, shall be grounded by a continuous equipment grounding conductor run with the circuit conductors from the service equipment or from the transformer of a secondary distribution system. Equipment grounding conductors shall be sized in accordance with Section 250-95.

The arrangement of equipment grounding connnections shall be such that the disconnection or removal of a receptacle or other device will not interfere with, or interrupt, the grounding continuity.

(b) Secondary Distribution System. Each secondary distribution system shall be grounded at the transformer.

(c) Neutral Conductor Not to Be Used as an Equipment Ground. The neutral conductor shall not be used as an equipment ground for recreational vehicles or equipment within the recreational vehicle park.

(d) No Connection on the Load Side. No connection to a grounding electrode shall be made to the neutral conductor on the load side of the service disconnecting means or tranformer distribution panelboard.

551-78. **Protection of Outdoor Equipment.**

(a) Wet Locations. All switches, circuit breakers, receptacles, control equipment, and metering devices located in wet locations or outside of a building shall be rainproof equipment.

(b) Meters. If secondary meters are installed, meter sockets without meters installed shall be blanked-off with an approved blanking plate.

Figure 551-1. *Recreational vehicle site supply equipment with receptacles per Section 551-52 and ground-fault circuit-interrupter protection for the 20-A, 125-volt receptacle outlet.*

551-79. **Clearance for Overhead Conductors.** Open conductors of not over 600 volts, nominal, shall have a vertical clearance of not less than 18 feet (5.49 m) and a horizontal clearance of not less than 3 feet (914 mm) in all areas subject to recreational vehicle movement. In all other areas, clearances shall conform to Sections 225-18 and 225-19.

(FPN): For clearances of conductors over 600 volts, nominal, see National Electrical Safety Code, ANSI C2-1990.

551-80. **Underground Service, Feeder, Branch-Circuit and Recreational Vehicle Site Feeder Circuit Conductors.**

(a) General. All direct-burial conductors, including the equipment grounding conductor if of aluminum, shall be insulated and identified for the use. All conductors shall be continuous from equipment to equipment. All splices and taps shall be made in approved junction boxes or by use of material listed and identified for the purpose.

(b) Protection Against Physical Damage. Direct-buried conductors and cables entering or leaving a trench shall be protected by rigid metal conduit, intermediate metal conduit, electrical metallic tubing with supplementary corrosion protection, rigid nonmetallic conduit, or other approved raceways or enclosures. Where subject to physical damage, the conductors or cables shall be protected by rigid metal conduit, intermediate conduit, or Schedule 80 rigid nonmetallic conduit. All such protection shall extend at least 18 inches (457 mm) into the trench from finished grade.

(FPN): See Section 300-5 and Article 339 for conductors or Type UF cable used underground or in direct burial in earth.

551-81. **Receptacles.** A receptacle to supply electric power to a recreational vehicle shall be one of the configurations shown in Figure 551-46(c) in the following ratings:

(a) 50-Ampere. 125/250 volts, 50-ampere, 3-pole, 4-wire, grounding type for 120/240-volt systems.

(b) 30-Ampere. 125-volt, 30-ampere, 2-pole, 3-wire, grounding type for 120-volt systems.

(c) 20-Ampere. 125-volt, 20-ampere, 2-pole, 3-wire, grounding type for 120-volt systems.

(FPN): Complete details of these configurations can be found in American National Standard Dimensions of Caps, Plugs and Receptacles, ANSI C73.17-1972; ANSI C73.13-1972; and C73.12-1972.

ARTICLE 553   Floating Buildings

Contents

A. General

B. Services and Feeders

A. General

553-1. **Scope.** This article covers wiring, services, feeders, and grounding for floating buildings.

553-2. **Definition.**

Floating Building. A building unit as defined in Article 100 that floats on water, is moored in a permanent location, and has a premises wiring system served through connection by permanent wiring to an electricity supply system not located on the premises.

553-3. **Application of Other Articles.** Wiring for floating buildings shall comply with the applicable provisions of other articles of this Code, except as modified by this article.

B. Services and Feeders

553-4. **Location of Service Equipment.** The service equipment for a floating building shall be located adjacent to, but not in or on, the building.

The intent here is to ensure that supply conductors to a floating building can be disconnected in an emergency, such as during a storm, where the floating dwelling unit has to be moved quickly.

Overcurrent protection for supply conductors is also provided where these conductors may develop excessive leakage, where underwater, or where a short circuit or fault may occur.

553-5. **Service Conductors.** One set of service conductors shall be permitted to serve more than one set of service equipment.

553-6. **Feeder Conductors.** Each floating building shall be supplied by a single set of feeder conductors from its service equipment.

Exception: Where the floating building has multiple occupancy, each occupant shall be permitted to be supplied by a single set of feeder conductors extended from the occupant's service equipment to the occupant's panelboard.

553-7. **Installation of Services and Feeders.**

(a) Flexibility. Flexibility of the wiring system shall be maintained between floating buildings and the supply conductors. All wiring shall be so installed that motion of the water surface and changes in the water level will not result in unsafe conditions.

(b) Wiring Methods. Liquidtight flexible metal conduit or liquidtight flexible nonmetallic conduit with approved fittings shall be permitted for feeders and where flexible connections are required for services. Extra-hard usage portable power cable listed for both wet locations and sunlight resistance shall be permitted for a feeder to a floating building where flexibility is required.

(FPN): See Sections 555-1 and 555-6.

Type W cables included in Table 400-4 are listed for wet locations. Liquidtight flexible nonmetallic conduit with approved fittings was added to the permitted wiring methods in the 1993 *Code.*

C. Grounding

553-8. **General Requirements.** Grounding of both electrical and nonelectrical parts in a floating building shall be through connection to a grounding bus in the building panelboard. The grounding bus shall be grounded through a green-colored insulated equipment grounding conductor run with the feeder conductors and connected to a grounding terminal in the service equipment. The grounding terminal in the service equipment shall be grounded by connection through a green insulated grounding electrode conductor to a grounding electrode on shore.

553-9. Insulated Neutral. The grounded circuit conductor (neutral) shall be a white insulated conductor. The neutral conductor shall be connected to the equipment grounding terminal in the service equipment, and, except for that connection, it shall be insulated from the equipment grounding conductors, equipment enclosures, and all other grounded parts. The neutral circuit terminals in the panelboard and in ranges, clothes dryers, counter-mounted cooking units, and the like shall be insulated from the enclosures.

553-10. Equipment Grounding.

(a) **Electrical Systems.** All enclosures and exposed metal parts of electrical systems shall be bonded to the grounding bus.

(b) **Cord-Connected Appliances.** Where required to be grounded, cord-connected appliances shall be grounded by means of an equipment grounding conductor in the cord and a grounding-type attachment plug.

553-11. Bonding of Noncurrent-Carrying Metal Parts. All metal parts in contact with the water, all metal piping, and all noncurrent-carrying metal parts that may become energized, shall be bonded to the grounding bus in the panelboard.

ARTICLE 555   Marinas and Boatyards

Contents

555-1. Scope. This article covers the installation of wiring and equipment in the areas comprising fixed or floating piers, wharfs, docks, and other areas in marinas, boatyards, boat basins, and similar establishments that are used, or intended for use, for the purpose of repair, berthing, launching, storage, or fueling of small craft and the moorage of floating buildings.

See Article 553 for requirements for floating buildings, including floating dwelling units.

555-2. Application of Other Articles. Wiring and equipment for marinas and boatyards shall comply with this article and also with the applicable provisions of other articles of this Code.

(FPN No. 1):   See fine print notes following Sections 210-19(a) and 215-2(b) for voltage drop on branch circuits and feeders, respectively.

(FPN No. 2):   For disconnection of auxiliary power from boats, see Pleasure and Commercial Motor Craft, NFPA 302-1989 (ANSI).

555-3. Receptacles. Where shore power is supplied, those accommodations for boats 20 feet (6.1 m) or less in length shall be equipped with shore-power receptacles of a locking and grounding type rated at not less than 20 amperes.

Where shore power is supplied to accommodations for boats longer than 20 feet (6.1 m) in length, shore-power receptacles of a locking and grounding type rated at 30 amperes or more shall be provided.

Fifteen- and 20-ampere, single-phase, 125-volt receptacles other than those supplying shore power to boats located at piers, wharfs, and other locations shall be protected by ground-fault circuit-interrupters.

(FPN No. 1):   For various configurations and ratings of locking- and grounding-type receptacles and caps, see Dimensions of Caps, Plugs, and Receptacles, ANSI C73-1972, and Supplement ANSI C73a-1980.

(FPN No. 2):   For locking- and grounding-type receptacles for auxiliary power to boats, see Marinas and Boatyards, NFPA 303-1990 (ANSI).

(FPN No. 3):   In locating receptacles, consideration should be given to the maximum tide level and wave action. See Marinas and Boatyards, NFPA 303-1990 (ANSI), for establishment of datum plane.

Single locking- and grounding-type receptacles are required for providing shore power to boats. See Figures 555-1 and 210-8 for a complete chart of grounding-type locking plug and receptacle configurations. See Figure 555-2 for a power outlet assembly used at marinas and boatyards.

Each single receptacle that supplies shore power to boats is required to be supplied from an individual branch circuit. Locking- and grounding-type receptacles and attachment caps are required to ensure proper connections to prevent unintentional disconnection of onboard equipment such as bilge pumps, refrigerators, etc. Fifteen- and 20-A, single-phase, 125-V receptacles, other than those supplying shore power to boats, that are used for maintenance or other purposes at piers, wharves, etc., may be of the general-purpose, nonlocking type and are required to be protected by ground-fault circuit-interrupters. See Figure 210-17.

Fine Print Note No. 3 calls attention to the possibility of high waves (4 to 5 feet) that are often created by large cruisers and freighter traffic. This condition causes outlets and boxes to become filled with water, which results in loss of power and corrosion of the receptacle and attachment plugs.

Figure 555-2. Power outlet assembly suitable for use at docks, wharves, piers, and other locations that provide shore power to boats. (Hubbell)

Receptacle

Attachment plug

20A 125V	30A 125V	30A 125/250V
2 pole, 3 wire	2 pole, 3 wire	3 pole, 4 wire
ANSI C-73.72	ANSI C-73.73	ANSI C-73.84

Figure 555-1. Typical configurations for single, locking- and grounding-type receptacles and attachment plug caps used to provide shore power for boats in marinas and boatyards.

555-4. **Branch Circuits.** Each single receptacle that supplies shore power to boats shall be supplied from a power outlet or panelboard by an individual or multiwire branch circuit of the voltage class and rating corresponding to the rating of the receptacle.

Either an individual or a multiwire branch circuit may be used with a common neutral. See commentary following Section 300-13(b) regarding device removal for multiwire branch circuits.

(FPN): Supplying receptacles at voltages other than the voltages marked on the receptacle may cause overheating or malfunctioning of connected equipment; for example, supplying single-phase, 120/240V, 3-wire loads for a 208Y/120V, 3-wire source.

555-5. **Feeders and Services.** The load for each ungrounded feeder and service conductor supplying receptacles that supply shore power for boats shall be calculated as follows:

For 1-4 receptacles	100%	of the sum of the rating of the receptacles			
For 5-8	90%	"	"	"	"
For 9-14	80%	"	"	"	"
For 15-30	70%	"	"	"	"
For 31-40	60%	"	"	"	"
For 41-50	50%	"	"	"	"
For 51-70	40%	"	"	"	"
For 71-100	30%	"	"	"	"
For 101 plus	20%	"	"	"	"

(FPN): These demand factors may be inadequate in areas of extreme hot or cold temperature with loaded circuits for heating, air-conditioning, or refrigerating equipment.

555-6. **Wiring Methods.** The wiring method shall be of a type identified for use in wet locations. Extra-hard usage portable power cable listed for both wet locations and sunlight resistance shall be permitted for a feeder where flexibility is required.

Open wiring shall be permitted only by special permission.

(FPN No. 1): In granting special permission, major factors include possible contact of open wires with masts, cranes, or similar structures or equipment.

(FPN No. 2): For further information on wiring methods for various locations and for establishment of datum plane, see Marinas and Boatyards, NFPA 303-1990 (ANSI).

555-7. **Grounding.**

(a) **Equipment to Be Grounded.** The following items shall be connected to an equipment grounding conductor run with the circuit conductors in a raceway or cable:

(1) Boxes, cabinets, and all other metal enclosures.
(2) Metal frames of utilization equipment.
(3) Grounding terminals of grounding-type receptacles.

(b) **Type of Equipment Grounding Conductor.** The equipment grounding conductor shall be an insulated copper conductor with a continuous outer finish that is either green or green with one or more yellow stripes.

Exception: The equipment grounding conductor of Type MI cable shall be permitted to be identified at terminations.

(c) **Size of Equipment Grounding Conductor.** The insulated copper equipment grounding conductor shall be sized in accordance with Section 250-95 but not smaller than No. 12.

(d) **Branch-Circuit Equipment Grounding Conductor.** The insulated equipment grounding conductor for branch circuits shall terminate at a grounding terminal in a remote panelboard or the grounding terminal in the main service equipment.

(e) **Feeder Equipment Grounding Conductors.** Where a feeder supplies a remote panelboard, an insulated equipment grounding conductor shall extend from a grounding terminal in the service equipment to a grounding terminal in the remote panelboard.

The purpose of Section 555-7 is to require an insulated equipment grounding conductor that will ensure a grounding circuit of high integrity. Because of corrosive conditions present in marinas and boatyards, metal raceways and boxes are not permitted to serve as equipment grounding conductors.

555-8. **Wiring Over and Under Navigable Water.** Wiring over and under navigable water shall be subject to approval by the authority having jurisdiction.

Some federal and local agencies have specific authority over navigable waterways; therefore, approval of any proposed installation over or under such a waterway should be obtained from the appropriate authority.

555-9. **Gasoline Dispensing Stations — Hazardous (Classified) Locations.** Electrical equipment and wiring located in gasoline dispensing stations shall comply with Article 514.

(FPN): For further information, see Automotive and Marine Service Station Code, NFPA 30A-1990, and Marinas and Boatyards, NFPA 303-1990 (ANSI).

Section 6-3 in NFPA 303-1990, *Fire Protection Standard for Marinas and Boatyards*, and NFPA 30A-1990, *Automotive and Marine Service Station Code*, include requirements pertaining to gasoline dispensing stations. See also Chapter 3 of NFPA 303 for electrical wiring and equipment requirements for marinas and boatyards.

555-10. **Location of Service Equipment.** The service equipment for floating docks or marinas shall be located adjacent to, but not on or in, the floating structure.

This section is new in the 1993 *Code*. It is similar to Section 553-4 for floating buildings.

6

Special Equipment

ARTICLE 600   Electric Signs and Outline Lighting

Contents

A. General

B. 1,000 Volts, Nominal, or Less

(e) Conductors Soldered to Terminals.

600-22. Lampholders.

600-23. Conductors within Signs and Troughs.

600-24. Protection of Leads.

C. Over 1,000 Volts, Nominal

600-31. Installation of Conductors.

    (a) Wiring Method.

    (b) Insulation and Size.

    (c) Bends in Conductors.

    (d) Concealed Conductors on Insulators — Indoors.

    (e) Conductors in Raceways.

    (f) Show Windows and Similar Locations.

    (g) Between Tubing and Grounded Midpoint.

600-32. Transformers.

    (a) Voltage.

    (b) Type.

    (c) Exposed to Weather.

    (d) Transformer Secondary Connections.

    (e) Accessibility.

    (f) Working Space.

    (g) Attic Locations.

600-33. Electric-Discharge Tubing.

    (a) Design.

    (b) Support.

    (c) Contact with Flammable Material and Other Surfaces.

600-34. Terminals and Electrode Receptacles for Electric-Discharge Tubing.

    (a) Terminals.

    (b) Tube Connections Other than with Receptacles.

    (c) Receptacles.

    (d) Bushings.

    (e) Show Windows.

    (f) Receptacles and Bushing Seals.

    (g) Enclosures of Metal.

    (h) Enclosures of Insulating Material.

    (i) Energized Parts.

600-35. Switches on Doors.

600-36. Fixed Outline Lighting and Skeleton-type Signs for Interior Use.

    (a) Tube Support.

    (b) Transformers.

    (c) Secondary Conductors.

600-37. Portable Gas Tube Signs for Show Windows and Interior Use.

    (a) Location.

    (b) Transformer.

    (c) Supply Conductors.

    (d) Secondary Conductors.

    (e) Grounding.

    (f) Support.

A. General

600-1. Scope. This article covers the installation of conductors and equipment for electric signs and outline lighting as defined in Article 100.

600-2. Disconnect Required. Each outline lighting installation, and each sign of other than the portable type, shall be controlled by an externally operable switch or breaker that will open all ungrounded conductors.

    (a) In Sight of Sign. The disconnecting means shall be within sight of the sign or outline lighting that it controls.

Exception No. 1: A disconnecting means shall not be required for an exit directional sign connected to a circuit within the scope of Article 700.

This exception is new in the 1993 *Code*. It clarifies that a disconnecting means is not required for exit illumination signs that are connected to an emergency system.

Exception No. 2: Signs or outline lighting operated by electronic or electromechanical controllers located external to the sign shall have a disconnecting means located within sight from the controller location. The disconnecting means shall disconnect the sign and the controller from all ungrounded supply conductors and shall be so designed that no pole can be operated independently. The disconnecting means shall be permitted to be in the same enclosure with the controller. The disconnecting means shall be capable of being locked in the open position.

The disconnecting means is required to be located in a direct line of sight from the sign or outline lighting that it controls. This requirement provides protection by enabling a worker to keep the disconnecting means within view while working on the sign. The exception permits disconnecting means capable of being locked in the open position to be located elsewhere.

Figure 600-1. *Example 1 depicts the disconnecting means placement that satisfies the requirements of Section 600-2(a). Example 2 illustrates the location of a disconnecting means as permitted by Section 600-2(a), Exception No. 2.*

See Figure 600-1.

(b) Control Switch Rating. Switches, flashers, and similar devices controlling transformers shall be either rated for controlling inductive load(s) or have an ampere rating not less than twice the ampere rating of the transformer.

(FPN):   See Section 380-14 for rating of snap switches.

A switching device that controls the primary circuit of a transformer supplying a luminous gas tube encounters unusually severe arcing of its contacts. Therefore, the switch, or flasher, is required to be a general-use ac snap switch or to have a current rating that is at least twice the rating of the transformer it controls.

600-3. **Enclosures as Pull Boxes.** The wiring method used to supply signs and outline lighting shall terminate in the sign or transformer enclosures.

Exception: Such signs and transformer boxes shall be permitted to be used as pull or junction boxes for conductors supplying other adjacent signs, outline lighting systems, and floodlights that are part of signs, provided the conductors extending from the equipment are protected by an overcurrent device rated 20 amperes or less.

600-4. **Listing Required.** Every electric sign of any type, fixed or portable, shall be listed and installed in conformance with that listing, unless otherwise permitted by special permission.

Section 600-4 requires every electric sign of any type to be listed, unless otherwise permitted by special permission (i.e., the written consent of the authority having jurisdiction). Large signs are often transported in several parts from the factory to the location where they are assembled. It is at this time that an inspection authority should be present to ensure that the components are assembled in conformance with their listing.

600-5. **Grounding.** Signs, troughs, tube terminal boxes, and other metal frames shall be grounded in the manner specified in Article 250.

Exception: Isolated Parts. Isolated noncurrent-carrying metal parts of outline lighting shall be permitted to be bonded by No. 14 conductors, protected from physical damage, and grounded in accordance with Article 250.

600-6. **Branch Circuits.**

(a) Rating. Circuits that supply lamps, ballasts, and transformers, or combinations, shall be rated not to exceed 20 amperes.

Circuits containing electric-discharge lighting transformers exclusively shall not be rated in excess of 30 amperes.

(b) Required Branch Circuit. Each commercial building and each commercial occupancy accessible to pedestrians shall be provided at an accessible location outside the entrance to each tenant space, with at least one outlet for sign or outline lighting use. The outlet(s) shall be supplied by a 20-ampere branch circuit that supplies no other load.

Exception: Interior service hallways or corridors shall not be considered outside the occupancy.

Signs for commercial occupancies are usually in use for three hours or longer and are therefore considered continuous loads and are not permitted to exceed 80 percent of the rating of the branch circuit (16 amperes for a 20-ampere branch circuit).

(c) Computed Load. The load for the required branch circuit installed for the supply of exterior signs or outline lighting shall be computed at a minimum of 1200 volt-amperes.

600-7. Marking.

(a) Signs. Signs shall be marked with the maker's name; and, for incandescent lamp signs, with the number of lampholders; and, for electric-discharge-lamp signs, with input amperes at full load and input voltage. The marking of the sign shall be visible after installation.

(b) Transformers. Transformers shall be marked with the maker's name; and transformers for electric-discharge-lamp signs shall be marked with the input rating in amperes or volt-amperes, the input voltage, and the open-circuit output voltage.

600-8. Enclosures.

(a) Conductors and Terminals. Conductors and terminals in sign boxes, cabinets, and outline troughs shall be enclosed in metal or other noncombustible material.

Exception: The supply leads shall not be required to be enclosed.

(b) Cutouts, Flashers, Etc. Cutouts, flashers, and similar devices shall be enclosed in metal boxes, the doors of which shall be arranged so they can be opened without removing obstructions or finished parts of the enclosure.

(c) Strength. Enclosures shall have ample strength and rigidity.

(d) Material. Signs and outline lighting shall be constructed of metal or other noncombustible material. Wood shall be permitted for external decoration if placed not less than 2 inches (50.8 mm) from the nearest lampholder or current-carrying part.

Exception: Portable signs of the indoor type shall not be required to meet this requirement.

(e) Minimum Thickness — Enclosure Metal. Sheet copper or aluminum shall be at least 0.020 inches (508 micrometers) thick. Sheet steel shall be of No. 28 MSG.

Exception: For outline lighting and for electric-discharge signs, sheet steel shall be of No. 24 MSG if not ribbed, corrugated, or embossed over its entire surface and of No. 26 MSG if it is so ribbed, corrugated, or embossed.

(f) Protection of Metal. All steel parts of enclosures shall be galvanized or otherwise protected from corrosion.

(g) Enclosures Exposed to Weather. Enclosures for outdoor use shall be weatherproof and shall have at least two drain holes, each not larger than $\frac{1}{2}$ inch (12.7 mm) or smaller than $\frac{1}{4}$ inch (6.35 mm).

600-9. Portable Signs or Sections.
Portable signs or sections, letters, fixtures, symbols, and similar displays used in conjunction with fixed outdoor signs shall only be used where in compliance with all applicable provisions of this Code and, in addition, shall meet all of the following requirements:

(a) Weatherproof Receptacle and Attachment Plug. A weatherproof receptacle and attachment plug having one pole for grounding shall be provided for each individual letter, fixture, or sign.

(b) Cords. All cords shall be of the junior hard service or hard service types as designated in Table 400-4 and shall be 3-conductor with one conductor grounded as provided in Section 600-9(a).

(c) Cord from Ground Level. No cord shall be less than 10 feet (3.05 m) from the ground level directly underneath.

Section 600-9 is not intended to apply to portable outdoor electric signs, such as those mounted on trailers. It is intended to apply only to portable parts used in conjunction with fixed outdoor signs.

600-10. Clearances.

(a) Vertical and Horizontal. Signs and outline system enclosures shall have not less than the vertical and horizontal clearances from open conductors specified in Article 225.

(b) Elevation. The bottom of sign and outline lighting enclosures shall not be less than 16 feet (4.88 m) above areas accessible to vehicles.

Exception: The bottom of such enclosures shall be permitted to be less than 16 feet (4.88 m) above areas accessible to vehicles where such enclosures are protected from physical damage.

600-11. Outdoor Portable Signs.

The wiring of an outdoor sign that is portable or mobile and is readily accessible shall be provided with factory-installed ground-fault circuit-interrupter protection for personnel. The ground-fault circuit-interrupter shall be an integral part of the attachment plug or shall be located in the power-supply cord within 12 inches (305 mm) of the attachment plug. Conductive supports of a sign specified in this section shall be considered part of the sign.

This section has been revised for the 1993 *Code.* It now requires outdoor portable signs to be provided with factory-installed ground-fault circuit-interrupter protection for personnel. The GFCI must be an integral part of the attachment plug or located in the supply cord within 12 inches of the attachment plug. A ground-fault circuit-interrupter installed within the sign would not satisfy this requirement because it would not provide GFCI protection for the cord.

See Figure 600-3.

See Figure 600-2 for a ground-fault circuit-interrupter that is designed to serve as an attachment plug, and is therefore capable of protecting both the sign and the supply cord.

It is the intent that a ground-fault circuit-interrupter identified for use with portable electric signs be provided with open neutral protection, so that the ground-fault circuit-interrupter will provide protection even if the neutral conductor supplying the sign and ground-fault circuit-interrupter opens.

B. 1000 Volts, Nominal, or Less

600-21. Installation of Conductors.

(a) Wiring Method. Conductors shall be installed using any wiring method included in Chapter 3 suitable for the conditions

Figure 600-2.   Raintight ground-fault circuit-interrupter with open neutral protection. This unit is designed for use on the line end of a flexible cord. (Pass & Seymour/Legrand)

Figure 600-3.   A factory installed GFCI is required as an integral part of the attachment plug or located in the power supply cord within 12 inches of the attachment plug.

that provides a means for equipment grounding, or in metal poles complying with all the requirements of Section 410-15(b).

(b) Insulation and Size. Conductors shall be of a type listed for general use and shall not be smaller than No. 14.

Exception No. 1: Conductors not smaller than No. 18 of a type listed in Table 402-3 shall be permitted:

a. In portable signs.

b. As short leads permanently attached to lampholders or electric-discharge ballasts.

c. As leads not more than 8 feet (2.44 m) long permanently attached to electric-discharge lampholders or electric-discharge ballasts, if the leads are enclosed in wiring channels.

d. For signs with multiple incandescent lamps requiring one conductor from a control to one or more lamps whose total load does not exceed 250 watts, if in an approved cable assembly of two or more conductors.

Exception No. 2: Conductors not smaller than No. 20 shall be permitted as short leads permanently attached to synchronous motors.

(c) Exposed to Weather. Conductors in raceways, metal-clad cable, or enclosures exposed to the weather shall be of a type listed for the conditions.

Exception: This shall not apply where rigid metal conduit, intermediate metal conduit, rigid nonmetallic conduit, electrical metallic tubing, or enclosures are made raintight and arranged to drain.

(d) Number of Conductors in Raceway. The number of conductors in a raceway for sign fixtures shall be in accordance with Table 1 of Chapter 9.

(e) Conductors Soldered to Terminals. Where the conductors are fastened to lampholders other than of the pin type, they shall be soldered to the terminals or made with wire connectors, and the exposed parts of conductors and terminals shall be treated to prevent corrosion. Where the conductors are fastened to pin-type lampholders that protect the terminals from the entrance of water, and that have been found acceptable for sign use, the conductors shall be of the stranded type but shall not be required to be soldered to the terminals.

Conductors are required to be sized No. 14 or larger (note exceptions) and installed in the specified raceways or metal-clad cables. Unless raceways or enclosures exposed to the weather are made raintight and arranged to drain, conductors are required to be lead-covered or approved for wet locations. See Table 310-13.

600-22. **Lampholders.** Lampholders shall be of the unswitched type having bodies of suitable insulating material and shall be so constructed and installed as to prevent turning. The screwshell of all sign lampholders shall be connected to the grounded conductor of the circuit. Lampholders for outdoor signs shall be suitable for the application.

600-23. **Conductors within Signs and Troughs.** Wires within the sign and outline lighting troughs shall be installed as to be mechanically secure.

600-24. **Protection of Leads.** Bushings shall be employed to protect wires feeding through enclosures.

C. Over 1000 Volts, Nominal

600-31. **Installation of Conductors.**

(a) Wiring Method. Conductors shall be installed as concealed conductors on insulators, in rigid metal conduit, in intermediate metal conduit, in rigid nonmetallic conduit, in flexible metal conduit, in liquidtight flexible metal conduit, or in electrical metallic tubing, or as Type MC cable.

(FPN):   See Section 600-5 for grounding requirements.

Exception: Liquidtight flexible nonmetallic conduit shall be permitted where requirements for flexibility exist and where weather conditions require corrosion protection.

(b) Insulation and Size. Conductors shall be of a type identified for voltage not less than the voltage of the circuit and shall not be smaller than No. 14.

Exception: Conductors not smaller than No. 18 shall be permitted:

a. As leads not more than 8 feet (2.44 m) long permanently attached to electric-discharge lampholders or electric-discharge ballasts, if the leads are enclosed in wiring channels.

b. In show window displays or small portable signs, as leads not more than 8 feet (2.44 m) long that run from the line ends of the tubing to the secondary windings of transformers, if the leads are permanently attached within the transformer enclosure.

(c) Bends in Conductors. Sharp bends in the conductors shall be avoided.

(d) Concealed Conductors on Insulators — Indoors. Concealed conductors on insulators shall be separated from each other and from all objects other than the insulators on which they are mounted by a spacing of not less than 1½ inches (38 mm) for voltages above 10,000 and not less than 1 inch (25.4 mm) for voltages of 10,000 or less. They shall be installed in channels lined with noncombustible material and used for no other purpose, except that the primary circuit conductors shall be permitted to be in the same channel. The insulators shall be of noncombustible, nonabsorbent material. Concealed conductors on insulators shall not be allowed outside the sign enclosure.

(e) Conductors in Raceways. Where conductors are covered with metal sheathing, the covering shall extend beyond the end of the raceway, and the surface of the cable shall not be damaged where the covering terminates.

(1) In damp or wet locations, the insulation on all conductors shall extend beyond the metal covering or raceway not less than 4 inches (102 mm) for voltages over 10,000, 3 inches (76 mm) for voltages over 5000 but not exceeding 10,000, and 2 inches (50.8 mm) for voltages of 5000 or less.

(2) In dry locations, the insulation shall extend beyond the end of the metal covering or raceways not less than 2½ inches (64 mm) for voltages over 10,000, 2 inches (50.8 mm) for voltages over 5000 but not exceeding 10,000, and 1½ inches (38 mm) for voltages of 5000 or less.

(3) For conductors at grounded midpoint terminals, no spacing shall be required.

(4) A metal raceway containing a single conductor from one secondary terminal of a transformer shall not exceed 20 feet (6.1 m) in length.

(f) Show Windows and Similar Locations. Conductors that hang freely in the air, away from combustible material, and where not subject to physical damage, as in some show window displays, shall be required to be insulated for the voltage but not otherwise protected.

(g) Between Tubing and Grounded Midpoint. Conductors shall be permitted to be run from the ends of tubing to the grounded midpoint of transformers specifically designed for the purpose and provided with terminals at the midpoint. Where such connections are made to the transformer grounded midpoint, the connections between the high-voltage terminals of the transformer and the line ends of the tubing shall be as short as possible.

600-32. Transformers.

(a) Voltage. The transformer secondary open-circuit voltage shall not exceed 15,000 volts with an allowance on test of 1000 volts additional. For end-grounded transformers, the secondary open-circuit voltage shall not exceed 7500 volts with an allowance on test of 500 volts additional.

(b) Type. Transformers shall be of a type identified for use with electrical-discharge tubing and shall be limited in rating to a maximum of 4500 volt-amperes.

Open core-and-coil-type transformers shall be limited to 5000 volts with an allowance on test of 500 volts and to indoor applications in small portable signs.

Transformers for outline lighting installations shall have secondary current ratings not more than 60 milliamperes.

Exception: Where the transformers and all wiring connected to them are installed in accordance with Article 410 for electric-discharge lighting of the same voltage.

(c) Exposed to Weather. Transformers used outdoors shall be of the weatherproof type or shall be protected from the weather by enclosure in the sign body or in a separate metal box.

(d) Transformer Secondary Connections. The secondary windings of transformers shall not be connected in parallel or in series.

Exception No. 1: Two transformers, each having one end of its secondary winding connected to the metal enclosure, shall be permitted to have their secondary windings connected in series to form the equivalent of a midpoint-grounded transformer. The grounded ends shall be connected by insulated conductors not smaller than No. 14.

Exception No. 2: Transformers for small portable signs in show windows and similar locations, listed for the purpose, shall be permitted to be connected in series where they are equipped with secondary leads permanently attached to the secondary winding within the transformer enclosure. The secondary leads shall not extend more than 8 feet (2.44 m) beyond the enclosure for attachment to the electrode ends of the tubing. The grounded ends shall be connected by insulated conductors not smaller than No. 18.

(e) Accessibility. Transformers shall be located where accessible and shall be securely fastened in place.

(f) Working Space. A work space at least 3 feet (914 mm) high and measuring at least 3 feet (914 mm) by 3 feet (914 mm) horizontally shall be provided about each transformer or its enclosure where not installed in a sign.

(g) Attic Locations. Transformers shall be permitted to be located in attics, provided there is a passageway at least 3 feet (914 mm) in height and at least 2 feet (610 mm) in width, provided with a suitable, permanent, fixed walkway or catwalk at least 12 inches (305 mm) in width extending from the point of entry into the attic to each transformer.

600-33. Electric-Discharge Tubing.

(a) Design. The tubing shall be of such length and design as not to cause a continuous overvoltage on the transformer.

(b) Support. Tubing shall be adequately supported on noncombustible, nonabsorbent supports. Tubing supports shall, where practicable, be adjustable.

(c) Contact with Flammable Material and Other Surfaces. The tubing shall be free from contact with flammable material and shall be located where not normally exposed to physical damage. Where operating at over 7500 volts, the tubing shall be supported on noncombustible, nonabsorbent insulating supports that maintain a spacing of not less than $1/4$ inch (6.35 mm) between the tubing and the nearest surface.

600-34. Terminals and Electrode Receptacles for Electric-Discharge Tubing.

(a) Terminals. Terminals of the tubing shall be inaccessible to unqualified persons and isolated from combustible material and grounded metal or shall be enclosed. Where enclosed, they shall be separated from grounded metal and combustible material by noncombustible, nonabsorbent insulating material or by not less than $1\frac{1}{2}$ inches (38 mm) of air. Terminals shall be relieved from stress by the independent support of the tubing.

(b) Tube Connections Other than with Receptacles. Where tubes do not terminate in receptacles designed for the purpose, all energized parts of tube terminals and conductors shall be separated from grounded metal and combustible material by noncombustible, nonabsorbent insulating material or be supported so as to maintain a separation of not less than $1\frac{1}{2}$ inches (38 mm) between conductors or between conductors and any grounded metal. Soldering or connection devices shall not be required for the connection of tube terminals to the conductors where they are spliced or joined so that they are mechanically and electrically secure.

(c) Receptacles. Electrode receptacles for the tubing shall be of noncombustible, nonabsorbent insulating material.

(d) Bushings. Where electrodes enter the enclosure of outdoor signs or of an indoor sign operating at a voltage in excess of 7500 volts, bushings shall be used unless receptacles are provided. Electrode terminal assemblies shall be supported not more than 6 inches (152 mm) from the electrode terminals. All electric-discharge tubing terminals shall be insulated with a material suitable for the voltages and environmental conditions expected during use.

(e) Show Windows. In the exposed type of show-window signs, terminals shall be enclosed by receptacles.

(f) Receptacles and Bushing Seals. A flexible, nonconducting seal shall be permitted to close the opening between the tubing and the receptacle or bushing against the entrance of dust or moisture. This seal shall not be in contact with grounded conductive material and shall not be depended upon for the insulation of the tubing.

(g) Enclosures of Metal. Enclosures of metal for electrodes shall not be less than No. 24 MSG sheet metal.

(h) Enclosures of Insulating Material. Enclosures of insulating material shall be noncombustible, nonabsorbent, and suitable for the voltage of the circuit.

(i) Energized Parts. Energized parts shall be enclosed or suitably guarded to prevent contact.

Electric-discharge tubing is required to be of such length and design that it will not cause a continuous overvoltage on the transformer. A tube too long or too small in diameter increases the impedance of the load and, thus, will stress the transformer insulation. Gas tube sign transformers are designed to operate at or near short-circuit current. Generally, primary voltages of transformers are 120 V, and proper installation and maintenance of transformers and high-voltage secondary conductors will minimize the possibility of injury or fire. Precautions should be taken to ensure that secondary conductors are properly terminated to the tube electrodes, and that these connections are protected from contact by unauthorized persons or by any flammable or combustible material. Broken tubes should be replaced or deenergized.

600-35. Switches on Doors.
Doors or covers giving access to uninsulated parts of indoor signs or outline lighting exceeding 600 volts, nominal, and accessible to unqualified persons shall either be provided with interlock switches that on the opening of the doors or covers disconnect the primary circuit, or shall be so fastened that the use of other than ordinary tools will be necessary to open them.

600-36. Fixed Outline Lighting and Skeleton-type Signs for Interior Use.

(a) Tube Support. Gas tubing shall be supported independently of the conductors by means of insulators of noncombustible, nonabsorptive materials such as glass or porcelain or by suspension from suitable wires or chains.

(b) Transformers. Transformers shall be installed in metal enclosures and as near as practicable to the gas tubing system.

(c) Secondary Conductors. Secondary conductors shall be insulated for the voltage of the circuit and shall be enclosed in grounded metal raceway.

Exception: Conductors not exceeding 4 feet (1.22 m) in length between gas tubing and adjacent metal enclosures shall be permitted to be enclosed in continuous glass or other insulating sleeves.

600-37. **Portable Gas Tube Signs for Show Windows and Interior Use.** This section shall apply to the installation and use of portable gas tube signs.

(a) Location. Portable gas tube signs shall be for indoor use only.

(b) Transformer. The transformer shall be of the window type or shall be within a metal enclosure.

(c) Supply Conductors. Supply conductors shall consist of hard or extra-hard usage-type cord containing an equipment grounding conductor. The cord shall not exceed 10 feet (3.05 m) in length.

(d) Secondary Conductors. Secondary conductors shall not be more than 6 feet (1.83 m) long and shall be located where not subject to physical damage, and shall be insulated for the voltage of the circuit and be protected by continuous glass or other insulating sleeves or tubing.

(e) Grounding. Transformers and attached noncurrent-carrying metal parts shall be grounded in the manner specified in Article 250.

(f) Support. Portable indoor signs shall be held in place by not more than two open hooks attached to the transformer case.

ARTICLE 604 Manufactured Wiring Systems

Contents

604-1. **Scope.** The provisions of this article apply to field-installed wiring using off-site manufactured subassemblies for branch circuits, remote-control circuits, signaling circuits, and communication circuits in accessible areas.

604-2. **Definition.**

Manufactured Wiring System: A system containing component parts that are assembled in the process of manufacture and cannot be inspected at the building site without damage or destruction to the assembly.

604-3. **Other Articles.** Except as modified by the requirements of this article, all other applicable articles of this Code shall apply.

604-4. **Uses Permitted.** The manufactured wiring systems shall be permitted in accessible and dry locations and in plenums and spaces used for environmental air, where listed for this application, and installed in accordance with Section 300-22.

Exception: In concealed spaces, one end of tapped cable shall be permitted to extend into hollow walls for direct termination at switch and outlet points.

604-5. **Uses Not Permitted.** Where conductors or cables are limited by the provisions in Articles 333 and 334.

604-6. **Construction.**

(a) Cable or Conduit Types.

(1) Cable shall be listed armored cable or metal-clad cable containing nominal 600-volt No. 10 or 12 copper insulated conductors with a bare or insulated copper equipment grounding conductor equivalent in size to the ungrounded conductor.

(2) Conduit shall be listed flexible metal conduit containing nominal 600-volt No. 10 or 12 copper insulated conductors with a bare or insulated copper equipment grounding conductor equivalent in size to the ungrounded conductor.

Exception No. 1 to (1) and (2): A fixture tap maximum 6 feet (1.83 m) long intended for connection to a single fixture shall be permitted to contain conductors smaller than No. 12 but not smaller than No. 18.

Exception No. 2 to (1) and (2): Conductors smaller than No. 12 shall be permitted for remote-control, signaling, or communications circuits. The assembly shall be listed for the purpose.

(3) Each section shall be marked to identify the type of cable or conduit.

(b) **Receptacles and Connectors.** Receptacles and connectors shall be locking type, uniquely polarized and identified for the purpose, and shall be part of a listed assembly for the appropriate system.

See Figure 604-2.

Figure 604-1. An example of metal-clad cable not longer than 6 feet containing conductors smaller than No. 12 as permitted by Exception No. 1 above. (AFC/A Nortek Company)

Figure 604-2. Components of a manufactured wiring system. (RELOC, Division of Lithonia Lighting)

(c) **Other Component Parts.** Other component parts shall be listed for the appropriate system.

604-7. **Unused Outlets.** All unused outlets shall be capped to effectively close the connector openings.

ARTICLE 605   Office Furnishings

(Consisting of Lighting Accessories and Wired Partitions)

Contents

605-1. Scope.

605-2. General.
  (a) Use.
  (b) Other Articles.
  (c) Hazardous (Classified) Locations.

605-3. Wireways.

605-4. Partition Interconnections.

605-5. Lighting Accessories.
  (a) Support.
  (b) Connection.
  (c) Receptacle Outlet.

605-6. Fixed-type Partitions.

605-7. Freestanding-type Partitions.

605-8. Freestanding-type Partitions, Cord- and Plug-Connected.
  (a) Flexible Power-Supply Cord.
  (b) Receptacle Supplying Power.
  (c) Receptacle Outlets, Maximum.
  (d) Multiwire Circuits, Not Permitted.

605-1. **Scope.** This article covers electrical equipment, lighting accessories, and wiring systems used to connect, or contained within, or installed on relocatable wired partitions.

605-2. **General.** Wiring systems shall be identified as suitable for providing power for lighting accessories and appliances in wired partitions. These partitions shall not extend from floor to ceiling.

Exception: Where permitted by the authority having jurisdiction, these relocatable wired partitions shall be permitted to extend to the ceiling but shall not penetrate the ceiling.

(a) Use. These assemblies shall be installed and used only as provided for by this article.

(b) Other Articles. Except as modified by the requirements of this article, all other articles of this Code shall apply.

(c) Hazardous (Classified) Locations. Where used in hazardous (classified) locations, these assemblies shall conform with Articles 500 through 517 in addition to this article.

605-3. **Wireways.** All conductors and connections shall be contained within wiring channels of metal or other material identified as suitable for the conditions of use. Wiring channels shall be free of projections or other conditions that may damage conductor insulation.

(FPN): Conductors as used in this section do not include flexible cord.

605-4. **Partition Interconnections.** The electrical connection between partitions shall be a flexible assembly identified for use with wired partitions.

Exception: Flexible cord shall be permitted for the connection between partitions, provided all of the following conditions are met:

a. The cord is extra-hard usage type.

b. The partitions are mechanically contiguous.

c. The cord is not longer than necessary for maximum positioning of the partitions but is in no case to exceed 2 feet (610 mm).

d. The cord is terminated at an attachment plug and cord-connector with strain relief.

605-5. **Lighting Accessories.** Lighting equipment listed and identified for use with wired partitions shall comply with all of the following:

(a) Support. A means for secure attachment or support shall be provided.

(b) Connection. Where cord- and plug-connection is provided, the cord length shall be suitable for the intended application but shall not exceed 9 feet (2.74 m) in length. The cord shall not be smaller than No. 18, shall contain an equipment grounding conductor, and shall be of the hard usage type. Connection by other means shall be identified as suitable for the condition of use.

(c) Receptacle Outlet. Convenience receptacles shall not be permitted in lighting accessories.

605-6. **Fixed-type Partitions.** Wired partitions that are fixed (secured to building surfaces) shall be permanently connected to the building electrical system by one of the wiring methods of Chapter 3.

605-7. **Freestanding-type Partitions.** Partitions of the freestanding type (not fixed) shall be permitted to be permanently connected to the building electrical system by one of the wiring methods of Chapter 3.

605-8. **Freestanding-type Partitions, Cord- and Plug-Connected.** Individual partitions of the freestanding type, or groups of individual partitions that are electrically connected, mechanically contiguous, and do not exceed 30 feet (9.14 m) when assembled, shall be permitted to be connected to the building electrical system by a single flexible cord and plug, provided all of the following conditions are met:

(a) Flexible Power-Supply Cord. The flexible power-supply cord shall be extra-hard-usage type with No. 12 or larger conductors with an insulated grounding conductor and not exceeding 2 feet (610 mm) in length.

(b) Receptacle Supplying Power. The receptacle(s) supplying power shall be on a separate circuit serving only panels and no other loads and shall be located not more than 12 inches (305 mm) from the partition that is connected to it.

(c) Receptacle Outlets, Maximum. Individual partitions or groups of interconnected individual partitions shall not contain more than thirteen 15-ampere, 125-volt receptacle outlets.

(d) Multiwire Circuits, Not Permitted. Individual partitions or groups of interconnected individual partitions shall not contain multiwire circuits.

(FPN): See Section 210-4 for circuits supplying partitions in Sections 605-6 and 605-7.

ARTICLE 610   Cranes and Hoists

Contents

A. General

B. Wiring

C. Contact Conductors

D. Disconnecting Means

E. Overcurrent Protection

F. Control

G. Grounding

A. General

610-1. **Scope.** This article covers the installation of electric equipment and wiring used in connection with cranes, monorail hoists, hoists, and all runways.

(FPN): For further information, see Safety Code for Cranes, Derricks, Hoists, Jacks, and Slings, (ANSI B-30).

610-2. **Special Requirements for Particular Locations.**

(a) **Hazardous (Classified) Locations.** All equipment that operates in a hazardous (classified) location shall conform to Article 500.

(1) Equipment used in locations that are hazardous because of the presence of flammable gases or vapors shall conform to Article 501.

(2) Equipment used in locations that are hazardous because of combustible dust shall conform to Article 502.

(3) Equipment used in locations that are hazardous because of the presence of easily ignitible fibers or flyings shall conform to Article 503.

See commentary following Section 503-13(d).

(b) Combustible Materials. Where a crane, hoist, or monorail hoist operates over readily combustible material, the resistors shall be placed in a well-ventilated cabinet composed of noncombustible material so constructed that it will not emit flames or molten metal.

Exception: Resistors shall be permitted to be located in a cage or cab constructed of noncombustible material that encloses the sides of the cage or cab from the floor to a point at least 6 inches (152 mm) above the top of the resistors.

(c) Electrolytic Cell Lines. See Section 668-32.

Special precautions are necessary on electrolytic cell lines to prevent introduction of exposed grounded parts, as described in Section 668-32.

B. Wiring

610-11. **Wiring Method.** Conductors shall be enclosed in raceways or be Type MC cable or Type MI cable.

Exception No. 1: Contact conductors.

Exception No. 2: Short lengths of open conductors at resistors, collectors, and other equipment.

Exception No. 3: Where flexible connections are necessary to motors and similar equipment, flexible stranded conductors shall be installed in flexible metal conduit, liquidtight flexible metal conduit, multiconductor cable, or an approved nonmetallic enclosure.

Exception No. 4: Where multiconductor cable is used with a suspended pushbutton station, the station shall be supported in some satisfactory manner that protects the electric conductors against strain.

Use of short lengths of open wiring is a permitted wiring method on cranes and hoists where a separately bushed hole from a box or fitting is provided for each conductor, and the method is used for the connection of resistors, collectors, or similar equipment. In addition to other types of raceways, flexible metal conduit, liquidtight flexible metal conduit, multiconductor cable, or an approved nonmetallic enclosure (tubing) is permissible where flexibility is necessary.

Figure 610-1. A suitable grip for strain relief with a suspended pushbutton station. (Hubbell, Kellems Div.)

Exception No. 5: Where flexibility is required for power or control to moving parts, a cord suitable for the purpose shall be permitted provided:

a. Suitable strain relief and protection from physical damage is provided; and

b. In Class 1, Division 2 hazardous locations, cord shall be approved for extra-hard usage.

610-12. **Raceway or Cable Terminal Fittings.** Conductors leaving raceways or cables shall comply with one of the following:

(a) Separately Bushed Hole. A box or terminal fitting having a separately bushed hole for each conductor shall be used wherever a change is made from rigid metal conduit, intermediate metal conduit, electrical metallic tubing, metal-clad cable, mineral-insulated cable, or surface raceway wiring to open wiring. A fitting used for this purpose shall not contain taps or splices and shall not be used at fixture outlets.

(b) Bushing in Lieu of a Box. A bushing shall be permitted to be used in lieu of a box at the end of a rigid metal conduit, intermediate metal conduit, or electrical metallic tubing where the raceway terminates at unenclosed controls or similar equipment including contact conductors, collectors, resistors, brakes, power circuit limit switches, and dc split frame motors.

Table 610-14(a). Ampacities of Insulated Copper Conductors Used with Short-Time Rated Crane and Hoist Motors. Based on Ambient Temperature of 30°C (86°F). Up to Four Conductors in Raceway or Cable* Up to 3 ac** or 4 dc* Conductors in Raceway or Cable.

Maximum Operating Temp.	75°C (167°F)		90°C (194°F)		125°C (257°F)		Maximum Operating Temp.
Size AWG (kcmil)	Types MTW, RH, RHW, THW, THWN, XHHW, USE, ZW		Types TA, TBS, SA, SIS, PFA, FEP, FEPB, RHH, THHN, XHHW, Z, ZW		Types FEP, FEPB, PFA, PFAH, SA, TFE, Z, ZW		Size AWG (kcmil)
	60 Min	30 Min	60 Min	30 Min	60 Min	30 Min	
16	10	12	—	—	—	—	16
14	25	26	31	32	38	40	14
12	30	33	36	40	45	50	12
10	40	43	49	52	60	65	10
8	55	60	63	69	73	80	8
6	76	86	83	94	101	119	6
5	85	95	95	106	115	134	5
4	100	117	111	130	133	157	4
3	120	141	131	153	153	183	3
2	137	160	148	173	178	214	2
1	143	175	158	192	210	253	1
1/0	190	233	211	259	253	304	1/0
2/0	222	267	245	294	303	369	2/0
3/0	280	341	305	372	370	452	3/0
4/0	300	369	319	399	451	555	4/0
250	364	420	400	461	510	635	250
300	455	582	497	636	587	737	300
350	486	646	542	716	663	837	350
400	538	688	593	760	742	941	400
450	600	765	660	836	818	1042	450
500	660	847	726	914	896	1143	500

AMPACITY CORRECTION FACTORS

Ambient Temp. °C	For ambient temperatures other than 30°C (86°F), multiply the ampacities shown above by the appropriate factor shown below.						Ambient Temp. °F
21-25	1.05	1.05	1.04	1.04	1.02	1.02	70-77
26-30	1.00	1.00	1.00	1.00	1.00	1.00	79-86
31-35	.94	.94	.96	.96	.97	.97	88-95
36-40	.88	.88	.91	.91	.95	.95	97-104
41-45	.82	.82	.87	.87	.92	.92	106-113
46-50	.75	.75	.82	.82	.89	.89	115-122
51-55	.67	.67	.76	.76	.86	.86	124-131
56-60	.58	.58	.71	.71	.83	.83	133-140
61-70	.33	.33	.58	.58	.76	.76	142-158
71-80	—	—	.41	.41	.69	.69	160-176
81-90	—	—	—	—	.61	.61	177-194
91-100	—	—	—	—	.51	.51	195-212
101-120	—	—	—	—	.40	.40	213-248

Other insulations shown in Table 310-13 and approved for the temperature and location shall be permitted to be substituted for those shown in Table 610-14(a). The allowable ampacities of conductors used with 15-minute motors shall be the 30-minute ratings increased by 12%.
* For 5 to 8 simultaneously energized power conductors in raceway or cable, the ampacity of each power conductor shall be reduced to a value of 80% of that shown in the table.
** For 4 to 6 simultaneously energized 125°C (257°F) ac power conductors in raceway or cable, the ampacity of each power conductor shall be reduced to a value of 80% of that shown in the table.

610-13. Types of Conductors. Conductors shall comply with Table 310-13.

Exception No. 1: Conductor(s) exposed to external heat or connected to resistors shall have a flame-resistant outer covering or be covered with flame-resistant tape individually or as a group.

Exception No. 2: Contact conductors along runways, crane bridges, and monorails shall be permitted to be bare, and shall be copper, aluminum, steel, or other alloys or combinations thereof in the form of hard drawn wire, tees, angles, tee rails, or other stiff shapes.

Exception No. 3: Flexible conductors shall be permitted to be used to conduct current and, where practicable, cable reels or take-up devices shall be used.

610-14. Rating and Size of Conductors.

(a) Ampacity. The allowable ampacities of conductors shall be as shown in Table 610-14(a).

(FPN): For the ampacities of conductors between controllers and resistors, see Section 430-23.

(b) Secondary Resistor Conductors. Where the secondary resistor is separate from the controller, the minimum size of the conductors between controller and resistor shall be calculated by multiplying the motor secondary current by the appropriate factor from Table 610-14(b) and selecting a wire from Table 610-14(a).

Table 610-14(b). Secondary Conductor Rating Factors

Time in Seconds		Ampacity of Wire in Percent of Full-Load Secondary Current
On	Off	
5	75	35
10	70	45
15	75	55
15	45	65
15	30	75
15	15	85
Continuous Duty		110

(c) Minimum Size. Conductors external to motors and controls shall not be smaller than No. 16.

Exception No. 1: No. 18 wire in multiple conductor cord shall be permitted for control circuits at not over 7 amperes.

Exception No. 2: Wires not smaller than No. 20 shall be permitted for electronic circuits.

(d) Contact Conductors. Contact wires shall have an ampacity not less than that required by Table 610-14(a) for 75°C (167°F) wire, and in no case shall they be smaller than the following:

Distance Between End Strain Insulators or Clamp-type Intermediate Supports	Size of Wire
0-30 feet	No. 6
30-60 feet	No. 4
Over 60 feet	No. 2

For SI units: one foot = 0.3048 meter.

(e) Calculation of Motor Load.

(1) For one motor, use 100 percent of motor nameplate full-load ampere rating.

(2) For multiple motors on a single crane or hoist, the minimum ampacity of the power supply conductors shall be the nameplate full-load ampere rating of the largest motor or group of motors for any single crane motion, plus 50 percent of the nameplate full-load ampere rating of the next largest motor or group of motors, using that column of Table 610-14(a) that applies to the longest time-rated motor.

(3) For multiple cranes and/or hoists supplied by a common conductor system, compute the motor minimum ampacity for each crane as defined in Section 610-14(e), add them together, and multiply the sum by the appropriate demand factor from Table 610-14(e).

Table 610-14(e). Demand Factors

Number of Cranes of Hoists	Demand Factor
2	0.95
3	0.91
4	0.87
5	0.84
6	0.81
7	0.78

(f) Other Loads. Additional loads, such as heating, lighting, and air conditioning, shall be provided for by application of the appropriate sections of this Code.

(g) Nameplate. Each crane, monorail, or hoist shall be provided with a visible nameplate marked with the maker's name, the rating in volts, frequency, number of phases, and circuit amperes as calculated in Sections 610-14(e) and (f).

610-15. **Common Return.** Where a crane or hoist is operated by more than one motor, a common-return conductor of proper ampacity shall be permitted.

C. Contact Conductors

610-21. **Installation of Contact Conductors.** Contact conductors shall comply with (a) through (h) below.

(a) Locating or Guarding Contact Conductors. Runway contact conductors shall be guarded, and bridge contact conductors shall be located or guarded in a manner that persons cannot inadvertently touch energized current-carrying parts.

(b) Contact Wires. Wires that are used as contact conductors shall be secured at the ends by means of approved strain insulators and shall be so mounted on approved insulators that the extreme limit of displacement of the wire will not bring the latter within less than 1½ inches (38 mm) from the surface wired over.

(c) Supports Along Runways. Main contact conductors carried along runways shall be supported on insulating supports placed at intervals not exceeding 20 feet (6.1 m).

Exception: Supports for grounded rail conductors as provided in (f) below shall not be required to be of the insulating type.

Such conductors shall be separated not less than 6 inches (152 mm) other than for monorail hoists where a spacing of not less than 3 inches (76 mm) shall be permitted. Where necessary, intervals between insulating supports shall be permitted to be increased up to 40 feet (12.2 m), the separation between conductors being increased proportionately.

(d) Supports on Bridges. Bridge wire contact conductors shall be kept at least 2½ inches (64 mm) apart, and, where the span exceeds 80 feet (24.4 m), insulating saddles shall be placed at intervals not exceeding 50 feet (15.2 m).

(e) Supports for Rigid Conductors. Conductors along runways and crane bridges, that are of the rigid type specified in Section 610-13, Exception No. 2 and not contained within an approved enclosed assembly, shall be carried on insulating supports spaced at intervals of not more than eighty times the vertical dimension of the conductor, but in no case greater than 15 feet (4.57 m), and spaced apart sufficiently to give a clear electrical separation of conductors or adjacent collectors of not less than 1 inch (25.4 mm).

(f) Track as Circuit Conductor. Monorail, tramrail, or crane-runway tracks shall be permitted as a conductor of current for one phase of a 3-phase, alternating-current system furnishing power to the carrier, crane, or trolley, provided all of the following conditions are met:

(1) The conductors supplying the other two phases of the power supply are insulated.

(2) The power for all phases is obtained from an insulating transformer.

(3) The voltage does not exceed 300 volts.

(4) The rail serving as a conductor is effectively grounded at the transformer and also shall be permitted to be grounded by the fittings used for the suspension or attachment of the rail to a building or structure.

Crane-runway tracks are permitted as a current-carrying conductor where part of a 3-phase system is furnishing power to the crane. Figure 610-2 illustrates a 3-phase, isolated-delta secondary with one phase grounded at the transformer. It is also permitted to be grounded through the metal supporting means attached to the metal frame of a building.

(g) Electrical Continuity of Contact Conductors. All sections of contact conductors shall be mechanically joined to provide a continuous electrical connection.

(h) Not to Supply Other Equipment. Contact conductors shall not be used as feeders for any equipment other than the crane or cranes that they are primarily designed to serve.

610-22. **Collectors.** Collectors shall be so designed as to reduce to a minimum sparking between them and the contact conductor; and, where operated in rooms used for the storage of easily ignitible combustible fibers and materials, they shall comply with Section 503-13.

Figure 610-2. Three-phase, delta-isolating transformer.

To power supply disconnecting means and overcurrent protection

To collector conductors

To track

D. Disconnecting Means

610-31. **Runway Conductor Disconnecting Means.** A disconnecting means having a continuous ampere rating not less than that computed in Sections 610-14(e) and (f) shall be provided between the runway contact conductors and the power supply. Such disconnecting means shall consist of a motor circuit switch or circuit breaker. This disconnecting means shall:

(1) Be readily accessible and operable from the ground or floor level.

(2) Be arranged to be locked in the open position.

(3) Open all ungrounded conductors simultaneously.

(4) Be placed within view of the crane or hoist and the runway contact conductors.

610-32. **Disconnecting Means for Cranes and Monorail Hoists.** A motor circuit switch or circuit breaker arranged to be locked in the open position shall be provided in the leads from the runway contact conductors or other power supply on all cranes and monorail hoists.

Exception: Where a monorail hoist or hand-propelled crane bridge installation meets all of the following, the disconnect shall be permitted to be omitted.

a. The unit is floor controlled.

b. The unit is within view of the power supply disconnecting means.

c. No fixed work platform has been provided for servicing the unit.

Where the disconnecting means is not readily accessible from the crane or monorail hoist operating station, means shall be provided at the operating station to open the power circuit to all motors of the crane or monorail hoist.

Many crane installations are not arranged so that the unit is within view of the power supply disconnecting means;

therefore, it is required that a disconnecting means (lock-open type) be provided in the contact conductors. However, personnel should be aware that while servicing one crane, another unit on the same system could remain energized and could be run into the person performing maintenance on the locked-out unit.

610-33. **Rating of Disconnecting Means.** The continuous ampere rating of the switch or circuit breaker required by Section 610-32 shall not be less than 50 percent of the combined short-time ampere rating of the motors, nor less than 75 percent of the sum of the short-time ampere rating of the motors required for any single motion.

E. Overcurrent Protection

610-41. **Feeders, Runway Conductors.** The runway supply conductors and main contact conductors of a crane or monorail shall be protected by an overcurrent device(s) that shall not be greater than the largest rating or setting of any branch-circuit protective device, plus the sum of the nameplate ratings of all the other loads with application of the demand factors from Table 610-14(e).

610-42. **Branch-Circuit Short-Circuit and Ground-Fault Protection.** Branch circuits shall be protected as follows:

(a) **Fuse or Circuit Breaker Rating.** Crane, hoist, and monorail hoist motor branch circuits shall be protected by fuses or inverse-time circuit breakers having a rating in accordance with Table 430-152. Taps to control circuits shall be permitted to be taken from the load side of a branch-circuit protective device, provided each tap and piece of equipment is properly protected.

Exception No. 1: When two or more motors operate a single motion, the sum of their nameplate current ratings shall be considered as a single motor current in the above calculations.

Exception No. 2: Two or more motors shall be permitted to be connected to the same branch circuit if no tap conductor to an individual motor has an ampacity less than one-third that of the branch circuit and if each motor is protected from overload according to Section 610-43.

(b) Taps to Brake Coils. Taps to brake coils do not require separate overcurrent protection.

610-43. **Motor and Branch-Circuit Overload Protection.** Each motor, motor control, and branch-circuit conductor shall be protected from overload by one of the following means:

(1) A single motor shall be considered as protected where the branch-circuit overcurrent device meets the rating requirements of Section 610-42.

(2) Overload relay elements in each ungrounded circuit conductor, with all relay elements protected from short circuit by the branch-circuit protection.

(3) Thermal sensing device(s), sensitive to motor temperature or to temperature and current that are thermally in contact with the motor winding(s). A hoist or trolley is considered to be protected if the sensing device is connected in the hoist's upper limit switch circuit so as to prevent further hoisting during an overload condition of either motor.

Exception No. 1: If the motor is manually controlled, with spring return controls, the overload protective device shall not be required to protect the motor against stalled rotor conditions.

Exception No. 2: Where two or more motors drive a single trolley, truck, or bridge and are controlled as a unit by a single set of overload devices with a rating equal to the sum of their rated full-load currents. A hoist or trolley shall be considered to be protected if the sensing device is connected in the hoist's upper limit switch circuit so as to prevent further hoisting during an over-temperature condition of either motor.

Exception No. 3: Hoists and monorail hoists and their trolleys that are not used as part of an overhead traveling crane shall not require individual motor overload protection, provided the largest motor does not exceed 7½ horsepower and all motors are under manual control of the operator.

F. Control

610-51. **Separate Controllers.** Each motor shall be provided with an individual controller.

Exception No. 1: Where two or more motors drive a single hoist, carriage, truck, or bridge, they shall be permitted to be controlled by a single controller.

Exception No. 2: One controller shall be permitted to be switched between motors, provided:

a. The controller shall have a horsepower rating that shall not be lower than the horsepower rating of the largest motor.

b. Only one motor is operated at one time.

610-53. **Overcurrent Protection.** Conductors of control circuits shall be protected against overcurrent. Control circuits shall be considered as protected by overcurrent devices that are rated or set at not more than 300 percent of the ampacity of the control conductors.

Exception No. 1: Taps to control transformers shall be considered as protected where the secondary circuit is protected by a device rated or set at not more than 200 percent of the rated secondary current of the transformer and not more than 200 percent of the ampacity of the control circuit conductors.

Exception No. 2: Such conductors shall be considered as being properly protected by the branch-circuit overcurrent devices where the opening of the control circuit would create a hazard, as for example, the control circuit of a hot metal crane.

610-55. **Limit Switch.** A limit switch or other device shall be provided to prevent the load block from passing the safe upper limit of travel of all hoisting mechanisms.

610-57. **Clearance.** The dimension of the working space in the direction of access to live parts that are likely to require examination, adjustment, servicing, or maintenance while energized shall be a minimum of 2½ feet (762 mm). Where controls are enclosed in cabinets, the door(s) shall either open at least 90 degrees or be removable.

G. Grounding

610-61. **Grounding.** All exposed noncurrent-carrying metal parts of cranes, monorail hoists, hoists, and accessories including pendant controls shall be metallically joined together into a continuous electrical conductor so that the entire crane or hoist will be grounded in accordance with Article 250. Moving parts, other than removable accessories or attachments, having metal-to-metal bearing surfaces shall be considered to be electrically connected to each other through the bearing surfaces for grounding purposes. The trolley frame and bridge frame shall be considered as electrically grounded through the bridge and trolley wheels and its respective tracks unless local conditions, such as paint or other insulating material, prevent reliable metal-to-metal contact. In this case, a separate bonding conductor shall be provided.

It is not the intent that the trolley frame or bridge frame serve as the equipment grounding conductor for electric equipment (such as motors, motor controllers, lighting fixtures, transformers, etc.) on a crane. The equipment grounding conductors that are run with the circuit conductors are required, in accordance with Article 250. See Section 250-91(b) for acceptable types of equipment grounding conductors. The trolley frame and bridge frame can be bonded together and grounded. The bonding of these nonelectrical structural parts can be made through the bridge and trolley wheels and their respective tracks, unless local conditions prevent reliable metal-to-metal contact.

ARTICLE 620   Elevators, Dumbwaiters, Escalators, Moving Walks, Wheelchair Lifts, and Stairway Chair Lifts

Contents

(a) Single- and Multi-Car Installations.

(b) Warning Sign for Multiple Disconnecting Means.

(c) Interconnection Multi-Car Control Panels.

620-53. Car Light and Accessories Disconnecting Means.

620-54. Heating and Air-Conditioning Disconnecting Means.

G. Overcurrent Protection

620-61. Overcurrent Protection.

(a) Control and Operating Circuits.

(b) Overload Protection for Motors.

H. Machine Room

620-71. Guarding Equipment.

620-72. Clearance Around Control Panels and Disconnecting Means.

J. Grounding

620-81. Metal Raceways Attached to Cars.

620-82. Electric Elevators.

620-83. Nonelectric Elevators.

620-84. Escalators, Moving Walks, Wheelchair Lifts, and Stairway Chair Lifts.

620-85. Ground-Fault Circuit-Interrupter Protection for Personnel.

K. Overspeed

620-91. Overspeed Protection for Elevators.

620-92. Motor-Generator Overspeed Device.

620-101. Emergency Power.

(a) Other Building Loads.

(b) Disconnecting Means.

A. General

620-1. Scope. This article covers the installation of electric equipment and wiring used in connection with elevators, dumbwaiters, escalators, moving walks, wheelchair lifts, and stairway chair lifts.

(FPN): For further information, see Safety Code for Elevators and Escalators, ASME/ANSI A17.1-1990.

This article is also applicable to similar equipment, such as moving theater stages. The fine print note is necessary to provide for lighting requirements for and about the equipment, including workspace areas.

620-2. Voltage Limitations. The nominal voltage used for elevator, dumbwaiter, escalator, moving walk, wheelchair lift, and stairway chair lift operating control and signaling circuits, operating equipment, driving machine motors, machine brakes, and motor-generator sets shall not exceed the following:

(a) 300 Volts. For operating control and signaling circuits and related equipment, including door operator motors.

Exception: Higher voltages shall be permitted for frequencies of 25- through 60-hertz alternating current or for direct current, provided the current in the system cannot, under any conditions, exceed 8 milliamperes for alternating current or 30 milliamperes for direct current.

(b) 600 Volts. Driving machine motors, machine brakes, and motor-generator sets.

Exception: Higher voltages shall be permitted for driving motors of motor-generator sets.

620-3. Live Parts Enclosed. All live parts of electric apparatus in the hoistways, at the landings, or in or on the cars of elevators and dumbwaiters or in the wellways or the landings of escalators or moving walks, or in the runways and machinery spaces of wheelchair lifts and stairway chair lifts shall be enclosed to protect against accidental contact.

B. Conductors

620-11. Insulation of Conductors. The insulation of conductors installed in connection with elevators, dumbwaiters, escalators, moving walks, wheelchair lifts, and stairway chair lifts shall comply with (a) through (d) below.

(a) Hoistway Door Interlock Wiring. The conductors to the hoistway door interlocks from the hoistway riser shall be flame-retardant and suitable for a temperature of not less than 200°C (392°F). Conductors shall be Type SF or equivalent.

(b) Traveling Cables. Traveling cables used as flexible connections between the elevator or dumbwaiter car and the raceway shall be of the types of elevator cable listed in Table 400-4 or other approved types.

(c) Other Wiring. All conductors in raceways; in or on the cars of elevators and dumbwaiters; in the wellways of escalators and moving walks; in the runways and machinery spaces of wheelchair lifts and stairway chair lifts; and in the machine room of elevators, dumbwaiters, escalators, and moving walks shall have flame-retardant insulation.

(d) Insulation. All conductors shall have an insulation voltage rating equal to at least the maximum nominal circuit voltage rating of any conductor within the enclosure, cable, or raceway.

Hoistway door interlock wiring is required to be suitable for 200°C (392°F). See Table 310-13 for conductor application and insulation. See also Table 310-18.

See Table 400-4 for approved types of elevator cables to be used in hazardous (classified) and nonhazardous locations. See also Note 5 to Table 400-4. A characteristic equally important with respect to safety is the prevention of twisting of cables during their rise and fall with the elevator or dumbwaiter.

Conductors shall be Type MTW, TF, TFF, TFN, TFFN, THHN, THW, THWN, TW, XHHW, hoistway cable, or any other conductor with insulation designated as flame-retardant. Shielded conductors shall be permitted, provided such conductors are insulated for the maximum voltage found in the cable or raceway system.

620-12. **Minimum Size of Conductors.** The minimum size of conductors used for elevator, dumbwaiter, escalator, moving walk, wheelchair lift, and stairway chair lift wiring, other than conductors that form an integral part of control equipment, shall be as follows:

(a) Traveling Cables.

(1) For lighting circuits: No. 14.

Exception: No. 20 or larger conductors shall be permitted in parallel, provided the ampacity is equivalent to at least that of No. 14 wire.

(2) Operating control and signaling circuits: No. 20.

(b) Other Wiring. All operating control and signaling circuits: No. 24.

Extensive use of electronics with correspondingly lower currents permits the use of smaller wire sizes; therefore,

conductors of elevator cables may be sized as small as No. 20, conforming to the description in Table 400-4. Operating control and signaling circuits in other-than-traveling cables may be as small as No. 24. They should, of course, have the necessary strength and durability for the conditions to which they will be exposed.

620-13. **Motor Circuit Conductors.** Conductors supplying elevator, dumbwaiter, escalator, moving walk, wheelchair lift, and stairway chair lift motors shall have an ampacity in accordance with (a) and (b) below based on the nameplate current rating of the motors. With generator field control, the ampacity shall be based on the nameplate current rating of the driving motor of the motor-generator set that supplies power to the elevator motor.

(FPN): The heating of conductors depends on root-mean-square current values, which, with generator field control, are reflected by the nameplate current rating of the motor-generator set driving motor rather than by the rating of the elevator motor, which represents actual but short-time and intermittent full-load current values.

(a) Conductors Supplying Single Motor. Conductors supplying a single motor shall have an ampacity in conformance with Section 430-22 and Table 430-22(a), Exception.

(b) Conductors Supplying Several Motors. Conductors supplying two or more motors shall have an ampacity of not less than 125 percent of the nameplate current rating of the highest rated motor in the group plus the sum of the nameplate current ratings of the remainder of the motors in the group.

620-14. **Adjustable Speed Drive Systems.** Conductors supplying elevators, dumbwaiters, escalators, moving walks, wheelchair lifts, or stairway chair lifts shall have an ampacity in accordance with the following:

(a) Drive Power Transformer Integral with the Power Conversion Equipment. Conductor ampacity shall be based on the nameplate current rating of the power conversion equipment.

(b) Drive Power Transformer Not Integral with the Power Conversion Equipment. Conductor ampacity shall be based on the nameplate current rating of the drive power transformer and all other connected loads, or the nameplate current rating of the power conversion equipment reflected to the primary side of the transformer, plus all other connected loads, whichever is the larger.

(FPN): Diagram 620-14 is for information only.

To supply
620-14(a)

To supply
620-14(b)

Common feeder

Feeder demand
factor — Sec. 620-15

Disconnecting means — Part F

Overcurrent
protection — Part G

Short-circuit and
ground-fault
protection — Art. 430
Part D

Branch circuit
conductors to
external transformer — Sec. 620-14

External transformer — Art. 450

Branch circuit
conductors to
controller — Sec. 620-14
Sec. 620-13

Controller
cabinet
rating — Sec. 620-14

Motor conductors — Sec. 620-13(a)

Motor — Part G

Thermal protection — Art. 430
Parts A and C

(FPN): Diagram 620-14

620-15. **Feeder Demand Factor.** Feeder conductors of less ampacity than required by Sections 620-13 and 620-14 shall be permitted subject to the requirements of Section 430-26 and Table 620-15.

C. Wiring

620-21. **Wiring Methods.** Conductors located in hoistways, in escalator and moving walk wellways, in wheelchair lifts, stairway chair lift runways, and machinery spaces, in or on cars, and in machine and control rooms, not including the traveling cables connecting the car and hoistway wiring, shall be installed in rigid

Table 620-15. Feeder Demand Factors for Elevators

Number of Elevators on a Single Feeder	DF
1	1.00
2	.95
3	.90
4	.85
5	.82
6	.79
7	.77
8	.75
9	.73
10 or more	.72

(FPN): Demand Factors (DF) are based on 50 percent duty cycle (i.e., half time on and half time off).

metal conduit, intermediate metal conduit, electrical metallic tubing, rigid nonmetallic conduit, or wireways, or shall be Type MC, MI, or AC cable.

Exception No. 1: Flexible metal conduit or liquidtight flexible metal conduit shall be permitted in hoistways and in escalator and moving walk wellways between risers and limit switches, interlocks, operating buttons, and similar devices. Cables used in Class 2 power-limited circuits (30 volts RMS or less or 42 VDC or less) shall be permitted to be installed between risers and signal fixtures and operating devices and within escalators and moving walkways and wheelchair lifts, and stairway chair lift runways and machinery spaces provided the cables are supported and protected from physical abuse and are of a jacketed and flame-retardant type.

(FPN): Signal fixtures include audible and visual equipment such as chimes, gongs, lights, and displays that convey information to the elevator user.

Exception No. 2: Flexible metal conduit or liquidtight flexible metal conduit not exceeding 6 feet (1.83 m) in length shall be permitted on cars where so located as to be free from oil and if securely fastened in place.

Exception No. 3: Hard-service cords and junior hard-service cords conforming to the requirements of Article 400 (Table 400-4) shall be permitted as flexible connections between the fixed wiring on the car and devices on the car doors or gates. Hard-service cords only shall be permitted as flexible connections for the top-of-car operating device or the car-top work light. Devices or fixtures shall be grounded by means of an equipment grounding conductor run with the circuit conductors. Cables with smaller conductors and other types and thicknesses of insulation and jackets shall be permitted as flexible connections between the fixed wiring on the car and devices on the car doors or gates, if listed for this use.

Exception No. 4: Flexible metal conduit or liquidtight flexible metal conduit, not exceeding 6 feet (1.83 m) in length, shall be permitted between control panels and machine motors, machine brakes, motor-generator sets, disconnecting means, and pumping unit motors and valves. Conductors shall also be permitted to be grouped together and taped or corded without being installed in a raceway. Such cable groups shall be supported at intervals not over 3 feet (914 mm) and so located as to be free from physical damage.

Exception No. 5: Flexible metal conduit or liquidtight flexible metal conduit, of ⅜-inch nominal trade size, shall be permitted in lengths not in excess of 6 feet (1.83 m).

Exception No. 6: Flexible metal conduit, conforming to Article 350, or liquidtight flexible metal conduit, or hard-service cords conforming to the requirements of Article 400 (Table 400-4) shall be permitted as flexible connections on escalators, moving walk or elevator control panels and disconnecting means where the entire control panel and disconnecting means are arranged for removal from machine spaces as permitted in Section 620-72, Exception Nos. 1 and 2.

Exception No. 7: Flexible metal conduit, liquidtight flexible metal conduit, or flexible cords and cables, or conductors grouped together and taped or corded that are part of listed equipment, a driving machine, or a driving machine brake shall be permitted on the counterweight assembly, in lengths not to exceed 6 feet (1.83 mm), without being installed in a raceway and where located to be free from physical damage.

Where motor-generators, machine motors, or pumping unit motors and valves are located adjacent to or underneath control equipment and are provided with extra-length terminal leads not exceeding 6 feet (1.83 m) in length, such leads shall be permitted to be extended to connect directly to controller terminal studs without regard to the carrying-capacity requirements of Articles 430 and 445. Auxiliary gutters shall be permitted in machine and control rooms between controllers, starters, and similar apparatus.

620-22. **Branch Circuits for Car Lighting, Accessories, Heating, and Air Conditioning.**

(a) **Car Light Source.** A dedicated branch circuit shall supply the car lights and accessories on each elevator car.

(b) **Air Conditioning and Heating Source.** A dedicated branch circuit shall supply the air-conditioning and heating units on each elevator car.

D. Installation of Conductors

620-31. **Raceway Terminal Fittings.** Conductors shall comply with Section 300-16(b). In locations where raceways project from the floor and terminate in other than a wiring enclosure, they shall extend at least 6 inches (152 mm) above the floor.

620-32. **Wireways.** Section 362-5 shall not apply to wireways. The sum of the cross-sectional area of the individual conductors in a wireway shall not be more than 50 percent of the interior cross-sectional area of the wireway.

Vertical runs of wireways shall be securely supported at intervals not exceeding 15 feet (4.57 m) and shall have not more than one joint between supports. Adjoining wireway sections shall be securely fastened together to provide a rigid joint.

620-33. **Number of Conductors in Raceways.** The sum of the cross-sectional area of the operating and control circuit conductors in raceways shall not exceed 40 percent of the interior cross-sectional area of the raceway.

Exception: In wireways as permitted in Section 620-32.

620-34. **Supports.** Supports for cables or raceways in a hoistway or in an escalator or moving walk wellway or wheelchair lift and stairway chair lift runway shall be securely fastened to the guide rail, escalator or moving walk truss, or to the hoistway, wellway, or runway construction.

620-35. **Auxiliary Gutters (Wiring Troughs).** Auxiliary gutters shall not be subject to the restrictions of Section 374-2 as to length or of Section 374-5 as to number of conductors.

620-36. **Different Systems in One Raceway or Traveling Cable.** Conductors for operating, control, power, signaling, and lighting circuits of 600 volts or less shall be permitted to be run in the same traveling cable or raceway system if all conductors are insulated for the maximum voltage found in the cables or raceway system and if all live parts of the equipment are insulated from ground for this maximum voltage. Such a traveling cable or raceway shall also be permitted to include shielded conductors and/or one or more coaxial cables, if such conductors are insulated for the maximum voltage found in the cable or raceway system. Conductors shall be permitted to be covered with suitable shielding for telephone, audio, video, or higher frequency communication circuits.

With the use of greater numbers of individual cables and the use of much longer cables in tall buildings, there is a possibility of intertwisting cable loops. In order to eliminate the practice of tying a cable to the traveling cable, one elevator cable or raceway is permitted to enclose all the conductors of power, control, lighting, video, and communication circuits, where all conductors are insulated for the maximum voltage of any conductor within the cable or raceway.

620-37. **Wiring in Hoistways and Machine Rooms.** Only such electric wiring, raceways, and cables used directly in connection with the elevator or dumbwaiter, including wiring for signals, for communication with the car, for lighting, heating, air conditioning, and ventilating the car, for fire detecting systems, for pit sump pumps, and for heating and lighting the hoistway, shall be permitted inside the hoistway and the machine room. Main feeders for supplying power to elevators and dumbwaiters shall be installed outside the hoistway.

Exception No. 1: By special permission, feeders for elevators shall be permitted within an existing hoistway if no conductors are spliced within the hoistway.

Exception No. 2: Feeders shall be permitted inside the hoistway for elevators with driving machine motors located in the hoistway or on the car or counterweight.

620-38. **Electric Equipment in Garages and Similar Occupancies.** Electric equipment and wiring used for elevators, dumbwaiters, escalators, moving walks, and wheelchair lifts and stairway chair lifts in garages shall comply with the requirements of Article 511. Wiring and equipment located on the underside of the car platform shall be considered as being located in the hazardous area.

(FPN): Garages used for parking or storage and where no repair work is done in accordance with Section 511-2 are not classified.

620-39. **Sidewalk Elevators.** Sidewalk elevators with sidewalk doors located exterior to the building shall have all electric wiring in rigid metal conduit, rigid nonmetallic conduit, intermediate metal conduit, liquidtight flexible metal conduit, liquidtight flexible nonmetallic conduit, or electrical metallic tubing, and all electrical outlets, switches, junction boxes, and fittings shall be weatherproof.

E. Traveling Cable

620-41. **Suspension of Traveling Cables.** Traveling cables shall be so suspended at the car and hoistways' ends, or counterweight end where applicable, as to reduce the strain on the individual copper conductors to a minimum.

Traveling cables shall be supported by one of the following means: (1) by its steel supporting member(s); (2) by looping the cables around supports for unsupported lengths less than 100 feet (30.5 m); (3) by suspending from the supports by a means that automatically tightens around the cable when tension is increased for unsupported lengths up to 200 feet (61 m).

(FPN): Unsupported length for the hoistway suspension means is that length of cable as measured from the point of suspension in the hoistway to the bottom of the loop, with the elevator car located at the bottom landing. Unsupported length for the car suspension means is that length of cable as measured from the point of suspension on the car to the bottom of the loop, with the elevator car located at the top landing.

620-42. **Hazardous (Classified) Locations.** In hazardous (classified) locations, traveling cables shall be of a type approved for hazardous (classified) locations and shall comply with Section 501-11, 502-12, or 503-10, as applicable.

620-43. **Location of and Protection for Cables.** Traveling cable supports shall be so located as to reduce to a minimum the possibility of damage due to the cables coming in contact with the hoistway construction or equipment in the hoistway. Where necessary, suitable guards shall be provided to protect the cables against damage.

620-44. **Installation of Traveling Cables.** Traveling cable shall be permitted to be run without the use of a raceway for a distance not exceeding 6 feet (1.83 m) in length as measured from the first point of support on the elevator car or hoistway wall, or counterweight where applicable, provided the conductors are grouped together and taped or corded, or in the original sheath.

Traveling cables shall be permitted to be continued to elevator control panels and to elevator car and machine room connections, as fixed wiring, provided they are suitably supported and protected from physical damage.

F. Disconnecting Means and Control

620-51. Disconnecting Means. Elevators, dumbwaiters, escalators, moving walks, wheelchair lifts, and stairway chair lifts shall have a single means for disconnecting all ungrounded main power supply conductors for each unit. Where multiple driving machines are connected to a single elevator, escalator, moving walk, or pumping unit, there shall be one disconnecting means to disconnect the motor(s) and control valve operating magnets.

Where there is more than one driving machine in a machine room, disconnecting means shall be numbered to correspond to the number of the driving machine that they control.

(a) Type. The disconnecting means shall be an enclosed externally operable fused motor circuit switch or circuit breaker arranged to be locked in the open position. No provision shall be made to open or close this disconnecting means from outside of the hoistway, machine room, or machinery spaces.

The fuses or circuit breakers provided for in the disconnecting means shall be selectively coordinated with any and all other supply side overcurrent-protective devices.

Coordination of the overcurrent protective devices is important. For example, if a building contains three elevators and a fault occurs in one elevator, then only the overcurrent device ahead of the faulted elevator should open. This leaves the remaining two elevators in operation.

If the overcurrent devices in the elevator room do not have proper coordination with the feeder overcurrent device, then all three elevators might be disconnected from the power source.

To selectively coordinate overcurrent protective devices, manufacturers' time-current curves, let-thru and withstand capacity data, and the unlatching times data must be referenced.

(FPN): For additional information, see Safety Code for Elevators and Escalators, ASME/ANSI A17.1-1990.

Figure 620-1. *To be selectively coordinated, for a fault at X_1, only the overcurrent devices in switch "A" should open. The feeder overcurrent devices in main distribution panel should not open. Thus, two elevators will remain in use. See Section 620-51(a).*

(b) Location. The disconnecting means shall be located where it is readily accessible to qualified persons.

(1) On elevators without generator field control, the disconnecting means shall be located within sight of the power converter or motor starter. Where the disconnecting means is not within sight of the hoist machine or control panel, an additional manually operated switch shall be installed adjacent to the remote equipment, connected in the control circuit to prevent starting.

(2) On elevators with generator field control, the disconnecting means shall be located within sight of the motor starter for the driver motor of the motor-generator set. Where the disconnecting means is not within sight of the hoist machine, the control panel, or the motor-generator set, an additional manually operated switch shall be installed adjacent to the remote equipment, connected in the control circuit to prevent starting.

(3) On escalators and moving walks, the disconnecting means shall be installed in the space where the controller is located.

(4) On wheelchair lifts and stairway chair lifts, the disconnecting means shall be located within sight of the motor controller. The disconnecting means shall be permitted in the same enclosure with the motor controller.

620-52. **Power from More than One Source.**

(a) Single- and Multi-Car Installations. On single- and multi-car installations, equipment receiving electrical power from more than one source shall be provided with a disconnecting means for each source of electrical power. The disconnecting means shall be within sight of the equipment served.

(b) Warning Sign for Multiple Disconnecting Means. Where multiple disconnecting means are used and parts of the control panel remain energized from a source other than the one disconnected, a warning sign shall be mounted on or adjacent to the disconnecting means. The sign shall be clearly legible and shall read "Warning — Parts of the Control Panel Are Not Deenergized by This Switch."

(c) Interconnection Multi-Car Control Panels. Where interconnections between control panels are necessary for the operation of the system on multi-car installations that remain energized from a source other than the one disconnected, a warning sign in accordance with Section 620-52(b) shall be mounted on or adjacent to the disconnecting means.

620-53. **Car Light and Accessories Disconnecting Means.** Elevators shall have a single means for disconnecting all ungrounded car light and accessories power-supply conductors for each unit.

Where there is equipment for more than one car in the machine room, disconnecting means shall be numbered to correspond to the number of the elevator car whose light source they control.

The disconnecting means shall be arranged to be locked in the open position and shall be located in the machine room for that car.

620-54. **Heating and Air-Conditioning Disconnecting Means.** Elevators shall have a single means for disconnecting all ungrounded car heating and air-conditioning power-supply conductors for each unit.

Where there is equipment for more than one car in the machine room, disconnecting means shall be numbered to correspond to the number of the elevator car whose heating and

air-conditioning source they control. The disconnecting means shall be arranged to be locked in the open position and shall be located in the machine room for that car.

G. Overcurrent Protection

620-61. **Overcurrent Protection.** Overcurrent protection shall be provided as follows:

(a) Control and Operating Circuits. Control and operating circuits and signaling circuits shall be protected against overcurrent in accordance with the requirements of Section 725-12.

(b) Overload Protection for Motors.

(1) Duty on elevator and dumbwaiter driving machine motors and driving motors of motor-generators used with generator field control shall be classed as intermittent. Such motors shall be protected against overload in accordance with Section 430-33.

(2) Duty on escalator and moving walk driving machine motors shall be classed as continuous. Such motors shall be protected against overload in accordance with Section 430-32.

(3) Escalator and moving walk driving machine motors and driving motors of motor-generator sets shall be protected against running overload as provided in Table 430-37.

(4) Duty on wheelchair lift and stairway chair lift driving machine motors shall be classed as intermittent. Such motors shall be protected against overload in accordance with Section 430-33.

H. Machine Room

620-71. **Guarding Equipment.** Elevator, dumbwaiter, escalator, and moving walk driving machines, motor-generator sets, motor controllers, and disconnecting means shall be installed in a room or enclosure set aside for that purpose. The room or enclosure shall be secured against unauthorized access.

Exception No. 1: Dumbwaiter, escalator, moving walk, or wheelchair lift and stairway chair lift motor controllers shall be permitted outside the spaces herein specified, provided they are enclosed in cabinets with doors or removable panels capable of being locked in the closed position and the disconnecting means is located adjacent to or is an integral part of the motor controller. Motor controller cabinets for escalator or moving walks shall be permitted in the balustrading on the side located away from the moving steps or moving treadway. If the disconnecting means is an integral part of the controller, it must be operable without opening the cabinet.

Exception No. 2: Elevator motor controllers and driving machines shall be permitted outside the spaces herein specified, provided the motor controllers are enclosed in cabinets with doors or removable panels capable of being locked in the closed position and the disconnecting means is located adjacent to or is an integral part of the controller. If the disconnecting means is an integral part of the controller, it must be operable without opening the cabinet.

620-72. **Clearance Around Control Panels and Disconnecting Means.** Sufficient clear working space shall be provided around control panels and disconnecting means to provide safe and convenient access to all live parts of the equipment necessary for maintenance and adjustment. The minimum clear working space about live parts on control panels and disconnecting means shall not be less than specified in Section 110-16.

Exception No. 1: Where an escalator or moving walk control panel and disconnecting means are mounted in the same space as the escalator or moving walk drive machine and the clearances specified cannot be provided, the clearance requirements of Section 110-16 shall be permitted to be waived where the entire panel and disconnecting means are arranged so that they can be readily removed from the machine space and are provided with flexible leads to all external connections.

Exception No. 2: Where an elevator motor control panel and disconnecting means are mounted in the hoistway or on the car, and the clearances specified cannot be provided, the clearance requirements of Section 110-16 shall be permitted to be waived where the entire panel and disconnecting means are arranged so that they can be readily removed from the machine space and are provided with flexible leads to all external connections.

Where control panels are not located in the same space as the drive machine, they shall be located in cabinets with doors or removable panels capable of being locked in the closed position. Such cabinets shall be permitted in the balustrading on the side away from the moving steps or moving treadway.

J. Grounding

620-81. **Metal Raceways Attached to Cars.** Metal raceways, Type MC cable, Type MI cable, or Type AC cable attached to elevator cars shall be bonded to grounded metal parts of the car that they contact.

620-82. **Electric Elevators.** For electric elevators, the frames of all motors, elevator machines, controllers, and the metal enclosures for all electric devices in or on the car or in the hoistway shall be grounded in accordance with Article 250.

620-83. **Nonelectric Elevators.** For elevators other than electric having any electric conductors attached to the car, the metal frame of the car, where normally accessible to persons, shall be grounded in accordance with Article 250.

620-84. **Escalators, Moving Walks, Wheelchair Lifts, and Stairway Lifts.** Escalators, moving walks, wheelchair lifts, and stairway chair lifts shall comply with Article 250.

620-85. **Ground-Fault Circuit-Interrupter Protection for Personnel.** All 125-volt, single-phase, 15- and 20-ampere receptacles installed in machine rooms, machinery spaces, pits, and elevator car tops shall have ground-fault circuit-interrupter protection.

This section is new in the 1993 *Code*. It requires all 15- and 20-ampere receptacles in elevator machine rooms, machinery spaces, pits, and elevator car tops to have ground-fault circuit-interrupter protection for personnel. It is intended to reduce the shock hazard to maintenance personnel who may service equipment using portable hand tools and temporary lighting.

K. Overspeed

620-91. **Overspeed Protection for Elevators.** Under overhauling load conditions, a means shall be provided on the load side of each elevator power disconnecting means to prevent the elevator from attaining a speed equal to the governor tripping speed or a speed in excess of 125 percent of the elevator rated speed, whichever is the lesser.

Overhauling load conditions shall include all loads up to rated elevator loads for freight elevators and all loads up to 125 percent of rated elevator loads for passenger elevators.

620-92. **Motor-Generator Overspeed Device.** Motor-generators driven by direct-current motors and used to supply direct current for the operation of elevator machine motors shall be provided with speed-limiting devices as required by Section 430-89(c) that will prevent the elevator from attaining at any time a speed of more than 125 percent of its rated speed.

620-101. **Emergency Power.** An elevator can be powered by an emergency power system, provided that when operating on such emergency power there is conformance with Section 620-91.

Exception: Where the emergency power system is designed to operate only one elevator at a time, the energy absorption means, if required, shall be permitted on the line side of the disconnecting means, provided all other requirements of Section 620-91 are conformed to when operating any of the elevators the system might serve.

(a) **Other Building Loads.** Other building loads, such as power and light that can be supplied by the emergency power system, shall not be considered as means of absorbing the regenerated energy for the purpose of conforming to Section 620-91, unless such loads are using their normal power from the emergency power system when it is activated.

(b) **Disconnecting Means.** The disconnecting means required by Section 620-51 shall disconnect the emergency power service and the normal power service.

ARTICLE 630   Electric Welders

Contents

A. General

A. General

630-1. **Scope.** This article covers electric arc welding, resistance welding apparatus, and other similar welding equipment that is connected to an electric supply system.

The two general types of electric welding are resistance welding and arc welding. Resistance welding or "spot" welding is the process of joining or fusing together electrically two or more metal sheets or parts without any preparation of stock. The metal parts are placed between two electrodes, or welding points, and a heavy current at a low voltage is passed through the electrodes. The metal parts offer resistance to the flow of current so that they heat to a molten state and a weld is made.

Arc welding is the butting of two metal parts to be welded and then striking an arc at this joint with a metal electrode (a flux-coated wire rod). The electrode itself is melted and supplies the extra metal necessary for joining the metal parts.

A transformer supplies current for one ac arc welder, and a generator or rectifier supplies current for one or more dc arc welders.

B. AC Transformer and DC Rectifier Arc Welders

630-11. **Ampacity of Supply Conductors.** The ampacity of conductors for ac transformer and dc rectifier arc welders shall be as follows:

(a) Individual Welders. The ampacity of the supply conductors shall not be less than the current values determined by multiplying the rated primary current in amperes given on the welder nameplate and the following factor based upon the duty cycle or time rating of the welder.

Duty Cycle

(percent) . . . 100 90 80 70 60 50 40 30 20 or less
Multiplier . . . 1.00 .95 .89 .84 .78 .71 .63 .55 .45

For a welder having a time rating of 1 hour, the multiplying factor shall be 0.75.

(b) Group of Welders. The ampacity of conductors that supply a group of welders shall be permitted to be less than the sum of the currents, as determined in accordance with (a) above, of the welders supplied. The conductor rating shall be determined in each case according to the welder loading based on the use to be made of each welder and the allowance permissible in the event that all the welders supplied by the conductors will not be in use at the same time. The load value used for each welder shall take into account both the magnitude and the duration of the load while the welder is in use.

(FPN): Conductor ratings based on 100 percent of the current, as determined in accordance with (a) above, of the two largest welders, 85 percent for the third largest welder, 70 percent for the fourth largest welder, and 60 percent for all the remaining welders, can be assumed to provide an ample margin of safety under high-production conditions with respect to the maximum permissible temperature of the conductors. Percentage values lower than those given are permissible in cases where the work is such that a high-operating duty cycle for individual welders is impossible.

Even under high-production conditions, the loads on transformer arc welders are considered intermittent; therefore, it is permissible to reduce the ampacity of feeder conductors supplying several transformers (three or more) to the allowable percentages described in the fine print note. It is obvious that intermittent transformer arc welder loads would be considerably less than a continuous load equal to the sum of the full-load current ratings of all the transformers. See also Section 630-31(b).

630-12. **Overcurrent Protection.** Overcurrent protection for ac transformer and dc rectifier arc welders shall be as provided in (a) and (b) below. Where the nearest standard rating of the overcurrent device used is under the value specified in this section, or where the rating or setting specified results in unnecessary opening of the overcurrent device, the next higher standard rating or setting shall be permitted.

(a) For Welders. Each welder shall have overcurrent protection rated or set at not more than 200 percent of the rated primary current of the welder.

Exception: An overcurrent device shall not be required for a welder having supply conductors protected by an overcurrent device rated or set at not more than 200 percent of the rated primary current of the welder.

(b) For Conductors. Conductors that supply one or more welders shall be protected by an overcurrent device rated or set at not more than 200 percent of the conductor rating.

Some arc-welding machines have a welding range involving an excess secondary-current output capacity beyond that indicated by the secondary rating marked on the machines. This excess capacity (generally not more than 150 percent of the marked output capacity) is usually supplied by means of one or more secondary taps in addition to the tap, or taps, intended for normal output current; the higher currents thus available are intended to provide for heavier welding work, including the use of larger-size electrodes. This excess capacity is somewhat analogous to the inherent overload capacity of motors and transformers. However, the use of this excess current capacity and the overloading of welding machines, except for relatively short periods of time, may be hazardous and should be undertaken with caution by those involved.

630-13. **Disconnecting Means.** A disconnecting means shall be provided in the supply circuit for each ac transformer and dc rectifier arc welder that is not equipped with a disconnect mounted as an integral part of the welder.

The disconnecting means shall be a switch or circuit breaker, and its rating shall not be less than that necessary to accommodate overcurrent protection as specified under Section 630-12.

630-14. **Marking.** A nameplate shall be provided for ac transformer and dc rectifier arc welders giving the following information: name of manufacturer; frequency; number of phases; primary voltage; rated primary current; maximum open-circuit voltage; rated secondary current; basis of rating, such as the duty cycle or time rating.

C. Motor-Generator Arc Welders

630-21. **Ampacity of Supply Conductors.** The ampacity of conductors for motor-generator arc welders shall be as follows:

(a) **Individual Welders.** The ampacity of the supply conductors shall not be less than the current values determined by multiplying the rated primary current in amperes given on the welder nameplate and the following factor based upon the duty cycle or time rating of the welder.

Duty Cycle

(percent) . . . 100 90 80 70 60 50 40 30 20 or less

Multiplier . . . 1.00 .96 91 .86 .81 .75 .69 .62 .55

For a welder having a time rating of 1 hour, the multiplying factor shall be 0.80.

(b) **Group of Welders.** The ampacity of conductors that supply a group of welders shall be permitted to be less than the sum of the currents, as determined in accordance with (a) above, of the welders supplied. The conductor rating shall be determined in each case according to the welder loading based on the use to be made of each welder and the allowance permissible in the event that all the welders supplied by the conductors will not be in use at the same time. The load value used for each welder shall take into account both the magnitude and the duration of the load while the welder is in use.

(FPN): Conductor ratings based on 100 percent of the current, as determined in accordance with (a) above, of the two largest welders, 85 percent for the third largest welder, 70 percent for the fourth

largest welder, and 60 percent for all the remaining welders, can be assumed to provide an ample margin of safety under high-production conditions with respect to the maximum permissible temperature of the conductors. Percentage values lower than those given are permissible in cases where the work is such that a high-operating duty cycle for individual welders is impossible.

630-22. **Overcurrent Protection.** Overcurrent protection for motor-generator arc welders shall be as provided in (a) and (b) below. Where the nearest standard rating of the overcurrent device used is under the value specified in this section, or where the rating or setting specified results in unnecessary opening of the overcurrent device, the next higher standard rating or setting shall be permitted.

(a) **For Welders.** Each welder shall have overcurrent protection rated or set at not more than 200 percent of the rated primary current of the welder.

Exception: An overcurrent device shall not be required for a welder having supply conductors protected by an overcurrent device rated or set at not more than 200 percent of the rated primary current of the welder.

(b) **For Conductors.** Conductors that supply one or more welders shall be protected by an overcurrent device rated or set at not more than 200 percent of the conductor rating.

Conductors for resistance welders and arc welders are provided with overcurrent protection against short circuits. Proper application and operation of the welder will safeguard against overload conditions. See commentary following Section 630-12(b).

630-23. **Disconnecting Means.** A disconnecting means shall be provided in the supply connection of each motor-generator arc welder.

The disconnecting means shall be a circuit breaker or motor-circuit switch, and its rating shall not be less than that necessary to accommodate overcurrent protection as specified under Section 630-22.

630-24. **Marking.** A nameplate shall be provided for each motor-generator arc welder giving the following information: name of manufacturer; rated frequency; number of phases; input voltage; input current; maximum open-circuit voltage; rated output current; basis of rating, such as duty cycle or time rating.

D. Resistance Welders

630-31. **Ampacity of Supply Conductors.** The ampacity of the supply conductors for resistance welders necessary to limit the voltage drop to a value permissible for the satisfactory performance of the welder is usually greater than that required to prevent overheating as prescribed in (a) and (b) below.

(a) **Individual Welders.** The rated ampacity for conductors for individual welders shall comply with the following:

(1) The ampacity of the supply conductors for a welder that may be operated at different times at different values of primary current or duty cycle shall not be less than 70 percent of the rated primary current for seam and automatically fed welders, and 50 percent of the rated primary current for manually operated nonautomatic welders.

(2) The ampacity of the supply conductors for a welder wired for a specific operation for which the actual primary current and duty cycle are known and remain unchanged shall not be less than the product of the actual primary current and the multiplier given below for the duty cycle at which the welder will be operated.

Duty Cycle (percent) ...	50	40	30	25	20	15	10	7.5	5.0 or less
Multiplier	.71	.63	.55	.50	.45	.39	.32	.27	.22

(b) **Groups of Welders.** The ampacity of conductors that supply two or more welders shall not be less than the sum of the value obtained in accordance with (a) above for the largest welder supplied and 60 percent of the values obtained for all the other welders supplied.

(FPN): Explanation of Terms. (1) The rated primary current is the rated kVA multiplied by 1000 and divided by the rated primary voltage, using values given on the nameplate. (2) The actual primary current is the current drawn from the supply circuit during each welder operation at the particular heat tap and control setting used. (3) The duty cycle is the percentage of the time during which the welder is loaded. For instance, a spot welder supplied by a 60-hertz system (216,000 cycles per hour) making four hundred 15-cycle welds per hour would have a duty cycle of 2.8 percent (400 multiplied by 15, divided by 216,000, multiplied by 100). A seam welder operating 2 cycles "on" and 2 cycles "off" would have a duty cycle of 50 percent.

The ampacity of supply conductors for a welder that is not wired for a specific function, that is, one operated at varying intervals for different applications such as dissimilar metals or thicknesses, is permitted to be 70 percent of the rated primary current for automatically fed welders and 50 percent of the rated primary current for manually operated welders.

$$\text{Rated primary current} = \frac{\text{kVA} \times 1{,}000}{\text{rated primary voltage}}$$

(using values given on nameplate).

Where the actual primary current and duty cycle are known, such as for a welder wired for a specific operation, the ampacity of the supply conductors is not permitted to be less than the product of the actual primary current (current drawn during weld operation) and the multiplier, as provided in Section 630-31(a)(2), for the duty cycle at which the welder will be operated. For example, a spot welder is specifically set to perform 300 welds per hour on a 60-Hz system. Each weld draws current for 16 cycles. During the 1-hour period, the welder draws current for 4,800 cycles (300 × 16). There are 216,000 cycles per hour (60 × 60 × 60);

$$\frac{4{,}800}{216{,}000} \times 100 \text{ percent} = 2.2 \text{ percent (duty cycle)}$$

or a seam welder draws current for 3 cycles and is off for 4 cycles during every 7-cycle period.

$$\frac{3}{7} \times 100 \text{ percent} = 42.9 \text{ percent (duty cycle)}$$

An instrument capable of measuring current impulses for 3 cycles ($\frac{1}{20}$ second), as shown in the example, is required to measure the actual primary current. The duty cycle is set for a specific operation by adjusting the controller for the welder. When sizing supply conductors, voltage drop should be limited to a value permissible for the satisfactory performance of the welder.

630-32. **Overcurrent Protection.** Overcurrent protection for resistance welders shall be as provided in (a) and (b) below. Where the nearest standard rating of the overcurrent device used is under the value specified in this section, or where the rating or setting specified results in unnecessary opening of the overcurrent device, the next higher standard rating or setting shall be permitted.

(a) For Welders. Each welder shall have an overcurrent device rated or set at not more than 300 percent of the rated primary current of the welder.

Exception: An overcurrent device shall not be required for a welder having a supply circuit protected by an overcurrent device rated or set at not more than 300 percent of the rated primary current of the welder.

(b) For Conductors. Conductors that supply one or more welders shall be protected by an overcurrent device rated or set at not more than 300 percent of the conductor rating.

630-33. **Disconnecting Means.** A switch or circuit breaker shall be provided by which each resistance welder and its control equipment can be disconnected from the supply circuit. The ampere rating of this disconnecting means shall not be less than the supply conductor ampacity determined in accordance with Section 630-31. The supply circuit switch shall be permitted as the welder disconnecting means where the circuit supplies only one welder.

630-34. **Marking.** A nameplate shall be provided for each resistance welder giving the following information: name of manufacturer; frequency; primary voltage rated kVA at 50 percent duty cycle; maximum and minimum open-circuit secondary voltage; short-circuit secondary current at maximum secondary voltage; and specified throat and gap setting.

E. Welding Cable

630-41. **Conductors.** Insulation of conductors intended for use in the secondary circuit of electric welders shall be flame-retardant.

630-42. **Installation.** Cables shall be permitted to be installed in a dedicated cable tray as provided in (a), (b), and (c) below.

(a) Cable Support. The cable tray shall provide support at not greater than 6-inch (152-mm) intervals.

(b) Spread of Fire and Products of Combustion. The installation shall comply with Section 300-21.

(c) Signs. A permanent sign shall be attached to the cable tray at intervals not greater than 20 feet (6.1 m). The sign shall read "Cable tray for welding cables only."

See Section 318-3(b)(1), Exception No. 1.

ARTICLE 640   Sound-Recording and Similar Equipment

Contents

640-1. **Scope.** This article covers equipment and wiring for sound-recording and reproduction, centralized distribution of sound, public address, speech-input systems, and electronic organs.

Equipment covered by this article includes amplifiers; public address (PA) and centralized sound systems such as those utilized in schools, factories, and similar locations; intercommunication devices and systems; and devices used for recording and reproducing voice or music.

640-2. Application of Other Articles.

(a) Wiring to and Between Devices. Wiring and equipment from source of power to and between devices connected to the interior wiring systems shall comply with the requirements of Chapters 1 through 4, except as modified by this article.

(b) Wiring and Equipment. Wiring and equipment for public-address, speech-input, radio-frequency and audio-frequency systems, and amplifying equipment associated with radio receiving stations in centralized distribution systems shall comply with Article 725.

Chapters 1 through 4 apply generally to branch-circuit wiring that supplies power to sound systems and to wiring that supplies power between components of the system, unless modified by this article. See Sections 640-3 and 640-4, Exceptions.

Wiring and equipment with electrical power limitations that differentiate them from light and power circuits are required to comply with Article 725. See Section 640-5.

Radio equipment is required to comply with Article 810 unless specifically referenced therein, such as in Section 810-2.

640-3. Number of Conductors in Conduit or Tubing. The number of conductors in a conduit or tubing shall comply with Tables 1 through 6 of Chapter 9.

Exception No. 1: Special permission may be granted for the installation of two 2-conductor lead-covered cables in ¾-inch conduit or tubing, provided the cross-sectional area of each cable does not exceed .11 square inch (70.97 mm²).

Exception No. 2: Special permission may be granted for the installation of two 2-conductor No. 19 lead-covered cables in ½-inch conduit or tubing, provided the sum of the cross-sectional areas of the cables does not exceed 32 percent of the internal cross-sectional area of the conduit or tubing.

640-4. Wireways and Auxiliary Gutters. Wireways shall comply with the requirements of Article 362, and auxiliary gutters shall comply with the requirements of Article 374.

Exception: Where used for sound-recording and reproduction, the following shall be complied with:

a. Conductors in wireways or gutters shall not fill the raceway to more than 75 percent of its depth.

b. Where the cover of auxiliary gutters is flush with the flooring and is subject to the moving of heavy objects, it shall be of steel at least ¼ inch (6.35 mm) in thickness; where not subject to moving of heavy objects, as in the rear of patch or other equipment panels, the cover shall be at least No. 10 MSG.

c. Wireways shall be permitted in concealed places, provided they are run in a straight line between outlets or junction boxes. Covers of boxes shall be accessible. Edges of metal shall be rounded at outlet or junction boxes and all rough projections smoothed to prevent abrasion of insulation or conductors.

d. Wireways and auxiliary gutters shall be grounded and bonded in accordance with the requirements of Article 250. Where the wireway or auxiliary gutter does not contain power-supply wires, the equipment grounding conductor shall not be required to be larger than No. 14 copper or its equivalent. Where the wireway or auxiliary gutter contains power-supply wires, the equipment grounding conductor shall not be smaller than specified in Section 250-95.

640-5. Conductors. Amplifier output circuits carrying audio-program signals of 70 volts or less and whose open-circuit voltage will not exceed 100 volts shall be permitted to employ Class 2 or Class 3 wiring as covered in Article 725.

(FPN): The above is based on amplifiers whose open-circuit voltage will not exceed 100 volts when driven with a signal at any frequency from 60 to 100 hertz sufficient to produce rated output (70.7 volts) into its rated load. This also accepts the known fact that the average program material is 12 db below the amplifier rating; thus, the average rms voltage for an open-circuit 70-volt output would be only 25 volts.

640-6. Grouping of Conductors. Conductors of different systems grouped in the same raceway or other enclosure or in portable cords or cables shall comply with (a) through (c) below.

(a) Power-Supply Conductors. Power-supply conductors shall be properly identified and shall be used solely for supplying power to the equipment to which the other conductors are connected.

(b) Leads to Motor-Generator or Rotary Converter. Input leads to a motor-generator or rotary converter shall be run separately from the output leads.

(c) Conductor Insulation. The conductors shall be insulated individually, or collectively in groups, by insulation at least equivalent to that on the power supply and other conductors.

Exception: Where the power supply and other conductors are separated by a lead sheath or other continuous metallic covering.

640-7. Flexible Cords. Flexible cords and cables shall be of Type S, SJ, ST, SJO, or SJT or other approved type. The conductors of flexible cords, other than power-supply conductors, shall be permitted to be of a size not smaller than No. 26, provided such conductors are not in direct electrical connection with the power-supply conductors and are equipped with a current-limiting means so that the maximum power under any condition will not exceed 150 watts.

640-8. Terminals. Terminals shall be marked to show their proper connections. Terminals for conductors other than power-supply conductors shall be separated from the terminals of the power-supply conductors by a spacing at least as great as the spacing between power-supply terminals of opposite polarity.

Branch-circuit wiring that supplies power to sound systems and their components is usually 120-V or 240-V power circuit wiring and is not considered to be a part of the sound system; therefore, it is kept separate from sound system cables or conductors. However, it is permitted in the same enclosure where terminals are spaced according to this section.

640-9. Storage Batteries. Storage batteries shall comply with (a) and (b) below.

(a) Installation. Storage batteries shall be installed in accordance with Article 480.

(b) Conductor Insulation. Storage-battery leads shall be rubber-covered or thermoplastic-covered.

640-10. Circuit Overcurrent Protection. Overcurrent protection shall be provided as follows:

(a) Heater or Filament (Cathode). Circuits to the heater or filament (cathode) of an electronic tube shall have overcurrent protection not exceeding 15 amperes where supplied by lighting branch circuits or by storage batteries exceeding 20 ampere-hour capacity.

(b) Plate (Anode-Positive). Circuits to the plate (anode-positive) and to the screen grid of an electronic tube shall have overcurrent protection not exceeding 1.0 ampere.

(c) Control Grid. Circuits to the control grid of an electronic tube shall have overcurrent protection not exceeding 1.0 ampere where supplied by lighting branch circuits or by storage batteries exceeding 20 ampere-hour capacity.

(d) Location. Overcurrent devices shall be located as near as practicable to the source of power supply.

Overcurrent protection is required to be located at the point where the conductor to be protected receives its supply from a battery or other power source. The three circuits specified above in subparagraphs (a), (b), and (c) are defined for clarity to ensure proper application and value of overcurrent protective devices.

640-11. Amplifiers and Rectifiers — Type.

(a) Approved Type. Amplifiers and rectifiers shall be of an approved type and shall be suitably housed.

(b) Readily Accessible. Amplifiers and rectifiers shall be so located as to be readily accessible.

(c) Ventilation. Amplifiers and rectifiers shall be so located as to provide sufficient ventilation to prevent undue temperature rise within the housing.

640-12. Hazardous (Classified) Locations. Equipment used in hazardous (classified) locations shall comply with Article 500.

640-13. Protection Against Physical Damage. Amplifiers, rectifiers, loudspeakers, and other equipment shall be so located or protected as to guard against physical damage, such as might result in fire or personal hazard.

ARTICLE 645　Electronic Computer/Data Processing Equipment

Contents

(e) Securing in Place.

645-6. Cables Not in Computer Room.

645-7. Penetrations.

645-10. Disconnecting Means.

645-11. Uninterruptible Power Supplies (UPS).

645-15. Grounding.

645-16. Marking.

645-1. **Scope.** This article covers equipment, power-supply wiring, equipment interconnecting wiring, and grounding of electronic computer/data processing equipment and systems, including terminal units, in an electronic computer/data processing room.

(FPN): For further information, see Protection of Electronic Computer/Data Processing Equipment, NFPA 75-1992 (ANSI).

645-2. **Special Requirements for Electronic Computer/Data Processing Equipment Room.** This article applies provided all the following conditions are met:

(1) Disconnecting means complying with Section 645-10 are provided.

(2) A separate heating/ventilating/air conditioning (HVAC) system is provided that is dedicated for electronic computer/data processing equipment use and is separated from other areas of occupancy. Any HVAC system that serves other occupancies may also serve the electronic computer/data processing equipment room if fire/smoke dampers are provided at the point of penetration of the room boundary. Such dampers shall operate on activation of smoke detectors and also by operation of the disconnecting means required by Section 645-10.

(FPN): For further information, see Protection of Electronic Computer/Data Processing Equipment, NFPA 75-1992 (ANSI).

(3) Listed electronic computer/data processing equipment is installed.

(FPN): For further information, see Protection of Electronic Computer/Data Processing Equipment, NFPA 75-1992 (ANSI), Section 5-1.1.

(4) Occupied only by those personnel needed for the maintenance and functional operation of the installed electronic computer/data processing equipment.

(FPN): The computer room is not to be used for the storage of combustibles beyond that necessary for the day-to-day operation of the

equipment. For further information, see Protection of Electronic Computer/Data Processing Equipment, NFPA 75-1992 (ANSI).

(5) The room is separated from other occupancies by fire-resistant-rated walls, floors, and ceilings with protected openings.

(6) The building construction, rooms, or areas and occupancy comply with the applicable building code.

Article 645 applies only to equipment and wiring located in the data processing room. A data processing room is usually an enclosed area, with one or more means of entry, that contains data processing equipment. Small terminals, such as remote telephone terminal units, remote data terminals, personal computers, and cash registers in stores and supermarkets, are not covered by Article 645.

A data processing room is a room designed to comply with the special construction and fire protection provisions of NFPA 75-1992, *Standard for the Protection of Electronic Computer/Data Processing Equipment,* and Section 645-2 of the *Code.* The requirements in Article 645 are based on the assumption that the room will comply with NFPA 75.

645-5. **Supply Circuits and Interconnecting Cables.**

(a) **Branch Circuit Conductors.** The branch circuit conductors supplying one or more units of a data processing system shall have an ampacity not less than 125 percent of the total connected load.

(b) **Connecting Cables.** The data processing system shall be permitted to be connected to a branch circuit by any of the following means listed for the purpose:

(1) Computer/data processing cable and attachment plug cap.

(2) Flexible cord and an attachment plug cap.

(3) Cord-set assembly. Where run on the surface of the floor, they shall be protected against physical damage.

(c) **Interconnecting Cables.** Separate data processing units shall be permitted to be interconnected by means of cables and cable assemblies listed for the purpose. Where run on the surface of the floor, they shall be protected against physical damage.

(d) **Under Raised Floors.** Power cables, communications cables, connecting cables, interconnecting cables, and receptacles associated with the data processing equipment shall be permitted under a raised floor, provided:

(1) The raised floor is of suitable construction and the area under the floor is accessible.

(FPN): See Protection of Electronic Computer/Data Processing Equipment, NFPA 75-1992 (ANSI).

(2) The branch-circuit supply conductors to receptacles or field-wired equipment are in rigid metal conduit, rigid nonmetallic conduit, intermediate metal conduit, electrical metallic tubing, metal wireway, surface metal raceway with metal cover, flexible metal conduit, liquidtight flexible metal or nonmetallic conduit, Type MI cable, Type MC cable, or Type AC cable. These supply conductors shall be installed in accordance with the requirements of Section 300-11.

Branch-circuit conductors, installed under the raised floor of a data processing room in any of the wiring methods listed in Section 645-5(d)(2), are required to conform to the specific article for the wiring method used. In addition, Article 300 applies except where modified in Article 645. For example, Section 300-11 requires raceways and boxes to be securely fastened in place even though they are installed below a raised floor.

(3) Ventilation in the underfloor area is used for the data processing equipment and data processing area only.

(4) Openings in raised floors for cables protect cables against abrasions and minimize the entrance of debris beneath the floor.

(5) Cables, other than those covered in (2) above, shall be listed as Type DP cable having adequate fire-resistance characteristics suitable for use under raised floors of a computer room. This listing requirement shall become effective July 1, 1994.

Exception No. 1: Where the interconnecting cables are enclosed in conduit or raceway.

Exception No. 2: Interconnecting cables listed with equipment manufactured prior to July 1, 1994 shall be permitted to be reinstalled with that equipment.

Exception No. 3: Other cable type designations that satisfy the above requirement are Type TC (Article 340); Types CL2, CL3, and PLTC (Article 725); Type FPL (Article 760); Types OFC and OFN (Article 770); Types CM and MP (Article 800); Type CATV (Article 820). These designations shall be permitted to have an additional letter P or R.

(FPN): One method of defining fire resistance is by establishing that the cables do not spread fire to the top of the tray in the "Vertical Tray Flame Test" referenced in the Standard for Electrical Wires, Cables, and Flexible Cords, ANSI/UL 1581-1985.

Another method of defining fire resistance is for the damage (char length) not to exceed 4 feet 11 inches (1.5 m) when performing the CSA "Vertical Flame Test — Cables in Cable Trays," as described in Test Methods for Electrical Wires and Cables, CSA C22.2 No. 0.3-M-1985.

A new Section 645-5(d)(5) has been added to the 1993 *Code* that will require interconnecting cables other than branch circuit conductors to be listed as Type DP cables. The effective date of this requirement is July 1, 1994. Cables that were listed with equipment that was manufactured before the effective date are not required to be listed. Cables in raceways are also exempted. Exception No. 3 allows cables that pass the "Vertical Tray Flame Test," ANSI/UL 1581-1985, or the "Vertical Flame Test — Cables in Cable Trays," CSA C22.2 No. 0.3-M-1985, where not more than four feet of cable is damaged during the CSA test, to be installed under raised floors of computer rooms. This section now recognizes Type DP cables that satisfy the tests specified above.

(e) Securing in Place. Power cables, communications cables, connecting cables, interconnecting cables, and associated boxes, connectors, plugs, and receptacles that are listed as part of, or for, electronic computer/data processing equipment shall not be required to be secured in place.

645-6. **Cables Not in Computer Room.** Cables extending beyond the computer room shall be subject to the applicable requirements of this Code.

(FPN): For signaling circuits, refer to Article 725; for fiber optic circuits, refer to Article 770; and for communication circuits, refer to Article 800. For fire protective signaling systems, refer to Article 760.

645-7. **Penetrations.** Penetrations of the fire resistant room boundary shall be in accordance with Section 300-21.

645-10. **Disconnecting Means.** A means shall be provided to disconnect power to all electronic equipment in the electronic computer/data processing equipment room. There shall also be a similar means to disconnect the power to all dedicated HVAC systems serving the room and cause all required fire/smoke dampers to close. The control for these disconnecting means shall be grouped and identified and shall be readily accessible at the principal exit doors. A single means to control both the electronic equipment and HVAC systems shall be permitted.

This section requires two separate disconnecting means but permits a single control, such as one pushbutton, to operate both disconnecting means. The disconnecting means is required to disconnect the conductors of each circuit from their supply source and close all required fire/smoke dampers. See definition of "disconnecting means" in Article 100. The disconnecting means is permitted to be remote-controlled switching devices, such as relays, with pushbutton stations at the principal exit doors.

This requirement and the requirement in Section 645-7 for sealing of penetrations are intended to minimize the passage of smoke or fire to other parts of the building.

See also Section 645-11.

Exception: Installations qualifying under the provisions of Article 685.

645-11. **Uninterruptible Power Supplies (UPS).** UPS systems installed within the electronic computer/data processing room, and their supply and output circuits, shall comply with Section 645-10. The disconnecting means shall also disconnect the battery from its load.

Exception No. 1: Installations qualifying under the provisions of Article 685.

Exception No. 2: A disconnecting means complying with Section 645-10 shall not be required for power sources capable of supplying 750 volt-amperes or less derived from UPS equipment or from battery circuits integral to electronic equipment, provided all other requirements of Section 645-11 are met.

645-15. **Grounding.** All exposed noncurrent-carrying metal parts of an electronic computer/data processing system shall be grounded in accordance with Article 250 or shall be double-insulated. Power systems derived within listed electronic computer/data processing equipment that supply electronic computer/data processing systems through receptacles or cable assemblies supplied as part of this equipment shall not be considered separately derived for the purpose of applying Section 250-5(d).

(FPN No. 1): This listed equipment provides the bonding and grounding requirements in accordance with the intent of Article 250.

(FPN No. 2): Where isolated grounding-type receptacles are used, see Section 250-74, Exception No. 4.

645-16. **Marking.** Each unit of an electronic computer/data processing system supplied by a branch-circuit shall be provided with a manufacturer's nameplate, which shall also include the input power requirements for voltage, frequency, and maximum rated load in amperes.

ARTICLE 650   Pipe Organs

Contents

650-1. **Scope.** This article covers those electrical circuits and parts of electrically operated pipe organs that are employed for the control of the sounding apparatus and keyboards.

650-2. **Other Articles.** Electronic organs shall comply with the appropriate provisions of Article 640.

650-3. **Source of Energy.** The source of power shall be a transformer-type rectifier, the dc potential of which shall not exceed 30 volts dc.

The permitted level of energy was increased to 30 volts in the 1990 *NEC* to provide greater compatibility with other permitted low-voltage levels and to accommodate the use of solid-state switching of electromagnetic valves. Generators are no longer permitted.

650-4. **Grounding.** The rectifier shall be grounded according to the provisions in Article 250.

650-5. **Conductors.** Conductors shall comply with (a) through (d) below:

(a) Size. Not less than No. 28 for electronic signal circuits and not less than No. 26 for electromagnetic valve supply and the like. A main common-return conductor in the electromagnetic supply shall not be less than No. 14.

Note that No. 14 wire is required only for a main common return conductor in the electromagnetic supply.

(b) Insulation. Conductors shall have thermoplastic or thermosetting insulation.

(c) Conductors to Be Cabled. Except for the common-return conductor and conductors inside the organ proper, the organ sections and the organ console conductors shall be cabled. The common-return conductors shall be permitted under an additional covering enclosing both cable and return conductor, or shall be permitted as a separate conductor and shall be permitted to be in contact with the cable.

(d) Cable Covering. Each cable shall be provided with an outer covering, either overall or on each of any subassemblies of grouped conductors. Tape shall be permitted in place of a covering. Where not installed in metal raceway, the covering shall be flame-retardant or the cable or each cable subassembly shall be covered with a closely wound fireproof tape.

The reference to braided outer coverings was deleted in the 1990 *NEC* to recognize thermoplastic and thermosetting types of insulation required by Section 650-5(b).

650-6. **Installation of Conductors.** Cables shall be securely fastened in place and shall be permitted to be attached directly to the organ structure without insulating supports. Cables shall not be placed in contact with other conductors.

Insulating supports are not required; however, measures should be taken to prevent contact between cables and conductors of other systems.

650-7. **Overcurrent Protection.** Circuits shall be so arranged that all conductors shall be protected from overcurrent by an overcurrent device rated at not more than 6 amperes.

Exception: The main supply conductors and the common-return conductors.

The overcurrent protection was reduced in the 1990 *Code* from 15 amperes to 6 amperes to compensate for the increase in permitted voltage from 15 volts to 30 volts.

ARTICLE 660   X-Ray Equipment

Contents

A. General

B. Control

C. Transformers and Capacitors

D. Guarding and Grounding

A. General

660-1. **Scope.** This article covers all X-ray equipment operating at any frequency or voltage for industrial or other nonmedical or nondental use.

(FPN): See Article 517, Part E, for X-ray installations in health care facilities.

Nothing in this article shall be construed as specifying safeguards against the useful beam or stray X-ray radiation.

(FPN No. 1): Radiation safety and performance requirements of several classes of X-ray equipment are regulated under Public Law 90-602 and are enforced by the Department of Health and Human Services.

(FPN No. 2): In addition, information on radiation protection by the National Council on Radiation Protection and Measurements is published as Reports of the National Council on Radiation Protection and Measurement. These reports are obtainable from NCRP Publications, 7910 Woodmont Ave., Suite 1016, Bethesda, MD 20814.

660-2. **Definitions.**

Long-Time Rating: A rating based on an operating interval of 5 minutes or longer.

Mobile: X-ray equipment mounted on a permanent base with wheels and/or casters for moving while completely assembled.

Momentary Rating: A rating based on an operating interval that does not exceed 5 seconds.

Portable: X-ray equipment designed to be hand-carried.

Transportable: X-ray equipment to be installed in a vehicle or that may be readily disassembled for transport in a vehicle.

660-3. **Hazardous (Classified) Locations.** Unless approved for the location, X-ray and related equipment shall not be installed or operated in hazardous (classified) locations.

(FPN): See Article 517, Part D.

X-ray equipment in industrial establishments or similar locations is usually used for the purpose of inspecting a process or product. This method permits testing without dismantling or applying stress to detect cracks, flaws, or structural defects. Welded joints are frequently inspected with X-ray equipment to detect hidden defects that may cause failure under stress.

Among the industrial applications of X-rays, the most common is radiography, where shadow pictures of the subject matter are produced on photographic film. The type and thickness of the material involved governs the voltage to be employed and may range from a few thousand volts (kilovolts) to millions of volts (megavolts). It is possible to x-ray metal objects that are 20 inches (508 mm) thick.

Fluoroscopy is another X-ray technique that is used for industrial or commercial applications. This method is similar to radiography but operates at a much lower voltage range (less than 250 kilovolts) and, instead of producing a film, a shadow picture is projected on a screen such as is used for security checks of luggage at airport terminals. Fluoroscopy is capable of detecting extremely minute flaws or defects.

660-4. **Connection to Supply Circuit.**

(a) Fixed and Stationary Equipment. Fixed and stationary X-ray equipment shall be connected to the power supply by means of a wiring method meeting the general requirements of this Code.

Exception: Equipment properly supplied by a branch circuit rated at not over 30 amperes shall be permitted to be supplied through a suitable attachment plug cap and hard-service cable or cord.

(b) Portable, Mobile, and Transportable Equipment. Individual branch circuits shall not be required for portable, mobile, and transportable X-ray equipment requiring a capacity of not over 60 amperes. Portable and mobile types of X-ray equipment of any capacity shall be supplied through a suitable hard-service cable or cord. Transportable X-ray equipment of any capacity shall be permitted to be connected to its power supply by suitable connections and hard-service cable or cord.

(c) Over 600 Volts, Nominal. Circuits and equipment operated at more than 600 volts, nominal, shall comply with Article 710.

660-5. **Disconnecting Means.** A disconnecting means of adequate capacity for at least 50 percent of the input required for the momentary rating or 100 percent of the input required for the long-time rating of the X-ray equipment, whichever is greater, shall be provided in the supply circuit. The disconnecting means shall be operable from a location readily accessible from the X-ray control. For equipment connected to a 120-volt, nominal, branch circuit of 30 amperes or less, a grounding-type attachment plug cap and receptacle of proper rating shall be permitted to serve as a disconnecting means.

660-6. Rating of Supply Conductors and Overcurrent Protection.

(a) Branch-Circuit Conductors. The ampacity of supply branch-circuit conductors and the overcurrent protective devices shall not be less than 50 percent of the momentary rating or 100 percent of the long-time rating, whichever is the greater.

(b) Feeder Conductors. The rated ampacity of conductors and overcurrent devices of a feeder for two or more branch circuits supplying X-ray units shall not be less than 100 percent of the momentary demand rating [as determined by (a)] of the two largest X-ray apparatus plus 20 percent of the momentary ratings of other X-ray apparatus.

(FPN): The minimum conductor size for branch and feeder circuits is also governed by voltage regulation requirements. For a specific installation, the manufacturer usually specifies minimum distribution transformer and conductor sizes, rating of disconnect means, and overcurrent protection.

660-7. Wiring Terminals.
X-ray equipment shall be provided with suitable wiring terminals or leads for the connection of power-supply conductors of the size required by the rating of the branch circuit for the equipment.

Exception: Where provided with a permanently attached cord or a cord set.

660-8. Number of Conductors in Raceway.
The number of control circuit conductors installed in a raceway shall be determined in accordance with Section 300-17.

660-9. Minimum Size of Conductors.
Size No. 18 or 16 fixture wires, as specified in Section 725-16, and flexible cords shall be permitted for the control and operating circuits of X-ray and auxiliary equipment where protected by not larger than 20-ampere overcurrent devices.

660-10. Equipment Installations.
All equipment for new X-ray installations and all used or reconditioned X-ray equipment moved to and reinstalled at a new location shall be of an approved type.

B. Control

660-20. Fixed and Stationary Equipment.

(a) Separate Control Device. A separate control device, in addition to the disconnecting means, shall be incorporated in the X-ray control supply or in the primary circuit to the high-voltage transformer. This device shall be a part of the X-ray equipment but shall be permitted in a separate enclosure immediately adjacent to the X-ray control unit.

(b) Protective Device. A protective device, which shall be permitted to be incorporated into the separate control device, shall be provided to control the load resulting from failures in the high-voltage circuit.

660-21. Portable and Mobile Equipment.
Portable and mobile equipment shall comply with Section 660-20, but the manually controlled device shall be located in or on the equipment.

660-23. Industrial and Commercial Laboratory Equipment.

(a) Radiographic and Fluoroscopic Types. All radiographic- and fluoroscopic-type equipment shall be effectively enclosed or shall have interlocks that deenergize the equipment automatically to prevent ready access to live current-carrying parts.

(b) Diffraction and Irradiation Types. Diffraction- and irradiation-type equipment shall be provided with a positive means to indicate when it is energized. The indicator shall be a pilot light, readable meter deflection, or equivalent means.

Exception: Equipment or installations effectively enclosed or provided with interlocks to prevent access to live current-carrying parts during operation.

660-24. Independent Control.
Where more than one piece of equipment is operated from the same high-voltage circuit, each piece or each group of equipment as a unit shall be provided with a high-voltage switch or equivalent disconnecting means. This disconnecting means shall be constructed, enclosed, or located so as to avoid contact by persons with its live parts.

A control device provides means for initiating and terminating X-ray exposures and automatically times their duration.

C. Transformers and Capacitors

660-35. **General.** Transformers and capacitors that are part of an X-ray equipment shall not be required to comply with Articles 450 and 460.

High-ratio step-up transformers that are an integral part of an X-ray are not required to comply with Article 450 and are generally used to provide the high voltage necessary for X-ray tubes. There is a lesser degree of fire hazard due to the low primary voltage; therefore, X-ray transformers are not required to be installed in fire-resistant vaults.

660-36. **Capacitors.** Capacitors shall be mounted within enclosures of insulating material or grounded metal.

D. Guarding and Grounding

660-47. **General.**

(a) High-Voltage Parts. All high-voltage parts, including X-ray tubes, shall be mounted within grounded enclosures. Air, oil, gas, or other suitable insulating media shall be used to insulate the high voltage from the grounded enclosure. The connection from the high-voltage equipment to X-ray tubes and other high-voltage components shall be made with high-voltage shielded cables.

(b) Low-Voltage Cables. Low-voltage cables connecting to oil-filled units that are not completely sealed, such as transformers, condensers, oil coolers, and high-voltage switches, shall have insulation of the oil-resistant type.

Grounded enclosures are required to be provided for all high-voltage X-ray equipment, including X-ray tubes. High-voltage shielded cables are required to be used to connect high-voltage equipment to X-ray tubes, and the shield is required to be grounded as specified in Section 660-48.

660-48. **Grounding.** Noncurrent-carrying metal parts of X-ray and associated equipment (controls, tables, X-ray tube supports, transformer tanks, shielded cables, X-ray tube heads, etc.) shall be grounded in the manner specified in Article 250. Portable and mobile equipment shall be provided with an approved grounding-type attachment plug cap.

Exception: Battery-operated equipment.

ARTICLE 665 Induction and Dielectric Heating Equipment

Contents

A. General

B. Guarding, Grounding, and Labeling

C. Motor-Generator Equipment

D. Equipment Other than Motor-Generator

A. General

665-1. **Scope.** This article covers the construction and installation of induction and dielectric heating equipment and accessories for industrial and scientific applications, but not for medical or dental applications, appliances, or line frequency pipelines and vessels heating.

(FPN No. 1): See Article 422 for appliances.

(FPN No. 2): See Article 427, Part E, for line frequency pipelines and vessels heating.

To prevent spurious radiation caused by induction and dielectric heating equipment and to ensure that the frequency spectrum is utilized equitably, the Federal Communications Commission (FCC) has established rules (Code of Federal Regulations, Title 47, Part 18) that govern the use of this type of industrial heating equipment operating above 10 kHz.

665-2. **Definitions.**

Dielectric Heating: Dielectric heating is the heating of a nominally insulating material due to its own dielectric losses when the material is placed in a varying electric field.

Heating Equipment: The term "heating equipment" as used in this article includes any equipment used for heating purposes whose heat is generated by induction or dielectric methods.

Induction Heating: Induction heating is the heating of a nominally conductive material due to its own I^2R losses when the material is placed in a varying electromagnetic field.

Induction and dielectric heating are used for ovens, furnaces, and industrial equipment where pieces of material are heated by a rapidly alternating magnetic or electric field. For further information on electric heating systems using an induction heater or a dielectric heater in ovens and furnaces, see NFPA 86-1990, *Standard for Ovens and Furnaces*, and NFPA 86D-1990, *Standard for Industrial Furnaces Using Vacuum as an Atmosphere*.

Theory of Operation — Solid-State Converter Power Circuit

The circuit consists of three sections: the rectifier section, the inverter section, and the tank circuit, which includes the load coil located on the outside. The rectifier section input power is 480 V ac nominal, 3-phase, 60 Hz. See Figure 665-1. The output of the rectifier section is most generally a fixed 600-V dc, nominal. This feeds the inverter section, which is a tuned variable frequency switching network that converts the dc power to single-phase, nominal, 180-Hz, 1-kHz, 3-kHz, or 10-kHz square wave or sinusoidal power. The operating frequency is determined by the control section. The single-phase output drives the tank circuit, which consists of a load coil and tuning capacitors.

Variable output power is achieved by frequency variation of the inverter section. Since the tank circuit is a tuned load, as the output approaches the frequency of the tank circuit, the power into the load approaches the maximum output. At minimum frequency, the output power is very low. As the frequency increases, the power increases until a maximum is reached. This is the resonant frequency of the tank circuit.

Induction heating loads that are magnetic (carbon steel) exhibit a dynamic change as the work piece passes through the Curie temperature point (where the work load changes from the magnetic to the nonmagnetic state). The converter automatically adjusts to maintain a constant output power during this dynamic load change.

Induction Heating

Induction heating is accomplished with the aid of a current-carrying coil that induces an eddy current in the work piece. Induction heating, in general, involves frequencies ranging from 50 Hz to approximately 500 kHz, and power outputs from a few hundred watts to several thousand kilowatts.

Where induction heating is employed, a nominally conductive material is placed in an inductor coil. The effective intensity of inductance is caused by a current flow in the coil at a high frequency, which produces a rapidly alternating magnetic field, thereby inducing a voltage in the material to be heated and causing a current to flow through the

Figure 665-1. *Simplified diagram of the components of a solid-state converter used for induction heating. (Tocco Div., Park Ohio Industries)*

resistance of the material (I²R loss), producing induction heating. See Figure 665-2.

Dielectric Heating

Dielectric heating equipment is similar to induction heating equipment; however, the frequencies are generally higher (in the order of 3 MHz or more) than those in induction heating. This type of heater is useful for heating materials that are commonly thought of as being nonconductive; for instance, heating plastic preforms before molding, curing glue and plywood, drying rayon cakes, and for many similar applications. Frequencies for this type of equipment range from 1 to 200 MHz, and they fall especially within the 1 to 50 MHz range. Vacuum-tube generators are used exclusively to supply dielectric heating power, and outputs range from a few hundred watts to several hundred kilowatts.

A typical wiring diagram of a vacuum-tube generator is shown in Figure 665-3. Whereas induction heating uses a varying magnetic field, dielectric heating employs a varying electric field. This is done by placing the material to be heated between a pair of metal plates, called electrodes, in the output circuit of the generator. When high-frequency voltage is applied to the electrodes, a rapidly alternating electric field is set up between them, passing through the material to be heated. Because of the electrical charges within the molecules of this material, the field causes the molecules to vibrate in proportion to its frequency. This internal molecular action generates the heat used for dielectric heating.

665-3. **Other Articles.** Wiring from the source of power to the heating equipment shall comply with Chapters 1 through 4. Circuits and equipment operated at more than 600 volts, nominal, shall comply with Article 710.

665-4. **Hazardous (Classified) Locations.** Induction and dielectric heating equipment shall not be installed in hazardous (classified) locations as defined in Article 500.

Exception: Where the equipment and wiring are designed and approved for the hazardous (classified) locations.

Figure 665-2. Simplified diagram of the components of a vacuum-tube generator used for induction heating. (Tocco Div., Park Ohio Industries)

B. Guarding, Grounding, and Labeling

665-20. **Enclosures.** The converting apparatus (including the dc line) and high-frequency electric circuits (excluding the output circuits and remote-control circuits) shall be completely contained within an enclosure or enclosures of noncombustible material.

665-21. **Panel Controls.** All panel controls shall be of dead-front construction.

665-22. **Access to Internal Equipment.** Doors or detachable panels shall be employed for internal access. Where doors are used giving access to voltages from 500 to 1000 volts ac or dc, either door locks shall be provided or interlocking shall be installed. Where doors are used giving access to voltages of over 1000 volts ac or dc, either mechanical lockouts with a

disconnecting means to prevent access until voltage is removed from the cubicle, or both door interlocking and mechanical door locks, shall be provided. Detachable panels not normally used for access to such parts shall be fastened in a manner that will make them inconvenient to remove.

665-23. **Warning Labels or Signs.** Warning labels or signs that read "DANGER — HIGH VOLTAGE — KEEP OUT" shall be attached to the equipment and shall be plainly visible where unauthorized persons might come in contact with energized parts, even when doors are open or when panels are removed from compartments containing over 250 volts ac or dc.

665-24. **Capacitors.** Where capacitors in excess of 0.1 microfarad are used in dc circuits, either as rectifier filter components or suppressors, etc., having circuit voltages of over 240 volts to

Figure 665-3. Simplified diagram of the components of a vacuum-tube generator used for dielectric heating. (Tocco Div., Park Ohio Industries)

ground, bleeder resistors or grounding switches shall be used as grounding devices. The time of discharge shall be in accordance with Section 460-6(a).

Where capacitors are individually switched out of a circuit, a bleeder resistor or automatic switch shall be used as a discharge means.

Where auxiliary rectifiers are used with filter capacitors in the output for bias supplies, tube keyers, etc., bleeder resistors shall be used, even though the dc voltage may not exceed 240 volts.

665-25. **Work Applicator Shielding.** Protective cages or adequate shielding shall be used to guard work applicators other than induction heating coils. Induction heating coils shall be permitted to be protected by insulation and/or refractory materials. Interlock switches shall be used on all hinged access doors, sliding panels, or other easy means of access to the applicator. All

interlock switches shall be connected in such a manner as to remove all power from the applicator when any one of the access doors or panels is open. Interlocks on access doors or panels shall not be required if the applicator is an induction heating coil at dc ground potential or operating at less than 150 volts ac.

665-26. **Grounding and Bonding.** Grounding and/or inter-unit bonding shall be used wherever required for circuit operation, for limiting to a safe value radio frequency potentials between all exposed noncurrent-carrying parts of the equipment and earth ground, between all equipment parts and surrounding objects, and between such objects and earth ground. Such grounding and bonding shall be installed in accordance with Article 250.

Because of stray currents flowing between units of the equipment or to ground, bonding presents special problems at radio frequencies. These special bonding requirements are needed particularly at dielectric heating frequencies (100 to 200 MHz) due to the differences in radio-frequency potential that can exist between the equipment and surrounding metal units or other units of the installation. Satisfactory bonding can be accomplished by placing all of the units of the equipment on a flooring or base consisting of a copper or aluminum sheet and by thoroughly bonding where necessary by soldering, welding, or bolting.

By use of such special bonding, the radio-frequency resistance and reactance between units is held to a minimum, and any stray circulating currents flowing through this bonding will not cause a dangerous voltage drop.

It is necessary to provide operator protection from high radio-frequency potentials by shielding at dielectric heating frequencies. Interference with radio communication systems at such high frequencies may be eliminated by totally enclosing all components in a shielding of copper or aluminum.

665-27. Marking. Each heating equipment shall be provided with a nameplate giving the manufacturer's name and model identification and the following input data: line volts, frequency, number of phases, maximum current, full-load kVA, and full-load power factor.

665-28. Control Enclosures. Direct current or low-frequency ac shall be permitted in the control portion of the heating equipment. This shall be limited to not over 150 volts. Solid or stranded wire No. 18 or larger shall be used. A step-down transformer with proper overcurrent protection shall be permitted in the control enclosure to obtain an ac voltage of less than 150 volts. The higher-voltage terminals shall be guarded to prevent accidental contact. 60-hertz components shall be permitted to control high frequency where properly rated by the induction heating equipment manufacturer. Electronic circuits utilizing solid-state devices and tubes shall be permitted printed circuits or wires smaller than No. 18.

C. Motor-Generator Equipment

665-40. General. Motor-generator equipment shall include all rotating equipment designed to operate from an ac or dc motor or by mechanical drive from a prime mover, producing an alternating current of any frequency for induction and/or dielectric heating.

665-41. Ampacity of Supply Conductors. The ampacity of supply conductors shall be determined in accordance with Article 430.

665-42. Overcurrent Protection. Overcurrent protection shall be provided as specified in Article 430 for the electric supply circuit.

665-43. Disconnecting Means. The disconnecting means shall be provided as specified in Article 430.

A readily accessible disconnecting means shall be provided by which each heating equipment can be isolated from its supply circuit. The ampere rating of this disconnecting means shall not be less than the nameplate current rating of the equipment. The supply circuit disconnecting means shall be permitted as a heating equipment disconnecting means where the circuit supplies only one equipment.

665-44. Output Circuit. The output circuit shall include all output components external to the generator, including contactors, transformers, busbars, and other conductors, and shall comply with (a) and (b) below.

(a) Generator Output. The output circuit shall be isolated from ground.

Exception No. 1: Where the capacitive coupling inherent in the generator causes the generator terminals to have voltages from terminal to ground that are equal.

Exception No. 2: Where a vacuum or controlled atmosphere is used with a coil in a tank or chamber, the center point of the coil shall be grounded to maintain an equal potential between each terminal and ground.

Where rated at over 500 volts, the output circuit shall incorporate a dc ground protector unit. The dc impressed on the output circuit shall not exceed 30 volts and shall not exceed a current capability of 5 milliamperes.

An isolating transformer for matching the load and the source shall be permitted in the output circuit if the output secondary is not at dc ground potential.

(b) Component Interconnections. The various components required for a complete induction heating equipment installation shall be connected by properly protected multiconductor cable, busbar, or coaxial cable. Cables shall be installed in nonferrous raceways. Busbars shall be protected, where required, by non-ferrous enclosures.

665-47. **Remote Control.**

(a) **Selector Switch.** Where remote controls are used for applying power, a selector switch shall be provided and interlocked to provide power from only one control point at a time.

(b) **Foot Switches.** Switches operated by foot pressure shall be provided with a shield over the contact button to avoid accidental closing of a switch.

D. Equipment Other than Motor-Generator

665-60. **General.** Equipment other than motor-generators shall consist of all static multipliers and oscillator-type units utilizing vacuum tubes and/or solid-state devices. The equipment shall be capable of converting ac or dc to an ac frequency suitable for induction and/or dielectric heating.

665-61. **Ampacity of Supply Conductors.** The ampacity of supply conductors shall be determined in accordance with (a) and (b) below.

(a) **Nameplate Rating.** The ampacity of the circuit conductors shall not be less than the nameplate current rating of the equipment.

(b) **Two or More.** The ampacity of conductors supplying two or more equipments shall not be less than the sum of the nameplate current ratings on all equipments.

Exception: If simultaneous operation of two or more equipments supplied from the same feeder is not possible, the ampacity of the feeder shall not be less than the sum of the nameplate ratings for the largest group of machines capable of simultaneous operation, plus 100 percent of the stand-by currents of the remaining machines supplied.

665-62. **Overcurrent Protection.** Overcurrent protection shall be provided as specified in Article 240 for the equipment as a whole. This overcurrent protection shall be provided separately or as a part of the equipment.

665-63. **Disconnecting Means.** A readily accessible disconnecting means shall be provided by which each heating equipment can be isolated from its supply circuit. The rating of this disconnecting means shall not be less than the nameplate rating of the equipment. The supply circuit disconnecting means shall be permitted for disconnecting the heating equipment where the circuit supplies only one equipment.

665-64. **Output Circuit.** The output circuit shall include all output components external to the converting device, including contactors, transformers, busbars, and other conductors, and shall comply with (a) and (b) below.

(a) **Converter Output.** The output circuit shall be isolated from ground.

Exception: Where a dc voltage can exist at the terminals because of an internal component failure, then the output circuit (direct or coupled) shall be at dc ground potential.

(b) **Converter and Applicator Connection.** Where the connections between the converter and the work applicator exceed 2 feet (610 mm) in length, the connections shall be enclosed or guarded with nonferrous, noncombustible material.

Figure 665-4. An 80-kW oscillator used to harden the exhaust valve seats of an automotive engine. (Tocco Div., Park Ohio Industries)

665-66. **Line Frequency in Converter Equipment Output.** Commercial frequencies of 25- to 60-hertz alternating-current output shall be permitted to be coupled for control purposes, but shall be limited to not over 150 volts during periods of circuit operation.

665-67. **Keying.** Where high-speed keying circuits dependent on the effect of "oscillator blocking" are employed, the peak radio-frequency output voltage during the blocked portion of the cycle shall not exceed 100 volts in units employing radio-frequency converters.

665-68. **Remote Control.**

(a) Selector Switch. Where remote controls are used for applying power, a selector switch shall be provided and interlocked to provide power from only one control point at a time.

(b) Foot Switches. Switches operated by foot pressure shall be provided with a shield over the contact button to avoid accidental closing of the switch.

ARTICLE 668 Electrolytic Cells

Contents

668-1. **Scope.** The provisions of this article apply to the installation of the electrical components and accessory equipment of electrolytic cells, electrolytic cell lines and process power supply for the production of aluminum, cadmium, chlorine, copper, fluorine, hydrogen peroxide, magnesium, sodium, sodium chlorate, and zinc.

Not covered by this article are cells used as a source of electric energy and for electroplating processes and cells used for the production of hydrogen.

(FPN No. 1): In general, any cell line or group of cell lines operated as a unit for the production of a particular metal, gas, or chemical compound may differ from any other cell lines producing the same product because of variations in the particular raw materials used, output capacity, use of proprietary methods or process practices, or other modifying factors to the extent that detailed Code requirements become overly restrictive and do not accomplish the stated purpose of this Code.

(FPN No. 2): For further information, see IEEE Standard for Electrical Safety Practices in Electrolytic Cell Line Working Zones: IEEE Std. 463-1977.

An electrolytic cell line and its dc process power supply circuit, both within a cell line working zone, constitute and are treated as an individual machine supplied from a single source, even though they may cover acres of space, have a load current in excess of 400,000 A dc, or have a circuit voltage in excess of 1,000 V dc. The cell line process current passes through each cell in a series connection, and the load current cannot be subdivided, as it can, for example, in the heating circuit of a resistance-type electric furnace.

Because a cell line is supplied by its individual dc rectifier system, the rectifier or the entire cell line circuit is deenergized by removing its source of primary power.

In some electrolytic cell systems, the terminal voltage of the process supply can be appreciable. The voltage-to-ground of exposed live parts from one end of a cell line to the other is variable between the limits of the terminal voltage. Hence, operating and maintenance personnel and their tools are required to be insulated from ground.

Figure 668-1. *A typical pot room in an aluminum reduction plant. (Alcoa)*

668-2. Definitions.

Cell Line: An assembly of electrically interconnected electrolytic cells supplied by a source of direct-current power.

Cell Line Attachments and Auxiliary Equipment: As applied to Article 668, cell line attachments and auxiliary equipment include, but are not limited to, auxiliary tanks; process piping; duct work; structural supports; exposed cell line conductors; conduits and other raceways; pumps, positioning equipment, and cell cutout or bypass electrical devices. Auxiliary equipment includes tools, welding machines, crucibles, and other portable equipment used for operation and maintenance within the electrolytic cell line working zone.

In the cell line working zone, auxiliary equipment includes the exposed conductive surfaces of ungrounded cranes and crane-mounted cell-servicing equipment.

Electrolytic Cell: A receptacle or vessel in which electrochemical reactions are caused by applying electrical energy for the purpose of refining or producing usable materials.

Electrolytic Cell Line Working Zone: The cell line working zone is the space envelope wherein operation or maintenance is normally performed on or in the vicinity of exposed energized surfaces of electrolytic cell lines or their attachments.

668-3. Other Articles.

(a) Lighting, Ventilating, Material Handling. Chapters 1 through 4 shall apply to services, feeders, branch circuits, and apparatus for supplying lighting, ventilating, material handling, and the like, that are outside the electrolytic cell line working zone.

(b) Systems Not Electrically Connected. Those elements of a cell line power-supply system that are not electrically connected to the cell supply system, such as the primary winding of a two-winding transformer, the motor of a motor-generator set, feeders, branch circuits, disconnecting means, motor controllers, and overload protective equipment shall be required to comply with all applicable provisions of this Code.

(FPN): For the purpose of this section, "electrically connected" means connection capable of carrying current as distinguished from connection through electromagnetic induction.

(c) Electrolytic Cell Lines. Electrolytic cell lines shall comply with the provisions of Chapters 1, 2, 3, and 4.

Exception No. 1: The electrolytic cell line conductors shall not be required to comply with the provisions of Articles 110, 210, 215, 220, and 225. See Section 668-11.

Exception No. 2: Overcurrent protection of electrolytic cell dc process power circuits shall not be required to comply with the requirements of Article 240.

Exception No. 3: Equipment located or used within the electrolytic cell line working zone or associated with the cell line dc power circuits shall not be required to comply with the provisions of Article 250.

Exception No. 4: The electrolytic cells, cell line attachments, and the wiring of auxiliary equipments and devices within the cell line working zone shall not be required to comply with the provisions of Articles 110, 210, 215, 220, and 225. See Section 668-30.

(FPN): See Section 668-15 on equipment, apparatus, and structural component grounding.

668-10. **Cell Line Working Zone.**

(a) **Area Covered.** The space envelope of the cell line working zone shall encompass any space:

(1) Within 96 inches (2.44 m) above energized surfaces of electrolytic cell lines or their energized attachments.

(2) Below energized surfaces of electrolytic cell lines or their energized attachments, provided the head room in the space beneath is less than 96 inches (2.44 m).

(3) Within 42 inches (1.07 m) horizontally from energized surfaces of electrolytic cell lines or their energized attachments or from the space envelope described in Section 668-10(a)(1) or (a)(2).

(b) **Area Not Covered.** The cell line working zone shall not be required to extend through or beyond walls, floors, roofs, partitions, barriers, or the like.

668-11. **DC Cell Line Process Power Supply.**

(a) **Not Grounded.** The dc cell line process power supply conductors shall not be required to be grounded.

(b) **Metal Enclosures Grounded.** All metal enclosures of dc cell line process power supply apparatus operating at a power supply potential between terminals of over 50 volts shall be grounded:

(1) Through protective relaying equipment, or

(2) By No. 2/0 minimum copper grounding conductor or a conductor of equal ampacity.

(c) **Grounding Requirements.** The grounding connections required by Section 668-11(b) shall be installed in accordance with Sections 250-112, 250-113, 250-115, 250-117, and 250-118.

668-12. **Cell Line Conductors.**

(a) **Insulation and Material.** Cell line conductors shall be either bare, covered, or insulated and of copper, aluminum, copper-clad aluminum, steel, or other suitable material.

(b) **Size.** Cell line conductors shall be of such cross-sectional area that the temperature rise under maximum load conditions and at maximum ambient shall not exceed the safe operating temperature of the conductor insulation or the material of the conductor supports.

(c) **Connections.** Cell line conductors shall be joined by bolted, welded, clamped, or compression connectors.

668-13. **Disconnecting Means.**

(a) **More than One Process Power Supply.** Where more than one dc cell line process power supply serves the same cell line, a disconnecting means shall be provided on the cell line circuit side of each power supply to disconnect it from the cell line circuit.

(b) **Removable Links or Conductors.** Removable links or removable conductors shall be permitted to be used as the disconnecting means.

668-14. **Shunting Means.**

(a) **Partial or Total Shunting.** Partial or total shunting of cell line circuit current around one or more cells shall be permitted.

(b) **Shunting One or More Cells.** The conductors, switches, or combination of conductors and switches used for shunting one or more cells shall comply with the applicable requirements of Section 668-12.

668-15. **Grounding.** For equipment, apparatus, and structural components that are required to be grounded by provisions of Article 668, the provisions of Article 250 shall apply.

Exception No. 1: A water pipe electrode shall not be required to be used.

Exception No. 2: Any electrode or combination of electrodes described in Sections 250-81 and 250-83 shall be permitted.

668-20. Portable Electrical Equipment.

(a) Portable Electrical Equipment Not to Be Grounded. The frames and enclosures of portable electrical equipment used within the cell line working zone shall not be grounded.

Exception No. 1: Where the cell line circuit voltage does not exceed 200 volts dc, these frames and enclosures shall be permitted to be grounded.

Exception No. 2: These frames and enclosures shall be permitted to be grounded where guarded.

(b) Isolating Transformers. Electrically powered, hand-held, cord-connected portable equipment with ungrounded frames or enclosures used within the cell line working zone shall be connected to receptacle circuits having only ungrounded conductors such as a branch circuit supplied by an isolating transformer with an ungrounded secondary.

(c) Marking. Ungrounded portable electrical equipment shall be distinctively marked and shall employ plugs and receptacles of a configuration that prevents connection of this equipment to grounding receptacles and that prevents inadvertent interchange of ungrounded and grounded portable electrical equipments.

668-21. Power Supply Circuits and Receptacles for Portable Electrical Equipment.

(a) Isolated Circuits. Circuits supplying power to ungrounded receptacles for hand-held, cord-connected equipments shall be electrically isolated from any distribution system supplying areas other than the cell line working zone and shall be ungrounded. Power for these circuits shall be supplied through isolating transformers. Primaries of such transformers shall operate at not more than 600 volts between conductors and shall be provided with proper overcurrent protection. The secondary voltage of such transformers shall not exceed 300 volts between conductors, and all circuits supplied from such secondaries shall be ungrounded and shall have an approved overcurrent device of proper rating in each conductor.

(b) Noninterchangeability. Receptacles and their mating plugs for ungrounded equipment shall not have provision for a grounding conductor and shall be of a configuration that prevents their use for equipment required to be grounded.

(c) Marking. Receptacles on circuits supplied by an isolating transformer with an ungrounded secondary shall be a distinctive configuration, distinctively marked, and shall not be used in any other location in the plant.

668-30. Fixed and Portable Electrical Equipment.

(a) Electrical Equipment Not Required to Be Grounded. AC systems supplying fixed and portable electrical equipments within the cell line working zone shall not be required to be grounded.

(b) Exposed Conductive Surfaces Not Required to Be Grounded. Exposed conductive surfaces, such as electrical equipment housings, cabinets, boxes, motors, raceways, and the like that are within the cell line working zone shall not be required to be grounded.

(c) Wiring Methods. Auxiliary electrical devices such as motors, transducers, sensors, control devices, and alarms, mounted on an electrolytic cell or other energized surface, shall be connected to premises wiring systems by any of the following means:

(1) Multiconductor hard usage cord;

(2) Wire or cable in suitable raceways or metal or nonmetallic cable trays. If metal conduit, cable tray, armored cable, or similar metallic systems are used, they shall be installed with insulating breaks such that they will not cause a potentially hazardous electrical condition.

(d) Circuit Protection. Circuit protection shall not be required for control and instrumentation that are totally within the cell line working zone.

(e) Bonding. Bonding of fixed electrical equipment to the energized conductive surfaces of the cell line, its attachments, or auxiliaries shall be permitted. Where fixed electrical equipment is mounted on an energized conductive surface, it shall be bonded to that surface.

668-31. Auxiliary Nonelectric Connections.
Auxiliary nonelectric connections, such as air hoses, water hoses, and the like, to an electrolytic cell, its attachments, or auxiliary equipments shall not have continuous conductive reinforcing wire, armor, braids, and the like. Hoses shall be of a nonconductive material.

668-32. Cranes and Hoists.

(a) Conductive Surfaces to Be Insulated from Ground. The conductive surfaces of cranes and hoists that enter the cell line working zone shall not be required to be grounded. The portion of an overhead crane or hoist that contacts an energized electrolytic cell or energized attachments shall be insulated from ground.

(b) Hazardous Electrical Conditions. Remote crane or hoist controls that may introduce hazardous electrical conditions into the cell line working zone shall employ one or more of the following systems:

(1) Insulated and ungrounded control circuit in accordance with Section 668-21(a);

(2) Nonconductive rope operator;

(3) Pendant pushbutton with nonconductive supporting means and having nonconductive surfaces or ungrounded exposed conductive surfaces;

(4) Radio.

668-40. **Enclosures.** General-purpose electrical equipment enclosures shall be permitted where a natural draft ventilation system prevents the accumulation of gases.

ARTICLE 669   Electroplating

Contents

669-1. **Scope.** The provisions of this article apply to the installation of the electrical components and accessory equipment that supply the power and controls for electroplating, anodizing, electropolishing, and electrostripping. For purposes of this article, the term electroplating shall be used to identify any or all of these processes.

Because of the extremely high currents and low voltages normally involved, conventional wiring methods cannot be used in electroplating, anodizing, electropolishing, and electrostripping processes. Note the permission to use bare conductors even in systems exceeding 50 V dc. See Figures 669-1 and 669-2. Some systems in the aluminum anodizing process have potentials up to 240 V. Warning signs are required to be posted to indicate the presence of bare conductors.

669-2. **Other Articles.** Except as modified by this article, wiring and equipment used for electroplating processes shall comply with the applicable requirements of Chapters 1 through 4.

669-3. **General.** Equipment for use in electroplating processes shall be identified for such service.

669-5. **Branch-Circuit Conductors.** Branch-circuit conductors supplying one or more units of equipment shall have an ampacity of not less than 125 percent of the total connected load. The ampacities for busbars shall be in accordance with Section 374-6.

669-6. **Wiring Methods.** Conductors connecting the electrolyte tank equipment to the conversion equipment shall be as follows:

(a) Systems Not Exceeding 50 Volts DC. Insulated conductors shall be permitted to be run without insulated support provided they are protected from physical damage. Bare copper or aluminum conductors shall be permitted where supported on insulators.

(b) Systems Exceeding 50 Volts DC. Insulated conductors shall be permitted to be run on insulated supports, provided they are protected from physical damage. Bare copper or aluminum conductors shall be permitted where supported on insulators and guarded against accidental contact in accordance with Section 110-17.

Exception: Unguarded bare conductors shall be permitted at the terminals.

669-7. **Warning Signs.** Warning signs shall be posted to indicate the presence of bare conductors.

669-8. Disconnecting Means.

    (a) More than One Power Supply. Where more than one power supply serves the same dc system, a disconnecting means shall be provided on the dc side of each power supply.

    (b) Removable Links or Conductors. Removable links or removable conductors shall be permitted to be used as the disconnecting means.

Figure 669-1. A typical electroplating line.

669-9. **Overcurrent Protection.** DC conductors shall be protected from overcurrent by one or more of the following: (1) fuses or circuit breakers; (2) a current-sensing device that operates a disconnecting means; or (3) other approved means.

Figure 669-2. Bare busbar to supply an electroplating tank.

ARTICLE 670   Industrial Machinery

Contents

670-1. **Scope.** This article covers the definition of, the size and overcurrent protection of supply conductors to, and the nameplate data required on industrial metalworking machine tools, woodworking machinery, plastics machinery, and mass production equipment, not portable by hand.

(FPN):   For further information, see Electrical Standard for Industrial Machinery, NFPA 79-1991 (ANSI).

670-2. **Definition of Industrial Machinery.** For the purposes of this article, a machine tool is defined as a power-driven machine not portable by hand, used to shape or form metal or plastic by cutting, impact, pressure, electrical techniques, or a combination of these processes. Plastics machinery is defined as a power-driven machine not portable by hand, used to shape or form plastic by application of thermal and/or mechanical energy, by cutting, impact, pressure, or a combination of these processes.

    Mass production industrial equipment is defined as a systematic array of one or more machine tools, plastics machinery, or assembly machines that is not portable by hand and that includes any associated material handling, manipulating, gaging, measuring, or inspection equipment.

    The requirements of this article do not apply to any motor-driven machine not covered by this definition. Thus, these provisions do not apply to portable machines or tools that can be carried from place to place by hand and that are not normally in a fixed location.

670-3. Machine Nameplate Data.

(a) Permanent Nameplate. A permanent nameplate that lists supply voltage, phase, frequency, full-load current, the maximum ampere rating of the short-circuit and ground-fault protective device, ampere rating of largest motor or load, short-circuit interrupting capacity of the machine overcurrent-protective device, if furnished, and diagram number shall be attached to the control equipment enclosure or machine where plainly visible after installation.

The full-load current shown on the nameplate shall not be less than the sum of the full-load currents required for all motors and other equipment that may be in operation at the same time under normal conditions of use. Where unusual type loads, duty cycles, etc., require oversized conductors, the required capacity shall be included in the marked "full-load current."

Where more than one incoming supply circuit is to be provided, the nameplate shall state the above information for each circuit.

(b) Overcurrent Protection. Where overcurrent protection is provided in accordance with Section 670-4(b), the machine shall be marked "overcurrent protection provided at machine supply terminals."

670-4. Supply Conductors and Overcurrent Protection.

(a) Size. The size of the supply conductor shall be such as to have an ampacity not less than 125 percent of the full-load current rating of all resistance heating loads plus 125 percent of the full-load current rating of highest rated motor plus the sum of the full-load current ratings of all other connected motors and apparatus that may be in operation at the same time.

(FPN): See the 0-2000 volt ampacity tables of Article 310 for ampacity of conductors rated 600 volts and below.

(b) Overcurrent Protection. A machine shall be considered as an individual unit and therefore shall be provided with a disconnecting means. The disconnecting means shall be permitted to be supplied by branch circuits protected by either fuses or circuit breakers. The disconnecting means shall not be required to incorporate overcurrent protection. Where furnished as part of the machine, overcurrent protection shall consist of a single circuit breaker or set of fuses, the machine shall bear the marking required in Section 670-3, and the supply conductors shall be considered either as feeders or taps as covered by Section 240-21.

Section 5-10 in NFPA 79-1991, *Electrical Standard for Industrial Machinery*, states in part: "The operating handle of the disconnecting means shall be readily accessible. The center of the grip of the operating handle of the disconnecting means, when in its highest position, shall not be more than 6½ feet (2 m) above the floor. A permanent operating platform, readily accessible by means of a permanent stair or ladder, shall be considered as the floor for the purpose of this requirement. The operating handle shall be capable of being locked only in the open (off) position. When the control enclosure door is closed, the operating handle shall positively indicate whether the disconnecting means is in the open (off) or closed position."

The rating or setting of the overcurrent-protective device for the circuit supplying the machine shall not be greater than the sum of the largest rating or setting of the branch-circuit short-circuit and ground-fault protective device provided with the machine, plus 125 percent of the full-load current rating of all resistance heating loads, plus the sum of the full-load currents of all other motors and apparatus that may be in operation at the same time.

Exception: Where one or more instantaneous trip circuit breakers or motor short-circuit protectors are used for motor branch-circuit short-circuit and ground-fault protection as permitted by Section 430-52(a), the procedure specified above for determining the maximum rating of the protective device for the circuit supplying the machine shall apply with the following provision. For the purpose of the calculation, each instantaneous trip circuit breaker or motor short-circuit protector shall be assumed to have a rating not exceeding the maximum percentage of motor full-load current permitted by Table 430-152 for the type of machine supply circuit protective device employed.

Where no branch-circuit short-circuit and ground-fault protective device is provided with the machine, the rating or setting of the overcurrent-protective device shall be based on Sections 430-52 and 430-53 as applicable.

670-5. Clearance.
Where the conditions of maintenance and supervision assure that only qualified persons will service the installation, the dimensions of the working space in the direction of access to live parts operating at not over 150 volts that are likely to require examination, adjustment, servicing, or maintenance while energized shall be a minimum of 2½ feet (762 mm).

Where controls are enclosed in cabinets, the door(s) shall open at least 90 degrees or be removable.

Exception: Where the enclosure requires a tool to open, and where only diagnostic and troubleshooting testing is involved on live parts operating at not over 150 volts, line-to-line, the clearances shall be permitted to be less than 2½ feet (762 mm).

According to the *NEC Style Manual*, "live parts" include conductors, buses, terminals, or components that are uninsulated or exposed and a shock hazard exists.

It is essential that ONLY *qualified persons* perform the service or maintenance on energized live parts.

ARTICLE 675 Electrically Driven or Controlled Irrigation Machines

Contents

A. General

B. Center Pivot Irrigation Machines

A. General

675-1. Scope. The provisions of this article apply to electrically driven or controlled irrigation machines, and to the branch circuits and controllers for such equipment.

Electric pump motors used to supply water to irrigation machines are governed by the general requirements of the *Code*, not by Article 675.

675-2. Definitions.

Center Pivot Irrigation Machines: A center pivot irrigation machine is a multimotored irrigation machine that revolves around a central pivot and employs alignment switches or similar devices to control individual motors.

Collector Rings: A collector ring is an assembly of slip rings for transferring electrical energy from a stationary to a rotating member.

Irrigation Machines: An irrigation machine is an electrically driven or controlled machine, with one or more motors, not hand portable, and used primarily to transport and distribute water for agricultural purposes.

675-3. Other Articles. These provisions are in addition to, or amendatory of, the provisions of Article 430 and other articles in this Code that apply except as modified in this article.

The requirements of this article apply to special equipment for a particular condition and supplement or modify the general rules. See Section 90-3, Code Arrangement.

675-4. Irrigation Cable.

(a) **Construction.** The cable used to interconnect enclosures on the structure of an irrigation machine shall be an assembly of stranded, insulated conductors with nonhygroscopic and nonwicking filler in a core of moisture- and flame-resistant nonmetallic material overlaid with a metallic covering and jacketed with a moisture-, corrosion-, and sunlight-resistant nonmetallic material.

The conductor insulation shall be of a type listed in Table 310-13 for an operating temperature of 75°C (167°F) and for use in wet locations. The core insulating material thickness shall not be less than 30 mils (762 micrometers), and the metallic overlay thickness shall not be less than 8 mils (203 micrometers). The jacketing material thickness shall not be less than 50 mils (1.27 mm).

A composite of power, control, and grounding conductors in the cable shall be permitted.

(b) **Alternate Wiring Methods.** Other cables listed for the purpose.

(c) **Supports.** Irrigation cable shall be secured by straps, hangers, or similar fittings identified for the purpose and installed as not to damage the cable. Cable shall be supported at intervals not exceeding 4 feet (1.22 m).

(d) **Fittings.** Fittings shall be used at all points where irrigation cable terminates. The fittings shall be designed for use with the cable and shall be suitable for the conditions of service.

675-5. More than Three Conductors in a Raceway or Cable.

The signal and control conductors of a raceway or cable shall not be counted for the purpose of derating the conductors as required in Article 310, Note 8 (a) of Notes to Ampacity Tables of 0 to 2000 Volts.

675-6. Marking on Main Control Panel.

The main control panel shall be provided with a nameplate that shall give the following information: (1) the manufacturer's name, the rated voltage, the phase, and the frequency; (2) the current rating of the machine; and (3) the rating of the main disconnecting means and size of overcurrent protection required.

675-7. Equivalent Current Ratings.

Where intermittent duty is not involved, the provisions of Article 430 shall be used for determining ratings for controllers, disconnecting means, conductors, and the like. Where irrigation machines have inherent intermittent duty, the following determinations of equivalent current ratings shall be used.

(a) **Continuous-Current Rating.** The equivalent continuous-current rating for the selection of branch-circuit conductors and overcurrent protection shall be equal to 125 percent of the motor nameplate full-load current rating of the largest motor plus a quantity equal to the sum of each of the motor nameplate full-load current ratings of all remaining motors on the circuit multiplied by the maximum percent duty cycle at which they can continuously operate.

(b) **Locked-Rotor Current.** The equivalent locked-rotor current rating shall be equal to the numerical sum of the locked-rotor current of the two largest motors plus 100 percent of the sum of the motor nameplate full-load current ratings of all the remaining motors on the circuit.

675-8. Disconnecting Means.

(a) **Main Controller.** A controller that is used to start and stop the complete machine shall meet all of the following requirements:

(1) An equivalent continuous current rating not less than specified in Section 675-7(a) or 675-22(a).

(2) A horsepower rating not less than the value from Table 430-151 based on the equivalent locked-rotor current specified in Section 675-7(b) or 675-22(b).

(b) **Main Disconnecting Means.** The main disconnecting means for the machine shall be at the point of connection of electrical power to the machine or shall be visible and not more than 50 feet (15.2 m) from the machine and shall be readily accessible and capable of being locked in the open position. This disconnecting means shall have a horsepower and current rating not less than required for the main controller.

This section permits the main disconnecting means to be up to 50 feet from the machine if readily accessible and capable of being locked in the open position. This eliminates one set of overcurrent protective devices and one disconnecting means where the circuit originates at the motor control panel for the irrigation pump and this panel is within

50 feet of the center pivot machine. It also alleviates some potential problems with machines designed to be towed to a second site.

Exception: Circuit breakers without marked horsepower ratings shall be permitted in accordance with Section 430-109.

(c) Disconnecting Means for Individual Motors and Controllers. A disconnecting means shall be provided to simultaneously disconnect all ungrounded conductors for each motor and controller and shall be located as required by Article 430, Part I. The disconnecting means shall not be required to be readily accessible.

Article 430, Part I, provides for safety during maintenance and inspection shutdown periods. See commentary following Section 430-103.

675-9. **Branch-Circuit Conductors.** The branch-circuit conductors shall have an ampacity not less than specified in Section 675-7(a) or 675-22(a).

675-10. **Several Motors on One Branch Circuit.**

Section 430-53 provides for motor branch-circuit short-circuit and ground-fault protection for several motors on one branch circuit. A combination of these requirements, which are modified for this special equipment application, is found in Section 675-10.

(a) Protection Required. Several motors, each not exceeding 2-horsepower rating, shall be permitted to be used on an irrigation machine circuit protected at not more than 30 amperes at 600 volts, nominal, or less, provided all of the following conditions are met:

(1) The full-load rating of any motor in the circuit shall not exceed 6 amperes.

(2) Each motor in the circuit shall have individual overload protection in accordance with Section 430-32.

(3) Taps to individual motors shall not be smaller than No. 14 copper and not more than 25 feet (7.62 m) in length.

(b) Individual Protection Not Required. Individual branch-circuit short-circuit protection for motors and motor controllers shall not be required where the requirements of Section 675-10(a) are met.

675-11. **Collector Rings.**

(a) Transmitting Current for Power Purposes. Collector rings shall have a current rating not less than 125 percent of the full-load current of the largest device served plus the full-load current of all other devices served, or as determined from Section 675-7(a) or 675-22(a).

(b) Control and Signal Purposes. Collector rings for control and signal purposes shall have a current rating not less than 125 percent of the full-load current of the largest device served plus the full-load current of all other devices served.

(c) Grounding. The collector ring used for grounding shall have a current rating of not less than that sized in accordance with Section 675-11(a).

(d) Protection. Collector rings shall be protected from the expected environment and from accidental contact by means of a suitable enclosure.

675-12. **Grounding.** The following equipment shall be grounded: (1) All electrical equipment on the irrigation machine; (2) all electrical equipment associated with the irrigation machine; (3) metal junction boxes and enclosures; and (4) control panels or control equipment that supply or control electrical equipment to the irrigation machine.

Exception: Grounding shall not be required on machines where all of the following provisions are met:

a. The machine is electrically controlled but not electrically driven.
b. The control voltage is 30 volts or less.
c. The control or signal circuits are current-limited as specified in Section 725-31.

675-13. **Methods of Grounding.** Machines that require grounding shall have a noncurrent-carrying equipment grounding conductor provided as an integral part of each cord, cable, or raceway. This grounding conductor shall be sized not less than the largest supply conductor in each cord, cable, or raceway. Feeder circuits supplying power to irrigation machines shall have an equipment grounding conductor sized according to Table 250-95.

675-14. **Bonding.** Where electrical grounding is required on an irrigation machine, the metallic structure of the machine, metallic conduit, or metallic sheath of cable shall be bonded to the grounding conductor. Metal-to-metal contact with a part that is bonded to the grounding conductor and the noncurrent-carrying parts of the machine shall be considered as an acceptable bonding path.

675-15. **Lightning Protection.** If an irrigation machine has a stationary point, a grounding electrode system in accordance with Article 250, Part H, shall be connected to the machine at the stationary point for lightning protection.

Where the electrical power supply to irrigation machine equipment is a service, provisions in Sections 250-81 and 250-83 require a made grounding electrode, such as a driven ground rod. Consideration should be given to Section 250-86 and NFPA 780-1992, *Lightning Protection Code,* in areas where lightning protection is critical.

675-16. **Energy from More than One Source.** Equipment within an enclosure receiving electrical energy from more than one source shall not be required to have a disconnecting means for the additional source, provided that its voltage is 30 volts or less and meets the requirements of Section 725-31.

675-17. **Connectors.** External plugs and connectors on the equipment shall be of the weatherproof type.

Unless provided solely for the connection of circuits meeting the requirements of Section 725-31, external plugs and connectors shall be constructed as specified in Section 250-99(a).

B. Center Pivot Irrigation Machines

675-21. **General.** The provisions of Part B are intended to cover additional special requirements that are peculiar to center pivot irrigation machines. See Section 675-2 for definition of "Center Pivot Irrigation Machines."

675-22. **Equivalent Current Ratings.** In order to establish ratings of controllers, disconnecting means, conductors, and the like, for the inherent intermittent duty of center pivot irrigation machines, the following determination shall be used:

The ratings of electrical components of any circuit should be selected so as to avoid extensive damage to the equipment during a short-circuit or a ground-fault condition. Section 675-22 contains requirements for establishing ratings of components of special equipment for inherent intermittent duty. Also see commentary following Sections 110-10 and 430-52.

Figure 675-1. *A center pivot irrigation machine. (Lockwood Corp.)*

(a) Continuous-Current Rating. The equivalent continuous-current rating for the selection of branch-circuit conductors and branch-circuit devices shall be equal to 125 percent of the motor nameplate full-load current rating of the largest motor plus 60 percent of the sum of the motor nameplate full-load current ratings of all remaining motors on the circuit.

(b) Locked-Rotor Current. The equivalent locked-rotor current rating shall be equal to the numerical sum of two times the locked-rotor current of the largest motor plus 80 percent of the sum of the motor nameplate full-load current ratings of all the remaining motors on the circuit.

ARTICLE 680 Swimming Pools, Fountains, and Similar Installations

Contents

A. General

(b) Cord Type.

(c) Sealing.

(d) Terminations.

F. Therapeutic Pools and Tubs in Health Care Facilities

680-60. General.

680-61. Permanently Installed Therapeutic Pools.

680-62. Therapeutic Tubs (Hydrotherapeutic Tanks).

(a) Ground-Fault Circuit-Interrupter.

(b) Bonding.

(c) Methods of Bonding.

(d) Grounding.

(e) Methods of Grounding.

(f) Receptacles.

(g) Lighting Fixtures.

G. Hydromassage Bathtubs

680-70. Protection.

680-71. Other Electric Equipment.

A. General

680-1. **Scope.** The provisions of this article apply to the construction and installation of electric wiring for and equipment in or adjacent to all swimming, wading, therapeutic, and decorative pools, fountains, hot tubs, spas, and hydromassage bathtubs, whether permanently installed or storable, and to metallic auxiliary equipment, such as pumps, filters, and similar equipment.

(FPN): The term "pool" as used in the balance of this article includes swimming, wading, and permanently installed therapeutic pools. The term "fountain" as used in the balance of this article includes fountains, ornamental pools, display pools, and reflection pools. The term is not intended to include drinking water fountains.

This article applies to swimming pools and similar installations, indoors or outdoors, permanent or storable, whether or not served by electrical circuits of any nature. Studies conducted by Underwriters Laboratories Inc., various manufacturers, and others indicate that a person in a swimming pool can receive a severe electric shock by reaching over and touching the energized casing of a faulty appliance, such as a radio, hair dryer, etc., as the person's body establishes a conductive path through the water and pool to earth. Also, a person not in contact with a faulty appliance or any grounded object may receive an electric shock and be rendered immobile by a potential gradient in the water itself. Accordingly, requirements of this article covering effective bonding and grounding, installation of receptacles and lighting fixtures, use of ground-fault circuit-interrupters, modified wiring methods, etc., apply not only to the installation of the pool, but also to installations and equipment adjacent to, or associated with, the pool.

680-2. **Approval of Equipment.** All electric equipment installed in the water, walls, or decks of pools, fountains, and similar installations shall comply with the provisions of this article.

680-3. **Other Articles.** Except as modified by this article, wiring and equipment in or adjacent to pools and fountains shall comply with the applicable requirements of Chapters 1 through 4.

(FPN): See Section 370-23 for junction boxes and Section 347-3 for rigid nonmetallic conduit.

Note that Section 370-23(d) specifies the requirements for the support of threaded boxes that do not contain devices, and Section 347-3(b) does not permit equipment to be supported by rigid nonmetallic conduit. See Figure 680-1. See also commentary following Section 370-23(d).

680-4. **Definitions.**

Cord- and Plug-Connected Lighting Assembly: A lighting assembly consisting of a lighting fixture intended for installation in the wall of a spa, hot tub, or storable pool, and a cord- and plug-connected transformer.

Dry-Niche Lighting Fixture: A lighting fixture intended for installation in the wall of a pool or fountain in a niche that is sealed against the entry of pool water.

Forming Shell: A structure designed to support a wet-niche lighting fixture assembly and intended for mounting in a pool or fountain structure.

Hydromassage Bathtub: A permanently installed bathtub equipped with a recirculating piping system, pump, and associated equipment. It is designed so it can accept, circulate, and discharge water upon each use.

See commentary following Part G, Hydromassage Bathtubs.

No-Niche Lighting Fixture: A lighting fixture intended for installation above or below the water without a niche.

This definition was new in the 1990 *Code*. See Section 680-20(d).

Permanently Installed Decorative Fountains and Reflection Pools: Those that are constructed in the ground, on the ground, or in a building in such a manner that the fountain cannot be readily disassembled for storage, whether or not served by electrical circuits of any nature. These units are primarily constructed for their aesthetic value and not intended for swimming or wading.

Permanently Installed Swimming, Wading, and Therapeutic Pools: Those that are constructed in the ground, on the ground, or in a building in such a manner that the pool cannot be readily disassembled for storage, whether or not served by electrical circuits of any nature.

See commentary following Part F, Therapeutic Pools and Tubs in Health Care Facilities.

Pool Cover, Electrically Operated: Motor-driven equipment designed to cover and uncover the water surface of a pool by means of a flexible sheet or rigid frame.

See Section 680-26.

Spa or Hot Tub: A hydromassage pool, or tub for recreational or therapeutic use, not located in health care facilities, designed for immersion of users and usually having a filter, heater, and motor-driven blower. It may be installed indoors or outdoors, on the ground or supporting structure, or in the ground or supporting structure. Generally, a spa or hot tub is not designed or intended to have its contents drained or discharged after each use.

See commentary following Part D, Spas and Hot Tubs.

Storable Swimming or Wading Pool: A pool with a maximum dimension of 18 feet (5.49 m) and a maximum wall height of 42 inches (1.07 m) and so constructed that it may be readily disassembled for storage and reassembled to its original

integrity. A pool with nonmetallic inflatable walls regardless of dimensions is considered to be a storable pool.

See commentary following Section 680-31 and Figure 680-10.

Wet-Niche Lighting Fixture: A lighting fixture intended for installation in a forming shell mounted in a pool or fountain structure where the fixture will be completely surrounded by water.

Figure 680-1. *Wet-niche fixture installation with J-box supported in accordance with Sections 370-23(d) and 347-3(b) above pool deck.*

680-5. **Transformers and Ground-Fault Circuit-Interrupters.**

(a) **Transformers.** Transformers used for the supply of underwater fixtures, together with the transformer enclosure, shall be identified for the purpose. The transformer shall be an isolated winding type having a grounded metal barrier between the primary and secondary windings.

Unless marked otherwise, UL-listed swimming pool and spa transformers are not suitable for connection to a conduit that extends directly to an underwater pool light forming shell. Swimming pool and spa transformers are not permitted to be used outdoors unless they are marked "For

Outdoor Use" or in an equivalent manner that signifies they have been found to be acceptable for both outdoor and indoor use. See Section 110-3(b).

(b) Ground-Fault Circuit-Interrupters. Ground-fault circuit-interrupters shall be self-contained units, circuit-breaker types, receptacle types, or other approved types.

See definition of "Ground-Fault Circuit-Interrupter" in Article 100.

A ground-fault circuit-interrupter is intended to be used only in a circuit that has a solidly grounded conductor; however, an equipment grounding conductor is not necessary in order for the GFCI to function. A Class A GFCI trips where the current to ground has a value in the range of 4 through 6 milliamperes and is suitable for use in swimming pool circuits. It should be noted, however, that swimming pool circuits installed before local adoption of the 1965 edition of the *National Electrical Code* may have sufficient leakage current to cause a Class A GFCI to trip. A Class B GFCI trips where the current to ground exceeds 20 milliamperes and is suitable for use with underwater swimming pool lighting fixtures only.

(c) Wiring. Conductors on the load side of a ground-fault circuit-interrupter or of a transformer, used to comply with provisions of Section 680-20(a)(1), shall not occupy raceway, boxes, or enclosures containing other conductors.

Exception No. 1: Ground-fault circuit-interrupters shall be permitted in a panelboard that contains circuits protected by other than ground-fault circuit-interrupters.

Exception No. 2: Supply conductors to a feed-through, receptacle-type, ground-fault circuit-interrupter shall be permitted in the same enclosure.

Exception No. 3: Conductors on the load side of a ground-fault circuit-interrupter shall be permitted to occupy raceway, boxes, or enclosures containing only conductors protected by ground-fault circuit-interrupters.

Exception No. 4: Grounding conductors.

680-6. **Receptacles, Lighting Fixtures, Lighting Outlets, Switching Devices, and Ceiling Fans.**

(a) Receptacles.

(1) Receptacles on the property shall be located at least 10 feet (3.05 m) from the inside walls of a pool or fountain.

Exception: Receptacle(s) that provide power for water-pump motor(s) for a permanently installed pool or fountain, as permitted in Section 680-7, shall be permitted between 5 and 10 feet (1.52 and 3.05 m) from the inside walls of the pool or fountain, and, where so located, shall be single and of the locking and grounding types and shall be protected by ground-fault circuit-interrupter(s).

(2) Where a permanently installed pool is installed at a dwelling unit(s), at least one 125-volt receptacle shall be located a minimum of 10 feet (3.05 m) from and not more than 20 feet (6.08 m) from the inside wall of the pool.

(3) All 125-volt receptacles located within 20 feet (6.08 m) of the inside walls of a pool shall be protected by a ground-fault circuit-interrupter. See Section 210-8(a)(3).

Section 680-6(a)(1), Exception makes it clear that a single locking- and grounding-type receptacle used for a recirculating pump motor is permitted where it will be not less than 5 feet from the inside walls of the pool or fountain and is protected by a GFCI.

Section 680-8(a)(3) also makes it clear that all receptacles located within 20 feet of a permanently installed pool or fountain (outdoors or indoors, for dwelling unit or commercial use) are required to be protected by GFCIs. This distance of 20 feet is intended to provide for location of receptacles beyond a pool deck. If located within the perimeter of a pool deck, the receptacle installation is likely to create a tripping hazard when the receptacle is in use.

See Figure 680-2.

Figure 680-2. *For permanently installed pools at dwelling unit(s), it is mandatory to install a 125-V receptacle between 10 and 20 feet from the inside wall of the pool.*

Figure 680-3. *This figure illustrates the shortest path a supply cord of an appliance connected to the receptacle would follow without piercing the wall.*

Figure 680-4. *Acceptable receptacle locations within 20 feet of a swimming pool.*

(FPN): In determining the above dimensions, the distance to be measured is the shortest path the supply cord of an appliance connected to the receptacle would follow without piercing a floor, wall, ceiling, doorway with hinged or sliding door, window opening, or other effective permanent barrier.

See Figures 680-3 and 680-4.

(b) Lighting Fixtures, Lighting Outlets, and Ceiling Fans.

(1) Lighting fixtures, lighting outlets, and ceiling fans shall not be installed over the pool or over the area extending

5 feet (1.52 m) horizontally from the inside walls of a pool unless no part of the lighting fixture or ceiling fan is less than 12 feet (3.66 m) above the maximum water level.

Exception No. 1: Existing lighting fixtures and lighting outlets located less than 5 feet (1.52 m) measured horizontally from the inside walls of a pool shall be at least 5 feet (1.52 m) above the surface of the maximum water level and shall be rigidly attached to the existing structure.

See Figures 680-5A and B.

Exception No. 2: In indoor pool areas, the limitations of Section 680-6(b)(1) shall not apply if all of the following conditions are complied with: (1) fixtures are of totally enclosed type; (2) a ground-fault circuit-interrupter is installed in the branch circuit supplying the fixture(s) or ceiling fans; and (3) the distance from the bottom of the fixture or ceiling fan to the maximum water level is not less than 7.5 feet (2.29 m).

(2) Lighting fixtures and lighting outlets installed in the area extending between 5 feet (1.52 m) and 10 feet (3.05 m) horizontally from the inside walls of a pool shall be protected by a ground-fault circuit-interrupter unless installed 5 feet (1.52 m) above the maximum water level and rigidly attached to the structure adjacent to or enclosing the pool.

(3) Cord-connected lighting fixtures shall meet the same specifications as other cord- and plug-connected equipment as set forth in Section 680-7 where installed within 16 feet (4.88 m) of any point on the water surface, measured radially.

(c) Switching Devices. Switching devices on the property shall be located at least 5 feet (1.52 m) horizontally from the inside walls of a pool unless separated from the pool by a solid fence, wall, or other permanent barrier.

Panelboards, time clocks, and pool light switches, etc., where located not less than 5 feet horizontally from the inside walls of a pool, without a solid fence, wall, or other permanent barrier, will be out of reach of persons who are in a pool, preventing contact and possible shock hazards.

680-7. **Cord- and Plug-Connected Equipment.** Fixed or stationary equipment rated 20 amperes or less, other than an underwater lighting fixture for a permanently installed pool, shall be

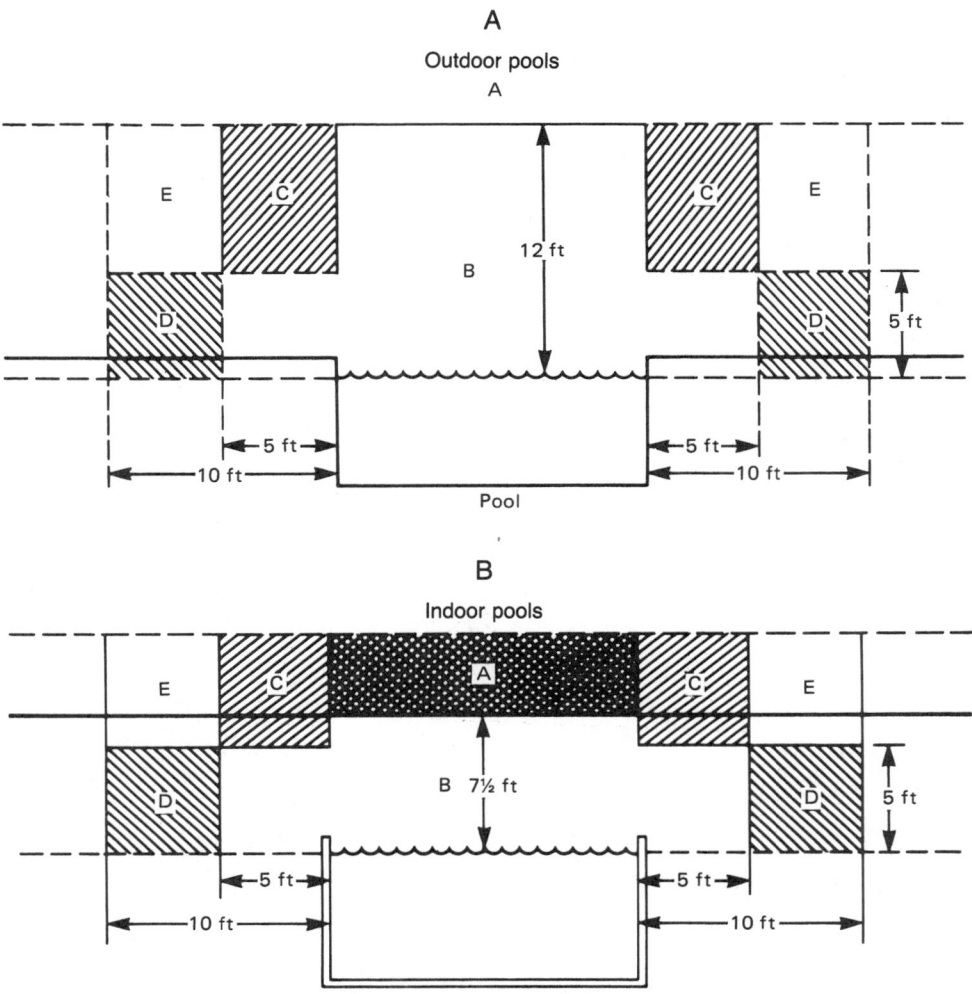

A
Outdoor pools
A

12 ft

5 ft

E   C   B   C   E

D   D

5 ft   5 ft

10 ft   Pool   10 ft

B
Indoor pools

E   C   A   C   E

B 7½ ft

D   D

5 ft

5 ft   5 ft

10 ft   10 ft

Figures 680-5A and 5B. *These diagrams clarify the limitations applicable to certain zones surrounding outdoor and indoor pools.*

Outdoor Pools
Area A. *Lighting fixtures, lighting outlets, and ceiling fans permitted above 12 feet. Section 680-6(b)(1)*
Area B. *Lighting fixtures, lighting outlets, and ceiling fans **not** permitted below 12 feet. Section 680-6(b)(1)*
Area C. *Existing lighting fixtures and lighting outlets permitted in this space if rigidly attached to existing structure (GFCI not required). Section 680-6(b)(1), Exception No. 1*
Area D. *Lighting fixtures and lighting outlets permitted if protected by a GFCI. Section 680-6(b)(2)*
Area E. *Lighting fixtures and lighting outlets permitted if rigidly attached. Section 680-6(b)(2)*

Indoor Pools
Area A. *Totally enclosed lighting fixtures protected by a GFCI and ceiling fans protected by a GFCI permitted above 7½ feet. Section 680-6(b)(1), Exception No. 2*
Area B. *Lighting fixtures, lighting outlets, and ceiling fans **not** permitted below 7½ feet. Section 680-6(b)(1), Exception No. 2.*
Areas C, D, and E. *Same as outdoor pools.*

permitted to be connected with a flexible cord to facilitate the removal or disconnection for maintenance or repair. For other than storable pools, the flexible cord shall not exceed 3 feet (914 mm) in length and shall have a copper equipment grounding conductor not smaller than No. 12 with a grounding-type attachment plug.

(FPN):   See Section 680-25(e) for connection with flexible cords.

In some climates, it is preferable to disconnect a permanent pool's filter pump during the cold weather months, and a 3-foot cord is permitted to facilitate the

removal of fixed or stationary equipment for purposes of maintenance and storage.

The 3-foot (914-mm) cord limitation does not apply to cord- and plug-connected filter pumps used with storable-type pools (covered in Part C of this article) since these pumps are neither fixed nor stationary. Listed filter pumps for use with storable pools are considered portable and are permitted to be equipped with cords longer than 3 feet.

680-8. **Overhead Conductor Clearances.** The following parts of pools shall not be placed under existing service-drop conductors or any other open overhead wiring; nor shall such wiring be installed above the following: (1) pools and the area extending 10 feet (3.05 m) horizontally from the inside of the walls of the pool; (2) diving structure; or (3) observation stands, towers, or platforms.

Exception No. 1: Structures listed in items (1), (2), and (3) above shall be permitted under supply lines or service drops where such installations provide the following clearances:

	Insulated supply or service drop cables, 0-750 volts to ground, supported on and cabled together with an effectively grounded bare messenger or effectively grounded neutral conductor	All other supply or service drop conductors	
		Voltage to Ground	
		0-15 kV	greater than 15 to 50kV
A. Clearance in any direction to the water level, edge of water surface, base of diving platform, or permanently-anchored raft	18 feet (5.49 m)	25 feet (7.62 m)	27 feet (8.23 m)
B. Clearance in any direction to the diving platform or tower	14 feet (4.27 m)	16 feet (4.88 m)	18 feet (5.49 m)
C. Horizontal limit of clearance measured from inside wall of the pool	This limit shall extend to the outer edge of the structures listed in (1) and (2) above but not less than 10 feet (3.05 m).		

Figure 680-8, Exception No. 1

Exception No. 2: Utility-owned, -operated, and -maintained communication conductors, community antenna system coaxial cables complying with Article 820, and the supporting messengers shall be permitted at a height of not less than 10 feet (3.05 m) above swimming and wading pools, diving structures, and observation stands, towers, or platforms.

(FPN): See Sections 225-18 and 225-19 for clearances for conductors not covered by this section.

680-9. **Electric Pool Water Heaters.** All electric pool water heaters shall have the heating elements subdivided into loads not exceeding 48 amperes and protected at not more than 60 amperes.

The ampacity of the branch-circuit conductors and the rating or setting of overcurrent protective devices shall not be less than 125 percent of the total load of the nameplate rating.

680-10. **Underground Wiring Location.** Underground wiring shall not be permitted under the pool or within the area extending 5 feet (1.52 m) horizontally from the inside wall of the pool.

Exception No. 1: Wiring necessary to supply pool equipment permitted by this article shall be allowed within this area.

Exception No. 2: Where space limitations prevent wiring from being routed 5 feet (1.52 m) or more from the pool, such wiring shall be permitted where installed in rigid metal conduit, intermediate metal conduit, or a nonmetallic raceway system. All metal conduit shall be corrosion-resistant and suitable for the location. The minimum burial depth shall be as follows:

Wiring Method	Minimum Burial (inches)
Rigid Metal Conduit	6
Intermediate Metal Conduit	6
Rigid Nonmetallic Conduit Approved for Direct Burial without Concrete Encasement	18
Other Approved Raceways*	18

For SI units: one inch = 25.4 millimeters
*Note: Raceways approved for burial only where concrete-encased shall require a concrete envelope not less than 2 inches (50.8 mm) thick.

680-11. **Equipment Rooms and Pits.** Electric equipment shall not be installed in rooms or pits that do not have adequate drainage to prevent water accumulation during normal operation or filter maintenance.

B. Permanently Installed Pools

680-20. **Underwater Lighting Fixtures.** Paragraphs (a) through (d) of this section apply to all lighting fixtures installed below the normal water level of the pool.

(a) General.

(1) The design of an underwater lighting fixture supplied from a branch circuit either directly or by way of a transformer meeting the requirements of Section 680-5(a) shall be such that, where the fixture is properly installed without a ground-fault circuit-interrupter, there is no shock hazard with any likely combination of fault conditions during normal use (not relamping).

In addition, a ground-fault circuit-interrupter shall be installed in the branch circuit supplying fixtures operating at more than 15 volts, so that there is no shock hazard during relamping. The installation of the ground-fault circuit-interrupter shall be such that there is no shock hazard with any likely fault-condition combination that involves a person in a conductive path from any ungrounded part of the branch circuit or the fixture to ground.

Compliance with this requirement shall be obtained by the use of an approved underwater lighting fixture and by installation of an approved ground-fault circuit-interrupter in the branch circuit.

(2) No lighting fixtures shall be installed for operation on supply circuits over 150 volts between conductors.

(3) Lighting fixtures mounted in walls shall be installed with the top of the fixture lens at least 18 inches (457 mm) below the normal water level of the pool. A lighting fixture facing upward shall have the lens adequately guarded to prevent contact by any person.

Exception: Lighting fixtures identified for use at a depth of not less than 4 inches (102 mm) below the normal water level of the pool shall be permitted.

The reason for the 18-inch minimum submergence requirement is to reduce the likelihood that a person who is in the water hanging onto the side of the pool directly over the fixture will have his or her chest cavity in line with the fixture. The exception covers fixtures that have been investigated and found acceptable for use where the chest cavity may be directly in front of the fixture. The highest level of leakage current in the pool coming from a wet-niche fixture with a broken lens and bulb will be found directly in front of the fixture.

(4) Fixtures that depend on submersion for safe operation shall be inherently protected against the hazards of overheating when not submerged.

Fixtures that depend on submersion for safe operation are required to be inherently protected against the hazards of overheating when not submerged; for instance, during a relamping process. Protection against overheating is required to be built into or be a part of the fixture. A remotely located low-water cutoff switch will not provide the intended protection.

(b) Wet-Niche Fixtures.

(1) Forming shells shall be installed for the mounting of all wet-niche underwater fixtures and shall be equipped with provisions for conduit entries.

Conduit shall extend from the forming shell to a suitable junction box or other enclosure located as provided in Section 680-21. Conduit shall be rigid metal, intermediate metal, or rigid nonmetallic.

Metal conduit shall be of brass or other approved corrosion-resistant metal.

Where rigid nonmetallic conduit is used, a No. 8 insulated copper conductor shall be installed in this conduit with provisions for terminating in the forming shell, junction box or transformer enclosure, or ground-fault circuit-interrupter enclosure. The termination of the No. 8 conductor in the forming shell shall be covered with, or encapsulated in, a listed potting compound to protect such connection from the possible deteriorating effect of pool water. Metal parts of the fixture and forming shell in contact with the pool water shall be of brass or other approved corrosion-resistant metal.

(2) The end of the flexible-cord jacket and the flexible-cord conductor terminations within a fixture shall be covered with, or encapsulated in, a suitable potting compound to prevent the entry of water into the fixture through the cord or its conductors. In addition, the grounding connection within a fixture shall be similarly treated to protect such connection from the deteriorating effect of pool water in the event of water entry into the fixture.

(3) The fixture shall be bonded to and secured to the forming shell by a positive locking device that assures a low-resistance contact and requires a tool to remove the fixture from the forming shell.

(c) Dry-Niche Fixtures. A dry-niche lighting fixture shall be provided with (1) provision for drainage of water and (2) means for accommodating one equipment grounding conductor for each conduit entry.

Approved rigid metal conduit, intermediate metal conduit, or rigid nonmetallic conduit shall be installed from the fixture to the service equipment or panelboard. A junction box shall not be required but, if used, shall not be required to be elevated or located as specified in Section 680-21(a)(4) if the fixture is specifically identified for the purpose.

Exception: Electrical metallic tubing shall be permitted to be used to protect conductors where installed on or within buildings.

Underwater lighting fixtures of either dry-niche, no-niche, or wet-niche types operating at more than 15 V require ground-fault circuit-interrupter protection. See commentary following Section 680-5(b).

Branch-circuit conductors for dry-niche fixtures are required to be installed in approved rigid metal conduit, intermediate metal conduit, or rigid nonmetallic conduit from the fixture to a panelboard or to the service equipment. Branch-circuit conductors for wet-niche fixtures leaving the pool junction box are required to be enclosed in rigid metal conduit, intermediate metal conduit, or rigid nonmetallic conduit, except where located in or on buildings where the conductors are permitted to be installed in electrical metallic tubing. However, unlike wet-niche fixtures, a junction box is not required for dry-niche fixtures. If one is used, it is not required to be elevated or located as specified in Section 680-21(a)(4). See Figures 680-1 and 680-5.

Where rigid nonmetallic conduit is used between a forming shell for a wet-niche fixture and a junction box or other enclosure, a No. 8 insulated, copper bonding conductor is required to be installed within this conduit to provide electrical continuity between the forming shell and the junction box or other enclosure. This rigid nonmetallic conduit should be sized large enough to enclose both the No. 8 insulated copper bonding conductor and the approved flexible cord that supplies the wet-niche fixture to facilitate easy withdrawal and insertion of the bonding conductor and the cord.

Figure 680-6. *Installation requirements for wet-niche forming shell and flush deck box installed in accordance with Section 680-21, Exception. See Figure 680-1 for surface deck boxes.*

(d) No-Niche Fixtures. A no-niche fixture shall:

(1) Be listed for the purpose.

(2) Be installed in accordance with the requirements of Section 680-20(b).

Where connection to a forming shell is specified, the connection shall be to the mounting bracket.

Requirements for no-niche fixtures were added in the 1990 *Code*.

680-21. Junction Boxes and Enclosures for Transformers or Ground-Fault Circuit-Interrupters.

(a) Junction Boxes. A junction box connected to a conduit that extends directly to a forming shell or mounting bracket of a no-niche fixture shall be:

(1) Equipped with threaded hubs or bosses or a nonmetallic hub listed for the purpose; and

(2) Of copper, brass, suitable plastic, or other approved corrosion-resistant material; and

(3) Provided with electrical continuity between every connected metal conduit and the grounding terminals by means of copper, brass, or other approved corrosion-resistant metal that is integral with the box; and

(4) Located not less than 4 inches (102 mm), measured from the inside of the bottom of the box, above the ground level, or pool deck, or not less than 8 inches (203 mm) above the maximum pool water level, whichever provides the greatest elevation, and located not less than 4 feet (1.22 m) from the inside wall of the pool, unless separated from the pool by a solid fence, wall, or other permanent barrier.

Exception: On lighting systems of 15 volts or less, a flush deck box shall be permitted provided:

a. An approved potting compound is used to fill the box to prevent the entrance of moisture; and

b. The flush deck box is located not less than 4 feet (1.22 m) from the inside wall of the pool.

(b) Other Enclosures. An enclosure for a transformer, ground-fault circuit-interrupter, or a similar device connected to a conduit that extends directly to a forming shell or mounting bracket of a no-niche fixture shall be:

(1) Equipped with threaded hubs or bosses or a nonmetallic hub listed for the purpose; and

(2) Provided with an approved seal, such as duct seal at the conduit connection, that prevents circulation of air between the conduit and the enclosures; and

(3) Provided with electrical continuity between every connected metal conduit and the grounding terminals by means of copper, brass, or other approved corrosion-resistant metal that is integral with the enclosures; and

(4) Located not less than 4 inches (102 mm), measured from the inside bottom of the enclosure, above the ground level or pool deck, or not less than 8 inches (203 mm) above the maximum pool water level, whichever provides the greater elevation, and located not less than 4 feet (1.22 mm) from the inside wall of the pool, unless separated from the pool by a solid fence, wall, or other permanent barrier.

(c) Protection. Junction boxes and enclosures mounted above the grade of the finished walkway around the pool shall not be located in the walkway unless afforded additional protection, such as by location under diving boards, adjacent to fixed structures, and the like.

(d) Grounding Terminals. Junction boxes, transformer enclosures, and ground-fault circuit-interrupter enclosures connected to a conduit that extends directly to a forming shell or mounting bracket of a no-niche fixture shall be provided with a number of grounding terminals that shall be at least one more than the number of conduit entries.

(e) Strain Relief. The termination of a flexible cord of an underwater lighting fixture within a junction box, transformer enclosure, ground-fault circuit-interrupter, or other enclosure shall be provided with a strain relief.

680-22. Bonding.

(FPN): It is not the intent of this subsection to require that the No. 8 or larger solid copper bonding conductor be extended or attached to any remote panelboard, service equipment, or any electrode, but only that it be employed to eliminate voltage gradients in the pool area as prescribed.

(a) Bonded Parts. The following parts shall be bonded together:

(1) All metallic parts of the pool structure, including the reinforcing metal of the pool shell, coping stones, and deck.

(2) All forming shells and mounting brackets of a no-niche fixture.

(3) All metal fittings within or attached to the pool structure.

(4) Metal parts of electric equipment associated with the pool water circulating system, including pump motors.

(5) Metal parts of equipment associated with pool covers, including electric motors.

(6) Metal-sheathed cables and raceways, metal piping, and all fixed metal parts that are within 5 feet (1.52 m) horizontally of the inside walls of the pool, and within 12 feet (3.66 m) above the maximum water level of the pool, or any observation stands, towers, or platforms, or from any diving structures, and that are not separated from the pool by a permanent barrier.

This section would also include, for example, a metal door frame or metal window frame.

Exception No. 1: The usual steel tie wires shall be considered suitable for bonding the reinforcing steel together, and welding or special clamping shall not be required. These tie wires shall be made tight.

Exception No. 2: Isolated parts that are not over 4 inches (102 mm) in any dimension and do not penetrate into the pool structure more than 1 inch (25.4 mm) shall not require bonding.

Exception No. 3: Structural reinforcing steel or the walls of bolted or welded metal pool structures shall be permitted as a common bonding grid for nonelectrical parts where connections can be made in accordance with Section 250-113.

Section 250-113 requires that the connection be made by exothermic welding or listed clamps, connectors, etc.

(b) Common Bonding Grid. These parts shall be connected to a common bonding grid with a solid, copper conductor, insulated, covered, or bare, not smaller than No. 8. Connection shall be made by pressure connectors or clamps of stainless steel, brass, copper, or copper alloy. The common bonding grid shall be permitted to be any of the following:

(1) The structural reinforcing steel of a concrete pool where the reinforcing rods are bonded together by the usual steel tie wires or the equivalent; or

(2) The wall of a bolted or welded metal pool; or

(3) A solid, copper conductor, insulated, covered, or bare, not smaller than No. 8.

(c) Pool Water Heaters. For pool water heaters rated at more than 50 amperes that have specific instructions regarding bonding and grounding, only those parts designated to be bonded shall be bonded, and only those parts designated to be grounded shall be grounded.

It is important to know the difference between the terms "bonding" and "grounding" as they apply to this article. As defined in Article 100, "bonding" is "the permanent joining of metallic parts to form an electrically conductive path that will assure electrical continuity and the capacity to

conduct safely any current likely to be imposed." See commentary following Section 680-25(f).

This section identifies the metal parts that are required to be bonded, including all metal parts of electrical equipment associated with the pool water circulating system, all metal parts of the pool structure, and all fixed metal parts, which include conduit and piping, metal door frames, and metal window frames, etc., within 5 feet of the inside walls of the pool and that are not separated by a permanent barrier. It should be understood that the bonding of these parts does not mean that they are required to be connected to each other; it means that they are required to be connected to a common bonding grid with an insulated, covered, or bare solid copper conductor not smaller than No. 8. See Figures 680-7 and 680-8. Connections are required to be made by exothermic welds or by listed pressure connectors, clamps, or other listed means in accordance with Section 250-113. See fine print note following Section 680-22.

The reason for connecting metal parts (ladders, handrails, water-circulating equipment, forming shells, diving boards, etc.) to a common bonding grid (pool reinforcing steel, pool metal wall, or a No. 8 solid conductor) is to ensure that all such metal parts will be at the same electrical potential. This

Figure 680-7. Illustrated is a metal (e.g., steel or aluminum) perimeter pool with bolted (or welded) sections. The metal perimeter serves as the common bonding grid to which the metal ladder, the metal diving board, and the pump motor are connected. Note that the pump motor is connected to a receptacle as specified in Sections 680-6 and 680-7.

Figure 680-8. A poured concrete pool. The structural reinforcing steel serves as the common bonding grid to which all metal appurtenances associated with the pool are connected. Safety rope hooks are not required to be bonded as specified in Section 680-22(a), Exception No. 2. The flush deck box meets the provisions of Section 680-21(a), Exception.

will reduce any possible shock hazard created by stray currents in the ground or piping connected to the swimming pool. Stray currents can also exist in nonmetallic piping because of the low resistivity of chlorinated water.

Since corrosion is normally associated with the wet conditions of swimming pool areas, wiring and connections should be checked periodically, especially bonding connections between the No. 8 copper conductor and, for instance, an aluminum (or other dissimilar metal) ladder.

680-23. **Underwater Audio Equipment.** All underwater audio equipment shall be identified for the purpose.

(a) Speakers. Each speaker shall be mounted in an approved metal forming shell, the front of which is enclosed by a captive metal screen, or equivalent, that is bonded to and secured to the forming shell by a positive locking device that assures a low-resistance contact and requires a tool to open for installation or servicing of the speaker. The forming shell shall be installed in a recess in the wall or floor of the pool.

(b) Wiring Methods. Rigid metal conduit or intermediate metal conduit of brass or other identified corrosion-resistant metal or rigid nonmetallic conduit shall extend from the forming shell to a suitable junction box or other enclosure as provided in Section 680-21. Where rigid nonmetallic conduit is used, a No. 8 insulated copper conductor shall be installed in this conduit with provisions for terminating in the forming shell and the junction box. The termination of the No. 8 conductor in the forming shell shall be covered with, or encapsulated in, a suitable potting compound to protect such connection from the possible deteriorating effect of pool water.

(c) Forming Shell and Metal Screen. The forming shell and metal screen shall be of brass or other approved corrosion-resistant metal.

680-24. **Grounding.** The following equipment shall be grounded: (1) wet-niche and no-niche underwater lighting fixtures; (2) dry-niche underwater lighting fixtures; (3) all electric equipment located within 5 feet (1.52 m) of the inside wall of the pool; (4) all electric equipment associated with the recirculating system of the pool; (5) junction boxes; (6) transformer enclosures; (7) ground-fault circuit-interrupters; (8) panelboards that are not part of the service equipment and that supply any electric equipment associated with the pool.

680-25. **Methods of Grounding.**

(a) General. The following provisions shall apply to the grounding of underwater lighting fixtures, junction boxes, metal transformer enclosures, panelboards, motors, and other electrical enclosures and equipment.

(b) Pool Lighting Fixtures and Related Equipment.

(1) Wet-niche, dry-niche, or no-niche lighting fixtures shall be connected to an equipment grounding conductor sized in accordance with Table 250-95 but not smaller than No. 12. It shall be an insulated copper conductor and shall be installed with the circuit conductors in rigid metal conduit, intermediate metal conduit, or rigid nonmetallic conduit.

Exception No. 1: Electrical metallic tubing shall be permitted to be used to protect conductors where installed on or within buildings.

Exception No. 2: The equipment grounding conductor between the wiring chamber of the secondary winding of a transformer and a junction box shall be sized in accordance with the over-current device in this circuit.

(2) The junction box, transformer enclosure, or other enclosure in the supply circuit to a wet-niche or no-niche lighting fixture and the field-wiring chamber of a dry-niche lighting fixture shall be grounded to the equipment grounding terminal of the panelboard. This terminal shall be directly connected to the panelboard enclosure. The equipment grounding conductor shall be installed without joint or splice.

See commentary following Section 680-5(a).

Exception No. 1: Where more than one underwater lighting fixture is supplied by the same branch circuit, the equipment grounding conductor, installed between the junction boxes, transformer enclosures, or other enclosures in the supply circuit to wet-niche fixtures, or between the field-wiring compartments of dry-niche fixtures, shall be permitted to be terminated on grounding terminals.

Exception No. 2: Where the underwater lighting fixture is supplied from a transformer, ground-fault circuit-interrupter, clock-operated switch, or a manual snap switch that is located between the panelboard and a junction box connected to the conduit that extends directly to the underwater lighting fixture, the equipment grounding conductor shall be permitted to terminate on grounding terminals on the transformer, ground-fault circuit-interrupter, clock-operated switch enclosure, or an outlet box used to enclose a snap switch.

(3) Wet-niche or no-niche lighting fixtures that are supplied by a flexible cord or cable shall have all exposed noncurrent-carrying metal parts grounded by an insulated copper equipment grounding conductor that is an integral part of the cord or cable. This grounding conductor shall be connected to a grounding terminal in the supply junction box, transformer enclosure, or other enclosure. The grounding conductor shall not be smaller than the supply conductors and not smaller than No. 16.

(c) **Motors.** Pool-associated motors shall be connected to an equipment grounding conductor sized in accordance with Table 250-95 but not smaller than No. 12. It shall be an insulated copper conductor and shall be installed with the circuit conductors in rigid metal conduit, intermediate metal conduit, rigid nonmetallic conduit, or Type MC cable listed for the application.

Type MC cable listed for the application has been added to the list of wiring methods permitted for swimming pool motor circuits.

Exception No. 1: Electrical metallic tubing shall be permitted to be used to protect conductors where installed on or within buildings.

Exception No. 2: Where necessary to employ flexible connections at or adjacent to the motor, liquidtight flexible metal or nonmetallic conduit with approved fittings shall be permitted.

Exception No. 3: Any of the wiring methods recognized in Chapter 3 of this Code that contain an insulated or covered equipment grounding conductor not smaller than No. 12 shall be permitted to be used in the interior of a one-family dwelling.

Exception No. 3 permits wiring methods such as nonmetallic-sheathed cable, MC cable, and armored cable in the interior of one-family dwelling units. It does not permit less than a No. 12 copper conductor for the equipment grounding conductor. It is not the intent to require an insulated grounding conductor for this exception.

Exception No. 4: Flexible cord shall be permitted in accordance with Section 680-7.

See Figure 680-7.

(d) **Panelboards.** A panelboard, not part of the service equipment, shall have an equipment grounding conductor installed between its grounding terminal and the grounding terminal of the service equipment. This conductor shall be sized in accordance with Table 250-95 but not smaller than No. 12. It shall be an insulated conductor and shall be installed with the feeder conductors in rigid metal conduit, intermediate metal conduit, or rigid nonmetallic conduit. The equipment grounding conductor shall be connected to an equipment grounding terminal of the panelboard.

The insulated equipment grounding conductor may be aluminum or copper and installed in a raceway. It should be understood that, for an existing remote panelboard, Exception No. 1 permits an approved cable assembly with an insulated or covered aluminum or copper equipment grounding conductor. See Figure 680-9.

Exception No. 1: The equipment grounding conductor between an existing remote panelboard and the service equipment shall not be required to be in one of the conduits listed in paragraph (d) if the interconnection is by means of a flexible metal conduit or an approved cable assembly with an insulated or covered equipment grounding conductor.

Exception No. 2: Electrical metallic tubing shall be permitted to be used to protect conductors where installed on or within the building.

(FPN): For permitted use of electrical metallic tubing, see Section 348-1.

(e) **Cord-Connected Equipment.** Where fixed or stationary equipment is connected with a flexible cord to facilitate removal or disconnection for maintenance, repair, or storage as provided in Section 680-7, the equipment grounding conductors shall be connected to a fixed metal part of the assembly. The removable part shall be mounted on or bonded to the fixed metal part.

(f) **Other Equipment.** Other electrical equipment shall be grounded in accordance with Article 250 and connected by wiring methods of Chapter 3.

Equipment, other than underwater lighting fixtures and pool-associated motors, is required to be connected by the wiring methods of Chapter 3 and grounded in accordance with Article 250. For example, an outdoor receptacle is permitted to be wired with Type UF cable containing an insulated or bare conductor for equipment grounding purposes. See Figure 680-9.

Figure 680-9. *Circuits for pools may be derived from an existing remote panelboard that is supplied by an approved cable assembly as specified in Section 680-25(d), Exception No. 1. Section 680-25(f) permits Type UF cable to be used for the receptacle required by Section 680-6(a)(2), and other equipment; but circuit conductors for underwater lighting fixtures are required to be run in raceways. Circuit conductors for pool-associated motors other than flexible cord, as permitted by Section 680-7, are required to be run in raceway. An exception is the interior of one-family dwelling units where any wiring method permitted by Chapter 3 is acceptable if the grounding conductor is at least No. 12 copper.*

Sections 680-24 and 680-25 provide requirements for equipment grounding. These sections require equipment grounding conductors to be connected to noncurrent-carrying metal parts of the specified equipment. These equipment grounding conductors are required to be run with the circuit conductors in rigid metal conduit, intermediate conduit, listed MC cable for motors, or rigid nonmetallic conduit, and they must be terminated at the grounding terminal bus at the service panelboard or subpanel. This equipment grounding conductor provides a path of low impedance that limits the voltage to ground and facilitates the operation of the circuit overcurrent protective device(s). Furthermore, the equipment grounding conductor is required to be an insulated copper conductor that is not smaller than No. 12. Where installed on or in buildings, the conductor may be run with the circuit conductors in EMT. See also 680-25(c), Exception No. 3.

The requirements in Sections 680-24 and 680-25 are in addition to the bonding requirements in Section 680-22. The intent of the bonding requirements is to establish an equipotential plane to limit the voltage between all noncurrent-carrying parts of electrical and nonelectrical equipment in the pool area.

Bonding conductors may be insulated, covered, or bare and are required to be No. 8 solid copper or larger. They may be direct buried, and, where connected to metal parts of the pool structure or metal parts of electric equipment,

they may be externally clamped or attached and are not required to be accessible. All of these parts form a common bonding grid that establishes an equipotential grounding system, and they do not have to be run to the equipment grounding terminals of panelboards or service equipment.

680-26. **Electrically Operated Pool Covers.**

(a) **Motors and Controllers.** The electric motors, controllers, and wiring shall be located at least 5 feet (1.52 m) from the inside wall of the pool unless separated from the pool by a wall, cover, or other permanent barrier. Electric motors installed below grade level shall be of the totally enclosed type.

(FPN No. 1): For cabinets installed in damp and wet locations, see Section 373-2(a).

(FPN No. 2): For switches or circuit breakers installed in a wet location, see Section 380-4.

(FPN No. 3): For protection against liquids, see Section 430-11.

(b) **Wiring Methods.** The electric motor and controller shall be connected to a circuit protected by a ground-fault circuit-interrupter.

680-27. **Deck Area Heating.** The provisions of this section apply to all pool deck areas, including a covered pool, where electrically operated comfort heating units are installed within 20 feet (6.1 m) of the inside wall of the pool.

(a) **Unit Heaters.** Unit heaters shall be rigidly mounted to the structure and shall be of the totally enclosed or guarded types. Unit heaters shall not be mounted over the pool or within the area extending 5 feet (1.52 m) horizontally from the inside walls of a pool.

(b) **Permanently Wired Radiant Heaters.** Radiant electric heaters shall be suitably guarded and securely fastened to their mounting device(s). Heaters shall not be installed over a pool or within the area extending 5 feet (1.52 m) horizontally from the inside walls of the pool and shall be mounted at least 12 feet (3.66 m) vertically above the pool deck unless otherwise approved.

(c) **Radiant Heat Cables Not Permitted.** Radiant heating cables embedded in or below the deck shall not be permitted.

Only unit heaters and permanently connected radiant heaters are permitted in the area that extends 5 to 20 feet horizontally from the inside walls of a pool. Radiant heat cables embedded in the deck are not permitted.

C. Storable Pools

680-30. **Pumps.** A cord-connected pool filter pump shall incorporate an approved system of double insulation or its equivalent and shall be provided with means for grounding only the internal and nonaccessible noncurrent-carrying metal parts of the appliance.

The means for grounding shall be an equipment grounding conductor run with the power-supply conductors in the flexible cord that is properly terminated in a grounding-type attachment plug having a fixed grounding contact member.

680-31. **Ground-Fault Circuit-Interrupters Required.** All electric equipment, including power-supply cords, used with storable pools shall be protected by ground-fault circuit-interrupters.

A storable pool may be readily disassembled and has a maximum dimension of 18 feet and a maximum wall height of 42 inches. Pools of any dimension with inflatable walls are considered to be storable. See definition in Section 680-4. This type of pool and its associated equipment do not require bonding conductors. However, the filter pump is required to be double insulated or equivalent, and grounding means consisting of an equipment grounding conductor that is an integral part of the flexible cord is required to be provided. There are portable filter pumps for use with storable pools listed by Underwriters Laboratories Inc.

The receptacle is required to be located at least 10 feet from pool [see Section 680-6(a)], and all electric equipment is required to have ground-fault circuit-interrupter protection for personnel. See Figure 680-10.

(FPN): Where flexible cords are used, see Section 400-4.

680-32. **Lighting Fixtures.** A lighting fixture installed in or on the wall of a storable pool shall be part of a cord- and plug-connected lighting assembly. This assembly shall:

(1) Have no exposed metal parts;

(2) Have a fixture lamp that operates at 15 volts or less;

(3) Have an impact-resistant polymeric lens, fixture body, and transformer enclosure;

Figure 680-10. *Illustrated are the requirements for a storable-type pool. Metal appurtenances are not required to be bonded. The 3-wire cord may be longer than 3 feet. (Some listed filter pumps are equipped with cords 25 ft long.) The receptacle shown can be a GFCI-type receptacle, a receptacle supplied through a GFCI-type receptacle, or a receptacle protected by a GFCI-type circuit breaker.*

(4) Have a transformer meeting the requirements of Section 680-5(a) with a primary rating not over 150 volts; and

(5) Be listed as an assembly for the purpose.

This section was new in the 1990 *Code*. It recognizes lighting fixtures installed in, or on, storable pools. It should be understood that these cord- and plug-connected fixtures are required to be listed as an assembly.

Exception: A lighting assembly without a transformer, and with the fixture lamp(s) operating at not over 150 volts, shall be permitted to be cord- and plug-connected where the assembly complies with all of the following:

a. It has no exposed metal parts.

b. It has an impact-resistant polymeric lens and fixture body.

c. A ground-fault circuit-interrupter with open neutral protection is provided as an integral part of the assembly.

d. The fixture lamp is permanently connected to the ground-fault circuit-interrupter with open-neutral protection.

e. It complies with the requirements of Section 680-20(a).

f. It is listed as an assembly for the purpose.

D. Spas and Hot Tubs

The requirements of Part D are divided into two categories: outdoor installations and indoor installations. See Part G for hydromassage bathtub requirements.

Outdoor installations fall under the requirements of both Parts A and B of Article 680 with three exceptions:

1. Metal bands or hoops used to secure wooden staves are not required to be bonded.

2. Listed packaged units may be cord connected and are required to be protected by a GFCI.

3. Bonding by metal-to-metal mounting on a common frame or base is permitted.

Indoor installations are subject to the same basic requirements but take into consideration the confines of an indoor location.

Receptacles, wall switches, and electrical devices and controls not associated with a spa or hot tub are required to be located at least 5 feet away. Receptacles within 10 feet, and those providing power to a spa or hot tub, are required to be protected by a GFCI. Effective January 1, 1994, spas and hot tubs will also require ground-fault circuit-interrupter protection. See Section 680-42.

Lighting fixtures, lighting outlets, and ceiling fans located over a spa or hot tub or within 5 feet horizontally are required to be protected by a GFCI.

Bonding and grounding requirements are similar to those in Parts A and B of Article 680, except that metal-to-metal mounting on a common frame or base is an acceptable bonding method.

Small conductive surfaces such as air and water jets, drain fittings, towel bars, etc., are not required to be bonded. See Section 680-41(d)(5), Exception.

Listed packaged units may be cord connected.

680-40 . Outdoor Installations. A spa or hot tub installed outdoors shall comply with the provisions of Parts A and B.

Exception No. 1: Metal bands or hoops used to secure wooden staves shall be exempt from Section 680-22.

Exception No. 2: Listed packaged units shall be permitted to be cord- and plug-connected with a cord no longer than 15 feet (4.57 m) if protected by a ground-fault circuit-interrupter.

Exception No. 3: Bonding by metal-to-metal mounting on a common frame or base shall be permitted.

Exception No. 4: Listed packaged units utilizing a factory-installed remote panelboard shall be permitted to be connected with not more than 3 feet (914 mm) of liquidtight flexible conduit.

Exception No. 4 permits the use of liquidtight flexible metal or nonmetallic conduit. This modifies the requirements for wiring methods provided in Section 680-25(d).

680-41 . Indoor Installations. A spa or hot tub installed indoors shall conform to the requirements of this part and shall be connected by wiring methods of Chapter 3.

Exception: Listed packaged units rated 20 amperes or less shall be permitted to be cord- and plug-connected to facilitate the removal or disconnection for maintenance and repair.

(a) Receptacles. At least one convenience receptacle shall be located a minimum of 5 feet (1.52 m) from and not more than 10 feet (3.05 m) from the inside wall of the spa or hot tub.

(1) Receptacles on the property shall be located at least 5 feet (1.52 m) from the inside walls of the spa or hot tub.

(2) 125-volt receptacles located within 10 feet (3.05 m) of the inside walls of a spa or hot tub shall be protected by a ground-fault circuit-interrupter.

(FPN): In determining the above dimensions, the distance to be measured is the shortest path the supply cord of an appliance connected to the receptacle would follow without piercing a floor, wall, or ceiling of a building or other effective permanent barrier.

See also Section 680-6(a)(3), FPN, and Figure 680-4.

(3) Receptacles that provide power for a spa or hot tub shall be ground-fault circuit-interrupter protected.

(b) Lighting Fixtures, Lighting Outlets, and Ceiling Fans.

(1) Lighting fixtures, lighting outlets, and ceiling fans located over the spa or hot tub or within 5 feet (1.52 m) from the inside walls of the spa or hot tub shall be a minimum of 7 feet 6 inches (2.29 m) above the maximum water level and shall be protected by a ground-fault circuit-interrupter.

Exception No. 1: Lighting fixtures, lighting outlets, and ceiling fans located 12 feet (3.66 m) or more above the maximum water level shall not require protection by a ground-fault circuit-interrupter.

Exception No. 2: Lighting fixtures meeting the requirements of items a or b below and protected by a ground-fault circuit-interrupter shall be permitted to be installed less than 7 feet 6 inches (2.29 m) over a spa or hot tub.

a. *Recessed fixtures with a glass or plastic lens and nonmetallic or electrically isolated metal trim, suitable for use in damp locations.*

b. *Surface-mounted fixtures with a glass or plastic globe and a nonmetallic body or a metallic body isolated from contact. Such fixtures shall be suitable for use in damp locations.*

(2) Underwater lighting fixtures shall comply with the provisions of Part B or Part C of this article.

(c) **Wall Switches.** Switches shall be located at least 5 feet (1.52 m), measured horizontally, from the inside walls of the spa or hot tub.

(d) **Bonding.** The following parts shall be bonded together:

(1) All metal fittings within or attached to the spa or hot tub structure.

(2) Metal parts of electric equipment associated with the spa or hot tub water circulating system, including pump motors.

(3) Metal conduit and metal piping within 5 feet (1.52 m) of the inside walls of the spa or hot tub and that are not separated from the spa or hot tub by a permanent barrier.

(4) All metal surfaces that are within 5 feet (1.52 m) of the inside walls of the spa or hot tub and not separated from the spa or hot tub area by a permanent barrier.

Exception: Small conductive surfaces not likely to become energized, such as air and water jets and drain fittings, where not connected to metallic piping, towel bars, mirror frames, and similar nonelectric equipment, need not be bonded.

(5) Electrical devices and controls not associated with the spas or hot tubs shall be located a minimum of 5 feet (1.52 m) away from such units or be bonded to the spa or hot tub system.

(e) **Methods of Bonding.** All metal parts associated with the spa or hot tub shall be bonded by any of the following methods: the interconnection of threaded metal piping and fittings; metal-to-metal mounting on a common frame or base; or by the provisions of a copper bonding jumper, insulated, covered, or bare, not smaller than No. 8 solid.

(f) **Grounding.** The following equipment shall be grounded:

(1) All electric equipment located within 5 feet (1.52 m) of the inside wall of the spa or hot tub.

(2) All electric equipment associated with the circulating system of the spa or hot tub.

(g) **Methods of Grounding.**

(1) All electric equipment shall be grounded in accordance with Article 250 and connected by the wiring methods of Chapter 3.

(2) Where equipment is connected with a flexible cord, the equipment grounding conductor shall be connected to a fixed metal part of the assembly.

(h) **Electric Water Heaters.** All electric spa or hot tub water heaters shall be listed and have the heating elements subdivided into loads not exceeding 48 amperes and protected at not more than 60 amperes.

The ampacity of the branch-circuit conductors, and the rating or setting of overcurrent protective devices, shall not be less than 125 percent of the total load of the nameplate rating.

(i) **Underwater Audio Equipment.** Underwater audio equipment shall comply with the provisions of Part B or Part C of this article.

680-42. **Protection.** Spas and hot tubs and associated electrical components shall be protected by ground-fault circuit-interrupters. This requirement shall become effective on January 1, 1994.

E. Fountains

680-50. **General.** The provisions of Part E shall apply to all fountains as defined in Section 680-4. Fountains that have water common to a pool shall comply with the pool requirements of this article.

Exception: Self-contained, portable fountains no larger than 5 feet (1.52 m) in any dimension are not covered by Part E.

680-51. **Lighting Fixtures, Submersible Pumps, and Other Submersible Equipment.**

(a) **Ground-Fault Circuit-Interrupter.** A ground-fault circuit-interrupter shall be installed in the branch circuit supplying fountain equipment.

Exception: Ground-fault circuit-interrupters shall not be required for equipment operating at 15 volts or less and supplied by a transformer complying with Section 680-5(a).

(b) Operating Voltage. All lighting fixtures shall be installed for operation at 150 volts or less between conductors. Submersible pumps and other submersible equipment shall operate at 300 volts or less between conductors.

(c) Lighting Fixture Lenses. Lighting fixtures shall be installed with the top of the fixture lens below the normal water level of the fountain unless approved for above-water locations. A lighting fixture facing upward shall have the lens adequately guarded to prevent contact by any person.

(d) Overheating Protection. Electric equipment that depends on submersion for safe operation shall be protected against overheating by a low-water cutoff or other approved means when not submerged.

(e) Wiring. Equipment shall be equipped with provisions for threaded conduit entries or be provided with a suitable flexible cord. The maximum length of exposed cord in the fountain shall be limited to 10 feet (3.05 m). Cords extending beyond the fountain perimeter shall be enclosed in approved wiring enclosures. Metal parts of equipment in contact with water shall be of brass or other approved corrosion-resistant metal.

(f) Servicing. All equipment shall be removable from the water for relamping or normal maintenance. Fixtures shall not be permanently imbedded into the fountain structure so that the water level must be reduced or the fountain drained for relamping, maintenance, or inspection.

(g) Stability. Equipment shall be inherently stable or be securely fastened in place.

680-52. Junction Boxes and Other Enclosures.

(a) General. Junction boxes and other enclosures used for other than underwater installation shall comply with Sections 680-21(a) (1), (2), and (3); and (b), (c), and (d).

(b) Underwater Junction Boxes and Other Underwater Enclosures. Junction boxes and other underwater enclosures shall be submersible and (1) be equipped with provisions for threaded conduit entries or compression glands or seals for cord entry; (2) be of copper, brass, or other approved corrosion-resistant material; (3) be filled with an approved potting compound to prevent the entry of moisture; and (4) be firmly attached to the supports or directly to the fountain surface and bonded as required. Where the junction box is supported only by the conduit, the conduit shall be of copper, brass, or other approved corrosion-resistant metal. Where the box is fed by nonmetallic

conduit, it shall have additional supports and fasteners of copper, brass, or other approved corrosion-resistant material.

(FPN): See Section 370-23 for support of enclosures.

680-53. Bonding. All metal piping systems associated with the fountain shall be bonded to the equipment grounding conductor of the branch circuit supplying the fountain.

(FPN): See Section 250-95 for sizing of these conductors.

680-54. Grounding. The following equipment shall be grounded: (1) all electric equipment located within the fountain or within 5 feet (1.52 m) of the inside wall of the fountain; (2) all electric equipment associated with the recirculating system of the fountain; (3) panelboards that are not part of the service equipment and that supply any electric equipment associated with the fountain.

680-55. Methods of Grounding.

(a) Applied Provisions. The provisions of Section 680-25 shall apply, excluding paragraph (e).

(b) Supplied by a Flexible Cord. Electric equipment that is supplied by a flexible cord shall have all exposed noncurrent-carrying metal parts grounded by an insulated copper equipment grounding conductor that is an integral part of this cord. This grounding conductor shall be connected to a grounding terminal in the supply junction box, transformer enclosure, or other enclosure.

680-56. Cord- and Plug-Connected Equipment.

(a) Ground-Fault Circuit-Interrupter. All electric equipment, including power-supply cords, shall be protected by ground-fault circuit-interrupters.

(b) Cord Type. Flexible cord immersed in or exposed to water shall be of the hard service type as designated in Table 400-4 and shall be marked water-resistant.

(c) Sealing. The end of the flexible cord jacket and the flexible cord conductor termination within equipment shall be covered with, or encapsulated in, a suitable potting compound to prevent the entry of water into the equipment through the cord or its conductors. In addition, the ground connection within equipment shall be similarly treated to protect such connections from the deteriorating effect of water that may enter into the equipment.

(d) Terminations. Connections with flexible cord shall be permanent, except that grounding-type attachment plugs and receptacles shall be permitted to facilitate removal or disconnection for maintenance, repair, or storage of fixed or stationary equipment not located in any water-containing part of a fountain.

F. Therapeutic Pools and Tubs in Health Care Facilities

Portable therapeutic appliances are covered by the provisions of Article 422. They are required to provide protection from electrocution while in the on or off position. The device used is an immersion-detection circuit-interrupter (IDCI).

Permanently installed therapeutic pools that cannot be readily disassembled are required to comply with Parts A and B of Article 680. The limitations regarding lighting fixtures over and around a swimming pool do not apply to therapeutic pools and tubs if the lighting fixtures are totally enclosed.

Therapeutic tubs that cannot be easily moved are subject to the same basic requirements.

Bonding and grounding requirements are similar to those in Parts A and B of Article 680, except that metal-to-metal mounting on a common frame or base is permitted. Where equipment is connected by a flexible cord, the equipment grounding conductor is required to be connected to a fixed metal part of the assembly.

680-60. **General.** The provisions of Part F include therapeutic pools and tubs in health care facilities. See Section 517-2 for definition of health care facilities. Portable therapeutic appliances shall comply with Article 422.

680-61. **Permanently Installed Therapeutic Pools.** Therapeutic pools that are constructed in the ground, on the ground, or in a building in such a manner that the pool cannot be readily disassembled shall comply with Parts A and B of this article.

Exception: The limitations of Sections 680-6(b)(1) and (2) shall not apply where all lighting fixtures are of the totally enclosed type.

680-62. **Therapeutic Tubs (Hydrotherapeutic Tanks).** Therapeutic tubs, used for the submersion and treatment of patients, that are not easily moved from one place to another in normal use or that are fastened or otherwise secured at a specific location, including associated piping systems, shall conform to this part.

(a) Ground-Fault Circuit-Interrupter. A ground-fault circuit-interrupter shall protect all therapeutic equipment.

Exception: Portable therapeutic appliances shall comply with Section 250-45.

(b) Bonding. The following parts shall be bonded together:

(1) All metal fittings within or attached to the tub structure.

(2) Metal parts of electric equipment associated with the tub water circulating system, including pump motors.

(3) Metal-sheathed cables and raceways and metal piping that are within 5 feet (1.52 m) of the inside walls of the tub and not separated from the tub by a permanent barrier.

(4) All metal surfaces that are within 5 feet (1.52 m) of the inside walls of the tub and not separated from the tub area by a permanent barrier.

(5) Electrical devices and controls not associated with the therapeutic tubs shall be located a minimum of 5 feet (1.52 m) away from such units or be bonded to the therapeutic tub system.

(c) Methods of Bonding. All metal parts associated with the tub shall be bonded by any of the following methods: the interconnection of threaded metal piping and fittings; metal-to-metal mounting on a common frame or base; connections by suitable metal clamps; or by the provisions of a solid copper bonding jumper, insulated, covered, or bare, not smaller than No. 8.

(d) Grounding. The following equipment shall be grounded:

(1) All electric equipment located within 5 feet (1.52 m) of the inside wall of the tub.

(2) All electric equipment associated with the circulating system of the tub.

(e) Methods of Grounding.

(1) All electric equipment shall be grounded in accordance with Article 250 and connected by wiring methods of Chapter 3.

(2) Where equipment is connected with a flexible cord, the equipment grounding conductor shall be connected to a fixed metal part of the assembly.

(f) Receptacles. All receptacles within 5 feet (1.52 m) of a therapeutic tub shall be protected by a ground-fault circuit-interrupter.

(g) Lighting Fixtures. All lighting fixtures used in therapeutic tub areas shall be of the totally enclosed type.

G. Hydromassage Bathtubs

Hydromassage bathtubs (see definition in Section 680-4) are required to be protected by a GFCI. Except for this protection, they are treated the same as ordinary bathtubs. See Section 410-4(d) for special requirements relating to cord-connected fixtures, hanging fixtures, and pendants near bathtubs. Also see Sections 210-8(a)(1) and 210-8(b)(1) for requirements for GFCI protection of bathroom receptacles.

680-70. **Protection.** Hydromassage bathtubs and their associated electric components shall be protected by a ground-fault circuit-interrupter.

680-71. **Other Electric Equipment.** Lighting fixtures, switches, receptacles, and other electric equipment located in the same room, and not directly associated with a hydromassage bathtub, shall be installed in accordance with the requirements of Chapters 1 through 4 in this Code covering the installation of that equipment in bathrooms.

ARTICLE 685 Integrated Electrical Systems

Contents

A. General

B. Orderly Shutdown

A. General

685-1. **Scope.** This article covers integrated electrical systems, other than unit equipment, in which orderly shutdown is necessary to assure safe operation. An integrated electrical system as used in this article is a unitized segment of an industrial wiring system where all of the following conditions are met: (1) an orderly shutdown is required to minimize personnel hazard and equipment damage; (2) the conditions of maintenance and supervision assure that qualified persons will service the system; and (3) effective safeguards, acceptable to the authority having jurisdiction, are established and maintained.

Integrated electrical systems are commonly used in large industrial establishments where the electrical system and equipment are designed, installed, and operated by engineering work forces. The control equipment, including overcurrent devices, are located to be accessible to qualified personnel, but may not be readily accessible as defined in Article 100.

685-2. **Application of Other Articles.** In other articles applying to particular cases of installation of conductors and equipment, there are orderly shutdown requirements that are in addition to those of this article or are modifications of them:

	Section
More than One Building or Other Structure	225-8
Ground-Fault Protection of Equipment	230-95, Exception No. 1
Protection of Conductors	240-3(a)
Electrical System Coordination	240-12
Ground-Fault Protection of Equipment	240-13, Exception No. 1
Grounding ac Systems of 50 to 1000 Volts	250-5(b), Exception No. 3
Orderly Shutdown	430-44
Disconnection	430-74, Exception Nos. 1 and 2
Disconnecting Means in Sight from Controller	430-102, Exception No. 2
Energy from More than One Source	430-113, Exception Nos. 1 and 2
Disconnecting Means	645-110, Exception
Point of Connection	705-12, Exception No. 1

B. Orderly Shutdown

685-10. **Location of Overcurrent Devices in or on Premises.** Location of overcurrent devices that are critical to integrated electrical systems shall be permitted to be accessible, with mounting heights allowed to assure security from operation by nonqualified personnel.

685-12. **Direct-Current System Grounding.** Two-wire direct-current circuits shall be permitted to be ungrounded.

685-14. **Ungrounded Control Circuits.** Where operational continuity is required, control circuits of 150 volts or less from separately derived systems shall be permitted to be ungrounded.

ARTICLE 690 Solar Photovoltaic Systems

Contents

(a) Supply Side.

(b) Load Side.

H. Storage Batteries

690-71. Installation.

(a) General.

(b) Dwellings.

690-72. State of Charge.

690-73. Grounding.

A. General

690-1. **Scope.** The provisions of this article apply to solar photovoltaic electrical energy systems including the array circuit(s), power conditioning unit(s) and controller(s) for such systems. Solar photovoltaic systems covered by this article may be interactive with other electric power production sources or stand alone, with or without electrical energy storage such as batteries. These systems may have alternating- or direct-current output for utilization.

In accordance with Section 705-3, Article 705 is also applicable to a solar photovoltaic system if it is interconnected with another power production source, which may be an electric utility or an on-site generating system, such as a wind turbine, a hydroelectric generator, or the like.

A typical utility-interactive solar photovoltaic system at a dwelling is illustrated in Figure 690-1. Other circuit arrangements are permissible.

690-2. **Definitions.**

Array: A mechanically integrated assembly of modules or panels with a support structure and foundation, tracking, thermal control, and other components, as required, to form a direct-current power-producing unit.

Blocking Diode: A diode used to block reverse flow of current into a photovoltaic source circuit.

Interactive System: A solar photovoltaic system that operates in parallel with and may be designed to deliver power to another electric power production source connected to the same load. For the purpose of this definition, an energy storage subsystem of a solar photovoltaic system, such as a battery, is not another electric power production source.

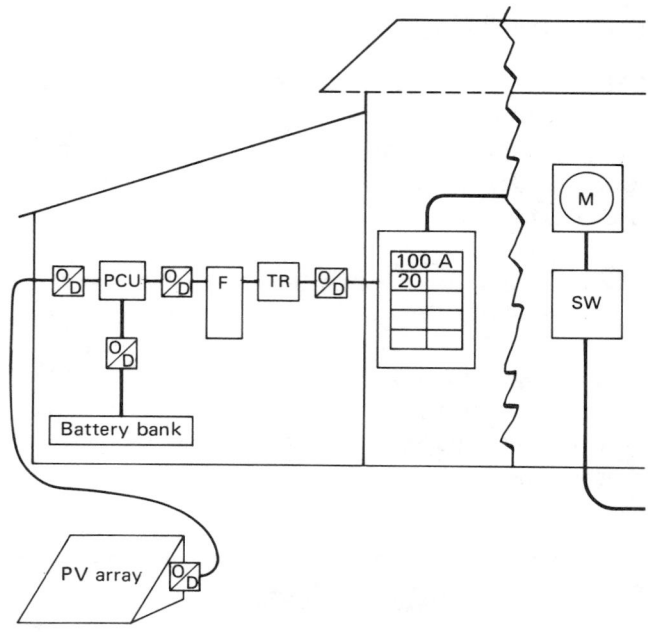

—Overcurrent device and disconnecting means
F—Filter assembly
M—Meter
PCU—Power conditioning unit
SW—A visibly verifiable disconnecting device that may be required by the utility company. This device may be required to be capable of being locked in the open position. Reference: FPN under Section 705—22
TR—Transformer

Figure 690-1. *Utility-interactive solar photovoltaic system at a dwelling. *Battery storage is more likely to be used with a stand-alone system.*

Module: The smallest complete, environmentally protected assembly of solar cells, optics, and other components, exclusive of tracking, designed to generate direct-current power under sunlight.

Panel: A collection of modules mechanically fastened together, wired, and designed to provide a field-installable unit.

Photovoltaic Output Circuit: Circuit conductors between the photovoltaic source circuit(s) and the power conditioning unit or direct-current utilization equipment. See Diagram 690-1.

Photovoltaic Power Source: An array or aggregate of arrays that generates direct-current power at system voltage and current.

Array

Panel

Module

Cell

Figure 690-2. Array components.

Photovoltaic Source Circuit: Conductors between modules and from modules to the common connection point(s) of the direct-current system. See Diagram 690-1.

Power Conditioning Unit: Equipment that is used to change voltage level or waveform, or both, of electrical energy. Commonly, a power conditioning unit is an inverter that changes a direct-current input to an alternating-current output.

Power Conditioning Unit Output Circuit: Conductors between the power conditioning unit and the connection to the service equipment or another electric power production source, such as a utility. See Diagram 690-1.

Solar Cell: The basic photovoltaic device that generates electricity when exposed to light.

Solar Photovoltaic System: The total components and subsystems that, in combination, convert solar energy into electrical energy suitable for connection to a utilization load.

Stand-Alone System: A solar photovoltaic system that supplies power independently but that may receive control power from another electric power production source.

Diagram 690-1. Solar Photovoltaic System (Simplified Circuit-grounding system not shown)

A: Disconnecting means required by Section 690–13.
B: Equipment permitted to be on the photovoltaic power source side of the photovoltaic power
   source disconnecting means, per Section 690–14, Exception No. 2. See Section 690–16.

The simplified circuit diagram demonstrates the use of various components in a photovoltaic system. Specific requirements for overcurrent protection, disconnecting means, and grounding are covered in other sections of Article 690 and should not be inferred from the diagram.

690-3. **Other Articles.** Wherever the requirements of other articles of this Code and Article 690 differ, the requirements of Article 690 shall apply. Solar photovoltaic systems operating as interconnected power production sources shall be installed in accordance with the provisions of Article 705.

690-4. **Installation.**

(a) Photovoltaic System. A solar photovoltaic system shall be permitted to supply a building or other structure in addition to any service(s) of another electricity supply system(s).

(b) Conductors of Different Systems. Photovoltaic source circuits and photovoltaic output circuits shall not be contained in the same raceway, cable tray, cable, outlet box, junction box, or similar fitting as feeders or branch circuits of other systems.

Exception: Where the conductors of the different systems are separated by a partition or are connected together.

As an example, Section 690-4(b) requires the conductors of a yard light located near a roof-mounted photovoltaic (PV) array to be in a separate raceway or cable from the conductors of PV source circuits or PV output circuits.

(c) Module Connection Arrangement. The connections to a module or panel shall be so arranged that removal of a module or panel from a photovoltaic source circuit does not interrupt a grounded conductor to another photovoltaic source circuit.

In general, this section requires installation of a jumper between a module terminal or lead and the connection point to the grounded photovoltaic source circuit conductor so that a module can be removed without interrupting the grounded conductor to other photovoltaic source circuits. If interrupted, such conductors, although identified as grounded conductors, would be operating at the system potential with respect to ground, and a shock hazard could result.

(d) Equipment. Inverters or motor generators shall be identified for use in solar photovoltaic systems.

690-5. **Ground Fault Detection and Interruption.** Roof-mounted photovoltaic arrays located on dwellings shall be provided with ground-fault protection to reduce fire hazard. The ground-fault protection circuit shall be capable of detecting a ground fault, interrupting the fault path, and disabling the array.

Ground fault detection and interruption for solar photovoltaic systems should not be confused with the requirements for a ground-fault circuit-interrupter (GFCI) protection as defined in Article 100. A GFCI is intended for the protection of personnel in single-phase *ac systems*. It functions to *open the ungrounded* conductor when a 5mA-fault current is detected. In contrast, Section 690-5 is intended to prevent fires in dc photovoltaic circuits. To accomplish this, the device must: 1) *detect a ground fault* in the photovoltaic system, 2) *open the grounded conductor* to interrupt the ground fault, and 3) open the ungrounded conductors and *short the photovoltaic array source* to disable it.

B. Circuit Requirements

690-7. **Maximum Voltage.**

(a) Voltage Rating. In a photovoltaic power source and its direct-current circuits, the voltage considered shall be the rated open-circuit voltage.

A photovoltaic source is not a constant voltage source, and the difference between the rated open-circuit voltage and operating voltage is significant. Consequently, there is a need to use the rated open-circuit voltage to select circuit components with proper voltage ratings.

The voltage potential of a photovoltaic power source increases with decreasing temperature. The installer should note the temperature conditions under which the photovoltaic device was rated. If the anticipated temperature conditions at the photovoltaic site are lower than the rating conditions, insulation and components should be appropriately rated.

(b) Direct-Current Utilization Circuits. The voltage of direct-current utilization circuits shall conform with Section 210-6.

This covers installations where the photovoltaic output is connected to direct-current utilization circuits.

(c) Photovoltaic Source and Output Circuits. Photovoltaic source circuits and photovoltaic output circuits that do not include lampholders, fixtures, or receptacles shall be permitted up to 600 volts.

Photovoltaic direct-current circuits in buildings are permanently connected using wiring systems recognized by this *Code,* and requirements for protecting unqualified persons from contact with these circuits are included in Sections 690-5(b) and (d). Unqualified persons are not likely to service equipment in these circuits due to its complexity. There is a significant difference between the rated open-circuit voltage and the operating voltage in photovoltaic direct-current circuits. In order for the photovoltaic system to perform its intended function, rated direct-current open-circuit voltages of up to 600 volts may be present.

(d) Circuits Over 150 Volts to Ground. In one- and two-family dwellings, live parts in photovoltaic source circuits and photovoltaic output circuits over 150 volts to ground shall not be accessible while energized to other than qualified persons.

(FPN): See Section 110-17 for guarding of live parts, and Section 210-6 for voltage to ground and between conductors.

Where direct-current circuitry over 150 volts to ground is present in one- and two-family dwellings, additional protection for unqualified persons is needed. Protection may be in the form of a locked cabinet or an enclosure that requires tools to be opened and that necessitates entry only for servicing purposes.

690-8. Circuit Sizing and Current.

(a) Ampacity and Overcurrent Devices. The ampacity of the conductors and the rating or setting of overcurrent devices in a circuit of a solar photovoltaic system shall not be less than 125 percent of the current computed in accordance with (b) below. The rating or setting of overcurrent devices shall be permitted in accordance with Section 240-3 (b) and (c).

Exception: Circuits containing an assembly together with its overcurrent device(s) that is listed for continuous operation at 100 percent of its rating.

Sizing of the circuits for 125 percent of the rating is necessary because of continuous (3-hour or more) loads.

The exception permits use at the full rating of assemblies, such as panelboards, incorporating overcurrent devices that are listed for continuous operation at 100 percent of the rating.

(b) Computation of Circuit Current. The current for the individual type of circuit shall be computed as follows:

(1) Photovoltaic Source Circuits. The sum of parallel module short-circuit current ratings.

The use of the array short-circuit current will allow proper sizing of conductors to handle current generated during extended periods of operation under a short-circuit condition.

(2) Photovoltaic Output Circuit. The photovoltaic power source short-circuit current rating.

(3) Power Conditioning Unit Output Circuit. The power conditioning unit output current rating.

Exception: The current rating of a circuit without an overcurrent device shall be the short-circuit current, and it shall not exceed the ampacity of the circuit conductors.

Because photovoltaic arrays have a limited capacity, the power conditioning unit supplies to the load (or the utility system) whatever power is available from the arrays. Therefore, the sizing of photovoltaic circuits has to be based on the source rather than the load.

The exception specifies the use of the short-circuit current rating rather than the operating current rating to determine the current rating of a photovoltaic source circuit, photovoltaic output circuit, or the power conditioning unit output circuit, if these circuits do not incorporate an overcurrent device. The short-circuit current rating is then used to determine the needed ampacity for the conductors in these circuits.

(c) Systems with Multiple DC Voltages. For a photovoltaic power source having multiple output circuit voltages and employing a common-return conductor, the ampacity of the common-return conductor shall not be less than the sum of the ampere ratings of the overcurrent devices of the individual output circuits.

690-9. Overcurrent Protection.

(a) Circuits and Equipment. Photovoltaic source circuit, photovoltaic output circuit, power conditioning unit output circuit, and storage battery circuit conductors and equipment shall be protected in accordance with the requirements of Article 240. Circuits connected to more than one electrical source shall have overcurrent devices so located as to provide overcurrent protection from all sources.

(FPN): Possible backfeed of current from any source of supply, including a supply through a power conditioning unit into the photovoltaic output circuit and photovoltaic source circuits, must be considered in determining whether adequate overcurrent protection from all sources is provided for conductors and modules.

In the circuit illustrated in Figure 690-3, the photovoltaic source circuit overcurrent devices are required to be rated so that the source circuit conductors are protected in accordance with Article 240, and the overcurrent device ratings do not exceed the maximum overcurrent device rating marked on the modules. Possible backfeed from the other photovoltaic source circuits, from other supply sources through the power conditioning unit, and from storage battery circuits, if any, has to be considered.

Figure 690-3. Application of blocking diodes and source circuit overcurrent devices.

Because the diodes may lose their blocking ability (due to over-temperature conditions or internal breakdown), overcurrent protection has to be considered with a condition of shorted blocking diodes, if used in the circuit.

If the rated short-circuit current of the photovoltaic power source does not exceed the ampacity of the photovoltaic output circuit conductors, overcurrent protective devices at the connections to the photovoltaic power source are not necessary. At the power conditioning unit end of the photovoltaic output circuit, the need for overcurrent protection has to be considered with respect to the maximum backfeed fault current available from the power conditioning unit.

(b) Power Transformers. Overcurrent protection for a transformer with a source(s) on each side shall be provided in accordance with Section 450-3 by considering first one side of the transformer, then the other side of the transformer, as the primary.

Exception: A power transformer with a current rating on the side connected toward the photovoltaic power source not less than the short-circuit output current rating of the power conditioning unit shall be permitted without overcurrent protection from that source.

(c) Photovoltaic Source Circuits. Branch-circuit or supplementary type overcurrent devices shall be permitted to provide overcurrent protection in photovoltaic source circuits. The overcurrent devices shall be accessible, but shall not be required to be readily accessible.

By considering the overcurrent protection of photovoltaic source circuits as supplementary overcurrent protection, use of overcurrent device types and ratings, other than those suitable for branch-circuit protection, can be permitted. Use of such devices permits module protection closer to the specified ratings. It is anticipated that replacement or resetting of overcurrent devices in photovoltaic source circuits will be done by qualified service personnel. Consequently, ready access to the user need not be provided.

C. Disconnecting Means

690-13. **All Conductors.** Means shall be provided to disconnect all current-carrying conductors of a photovoltaic power source from all other conductors in a building or other structure.

Exception: Where a circuit grounding connection is not designed to be automatically interrupted as part of the ground-fault protection system required by Section 690-5, a switch or circuit breaker used as a disconnecting means shall not have a pole in the grounded conductor.

(FPN): It is intended that the grounded conductor be permitted to have a bolted or terminal disconnecting means to allow maintenance or troubleshooting by qualified personnel.

690-14. **Additional Provisions.** The provisions of Article 230, Part F, shall apply to the photovoltaic power source disconnecting means.

Exception No. 1: The disconnecting means shall not be required to be suitable as service equipment and shall be rated in accordance with Section 690-17.

Exception No. 1 permits use of disconnecting means that are rated in accordance with Section 690-17, but that are not required to be marked as suitable for use as service equipment.

Exception No. 2: Equipment such as photovoltaic source circuit isolating switches, overcurrent devices, and blocking diodes shall be permitted on the photovoltaic power source side of the photovoltaic power source disconnecting means.

In general, there is a need to disconnect equipment from sources of supply for servicing, etc. However, in a solar photovoltaic system, some equipment, as indicated in Exception No. 2, is permitted to be located on the photovoltaic power source side of the disconnecting means. See Figure 690-4. In order to service the exempted equipment, the array or portions of the array may have to be disabled, as explained under Section 690-18.

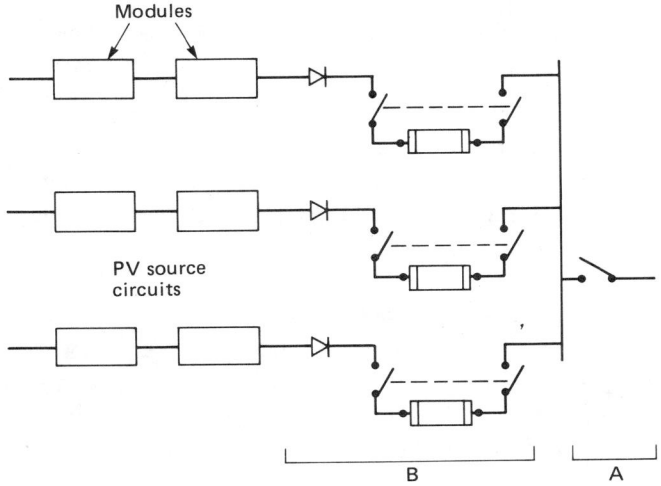

A—Disconnecting means required by Section 690–13
B—Equipment permitted to be on the photovoltaic power source side of the photovoltaic power source disconnecting means, per Section 690–14, Exception 2

Figure 690-4. Equipment permitted on the photovoltaic power source side of the photovoltaic power source disconnecting means.

690-15. **Disconnection of Photovoltaic Equipment.** Means shall be provided to disconnect equipment, such as a power conditioning unit, filter assembly, and the like, from all ungrounded conductors of all sources. If the equipment is energized from more than one source, the disconnecting means shall be grouped and identified.

690-16. **Fuses.** Disconnecting means shall be provided to disconnect a fuse from all sources of supply if the fuse is energized from both directions and is accessible to other than qualified persons. Such a fuse in a photovoltaic source circuit shall be capable of being disconnected independently of fuses in other photovoltaic source circuits.

Switches, pullouts, or similar devices having suitable ratings may serve as means to disconnect fuses from all sources of supply.

690-17. **Switch or Circuit Breaker.** The disconnecting means for ungrounded conductors shall consist of a manually operable switch(es) or circuit breaker(s) (1) located where readily accessible, (2) externally operable without exposing the operator to contact with live parts, (3) plainly indicating whether in the open or closed position, and (4) having ratings not less than the load to be carried. Where all terminals of the disconnecting means may be energized in the open position, a warning sign shall be mounted on or adjacent to the disconnecting means. The sign shall be clearly legible and shall read substantially: WARNING — ELECTRIC SHOCK — DO NOT TOUCH — TERMINALS ENERGIZED IN OPEN POSITION.

Exception: A disconnecting means located on the direct-current side shall be permitted to have an interrupting rating less than the current-carrying rating where the system is designed so that the direct-current switch cannot be opened under load.

690-18. **Disablement of an Array.** Means shall be provided to disable an array or portions of an array.

(FPN): Photovoltaic modules are energized while exposed to light. Installation, replacement, or servicing of array components while a module(s) is irradiated may expose persons to electric shock.

There are a number of methods that may accomplish disablement of an array or portions of an array for purposes of installation, servicing, or other functions during which persons may come in contact with energized parts.

One method is to cover all or portions of an array with an opaque material. Care must be taken that all of the area to be covered is shielded from light.

Another method is to provide for the array to be divided into nonhazardous segments. This may be accomplished by switches or connectors. Also see Section 690-33.

Short-circuiting all or portions of an array by means of switches or plug-in connectors in conjunction with bypass diodes may also provide the necessary disablement. (Bypass diodes are incorporated in photovoltaic power sources for performance purposes.)

D. Wiring Methods

690-31. **Methods Permitted.**

(a) Wiring Systems. All raceway and cable wiring methods included in this Code and other wiring systems and fittings specifically intended and identified for use on photovoltaic arrays shall be permitted. Where wiring devices with integral enclosures are used, sufficient length of cable shall be provided to facilitate replacement.

(b) Single Conductor Cable. Types SE, UF, and USE conductor cable shall be permitted in photovoltaic source circuits where installed in the same manner as a Type UF multiconductor cable in accordance with Article 339. Where exposed to direct rays of the sun, Type UF cable identified as sunlight-resistant or Type USE cable shall be used.

Some photovoltaic modules are designed for a direct series connection by having terminations located at both ends. To accommodate such a direct series connection without the waste of one or more conductors in a multiconductor cable, use of a single-conductor Type UF cable is permitted in photovoltaic source circuits. The reference to installation as a multiconductor cable permits the single-conductor cable to be routed separately, not necessarily with the other conductors of a circuit. Since photovoltaic source circuits are direct-current circuits, increased impedance due to separated circuit conductors is not a problem. Thermoplastic insulation (e.g. PVC), where used on dc circuits in wet locations, may result in electroendosmosis between insulation and conductor, which may cause eventual failure of the insulation. In wet locations, USE insulated conductors with cross linked polyethylene (XLP, XLPE) or rubber insulation may be the more suitable alternative.

690-32. **Component Interconnections.** Fittings and connectors that are intended to be concealed at the time of on-site assembly, where listed for such use, shall be permitted for on-site interconnection of modules or other array components. Such fittings and connectors shall be equal to the wiring method employed in insulation, temperature rise and fault-current withstand, and shall be capable of resisting the effects of the environment in which they are used.

690-33. **Connectors.** The connectors permitted by Section 690-32 shall comply with (a) through (e) below.

(a) Configuration. The connectors shall be polarized and shall have a configuration that is noninterchangeable with receptacles in other electrical systems on the premises.

(b) Guarding. The connectors shall be constructed and installed so as to guard against inadvertent contact with live parts by persons.

(c) Type. The connectors shall be of the latching or locking type.

(d) Grounding Member. The grounding member shall be the first to make and the last to break contact with the mating connector.

(e) Interruption of Circuit. The connectors shall be capable of interrupting the circuit current without hazard to the operator.

The connectors discussed in this article are those concealed connectors used in the installation of the photovoltaic modules. This article does not refer to other connectors that might be used elsewhere in the system.

690-34. **Access to Boxes.** Junction, pull, and outlet boxes located behind modules or panels shall be installed so that the wiring contained in them can be rendered accessible directly or by displacement of a module(s) or panel(s) secured by removable fasteners and connected by a flexible wiring system.

E. Grounding

690-41. **System Grounding.** For a photovoltaic power source, one conductor of a 2-wire system rated over 50 volts and a neutral conductor of a 3-wire system shall be solidly grounded.

Exception: Other methods that accomplish equivalent system protection and that utilize equipment listed and identified for the use shall be permitted.

(FPN): See the first Fine Print Note under Section 250-1.

With respect to the exception, other methods that employ available equipment may be used to achieve objectives contained in the first fine print note to Section 250-1, thereby providing protection for the photovoltaic power source circuits equivalent to solid grounding.

690-42. **Point of System Grounding Connection.** The direct-current circuit grounding connection shall be made at any single point on the photovoltaic output circuit.

(FPN): Locating the grounding connection point as close as practicable to the photovoltaic source will better protect the system from voltage surges due to lightning.

If other-than-solid grounding is utilized as permitted by Section 690-41, Exception, the connections should be made in accordance with the markings on the equipment or its installation instructions.

690-43. **Size of Equipment Grounding Conductor.** The equipment grounding conductor shall be no smaller than the required size of the circuit conductors in systems where the available photovoltaic power source short-circuit current is less than twice the current rating of the overcurrent device. In other systems, the equipment grounding conductor shall be sized in accordance with Section 250-95.

Photovoltaic power systems, regardless of system voltage, must have all noncurrent-carrying, exposed metal surfaces grounded with an equipment grounding system as required by Article 250.

690-44. **Common Grounding Electrode.** Exposed noncurrent-carrying metal parts of equipment and conductor enclosures of a photovoltaic system shall be grounded to the grounding electrode that is used to ground the direct-current system. Two or more electrodes that are effectively bonded together shall be considered as a single electrode in this sense.

This requirement ensures that direct-current circuits from the photovoltaic system do not enter enclosures that are grounded only by the grounding electrode of an alternating-current system without the grounding electrodes of both systems being effectively bonded. For example, if the electrodes are not bonded, it is possible that a small current flow

through the alternating-current electrode, through the earth, and back through the direct-current electrode could result in raising the voltage on the array frame almost to line voltage.

F. Marking

690-51. **Modules.** Modules shall be marked with identification of terminals or leads as to polarity, maximum overcurrent device rating for module protection, and with rated: (1) open-circuit voltage, (2) operating voltage, (3) maximum permissible system voltage, (4) operating current, (5) short-circuit current, and (6) maximum power.

690-52. **Photovoltaic Power Source.** A marking, specifying the photovoltaic power source rated: (1) operating current, (2) operating voltage, (3) open-circuit voltage, and (4) short-circuit current, shall be provided at an accessible location at the disconnecting means for the photovoltaic power source.

(FPN): Reflecting systems used for irradiance enhancement may result in increased levels of output current and power.

After installation of photovoltaic arrays, it may be difficult to determine the system's rated voltage and current. These ratings, along with the open-circuit voltage and short-circuit current, are necessary to size the remainder of the system components as specified elsewhere in Article 690.

Generally, this marking is required to be provided by the installer. The rated values for the photovoltaic power source can be calculated by adding voltage ratings of series-connected modules and adding current ratings of parallel-connected modules or photovoltaic source circuits.

With respect to the fine print note, deliberate increase in the level of irradiance by reflectors or the like can cause the power source to operate at levels above those recommended by the manufacturer. See Section 110-3.

G. Connection to Other Sources

690-61. **Loss of System Voltage.** The power output from a power conditioning unit in a solar photovoltaic system that is interactive with another electric system(s) shall be automatically disconnected from all ungrounded conductors in such other electric system(s) upon loss of voltage in that electric system(s) and shall not reconnect to that electric system(s) until its voltage is restored.

(FPN): For other interconnected electric power production sources, see Article 705.

A normally interactive solar photovoltaic system shall be permitted to operate as a stand-alone system to supply premises wiring.

This requirement prevents energizing of otherwise deenergized system conductors or output conductors of other on-site sources and is intended to prevent electric shock. This feature is normally provided as part of the power conditioning unit.

690-62. **Ampacity of Neutral Conductor.** If a single-phase, 2-wire power conditioning unit output is connected to the neutral and one ungrounded conductor (only) of a 3-wire system or of a 3-phase, 4-wire wye-connected system, the maximum load connected between the neutral and any one ungrounded conductor plus the power conditioning unit output rating shall not exceed the ampacity of the neutral conductor.

690-63. **Unbalanced Interconnections.**

(a) **Single-Phase.** The output of a single-phase power conditioning unit shall not be connected to a 3-phase, 3- or 4-wire electrical service derived directly from a delta-connected transformer.

(b) **Three-Phase.** A 3-phase power conditioning unit shall be automatically disconnected from all ungrounded conductors of the interconnected system when one of the phases opens in either source.

Exception for (a) and (b): Where the interconnected system is designed so that significant unbalanced voltages will not result.

With respect to connections to other sources, the point of interconnection has not been specified. Section 230-82, Exception No. 6 permits connection of interconnected electric power production sources to the supply side of service disconnecting means of a premises. This could be a point of interconnection.

If the interconnections are made on the load side of the service disconnecting means, such as at a distribution panelboard, possible overloading of panelboard buses, suitability of equipment such as circuit breakers for backfeeding, and a need for cautionary markings to indicate the presence of two sources should be considered.

690-64. **Point of Connection.** The output of a power production source shall be connected as specified in (a) or (b) below.

Also see Section 705-12 for additional limitations on the location of the point of interconnection. If the aggregate of all nonutility sources of electricity on the premises does not exceed 100 kW, the interconnection point is required to be located at the premises service disconnecting means. Other conditions also apply to interconnections remote from the premises service disconnecting means.

(FPN): For the purposes of this section, a power production source is considered to be (1) the output of a power conditioning unit where connected to an alternating-current electric source; and (2) the photovoltaic output circuit where interactive with a direct-current electric source.

(a) **Supply Side.** To the supply side of the service disconnecting means as permitted in Section 230-82, Exception No. 6.

(b) **Load Side.** To the load side of the service disconnecting means of the other source(s), if all of the following conditions are met:

(1) Each source interconnection shall be made at a dedicated circuit breaker or fusible disconnecting means.

(2) The sum of the ampere ratings of overcurrent devices in circuits supplying power to a busbar or conductor shall not exceed the rating of the busbar or conductor.

Exception: For a dwelling unit, the sum of the ampere ratings of the overcurrent devices shall not exceed 120 percent of the rating of the busbar or conductor.

(3) The interconnection point shall be on the line side of all ground-fault protection equipment.

Exception: Connection shall be permitted to be made to the load side of ground-fault protection, provided that there is ground-fault protection for equipment from all ground-fault current sources.

(4) Equipment containing overcurrent devices in circuits supplying power to a busbar or conductor shall be marked to indicate the presence of all sources.

Exception: Equipment with power supplied from a single point of connection.

(5) Equipment such as circuit breakers, if back-fed, shall be identified for such operation.

H. Storage Batteries

690-71. Installation.

(a) General. Storage batteries in a solar photovoltaic system shall be installed in accordance with the provisions of Article 480.

Exception: As provided in Section 690-73.

Large banks of storage batteries can deliver significant amounts of short-circuit current. Current-limiting overcurrent devices should be used where necessary.

(b) Dwellings.

(1) Storage batteries for dwellings shall have the cells connected so as to operate at less than 50 volts.

Exception: Where live parts are not accessible during routine battery maintenance, a battery system voltage in accordance with Section 690-7 shall be permitted.

(2) Live parts of battery systems for dwellings shall be guarded to prevent accidental contact by persons or objects, regardless of voltage or battery type.

At any voltage, a primary safety concern in battery systems is that a fault (e.g., a metal tool dropped onto terminals) may create a fire or explosive hazard. "Guarded," as defined in Article 100, describes the best method to reduce this hazard.

(FPN): Batteries in solar photovoltaic systems are subject to extensive charge-discharge cycles and typically require frequent maintenance, such as checking electrolyte and cleaning connections.

690-72. State of Charge.
Equipment shall be provided to control the state of charge of the battery. All adjusting means for control of the state of charge shall be accessible only to qualified persons.

Exception: Where the design of the photovoltaic power source is matched to the voltage rating and charge current requirements for the interconnected battery cells.

690-73. Grounding.
The interconnected battery cells shall be considered grounded where the photovoltaic power source is installed in accordance with Section 690-41, Exception.

The battery circuit need not be grounded where equivalent protection is provided in accordance with Section 690-41.

7
Special Conditions

ARTICLE 700   Emergency Systems

Contents

A. General

B. Circuit Wiring

C. Sources of Power

D. Emergency System Circuits for Lighting and Power

700-15. Loads on Emergency Branch Circuits.
700-16. Emergency Illumination.
700-17. Circuits for Emergency Lighting.
700-18. Circuits for Emergency Power.

E. Control — Emergency Lighting Circuits

700-20. Switch Requirements.
700-21. Switch Location.
700-22. Exterior Lights.

F. Overcurrent Protection

700-25. Accessibility.
700-26. Ground-Fault Protection of Equipment.

A. General

700-1. **Scope.** The provisions of this article apply to the electrical safety of the design, installation, operation, and maintenance of emergency systems consisting of circuits and equipment intended to supply, distribute, and control electricity for illumination or power, or both, to required facilities when the normal electrical supply or system is interrupted.

Emergency systems are those systems legally required and classed as emergency by municipal, state, federal, or other codes, or by any governmental agency having jurisdiction. These systems are intended to automatically supply illumination or power, or both, to designated areas and equipment in the event of failure of the normal supply or in the event of accident to elements of a system intended to supply, distribute, and control power and illumination essential for safety to human life.

The provisions of this article apply to the installation of emergency systems essential for safety to human life where such systems are legally required by municipal, state, federal, or other codes or a governmental agency having jurisdiction.

This article of the *Code* does not determine whether emergency systems are required or the location of emergency or exit lights. This function is covered in NFPA 101-1991, *Life Safety Code*.

(FPN No. 1): For further information regarding wiring and installation of emergency systems in health care facilities, see Article 517.

(FPN No. 2): For further information regarding performance and maintenance of emergency systems in health care facilities, see Health Care Facilities, NFPA 99-1990 (ANSI).

(FPN No. 3): Emergency systems are generally installed in places of assembly where artificial illumination is required for safe exiting and for panic control in buildings subject to occupancy by large numbers of persons, such as hotels, theaters, sports arenas, health care facilities, and similar institutions. Emergency systems may also provide power for such functions as ventilation where essential to maintain life, fire detection and alarm systems, elevators, fire pumps, public safety communication systems, industrial processes where current interruption would produce serious life safety or health hazards, and similar functions.

(FPN No. 4): For specification of locations where emergency lighting is considered essential to life safety, see Life Safety Code, NFPA 101-1991 (ANSI).

(FPN No. 5): For further information regarding performance of emergency and standby power systems, see Emergency and Standby Power Systems, NFPA 110-1988 (ANSI).

Emergency systems are designed to maintain a specific degree of illumination or provide power for essential equipment, such as fire pumps or operating room and life-support equipment in hospitals, in the event of failure of the normal power supply.

Where authorities determine that emergency lighting, including the proper placement of exit signs, is required for safe egress from various classes of buildings or parts of buildings, sufficient illumination is required to be provided for corridors, passageways, stairways, lobbies, etc.

700-2. **Application of Other Articles.** Except as modified by this article, all applicable articles of this Code shall apply.

700-3. **Equipment Approval.** All equipment shall be approved for use on emergency systems.

700-4. **Tests and Maintenance.**

(a) Conduct or Witness Test. The authority having jurisdiction shall conduct or witness a test on the complete system upon installation and periodically afterward.

(b) Tested Periodically. Systems shall be tested periodically on a schedule acceptable to the authority having jurisdiction to assure their maintenance in proper operating condition.

(c) Battery Systems Maintenance. Where battery systems or unit equipments are involved, including batteries used for starting, control, or ignition in auxiliary engines, the authority having jurisdiction shall require periodic maintenance.

(d) Written Record. A written record shall be kept of such tests and maintenance.

(e) Testing Under Load. Means for testing all emergency lighting and power systems during maximum anticipated load conditions shall be provided.

700-5. Capacity.

(a) Capacity and Rating. An emergency system shall have adequate capacity and rating for all loads to be operated simultaneously. The emergency system equipment shall be suitable for the maximum available fault current at its terminals.

It is essential that the emergency system be designed with adequate capacity and rating to safely carry the entire load connected to the emergency system at one time. The emergency system is required to be capable of restarting emergency loads, such as motors, that may have stopped. Emergency system equipment is required to be suitable for the available fault current. The use of devices that limit the available fault current is one method of achieving suitability.

(b) Selective Load Pickup, Load Shedding, and Peak Load Shaving. The alternate power source shall be permitted to supply emergency, legally required standby, and optional standby system loads where automatic selective load pickup and load shedding is provided as needed to assure adequate power to (1) the emergency circuits; (2) the legally required standby circuits; and (3) the optional standby circuits, in that order of priority. The alternate power source shall be permitted to be used for peak load shaving, provided the above conditions are met.

(FPN): Peak load shaving operation may be acceptable for satisfying the test requirements of Section 700-4(b) where all conditions of Section 700-4 are met.

This section permits a generator to serve more than one level of emergency, standby, or other loads. It also permits the use of a generator for peak load shaving, supplying backup power, and other uses. However, assurance is required that priority loads will be properly and reliably served. To provide the necessary assurance, such systems are required to be maintained and tested periodically.

A portable or temporary alternate source shall be available whenever the emergency generator is out of service for major maintenance or repair.

The additional use that may result from serving other loads may necessitate major maintenance of emergency generator sets. On the other hand, use of the emergency generator on a regular basis for nonemergency loads provides assurance that the emergency generator will supply emergency power when called upon. The requirement for a portable or temporary alternate source is to provide emergency power when the generator set is out of service for a long time. A major maintenance or repair procedure is one that keeps the generator set out of service for more than a few hours.

700-6. Transfer Equipment.
Transfer equipment, including automatic transfer switches, shall be automatic and identified for emergency use and approved by the authority having jurisdiction. Transfer equipment shall be designed and installed to prevent the inadvertent interconnection of normal and emergency sources of supply in any operation of the transfer equipment. See Section 230-83.

Means shall be permitted to bypass and isolate the transfer equipment. Where bypass isolation switches are used, inadvertent parallel operation shall be avoided.

700-7. Signals.
Audible and visual signal devices shall be provided, where practicable, for the following purposes:

(a) Derangement. To indicate derangement of the emergency source.

(b) Carrying Load. To indicate that the battery is carrying load.

(c) Not Functioning. To indicate that the battery charger is not functioning.

(d) Ground Fault. To indicate a ground fault in solidly grounded wye emergency systems of more than 150 volts to ground and circuit protective devices rated 1000 amperes or more. The sensor for the ground-fault signal devices shall be located at, or ahead of, the main system disconnecting means for the emergency source, and the maximum setting of the signal devices shall be for a ground-fault current of 1200 amperes. Instructions on the course of action to be taken in event of indicated ground fault shall be located at or near the sensor location.

(FPN): For signals for generator sets, see Emergency and Standby Power Systems, NFPA 110-1988 (ANSI).

Improper testing or lack of testing, inadequate maintenance, and failure by attendants to observe visual signals indicating a malfunction of battery-charging equipment are the major causes of emergency equipment failures.

Signal devices should be located in an area where they will be readily visible to or heard by attendants or other personnel familiar with the operation of the emergency equipment.

In locations such as theaters or assembly halls, audible signal bells or horns intended to annunciate the functions specified in Section 700-7 should be located where their sounding will not cause panic.

Battery-operated unit equipment generally has a test switch to simulate a failure of the normal system and an indicating light that glows brightly while charging and that dims when ready. Transparent plastic cases are required to be provided for lead-acid batteries for easy viewing of electrolyte levels.

A storage battery system is normally capable of delivering 12 V, 24 V, 32 V, or 120 V and consists of monitoring and distribution cabinets and console with battery and charger. It generally includes audio, visual, and remote signal devices, a test switch, and may be provided with a trouble bell and silence switch.

Although Section 700-26 indicates that ground-fault protection of equipment is not required on the alternate source for emergency systems, ground-faults can occur on such systems, and they can result in equipment burn-down. Because of the emergency nature of such systems, automatic disconnect in the event of a ground fault is not appropriate. However, detection of such a fault is desirable.

700-8. Signs.

(a) **Emergency Sources.** A sign shall be placed at the service entrance equipment indicating type and location of on-site emergency power sources.

(b) **Grounding.** Where the grounded circuit conductor connected to the emergency source is connected to a grounding electrode conductor at a location remote from the emergency source, there shall be a sign at the grounding location that shall identify all emergency and normal sources connected at that location.

Section 700-8(b) has been added to the 1993 *Code* to require a sign at the grounding location where the emergency source is connected to a grounding electrode conductor at a location remote from the emergency source. The sign is required to indicate all sources grounded at that location. This applies to installation where the neutral conductor is not switched by the transfer switch (i.e., an installation where a 3-phase, 4-wire generator is connected to a 3-pole transfer switch.)

B. Circuit Wiring

700-9. Wiring, Emergency System.

(a) **Identification.** All boxes, and enclosures (including transfer switches, generators, and power panels) for emergency circuits shall be permanently marked so they will be readily identified as a component of an emergency circuit or system.

The marking may be a color code, may be marked "Emergency System," or may be any other type of identification that will identify the box or enclosure as a component of the emergency system.

(b) **Wiring.** Wiring from emergency source or emergency source distribution overcurrent protection to emergency loads shall be kept entirely independent of all other wiring and equipment and shall not enter the same raceway, cable, box, or cabinet with other wiring.

Exception No. 1: In transfer equipment enclosures.

Exception No. 2: In exit or emergency lighting fixtures supplied from two sources.

Exception No. 3: In a common junction box attached to exit or emergency lighting fixtures supplied from two sources.

Exception No. 4: Wiring of two or more emergency circuits supplied from the same source shall be permitted in the same raceway, cable, box, or cabinet.

Exception No. 5: In a common junction box attached to a unit equipment, and that contains only the branch circuit supplying the unit equipment and the emergency circuit supplied by the unit equipment.

Emergency circuit wiring is not permitted to enter the same raceway, cable, box, or cabinet with the regular or normal wiring of the building concerned. Wiring for the emergency circuits is required to be completely independent of all other wiring and equipment, thus ensuring that any fault on the normal wiring circuits will not affect the performance of the emergency wiring or equipment.

To effect an immediate transfer from one system to the other, it is necessary for both the normal source and the emergency source to be present within a transfer switch enclosure per Exception No. 1.

Exception Nos. 2 and 3 permit the use of two-lamp exit or two-lamp emergency fixtures where one lamp is connected to the normal supply and one lamp is connected to the alternate supply. It should be understood that both lamps may be illuminated as part of the regular lighting operation.

Wiring on the load side of a transfer switch serves as both the emergency circuit wiring and normal circuit wiring. It is not intended that two sets of wiring supply emergency loads from the transfer switch to the emergency load distribution panel shown in Figures 700-3, 700-4, and 700-5, or from these emergency distribution panels to the emergency loads.

Emergency wiring circuit(s) shall be designed and located to minimize the hazards that might cause failure due to flooding, fire, icing, vandalism, and other adverse conditions.

This requirement was revised for the 1993 *Code* to mandate design and installation that minimizes the likelihood of impairment of the emergency system due to flood, fire, icing, vandalism, and other adverse conditions. The same requirement applies to sources of power covered in Section 700-12.

C. Sources of Power

700-12. **General Requirements.** Current supply shall be such that, in the event of failure of the normal supply to, or within, the building or group of buildings concerned, emergency lighting, emergency power, or both will be available within the time required for the application but not to exceed 10 seconds. The supply system for emergency purposes, in addition to the normal services to the building and meeting the general requirements of this section, shall be permitted to comprise one or more of the types of systems described in (a) through (e) below. Unit equipment in accordance with Section 700-12(f) shall satisfy the applicable requirements of this article.

In selecting an emergency source of power, consideration shall be given to the occupancy and the type of service to be rendered, whether of minimum duration, as for evacuation of a theater, or longer duration, as for supplying emergency power and lighting due to an indefinite period of current failure from trouble either inside or outside the building.

Equipment shall be designed and located to minimize the hazards that might cause complete failure due to flooding, fires, icing, and vandalism.

(FPN): Assignment of degree of reliability of the recognized emergency supply system depends upon the careful evaluation of the variables at each particular installation.

(a) Storage Battery. Storage batteries used as source of power for emergency systems shall be of suitable rating and capacity to supply and maintain the total load for a period of 1½ hours minimum, without the voltage applied to the load falling below 87½ percent of normal.

Batteries, whether of the acid or alkali type, shall be designed and constructed to meet the requirements of emergency service and shall be compatible with the charger for that particular installation.

For a sealed battery, the container shall not be required to be transparent. However, for the lead acid battery that requires water additions, transparent or translucent jars shall be furnished. Automotive-type batteries shall not be used.

An automatic battery charging means shall be provided.

(b) Generator Set.

(1) A generator set driven by a prime mover acceptable to the authority having jurisdiction and sized in accordance with Section 700-5. Means shall be provided for automatically starting the prime mover on failure of the normal service and for automatic transfer and operation of all required electrical circuits. A time-delay feature permitting a 15-minute setting shall be provided to avoid retransfer in case of short-time reestablishment of the normal source.

(2) Where internal combustion engines are used as the prime mover, an on-site fuel supply shall be provided with an on-premise fuel supply sufficient for not less than 2 hours full-demand operation of the system.

(3) Prime movers shall not be solely dependent upon a public utility gas system for their fuel supply or municipal water supply for their cooling systems. Means shall be provided for automatically transferring from one fuel supply to another where dual fuel supplies are used.

Exception: Where acceptable to the authority having jurisdiction, the use of other than on-site fuels shall be permitted where there is a low probability of a simultaneous failure of both the off-site fuel delivery system and power from the outside electrical utility company.

(4) Where a storage battery is used for control or signal power, or as the means of starting the prime mover, it shall be suitable for the purpose and shall be equipped with an automatic charging means independent of the generator set.

(5) Generator sets that require more than 10 seconds to develop power are acceptable, provided an auxiliary power supply will energize the emergency system until the generator can pick up the load.

(c) Uninterruptible Power Supplies. Uninterruptible power supplies used to provide power for emergency systems shall comply with the applicable provisions of Sections 700-12(a) and (b).

(d) Separate Service. Where acceptable to the authority having jurisdiction as suitable for use as an emergency source, a second service shall be permitted. This service shall be in accordance with Article 230, with separate service drop or lateral, widely separated electrically and physically from the normal service to minimize the possibility of simultaneous interruption of supply.

(e) Connection Ahead of Service Disconnecting Means. Where acceptable to the authority having jurisdiction as suitable for use as an emergency source, connection ahead of, but not within, the main service disconnecting means shall be permitted. The emergency service shall be sufficiently separated from the normal main service disconnecting means to prevent simultaneous interruption of supply through an occurrence within the building or groups of buildings served.

When designing emergency systems, whether for lighting, power, or both, it is required that consideration be given to the type of service to be rendered.

Supply systems for emergency systems can be designed as one or more of the following:

1. One storage battery or a group of storage batteries provided with an automatic battery-charging means. See also Article 480 and paragraph (a) of this section.

2. A generator set driven by a prime mover, acceptable to the authority having jurisdiction, and with adequate capacity to carry the maximum load connected. Prime movers may be internal-combustion engines, steam or gas turbines, or other approved types. A storage battery used to start the prime mover is required to be provided with an automatic battery-charging means. An on-site fuel supply sufficient to operate internal-combustion engines at full load for 2 hours is required to be available.

Off-site fuel supplies may be used where experience has demonstrated their reliability. Off-site fuel supplies may also be used where they will provide greater reliability than gasoline or diesel engines or in isolated areas where maintenance or refueling could be a problem.

Some types of drivers, particularly large ones, may take longer than 10 seconds to accelerate and develop generator voltage. Gas and steam turbines and large internal-combustion engines may have prolonged starting times. Depending on the specific loads, short-time supply could be provided by an uninterruptible power supply; a generator shared with other loads; or a generator with limited emergency supply, such as an expander, steam turbine, or waste heat system.

3. Two services, overhead or underground, widely separated electrically and physically, and preferred by some authorities to be completely independent of each other; that is, separate service locations and separate transformers, and supplied from separate utility substations where practical.

4. Uninterruptible power supplies (UPS) generally include a rectifier, storage battery, and inverter to ac. These may be very complex systems with redundant components and high-speed solid-state switching. It is common practice to include an automatic bypass for UPS malfunction to permit maintenance.

5. The use of a separate service or connection ahead of the service disconnect requires a judgment by the authority having jurisdiction. Such judgment should be based on the nature of the emergency loads and the expected reliability of the other available sources.

(FPN): See Section 230-82 for equipment permitted on the supply side of a service disconnecting means.

(f) Unit Equipment. Individual unit equipment for emergency illumination shall consist of (1) a rechargeable battery; (2) a battery charging means; (3) provisions for one or more lamps mounted on the equipment, or shall be permitted to have terminals for remote lamps, or both; and (4) a relaying device arranged to energize the lamps automatically upon failure of the supply to the unit equipment. The batteries shall be of suitable rating and capacity to supply and maintain at not less than 87½ percent of the nominal battery voltage for the total lamp load associated with the unit for a period of at least 1½ hours, or the unit equipment shall supply and maintain not less than 60 percent of the initial emergency illumination for a period of at least 1½ hours. Storage batteries, whether of the acid or alkali type, shall be designed and constructed to meet the requirements of emergency service.

Figure 700-1. A typical generator installation supplying standby power in ratings from 55 kW to 930 kW, 60 Hz. (Caterpillar)

Unit equipment shall be permanently fixed in place (i.e., not portable) and shall have all wiring to each unit installed in accordance with the requirements of any of the wiring methods in Chapter 3. Flexible cord- and plug-connection shall be permitted, provided that the cord does not exceed 3 feet (914 mm) in length. The branch circuit feeding the unit equipment shall be the same branch circuit as that serving the normal lighting in the area and connected ahead of any local switches. The branch circuit feeding unit equipment shall be clearly identified at the distribution panel. Emergency illumination fixtures that obtain power from a unit equipment and are not part of the unit equipment shall be wired to the unit equipment as required by Section 700-9 and by one of the wiring methods of Chapter 3.

Exception: In a separate and uninterrupted area supplied by a minimum of three normal lighting circuits, a separate branch circuit for unit equipment shall be permitted if it originates from the same panelboard as that of the normal lighting circuits and is provided with a lock-on feature.

Unit equipment may be wired with a flexible cord (not exceeding 3 feet) and attachment plug cap. This equipment must be permanently fixed in place, usually by mounting screws accessible only from within the unit. One or more lamps may be mounted on, or remote from, the unit. The unit should be located where it can be readily checked or tested for proper performance.

Unit equipment is intended to provide illumination for the area where it is installed. For instance, if a unit is located in a corridor, it is required to be connected to the branch circuit supplying the normal corridor lights (on the line side of any switching arrangements) and, in the event of loss of normal power, the unit would automatically energize the unit lamps, restoring illumination to the corridor. A separate circuit is not permitted for unit equipment (except as noted in the exception) because, if applied to the above example, failure of the normal corridor circuit would not affect the unit equipment, and the corridor would remain in darkness. The branch circuit feeding the unit must be identified at the panelboard.

Notes on General Requirements for Emergency Lighting Systems

At least two sources of power are required to be provided; that is, one normal supply and one or more types of emergency systems described in Section 700-12. The sources may be (1) two services, one normal supply and one emergency supply (preferably from separate utility stations), (2) one normal service and a storage battery (or unit equipment) system, (3) one normal service and a generator set, or (4) one normal service and one emergency service connected to the line side of the normal service (usually outside the building). See Figures 700-3, 700-4, and 700-5.

A transfer means (or throw-over switch) is required to be provided to energize the emergency equipment from the alternate supply when the normal source of supply is interrupted.

Where two services are used, both may operate normally, but equipment for emergency lighting and power is required to be arranged to be energized from either service.

Where the alternate or emergency source of supply is a storage battery or a generator set, the single emergency system is usually operated on the normal service, and the battery (or batteries) or generator operates only if the normal service fails. See Figure 700-5. However, a generator may be used for peak load shaving, etc., in accordance with Section 700-5(b).

Two or more separate and complete systems may be used to provide current for emergency lighting, but means are required to be provided for energizing one system upon the failure of the other.

It should be noted that provisions for disconnecting means and overcurrent protection (see Figures 700-3, 700-4, and 700-5) are to be provided for emergency systems as required by Article 230. See also Section 230-83.

D. Emergency System Circuits for Lighting and Power

700-15. Loads on Emergency Branch Circuits. No appliances and no lamps, other than those specified as required for emergency use, shall be supplied by emergency lighting circuits.

700-16. Emergency Illumination. Emergency illumination shall include all required means of egress lighting, illuminated exit signs,

Figure 700-2. *Self-contained, fully automatic unit equipment for operating emergency lighting located on the unit or for remotely located exit signs or lighting heads. (Dual-Lite Inc.)*

and all other lights specified as necessary to provide required illumination.

Emergency lighting systems shall be so designed and installed that the failure of any individual lighting element, such as the burning out of a light bulb, cannot leave in total darkness any space that requires emergency illumination.

Where high-intensity discharge lighting such as high- and low-pressure sodium, mercury vapor, and metal halide is used as the sole source of normal illumination, the emergency lighting system shall be required to operate until normal illumination has been restored.

Exception: Where alternative means have been taken to ensure that the emergency lighting illumination level is maintained.

High-intensity discharge (HID) fixtures take some time to start once they are energized, so if they are the sole source of normal illumination in an area, the *Code* requires that the emergency lighting system operate not only until the normal system is returned to service, but also until the HID fixtures provide illumination. This may require a timing circuit, a photoelectric monitoring system, or the equivalent.

700-17. Circuits for Emergency Lighting. Branch circuits that supply emergency lighting shall be installed to provide service from a source complying with Section 700-12 when the normal supply for lighting is interrupted. Such installations shall provide either one of the following: (1) an emergency lighting supply, independent of the general lighting supply, with provisions for automatically transferring the emergency lights upon the event of failure of the general lighting system supply, or (2) two or more separate and complete systems with independent power supply, each system providing sufficient current for emergency lighting purposes. Unless both systems are used for regular lighting purposes and are both kept lighted, means shall be provided for automatically energizing either system upon failure of the other. Either or both systems shall be permitted to be a part of the general lighting system of the protected occupancy if circuits supplying lights for emergency illumination are installed in accordance with other sections of this article.

1. *General Considerations for Transfer Switches*

Automatic transfer switches of double-throw construction are used primarily for emergency and standby power generation systems rated 600 V or less. These transfer switches do not normally incorporate overcurrent protection and are designed and applied in accordance with the *Code*, particularly Articles 700 and 701. They are available in ratings from 30 to 3,000 amperes. For reliability, most automatic transfer switches rated above 100 A are mechanically held and electrically operated from the power source to which the load is to be transferred.

An automatic transfer switch is usually located in the main or secondary distribution bus that feeds the branch circuits. Because of its location in the system, the capabilities that must be designed into the transfer switch are unique and extensive as compared with the design requirements for other branch-circuit and feeder devices. For example, special consideration should be given to the following

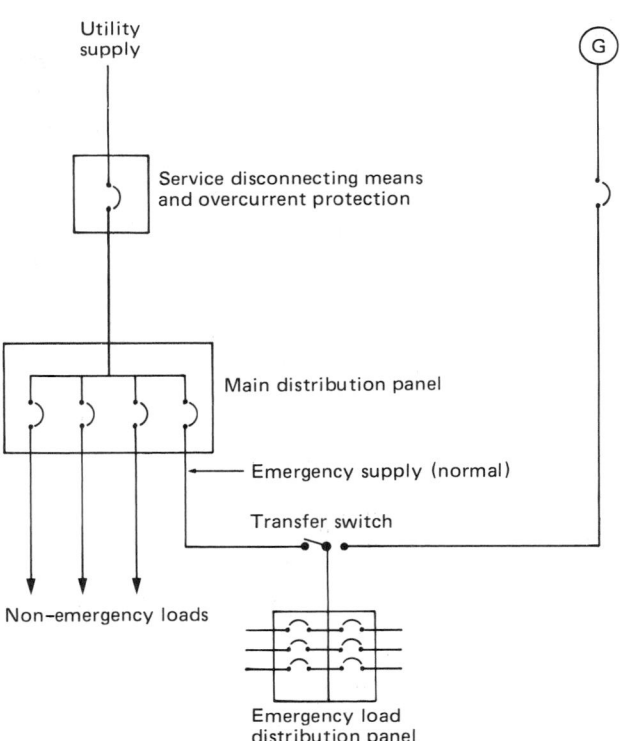

Figure 700-3. *Emergency load arranged to be supplied from two widely separated services as permitted by Section 700-12(d). Upon failure of one service, the emergency load will be transferred to the other service.*

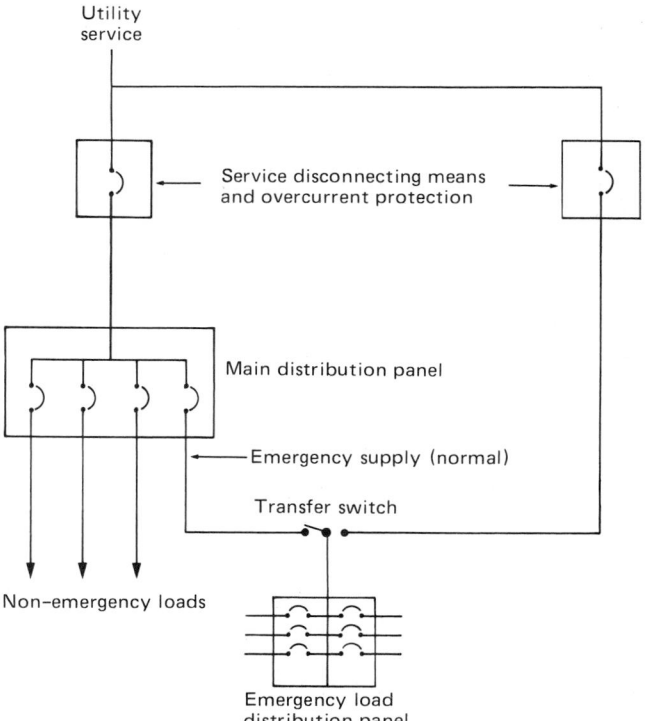

Figure 700-4. *Emergency service arranged to be supplied by the tap ahead of the main as permitted by Section 700-12(e).*

Figure 700-5. *Emergency load arranged to be supplied from a generator as permitted by Section 700-12(b).*

characteristics of an automatic transfer: (1) its ability to close against high in-rush currents, (2) its ability to carry full-rated current continuously from normal and emergency sources, (3) its ability to withstand fault currents, and (4) its ability to interrupt six times the full-load current. In addition to considering each of the above characteristics individually, it is also necessary to consider the effect each has on the other.

In arrangements that provide protection against failure of the utility service, consideration should also be given to (1) an open circuit within the building area on the load side of the incoming service, (2) overload or fault condition, and (3) electrical or mechanical failure of the electric power distribution system within the building. It is therefore desirable to locate transfer switches close to the load and to keep the operation of the transfer switches independent of overcurrent protection. It is often desirable to use multiple transfer switches of lower current rating located near the

load rather than one large transfer switch at the point of incoming service.

2. *Location of Overcurrent Devices*

The location of overcurrent devices for both normal and emergency power is covered by Section 240-21 and is not affected by the installation of an automatic transfer switch. Transfer switches should be rated for continuous duty and have low contact temperature rise.

3. *Solid Neutral on AC and DC Systems*

Where automatic ac-to-ac transfer switches are used, solid neutrals can be used with the grounding connections, as required in Section 250-23. Where multiple grounding creates objectionable ground current, corrective action as specified in Section 250-21(b) is required to be made.

Section 230-95 requires ground-fault protection of equipment. Because the normal source and emergency source are typically grounded at their locations, the multiple neutral-to-ground connections usually require some additional means or devices to ensure proper ground-fault sensing by the ground-fault protection device. Additional means or devices are generally required because the usual alterations used to stop objectionable current, per Section 250-21(b), do not apply where the objectionable current is a ground-fault current. See Section 250-21(c). Rather, solutions often include adding an overlapping neutral transfer pole or conventional fourth pole to the transfer switch. Other solutions include the use of isolation transformers and special ground-fault circuits, or the use of the service ground to also ground the generator neutral with 3-pole transfer switches.

On ac-to-dc automatic transfer switches, a solid neutral tie between the ac and dc neutrals is not permitted where both sources of supply are exterior distribution systems. Section 250-22, which addresses location of grounds for dc exterior systems, clearly specifies that the dc system can be grounded only at the supply station.

Where the dc system is an interior isolated system, such as a storage battery, solid neutral connection between the ac system neutral and the dc source is acceptable.

On an ac-to-dc automatic transfer switch where the neutral must be switched, the size of the neutral switching pole must be considered. A 4-pole, double-throw switch must be used where a 3-phase, 4-wire normal source and a 2-wire dc emergency source are transferred. Because the neutral is switched, a 4-pole, double-throw transfer switch is required. In this instance, one pole of the dc emergency source carries three times the current of the other poles.

4. *Close Differential Voltage Supervision of Normal Source*

Most often the normal source is an electric utility company whose power is transmitted many miles to the point of utilization. The automatic transfer switch control panel continuously monitors the voltage of all phases. (Because utility frequency is, for all practical purposes, constant, only the voltage need be monitored.) For single-phase power systems, the line-to-line voltage is monitored. For 3-phase power systems, all three line-to-line voltages should be monitored to provide full phase protection.

In addition, monitoring protects against operation at reduced voltage, such as during brownouts, which can damage loads such as motors. Since the voltage sensitivity of loads varies, the pickup (acceptable) voltage setting, and dropout (unacceptable) voltage setting of the monitors should be adjustable. Typical range of adjustment for the pickup is 85 percent to 100 percent of nominal, while the dropout setting, which is a function of the pickup setting, is 75 to 98 percent of the pickup selected. Typical settings for most loads are 95 percent of nominal for pickup and 85 percent of nominal for dropout (90 percent of pickup).

Consideration must be given to voltage supervision at closer differential for many installations where the load circuits are critical to voltage.

Starter-type fluorescent lighting is extremely voltage sensitive, and, at voltages below 105 V, it becomes uncertain as to whether a fluorescent lamp will operate. Therefore, a closer differential of transfer and retransfer is required for this type of lighting.

Electronic equipment load is frequently voltage critical. These installations include patient care equipment in health care facilities, X-ray equipment, television stations, cable TV centers, microwave communications, telephone communications, computers, computer-operated equipment, computer centers, and similar applications.

Polyphase motors operating at low load have a tendency to single-phase, despite the loss of voltage in one phase, leading to burnout of the motor. A close differential of voltage supervision should be applied to automatic transfer switches for motor installations of the polyphase type. Differential

voltage relays with a close adjustment of 2 percent for transfer and retransfer values will aid in the detection of phase outages and provide protection from single phasing.

Figure 700-6. *Automatic emergency transfer switch and control panel. (Automatic Switch Co.)*

5. *Automatic Transfer Switches with Emergency Source on Automatically Started Power Plant*

In these installations, the normal source is usually a utility power line, and the emergency source is an automatically started engine generator set that starts upon failure of the normal source. To ensure maximum reliability, a minimum installation should be arranged to:

1. Initiate engine starting of the power plant from a contact on the automatic transfer switch control panel (see Figure 700-7),

2. Sustain connection of load circuits to the normal source during the starting period to provide utilization of any existing service from the normal source,

3. Measure output voltage and frequency of emergency source through the use of a voltage-frequency-sensitive monitor (see Figure 700-7) and effect transfer of the load circuits to the power plant only when both voltage and frequency of the power plant are approximately normal. Sensing of the emergency source need only be single-phase since most applications involve an on-site engine generator with a relatively short line run to the automatic transfer switch. In addition to monitoring voltage, the emergency

source's frequency should also be monitored. Unlike the utility power, the engine generator frequency can vary during start-up. Frequency monitoring will avoid overloading the engine generator while it is starting and can thus prevent stalling the engine. Combined frequency and voltage monitoring will prevent loads from being transferred to an engine generator set with an unacceptable output, and

4. Provide visual signal and auxiliary contact for remote indication when power plant is feeding the load.

Figure 700-7. *Diagram of connections of the automatic transfer switch shown in Figure 700-6. TD, Time Delay; TO, Transfer; TC, Transfer Controls; V/FM, Voltage-Frequency-Sensitive Monitor; VM, Voltage Monitor. (Automatic Switch Co.)*

6. Time-Delay Devices on Automatic Transfer Switches

Time delays are provided to program operation of the automatic transfer switch. To avoid unnecessary starting and transfer to the alternate supply, a nominal 1-second time delay, adjustable up to 6 seconds, can override momentary interruptions and reductions in normal source voltage but still allow starting and transfer if the reduction or outage is sustained. See Figure 700-7. The advantages of this feature are realized in all types of automatic transfer installations. In standby plant installations, the reduced number of false starts is especially important to minimize wear on the starting gear, battery, and associated equipment. This delay is generally set at 1 second but may be set higher if reclosers on the high lines take

longer to operate or if momentary power dips exceed 1 second. If longer delay settings are used, care must be taken to ensure that sufficient time remains to meet 10-second power restoration requirements.

Once the load is transferred to the alternate source, another timer delays retransfer to the normal source until that source has time to stabilize. See commentary following Section 700-16. This timer is required by Section 700-12(b)(1) and is controlled by the preferred source voltage monitors. The timer is adjustable from 0 to 30 minutes and is normally set at 30 minutes. Another important function of this retransfer timer is to allow an engine generator to operate under load for a preselected minimum time to ensure continued good performance of the set and its starting system. This delay should be automatically nullified if the alternate source fails and the normal source is available, as determined by the voltage monitors.

Engine generator manufacturers often recommend a cooldown period for their sets that allows them to run unloaded after the load is retransferred to the normal source. A third time delay, usually 5 minutes, is provided for this purpose. Running an unloaded engine for more than 5 minutes is neither necessary nor recommended since it can cause deterioration in engine performance.

Where more than one automatic transfer switch is connected to the same engine generator, it is sometimes recommended that transfer of the loads be purposely sequenced to the alternate source. Utilization of such a sequencing scheme can reduce starting kVA capacity requirements of the generator. A fourth timer, adjustable from 0 to 5 minutes, will delay transfer to the emergency supply source for this and other similar requirements.

700-18. Circuits for Emergency Power. For branch circuits that supply equipment classed as emergency, there shall be an emergency supply source to which the load will be transferred automatically upon the failure of the normal supply.

E. Control — Emergency Lighting Circuits

700-20. Switch Requirements. The switch or switches installed in emergency lighting circuits shall be so arranged that only authorized persons will have control of emergency lighting.

Exception No. 1: Where two or more single-throw switches are connected in parallel to control a single circuit, at least one of these switches shall be accessible only to authorized persons.

Exception No. 2: Additional switches that act only to put emergency lights into operation but not disconnect them are permissible.

Switches connected in series or 3- and 4-way switches shall not be used.

700-21. **Switch Location.** All manual switches for controlling emergency circuits shall be in locations convenient to authorized persons responsible for their actuation. In places of assembly, such as theaters, a switch for controlling emergency lighting systems shall be located in the lobby or at a place conveniently accessible thereto.

In no case shall a control switch for emergency lighting in a theater, or motion-picture theater or place of assembly, be placed in a motion-picture projection booth or on a stage or platform.

Exception: Where multiple switches are provided, one such switch shall be permitted in such locations where so arranged that it can energize the circuit only, but it cannot deenergize the circuit.

700-22. **Exterior Lights.** Those lights on the exterior of a building that are not required for illumination when there is sufficient daylight shall be permitted to be controlled by an automatic light-actuated device.

F. Overcurrent Protection

700-25. **Accessibility.** The branch-circuit overcurrent devices in emergency circuits shall be accessible to authorized persons only.

(FPN): Fuses and circuit breakers for emergency circuit overcurrent protection, where coordinated to ensure selective clearing of fault currents, increase overall reliability of the system.

700-26. **Ground-Fault Protection of Equipment.** The alternate source for emergency systems shall not be required to have ground-fault protection of equipment with automatic disconnecting means. Ground-fault indication of the emergency source shall be provided per Section 700-7(d).

This is an exception to the general ground-fault protection requirement of Section 230-95. It permits the designer to exercise judgment in risking equipment damage for the purpose of keeping emergency circuits in operation as long as they will continue to function. However a ground-fault indicator is required by Section 700-7(d).

ARTICLE 701   Legally Required Standby Systems

Contents

A. General

B. Circuit Wiring

C. Sources of Power

(d) Separate Service.

(e) Connection Ahead of Service Disconnecting Means.

(f) Unit Equipment.

D. Overcurrent Protection

701-15. Accessibility.

701-17. Ground-Fault Protection of Equipment.

A. General

701-1. **Scope.** The provisions of this article apply to the electrical safety of the design, installation, operation, and maintenance of legally required standby systems consisting of circuits and equipment intended to supply, distribute, and control electricity to required facilities for illumination or power, or both, when the normal electrical supply or system is interrupted.

The systems covered by this article consist only of those that are permanently installed in their entirety, including the power source.

(FPN No. 1): For additional information, see Health Care Facilities, NFPA 99-1990 (ANSI).

(FPN No. 2): For further information regarding performance of emergency and standby power systems, see Emergency and Standby Power Systems, NFPA 110-1988 (ANSI).

(FPN No. 3): For further information, see Recommended Practice for Emergency and Standby Power Systems for Industrial and Commercial Applications, ANSI/IEEE 446-1987.

In earlier editions of the *Code*, these requirements were included with those for optional standby systems in Article 750. This tended to obscure requirements for an important level of standby systems.

Legally required standby systems are intended to provide electric power to aid in fire fighting, rescue operations, control of health hazards, and similar operations. In comparison, emergency systems (Article 700) are those that are essential for safety to human life. Optional standby systems are those whose failure can cause such effects as physical discomfort, serious interruption of an industrial process, damage to process equipment, or disruption of business.

The requirements for legally required standby systems are much the same as for emergency systems; however, there are some differences. Upon loss of normal power, legally required systems are required to be able to supply standby power in 60 seconds or less instead of the 10 seconds or less required of emergency systems. Wiring for legally required standby systems may occupy the same raceways, cables, boxes, and cabinets as other general wiring. Wiring for emergency systems is required to be kept entirely independent of other wiring. Legally required standby systems take second priority to emergency systems where they are involved in sharing an alternate supply and/or load shedding or peak shaving schemes.

701-2. **Legally Required Standby Systems.** Legally required standby systems are those systems required and so classed as legally required standby by municipal, state, federal, or other codes or by any governmental agency having jurisdiction. These systems are intended to automatically supply power to selected loads (other than those classed as emergency systems) in the event of failure of the normal source.

(FPN): Legally required standby systems are typically installed to serve loads, such as heating and refrigeration systems, communication systems, ventilation and smoke removal systems, sewerage disposal, lighting systems, and industrial processes, that, when stopped during any interruption of the normal electrical supply, could create hazards or hamper rescue or fire fighting operations.

701-3. **Application of Other Articles.** Except as modified by this article, all applicable articles of this Code shall apply.

701-4. **Equipment Approval.** All equipment shall be approved for the intended use.

701-5. **Tests and Maintenance for Legally Required Standby Systems.**

(a) **Conduct or Witness Test.** The authority having jurisdiction shall conduct or witness a test on the complete system upon installation.

(b) **Tested Periodically.** Systems shall be tested periodically on a schedule and in a manner acceptable to the authority having jurisdiction to assure their maintenance in proper operating condition.

(c) **Battery Systems Maintenance.** Where batteries are used for control, starting, or ignition of prime movers, the authority having jurisdiction shall require periodic maintenance.

(d) **Written Record.** A written record shall be kept on such tests and maintenance.

(e) Testing under Load. Means for testing legally required standby systems under load shall be provided.

701-6. **Capacity and Rating.** A legally required standby system shall have adequate capacity and rating for the supply of all equipment intended to be operated at one time. Legally required standby system equipment shall be suitable for the maximum available fault current at its terminals.

The alternate power source shall be permitted to supply legally required standby and optional standby system loads when automatic selective load pickup and load shedding is provided as needed to assure adequate power to the legally required standby circuits.

701-7. **Transfer Equipment.** Transfer equipment, including automatic transfer switches, shall be automatic and identified for standby use and approved by the authority having jurisdiction. Transfer equipment shall be designed and installed to prevent the inadvertent interconnection of normal and alternate sources of supply in any operation of the transfer equipment. See Section 230-83.

Means to bypass and isolate the transfer switch equipment shall be permitted. Where bypass isolation switches are used, inadvertent parallel operation shall be avoided.

701-8. **Signals.** Audible and visual signal devices shall be provided, where practicable, for the following purposes:

(a) Derangement. To indicate derangement of the standby source.

(b) Carrying Load. To indicate that the standby source is carrying load.

(c) Not Functioning. To indicate that the battery charger is not functioning.

(FPN): For signals for generator sets, see Emergency and Standby Power Systems, NFPA 110-1988 (ANSI).

701-9. **Signs.**

(a) Mandated Standby. A sign shall be placed at the service entrance indicating type and location of on-site legally required standby power sources.

(b) Grounding. Where the grounded circuit conductor connected to the emergency source is connected to a grounding electrode conductor at a location remote from the emergency source, there shall be a sign at the grounding location that shall identify all emergency and normal sources connected at that location.

B. Circuit Wiring

701-10. **Wiring Legally Required Standby Systems.** The legally required standby system wiring shall be permitted to occupy the same raceways, cables, boxes, and cabinets with other general wiring.

C. Sources of Power

701-11. **Legally Required Standby Systems.** Current supply shall be such that, in event of failure of the normal supply to, or within, the building or group of buildings concerned, legally required standby power will be available within the time required for the application but not to exceed 60 seconds. The supply system for legally required standby purposes, in addition to the normal services to the building, shall be permitted to comprise one or more of the types of systems described in (a) through (f) below. Unit equipment in accordance with Section 701-11(f) shall satisfy the applicable requirements of this article.

In selecting a legally required standby source of power, consideration shall be given to the type of service to be rendered, whether of short-time duration or long duration.

Consideration shall be given to the location or design, or both, of all equipment to minimize the hazards that might cause complete failure due to floods, fires, icing, and vandalism.

(FPN): Assignment of degree of reliability of the recognized legally required standby supply system depends upon the careful evaluation of the variables at each particular installation.

(a) Storage Battery. A storage battery of suitable rating and capacity to supply and maintain at not less than $87\frac{1}{2}$ percent of system voltage the total load of the circuits supplying legally required standby power for a period of at least $1\frac{1}{2}$ hours.

Batteries, whether of the acid or alkali type, shall be designed and constructed to meet the service requirements of emergency service and shall be compatible with the charger for that particular installation.

For a sealed battery, the container shall not be required to be transparent. However, for the lead acid battery which requires water additions, transparent or translucent jars shall be furnished. Automotive-type batteries shall not be used.

An automatic battery charging means shall be provided.

(b) Generator Set.

(1) A generator set driven by a prime mover acceptable to the authority having jurisdiction and sized in accordance with Section 701-6. Means shall be provided for automatically starting the prime mover on failure of the normal service and for automatic transfer and operation of all required electrical circuits. A time-delay feature permitting a 15-minute setting shall be provided to avoid retransfer in case of short-time reestablishment of the normal source.

(2) Where internal combustion engines are used as the prime mover, an on-site fuel supply shall be provided with an on-premise fuel supply sufficient for not less than 2 hours full-demand operation of the system.

(3) Prime movers shall not be solely dependent upon a public utility gas system for their fuel supply or municipal water supply for their cooling systems. Means shall be provided for automatically transferring one fuel supply to another where dual fuel supplies are used.

Exception: Where acceptable to the authority having jurisdiction, the use of other than on-site fuels shall be permitted where there is a low probability of a simultaneous failure of both the off-site fuel delivery system and power from the outside electrical utility company.

(4) Where a storage battery is used for control or signal power, or as the means of starting the prime mover, it shall be suitable for the purpose and shall be equipped with an automatic charging means independent of the generator set.

(c) Uninterruptible Power Supplies. Uninterruptible power supplies used to provide power for legally required standby systems shall comply with the applicable provisions of Sections 701-11(a) and (b).

(d) Separate Service. Where acceptable to the authority having jurisdiction, a second service shall be permitted. This service shall be in accordance with Article 230, with separate service drop or lateral widely separated electrically and physically from the normal service to minimize the possibility of simultaneous interruption of supply.

(e) Connection Ahead of Service Disconnecting Means. Where acceptable to the authority having jurisdiction, connections ahead of, but not within, the main service disconnecting means shall be permitted. The legally required standby service shall be sufficiently separated from the normal main service disconnecting means to prevent simultaneous interruption of supply through an occurrence within the building or groups of buildings served.

(FPN): See Section 230-82 for equipment permitted on the supply side of a service disconnecting means.

(f) Unit Equipment. Individual unit equipment for legally required standby illumination shall consist of (1) a rechargeable battery; (2) a battery charging means; (3) provisions for one or more lamps mounted on the equipment and shall be permitted to have terminals for remote lamps; and (4) a relaying device arranged to energize the lamps automatically upon failure of the supply to the unit equipment. The batteries shall be of suitable rating and capacity to supply and maintain at not less than $87\frac{1}{2}$ percent of the nominal battery voltage for the total lamp load associated with the unit for a period of at least $1\frac{1}{2}$ hours, or the unit equipment shall supply and maintain not less than 60 percent of the initial legally required standby illumination for a period of at least $1\frac{1}{2}$ hours. Storage batteries, whether of the acid or alkali type, shall be designed and constructed to meet the requirements of emergency service.

Unit equipment shall be permanently fixed in place (i.e., not portable) and shall have all wiring to each unit installed in accordance with the requirements of any of the wiring methods in Chapter 3. Flexible cord- and plug-connection shall be permitted, provided that the cord does not exceed 3 feet (914 mm) in length. The branch circuit feeding the unit equipment shall be the same branch circuit as that serving the normal lighting in the area and connected ahead of any local switches. Legally required standby illumination fixtures that obtain power from a unit equipment and are not part of the unit equipment shall be wired to the unit equipment by one of the wiring methods of Chapter 3.

D. Overcurrent Protection

701-15. **Accessibility.** The branch-circuit overcurrent devices in legally required standby circuits shall be accessible to authorized persons only.

701-17. **Ground-Fault Protection of Equipment.** The alternate source for legally required standby systems shall not be required to have ground-fault protection of equipment.

ARTICLE 702 Optional Standby Systems

Contents

A. General

B. Circuit Wiring

A. General

702-1. **Scope.** The provisions of this article apply to the installation and operation of optional standby systems.

The systems covered by this article consist only of those that are permanently installed in their entirety, including prime movers.

702-2. **Optional Standby Systems.** Optional standby systems are intended to protect private business or property where life safety does not depend on the performance of the system. Optional standby systems are intended to supply on-site generated power to selected loads either automatically or manually.

(FPN): Optional standby systems are typically installed to provide an alternate source of electric power for such facilities as industrial and commercial buildings, farms, and residences, and to serve loads such as heating and refrigeration systems, data processing and communications systems, and industrial processes that, when stopped during any power outage, could cause discomfort, serious interruption of the process, damage to the product or process, or the like.

702-3. **Application of Other Articles.** Except as modified by this article, all applicable articles of this Code shall apply.

702-4. **Equipment Approval.** All equipment shall be approved for the intended use.

702-5. **Capacity and Rating.** An optional standby system shall have adequate capacity and rating for the supply of all equipment intended to be operated at one time. Optional standby system equipment shall be suitable for the maximum available fault current at its terminals.

(FPN): The optional standby system rating need only be sufficient to carry loads selected by the user.

702-6. **Transfer Equipment.** Transfer equipment shall be suitable for the intended use and so designed and installed as to prevent the inadvertent interconnection of normal and alternate sources of supply in any operation of the transfer equipment.

Transfer equipment, located on the load side of branch-circuit protection, shall be permitted to contain supplementary overcurrent protection having an interrupting rating sufficient for the available fault current that the generator can deliver.

702-7. **Signals.** Audible and visual signal devices shall be provided, where practicable, for the following purposes:

(a) **Derangement.** To indicate derangement of the optional standby source.

(b) **Carrying Load.** To indicate that the optional standby source is carrying load.

702-8. **Signs.**

(a) **Standby.** A sign shall be placed at the service-entrance equipment indicating type and location of on-site optional standby power sources.

(b) **Grounding.** Where the grounded circuit conductor connected to the emergency source is connected to a grounding electrode conductor at a location remote from the emergency source, there shall be a sign at the grounding location that shall identify all emergency and normal sources connected at that location.

B. Circuit Wiring

702-9. **Wiring Optional Standby Systems.** The optional standby system wiring shall be permitted to occupy the same raceways, cables, boxes, and cabinets with other general wiring.

ARTICLE 705   Interconnected Electric Power Production Sources

Contents

705-1.   Scope. This article covers installation of one or more electric power production sources operating in parallel with a primary source(s) of electricity.

(FPN):   The primary source may be a utility supply, on-site electric power source(s), or other sources.

This article sets forth basic safety requirements for the installation of generators and other types of power production sources that are interconnected and operate in parallel. Power sources include any system that produces electric power. They include not only electric utility sources, but also on-premises sources ranging from rotating generators (see Article 445) to solar photovoltaic systems (see Article 690) to fuel cells.

The purpose of this article is to address the basic safety requirements, specifically related to parallel operation, for the generators and other power sources, the power system that interconnects the power sources, and equipment that is connected to these systems. Proper application of these systems requires a thorough review of the entire power system.

705-2.   Definition. For purposes of this article, the following definition applies:

Interactive System: An electric power production system that is operating in parallel with and capable of delivering energy to an electric primary source supply system.

705-3.   Other Articles. Interconnected electric power production sources shall comply with this article and also the applicable requirements of the following articles:

	Article
Generators	445
Solar Photovoltaic Systems	690
Emergency Systems	700
Legally Required Standby Systems	701
Optional Standby Systems	702

705-10.   Directory. A permanent plaque or directory, denoting all electrical power sources on or in the premises, shall be installed at each service equipment location and at locations of all electric power production sources capable of being interconnected.

Exception: Installations with large numbers of power production sources shall be permitted to be designated by groups.

705-12.   Point of Connection. The outputs of electric power production systems shall be interconnected at the premises service disconnecting means. See Section 230-82, Exception No. 6.

Exception No. 1: The outputs shall be permitted to be interconnected at a point or points elsewhere on the premises where the system qualifies as an integrated electric system and incorporates protective equipment in accordance with all applicable sections of Article 685.

Exception No. 2: The outputs shall be permitted to be interconnected at a point or points elsewhere on the premises where all of the following conditions are met:

a. The aggregate of nonutility sources of electricity has a capacity in excess of 100 kW, or the service is above 1000 volts;

b. The conditions of maintenance and supervision assure that qualified persons will service and operate the system; and c. Safeguards and protective equipment are established and maintained.

The point of interconnection is required to be at the premises service disconnecting means. This requirement may be difficult to meet for systems 100 kW or smaller. It is intended to prevent the indiscriminate interconnection of small generators or other sources of power without proper protection against fire and electric shock. See Figure 705-1. It is important to utilize disconnect devices (switches, etc.) that are suitable for the purpose.

Figure 705-1. *The point of connection is required to be at the premises service disconnecting means.*

The requirement specifying "at the premises service disconnecting means" permits connection ahead of the disconnect or on the load side. This is to accommodate the safe work practices of many utilities that provide a readily accessible disconnect for dispersed generation. It is a contract matter between the utility and the customer and does not adversely affect the safety of the premises wiring; therefore, it is not within the scope of the *Code.*

There are two exceptions that recognize that generators and other power sources can be safely connected elsewhere on the premises system. These locations include:

Where the premises has an integrated electrical system as set forth in Article 685, or

Where the total generator capacity on premises is greater than 100 kW, or

Where the service is greater than 1000 V.

Experience has proved that a higher level of design input and more responsible installation are used for larger systems than are commonly used for small systems (100 kW or less, 600 V or less services).

705-14. **Output Characteristics.** The output of a generator or other electric power production source operating in parallel with an electric supply system shall be compatible with the voltage, wave shape, and frequency of the system to which it is connected.

(FPN):   The term compatible does not necessarily mean matching the primary source wave shape.

The level of output voltage and frequency must be controlled to permit real power and reactive power to flow in the intended amount and proper direction. Control of the driver speed causes real power (kW) to flow from a rotating generator. Control of voltage causes reactive power (kVAR) to flow to or from a synchronous generator. The parallel operation of generators is a complex balance of several variables. These are design parameters and are beyond the scope of the *Code.* There is a considerable amount of data available for equipment application and design.

The output characteristics of a rotating generator are significantly different from those of a solid-state power source. Their compatibility with other sources, and with different types of loads, will be limited in different ways.

Where either the power source or the loads have solid-state equipment, such as inverters, uninterruptible power supply (UPS), or solid-state variable speed drives, there will be harmonic currents that flow in the system. See Figures 705-2, 705-3, and 705-4. These multiples of the basic supply frequency (usually 60 Hz) cause additional heating, which may require derating of generators, transformers, cables, and motors. Special generator voltage control systems are required to avoid erratic operation or destruction of control devices. Circuit breakers may require derating where the higher harmonics become significant.

Significant magnitudes of harmonics may be inadvertently matched to system resonance and result in opening of capacitor fuses, overheating of circuits, and erratic operation of controls. The usual solution is to detune the system by rearrangement or installation of reactors, or both.

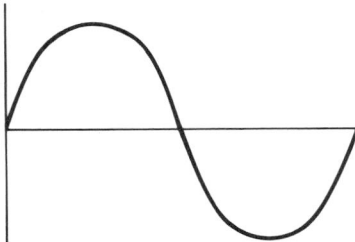

Figure 705-2. *Typical output wave shape of rotating generator and system wave shape normally encountered with motor, lighting, and heating loads.*

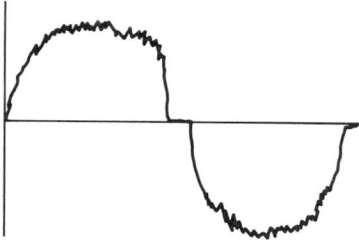

Figure 705-3. *Typical output wave shape with inverter source. Motors and transformers will be driven by harmonic-rich voltage and may require derating.*

Figure 705-4. *Wave shape typical of system with variable speed drive, rectifier, elevator, and uninterruptible power-supply loads. Source generator may require derating, and special voltage control may be needed.*

705-16. **Interrupting and Withstand Rating.** Consideration shall be given to the contribution of fault currents from all interconnected power sources for the interrupting and withstand ratings of equipment on interactive systems.

705-20. **Disconnecting Means, Sources.** Means shall be provided to disconnect all ungrounded conductors of an electric power production source(s) from all other conductors. See Article 230.

705-21. **Disconnecting Means, Equipment.** Means shall be provided to disconnect equipment, such as inverters or transformers, associated with a power production source, from all ungrounded conductors of all sources of supply.

Exception: Equipment intended to be operated and maintained as an integral part of a power production source exceeding 1000 volts.

An example of equipment covered under the exception is a generator designed for 4,160 V and connected to a 13,800-V system through a transformer. The transformer and generator are to be operated as a unit. It is not required that there be a disconnecting means between the generator and transformer. However, a disconnecting means is required between the transformer and the point of connection to the power system.

705-22. **Disconnect Device.** The disconnecting means for ungrounded conductors shall consist of a manually or power operable switch(es) or circuit breaker(s):

(1) Located where accessible;

(2) Externally operable without exposing the operator to contact with live parts and, if power operable, of a type that can be opened by hand in the event of a power supply failure;

(3) Plainly indicating whether in the open or closed position; and

(4) Having ratings not less than the load to be carried and the fault current to be interrupted.

For disconnect equipment energized from both sides, a marking shall be provided to indicate that all contacts of the disconnect equipment may be energized.

(FPN No. 1): In parallel generation systems, some equipment, including knife blade switches and fuses, may be energized from both directions. See Section 240-40.

(FPN No. 2): Interconnection to off-premises primary source may require a visibly verifiable disconnecting device.

The requirements of Section 705-22 for disconnects are probably the most significant and important requirements in Article 705. A disconnecting means is to serve each generating source. This device or another will be the service-entrance disconnect. Still another may be applied to separate the generating systems.

The basic requirement in Section 705-22 recognizes the success of applying switches as well as molded-case circuit breakers in this service. Most safe work practices on the premises utilize these disconnect devices.

The disconnect at the service entrance is required for disconnecting the premises wiring system from the utility. The utility safe work practices may also utilize this disconnect device. Utility work practices may require a visibly verifiable disconnect device. For this reason, some utility contracts require that a visible break be provided. The second fine print note is intended to bring attention to this common utility requirement.

705-30. **Overcurrent Protection.** Conductors shall be protected in accordance with Article 240. Equipment overcurrent protection shall be in accordance with the articles referenced in Article 240. Equipment and conductors connected to more than one electrical source shall have a sufficient number of overcurrent devices so located as to provide protection from all sources.

(1) Generators shall be protected in accordance with Section 445-4.

(2) Solar photovoltaic systems shall be protected in accordance with Article 690.

(3) Overcurrent protection for a transformer with a source(s) on each side shall be provided in accordance with Section 450-3 by considering first one side of the transformer, then the other side of the transformer, as the primary.

705-32. **Ground-Fault Protection.** Where ground-fault protection is used, the output of an interactive system shall be connected to the supply side of the ground-fault protection.

Exception: Connection shall be permitted to be made to the load side of ground-fault protection provided that there is ground-fault protection for equipment from all ground-fault current sources.

The larger systems have become very sophisticated and involve many special relays. The more common relays are under- and over-voltage, under- and over-frequency, voltage-restrained overcurrent, anti-motoring, loss-of-field, over-temperature, and shutdown for derangement of the

mechanical driver. Small-generator installations cannot justify the cost of these switchgear-type relays. Small-generator protection is comprised of more common devices with fewer features. Application guides are available in technical literature and manufacturer's data.

It is important to note that the requirements in Article 705 are only for protection against conditions that may occur because generating sources are being operated in parallel. It is essential that the installation also meet the requirements of the referenced articles to provide the basic protection and safeguards for all equipment, whether or not it is involved with more than one source.

705-40. **Loss of Primary Source.** Upon loss of primary source, an electric power production source shall be automatically disconnected from all ungrounded conductors of the primary source and shall not be reconnected until the primary source is restored.

(FPN No. 1): Risks to personnel and equipment associated with the primary source may occur if an interactive electric power production source can operate as an island. Special detection methods may be required to determine that a primary source supply system outage has occurred, and whether there should be automatic disconnection. When the primary source supply system is restored, special detection methods may be required to limit exposure of power production sources to out-of-phase reconnection.

(FPN No. 2): Induction generating equipment on systems with significant capacitance may become self-excited upon loss of primary source and experience severe over-voltage as a result.

When two interconnected power systems separate, they will drift out of synchronism. When the utility separates, there is a risk of damage to the system if restoration of the utility occurs out of phase. If the timing of the reconnection is random, there will be violent electromechanical stresses. These can destroy mechanical components such as gears, couplings, and shafts, and can displace coils. It is essential to disconnect the premises or generator from the primary source. There are many technical guides from which to select appropriate protective systems and equipment for large systems. There is still a limited choice of low-cost devices available for application to small systems.

Induction generators are commonly used today. They have characteristics quite different from synchronous machines. They are more rugged because of the construction of the rotor. They are less expensive because of their basic design, availability, and type of starting and control equipment. Theoretically, an induction machine can continue to run on an isolated system if there is a large capacitor bank to provide excitation. In reality, an induction machine will lose stability and be shut down quickly by one of the protective devices.

705-42. **Unbalanced Interconnections.** A 3-phase electric power production source shall be automatically disconnected from all ungrounded conductors of the interconnected systems when one of the phases of that source opens.

Exception: An electric power production source providing power for an emergency or legally required standby system.

705-43. **Synchronous Generators.** Synchronous generators in a parallel system shall be provided with the necessary equipment to establish and maintain a synchronous condition.

705-50. **Grounding.** Interconnected electric power production sources shall be grounded in accordance with Article 250.

Exception: For direct-current systems connected through an inverter directly to a grounded service, other methods that accomplish equivalent system protection and that utilize equipment listed and identified for the use shall be permitted.

ARTICLE 710   Over 600 Volts, Nominal General

Contents

A. General

B. Equipment — General Provisions

C. Equipment — Specific Provisions

A. General

710-1. Scope. This article covers the general requirements for all circuits and equipment operating at more than 600 volts, nominal.

710-2. Definition. For the purposes of this article, "high voltage" shall be defined as more than 600 volts, nominal.

710-3. Other Articles. Provisions applicable to specific types of installations are included in the following articles:

	Article
Busways	364
Cable Trays	318
Capacitors	460
Conductors for General Wiring	310
Definitions	100
Electric Signs and Outline Lighting	600
Flexible Cords and Cables	400
Grounding	250
Lighting Fixtures, Lampholders, Lamps, and Receptacles	410
Motors, Motor Circuits, and Controllers	430
Outlet, Device, Pull and Junction Boxes, Conduit Bodies, and Fittings	370
Outside Branch Circuits and Feeders	225
Overcurrent Protection	240
Requirements for Electrical Installations	110
Resistors and Reactors	470
Services	230
Surge Arresters	280
Transformers and Transformer Vaults	450
Wiring Methods	300

710-4. Wiring Methods.

In switch rooms, transformer vaults, and similar areas that are restricted to qualified personnel, any suitable wiring method may be used. Open wiring using bare or insulated conductors on insulators is commonly employed, as is rigid metal conduit and rigid nonmetallic conduit.

(a) Aboveground Conductors. Aboveground conductors shall be installed in rigid metal conduit, in intermediate metal conduit, in rigid nonmetallic conduit, in cable trays, as busways, as cablebus, in other identified raceways, or as open runs of metal-clad cable suitable for the use and purpose.

In locations accessible to qualified persons only, open runs of Type MV cables, bare conductors, and bare busbars shall also be permitted.

(b) Underground Conductors. Underground conductors shall be identified for the voltage and conditions under which they are installed.

Direct burial cables shall comply with the provisions of Section 310-7.

Underground cables shall be permitted to be direct buried or installed in raceways identified for the use and shall meet the depth requirements of Table 710-4(b).

Nonshielded cables shall be installed in rigid metal conduit, in intermediate metal conduit, or in rigid nonmetallic conduit encased in not less than 3 inches (76 mm) of concrete.

Exception No. 1: Type MC cable with nonshielded conductor where the metallic sheath is grounded through an effective grounding path meeting the requirements of Section 250-51.

Exception No. 2: Lead-sheath cable with nonshielded conductor where the lead sheath is grounded through an effective grounding path meeting the requirements of Section 250-51.

Table 710-4(b). Minimum Cover Requirements
Cover is defined as the shortest distance in inches measured between a point on the top surface of any direct buried conductor, cable, conduit, or other raceway and the top surface of finished grade, concrete, or similar cover.

Circuit Voltage	Direct Buried Cables	Rigid Nonmetallic Conduit Approved for Direct Burial*	Rigid Metal Conduit and Intermediate Metal Conduit
Over 600-22kV	30	18	6
Over 22kV-40kV	36	24	6
Over 40kV	42	30	6

For SI units: one inch = 25.4 millimeters.
* Listed by a qualified testing agency as suitable for direct burial without encasement. All other nonmetallic systems shall require 2 inches (50.8 mm) of concrete or equivalent above conduit in addition to above depth.

Exception No. 1: Areas subject to vehicular traffic, such as thoroughfares or commercial parking areas, shall have a minimum cover of 24 inches (610 mm).

Exception No. 2: The minimum cover requirements for other than rigid metal conduit and intermediate metal conduit shall be permitted to be reduced 6 inches (152 mm) for each 2 inches (50.8 mm) of concrete or equivalent protection placed in the trench over the underground installation.

Exception No. 3: The minimum cover requirements shall not apply to conduits or other raceways that are located under a building or exterior concrete slab not less than 4 inches (102 mm) in thickness and extending not less than 6 inches (152 mm) beyond the underground installation. A warning ribbon or other effective means suitable for the conditions shall be placed above the underground installation.

Exception No. 4: Lesser depths shall be permitted where cables and conductors rise for terminations or splices or where access is otherwise required.

Exception No. 5: In airport runways, including adjacent defined areas where trespass is prohibited, cable shall be permitted to be buried not less than 18 inches (457 mm) deep and without raceways, concrete enclosement, or equivalent.

Exception No. 6: Raceways installed in solid rock shall be permitted to be buried at lesser depth where covered by 2 inches (50.8 mm) of concrete, which shall be permitted to extend to the rock surface.

(1) Protection from Damage. Conductors emerging from the ground shall be enclosed in approved raceway. Raceways installed on poles shall be of rigid metal conduit, intermediate metal conduit, PVC Schedule 80, or equivalent extending from the ground line up to a point 8 feet (2.44 m) above finished grade. Conductors entering a building shall be protected by an approved enclosure from the ground line to the point of entrance. Metallic enclosures shall be grounded.

(2) Splices. Direct burial cables shall be permitted to be spliced or tapped without the use of splice boxes, provided they are installed using materials suitable for the application. The taps and splices shall be watertight and protected from mechanical damage. Where cables are shielded, the shielding shall be continuous across the splice or tap.

(3) Backfill. Backfill containing large rock, paving materials, cinders, large or sharply angular substance, or corrosive materials shall not be placed in an excavation where materials can damage raceways, cables, or other substructures or prevent adequate compaction of fill or contribute to corrosion of raceways, cables, or other substructures.

Protection in the form of granular or selected material or suitable sleeves shall be provided to prevent physical damage to the raceway or cable.

(4) Raceway Seal. Where a raceway enters from an underground system, the end within the building shall be sealed with an identified compound so as to prevent the entrance of moisture or gases, or it shall be so arranged to prevent moisture from contacting live parts.

(c) Busbars. Busbars shall be permitted to be either copper or aluminum.

710-5. **Braid-Covered Insulated Conductors — Open Installation.** Open runs of braid-covered insulated conductors shall have a flame-retardant braid. If the conductors used do not have this protection, a flame-retardant saturant shall be applied to the braid covering after installation. This treated braid covering shall be stripped back a safe distance at conductor terminals, according to the operating voltage. This distance shall not be less than 1 inch (25.4 mm) for each kilovolt of the conductor-to-ground voltage of the circuit, where practicable.

710-6. **Insulation Shielding.** Metallic and semiconducting insulation shielding components of shielded cables shall be removed for a distance dependent on the circuit voltage and insulation. Stress reduction means shall be provided at all terminations of factory-applied shielding.

Special kits that permit a quick and easy means of providing the required stress reductions when terminating solid dielectric cables are available from several manufacturers.

Metallic shielding components such as tapes, wires or braids, or combinations thereof and their associated conducting or semiconducting components shall be grounded.

710-7. **Grounding.** Wiring and equipment installations shall be grounded in accordance with the applicable provisions of Article 250.

710-8. **Moisture or Mechanical Protection for Metal-Sheathed Cables.** Where cable conductors emerge from a metal sheath and where protection against moisture or physical damage is necessary, the insulation of the conductors shall be protected by a cable sheath terminating device.

710-9. **Protection of Service Equipment, Metal-Enclosed Power Switchgear, and Industrial Control Assemblies.** Pipes or ducts foreign to the electrical installation that require periodic maintenance or whose malfunction would endanger the operation of the electrical system shall not be located in the vicinity of the service equipment, metal-enclosed power switchgear, or industrial control assemblies. Protection shall be provided where necessary to avoid damage from condensation leaks and breaks in such foreign systems. Piping and other facilities shall not be considered foreign if provided for fire protection of the electrical installation.

B. Equipment — General Provisions

710-11. **Indoor Installations.** See Section 110-31(a).

710-12. **Outdoor Installations.** See Section 110-31(b).

710-13. **Metal-Enclosed Equipment.** See Section 110-31(c).

710-14. **Oil-Filled Equipment.** Installation of electrical equipment, other than transformers, covered in Article 450, containing more than 10 gallons (37.85 L) of flammable oil per unit shall meet the requirements of Parts B and C of Article 450.

C. Equipment — Specific Provisions

(FPN): See also references to specific types of installations in Section 710-3.

710-20. Overcurrent Protection.

Overcurrent protection shall be provided for each ungrounded conductor by one of the following:

(a) **Overcurrent Relays and Current Transformers.** Circuit breakers used for overcurrent protection of ac 3-phase circuits shall have a minimum of three overcurrent relays operated from three current transformers.

Exception No. 1: On 3-phase, 3-wire circuits, an overcurrent relay in the residual circuit of the current transformers shall be permitted to replace one of the phase relays.

Exception No. 2: An overcurrent relay, operated from a current transformer that links all phases of a 3-phase, 3-wire circuit, shall be permitted to replace the residual relay and one of the phase conductor current transformers. Where the neutral is not regrounded on the load side of the circuit as permitted in Section 250-152(b), the current transformer shall be permitted to link all three phase conductors and the grounded circuit conductor (neutral).

(b) **Fuses.** A fuse shall be connected in series with each ungrounded conductor.

710-21. Circuit-Interrupting Devices.

(a) **Circuit Breakers.**

(1) Indoor installations shall consist of metal-enclosed units or fire-resistant cell-mounted units.

Exception: Open mounting of circuit breakers shall be permitted in locations accessible to qualified persons only.

(2) Circuit breakers used to control oil-filled transformers shall be either located outside the transformer vault or be capable of operation from outside the vault.

(3) Oil circuit breakers shall be so arranged or located that adjacent readily combustible structures or materials are safeguarded in an approved manner.

(4) Circuit breakers shall have the following equipment or operating characteristics:

  a. An accessible mechanical or other approved means for manual tripping, independent of control power.

  b. Be release free (trip free).

  c. If capable of being opened or closed manually while energized, the main contacts shall operate independently of the speed of the manual operation.

  d. A mechanical position indicator at the circuit breaker to show the open or closed position of the main contacts.

  e. A means of indicating the open and closed position of the breaker at the point(s) from which they may be operated.

  f. A permanent and legible nameplate showing manufacturer's name or trademark, manufacturer's type or identification number, continuous current rating, interrupting rating in mVA or amperes, and maximum voltage rating. Modification of a circuit breaker affecting its rating(s) shall be accompanied by an appropriate change of nameplate information.

For the control and protection of feeders leaving a substation, Figure 710-1 illustrates a typical example of modern, metal-enclosed switchgear. This industrial unit substation includes a high-voltage disconnect switch, transformer, and low-voltage switchgear with a fully functioning ground-fault relay protection system.

Indicator instruments, such as voltmeters, ammeters, wattmeters, and protective relays, may be mounted on the panel doors as desired. This switchgear affords a high degree of safety because all live parts are metal-enclosed, and interlocks are provided for safe operation.

(5) The continuous current rating of a circuit breaker shall be not less than the maximum continuous current through the circuit breaker.

(6) The interrupting rating of a circuit breaker shall not be less than the maximum fault current the circuit breaker will be required to interrupt, including contributions from all connected sources of energy.

(7) The closing rating of a circuit breaker shall not be less than the maximum asymmetrical fault current into which the circuit breaker can be closed.

(8) The momentary rating of a circuit breaker shall not be less than the maximum asymmetrical fault current at the point of installation.

(9) The rated maximum voltage of a circuit breaker shall not be less than the maximum circuit voltage.

(b) **Power Fuses and Fuseholders.**

(1) **Use.** Where fuses are used to protect conductors and equipment, a fuse shall be placed in each ungrounded conductor. Two power fuses shall be permitted to be used in parallel to protect the same load, if both fuses have identical

Figure 710-1. An assembly of metal-enclosed switchgear. (Square D Co.)

ratings, and both fuses are installed in an identified common mounting with electrical connections that will divide the current equally. Power fuses of the vented type shall not be used indoors, underground, or in metal enclosures unless identified for the use.

(2) Interrupting Rating. The interrupting rating of power fuses shall not be less than the maximum fault current the fuse will be required to interrupt, including contributions from all connected sources of energy.

(3) Voltage Rating. The maximum voltage rating of power fuses shall not be less than the maximum circuit voltage. Fuses having a minimum recommended operating voltage shall not be applied below this voltage.

(4) Identification of Fuse Mountings and Fuse Units. Fuse mountings and fuse units shall have permanent and legible nameplates showing the manufacturer's type or designation, continuous current rating, interrupting current rating, and maximum voltage rating.

(5) Fuses. Fuses that expel flame in opening the circuit shall be so designed or arranged that they will function properly without hazard to persons or property.

(6) Fuseholders. Fuseholders shall be designed or installed so that they will be deenergized while replacing a fuse.

Exception: Fuse and fuseholder designed to permit fuse replacement by qualified persons using equipment designed for the purpose without deenergizing the fuseholder.

(7) High-Voltage Fuses. Metal-enclosed switchgear and substations that utilize high-voltage fuses shall be provided with a gang-operated disconnecting switch. Isolation of the fuses from the circuit shall be provided by either connecting a switch between the source and the fuses or providing roll-out switch and fuse-type of construction. The switch shall be of the load-interrupter type, unless mechanically or electrically interlocked with a load-interrupting device arranged to reduce the load to the interrupting capability of the switch.

Exception: More than one switch shall be permitted as the disconnecting means for one set of fuses where the switches are installed to provide connection to more than one set of supply conductors. The switches shall be mechanically or electrically interlocked to permit access to the fuses only when all switches are open. A conspicuous sign shall be placed at the fuses reading: "WARNING—FUSES MAY BE ENERGIZED FROM MORE THAN ONE SOURCE."

(c) Distribution Cutouts and Fuse Links — Expulsion Type.

(1) Installation. Cutouts shall be so located that they may be readily and safely operated and re-fused, and so that the exhaust of the fuses will not endanger persons. Distribution cutouts shall not be used indoors, underground, or in metal enclosures.

(2) Operation. Where fused cutouts are not suitable to interrupt the circuit manually while carrying full load, an approved means shall be installed to interrupt the entire load. Unless the fused cutouts are interlocked with the switch to prevent opening of the cutouts under load, a conspicuous sign shall be placed at such cutouts reading, "WARNING — DO NOT OPEN UNDER LOAD."

(3) Interrupting Rating. The interrupting rating of distribution cutouts shall not be less than the maximum fault current the cutout will be required to interrupt, including contributions from all connected sources of energy.

(4) Voltage Rating. The maximum voltage rating of cutouts shall not be less than the maximum circuit voltage.

(5) Identification. Distribution cutouts shall have on their body, door, or fuse tube a permanent and legible nameplate or identification showing the manufacturer's type or designation, continuous current rating, maximum voltage rating, and interrupting rating.

(6) Fuse Links. Fuse links shall have a permanent and legible identification showing continuous current rating and type.

(7) Structure Mounted Outdoors. The height of cutouts mounted outdoors on structures shall provide safe clearance between lowest energized parts (open or closed position) and standing surfaces, in accordance with Section 110-34(e).

(d) Oil-Filled Cutouts.

(1) Continuous Current Rating. The continuous current rating of oil-filled cutouts shall not be less than the maximum continuous current through the cutout.

(2) Interrupting Rating. The interrupting rating of oil-filled cutouts shall not be less than the maximum fault current the oil-filled cutout will be required to interrupt, including contributions from all connected sources of energy.

(3) Voltage Rating. The maximum voltage rating of oil-filled cutouts shall not be less than the maximum circuit voltage.

(4) Fault Closing Rating. Oil-filled cutouts shall have a fault closing rating not less than the maximum asymmetrical fault current that can occur at the cutout location, unless suitable interlocks or operating procedures preclude the possibility of closing into a fault.

(5) Identification. Oil-filled cutouts shall have a permanent and legible nameplate showing the rated continuous current, rated maximum voltage, and rated interrupting current.

(6) Fuse Links. Fuse links shall have a permanent and legible identification showing the rated continuous current.

(7) Location. Cutouts shall be so located that they will be readily and safely accessible for re-fusing, with the top of the cutout not over 5 feet (1.52 m) above the floor or platform.

(8) Enclosure. Suitable barriers or enclosures shall be provided to prevent contact with nonshielded cables or energized parts of oil-filled cutouts.

(e) Load Interrupters. Load-interrupter switches shall be permitted if suitable fuses or circuit breakers are used in conjunction with these devices to interrupt fault currents. Where these devices are used in combination, they shall be so coordinated electrically that they will safely withstand the effects of closing, carrying, or interrupting all possible currents up to the assigned maximum short-circuit rating.

Where more than one switch is installed with interconnected load terminals to provide for alternate connection to different supply conductors, each switch shall be provided with a conspicuous sign reading: "WARNING — SWITCH MAY BE ENERGIZED BY BACKFEED."

(1) Continuous Current Rating. The continuous current rating of interrupter switches shall equal or exceed the maximum continuous current at the point of installation.

(2) Voltage Rating. The maximum voltage rating of interrupter switches shall equal or exceed the maximum circuit voltage.

(3) Identification. Interrupter switches shall have a permanent and legible nameplate including the following information: manufacturer's type or designation, continuous current rating, interrupting current rating, fault closing rating, maximum voltage rating.

(4) Switching of Conductors. The switching mechanism shall be arranged to be operated from a location where the operator is not exposed to energized parts and shall be arranged to open all ungrounded conductors of the circuit simultaneously with one operation. Switches shall be arranged to be locked in the open position. Metal-enclosed switches shall be operable from outside the enclosure.

(5) Stored Energy for Opening. The stored energy operator shall be permitted to be left in the uncharged position after the switch has been closed if a single movement of the operating handle charges the operator and opens the switch.

(6) Supply Terminals. Fused interrupter switches shall be so installed that all supply terminals shall be at the top of the switch enclosure.

Exception: Supply terminals shall not be required to be at the top of the switch enclosure if barriers are installed to prevent persons from accidentally contacting energized parts or dropping tools or fuses into energized parts.

710-22. **Isolating Means.** Means shall be provided to completely isolate an item of equipment. The use of isolating switches shall not be required where there are other ways of deenergizing the equipment for inspection and repairs, such as drawout-type metal-enclosed switchgear units and removable truck panels.

Isolating switches not interlocked with an approved circuit-interrupting device shall be provided with a sign warning against opening them under load.

A fuseholder and fuse, designed for the purpose, shall be permitted as an isolating switch.

710-23. Voltage Regulators.
Proper switching sequence for regulators shall be assured by use of one of the following: (1) mechanically sequenced regulator bypass switch(es); (2) mechanical interlocks; or (3) switching procedure prominently displayed at the switching location.

710-24. Metal-Enclosed Power Switchgear and Industrial Control Assemblies.

(a) Scope. This section covers assemblies of metal-enclosed power switchgear and industrial control, including but not limited to switches, interrupting devices and their control, metering, protection and regulating equipment, where an integral part of the assembly, with associated interconnections and supporting structures. This section also includes metal-enclosed power switchgear assemblies that form a part of unit substations, power centers, or similar equipment.

(b) Arrangement of Devices in Assemblies. Arrangement of devices in assemblies shall be such that individual components can safely perform their intended function without adversely affecting the safe operation of other components in the assembly.

(c) Guarding of High-Voltage Energized Parts Within a Compartment. Where access for other than visual inspection is required to a compartment that contains energized high-voltage parts, barriers shall be provided as follows:

(1) To prevent accidental contact with energized parts.

Exception No. 1: Fuse and fuseholder designed to permit fuse replacement by qualified persons using equipment designed for the purpose without deenergizing the fuseholder.

Exception No. 2: Exposed live parts shall be permitted within the compartment where accessible to qualified persons only.

(2) To prevent tools or other equipment from being dropped on energized parts.

Figure 710-2. A 300-kVa, 15-kV pad-mounted transformer integral unit containing a primary hook-stick-operated switch with a limited number of secondary breakers or switches. (Square D Co.)

(d) Guarding of Low-Voltage Energized Parts Within a Compartment. Energized bare parts mounted on doors shall be guarded where the door must be opened for maintenance of equipment or removal of drawout equipment.

(e) Clearance for Cable Conductors Entering Enclosure. The unobstructed space opposite terminals or opposite raceways or cables entering a switchgear or control assembly shall be adequate for the type of conductor and method of termination.

(f) Accessibility of Energized Parts.

(1) Doors that would provide nonqualified persons access to high-voltage energized parts shall be locked.

(2) Low-voltage control equipment, relays, motors, and the like shall not be installed in compartments with exposed high-voltage energized parts or high-voltage wiring unless the access door or cover is interlocked with the high-voltage switch or disconnecting means to prevent the door or cover from being opened or removed unless the switch or disconnecting means is in its isolating position.

Exception No. 1: Instrument or control transformers connected to high voltage.

Exception No. 2: Space heaters.

(g) Grounding. Frames of switchgear and control assemblies shall be grounded.

(h) Grounding of Devices. Devices with metal cases and/or frames, such as instruments, relays, meters, and instrument and control transformers, located in or on switchgear or control, shall have the frame or case grounded.

Figure 710-3. A 1,500-kVa, 15-kV unit substation transformer or power-center-type transformer that is adaptable to a lineup of a high-voltage switch, transformer, and low-voltage secondary. (Square D Co.)

(i) Door Stops and Cover Plates. External hinged doors or covers shall be provided with stops to hold them in the open position. Cover plates intended to be removed for inspection of energized parts or wiring shall be equipped with lifting handles and shall not exceed 12 square feet (1.11 sq m) in area or 60 pounds (27.22 kg) in weight, unless they are hinged and bolted or locked.

(j) Gas Discharge from Interrupting Devices. Gas discharged during operating of interrupting devices shall be so directed as not to endanger personnel.

(k) Inspection Windows. Windows intended for inspection of disconnecting switches or other devices shall be of suitable transparent material.

(l) Location of Devices. Control and instrument transfer switch handles or pushbuttons shall be in a readily accessible location at an elevation not over 78 inches (1.98 m).

Exception No. 1: Operating handles requiring more than 50 pounds (22.68 kg) of force shall not be higher than 66 inches (1.68 m) in either the open or closed position.

Exception No. 2: Operating handles for infrequently operated devices, such as drawout fuses, fused potential or control transformers and their primary disconnects, and bus transfer switches where they are otherwise safely operable and serviceable from a portable platform.

(m) Interlocks — Interrupter Switches. Interrupter switches equipped with stored energy mechanisms shall have mechanical interlocks to prevent access to the switch compartment unless the stored energy mechanism is in the discharged or blocked position.

(n) Stored Energy for Opening. The stored energy operator shall be permitted to be left in the uncharged position after the switch has been closed if a single movement of the operating handle charges the operator and opens the switch.

(o) Fused Interrupter Switches.

(1) Fused interrupter switches shall be so installed that all supply terminals shall be at the top of the switch enclosure.

Exception: Supply terminals shall not be required to be at the top of the switch enclosure if barriers are installed to prevent persons from accidentally contacting energized parts or dropping tools or fuses into energized parts.

(2) Where fuses can be energized by backfeed, a sign shall be placed on the enclosure door reading: "WARNING — FUSES MAY BE ENERGIZED BY BACKFEED."

(3) The switching mechanism shall be arranged to be operated from a location outside the enclosure where the operator is not exposed to energized parts and shall be arranged to open all ungrounded conductors of the circuit simultaneously with one operation. Switches shall be capable of being locked in the open position.

(p) Interlocks — Circuit Breakers.

(1) Circuit breakers equipped with stored energy mechanisms shall be designed to prevent the release of the stored energy unless the mechanism has been fully charged.

(2) Mechanical interlocks shall be provided in the housing to prevent the complete withdrawal of the circuit breaker from the housing when the stored energy mechanism is in the fully charged position.

Figure 710-4. Group-operated interrupter-switch and power-fuse combination rated at 13.8 kV, 600 A continuous and interrupting, 40,000 A momentary, 40,000 A fault closing.

Figure 710-5. Components of the indoor solid-material (SM) power fuseholder (boric-acid arc-extinguishing type) with a 14.4 kV, 400 E A max, 40,000 A RMS asymmetrical interrupting rating. Shown here are the spring and cable assembly, refill unit, holder, and snuffler. (S & C Electric Co.)

Exception: Where a suitable device is provided that prevents the complete withdrawal of the circuit breaker unless the closing function is blocked.

D. Installations Accessible to Qualified Persons Only

710-31. **Enclosure for Electrical Installations.** See Section 110-31.

710-32. **Circuit Conductors.** Circuit conductors shall be permitted to be installed in raceways, in cable trays, as metal-clad cable, as bare wire, cable, and busbars, or as Type MV cables, or conductors as provided in Sections 710-4 through 710-6. Bare live conductors shall conform with Sections 710-33 and 710-34.

Insulators, together with their mounting and conductor attachments, where used as supports for wires, single-conductor cables, or busbars, shall be capable of safely withstanding the maximum

magnetic forces that would prevail when two or more conductors of a circuit were subjected to short-circuit current.

Open runs of insulated wires and cables having a bare lead sheath or a braided outer covering shall be supported in a manner designed to prevent physical damage to the braid or sheath. Supports for lead-covered cables shall be designed to prevent electrolysis of the sheath.

710-33. **Minimum Space Separation.** In field-fabricated installations, the minimum air separation between bare live conductors and between such conductors and adjacent grounded surfaces shall not be less than the values given in Table 710-33. These values shall not apply to interior portions or exterior terminals of equipment designed, manufactured, and tested in accordance with accepted national standards.

710-34. **Work Space and Guarding.** See Section 110-34.

Table 710-33. Minimum Clearance of Live Parts*

Nominal Voltage Rating, kV	Impulse Withstand, B.I.L. kV		Minimum Clearance of Live Parts, in inches			
			Phase-to-Phase		Phase-to-Ground	
	Indoors	Outdoors	Indoors	Outdoors	Indoors	Outdoors
2.4-4.16	60	95	4.5	7	3.0	6
7.2	75	95	5.5	7	4.0	6
13.8	95	110	7.5	12	5.0	7
14.4	110	110	9.0	12	6.5	7
23	125	150	10.5	15	7.5	10
34.5	150	150	12.5	15	9.5	10
	200	200	18.0	18	13.0	13
46		200		18		13
		250		21		17
69		250		21		17
		350		31		25
115		550		53		42
138		550		53		42
		650		63		50
161		650		63		50
		750		72		58
230		750		72		58
		900		89		71
		1050		105		83

For SI units: one inch = 25.4 millimeters.
* The values given are the minimum clearance for rigid parts and bare conductors under favorable service conditions. They shall be increased for conductor movement or under unfavorable service conditions or wherever space limitations permit. The selection of the associated impulse withstand voltage for a particular system voltage is determined by the characteristics of the surge protective equipment.

E. Mobile and Portable Equipment

710-41. General.

(a) **Covered.** The provisions of this part shall apply to installations and use of high-voltage power distribution and utilization equipment that is portable and/or mobile, such as substations and switch houses mounted on skids, trailers, or cars, mobile shovels, draglines, cranes, hoists, drills, dredges, compressors, pumps, conveyors, underground excavators, and the like.

(b) **Other Requirements.** The requirements of this part shall be additional to, or amendatory of, those prescribed in Articles 100 through 725 of this Code. Special attention shall be paid to Article 250.

(c) **Protection.** Adequate enclosures and/or guarding shall be provided to protect portable and mobile equipment from physical damage.

(d) **Disconnecting Means.** Disconnecting means shall be installed for mobile and portable high-voltage equipment according to the requirements of Part H of Article 230 and shall disconnect all ungrounded conductors.

710-42. Overcurrent Protection.
Motors driving single or multiple dc generators supplying a system operating on a cyclic load basis do not require running overcurrent protection, provided that the thermal rating of the ac drive motor cannot be exceeded under any operating condition. The branch-circuit protective device(s) shall provide short-circuit and locked-rotor protection, and shall be permitted to be external to the equipment.

710-43. Enclosures.
All energized switching and control parts shall be enclosed in effectively grounded metal cabinets or enclosures. These cabinets or enclosures shall be marked "DANGER — HIGH VOLTAGE — KEEP OUT" and shall be locked so that only authorized and qualified persons can enter. Circuit breakers and protective equipment shall have the operating means projecting through the metal cabinet or enclosure so these units can be reset without opening locked doors. With doors closed, reasonable safe access for normal operation of these units shall be provided.

710-44. Collector Rings.
The collector ring assemblies on revolving-type machines (shovels, draglines, etc.) shall be guarded to prevent accidental contact with energized parts by personnel on or off the machine.

710-45. Power Cable Connections to Mobile Machines.
A metallic enclosure shall be provided on the mobile machine for enclosing the terminals of the power cable. The enclosure shall include provisions for a solid connection for the ground wire(s) terminal to effectively ground the machine frame. Ungrounded conductors shall be attached to insulators or terminated in approved high-voltage cable couplers (which include ground wire connectors) of proper voltage and ampere rating. The method of cable termination used shall prevent any strain or pull on the cable from stressing the electrical connections. The enclosure shall have provision for locking so only authorized and qualified persons may open it and shall be marked "DANGER — HIGH VOLTAGE — KEEP OUT."

710-46. High-Voltage Portable Cable for Main Power Supply.
Flexible high-voltage cable supplying power to portable or mobile equipment shall comply with Article 250 and Article 400, Part C.

710-47. **Grounding.** Mobile equipment shall be grounded in accordance with Article 250.

F. Tunnel Installations

710-51. **General.**

(a) **Covered.** The provisions of this part shall apply to installation and use of high-voltage power distribution and utilization equipment that is portable and/or mobile, such as substations, trailers, or cars, mobile shovels, draglines, hoists, drills, dredges, compressors, pumps, conveyors, underground excavators, and the like.

(b) **Other Articles.** The requirements of this part shall be additional to, or amendatory of, those prescribed in Articles 100 through 710 of this Code. Special attention shall be paid to Article 250.

(c) **Protection Against Physical Damage.** Conductors and cables in tunnels shall be located above the tunnel floor and so placed or guarded to protect them from physical damage.

710-52. **Overcurrent Protection.** Motor-operated equipment shall be protected from overcurrent in accordance with Article 430. Transformers shall be protected from overcurrent in accordance with Article 450.

710-53. **Conductors.** High-voltage conductors in tunnels shall be installed in (1) metal conduit or other metal raceway; (2) Type MC cable; or (3) other approved multiconductor cable. Multiconductor portable cable shall be permitted to supply mobile equipment.

710-54. **Bonding and Equipment Grounding Conductor.**

(a) **Grounded and Bonded.** All noncurrent-carrying metal parts of electric equipment and all metal raceways and cable sheaths shall be effectively grounded and bonded to all metal pipes and rails at the portal and at intervals not exceeding 1000 feet (305 m) throughout the tunnel.

(b) **Equipment Grounding Conductor.** An equipment grounding conductor shall be run with circuit conductors inside the metal raceway or inside the multiconductor cable jacket. The equipment grounding conductor shall be permitted to be insulated or bare.

710-55. **Transformers, Switches, and Electric Equipment.** All transformers, switches, motor controllers, motors, rectifiers, and other equipment installed below ground shall be protected from physical damage by location or guarding.

710-56. **Energized Parts.** Bare terminals of transformers, switches, motor controllers, and other equipment shall be enclosed to prevent accidental contact with energized parts.

710-57. **Ventilation System Controls.** Electrical controls for the ventilation system shall be so arranged that the airflow can be reversed.

710-58. **Disconnecting Means.** A switching device meeting the requirements of Article 430 or 450 shall be installed at each transformer or motor location for disconnecting the transformer or motor. The switching device shall open all ungrounded conductors of a circuit simultaneously.

710-59. **Enclosures.** Enclosures for use in tunnels shall be dripproof, weatherproof, or submersible as required by the environmental conditions. Switch or contactor enclosures shall not be used as junction boxes or raceways for conductors feeding through or tapping off to other switches, unless special designs are used to provide adequate space for this purpose.

710-60. **Grounding.** Tunnel equipment shall be grounded in accordance with Article 250.

G. Electrode-type Boilers

710-70. **General.** The provisions of this part shall apply to boilers operating over 600 volts, nominal, in which heat is generated by the passage of current between electrodes through the liquid being heated.

710-71. **Electric Supply System.** Electrode-type boilers shall be supplied only from a 3-phase, 4-wire solidly grounded wye system, or from isolating transformers arranged to provide such a system. Control circuit voltages shall not exceed 150 volts, shall be supplied from a grounded system, and shall have the controls in the ungrounded conductor.

710-72. **Branch Circuit Requirements.**

(a) **Rating.** Each boiler shall be supplied from an individual branch circuit rated not less than 100 percent of the total load.

(b) **Common-Trip Fault Interrupting Device.** The circuit shall be protected by a 3-phase common-trip fault interrupting device, which shall be permitted to automatically reclose the circuit upon removal of an overload condition but shall not reclose after a fault condition.

(c) Phase Fault Protection. Phase fault protection shall be provided in each phase, consisting of a separate phase overcurrent relay connected to a separate current transformer in the phase.

(d) Ground Current Detection. Means shall be provided for detection of the sum of the neutral and ground currents and shall trip the circuit interrupting device if the sum of those currents exceeds the greater of 5 amperes or $7\frac{1}{2}$ percent of the boiler full-load current for 10 seconds or exceeds an instantaneous value of 25 percent of the boiler full-load current.

(e) Grounded Neutral Conductor. The grounded neutral conductor shall:

(1) Be connected to the pressure vessel containing the electrodes.

(2) Be insulated for not less than 600 volts.

(3) Have not less than the ampacity of the largest ungrounded branch-circuit conductor.

(4) Be installed in the same raceway or cable tray with the ungrounded conductors.

(5) Not be used for any other circuit.

710-73. Pressure and Temperature Limit Control. Each boiler shall be equipped with a means to limit the maximum temperature and/or pressure by directly or indirectly interrupting all current flow through the electrodes. Such means shall be in addition to the temperature and/or pressure regulating systems and pressure relief or safety valves.

710-74. Grounding. All exposed noncurrent-carrying metal parts of the boiler and associated exposed grounded structures or equipment shall be bonded to the pressure vessel or to the neutral conductor to which the vessel is connected, in accordance with Section 250-79, except the ampacity of the bonding jumper shall be not less than the ampacity of the neutral conductor.

ARTICLE 720   Circuits and Equipment Operating at Less Than 50 Volts

Contents

720-1. Scope. This article covers installations operating at less than 50 volts, direct current or alternating current.

Exception: As covered in Articles 551, 650, 669, 690, 725, and 760.

720-2. Hazardous (Classified) Locations. Installations coming within the scope of this article and installed in hazardous (classified) locations shall also comply with the appropriate provisions of Articles 500 through 517.

It should be understood that low voltage alone does not render a circuit incapable of igniting flammable atmospheres. Under some conditions, even ordinary flashlights using two $1\frac{1}{2}$-V "D" cells can be a source of ignition in hazardous (classified) locations.

720-4. Conductors. Conductors shall not be smaller than No. 12 copper or equivalent. Conductors for appliance branch circuits supplying more than one appliance or appliance receptacle shall not be smaller than No. 10 copper or equivalent.

720-5. Lampholders. Standard lampholders having a rating of not less than 660 watts shall be used.

720-6. Receptacle Rating. Receptacles shall have a rating of not less than 15 amperes.

720-7. Receptacles Required. Receptacles of not less than 20-ampere rating shall be provided in kitchens, laundries, and other locations where portable appliances are likely to be used.

720-8. Overcurrent Protection. Overcurrent protection shall comply with Article 240.

720-9. Batteries. Installations of storage batteries shall comply with Article 480.

720-10. Grounding. Grounding shall comply with Sections 250-5(a) and 250-45.

ARTICLE 725   Class 1, Class 2, and Class 3 Remote-Control, Signaling, and Power-Limited Circuits

Contents

A. General

725-1. **Scope.** This article covers remote-control, signaling, and power-limited circuits that are not an integral part of a device or appliance.

(FPN): The circuits described herein are characterized by usage and electrical power limitations that differentiate them from electric light and power circuits and, therefore, alternative requirements to those of Chapters 1 through 4 are given with regard to minimum wire sizes, derating factors, overcurrent protection, insulation requirements, and wiring methods and materials.

Included within the scope of Article 725 are such systems as burglar alarm circuits (a signaling system) and the coaxial cable wiring often associated with interconnection of electronic data processing (EDP) and computer equipment not within a data processing room as covered in Article 645. If pieces of listed computer equipment are interconnected and in close proximity, the wiring is considered to be an integral part of the equipment and not subject to the requirements of Article 725. If the wiring leaves the group to connect to other devices in the same room or elsewhere in the building, the wiring is considered to be "wiring within buildings" and hence subject to the requirements of this article.

The format for this article is similar to the format for Articles 760, 770, 800, and 820.

725-2. **Locations and Other Articles.** Circuits and equipment shall comply with (a), (b), (c), (d), and (e) below.

(a) **Spread of Fire or Products of Combustion.** Section 300-21.

(b) **Ducts, Plenums, and Other Air-Handling Spaces.** Section 300-22, where installed in ducts or plenums or other space used for environmental air.

Exception to (b): As permitted in Section 725-53(a).

See commentary following Sections 300-22(b), 300-22(c), and 725-51(a) FPN.

(c) **Hazardous (Classified) Locations.** Articles 500 through 516, and Article 517, Part D, where installed in hazardous (classified) locations.

(d) **Cable Trays.** Article 318, where installed in cable tray.

(e) **Motor Control Circuits.** Article 430, Part F, where tapped from the load side of the motor branch-circuit protective device(s) as specified in Section 430-72(a).

725-3. **Classifications.** A remote-control, signaling, or power-limited circuit is the portion of the wiring system between the load side of the overcurrent device or the power-limited supply and all connected equipment, and shall be Class 1, Class 2, or Class 3 as defined in (a) and (b) below.

(a) **Class 1 Circuits.** Circuits that comply with Part B of this article and in which the voltage and power limitations are in accordance with Section 725-11.

(b) **Class 2 and Class 3 Circuits.** Circuits that comply with Part C of this article and in which the voltage and power limitations are in accordance with Section 725-31.

(FPN): Due to their power limitations, both Class 2 and 3 circuits consider safety from a fire initiation standpoint. In addition, Class 2 circuits provide acceptable protection from electric shock. However, since Class 3 circuits permit higher allowable levels of voltage and current, additional safeguards are specified to provide protection against the electric shock hazard that could be encountered.

725-4. **Safety-Control Equipment.** Remote-control circuits to safety-control equipment shall be classified as Class 1 if the failure of the equipment to operate introduces a direct fire or life hazard. Room thermostats, water temperature regulating devices, and similar controls used in conjunction with electrically controlled household heating and air conditioning shall not be considered safety-control equipment.

725-5. **Communications Cables.** Class 1 circuits shall not be run in the same cable with communications circuits. Class 2 and Class 3 circuit conductors shall be permitted in the same cable with communications circuits, in which case the Class 2 and Class 3 circuits shall be classified as communications circuits and shall meet the requirements of Article 800. The cables shall be listed as communications cables or multipurpose cables.

Exception: Cables constructed of individually listed Class 2, Class 3, and communications cables under a common jacket shall not be required to be classified as communications cables. The fire resistance rating of the composite cable shall be determined by the performance of the composite cable.

725-6. **Access to Electrical Equipment Behind Panels Designed to Allow Access.** Access to equipment shall not be denied by an accumulation of wires and cables that prevents removal of panels, including suspended ceiling panels.

This section is new in the 1993 *Code*. The excess accumulation of wires and cables can limit access to electrical equipment by preventing the removal of access panels. To service, rearrange, or install electrical equipment, the worker must have an accessible workspace for working safely on energized equipment. See Figure 725-1.

725-1. The excess accumulation of wires and cables that prevents access to equipment above the suspended ceiling is not permitted.

B. Class 1 Circuits

725-11. **Power Limitations for Class 1 Circuits.**

(a) Class 1 Power-Limited Circuits. These circuits shall be supplied from a source having a rated output of not more than 30 volts and 1000 volt-amperes. Power sources other than transformers shall be protected by overcurrent devices rated at not more than 167 percent of the volt-ampere rating of the source divided by the rated voltage. The overcurrent devices shall not be interchangeable with overcurrent devices of higher ratings. The overcurrent device shall be permitted to be an integral part of the power supply.

(1) **Transformers.** Transformers used to supply power-limited Class 1 circuits shall comply with Article 450.

(2) **Other Power Sources.** To comply with the 1000 volt-ampere limitation of Section 725-11(a), the maximum output of power sources other than transformers shall be limited to 2500 volt-amperes, and the product of the maximum current and maximum voltage shall not exceed 10,000 volt-amperes. These ratings shall be determined with any overcurrent-protective device bypassed.

(FPN): For definitions of V_{max}, I_{max}, and VA_{max}, see Note 1, Tables 725-31(a) and (b).

(b) Class 1 Remote-Control and Signaling Circuits. Class 1 remote-control and signaling circuits shall not exceed 600 volts; however, the power output of the source shall not be required to be limited.

725-12. **Overcurrent Protection.** Conductors No. 14 and larger shall be protected against overcurrent in accordance with Section 310-15. Derating factors shall not be applied. Overcurrent protection shall not exceed 7 amperes for No. 18 conductors and 10 amperes for No. 16.

Exception No. 1: Where other articles of this Code permit or require other overcurrent protection.

(FPN): For example, see Section 430-72 for motors, Section 610-53 for cranes and hoists, and Sections 517-74(b) and 660-9 for X-ray equipment.

See Section 240-4, Exception No. 2 for another example.

Exception No. 2: Transformer Secondary Conductors. Class 1 circuit conductors supplied by the secondary of a single-phase transformer having only a 2-wire (single-voltage) secondary shall be permitted to be protected by overcurrent protection provided on the primary (supply) side of the transformer, provided this protection is in accordance with Section 450-3 and does not exceed the value determined by multiplying the secondary conductor ampacity by the secondary-to-primary transformer voltage ratio. Transformer secondary conductors other than 2-wire shall not be considered to be protected by the primary overcurrent protection.

Exception No. 2 correlates with Section 240-3(i) and Section 430-72(b), Exception No. 3.

Exception No. 3: Class 1 circuit conductors No. 14 and larger that are tapped from the load side of the overcurrent-protective device(s) of a controlled light and power circuit shall require only short-circuit and ground-fault protection and shall be permitted to be protected by the branch-circuit overcurrent-protective device(s) where the rating of the protective device(s) is not more than 300 percent of the ampacity of the Class 1 circuit conductor.

Exception No. 3 correlates with Section 240-3(l).

725-13. Location of Overcurrent Devices. Overcurrent devices shall be located at the point where the conductor to be protected receives its supply.

Exception No. 1: Where the overcurrent device protecting the larger conductor also protects the smaller conductor.

Exception No. 2: Where overcurrent protection is provided in accordance with Section 725-12, Exception No. 2.

725-14. Wiring Method. Installations of Class 1 circuits shall be in accordance with the appropriate articles in Chapter 3.

Exception No. 1: As provided in Sections 725-15 through 725-17.

Exception No. 2: Where other articles of this Code permit or require other methods.

725-15. Conductors of Different Circuits in Same Cable, Enclosure, or Raceway. Class 1 circuits shall be permitted to occupy the same cable, enclosure, or raceway without regard to whether the individual circuits are alternating current or direct current, provided all conductors are insulated for the maximum voltage of any conductor in the cable, enclosure, or raceway. Power supply and Class 1 circuit conductors shall be permitted in the same cable, enclosure, or raceway only where the equipment powered is functionally associated.

Exception No. 1: Where installed in factory- or field-assembled control centers.

Exception No. 2: Underground conductors in a manhole where one of the following conditions is met:

a. The power supply or Class 1 circuit conductors are in a metal-enclosed cable, or Type UF cable;

b. The conductors are permanently separated from the power-supply conductors by a continuous firmly fixed nonconductor, such as flexible tubing, in addition to the insulation on the wire;

c. The conductors are permanently and effectively separated from the power supply conductors and securely fastened to racks, insulators, or other approved supports.

This section permits the installation of Class 1 power-limited circuit conductors in manholes with wiring of nonpower-limited systems where suitable separation provides the same degree of protection as is required for Class 2 and Class 3 power-limited circuits in Section 725-52(a),

for communication circuits in Section 800-52(a), for radio/television antennas and lead-in conductors in Section 810-18(a), and for CATV conductors in Section 820-52(a).

725-16. Conductors.

(a) Sizes and Use. Conductors of sizes No. 18 and 16 shall be permitted to be used, provided they supply loads that do not exceed the ampacities given in Section 402-5 and are installed in a raceway, an approved enclosure, or a listed cable. Conductors larger than No. 16 shall not supply loads greater than the ampacities given in Section 310-15. Flexible cords shall comply with Article 400.

(b) Insulation. Insulation on conductors shall be suitable for 600 volts. Conductors larger than No. 16 shall comply with Article 310.

Conductors in sizes No. 18 and 16 shall be Type FFH-2, KF-2, KFF-2, PAF, PAFF, PF, PFF, PGF, PGFF, PTF, PTFF, RFH-2, RFHH-2, RFHH-3, SF-2, SFF-2, TF, TFF, TFFN, TFN, ZF, or ZFF.

Conductors with other types and thicknesses of insulation shall be permitted if listed for Class 1 circuit use.

725-17. Number of Conductors in Cable Trays and Raceway, and Derating.

(a) Class 1 Circuit Conductors. Where only Class 1 circuit conductors are in a raceway, the number of conductors shall be determined in accordance with Section 300-17. The derating factors given in Article 310, Note 8(a) of Notes to Ampacity Tables of 0 to 2000 Volts shall apply only if such conductors carry continuous loads in excess of 10 percent of the ampacity of each conductor.

(b) Power-Supply Conductors and Class 1 Circuit Conductors. Where power-supply conductors and Class 1 circuit conductors are permitted in a raceway in accordance with Section 725-15, the number of conductors shall be determined in accordance with Section 300-17. The derating factors given in Article 310, Note 8(a) of Notes to Ampacity Tables of 0 to 2000 Volts shall apply as follows:

(1) To all conductors where the Class 1 circuit conductors carry continuous loads in excess of 10 percent of the ampacity of each conductor and where the total number of conductors is more than three.

(2) To the power-supply conductors only, where the Class 1 circuit conductors do not carry continuous loads in excess of 10 percent of the ampacity of each conductor and where the number of power-supply conductors is more than three.

(c) Class 1 Circuit Conductors in Cable Trays. Where Class 1 circuit conductors are installed in cable trays, they shall comply with the provisions of Sections 318-9 through 318-11.

725-18. **Physical Protection.** Where damage to remote-control circuits of safety control equipment would introduce a hazard, as covered in Section 725-4, all conductors of such remote-control circuits shall be installed in rigid metal conduit, intermediate metal conduit, rigid nonmetallic conduit, electrical metallic tubing, Type MI cable, Type MC cable, or be otherwise suitably protected from physical damage.

725-19. **Circuits Extending Beyond One Building.** Class 1 circuits that extend aerially beyond one building shall also meet the requirements of Article 225.

725-20. **Grounding.** Class 1 circuits and equipment shall be grounded in accordance with Article 250.

C. Class 2 and Class 3 Circuits

725-31. **Power Limitations of Class 2 and Class 3 Circuits.** As specified in Table 725-31(a) for ac circuits and Table 725-31(b) for dc circuits, the power for Class 2 and Class 3 circuits shall be either inherently limited requiring no overcurrent protection or limited by a combination of a power source and overcurrent protection.

Table 725-31(a). **Power Source Limitations for Alternating Current Class 2 and Class 3 Circuits**

Circuit	Inherently Limited Power Source (Overcurrent protection not required)				Not Inherently Limited Power Source (Overcurrent protection required)			
	Class 2			Class 3	Class 2		Class 3	
Circuit Voltage V_{max} (Volts) (Note 1)	0 through 20†	Over 20 and through 30†	Over 30 and through 150	Over 30 and through 100	0 through 20†	Over 20 and through 30†	Over 30 and through 100	Over 100 and through 150
Power Limitations $(VA)_{max}$ (Volt-Amps) (Note 1)	—	—	—	—	250 (Note 3)	250	250	N.A.
Current Limitations I_{max} (Amps) (Note 1)	8.0	8.0	0.005	$150/V_{max}$	$1000/V_{max}$	$1000/V_{max}$	$1000/V_{max}$	1.0
Maximum Overcurrent Protection (Amps)	—	—	—	—	5.0	$100/V_{max}$	$100/V_{max}$	1.0
Power Source Maximum Nameplate Ratings — VA (Volt-Amps)	$5.0 \times V_{max}$	100	$0.005 \times V_{max}$	100	$5.0 \times V_{max}$	100	100	100
Power Source Maximum Nameplate Ratings — Current (Amps)	5.0	$100/V_{max}$	0.005	$100/V_{max}$	5.0	$100/V_{max}$	$100/V_{max}$	$100/V_{max}$
Supply Conductors and Cables	See Section 725-37							
Circuit Conductors and Cables	See Sections 725-49 through 725-53							

† Voltage ranges shown are for sinusoidal ac in indoor locations or where wet contact is not likely to occur. For nonsinusoidal or wet contact conditions, see Note 2.

Table 725-31(b). Power Source Limitations for Direct Current Class 2 and Class 3 Circuits

Circuit	Inherently Limited Power Source (Note 4) (Overcurrent protection not required)					Not Inherently Limited Power Source (Overcurrent protection required)			
	Class 2				Class 3	Class 2		Class 3	
Circuit Voltage V_{max} (Volts) (Note 1)	0 through 20††	Over 20 and through 30††	Over 30 and through 60††	Over 60 and through 150	Over 60 and through 100	0 through 20††	Over 20 and through 60††	Over 60 and through 100	Over 100 and through 150
Power Limitations $(VA)_{max}$ (Volt-Amps) (Note 1)	—	—	—	—	—	250 (Note 3)	250	250	N.A.
Current Limitations I_{max} (Amps) (Note 1)	8.0	8.0	$150/V_{max}$	0.005	$150/V_{max}$	$1000/V_{max}$	$1000/V_{max}$	$1000/V_{max}$	1.0
Maximum Overcurrent Protection (Amps)	—	—	—	—	—	5.0	$100/V_{max}$	$100/V_{max}$	1.0
Power Source Maximum Nameplate Ratings — VA (Volt-Amps)	$5.0 \times V_{max}$	100	100	$0.005 \times V_{max}$	100	$5.0 \times V_{max}$	100	100	100
Power Source Maximum Nameplate Ratings — Current (Amps)	5.0	$100/V_{max}$	$100/V_{max}$	0.005	$100/V_{max}$	5.0	$100/V_{max}$	$100/V_{max}$	$100/V_{max}$
Supply Conductors and Cables	See Section 725-37								
Circuit Conductors and Cables	See Sections 725-49 through 725-53								

†† Voltage ranges shown are for continuous dc in indoor locations or where wet contact is not likely to occur. For interrupted dc or wet contact conditions, see Note 5.

Notes for Tables 725-31(a) and (b)

Note 1.

V_{max}: Maximum output voltage regardless of load with rated input applied.

I_{max}: Maximum output current under any noncapacitive load, including short circuit, and with overcurrent protection bypassed, if used. When a transformer limits the output current, I_{max} limits apply after one minute of operation. Where a current-limiting impedance, listed for the purpose, or as part of a listed product, is used in combination with a nonpower-limited transformer or a stored energy source, e.g., storage battery, to limit the output current, I_{max} limits apply after 5 seconds.

VA_{max}: Maximum volt-ampere output after one minute of operation regardless of load and overcurrent protection bypassed, if used.

Current-limiting impedance shall not be bypassed when determining I_{max} and VA_{max}.

Note 2. For nonsinusoidal ac, V_{max} shall be not greater than 42.4 volts peak. Where wet contact (immersion not included) is likely to occur, Class 3 wiring methods shall be used, or V_{max} shall be not greater than: 15 volts for sinusoidal ac: 21.2 volts peak for nonsinusoidal ac.

Note 3. If the power source is a transformer, $(VA)_{max}$ is 350 or less where V_{max} is 15 or less.

Note 4. A dry cell battery shall be considered an inherently limited power source, provided the voltage is 30 volts or less and the capacity is equal to or less than that available from series connected No. 6 carbon zinc cells.

Note 5. For dc interrupted at a rate of 10 to 200 Hz, V_{max} shall not be greater than 24.8 volts. Where wet contact (immersion not included) is likely to occur, Class 3 wiring methods shall be used, or V_{max} shall not be greater than: 30 volts for continuous dc; 12.4 volts for dc that is interrupted at a rate of 10 to 200 Hz.

725-32. **Interconnection of Power Supplies.** Class 2 or Class 3 power supplies shall not be paralleled or otherwise interconnected unless listed for such interconnection.

725-34. **Marking.** A Class 2 or Class 3 power supply unit shall be durably marked where plainly visible to indicate the class of supply and its electrical rating.

725-35. **Overcurrent Protection.** Where overcurrent protection is required, the overcurrent-protective devices shall not be interchangeable with devices of higher ratings. The overcurrent device shall be permitted as an integral part of the power supply.

725-36. **Location of Overcurrent Devices.** Overcurrent devices, where required, shall be located at the point where the conductor to be protected receives its supply.

725-37. **Wiring Methods on Supply Side.** Conductors and equipment on the supply side of overcurrent protection, transformers, or current-limiting devices shall be installed in accordance with the appropriate requirements of Chapter 3. Transformers or other devices supplied from electric light or power circuits shall be protected by an overcurrent device rated not over 20 amperes.

Exception: The input leads of a transformer or other power source supplying Class 2 and Class 3 circuits shall be permitted to be smaller than No. 14, but not smaller than No. 18 if they are not over 12 inches (305 mm) long and if they have insulation that complies with Section 725-16(b).

725-38. **Wiring Methods and Materials on Load Side.** Conductors on the load side of overcurrent protection, transformers, and current-limiting devices shall be insulated at not less than the requirements of Section 725-50 and shall be installed in accordance with Section 725-52.

725-42. **Circuit Conductors Extending Beyond One Building.** Where Class 2 or Class 3 circuit conductors that extend beyond one building and are so run as to be subject to accidental contact with electric light or power conductors operating at over 300 volts to ground, or are exposed to lightning on interbuilding circuits on the same premises, the requirements of the following shall also apply:

(1) Sections 800-10, 800-12, 800-13, 800-30, 800-31, 800-32, 800-33, and 800-40 for other than coaxial conductors, and

(2) Sections 820-10, 820-33, and 820-40 for coaxial conductors.

725-43. **Grounding.** Class 2 and Class 3 circuits and equipment shall be grounded in accordance with Article 250.

725-49. **Fire Resistance of Cables within Buildings.** Single- and multiconductor cables of Class 2 and Class 3 circuits, including PLTC cables, installed as wiring within buildings shall be listed as resistant to the spread of fire in accordance with Sections 725-50 and 725-51.

725-50. **Listing, Marking, and Installation of Class 2, Class 3, and PLTC Cables.**

(a) **Class 2 and Class 3 Cables.** Class 2 and Class 3 cables installed as wiring within buildings shall be listed as being suitable for the purpose, marked in accordance with Table 725-50, and installed in accordance with Section 725-38. The cable voltage ratings shall not be marked on the cable.

(FPN): Voltage markings on cables may be misinterpreted to suggest that the cables may be suitable for Class 1, electric light and power applications.

Exception No. 1: Voltage markings shall be permitted where the cable has multiple listings and voltage marking is required for one or more of the listings.

Exception No. 2: Cable substitutions as provided for in Section 725-53(g) shall be considered as suitable for the purpose and shall be permitted.

(b) **PLTC.** PLTC shall be marked in accordance with Section 310-11 and Table 725-50 and shall be listed as being suitable for use in cable trays.

(FPN No. 1): Class 2 and Class 3 Cable types are listed in descending order of fire resistance rating, and Class 3 cables are listed above Class 2 cables, since Class 3 cables may substitute for Class 2 cables.

(FPN No. 2): See the referenced sections for permitted uses.

725-51. **Additional Listing Requirements.** Class 2 and Class 3 cables shall be listed in accordance with (a) through (f), and, where single conductors are used for Class 3 circuits, with (g):

Table 725-50.   Cable Markings

Cable Marking	Type	Reference
CL3P	Class 3 Plenum Cable	725-51(a) and 725-53(a)
CL2P	Class 2 Plenum Cable	725-51(a) and 725-53(a)
CL3R	Class 3 Riser Cable	725-51(b) and 725-53(b)
CL2R	Class 2 Riser Cable	725-51(b) and 725-53(b)
PLTC	Power-Limited Tray Cable	725-51(e) and 725-53(c) and (d)
CL3	Class 3 Cable	725-51(c), 725-53(b), Exception No. 2, and 725-53(e)
CL2	Class 2 Cable	725-51(c), 725-53(b), Exception No. 2, and 725-53(e)
CL3X	Class 3 Cable, Limited Use	725-51(d), 725-53(b), Exception No. 2, and 725-53(e), Exception Nos. 1, 2, and 3
CL2X	Class 2 Cable, Limited Use	725-51(d), 725-53(b), Exception No. 2, and 725-53(e), Exception Nos. 1, 2, and 3

(a) Types CL2P and CL3P. Types CL2P and CL3P plenum cables shall be listed as being suitable for use in ducts, plenums, and other space used for environmental air and shall also be listed as having adequate fire-resistant and low-smoke-producing characteristics.

(FPN):   One method of defining low-smoke-producing cable is by establishing an acceptable value of the smoke produced when tested in accordance with Test for Fire and Smoke Characteristics of Wires and Cables, NFPA 262-1990 (ANSI) to a maximum peak optical density of 0.5 and a maximum average optical density of 0.15. Similarly, one method of defining fire-resistant cables is by establishing maximum allowable flame travel distance of 5 feet (1.52 m) when tested in accordance with the same test.

NFPA 262-1990, *Standard Method of Test for Fire and Smoke Characteristics of Wires and Cables*, is a test method for electrical wires and cables that are to be installed without raceways in plenums and other spaces used for environmental air. It was originally developed as UL 910, which is an adaptation of the Steiner Tunnel Test (NFPA 255/ASTM E84/UL723).

The test is conducted in a 25-foot long horizontal duct lined with insulating masonry faced with a row of refractory fire brick. One side of the duct is provided with a row of double-paned observation windows that permit monitoring of the progress of the test. One end of the chamber, designated as the "fire end," is provided with two gas burners that deliver flames upward to engulf the test specimen. The burners are positioned on each side of the centerline of the furnace so that flame is evenly distributed across the sample. Test specimens are installed in a cable tray that is 23.9 feet long.

Smoke output is measured in a metal vent pipe at the vent end of the furnace, which is opposite the fire end. Where smoke passes through the vent pipe, it passes between a light source and a photocell. The output signal of the photocell is directly proportional to the amount of light received.

The cable specimens are exposed to a fire source with an output of 300,000 Btu/hour for a period of 20 minutes. A graph is plotted illustrating the flame distance beyond $4\frac{1}{2}$ feet (measured from the end of the flame delivered by the burners) versus time taken for the duration of the test. This graph is plotted against a flame spread curve representative of a red oak specimen. A graph is also plotted for optical density versus time for the sample.

Optical Density $= \text{Log } 10 \, T°/T$
Where
$T°$ = Initial Light Transmission
T = Light Transmission During Test

NFPA 262 does not list pass/fail criteria. The criteria for acceptance of a given application are given in the appropriate sections of the *Code*. See fine print note above and Sections 760-51(a)(FPN), 770-51(a)(FPN), 800-51(a)(FPN), and 820-51(a)(FPN).

A Class 2 or Class 3 cable that has passed the requirements of this test may be used in ducts, plenums, or other air-handling spaces. In addition, such cable may be used anywhere in a building where Class 2 or Class 3 cable is permitted.

(b) Types CL2R and CL3R. Types CL2R and CL3R riser cables shall be listed as being suitable for use in a vertical run in a shaft or from floor to floor and shall also be listed as having fire-resistant characteristics capable of preventing the carrying of fire from floor to floor.

(FPN):   One method of defining fire-resistant characteristics capable of preventing the carrying of fire from floor to floor is that the cables pass the requirements of Test for Flame Propagation Height of Electrical and Optical-Fiber Cable Installed Vertically in Shafts, ANSI/UL 1666-1986.

In the fire test in UL 1666, cables are arranged in a simulated vertical shaft and subjected to an ignition source. The

Figure 725-2. *Steiner Tunnel Test chamber used in Standard Method of Test for Fire and Smoke Characteristics of Wires and Cables,* NFPA 262/UL910.

shaft is a 19-foot high concrete shaft that is divided into two compartments at the 12 foot level. There is a 1 foot × 2 foot opening between the two compartments. The ignition source is a burner with a heat output rate of 495,000 BTU/hr.

The individual cable lengths are suspended from a support system on the second floor and held in place just below the support system and at the first-floor slot.

The support frame consists of a steel bar located on the second floor above the slot opening. The individual cable lengths are suspended from the support frame by one of the following methods:

    a. The cables are draped over the support frame.

    b. The cables are arranged in a clamping device that is suspended from the support frame by two hooks.

    c. In the case of large-diameter cables, each individual cable is placed in a wire-mesh grip. Each grip is attached to a hook that is suspended from the support frame.

In order to pass, cables must not propagate flame to the top of the 12-foot high compartment during the 30-minute test.

    (c) Types CL2 and CL3. Types CL2 and CL3 cables shall be listed as being suitable for general-purpose use, with the exception of risers, ducts, plenums, and other space used for environmental air, and shall also be listed as being resistant to the spread of fire.

(FPN): One method of defining resistant to spread of fire is that the cables do not spread fire to the top of the tray in the "Vertical Tray Flame Test" in Reference Standard for Electrical Wires, Cables and Flexible Cords, ANSI/UL 1581-1985.

Another method of defining resistant to the spread of fire is for the damage (char length) not to exceed 4 feet 11 inches (1.5 m) when performing the CSA "Vertical Flame Test — Cables in Cable Trays," as described in Test Methods for Electrical Wires and Cables, CSA C22.2 No. 0.3-M-1985.

The Vertical Tray Flame Test determines whether cables installed in a ladder-type cable tray will propagate fire from a given exposure. The test flame is supplied by a strip or ribbon-type propane gas burner.

The cables are installed in a steel ladder-type cable tray that is 12 inches wide, 3 inches deep, and 96 inches long. Cables are installed in the tray spaced ½ diameter apart, filling 75 percent of the tray width. A burner supplying

Figure 725-3. *Fire test chamber for UL 1666 Riser Cable Flammability Test.*

70,000 Btu/hour (20.32 kW/hour) is positioned 18 inches above the bottom of the tray midway between two rungs. The burner flame is applied to the samples for a period of 20 minutes. The samples are considered to have passed the test if flame has not propagated to the top of the cable tray by the test's conclusion. See also commentary following Section 725-51(d).

    A cable that has passed this testing may be listed as a CL2 or CL3 cable.

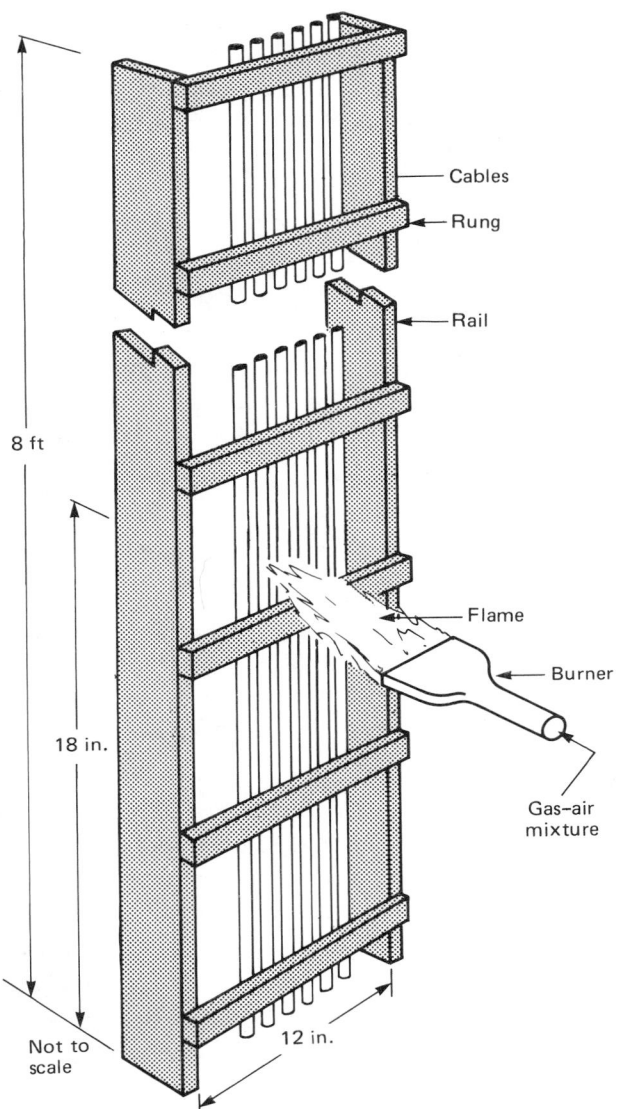

Figure 725-4.   UL Vertical Tray Flame Test.

(d) Types CL2X and CL3X. Types CL2X and CL3X limited use cables shall be listed as being suitable for use in dwellings and for use in raceway and shall also be listed as being flame-retardant.

(FPN): One method of determining that cable is flame-retardant is by testing the cable to the "VW-1 (Vertical-Wire) Flame Test" in the Reference Standard for Electrical Wires, Cables and Flexible Cords, ANSI/UL 1581-1985.

UL 1581, *Reference Standard for Electrical Wires, Cables, and Flexible Cords*, contains basic requirements for conductors, insulation, jackets, and other coverings and the methods of sample preparation, specimen selection and conditioning, and measurements and calculations that are required in the standards for UL 44, *Rubber-Insulated Wires and Cables*; UL 83, *Thermoplastic-Insulated Wires and Cables*; and UL 62, *Flexible Cord and Fixture Wire*. The flame test methods of these standards include the Vertical Wire Flame Test (VW-1) and the Vertical Tray Flame Test.

Figure 725-5.   UL Vertical Wire Flame Test.

The method used in the VW-1 test is a small-scale test of the flammability of insulating material. It is conducted using a single specimen secured in a vertical position in a three-sided metal enclosure that has a layer of untreated surgical cotton on the bottom. For thermoplastic or rubber-insulated wire and cable, the specimen used is an 18-inch insulated No. 14 copper or No. 12 aluminum conductor. A small kraft-paper indicator flag is attached to the specimen near its top. A flame is impinged 10 inches below the bottom of the flag for a period of 15 seconds. It is then removed for 15 seconds and reapplied for 15 seconds. This procedure is repeated until there have been five 15-second flame applications. The specimen is considered to be capable of propagating fire if:

1. More than 25 percent of the indicator flag is burned away or charred, or

2. Flaming or glowing particles are emitted that ignite the surgical cotton, or

3. The specimen continues to flame longer than 60 seconds after removal of the burner.

A sample that has passed this test may be listed as CL2X or CL3X, suitable for use as a limited-use, power-limited cable. This cable may be used in one-and two-family and multifamily dwellings.

(e) Type PLTC. Type PLTC nonmetallic-sheathed, power-limited tray cable shall be a factory assembly of two or more insulated conductors under a nonmetallic jacket. The insulated conductors shall be Nos. 22 through 12. The conductor material shall be copper (solid or stranded). Insulation on conductors shall be suitable for 300 volts. The cable core shall be either (1) two or more parallel conductors; (2) one or more group assemblies of twisted or parallel conductors; or (3) a combination thereof. A metallic shield or a metallized foil shield with drain wire(s) shall be permitted to be applied either over the cable core, over groups of conductors, or both. The cable shall be listed as being resistant to the spread of fire. The outer jacket shall be a sunlight- and moisture-resistant nonmetallic material.

Exception: Where a smooth metallic sheath, welded and corrugated metallic sheath, or interlocking tape armor is applied over the nonmetallic jacket, an overall nonmetallic jacket shall not be required. On metallic-sheathed cable without an overall nonmetallic jacket, the information required in Section 310-11 shall be located on the nonmetallic jacket under the sheath.

(FPN): One method of defining resistant to spread of fire is that the cables do not spread fire to the top of the tray in the "Vertical Tray Flame Test" in the Reference Standard for Electrical Wires, Cables and Flexible Cords, ANSI/UL 1581-1985.

Another method of defining resistant to the spread of fire is for the damage (char length) not to exceed 4 feet, 11 inches (1.5 m) when performing the CSA "Vertical Flame Test — Cables in Cable Trays," as described in Test Methods for Electrical Wires and Cables, CSA C22.2 No. 0.3-M-1985.

(f) Voltage Rating. Class 3 cables shall have a voltage rating of not less than 300 volts.

(g) Single Conductors. Class 3 single conductors shall not be smaller than No. 18 and shall be insulated in accordance with Section 725-16(b).

725-52. **Installation of Conductors and Equipment.** Conductors and equipment on the load side of overcurrent protection, transformers, and current-limiting devices shall comply with (a) and (b) below.

(a) Separation from Electric Light, Power, Class 1, and Nonpower-Limited Fire Protective Signaling Circuit Conductors.

(1) Open Conductors. Conductors of Class 2 and Class 3 circuits shall be separated by at least 2 inches (50.8 mm) from conductors of any electric light, power, Class 1, or nonpower-limited fire protective signaling circuits.

Exception No. 1: Where either (1) all of the electric light, power, Class 1, and nonpower-limited fire protective signaling circuit conductors, or (2) all of the Class 2 and Class 3 circuit conductors are in raceway or in metal-sheathed, metal-clad, nonmetallic-sheathed, or Type UF cables.

Exception No. 2: Where the conductors are permanently separated from the conductors of the other circuits by a continuous and firmly fixed nonconductor, such as porcelain tubes or flexible tubing, in addition to the insulation on the wire.

(2) In Cable, Cable Trays, Enclosures, and Raceways. Conductors of Class 2 and Class 3 circuits shall not be placed in any cable, cable tray, compartment, enclosure, outlet box, raceway, or similar fitting with conductors of electric light, power, Class 1, and nonpower-limited fire protective signaling circuits.

Exception No. 1: Where the conductors of the different circuits are separated by a barrier. In enclosures , Class 2 or Class 3 circuits shall be permitted to be installed in a raceway within the enclosure to separate them from Class 1, electric light and power circuits.

Exception No. 2: Conductors in compartments, enclosures, outlet boxes, or similar fittings, where electric light, power, Class 1, or nonpower-limited fire protective signaling circuit conductors are introduced solely to connect to the equipment connected to Class 2 or Class 3 circuits to which the other conductors in the enclosure are connected. The electric light, power, Class 1, and nonpower-limited fire protective signaling circuit conductors shall be routed within the enclosure to maintain a minimum 0.25-inch (6.35-mm) separation from the conductors of Class 2 and Class 3 circuits.

An example is power circuit and Class 2 circuit conductors in the same motor-starter enclosure where the Class 2 circuit source is the secondary of a control transformer in the same motor-starter enclosure. In such an installation, the Class 2 conductor insulation is not required to have the same voltage rating as the insulation on the power conductors in the same enclosure.

Exception No. 3: Underground conductors in a manhole where one of the following conditions is met:

a. The electric light, power, Class 1, and nonpower-limited fire protective signaling circuit conductors are in a metal-enclosed cable or Type UF cable;

b. The conductors are permanently and effectively separated from the conductors of the other circuits by a continuous and firmly fixed nonconductor, such as flexible tubing, in addition to the insulation or covering on the wire;

c. The conductors are permanently and effectively separated from conductors of the other circuits and securely fastened to racks, insulators, or other approved supports.

This section permits the installation of Class 2 and Class 3 power-limited circuit conductors in manholes having wiring for electric light, power, Class 1, and nonpower-limited systems where suitable separation provides the same degree of protection as is required in Section 725-52(a). See commentary following Section 725-15, Exception No. 2.

Exception No. 4: As permitted by Section 780-6(a) and installed in accordance with Article 780.

(3) In Hoistways. Class 2 or Class 3 circuit conductors shall be installed in rigid metal conduit, rigid nonmetallic conduit, intermediate metal conduit, or electrical metallic tubing in hoistways.

Exception: As provided for in Section 620-21, Exception Nos. 1 and 2 for elevators and similar equipment.

(4) In Shafts. Class 2 or Class 3 circuit conductors shall be separated by not less than 2 inches (50.8 mm) from electric light, power, Class 1, or nonpower-limited fire protective signaling circuit conductors run in the same shaft.

(b) Conductors of Different Circuits in Same Cable, Enclosure, or Raceway.

(1) Two or More Class 2 Circuits. Conductors of two or more Class 2 circuits shall be permitted within the same cable, enclosure, or raceway, provided all conductors in the cable, enclosure, or raceway are insulated for the maximum voltage of any conductor.

(2) Two or More Class 3 Circuits. Conductors of two or more Class 3 circuits shall be permitted within the same cable, enclosure, or raceway.

(3) Class 2 Circuits with Class 3 Circuits. Conductors of one or more Class 2 circuits shall be permitted within the same cable, enclosure, or raceway with conductors of Class 3 circuits, provided that the insulation of the Class 2 circuit conductors in the cable, enclosure, or raceway is at least that required for Class 3 circuits.

(4) Class 2 or Class 3 Circuits with Other Circuits. Jacketed cables of Class 2 or Class 3 circuits shall be permitted in the same enclosure or raceway with jacketed cables of any of the following:

a. Power-limited fire protective signaling systems in compliance with Article 760.

b. Nonconductive and conductive optical fiber cables in compliance with Article 770.

c. Communications circuits in compliance with Article 800.

d. Community antenna television and radio distribution systems in compliance with Article 820.

(c) Support of Conductors. Raceways shall not be used as a means of support for Class 2 or Class 3 circuit conductors.

Exception: Except as permitted by Section 300-11(b), Exception No. 2.

725-53. **Applications of Listed Class 2, Class 3, and PLTC Cables.** Class 2, Class 3, and PLTC cables shall comply with (a) through (g) below.

(a) Plenum. Cables installed in ducts, plenums, and other spaces used for environmental air shall be Type CL2P or CL3P.

Exception: Listed wires and cables installed in compliance with Section 300-22.

(b) Riser. Cables installed in vertical runs and penetrating more than one floor, or cables installed in vertical runs in a shaft, shall be Type CL2R or CL3R. Floor penetrations requiring Type CL2R or CL3R shall contain only cables suitable for riser or plenum use.

Exception No. 1: Other cables as covered in Table 725-53 and other listed wiring methods as covered in Chapter 3, where these are installed in metal raceways or located in a fireproof shaft having firestops at each floor.

Exception No. 2: Types CL2, CL3, CL2X, and CL3X cable in one- and two-family dwellings.

(FPN): See Section 300-21 for firestop requirements for floor penetrations.

(c) Cable Trays. Cables installed in cable trays shall be Type PLTC.

Exception: Conductors in PLTC cables used for Class 2 thermocouple circuits shall be permitted to be any of the materials used for thermocouple extension wire.

(d) Hazardous (Classified) Locations. Cables installed in hazardous (classified) locations shall be Type PLTC. Where the use of PLTC cable is permitted in Section 501-4(b), the cable shall be installed in cable trays, in raceways, supported by messenger wire, or directly buried where the cable is listed for this use.

Exception No. 1: For Class 2 circuits as permitted by Section 501-4(b), Exception.

Exception No. 2: Conductors in PLTC cables used for Class 2 thermocouple circuits shall be permitted to be any of the materials used for thermocouple extension wire.

(e) Other Wiring within Buildings. Cables installed in building locations other than the locations covered in (a) through (d) above shall be Type CL2 or CL3.

Exception No. 1: Type CL2X or CL3X where installed in a raceway, or other wiring methods as covered in Chapter 3.

Exception No. 2: In nonconcealed spaces where the exposed length of cable does not exceed 10 feet (3.05 m).

Exception No. 3: Listed Type CL2X, Class 2 cables less than 0.25 inch (6.4 mm) in diameter and listed Type CL3X, Class 3 cables less than 0.25 inch (6.4 mm) in diameter installed in one- or two-family or multifamily dwellings.

(f) Cross-Connect Arrays. Type CL2 or CL3 wire or cable shall be used.

(g) Cable Substitutions. The substitutions for Class 2 and Class 3 cables listed in Table 725-53 and illustrated in Figure 725-53 shall be permitted.

Table 725-53. Cable Substitutions

Cable Type	Permitted Substitutions
CL3P	MPP, CMP, FPLP
CL2P	MPP, CMP, FPLP, CL3P
CL3R	MPP, CMP, FPLP, CL3P, MPR, CMR, FPLR
CL2R	MPP, CMP, FPLP, CL3P, CL2P, MPR, CMR, FPLR, CL3R
CL3	MPP, CMP, FPLP, CL3P, MPR, CMR, FPLR, CL3R, MPG, MP, CMG, CM, FPL, PLTC
CL2	MPP, CMP, FPLP, CL3P, CL2P, MPR, CMR, FPLR, CL3R, CL2R, MPG, MP, CMG, CM, FPL, PLTC, CL3
CL3X	MPP, CMP, FPLP, CL3P, MPR, CMR, FPLR, CL3R, MPG, MP, CMG, CM, FPL, PLTC, CL3, CMX
CL2X	MPP, CMP, FPLP, CL3P, CL2P, MPR, CMR, FPLR, CL3R, CL2R, MPG, MP, CMG, CM, FPL, PLTC, CL3, CL2, CMX, CL3X

(FPN): For information on FPLP, FPLR, and FPL cables, see Section 760-50. For information on MPP, MPR, MPG, MP, CMP, CMR, CMG, and CM cables, see Section 800-50.

Type CM — Communications Wires and Cables
Types CL2 and CL3 — Class 2 and Class 3 Remote-Control, Signaling, and Power-Limited Cables
Type FPL — Power-Limited Fire Protective Signaling Cables
Type MP — Multipurpose Cables
Type PLTC — Power-Limited Tray Cable

Figure 725-53. *Cable Substitution Hierarchy*

General Discussion of Remote-Control, Signaling, and Power-Limited Circuits.

The wiring methods required by Chapters 1 through 4 of the *Code* apply to remote-control, signaling, and power-limited circuits, except as amended by Article 725 for specified conditions.

A remote-control, signaling, or power-limited circuit is the portion of the wiring system between the load side of the overcurrent device or the power-limited supply and all connected equipment, and it is separated into Class 1, Class 2, or Class 3 circuits.

Class 1 circuits are not permitted to exceed 600 V. A remote-control circuit to safety-control equipment is a Class 1 circuit if failure of the safety control introduces a hazard to life or property. Room thermostats and water-temperature regulating devices used in conjunction with household heating and air-conditioning systems are not considered safety-control equipment. In many cases, Class 1 circuits are extensions of power systems and are subject to the requirements of the power systems, except under the following conditions: (1) conductors sized Nos. 16 and 18 may be used if properly protected against overcurrent (see Section 725-12); (2) where damage to the circuit would introduce a hazard, the circuit is required to be mechanically protected by a suitable means (see Section 725-18); (3) the derating factors of Article 310 Note 8(a) of Notes to Ampacity Tables of 0 to 2000 Volts are to apply only if such conductors carry a continuous load. See Section 725-17.

Class 1 remote-control circuits are commonly used to operate motor controllers in conjunction with moving equipment or mechanical processes, elevators, conveyors, and other such equipment where it is necessary to control the equipment from one or more locations to prevent a hazard to life. Class 1 wiring is required in this case, even though a low-voltage, low-energy system is used. See Section 725-4.

Another example of such a Class 1 circuit is a hospital nurses' call system where it is intended that the system be used for issuing instructions during emergency conditions.

Class 1 signaling circuits often operate at 120 V, though not limited to this value, and are often used for alarm and security systems.

Conductors and equipment on the supply side of overcurrent protection, transformers, or current-limiting devices of Class 2 and Class 3 circuits are required to be installed according to the applicable requirements of Chapter 3. Load-side conductors and equipment are required to comply with Article 725. They are required to be separated from, and not occupy, the same raceways, cable trays, cables, or enclosures as electric light, power, and Class 1 conductors. Exceptions are noted in Section 725-52(a).

Primary batteries are satisfactory with respect to current limitations provided the voltage is 30 V or less and the capacity is equal to or less than that available from series-connected No. 6 carbon-zinc cells.

Where dry cells are used, the requirements of Note 4 to Tables 725-31(a) and 725-31(b) are applicable for inherent power limitation.

Figure 725-6 illustrates a simplified diagram of an automatic domestic oil burner unit. A thermostat is supplied by a current-limiting transformer at 24 V, and the opening and closing of the thermostat contacts controls a relay that operates the oil burner ignition and pump motor. Failure of the thermostat will not introduce a hazard. Assume that the thermostat fails in the closed-contact position, thereby energizing the ignition and motor. The Class 1 circuit, in this case an extension of the power circuit, would operate and open the circuit; that is, the high-limit control (forced warm air) or pressure switch control (circulating hot water or steam). Therefore, the safety controls and ignition circuit would be considered a Class 1 circuit, and the thermostat circuit would be considered a Class 2 circuit.

Figure 725-6. *Typical installation of an automatic oil burner unit.*

ARTICLE 760   Fire Protective Signaling Systems

Contents

A. General

760-1. **Scope.** This article covers the installation of wiring and equipment of fire protective signaling systems operating at 600 volts, nominal, or less.

(FPN No. 1):   Fire protective signaling systems include fire alarm, guard tour, sprinkler waterflow, and sprinkler supervisory systems. For further information on the installation and supervision requirements for fire protective signaling systems, refer to the following:

NFPA 71-1989 - Installation, Maintenance, and Use of Signaling Systems for Central Station Service.

NFPA 72-1990 - Installation, Maintenance, and Use of Protective Signaling Systems.

NFPA 72E-1990 - Automatic Fire Detectors.

NFPA 74-1989 - Installation, Maintenance, and Use of Household Fire Warning Equipment.

(FPN No. 2):   Class 1, 2, and 3 circuits are defined in Article 725.

The format for this article is similar to that for Articles 725, 770, 800, and 820.

Sections 760-7 and 760-22 in the 1987 *NEC*, which dealt with supervision, were deleted from the 1990 edition. Performance requirements for fire protective signaling systems are covered by the standard that addresses the specific type of system. See Section 760-1, FPN No. 1.

NFPA 71-1989, *Standard for the Installation, Maintenance, and Use of Signaling Systems for Central Station Service*, covers the installation, maintenance, and use of central station signaling systems. These systems include the central station physical plant, exterior communication channels, satellite stations, and the signaling facilities located at the protected premises.

This standard is intended to apply primarily to supervisory and alarm services staffed by operators in constant attendance at a central station, controlled by manual or automatic means and provided with the required maintenance and inspection, and furnished with a readily available testing force and runner service. Central station companies customarily follow this standard for maintenance, testing, and inspection with respect to other classes of contract service that they furnish.

Such systems are controlled and operated by an individual, firm, or corporation whose principal business is to furnish and maintain supervised signaling services.

NFPA 72-1990, *Standard for the Installation, Maintenance, and Use of Protective Signaling Systems* deals with the application, installation, performance, and maintenance of local, auxiliary, remote station, proprietary, and emergency voice/alarm protective signaling systems, and combinations thereof and their components. It is intended to provide information that will allow a system to perform as required for the preservation of life and property.

NFPA 72E-1990, *Automatic Fire Detectors*, provides minimum requirements for performance of automatic fire detectors to ensure warning in a timely manner for the purposes of life safety and property protection.

This standard is intended for use by persons knowledgeable in fire protection.

It covers minimum performance, location, mounting, testing, and maintenance requirements of automatic fire detectors for the protection of occupants, buildings, spaces, structures, areas, or objects in accordance with the stated purpose.

NFPA 72E is intended to be used with other NFPA standards that specifically address fire alarms, extinguishment, or control. Automatic fire detectors add to fire protection by initiating emergency action but only where used in conjunction with other equipment.

NFPA 74-1989, *Standard for the Installation, Maintenance, and Use of Household Fire Warning Equipment*, is primarily concerned with life protection, not with the protection of property. Its requirements are based on the premise that a family has an exit plan and covers requirements for the proper selection, installation, operation, and maintenance of fire warning equipment to be used within family living units.

A control and associated equipment, single or multiple station alarm device(s), or any combination thereof, may be used to form a household fire warning system.

Detection and alarm systems covered by this standard are solely for the use of a protected household. If the alarm is extended to any other location, such as a fire department, the system is then considered to be one of the aforementioned systems (as applicable), except that the requirements of detector location and spacing, as they apply to home warning systems, would continue to be followed.

NFPA 1221-1991, *Standard for the Installation, Maintenance, and Use of Public Fire Service Communication Systems*, covers the installation, maintenance, and use of all public fire service communication facilities. These facilities include public reporting, dispatching, telephone, and both two-way and microwave radio systems, all of which fulfill two principal functions: the receipt of fire alarms or other emergency calls from the public and the retransmission of these alarms and emergency calls to fire companies and other appropriate agencies.

760-2. **Locations and Other Articles.** Circuits and equipment shall comply with (a), (b), (c), (d), and (e) below.

(a) **Spread of Fire or Products of Combustion.** Section 300-21.

(b) **Ducts, Plenums, and Other Air-Handling Spaces.** Section 300-22, where installed in ducts or plenums or other spaces used for environmental air.

Exception to (b): As permitted in Sections 760-17(e)(1) and (2) and Section 760-53(a).

See commentary following Sections 300-22(b) and 300-22(c).

(c) **Hazardous (Classified) Locations.** Articles 500 through 516 and Article 517, Part D, where installed in hazardous (classified) locations.

(d) **Corrosive, Damp, or Wet Locations.** Sections 110-11, 300-6, and 310-9 where installed in corrosive, damp, or wet locations.

(e) **Building Control Circuits.** Article 725 where building control circuits (e.g., elevator capture, fan shutdown) are associated with the fire protective signaling system.

760-3. **Classifications.** Fire protective signaling circuits are the portion of the wiring system between the load side of the overcurrent device or the power-limited supply and all connected equipment, and shall be classified as nonpower-limited or power-limited. All fire protective signaling circuits shall comply with Part A, and, in addition, nonpower-limited circuits shall comply with Part B, and power-limited circuits shall comply with Part C. Circuits that do not comply with all of the requirements of Part C, including the markings required by Section 760-22, are classified as nonpower-limited circuits and shall comply with all of the requirements of Part B.

Section 760-28(a), Exception No. 3 permits power-limited, fire-protective signaling circuits to be reclassified as nonpower-limited if the markings required by Section 760-22

are eliminated and the entire circuit is wired as a nonpower-limited circuit.

760-4. **Identification.** Fire protective signaling circuits shall be identified at terminal and junction locations, in a manner that will prevent unintentional interference with the signaling circuit during testing and servicing.

760-5. **Circuits Extending Beyond One Building.** Fire protective signaling circuits that extend aerially beyond one building shall either meet the requirements of Article 800 and be classified as communications circuits, or shall meet the requirements of Article 225.

760-6. **Grounding.** Fire protective signaling circuits and equipment shall be grounded in accordance with Article 250.

Exception: DC power-limited fire protective signaling circuits having a maximum current of 0.030 amperes.

760-7. **Access to Electrical Equipment Behind Panels Designed to Allow Access.** Access to equipment shall not be denied by an accumulation of wires and cables that prevents removal of panels, including suspended ceiling panels.

See commentary following Section 725-7.

B. Nonpower-Limited Fire Protective Signaling Circuits

760-11. **Power Limitations.** The power supply of nonpower-limited fire protective signaling circuits shall comply with Chapters 1 through 4, and the output voltage shall not be more than 600 volts, nominal.

760-12. **Overcurrent Protection.** Conductors No. 14 and larger shall be protected against overcurrent in accordance with the values specified in Section 310-15, as applicable. Derating factors shall not be applied. Overcurrent protection shall not exceed 7 amperes for No. 18 conductors and 10 amperes for No. 16.

Exception: Where other articles of this Code permit or require other overcurrent protection.

See Section 240-4, Exception No. 2 for example.

760-13. **Location of Overcurrent Devices.** Overcurrent devices shall be located at the point where the conductor to be protected receives its supply.

Exception No. 1: Where the overcurrent device protecting the larger conductor also protects the smaller conductor.

Exception No. 2: Transformer secondary conductors. Nonpower-limited fire protective signaling circuit conductors supplied by the secondary of a single-phase transformer having only a 2-wire (single voltage) secondary shall be permitted to be protected by overcurrent protection provided by the primary (supply) side of the transformer, provided the protection is in accordance with Section 450-3 and does not exceed the value determined by multiplying the secondary conductor ampacity by the secondary-to-primary transformer voltage ratio. Transformer secondary conductors other than 2-wire shall not be considered to be protected by the primary overcurrent protection.

760-14. **Wiring Method.** Wiring installation shall be in accordance with the appropriate articles in Chapter 3.

Exception No. 1: As provided in Sections 760-15 through 760-18.

Exception No. 2: Where other articles of this Code require other methods.

760-15. **Conductors of Different Circuits in Same Cable, Enclosure, or Raceway.** Class 1 and nonpower-limited fire protective signaling circuits shall be permitted to occupy the same cable, enclosure, or raceway without regard to whether the individual circuits are alternating current or direct current, provided all conductors are insulated for the maximum voltage of any conductor in the enclosure or raceway. Power-supply and fire protective signaling circuit conductors shall be permitted in the same cable, enclosure, or raceway only where connected to the same equipment.

760-16. **Copper Conductors.**

(a) Types, Sizes, and Use. Only copper conductors shall be permitted to be used for fire protective signaling systems. Conductors of Nos. 18 and 16 shall be permitted to be used, provided they supply loads that do not exceed the ampacities given in Table 402-5 and are installed in a raceway or a listed cable. Conductors larger than No. 16 shall not supply loads greater than the ampacities given in Section 310-15, as applicable.

The minimum size conductors permitted to be used on nonpower limited fire protective signaling circuits is No. 18. The load must not exceed the conductor ampacities as specified in Table 402-5.

(b) Insulation. Insulation on conductors shall be suitable for 600 volts. Conductors larger than No. 16 shall comply with Article 310. Conductors in sizes No. 18 and 16 shall be Type KF-2, PF, PGF, RFH-2, RFHH-2, RFHH-3, SF-2, TF, TFN, or ZF. Conductors with other types and thickness of insulation shall be permitted if listed for nonpower-limited fire protective signaling circuit use.

(FPN): For application provisions, see Table 402-3.

(c) Conductor Materials. Conductors shall be solid or bunch-tinned (bonded) stranded copper.

See commentary following Section 760-51(a).

Exception No. 1: Stranded copper with a maximum of 7 strands for Nos. 16 and 18 shall be permitted.

Exception No. 2: Stranded copper with a maximum of 19 strands for Nos. 14 and larger shall be permitted.

Control of the stranding is required to prevent a single, fine strand of wire from completing a circuit, creating the false appearance of a circuit that is operational. The fine strand could remain intact under the current used for the supervisory signal, but could burn open when required to carry the higher current of an alarm signal.

Exception No. 2 permits, for example, No. 14 conductors that are dual rated THW/MTW.

Exception to (b) and (c): Wire Types PAF and PTF shall be permitted only for high-temperature applications between 90°C (194°F) and 250°C (482°F).

760-17. **Multiconductor Nonpower-Limited Fire Protective Signaling Circuit Cables for Circuits Operating at 150 Volts or Less.** Multiconductor nonpower-limited fire protective signaling circuit cables that meet the requirements of (a) through (e) below shall be permitted to be used on fire protective signaling circuits operating at 150 volts or less.

(a) Fire Resistance of Cables within Buildings. Multiconductor nonpower-limited fire protective signaling circuit cables installed as wiring within buildings shall be listed as being resistant to the spread of fire in accordance with sections (b) and (c) below.

(b) Listing and Markings. Multiconductor nonpower-limited fire protective signaling circuit cables in a building shall be listed as being suitable for the purpose, and cables shall be marked in accordance with Table 760-17(b).

Table 760-17(b). Cable Markings

Cable Marking	Type	Reference
NPLFP	nonpower-limited fire protective signaling circuit plenum cable	Sections 760-17(c)(4) and 760-17(e)(2)
NPLFR	nonpower-limited fire protective signaling circuit riser cable	Sections 760-17(c)(5) and 760-17(e)(3)
NPLF	nonpower-limited fire protective signaling circuit cable	Sections 760-17(c)(6) and 760-17(e)(4)

(FPN No. 1): See the referenced sections for listing requirements and permitted uses.

(FPN No. 2): Cable types are listed in descending order of fire resistance rating.

(c) Listing Requirements. Nonpower-limited fire protective signaling circuit cables shall be listed in accordance with (1) through (3) below and, depending on the type, (4) through (6) below.

(1) Conductor Materials. Conductors shall be solid copper or bunch-tinned (bonded) stranded copper.

Exception No. 1: Stranded copper with a maximum of 7 strands for No. 16 and No. 18 shall be permitted.

Exception No. 2: Stranded copper with a maximum of 19 strands for Nos. 14 and larger shall be permitted.

(2) Sizes and Number. The cables shall have two or more No. 18 or larger conductors.

(3) Ratings. Each insulated conductor of the cable shall have a voltage rating of not less than 300 volts. The combination of the insulated conductors and the cable jacket shall have a voltage rating of not less than 600 volts.

(4) Type NPLFP. Type NPLFP nonpower-limited fire protective signaling plenum cable shall be listed as being suitable for use in other space used for environmental air as described in Section 300-22(c) and shall also be listed as having adequate fire-resistant and low-smoke-producing characteristics.

(FPN): One method of defining low-smoke-producing cable is by establishing an acceptable value of the smoke produced when tested in accordance with the Test for Fire and Smoke Characteristics of Wires and Cables, NFPA 262-1990 (ANSI) to a maximum peak optical density of 0.5 and a maximum average optical density of 0.15. Similarly, one method of defining fire-resistant cables is by establishing maximum allowable flame travel distance of 5 feet (1.52 m) when tested in accordance with the same test.

For further information on the fire test method for plenum cables, see commentary following Section 725-51(a)(FPN).

(5) Type NPLFR. Type NPLFR nonpower-limited fire protective signaling riser cable shall be listed as being suitable for use in a vertical run in a shaft or from floor to floor and shall also be listed as having fire-resistant characteristics capable of preventing the carrying of fire from floor to floor.

(FPN): One method of defining fire-resistant characteristics capable of preventing the carrying of fire from floor to floor is that the cables pass the Test for Flame Propagation Height of Electrical and Optical-Fiber Cables Installed Vertically in Shafts, ANSI/UL 1666-1986.

For further information on the fire test method for riser cables, see commentary following Section 725-51(b)(FPN).

(6) Type NPLF. Type NPLF nonpower-limited fire protection signaling cable shall be listed as being suitable for general-purpose fire alarm use, with the exception of risers, ducts, plenums, and other space used for environmental air, and shall also be listed as being resistant to the spread of fire.

(FPN): One method of defining resistant to spread of fire is that the cables do not spread fire to the top of the tray in the "Vertical-Tray Flame Test" in the Reference Standard for Electrical Wires, Cables and Flexible Cords, ANSI/UL 1581-1985.

Another method of defining resistant to the spread of fire is for the damage (char length) not to exceed 4 feet 11 inches (1.5 m) when performing the CSA "Vertical Flame Test — Cables in Cable Trays," as described in Test Methods for Electrical Wires and Cables, CSA C22.2 No. 0.3-M-1985.

For further information on the fire test method for cables used as other wiring within buildings, see Section 725-51(c)(FPN).

(d) Wiring Method. Multiconductor nonpower-limited fire protective signaling circuit cables described in Section 760-17(a) shall be installed as follows:

(1) In raceway or exposed on surface of ceiling and sidewalls or "fished" in concealed spaces. Where installed exposed, cables shall be adequately supported and terminated in approved fittings and installed in such a way that maximum protection against physical damage is afforded by building construction such as baseboards, door frames, ledges, etc. Where located within 7 feet (2.13 m) of the floor, cables shall be securely fastened in an approved manner at intervals of not more than 18 inches (457 mm).

(2) In metal raceway or rigid nonmetallic conduit where passing through a floor or wall to a height of 7 feet (2.13 m) above the floor unless adequate protection can be afforded by building construction such as detailed in (1) above, or unless an equivalent solid guard is provided.

(3) In rigid metal conduit, rigid nonmetallic conduit, intermediate metal conduit, or electrical metallic tubing where installed in hoistways.

Exception: As provided for in Section 620-21, Exception Nos. 1 and 2 for elevators and similar equipment.

(e) **Applications of Listed Nonpower-Limited Fire Protective Signaling Circuit Cables.** The use of nonpower-limited fire protective signaling circuit cables shall comply with (1) through (4) below.

(1) **Ducts and Plenums.** Multiconductor nonpower-limited fire protective signaling circuit cables shall not be installed exposed in ducts or plenums. See Section 300-22(b).

(2) **Other Spaces Used for Environmental Air.** Cables installed in other spaces used for environmental air shall be Type NPLFP.

Exception No. 1: Types NPLF and NPLFR cables installed in compliance with Section 300-22(c).

Exception No. 2: Other wiring methods in accordance with Section 300-22(c) and conductors in compliance with Section 760-16(c).

(3) **Riser.** Cables installed in vertical runs and penetrating more than one floor or cables installed in vertical runs in a shaft shall be Type NPLFR. Floor penetrations requiring Type NPLFR shall contain only cables suitable for riser or plenum use.

Exception No. 1: Type NPLF or other cables specified in Chapter 3 that are in compliance with Section 760-16(c) and encased in metal raceway.

The conductors must be solid copper or bunch-tinned stranded copper. Stranded conductors are permitted with a maximum of 7 strands for Nos. 16 or 18, or 19 strands for Nos. 14 and larger.

Exception No. 2: Type NPLF cables located in a fireproof shaft having firestops at each floor.

(FPN): See Section 300-21 for firestop requirements for floor penetrations.

(4) **Other Wiring Within Buildings.** Cables installed in building locations other than the locations covered in (1), (2), and (3) above shall be Type NPLF.

Exception No. 1: Chapter 3 wiring methods with conductors in compliance with Section 760-16(c).

The conductors must be solid copper or bunch-tinned stranded copper. Stranded conductors are permitted with a maximum of 7 strands for Nos. 16 or 18, or 19 strands for Nos. 14 and larger.

Exception No. 2: Type NPLFP or Type NPLFR cables shall be permitted.

760-18. **Number of Conductors in Cable Trays and Raceways, and Derating.**

(a) **Nonpower-Limited Fire Protective Signaling Circuits and Class 1 Circuits.** Where only nonpower-limited fire protective signaling circuit and Class 1 circuit conductors are in a raceway, the number of conductors shall be determined in accordance with Section 300-17. The derating factors given in Article 310, Note 8(a) of Notes to Ampacity Tables of 0 to 2000 Volts shall apply if such conductors carry continuous load in excess of 10 percent of the ampacity of each conductor.

(b) **Power-Supply Conductors and Fire Protective Signaling Circuit Conductors.** Where power-supply conductors and fire protective signaling circuit conductors are permitted in a raceway in accordance with Section 760-15, the number of conductors shall be determined in accordance with Section 300-17. The derating factors given in Article 310, Note 8(a) of Notes to Ampacity Tables of 0 to 2000 Volts shall apply as follows:

(1) To all conductors where the fire protective signaling circuit conductors carry continuous loads in excess of 10 percent of the ampacity of each conductor and where the total number of conductors is more than three.

Table 760-21(a). Power Source Limitations for Alternating-Current Fire Protective Signaling Circuits

Circuit Voltage V_{max} (Volts) (Note 1)	Inherently Limited Power Source (Overcurrent protection not required)			Not Inherently Limited Power Source (Overcurrent protection required)		
	0 through 20	Over 20 and through 30	Over 30 and through 100	0 through 20	Over 20 and through 100	Over 100 and through 150
Power Limitations $(VA)_{max}$ (Volt-Amps) (Note 1)	—	—	—	250 (Note 2)	250	N.A.
Current Limitations I_{max} (Amps) (Note 1)	8.0	8.0	$150/V_{max}$	$1000/V_{max}$	$1000/V_{max}$	1.0
Maximum Overcurrent Protection (Amps)	—	—	—	5.0	$100/V_{max}$	1.0
Power Source Maximum Nameplate Ratings — VA (Volt-Amps)	$5.0 \times V_{max}$	100	100	$5.0 \times V_{max}$	100	100
Power Source Maximum Nameplate Ratings — Current (Amps)	5.0	$100/V_{max}$	$100/V_{max}$	5.0	$100/V_{max}$	$100/V_{max}$
Supply Conductors and Cables	See Section 760-25					
Circuit Conductors and Cables	See Sections 760-49 through 760-53					

(2) To the power-supply conductors only, where the fire protective signaling circuit conductors do not carry continuous loads in excess of 10 percent of the ampacity of each conductor and where the number of power-supply conductors is more than three.

(c) Cable Trays. Where fire protective signaling circuit conductors are installed in cable trays, they shall comply with Sections 318-9 through 318-11.

C. Power-Limited Fire Protective Signaling Circuits

760-21. **Power Limitations.** As specified in Table 760-21(a) for ac circuits and Table 760-21(b) for dc circuits, the power for power-limited fire protective signaling circuits shall be either inherently limited requiring no overcurrent protection or limited by a combination of a power source and overcurrent protection.

760-22. **Circuit Marking.** The equipment shall be durably marked where plainly visible to indicate each circuit that is a power-limited fire protective signaling circuit.

(FPN): See Section 760-28(a), Exception No. 3 where a power-limited circuit is to be reclassified as a nonpower-limited circuit.

760-23. **Overcurrent Protection.** Where overcurrent protection is required, the overcurrent protective devices shall not be interchangeable with devices of higher ratings. The overcurrent device shall be permitted as an integral part of the power supply.

760-24. **Location of Overcurrent Device.** Overcurrent device, where required, shall be located at the point where the conductor to be protected receives its supply.

760-25. **Wiring Methods on Supply Side.** Conductors and equipment on the supply side of overcurrent protection,

Table 760-21(b). Power Source Limitations for Direct-Current Fire Protective Signaling Circuits

Circuit Voltage V_{max} (Volts) (Note 1)	Inherently Limited Power Source (Overcurrent protection not required)				Not Inherently Limited Power Source (Overcurrent protection required)		
	0 through 20	Over 20 and through 30	Over 30 and through 100	Over 100 and through 250	0 through 20	Over 20 and through 100	Over 100 and through 150
Power Limitations $(VA)_{max}$ (Volt-Amps) (Note 1)	—	—	—	—	250 (Note 2)	250	N.A.
Current Limitations I_{max} (Amps) (Note 1)	8.0	8.0	$150/V_{max}$	0.030	$1000/V_{max}$	$1000/V_{max}$	1.0
Maximum Over-current Protection (Amps)	—	—	—	—	5.0	$100/V_{max}$	1.0
Power Source Maximum Nameplate Ratings — VA (Volt-Amps)	$5.0 \times V_{max}$	100	100	$0.030 \times V_{max}$	$5.0 \times V_{max}$	100	100
Power Source Maximum Nameplate Ratings — Current (Amps)	5.0	$100/V_{max}$	$100/V_{max}$	0.030	5.0	$100/V_{max}$	$100/V_{max}$
Supply Conductors and Cables	See Section 760-25						
Circuit Conductors and Cables	See Sections 760-49 through 760-53						

Notes for Tables 760-21(a) and (b)

Note 1. V_{max}: Maximum output voltage regardless of load with rated input applied.

I_{max}: Maximum output current under any noncapacitive load, including short circuit, and with overcurrent protection bypassed if used. When a transformer limits the output current, I_{max} limits apply after one minute of operation. Where a current-limiting impedance, listed for the purpose, is used in combination with a nonpower-limited transformer or a stored energy source, e.g., storage battery, to limit the output current, I_{max} limits apply after 5 seconds.

VA_{max}: Maximum volt-ampere output after one minute of operation regardless of load and overcurrent protection bypassed if used. Current-limiting impedance shall not be bypassed when determining I_{max} and VA_{max}.

Note 2. If the power source is a transformer, $(VA)_{max}$ is 350 or less when V_{max} is 15 or less.

transformers, or current-limiting devices shall be installed in accordance with the appropriate requirements of Part B and Chapter 3. Transformers or other devices supplied from power-supply conductors shall be protected by an overcurrent device rated not over 20 amperes.

Exception: The input leads of a transformer or other power source supplying power-limited fire protective signaling circuits shall be permitted to be smaller than No. 14, but not smaller than No. 18, if they are not over 12 inches (305 mm) long and if they have insulation that complies with Section 760-16(b).

760-28. **Wiring Methods and Materials on Load Side.** Circuits on the load side of overcurrent protection, transformers, and current-limiting devices shall be permitted to use wiring methods and materials in accordance with either (a) or (b) below.

(a) Nonpower-Limited Wiring Methods and Materials. The appropriate articles of Chapter 3, including Section 300-17, shall apply, and, in addition, conductors shall be copper, solid, bunch-tinned, or stranded with a maximum of 19 strands.

Article 760 — Fire Protective Signaling Systems

Exception No. 1: The derating factors given in Article 310, Note 8(a) of Notes to Ampacity Tables of 0 to 2000 Volts shall not apply.

Exception No. 2: Conductors and multiconductor cables described in and installed in accordance with Sections 760-16 and 760-17 shall be permitted.

Exception No. 3: Power-limited circuits shall be permitted to be reclassified and installed as nonpower-limited circuits if the markings required by Section 760-22 are eliminated (see Section 760-3) and the entire circuit is installed using the wiring methods and materials in accordance with Part B, Nonpower-Limited Fire Protective Signaling Circuits.

Section 760-28(a) permits any of the wiring methods in Chapter 3 to be used for power-limited circuits. In addition, Section 760-28(a), Exception No. 3, allows power-limited circuits to be reclassified and installed in accordance with the requirements for nonpower-limited circuits. Where installed as nonpower-limited circuits, separation of circuits must be maintained in accordance with Section 760-15.

(b) Power-Limited Wiring Methods and Materials. Power-limited circuit conductors and cables described in Sections 760-49 through 760-51 shall be installed as follows:

(1) In raceway or exposed on the surface of ceiling and sidewalls or "fished" in concealed spaces. Where installed exposed, cables shall be adequately supported and terminated in approved fittings and installed in such a way that maximum protection against physical damage is afforded by building construction such as baseboards, door frames, ledges, etc. Raceways shall not be used as a means of support for power-limited fire protective signaling circuit conductors. Where located within 7 feet (2.13 m) of the floor, cables shall be securely fastened in an approved manner at intervals of not more than 18 inches (457 mm).

(2) In metal raceways or rigid nonmetallic conduit where passing through a floor or wall to a height of 7 feet (2.13 m) above the floor, unless adequate protection can be afforded by building construction such as detailed in (1) above, or unless an equivalent solid guard is provided.

(3) In rigid metal conduit, rigid nonmetallic conduit, intermediate metal conduit, or electrical metallic tubing where installed in hoistways.

Exception: As provided for in Section 620-21, Exception Nos. 1 and 2 for elevators and similar equipment.

760-49. Fire Resistance of Cables within Buildings. Single and multiconductor power-limited fire protective signaling circuit cables installed as wiring within buildings shall be listed as being resistant to the spread of fire in accordance with Sections 760-50 and 760-51.

760-50. Listing, Marking, and Installation of Power-Limited Fire Protective Signaling Circuit Cables. Power-limited fire protective signaling circuit cables installed as wiring within buildings shall be listed as being suitable for the purpose, marked in accordance with Table 760-50, and installed in accordance with Section 760-52. The cable voltage rating shall not be marked on the cable.

(FPN): Voltage ratings on cables may be misinterpreted to suggest that the cables may be suitable for Class 1, electric light and power applications.

Exception No. 1: Voltage markings shall be permitted where the cable has multiple listings and voltage marking is required for one or more of the listings.

Exception No. 2: Cable substitutions as provided for in Section 760-53(d) shall be considered as suitable for the purpose and shall be permitted.

Table 760-50. Cable Markings

Cable Marking	Type	Reference
FPLP	Power-limited fire protective signaling circuit plenum cable	Sections 760-51(d) and 760-53(a)
FPLR	Power-limited fire protective signaling circuit riser cable	Sections 760-51(e) and 760-53(b)
FPL	Power-limited fire protective signaling circuit cable	Sections 760-51(f) and 760-53(c)

(FPN No. 1): See the referenced sections for listing requirements and permitted uses.

(FPN No. 2): Cable types are listed in descending order of fire resistance rating.

760-51. **Listing Requirements.** Power-limited fire protective signaling cables shall be listed in accordance with (a) through (c) below and, depending on the type, (d) through (g) below.

(a) Conductor Materials. Conductors shall be solid copper or bunch-tinned (bonded) stranded copper.

Bunch-tinned strands are strands that have been extruded through a solder bath so that the strands are bonded together by the solder.

Exception No. 1: Stranded copper with a maximum of 7 strands for Nos. 16 and 18 shall be permitted.

Exception No. 2: Stranded copper with a maximum of 19 strands for Nos. 14 and larger shall be permitted.

(b) Sizes and Number. The size and number of conductors in a cable shall meet the requirements of Table 760-51. Conductors of No. 26 shall only be permitted if spliced with a connector listed as suitable for No. 26 to No. 24 or larger conductors that are terminated on equipment or if the No. 26 conductors are terminated on equipment listed as suitable for No. 26 conductors.

Table 760-51. **Minimum Size and Number of Conductors Required in Cables Used for Power-Limited Fire Protective Signaling Circuits**

Size	Minimum Number of Conductors in Cable
26 AWG	10
24 AWG	6
22 AWG	4
19 AWG	2
16 AWG or larger	1

(c) Ratings. The cable shall have a voltage rating of not less than 300 volts.

(d) Type FPLP. Type FPLP power-limited fire alarm plenum cable shall be listed as being suitable for use in ducts, plenums, and other space used for environmental air and shall also be listed as having adequate fire-resistant and low-smoke-producing characteristics.

(FPN): One method of defining low-smoke-producing cable is by establishing an acceptable value of the smoke produced when tested in accordance with the Test for Fire and Smoke Characteristics of Wires and Cables, NFPA 262-1990 (ANSI) to a maximum peak optical density of 0.5 and a maximum average optical density of 0.15. Similarly, one method of defining fire-resistant cables is by establishing maximum allowable flame travel distance of 5 feet (1.52 m) when tested in accordance with the same test.

For further information on the fire test method for plenum cables, see commentary following Section 725-51(a)(FPN).

(e) Type FPLR. Type FPLR power-limited fire alarm riser cable shall be listed as being suitable for use in a vertical run in a shaft or from floor to floor and shall also be listed as having fire-resistant characteristics capable of preventing the carrying of fire from floor to floor.

(FPN): One method of defining fire-resistant characteristics capable of preventing the carrying of fire from floor to floor is that the cables pass the requirements of the Standard Test for Flame Propagation Height of Electrical and Optical-Fiber Cable Installed Vertically in Shafts, ANSI/UL 1666-1986.

For further information on the fire test method for riser cables, see commentary following Section 725-51(b)(FPN).

(f) Type FPL. Type FPL power-limited fire alarm cable shall be listed as being suitable for general-purpose fire alarm use, with the exception of risers, ducts, plenums, and other space used for environmental air and shall also be listed as being resistant to the spread of fire.

(FPN): One method of defining resistant to the spread of fire is that the cables do not spread fire to the top of the tray in the "Vertical-Tray Flame Test" in the Reference Standard for Electrical Wires, Cables and Flexible Cords, ANSI/UL 1581-1985.

Another method of defining resistant to the spread of fire is for the damage (char length) not to exceed 4 feet 11 inches (1.5 m) when performing the CSA "Vertical Flame Test — Cables in Cable Trays," as described in Test Methods for Electrical Wires and Cables, CSA C22.2 No. 0.3-M-1985.

For further information on the fire test method for cables used as other wiring within buildings, see Section 725-51(c)(FPN).

(g) Coaxial Cables. Coaxial cables shall have a minimum of No. 22 copper or 30 percent copper-covered steel center conductor, a voltage rating of not less than 300 volts, and shall be listed as a Type FPLP, FPLR, or FPL cable.

760-52. **Installation of Conductors and Equipment.** Conductors and cables on the load side of overcurrent protection, transformers, and current-limiting devices shall comply with (a) and (b) below.

(a) Separation from Electric Light, Power, Class 1, and Nonpower-Limited Fire Protective Signaling Circuit Conductors.

The requirements for separation from electric light, power, Class 1, and nonpower-limited, fire-protective signaling circuits as noted in Section 760-52 apply even if the power-limited circuits are wired using nonpower-limited circuit wiring methods.

(1) Open Conductors. Power-limited circuit conductors shall be separated at least 2 inches (50.8 mm) from conductors of any electric light, power, Class 1, or nonpower-limited fire protective signaling circuit conductors.

Exception No. 1: Where the electric light, power, Class 1, or nonpower-limited fire protective signaling circuit conductors are in raceway or in metal-sheathed, metal-clad, nonmetallic-sheathed, or Type UF cables.

Exception No. 2: Where the power-limited circuit conductors are permanently separated from the conductors of the other circuits by a continuous and firmly fixed nonconductor, such as porcelain tubes or flexible tubing in addition to the insulation on the wire.

(2) In Cables, Compartments, Enclosures, Outlet Boxes, or Raceways. Power-limited circuit conductors shall not be placed in any cable, compartment, enclosure, outlet box, raceway, or similar fitting containing conductors of electric light, power, Class 1, or nonpower-limited fire protective signaling circuit conductors.

Exception No. 1: Where the conductors of the different circuits are separated by a barrier.

Exception No. 2: Conductors in compartments, enclosures, outlet boxes, or similar fittings where electric light, power, Class 1 circuit, or nonpower-limited circuit conductors are introduced solely to connect to the equipment connected to the power-limited fire protective signaling system or to other circuits controlled by the fire protective signaling system to which the other conductors in the enclosure are connected.

The electric light, power, Class 1, and nonpower-limited fire protective signaling circuit conductors shall be routed within the enclosure to maintain a minimum 0.25-inch (6.35-mm) separation from the conductors of power-limited fire protective signaling circuits.

(3) In Shafts. Power-limited circuit conductors shall be separated by not less than 2 inches (50.8 mm) from electric light, power, Class 1, or nonpower-limited fire protective signaling circuit conductors run in the same shaft.

Exception No. 1: Where the conductors of either the electric light, power, Class 1, the nonpower-limited fire protective signaling circuits, or the power-limited fire protective signaling circuits are encased in metal raceways.

Exception No. 2: Where the electric light, power, Class 1, or the nonpower-limited fire protective signaling circuit conductors are in a raceway or are in metal-sheathed, metal-clad, nonmetallic-sheathed, or Type UF cables.

(4) In Hoistways. Power-limited circuit conductors shall be installed in rigid metal conduit, intermediate metal conduit, or electrical metallic tubing in hoistways.

Exception: As provided for in Section 620-21, Exception Nos. 1 and 2 for elevators and similar equipment.

(b) Conductors of Different Power-Limited Fire Protective Signaling Circuits, Class 2, Class 3, and Communications Circuits in Same Cable, Enclosure, or Raceway.

(1) Cables and conductors of two or more power-limited fire protective signaling circuits, communications circuits, or Class 3 circuits shall be permitted in the same cable, enclosure, or raceway.

(2) Conductors of one or more Class 2 circuits shall be permitted within the same cable, enclosure, or raceway with conductors of power-limited fire protective signaling circuits, provided that the insulation of the Class 2 circuit conductors in the cable, enclosure, or raceway is at least that required by the power-limited fire protective signaling circuits.

760-53. **Applications of Listed Power-Limited Fire Protective Signaling Circuit Cables.** Power-limited fire protective signaling circuit cables shall comply with (a) through (c) or, where cable substitution is being made, (d) below.

(a) Plenum. Cables installed in ducts, plenums, and other spaces used for environmental air shall be Type FPLP.

Exception: Types FPLP, FPLR, and FPL cable installed in compliance with Section 300-22.

(b) Riser. Cables installed in vertical runs and penetrating more than one floor or cables installed in vertical runs in a shaft shall be Type FPLR. Floor penetrations requiring Type FPLR shall contain only cables suitable for riser or plenum use.

Exception No. 1: Where the cables are encased in metal raceway or are located in a fireproof shaft having firestops at each floor.

Exception No. 2: Type FPL in one- and two-family dwellings.

(FPN): See Section 300-21 for firestop requirements for floor penetrations.

(c) Other Wiring within Buildings. Cables installed in building locations other than the locations covered in (a) and (b) above shall be Type FPL.

Exception No. 1: Where the cables are enclosed in raceway.

Exception No. 2: Cables specified in Chapter 3 that meet the requirements of Sections 760-51(a) and (b) and are installed in nonconcealed spaces where the exposed length of cable does not exceed 10 feet (3.05 m).

(d) Cable Substitutions. The substitutions for power-limited fire protective signaling circuit cables listed in Table 760-53 and illustrated in Figure 760-53 shall be permitted. Communications and Class 3 cables shall be permitted to substitute for power-limited fire protective signaling circuit cables only where the requirements of Sections 760-51(a), (b), and (c) for multiconductor cables and Section 760-51(g) for coaxial cables are satisfied.

Table 760-53. Cable Substitutions

Cable Type	Permitted Substitutions
FPLP	MPP, CMP, CL3P
FPLR	MPP, CMP, FPLP, CL3P, MPR, CMR, CL3R
FPL	MPP, CMP, FPLP, CL3P, MPR, CMR, CL3R, FPLR, MPG, MP, CMG, CM, PLTC, CL3

(FPN): For information on multipurpose cables (MPP, MRP, MPG, MP) and communications cables (CMP, CMR, CMG, CM), see Section 800-50. For information on Class 3 cables (CL3P, CL3R, CL3, PLTC), see Section 725-50.

Type CM — Communications Wires and Cables
Types CL2 and CL3 — Class 2 and Class 3 Remote-Control, Signaling, and Power-Limited Cables
Type FPL — Power-Limited Fire Protective Signaling Cables
Type MP — Multipurpose Cables
Type PLTC — Power-Limited Tray Cable

Figure 760-53. *Cable Substitution Hierarchy*

760-55. Current-Carrying Continuous Line-type Fire Detectors.

(a) Application. Listed continuous line-type fire detectors, including insulated copper tubing of pneumatically operated detectors, employed for both detection and carrying signaling currents shall be permitted to be used in circuits having power-limiting characteristics in accordance with Section 760-21.

(b) Insulation. Insulated continuous line-type fire detectors shall be listed as being resistant to the spread of fire in accordance with the requirements of Sections 760-49 and 760-50, have a voltage rating of not less than 300 volts, and the jacket compound shall have a high degree of abrasion resistance.

(c) Installation. Continuous line-type fire detectors shall be installed in accordance with Sections 760-22 through 760-28 and Section 760-52.

ARTICLE 770 Optical Fiber Cables and Raceways

Contents

A. General

(a) Spread of Fire or Products of Combustion.

(b) Ducts, Plenums, and Other Air-Handling Spaces.

770-3. Optical Fiber Cables.

770-4. Types.
(a) Nonconductive.
(b) Conductive.
(c) Composite.

770-5. Optical Fiber Raceway System.

770-6. Cable Trays.

770-7. Access to Electrical Equipment Behind Panels Designed to Allow Access.

B. Protection

770-33. Grounding of Entrance Cables.

C. Cables within Buildings.

770-49. Fire Resistance of Optical Fiber Cables.

770-50. Listing, Marking, and Installation of Optical Fiber Cables.

770-51. Listing Requirements for Optical Fiber Cables and Raceways.
(a) Types OFNP and OFCP.
(b) Types OFNR and OFCR.
(c) Types OFNG and OFCG.
(d) Types OFN and OFC.
(e) Plenum Optical Fiber Raceway.
(f) Riser Optical Fiber Raceway.

770-52. Installation of Optical Fibers and Electrical Conductors.
(a) With Conductors for Electric Light, Power, or Class 1 Circuits.
(b) With Other Conductors.
(c) Grounding.

770-53. Applications of Listed Optical Fiber Cables and Raceways.
(a) Plenum.
(b) Riser.
(c) Other Wiring within Buildings.
(d) Cable Substitutions.

A. General

770-1. Scope. The provisions of this article apply to the installation of optical fiber cables and raceways. This article does not cover the construction of optical fiber cables and raceways.

Article 770 is included to permit the orderly development and usage of optical fiber technology where used in conjunction with electrical conductors for communication, signaling, and control circuits in lieu of metallic conductors.

Optical fiber cables may be desirable in some circumstances where electrical noise is a problem, as they are not affected by electrical noise.

770-2. Locations and Other Articles. Circuits and equipment shall comply with (a) and (b) below.

(a) Spread of Fire or Products of Combustion. See Section 300-21.

(b) Ducts, Plenums, and Other Air-Handling Spaces. Section 300-22, where installed in ducts or plenums or other space used for environmental air.

See commentary following Sections 300-22(b) and 300-22(c).

Exception to (b): As permitted in Section 770-53(a).

770-3. Optical Fiber Cables. Optical fiber cables transmit light for control, signaling, and communications through an optical fiber.

770-4. Types. Optical fiber cables can be grouped into three types.

(a) Nonconductive. These cables contain no metallic members and no other electrically conductive materials.

(b) Conductive. These cables contain noncurrent-carrying conductive members such as metallic strength members and metallic vapor barriers.

(c) Composite. These cables contain optical fibers and current-carrying electrical conductors, and shall be permitted to contain noncurrent-carrying conductive members such as metallic strength members and metallic vapor barriers. Composite optical fiber cables shall be classified as electrical cables in accordance with the type of electrical conductors.

770-5. Optical Fiber Raceway System. A raceway system designed for enclosing and routing only nonconductive optical fiber cables. Where optical fiber cables are installed in a raceway, the raceway shall be of a type permitted in Chapter 3 and installed in accordance with Chapter 3.

Exception: Listed optical fiber raceway.

(FPN): Plastic innerduct commonly used for underground or outside plant construction may not have appropriate fire safety characteristics for use as an optical fiber optic cable wiring method within buildings.

770-6. **Cable Trays.** Optical fiber cables of the types listed in Table 770-50 shall be permitted to be installed in cable trays.

(FPN): It is not the intent to require that these optical fiber cables be listed specifically for use in cable trays.

770-7. **Access to Electrical Equipment Behind Panels Designed to Allow Access.** Access to equipment shall not be denied by an accumulation of wires and cables that prevents removal of panels, including suspended ceiling panels.

See commentary following Section 725-7.

B. Protection

770-33. **Grounding of Entrance Cables.** Where exposed to contact with electric light or power conductors, the noncurrent-carrying metallic members of optical fiber cables entering buildings shall be grounded as close to the point of entrance as practicable or shall be interrupted as close to the point of entrance as practicable by an insulating joint or equivalent device.

For purposes of this section, the point of entrance shall be considered to be at the point of emergence through an exterior wall, a concrete floor slab, or from a rigid metal conduit or an intermediate metal conduit grounded in accordance with Article 250.

C. Cables within Buildings

770-49. **Fire Resistance of Optical Fiber Cables.** Optical fiber cables installed as wiring within buildings shall be listed as being resistant to the spread of fire in accordance with Sections 770-50 and 770-51.

770-50. **Listing, Marking, and Installation of Optical Fiber Cables.** Optical fiber cables in a building shall be listed as being suitable for the purpose, and cables shall be marked in accordance with Table 770-50.

Exception No. 1: Optical fiber cables shall not be required to be listed and marked where the length of cable within the building does not exceed 50 feet (15.2 m) and the cable enters the building from the outside and is terminated in an enclosure.

(FPN): Splice cases or terminal boxes, both metallic and plastic types, are typically used as enclosures for splicing or terminating optical fiber cables.

Exception No. 2: Conductive optical fiber cable shall not be required to be listed and marked where the cable enters the building from the outside and is run in rigid metal conduit or intermediate metal conduit and such conduits are grounded to an electrode in accordance with Section 800-40(b).

Exception No. 3: Nonconductive optical fiber cables shall not be required to be listed and marked where the cable enters the building from the outside and is run in raceway installed in compliance with Chapter 3.

Table 770-50. **Cable Markings**

Cable Marking	Type	Reference
OFNP	Nonconductive optical fiber plenum cable	Sections 770-51(a) and 770-53(a)
OFCP	Conductive optical fiber plenum cable	Sections 770-51(a) and 770-53(a)
OFNR	Nonconductive optical fiber riser cable	Sections 770-51(b) and 770-53(b)
OFCR	Conductive optical fiber riser cable	Sections 770-51(b) and 770-53(b)
OFNG	Nonconductive optical fiber general-purpose cable	Sections 770-51(c) and 770-53(c)
OFCG	Conductive optical fiber general-purpose cable	Sections 770-51(c) and 770-53(c)
OFN	Nonconductive optical fiber general-purpose cable	Sections 770-51(d) and 770-53(c)
OFC	Conductive optical fiber general-purpose cable	Sections 770-51(d) and 770-53(c)

(FPN No. 1): Cable types are listed in descending order of fire resistance rating. Within each fire resistance rating, nonconductive cable is listed first, since it may substitute for the conductive cable.

(FPN No. 2): See the referenced sections for requirements and permitted uses.

770-51. **Listing Requirements for Optical Fiber Cables and Raceways.** Optical fiber cables shall be listed in accordance with (a) through (d) below, and optical fiber raceways shall be listed in accordance with (e) and (f) below.

(a) Types OFNP and OFCP. Types OFNP and OFCP nonconductive and conductive optical fiber plenum cables shall be listed as being suitable for use in ducts, plenums, and other space used for environmental air and shall also be listed as having adequate fire-resistant and low-smoke-producing characteristics.

(FPN): One method of defining low-smoke-producing cables is by establishing an acceptable value of the smoke produced when tested in accordance with the Test for Fire and Smoke Characteristics of Wires and Cables, NFPA 262-1990 (ANSI) to a maximum peak optical density of 0.5 and a maximum average optical density of 0.15. Similarly, one method of defining fire-resistant cables is by defining maximum allowable flame travel distance of 5 feet (1.52 m) when tested in accordance with the same test.

For further information on the fire test method for plenum cables, see commentary following Section 725-51(a)(FPN).

(b) Types OFNR and OFCR. Types OFNR and OFCR nonconductive and conductive optical fiber riser cables shall be listed as being suitable for use in a vertical run in a shaft or from floor to floor and shall also be listed as having fire-resistant characteristics capable of preventing the carrying of fire from floor to floor.

(FPN): One method of defining fire-resistant characteristics capable of preventing the carrying of fire from floor to floor is that the cables pass the requirements of the Standard Test for Flame Propagation Height of Electrical and Optical-Fiber Cable Installed Vertically in Shafts, ANSI/UL 1666-1986.

For further information on the fire test method for riser cables, see commentary following Section 725-51(b)(FPN).

(c) Types OFNG and OFCG. Types OFNG and OFCG nonconductive and conductive general-purpose optical fiber cables shall be listed as being suitable for general-purpose use, with the exception of risers and plenums, and shall also be listed as being resistant to the spread of fire.

(FPN): One method of defining resistance to the spread of fire is for the damage (char length) not to exceed 4 feet 11 inches (1.5 m) when performing the "Vertical Flame Test — Cables in Cable Trays," as described in Test Methods for Electrical Wires and Cables, CSA C22.2 No. 0.3-M 1985.

For further information on the fire test method for cables used as other wiring within buildings, see commentary following Section 725-51(c)(FPN).

(d) Types OFN and OFC. Types OFN and OFC nonconductive and conductive optical fiber cables shall be listed as being suitable for general-purpose use, with the exception of risers, plenums, and other space used for environmental air, and shall also be listed as being resistant to the spread of fire.

(FPN): One method of defining resistant to the spread of fire is that the cables do not spread fire to the top of the tray in the "Vertical-Tray Flame Test" in the Reference Standard for Electrical Wires, Cables and Flexible Cords, ANSI/UL 1581-1985.

Another method of defining resistant to the spread of fire is for the damage (char length) not to exceed 4 feet 11 inches (1.5 m) when performing the "Vertical Flame Test — Cables in Cable Trays," as described in Test Methods for Electrical Wires and Cables, CSA C22.2 No. 0.3-M 1985.

(e) Plenum Optical Fiber Raceway. Plenum optical fiber raceways shall be listed as having adequate fire-resistant and low-smoke-producing characteristics.

(f) Riser Optical Fiber Raceway. Riser optical fiber raceways shall be listed as having fire-resistant characteristics capable of preventing the carrying of fire from floor to floor.

770-52. **Installation of Optical Fibers and Electrical Conductors.**

(a) With Conductors for Electric Light, Power, or Class 1 Circuits. Optical fibers shall be permitted within the same composite cable for electric light, power, or Class 1 circuits operating at 600 volts or less only where the functions of the optical fibers and the electrical conductors are associated. Nonconductive optical fiber cables shall be permitted to occupy the same cable tray or raceway with conductors for electric light, power, or Class 1 circuits operating at 600 volts or less. Conductive optical fiber cables shall not be permitted to occupy the same cable tray or raceway with conductors for electric light, power, or Class 1 circuits. Composite optical fiber cables containing only current-carrying conductors for electric light, power, or Class 1 circuits rated 600 volts or less shall be permitted to occupy the same cabinet, cable tray, outlet box, panel, raceway, or other termination enclosure with conductors for electric light, power, or Class 1 circuits operating at 600 volts or less.

Nonconductive optical fiber cables shall not be permitted to occupy the same cabinet, outlet box, panel, or similar enclosure housing the electrical terminations of an electric light, power, or Class 1 circuit.

Exception No. 1: Occupancy of the same cabinet, outlet box, panel, or similar enclosure shall be permitted where nonconductive optical fiber cable is functionally associated with the electric light, power, or Class 1 circuit.

Exception No. 2: Occupancy of the same cabinet, outlet box, panel, or similar enclosure shall be permitted where nonconductive optical fiber cables are installed in factory- or field-assembled control centers.

Exception No. 3: In industrial establishments only, where conditions of maintenance and supervision assure that only qualified persons will service the installation, nonconductive optical fiber cables shall be permitted with circuits exceeding 600 volts.

Exception No. 4: In industrial establishments only, where conditions of maintenance and supervision assure that only qualified persons will service the installation, hybrid optical fiber cables shall be permitted to contain current-carrying conductors operating over 600 volts.

Installations in raceway shall comply with Section 300-17.

(b) With Other Conductors. Optical fibers shall be permitted in the same cable, and conductive and nonconductive optical fiber cables shall be permitted in the same cable tray, enclosure, or raceway with conductors of any of the following:

(1) Class 2 and Class 3 remote-control, signaling, and power-limited circuits in compliance with Article 725.

(2) Power-limited fire protective signaling systems in compliance with Article 760.

(3) Communications circuits in compliance with Article 800.

(4) Community antenna television and radio distribution systems in compliance with Article 820.

(c) Grounding. Noncurrent-carrying conductive members of optical fiber cables shall be grounded in accordance with Article 250.

770-53. Applications of Listed Optical Fiber Cables and Raceways. Nonconductive and conductive optical fiber cables shall comply with (a) through (d) below.

(a) Plenum. Cables installed in ducts, plenums, and other spaces used for environmental air shall be Type OFNP or OFCP.

Also, listed plenum optical fiber raceways shall be permitted to be installed in ducts and plenums as described in Section 300-22(b) and in other space used for environmental air as described in Section 300-22(c). Type OFNP cable shall be permitted to be installed in these raceways.

Exception: Types OFNR, OFCR, OFNG, OFN, OFCG, and OFC cables installed in compliance with Section 300-22.

(b) Riser. Cables installed in vertical runs and penetrating more than one floor or cables installed in vertical runs in a shaft shall be Types OFNR or OFCR. Floor penetrations requiring Types OFNR or OFCR shall contain only cables suitable for riser or plenum use.

Also, listed riser optical fiber raceways shall be permitted to be installed in vertical runs in a shaft or from floor to floor. Types OFNR and OFNP cables shall be permitted to be installed in these raceways.

Exception No. 1: Where Types OFNG, OFN, OFCG, and OFC cables are encased in metal raceway or are located in a fireproof shaft having firestops at each floor.

Exception No. 2: Type OFNG, OFN, OFCG, or OFC cable in one- and two-family dwellings.

(FPN): See Section 300-21 for firestop requirements for floor penetrations.

(c) Other Wiring within Buildings. Cables installed in building locations other than the locations covered in (a) and (b) above shall be Type OFNG, OFN, OFCG, or OFC.

(d) Cable Substitutions. The substitutions for optical fiber cables listed in Table 770-53 and illustrated in Figure 770-53 shall be permitted.

Table 770-53. Cable Substitutions

Cable Type	Permitted Substitutions
OFNP	None
OFCP	OFNP
OFNR	OFNP
OFCR	OFNP, OFCP, OFNR
OFNG, OFN	OFNP, OFNR
OFCG, OFC	OFNP, OFCP, OFNR, OFCR, OFNG, OFN

Type CM — Communications Wires and Cables
Types CL2 and CL3 — Class 2 and Class 3 Remote-Control, Signaling, and Power-Limited Cables
Type FPL — Power-Limited Fire Protective Signaling Cables
Type MP — Multipurpose Cables
Type PLTC — Power-Limited Tray Cable

Figure 770-53. *Cable Substitution Hierarchy*

ARTICLE 780 Closed-Loop and Programmed Power Distribution

Contents

780-1. Scope. The provisions of this article apply to premise power distribution systems jointly controlled by a signaling between the energy controlling equipment and utilization equipment.

This article provides requirements for the "smart house" concept, which involves universal cable terminating in universal outlets.

Buildings wired by conventional methods require separate sets of conductors for different systems. However, in the smart house, multiple conductors for 120-Vac power, 24-Vdc UPS, telephone, remote-control and signaling, as well as coaxial cable, are combined in a single construction known as hybrid cabling.

This hybrid cabling serves multipurpose receptacle outlets known as "convenience centers," which are capable of supplying different types of energy and signals to specific appliances or equipment.

The smart house utilizes an energy safety technique called closed-loop control to reduce shock hazard. In conventional wiring, receptacles are energized at all times under normal operating conditions. In the closed-loop configuration, receptacles are not energized until the insertion of an attachment plug generates a characteristic electrical identification.

Figure 780-1 illustrates a typical smart house installation. The 1987 *NEC Handbook* illustrated a system distributing power at both 120/240-Vac and 48-Vdc, with 12-Vdc UPS. However, present smart house technology utilizes only 120/240-Vac, with 24-Vdc UPS to maintain system electronics in the event of a transient or utility power outage.

780-2. General.

(a) Other Articles. Except as modified by the requirements of this article, all other applicable articles of this Code shall apply.

(b) Component Parts. All equipment and conductors shall be listed and identified.

Figure 780-1. *A typical smart house installation. (Smart House) Legend:* ▬ *hybrid branch cable,* ── *hybrid light fixture cable,* ── ── ── *hybrid switch/sensor cable.*

780-3. **Control.** The control equipment and all power switching devices operated by the control equipment shall be listed and identified. The system shall operate such that:

(a) Characteristic Electrical Identification Required. Outlets shall not be energized unless the utilization equipment first exhibits a characteristic electrical identification.

Receptacles are energized with 120-Vac power only when electronic circuitry in the convenience center receives this characteristic identification.

(b) Conditions for Deenergization. Outlets shall be deenergized when any of the following conditions occur:

(1) A nominal-operation acknowledgement signal is not being received from the utilization equipment connected to the outlet.

Convenience center receptacles are deenergized when the characteristic electrical identification ceases (when the attachment plug is withdrawn). In addition, appliances with built-in smart house communications chips transmit a continuous nominal-operation signal to the convenience center electronics. If this signal is interrupted, indicating a possible malfunction or safety problem, the receptacle is automatically deenergized.

(2) A ground-fault condition exists.

(3) An overcurrent condition exists.

(c) Additional Conditions for Deenergization When an Alternate Source of Power is Used. In addition to the requirements in Section 780-3(b), outlets shall be deenergized when any of the following conditions occur:

(1) The grounded conductor is not properly grounded.

(2) Any ungrounded conductor is not at nominal voltage.

(d) Controller Malfunction. In the event of a controller malfunction, all associated outlet(s) shall be deenergized.

780-5. **Power Limitation in Signaling Circuits.** For signaling circuits not exceeding 24 volts, the current required shall not exceed one ampere where protected by an overcurrent device or an inherently limited power source.

780-6. **Cables and Conductors.**

(a) Hybrid Cable. Listed hybrid cable consisting of power, communications, and signaling conductors shall be permitted under a common jacket. The jacket shall be applied so as to separate the power conductors from the communications and signaling conductors. An optional outer jacket shall be permitted to be applied. The individual conductors of a hybrid cable shall conform to the Code provisions applicable to their current, voltage, and insulation rating. The signaling conductors shall not be smaller than No. 24 copper.

(b) Cables and Conductors in the Same Cabinet, Panel, or Box. The power, communications, and signaling conductors of listed hybrid cable are permitted to occupy the same cabinet, panel, or outlet box (or similar enclosure housing the electrical terminations of electric light or power circuits) only if connectors specifically listed for hybrid cable are employed.

780-7. **Noninterchangeability.** Receptacles, cord connectors, and attachment plugs used on closed-loop power distribution systems shall be constructed so that they are not interchangeable with other receptacles, cord connectors, and attachment plugs.

Convenience center receptacles are constructed so that they will not accept an attachment plug with a different voltage or a different current rating than that for which the device is intended. Attachment plugs for use with closed-loop power distribution systems will not fit into conventional receptacles in order to ensure that "smart" appliances are not used on other power distribution systems that lack closed-loop control features.

8
Communications Systems

ARTICLE 800   Communications Circuits

Contents

A. General

800-41. Primary Protector Grounding and Bonding at Mobile Homes.
  (a) Grounding.
  (b) Bonding.

E. Conductors within Buildings

800-49. Fire Resistance of Communications Wires and Cables.

800-50. Listing, Marking, and Installation of Communications Wires and Cables.

800-51. Listing Requirements.
  (a) Type CMP.
  (b) Type CMR.
  (c) Type CMG.
  (d) Type CM.
  (e) Type CMX.
  (f) Type CMUC Undercarpet Wire and Cable.
  (g) Multipurpose (MP) Cables.
  (h) Communications Wires.
  (i) Hybrid Power and Communications Cable.

800-52. Installation of Communications Wires, Cables, and Equipment.
  (a) Separation from Other Conductors.
  (b) Spread of Fire or Products of Combustion.
  (c) Equipment in Other Space Used for Environmental Air.
  (d) Cable Trays.
  (e) Support of Conductors.

800-53. Applications of Listed Communications Wires and Cables.
  (a) Plenum.
  (b) Riser.
  (c) Distributing Frames and Cross-Connect Arrays.
  (d) Other Wiring within Buildings.
  (e) Hybrid Power and Communications Cable.
  (f) Cable Substitutions.

A. General

800-1. Scope. This article covers telephone, telegraph (except radio), outside wiring for fire alarm and burglar alarm, and similar central station systems; and telephone systems not connected to a central station system but using similar types of equipment, methods of installation, and maintenance.

(FPN No. 1): For further information for fire alarm, guard tour, sprinkler waterflow, and sprinkler supervisory systems, see Article 760.

(FPN No. 2): For installation requirements of optical fiber cables, see Article 770.

Section 90-3, Code Arrangement, states that Chapter 8, which includes Articles 800, 810, and 820, covers communications systems and is independent of the other chapters except where they are specifically referenced therein. For instance, Section 800-30(c) references Article 500, Section 800-52(c) references Section 300-22, and Section 800-10(a)(3) references Section 225-14(d).

Although electronic data processing (EDP) systems are often used for or with communications systems, Article 800 does not cover EDP system wiring. Article 645 provides wiring requirements for wiring contained solely within a computer room. See Section 645-2 for the definition of "Computer Room." Article 725 provides wiring requirements for wiring that extends beyond a computer room. See Article 760 for wiring requirements for a fire protective signaling system. In some cases, the telephone system wiring is also used for data transmission; and this use is covered by Article 800. Telephone company central offices are exempt from the requirements of Article 800. See Section 90-2(b)(4).

This article was rewritten and reorganized for the 1990 *Code*. The format for this article is similar to that for Articles 725, 760, 770, and 820.

800-2. Definitions. See Article 100. For purposes of this article, the following additional definitions apply:

Cable: A cable is a factory assembly of two or more conductors having an overall covering.

Cable Sheath: A sheath is a covering over the conductor assembly that may include one or more metallic members, strength members, or jackets.

Point of Entrance: The point of entrance within a building is the point at which the wire or cable emerges from an external wall, from a concrete floor slab, or from a rigid metal conduit or an intermediate metal conduit grounded to an electrode in accordance with Section 800-40(b).

Wire: A wire is a factory assembly of one or more insulated conductors without an overall covering.

See Article 100 for definitions of "Raceway," "Equipment," and "Conductors."

800-3. Hybrid Power and Communications Cables. The provisions of Section 780-6 shall apply for listed hybrid power and communications cables in closed-loop and programmed power distribution.

See Section 800-51(i) for listing requirements and use of hybrid power and communications cables in one- and two-family residences for applications other than closed-loop and programmed power distribution.

(FPN): See Section 800-51(i) for hybrid power and communications cable in other applications.

800-4. Equipment. Equipment intended to be electrically connected to a telecommunications network shall be listed for the purpose.

(FPN): One way to determine applicable requirements is to refer to the Standard for Telephone Equipment, UL 1459-1987, or Communication Circuit Accessories, UL 1863-1990.

Exception No. 1: For other than wires, cables, grounding conductors, and protectors, this listing requirement shall not apply to premises wiring components, such as plugs, jacks, connectors, terminal blocks, and cross-connect assemblies that were manufactured before October 1, 1990 and all other equipment manufactured before July 1, 1991.

Exception No. 2: This listing requirement shall not apply to test equipment intended for temporary connection to a telecommunications network by qualified persons during the course of installation, maintenance, or repair of telecommunications equipment or systems.

800-5. Access to Electrical Equipment Behind Panels Designed to Allow Access. Access to equipment shall not be denied by an accumulation of wires and cables that prevents removal of panels, including suspended ceiling panels.

800-6. Mechanical Execution of Work. Communication circuits and equipment shall be installed in a neat and workmanlike manner.

This requirement appears in Section 110-12 and is now applicable to communications circuits. See Section 90-3.

B. Conductors Outside and Entering Buildings

800-10. Overhead Communications Wires and Cables. Overhead communications wires and cables entering buildings shall comply with (a) and (b) below.

(a) On Poles and In-Span. Where communications wires and cables and electric light or power conductors are supported by the same pole or run in parallel in-span, the following conditions shall be met:

(1) Relative Location. Where practicable, the communications wires and cables shall be located below the electric light or power conductors.

(2) Attachment to Crossarms. Communications wires and cables shall not be attached to a crossarm that carries electric light or power conductors.

(3) Climbing Space. The climbing space through communications wires and cables shall comply with the requirements of Section 225-14(d).

(4) Clearance. Supply service drops of 0-750 volts running above and parallel to communications service drops shall be permitted to have a minimum separation of 12 inches (30.48 cm) at any point in the span, including the point of and at their attachment to the building, provided the nongrounded conductors are insulated and that a clearance of 40 inches (1.02 m) is maintained between the two services at the pole.

(b) Above Roofs. Communications wires and cables shall have a vertical clearance of not less than 8 feet (2.44 m) from all points of roofs above which they pass.

Exception No. 1: Auxiliary buildings, such as garages and the like.

Exception No. 2: A reduction in clearance above only the overhanging portion of the roof to not less than 18 inches (457 mm) shall be permitted if (1) not more than 4 feet (1.22 mm) of communications service-drop conductors pass above the roof overhang and (2) they are terminated at a through- or above-the-roof raceway or approved support.

Exception No. 3: Where the roof has a slope not less than 4 inches (102 mm) in 12 inches (305 mm), a reduction in clearance to not less than 3 feet (914 mm) shall be permitted.

800-11. **Underground Circuits Entering Buildings.** Underground communications wires and cables entering buildings shall comply with (a) and (b) below.

(a) With Electric Light or Power Conductors. Underground communications wires and cables in a raceway, handhole, or manhole containing electric light or power conductors shall be in a section separated from such conductors by means of brick, concrete, or tile partitions.

(b) Underground Block Distribution. Where the entire street circuit is run underground and the circuit within the block is so placed as to be free from likelihood of accidental contact with electric light or power circuits of over 300 volts to ground, the insulation requirements of Sections 800-12(a) and 800-12(c) shall not apply, insulating supports shall not be required for the conductors, and bushings shall not be required where the conductors enter the building.

800-12. **Circuits Requiring Primary Protectors.** Circuits that require primary protectors as provided in Section 800-30 shall comply with the following:

(a) Insulation, Wires, and Cables. Communications wires and cables without a metallic shield, running from the last outdoor support to the primary protector, shall be listed as being suitable for the purpose and having current-carrying capacity as specified in Section 800-30(a)(1)(b) or 800-30(a)(1)(c).

(b) On Buildings. Communications wires and cables in accordance with Section 800-12(a) shall be separated at least 4 inches (102 mm) from electric light or power conductors not in a raceway or cable, or be permanently separated from conductors of the other system by a continuous and firmly fixed nonconductor in addition to the insulation on the wires, such as porcelain tubes or flexible tubing. Communications wires and cables in accordance with Section 800-12(a) exposed to accidental contact with electric light and power conductors operating at over 300 volts to ground and attached to buildings shall be separated from woodwork by being supported on glass, porcelain, or other insulating material.

Exception: Separation from woodwork shall not be required where fuses are omitted as provided for in Section 800-31(a), or where conductors are used to extend circuits to a building from a cable having a grounded metal sheath.

(c) Entering Buildings. Where a primary protector is installed inside the building, the communications wires and cables shall enter the building either through a noncombustible, nonabsorbent insulating bushing, or through a metal raceway. The insulating bushing shall not be required where the entering communications wires and cables (1) are in metal-sheathed cable; (2) pass through masonry; (3) meet the requirements of Section 800-12(a) and fuses are omitted as provided in Section 800-31(a); or (4) meet the requirements of Section 800-12(a) above and are used to extend circuits to a building from a cable having a grounded metallic sheath. Raceways or bushings shall slope upward from the outside or, where this cannot be done, drip loops shall be formed in the communications wires and cables immediately before they enter the building.

Raceways shall be equipped with an approved service head. More than one communications wire and cable shall be permitted to enter through a single raceway or bushing. Conduits or other metal raceways located ahead of the primary protector shall be grounded.

800-13. **Lightning Conductors.** Where practicable, a separation of at least 6 feet (1.83 m) shall be maintained between open conductors of communications systems on buildings and lightning conductors.

C. Protection

800-30. **Protective Devices.**

(a) Application. A listed primary protector shall be provided on each circuit run partly or entirely in aerial wire or aerial cable not confined within a block. Also, a listed primary protector shall be provided on each circuit, aerial or underground, so located within the block containing the building served as to be exposed to accidental contact with electric light or power conductors operating at over 300 volts to ground. In addition, where there exists a lightning exposure, each interbuilding circuit on a premises shall be protected by a listed primary protector at each end of the interbuilding circuit. Installation of primary protectors shall also comply with Section 110-3(b).

(FPN No. 1): The word "block" as used in this article means a square or portion of a city, town, or village enclosed by streets and including the alleys so enclosed, but not any street. The word "premises" as used in this article means the land and buildings of a user located on the user side of the utility-user network point of demarcation.

(FPN No. 2): The word "exposed" as used in this article means that the circuit is in such a position that, in case of failure of supports or insulation, contact with another circuit may result.

(FPN No. 3): On a circuit not exposed to accidental contact with power conductors, providing a listed primary protector in accordance with this article will help protect against other hazards, such as lightning and above-normal voltages induced by fault currents on power circuits in proximity to the communications circuit.

Telephone utility companies ordinarily provide primary protectors where telephone lines are exposed to lightning. Installers of private networks that include interbuilding cables should also install primary protectors where these cables are exposed to lightning. Generally, cables are considered exposed to lightning unless one or more of the conditions in FPN No. 4 exist. A primary protector is required at each end of an interbuilding communications circuit where lighting exposure exists.

(FPN No. 4): Interbuilding circuits are considered to have a lightning exposure unless one or more of the following conditions exist:

1. Circuits in large metropolitan areas where buildings are close together and sufficiently high to intercept lightning.

2. Interbuilding cable runs of 140 feet (42.7 m) or less, directly buried or in underground conduit, where a continuous metallic cable shield or a continuous metallic conduit containing the cable is bonded to each building grounding electrode system.

3. Areas having an average of five or fewer thunderstorm days per year and earth resistivity of less than 100 ohm-meters. Such areas are found along the Pacific coast.

(1) **Fuseless Primary Protectors.** Fuseless-type primary protectors shall be permitted under any of the following conditions:

a. Where conductors enter a building through a cable with grounded metallic sheath member(s) and if the conductors in the cable safely fuse on all currents greater than the current-carrying capacity of the primary protector and of the primary protector grounding conductor.

b. Where insulated conductors in accordance with Section 800-12(a) are used to extend circuits to a building from a cable with effectively grounded metallic sheath member(s) and if the conductors in the cable or cable stub, or the connections between the insulated conductors and the exposed plant, safely fuse on all currents greater than the current-carrying capacity of the primary protector, or the associated insulated conductors and of the primary protector grounding conductor.

c. Where insulated conductors in accordance with Section 800-12(a) or (b) are used to extend circuits to a building from other than a cable with metallic sheath member(s) if (1) the primary protector is listed for this purpose, and (2) the connections of the insulated conductors to the exposed plant or the conductors of the exposed plant safely fuse on all currents greater than the current-carrying capacity of the primary protector, or the associated insulated conductors and of the primary protector grounding conductor.

d. Where insulated conductors in accordance with Section 800-12(a) are used to extend circuits aerially to a building from an unexposed buried or underground circuit.

e. Where insulated conductors in accordance with Section 800-12(a) are used to extend circuits to a building from cable with effectively grounded metallic sheath member(s) and if (1) the combination of the primary protector and insulated conductors is listed for this purpose, and (2) the insulated conductors safely fuse on all currents greater than the current-carrying capacity of the primary protector and of the primary protector grounding conductor.

(FPN): Effectively grounded means intentionally connected to earth through a ground connection or connections of sufficiently low impedance and having sufficient current-carrying capacity to prevent the buildup of voltages that may result in undue hazard to connected equipment or to persons.

(2) **Fused Primary Protectors.** Where the requirements listed under items a through e above are not met, fused-type primary protectors shall be used. Fused-type primary protectors shall consist of an arrester connected between each line conductor and ground, a fuse in series with each line conductor, and an appropriate mounting arrangement. Primary protector terminals shall be marked to indicate line, instrument, and ground, as applicable.

(b) **Location.** The primary protector shall be located in, on, or immediately adjacent to the structure or building served and as close as practicable to the point at which the exposed conductors enter or attach.

See Figure 800-2.

Figure 800-1. *A primary protector unit that is typically installed in commercial buildings. This is the interface to the outside plant cable. (AT&T)*

For purposes of this section, the point at which the exposed conductors enter shall be considered to be the point of emergence through an exterior wall, a concrete floor slab, or from a rigid metal conduit or an intermediate metal conduit grounded to an electrode in accordance with Section 800-40(b).

For purposes of this section, primary protectors located at mobile home service equipment located in sight from and not more than 30 feet (9.14 m) from the exterior wall of the mobile home it serves, or at a mobile home disconnecting means grounded in accordance with Section 250-24 and located in sight from and not more than 30 feet (9.14 m) from the exterior wall of the mobile home it serves, shall be considered to meet the requirements of this section.

(FPN): Selecting a primary protector location to achieve the shortest practicable primary protector grounding conductor will help limit potential differences between communications circuits and other metallic systems.

(c) Hazardous (Classified) Locations. The primary protector shall not be located in any hazardous (classified) location as defined in Article 500, nor in the vicinity of easily ignitible material.

Exception: As permitted in Sections 501-14, 502-14, and 503-12.

800-31. **Primary Protector Requirements.** The primary protector shall consist of an arrester connected between each line conductor and ground in an appropriate mounting. Primary protector terminals shall be marked to indicate line and ground as applicable.

(FPN): One way to determine applicable requirements for a listed primary protector is to refer to the Standard for Protectors for Communications Circuits, ANSI/UL 497-1978.

800-32. **Secondary Protector Requirements.** Where a secondary protector is installed in series with the indoor communications wire and cable between the primary protector and the equipment, it shall be listed for the purpose. The secondary protector shall provide means to safely limit currents to less than the current-carrying capacity of listed indoor communications wire and cable, listed telephone set line cords, and listed communications terminal equipment having ports for external wire line communications circuits. Any overvoltage protection, arresters, or grounding connection shall be connected on the equipment terminals side of the secondary protector current-limiting means.

(FPN No. 1): One way to determine applicable requirements for a listed secondary protector is to refer to the Standard for Secondary Protectors for Communications, UL497A-1990.

(FPN No. 2): Secondary protectors on exposed circuits are not intended for use without primary protectors.

800-33. **Cable Grounding.** The metallic sheath of communications cables entering buildings shall be grounded as close as practicable to the point of entrance or shall be interrupted as close to the point of entrance as practicable by an insulating joint or equivalent device.

For purposes of this section, the point of entrance shall be considered to be at the point of emergence through an exterior wall, a concrete floor slab, or from a rigid metal conduit or an intermediate metal conduit grounded to an electrode in accordance with Section 800-40(b).

D. Grounding Methods

800-40. **Cable and Primary Protector Grounding.** The metallic member(s) of the cable sheath, where required to be grounded by Section 800-33, and primary protectors shall be grounded as specified in (a) through (d) below.

(a) Grounding Conductor.

(1) Insulation. The grounding conductor shall be insulated and shall be listed as suitable for the purpose.

(2) Material. The grounding conductor shall be copper or other corrosion-resistant conductive material, stranded or solid.

(3) Size. The grounding conductor shall not be smaller than No. 14.

(4) Run in Straight Line. The grounding conductor shall be run to the grounding electrode in as straight a line as practicable.

(5) Physical Damage. Where necessary, the grounding conductor shall be guarded from physical damage. Where the grounding conductor is run in a metal raceway, both ends of the raceway shall be bonded to the grounding conductor or the same terminal or electrode to which the grounding conductor is connected.

(b) Electrode. The grounding conductor shall be connected as follows:

(1) To the nearest accessible location on (1) the building or structure grounding electrode system as covered in Section 250-81, (2) the grounded interior metal water piping system as covered in Section 250-80(a), (3) the power service accessible means external to enclosures as covered in Section 250-71(b), (4) the metallic power service raceway, (5) the service equipment enclosure, (6) the grounding electrode conductor or the grounding electrode conductor metal enclosure, or (7) to the grounding conductor or the grounding electrode of a building or structure disconnecting means that is grounded to an electrode as covered in Section 250-24.

For purposes of this section, the mobile home service equipment or the mobile home disconnecting means, as described in Section 800-30(b), shall be considered accessible.

(2) If the building or structure served has no grounding means, as described in b(1), to any one of the individual electrodes described in Section 250-81; or

(3) If the building or structure served has no grounding means, as described in b(1) or b(2), to (1) an effectively grounded metal structure or (2) to a ground rod or pipe not less than 5 feet (1.52 m) in length and ½ inch (12.7 mm) in diameter, driven, where practicable, into permanently damp earth and separated from lightning conductors as covered in Section 800-13 and at least 6 feet (1.83 m) from electrodes of other systems. Steam or hot water pipes or lightning-rod conductors shall not be employed as electrodes for protectors.

(c) Electrode Connection. Connections to grounding electrodes shall comply with Section 250-115. Connectors, clamps, fittings, or lugs used to attach grounding conductors and bonding jumpers to grounding electrodes or to each other that are to be concrete-encased or buried in the earth shall be suitable for its application.

(d) Bonding of Electrodes. A bonding jumper not smaller than No. 6 copper or equivalent shall be connected between the communications grounding electrode and power grounding electrode system at the building or structure served where separate electrodes are used. Bonding together of all separate electrodes shall be permitted.

This section requires bonding of communications and power grounding electrodes at the same building or structure. There are no requirements for separate grounding electrodes for communications systems.

Exception: At mobile homes as covered in Section 800-41.

(FPN No. 1):   See Section 250-86 for use of lightning rods.

(FPN No. 2):   Bonding together of all separate electrodes will limit potential differences between them and between their associated wiring systems.

800-41. Primary Protector Grounding and Bonding at Mobile Homes.

(a) Grounding. Where there is no mobile home service equipment located in sight from and not more than 30 feet (9.14 m) from the exterior wall of the mobile home it serves, or there is no mobile home disconnecting means grounded in accordance with Section 250-24 and located within sight from and not more than 30 feet (9.14 m) from the exterior wall of the mobile home it serves, the primary protector ground shall be in accordance with Section 800-40(b)(2) and (3).

(b) Bonding. The primary protector grounding terminal or grounding electrode shall be bonded to the metal frame or available grounding terminal of the mobile home with a copper grounding conductor not smaller than No. 12 under any of the following conditions:

(1) Where there is no mobile home service equipment or disconnecting means as in (a) above or;

(2) The mobile home is supplied by cord and plug.

E. Conductors within Buildings

800-49. Fire Resistance of Communications Wires and Cables. Communications wires and cables installed as wiring within a building shall be listed as being resistant to the spread of fire in accordance with Sections 800-50 and 800-51.

800-50. Listing, Marking, and Installation of Communications Wires and Cables. Communications wires and cables installed as wiring within buildings shall be listed as being suitable for the purpose, marked in accordance with Table 800-50, and installed in accordance with Section 800-52. The cable voltage rating shall not be marked on the cable.

(FPN):   Voltage markings on cables may be misinterpreted to suggest that the cables may be suitable for Class 1, electric light and power applications.

Exception No. 1: Voltage markings shall be permitted where the cable has multiple listings and voltage marking is required for one or more of the listings.

Exception No. 2: Listing and marking shall not be required where the cable enters the building from the outside and is continuously enclosed in rigid metal conduit or intermediate metal conduit and such conduits are grounded to an electrode in accordance with Section 800-40(b).

Exception No. 3: Listing and marking shall not be required where the length of cable within the building does not exceed 50 feet (15.2 m) and the cable enters the building from the outside and is terminated in an enclosure or on a listed primary protector.

(FPN No. 1):   Splice cases or terminal boxes, both metallic and plastic types, are typically used as enclosures for splicing or terminating telephone cables.

(FPN No. 2):   This exception limits the length of unlisted outside plant cable to 50 feet (15.2 m), while Section 800-30(b) requires that the primary protector shall be located as close as practicable to the point at which the cable enters the building. Hence, in installations requiring a primary protector, the outside plant cable may not be permitted to extend 50 feet (15.2 m) into the building if it is practicable to place the primary protector closer than 50 feet (15.2 m) to the entrance point.

Exception No. 4: Multipurpose cables shall be considered as being suitable for the purpose and shall be permitted to substitute for communications cables as provided for in Section 800-53(f).

(FPN No. 1):   Cable types are listed in descending order of fire resistance rating, and multipurpose cables are listed above communications cables because multipurpose cables may substitute for communications cables.

(FPN No. 2):   See the referenced sections for permitted uses.

800-51. Listing Requirements. Communications wires and cables shall have a voltage rating of not less than 300 V and shall be listed in accordance with (a) through (i) below.

A voltage rating of 300 V is necessary for four reasons: 1) to coordinate with protector installation requirements, i.e., protectors are not required within a block unless the cable is exposed to over 300 volts; 2) to recognize the fact that primary protectors are designed to allow voltages below 300 to pass; 3) to accommodate the voltages ordinarily found on a telephone line (48 V dc plus ringing voltage up to 130 V rms); and 4) to permit communications cables to substitute for 300-V power-limited fire protective signaling cables.

Table 800-50. Cable Markings

Cable Marking	Type	Reference
MPP	Multipurpose plenum cable	Sections 800-51(g) and 800-53(a)
CMP	Communications plenum cable	Sections 800-51(a) and 800-53(a)
MPR	Multipurpose riser cable	Sections 800-51(g) and 800-53(b)
CMR	Communications riser cable	Sections 800-51(b) and 800-53(b)
MPG	Multipurpose general purpose cable	Sections 800-51(g) and 800-53(d)
CMG	Communications general purpose cable	Sections 800-51(c) and 800-53(d)
MP	Multipurpose general purpose cable	Sections 800-51(g) and 800-52(d)
CM	Communications general purpose cable	Sections 800-51(d) and 800-53(d)
CMX	Communications cable, limited use	Sections 800-51(e) and 800-53(d), Exception Nos. 1, 2, 3, and 4
CMUC	Undercarpet communications wire and cable	Sections 800-51(f) and 800-53(d), Exception No. 5

(FPN): See Section 800-4 for listing requirement for equipment.

(a) Type CMP. Type CMP communications plenum cable shall be listed as being suitable for use in ducts, plenums, and other space used for environmental air and shall also be listed as having adequate fire-resistant and low-smoke-producing characteristics.

(FPN): One method of defining low-smoke-producing cables is by establishing an acceptable value of the smoke produced when tested in accordance with the Test for Fire and Smoke Characteristics of Wires and Cables, NFPA 262-1990 (ANSI) to a maximum peak optical density of 0.5 and a maximum average optical density of 0.15. Similarly, one method of defining fire-resistant cables is by establishing maximum allowable flame travel distance of 5 feet (1.52 m) when tested in accordance with the same test.

See commentary following Section 725-51(a), FPN.

(b) Type CMR. Type CMR communications riser cable shall be listed as being suitable for use in a vertical run in a shaft and shall also be listed as having fire-resistant characteristics capable of preventing the carrying of fire from floor to floor.

(FPN): One method of defining fire-resistant characteristics capable of preventing the carrying of fire from floor to floor is that the cables pass the requirements of the Standard Test for Flame Propagation Height of Electrical and Optical-Fiber Cable Installed Vertically in Shafts, ANSI/UL 1666-1986.

See commentary following Section 725-51(b), FPN.

(c) Type CMG. Type CMG general-purpose communications cable shall be listed as being suitable for general-purpose communications use, with the exception of risers and plenums, and shall also be listed as being resistant to the spread of fire.

(FPN): One method of defining resistant to the spread of fire is for the damage (char length) not to exceed 4 feet 11 inches (1.5 m) when performing the "Vertical Flame Test — Cables in Cable Trays," as described in Test Methods for Electrical Wires and Cables, CSA C22.2 No. 0.3-M 1985.

(d) Type CM. Type CM communications cable shall be listed as being suitable for general purpose communications use, with the exception of risers and plenums, and shall also be listed as being resistant to the spread of fire.

(FPN): One method of defining resistant to the spread of fire is that the cables do not spread fire to the top of the tray in the "Vertical-Tray Flame Test" in the Reference Standard for Electrical Wires, Cables and Flexible Cords, ANSI/UL 1581-1985.

Another method of defining resistant to the spread of fire is for the damage (char length) not to exceed 4 feet 11 inches (1.5 m) when performing the "Vertical Flame Test—Cables in Cable Trays," as described in Test Methods for Electrical Wires and Cables, CSA C22.2 No. 0.3-M-1985.

See commentary following Section 725-51(c), FPN.

(e) Type CMX. Type CMX limited use communications cable shall be listed as being suitable for use in dwellings and for use in raceway and shall also be listed as being flame-retardant.

(FPN): One method of determining that cable is flame-retardant is by testing the cable to the "VW-1 (Vertical-Wire) Flame Test" in the Reference Standard for Electrical Wires, Cables and Flexible Cords, ANSI/UL 1581-1985.

See commentary following Section 725-51(d), FPN.

(f) Type CMUC Undercarpet Wire and Cable. Type CMUC undercarpet communications wire and cable shall be listed as being suitable for undercarpet use and shall also be listed as being flame-retardant.

(FPN): One method of determining that cable is flame-retardant is by testing the cable to the "VW-1 (Vertical-Wire) Flame Test" in the Reference Standard for Electrical Wires, Cables and Flexible Cords, ANSI/UL 1581-1985.

(g) Multipurpose (MP) Cables. Cables that meet the requirements for Types CMP, CMR, CMG, and CM and also satisfy the requirements of Sections 760-51(a) and (b) for multiconductor cables and Section 760-51(g) for coaxial cables shall be permitted to be listed and marked as Types MPP, MPR, MPG, and MP, respectively.

In order for a cable to be listed as "multipurpose," it must meet the requirements of Type CMP, CMR, or CM and also satisfy the requirements of Sections 760-51(a) and (b). Most solid copper communications cables qualify for listing as multipurpose cables.

Sections 760-51(a) and (b) contain the gauge and stranding requirements for fire alarm use. The gauges permitted for use in power-limited, fire-protective signaling circuit applications have been expanded in the 1990 *Code* to include No. 26 conductors with a minimum of 10 conductors in the cable.

Typical communications cables used in buildings have No. 22-, No. 24-, or No. 26-gauge solid copper conductors. These cables may be used in place of Class 2 or Class 3 cable of equal or lower fire rating, and they may be used in place of power-limited, fire-protective signaling cables if there are a sufficient number of conductors in the cable; two pairs for No. 22-gauge, three pairs for No. 24-gauge, and five pairs for No. 26-gauge.

Conductors of fire-protective signaling circuits are required to be solid or bunch-tinned stranded copper with a minimum size of No. 18. Stranded conductors sized No. 16 and No. 18 are permitted with a maximum of seven strands. Nineteen strands are permitted for Nos. 14 and larger. Minimum conductor size and control of stranding are necessary requirements, providing physical strength to the conductor.

Control of the stranding is required to prevent a single, fine strand of wire from completing a circuit, causing the circuit to appear operational. The fine strand could remain intact under the current used for the supervisory signal but could burn open where required to carry the higher current of an alarm signal.

(h) Communications Wires. Communications wires, such as distributing frame wire and jumper wire, shall be listed as being resistant to the spread of fire.

(FPN): One method of defining resistant to the spread of fire is that the cables do not spread fire to the top of the tray in the "Vertical-Tray Flame Test" in the Reference Standard for Electrical Wires, Cables and Flexible Cords, ANSI/UL 1581-1985.

Another method of defining resistant to the spread of fire is for the damage (char length) not to exceed 4 feet 11 inches (1.5 m) when performing the "Vertical Flame Test—Cables in Cable Trays," as described in Test Methods for Electrical Wires and Cables, CSA C22.2 No. 0.3-M-1985.

(i) Hybrid Power and Communications Cable. Listed hybrid power and communications cable shall be permitted where the power cable is a listed Type NM conforming to the provisions of Article 336, and the communications cable is a listed Type CM, and the jackets on the listed NM and listed CM cables are rated for 600 volts minimum, and the hybrid cable is listed as being resistant to the spread of fire.

(FPN): One method of defining resistant to the spread of fire is that the cables do not spread fire to the top of the tray in the "Vertical-Tray Flame Test" in the Reference Standard for Electrical Wires, Cables and Flexible Cords, ANSI/UL 1581-1985.

Another method of defining resistant to the spread of fire is for the damage (char length) not to exceed 4 feet 11 inches (1.5 m) when performing the "Vertical Flame Test—Cables in Cable Trays," as described in Test Methods for Electrical Wires and Cables, CSA C22.2 No. 0.3-M-1985.

800-52. Installation of Communications Wires, Cables, and Equipment. Communications wires and cables from the protector to the equipment or, where no protector is required, communications wires and cables attached to the outside or inside of the building shall comply with (a) through (c) below.

(a) Separation from Other Conductors.

(1) Open Conductors. Communications wires and cables shall be separated at least 2 inches (50.8 mm) from conductors of any electric light or power circuits, Class 1, or nonpower-limited fire protective signaling circuits.

Exception No. 1: Where the electric light or power, Class 1, or nonpower-limited fire protective signaling circuit conductors are in a raceway or in metal-sheathed, metal-clad, nonmetallic-sheathed, Type AC, or Type UF cables.

Exception No. 2: Where the communications wires and cables are permanently separated from the conductors of the other circuit by a continuous and firmly fixed nonconductor, such as porcelain tubes or flexible tubing, in addition to the insulation on the wire.

(2) In Raceways, Boxes, and Cables.

a. Other Power-Limited Circuits. Communications cables shall be permitted in the same raceway or enclosure with cables of any of the following:

1. Class 2 and Class 3 remote-control, signaling, and power-limited circuits in compliance with Article 725.

2. Power-limited fire protective signaling systems in compliance with Article 760.

3. Nonconductive and conductive optical fiber cables in compliance with Article 770.

4. Community antenna television and radio distribution systems in compliance with Article 820.

b. Class 2 and Class 3 Circuits. Class 1 circuits shall not be run in the same cable with communications circuits. Class 2 and Class 3 circuit conductors shall be permitted in the same cable with communications circuits, in which case the Class 2 and Class 3 circuits shall be classified as communications circuits and shall meet the requirements of this article. The cables shall be listed as communications cables or multipurpose cables.

Exception: Cables constructed of individually listed Class 2, Class 3, and communications cables under a common jacket shall not be required to be classified as communications cable. The fire resistance rating of the composite cable shall be determined by the performance of the composite cable.

c. Electric Light or Power Circuits.

1. Communications conductors shall not be placed in any raceway, compartment, outlet box, junction box, or similar fitting with conductors of electric light or power circuits or Class 1 circuits.

Exception No. 1: Where all of the conductors of electric light or power, Class 1, or nonpower-limited fire protective signaling circuits are separated from all of the conductors of communications circuits by a barrier.

Exception No. 2: Electric light or power, Class 1, or nonpower-limited fire protective signaling circuit conductors in outlet boxes, junction boxes, or similar fittings or compartments where such conductors are introduced solely for power supply to

communications equipment or for connection to remote-control equipment. The electric light or power, Class 1, or nonpower-limited fire protective signaling circuit conductors shall be routed within the enclosure to maintain a minimum of 0.25 inch (6.35 mm) separation from the communications circuit conductors.

2. In shafts. Communications wires and cables run in the same shaft with conductors of electric light or power, Class 1, or nonpower-limited fire protective signaling circuits shall be separated from light or power conductors, Class 1, or nonpower-limited fire protective signaling circuit conductors by not less than 2 inches (50.8 mm).

Exception No. 1: Where either (1) all of the conductors of the electric light or power, Class 1 or nonpower-limited fire protective signaling circuits, or (2) all of the conductors of communications circuits are encased in raceway.

Exception No. 2: Where the electric light or power, Class 1 or nonpower-limited fire protective signaling conductors are in a raceway, or in metal-sheathed, metal-clad, nonmetallic-sheathed, or Type UF cables.

(b) Spread of Fire or Products of Combustion. Installations in hollow spaces, vertical shafts, and ventilation or air-handling ducts shall be so made that the possible spread of fire or products of combustion will not be substantially increased. Openings around penetrations through fire resistance-rated walls, partitions, floors, or ceilings shall be firestopped using approved methods.

(c) Equipment in Other Space Used for Environmental Air. Section 300-22(c) shall apply.

(d) Cable Trays. Types MPP, MPR, MPG, and MP multipurpose cables and Types CMP, CMR, CMG, and CM communications cables shall be permitted to be installed in cable trays.

(e) Support of Conductors. Raceways shall not be used as a means of support for communications wires and cables.

800-53. **Applications of Listed Communications Wires and Cables.** Communications wires and cables shall comply with (a) through (f).

Note that the length of unlisted outside plant cable permitted in the building depends on the location of the primary protector, in accordance with Sections 800-30(b) and 800-50, Exception No. 3.

Figure 800-2. *An example of applications of listed communications and multipurpose cables.*

MPP, CMP
(not in conduit)

MPR, CMR
(not in conduit)

MPR, CMR (in conduit–
only in plenum)

MP, CM, CMG
(not in conduit
and not in same
penetration as
riser cables)

Plenum

Basement

Outside plant
cable (not to
exceed 50 feet)

Primary protector
(as close as practicable
to cable entrance)

MPP, CMP
(not in conduit)

MPR, CMR
(not in conduit)

MPR, CMR
(in conduit–
only in plenum)

MP, CM, CMG
(not in conduit
and not in same
penetration as
riser cables)

Plenum

(a) Plenum. Cables installed in ducts, plenums, and other spaces used for environmental air shall be Type CMP.

Exception: Types CMP, CMR, CMG, CM, and CMX and communications wire installed in compliance with Section 300-22.

(b) Riser. Cables installed in vertical runs and penetrating more than one floor, or cables installed in vertical runs in a shaft, shall be Type CMR. Floor penetrations requiring Type CMR shall contain only cables suitable for riser or plenum use.

(FPN): See Section 800-52(b) for firestop requirements for floor penetrations.

Exception No. 1: Where the listed cables are encased in metal raceway or are located in a fireproof shaft having firestops at each floor.

Exception No. 2: Types CM and CMX cable in one- and two-family dwellings.

(c) Distributing Frames and Cross-Connect Arrays. Communications wires shall be used in distributing frames and cross-connect arrays.

Exception: Types CMP, CMR, CMG, and CM are permitted to be used.

(d) Other Wiring within Buildings. Cables installed in building locations other than the locations covered in (a), (b), and (c) above shall be Type CMG or Type CM.

Exception No. 1: Where listed communications wires and cables are enclosed in raceway.

Exception No. 2: Type CMX communications cable in nonconcealed spaces where the exposed length of cable does not exceed 10 feet (3.05 m).

Exception No. 3: Type CMX communications cables that are less than 0.25 inch (6.35 mm) in diameter and installed in one- or two-family dwellings.

Exception No. 4: Type CMX communications wires and cables that are less than 0.25 inch (6.35 mm) in diameter and installed in nonconcealed spaces in multifamily dwellings.

Exception No. 5: Type CMUC undercarpet communications wires and cables installed under carpet.

(e) Hybrid Power and Communications Cable. Hybrid power and communications cable listed in accordance with Section 800-51(i) shall be permitted to be installed in one-and two-family dwellings.

(f) Cable Substitutions. Substitutions for communications cables listed in Table 800-53 and illustrated in Figure 800-53 shall be permitted.

Table 800-53. Cable Substitutions

Cable Type	Permitted Substitutions
MPP	None
CMP	MPP
MPR	MPP
CMR	MPP, CMP, MPR
MPG, MP	MPP, MPR
CMG, CM	MPP, CMP, MPR, CMR, MPG, MP
CMX	MPP, CMP, MPR, CMR, MPG, MP, CMG, CM

(FPN): For the use of communications cable and multipurpose cable in place of Class 2 or Class 3 cables, see Section 725-53(g), and, for the use of communications cable and multipurpose cable in place of power-limited fire protective signaling cables, see Section 760-53(d). The permitted cable substitutions are illustrated in Figure 800-53.

Type CM — Communications Wires and Cables
Types CL2 and CL3 — Class 2 and Class 3 Remote-Control, Signaling, and Power-Limited Cables
Type FPL — Power-Limited Fire Protective Signaling Cables
Type MP — Multipurpose Cables
Type PLTC — Power-Limited Tray Cable

Figure 800-53.   *Cable Substitution Hierarchy*

ARTICLE 810   Radio and Television Equipment

Contents

A. General

A. General

810-1. Scope. This article covers radio and television receiving equipment and amateur radio transmitting and receiving equipment, but not equipment and antennas used for coupling carrier current to power line conductors.

810-2. Other Articles. Wiring from the source of power to and between devices connected to the interior wiring system shall comply with Chapters 1 through 4 other than as modified by Sections 640-3, 640-4, and 640-5. Wiring for radio-frequency and audio-frequency equipment and loud speakers shall comply with Article 640. Where optical fiber is used Article 770 shall apply. Coaxial cable wiring for television receiving shall comply with Article 820.

810-3. Community Television Antenna. The antenna shall comply with this article. The distribution system shall comply with Article 820.

810-4. Radio Noise Suppressors. Radio interference eliminators, interference capacitors, or noise suppressors connected to power-supply leads shall be of a listed type. They shall not be exposed to physical damage.

810-5. Definitions. See Article 100.

B. Receiving Equipment — Antenna Systems

810-11. Material. Antennas and lead-in conductors shall be of hard-drawn copper, bronze, aluminum alloy, copper-clad steel, or other high-strength, corrosion-resistant material.

Exception: Soft-drawn or medium-drawn copper shall be permitted for lead-in conductors where the maximum span between points of support is less than 35 feet (10.67 m).

810-12. Supports. Outdoor antennas and lead-in conductors shall be securely supported. The antennas shall not be attached to the electric service mast. They shall not be attached to poles or similar structures carrying open electric light or power wires or trolley wires of over 250 volts between conductors. Insulators supporting the antenna conductors shall have sufficient mechanical strength to safely support the conductors. Lead-in conductors shall be securely attached to the antennas.

810-13. **Avoidance of Contacts with Conductors of Other Systems.** Outdoor antennas and lead-in conductors from an antenna to a building shall not cross over open conductors of electric light or power circuits and shall be kept well away from all such circuits so as to avoid the possibility of accidental contact. Where proximity to open electric light or power service conductors of less than 250 volts between conductors cannot be avoided, the installation shall be such as to provide a clearance of at least 2 feet (610 mm).

Where practicable, antenna conductors shall be so installed as not to cross under open electric light or power conductors.

One of the leading causes of electrical shock and electrocution, according to statistical reports, is the accidental contact of radio and television receiving antennas and equipment, and amateur radio transmitting and receiving antennas and equipment, with light or power conductors. Extreme caution should therefore be exercised during this type of installation, and periodic visual inspections should be conducted thereafter.

810-14. **Splices.** Splices and joints in antenna spans shall be made mechanically secure with approved splicing devices or by such other means as will not appreciably weaken the conductors.

Conductor spans from antennas should be of sufficient size and strength to maintain clearances and avoid possible contact with light or power conductors. Splices and joints should be made with approved connectors or other means that provide sufficient mechanical strength so conductors are not weakened appreciably.

810-15. **Grounding.** Masts and metal structures supporting antennas shall be grounded in accordance with Section 810-21.

810-16. **Size of Wire-Strung Antenna — Receiving Station.**

(a) **Size of Antenna Conductors.** Outdoor antenna conductors for receiving stations shall be of a size not less than given in Table 810-16(a).

Table 810-16(a). **Size of Receiving-Station Outdoor Antenna Conductors**

	Minimum Size of Conductors		
	When Maximum Open Span Length is		
Material	Less than 35 feet	35 feet to 150 feet	Over 150 feet
Aluminum alloy, hard-drawn copper	19	14	12
Copper-clad steel, bronze, or other high-strength material	20	17	14

For SI units: one foot = 0.3048 meter.

(b) **Self-Supporting Antennas.** Outdoor antennas, such as vertical rods, dishes, or dipole structures, shall be of corrosion-resistant materials and of strength suitable to withstand ice and wind loading conditions, and shall be located well away from overhead conductors of electric light and power circuits of over 150 volts to ground, so as to avoid the possibility of the antenna or structure falling into or making accidental contact with such circuits.

This section was expanded in the 1990 *Code* to include dish-type (parabolic) antennas.

810-17. **Size of Lead-in — Receiving Station.** Lead-in conductors from outside antennas for receiving stations shall, for various maximum open span lengths, be of such size as to have a tensile strength at least as great as that of the conductors for antennas as specified in Section 810-16. Where the lead-in consists of two or more conductors that are twisted together, are enclosed in the same covering, or are concentric, the conductor size shall, for various maximum open span lengths, be such that the tensile strength of the combination will be at least as great as that of the conductors for antennas as specified in Section 810-16.

810-18. **Clearances — Receiving Stations.**

(a) **Outside of Buildings.** Lead-in conductors attached to buildings shall be so installed that they cannot swing closer than 2 feet (610 mm) to the conductors of circuits of 250 volts or less between conductors, or 10 feet (3.05 m) to the conductors of circuits of over 250 volts between conductors, except that in the case of circuits not over 150 volts between conductors, where all conductors involved are supported so as to ensure permanent separation, the clearance shall be permitted to be reduced but shall not be less than 4 inches (102 mm). The clearance between lead-in conductors and any conductor forming a part of a lightning-rod system shall be not less than 6 feet (1.83 m) unless the bonding referred to in Section 250-86 is accomplished. Underground conductors shall be separated at least 12 inches (305 mm) from conductors of any light or power circuits, or Class 1 circuits.

Exception: Where the electric light or power conductors, Class 1 conductors, or lead-in conductors are installed in raceways or metal cable armor.

(b) Antennas and Lead-ins — Indoors. Indoor antennas and indoor lead-ins shall not be run nearer than 2 inches (50.8 mm) to conductors of other wiring systems in the premises.

Exception No. 1: Where such other conductors are in metal raceways or cable armor.

Exception No. 2: Where permanently separated from such other conductors by a continuous and firmly fixed nonconductor, such as porcelain tubes or flexible tubing.

(c) In Boxes or Other Enclosures. Indoor antennas and indoor lead-ins shall be permitted to occupy the same box or enclosure with conductors of other wiring systems where separated from such other conductors by an effective permanently installed barrier.

810-19. **Electric Supply Circuits Used in Lieu of Antenna — Receiving Stations.** Where an electric supply circuit is used in lieu of an antenna, the device by which the radio receiving set is connected to the supply circuit shall be listed.

The approved device is usually a small, fixed capacitor connecting the antenna terminal of the receiver and one wire of the supply circuit. As is the case with most receivers, the capacitor should be designed for operation at not less than 300 V. This ensures a high degree of safety and minimizes the possibility of a breakdown in the capacitor, thereby avoiding a short circuit to ground through the antenna coil of the set.

810-20. **Antenna Discharge Units — Receiving Stations.**

(a) Where Required. Each conductor of a lead-in from an outdoor antenna shall be provided with a listed antenna discharge unit.

Exception: Where the lead-in conductors are enclosed in a continuous metallic shield that is either permanently and effectively grounded, or is protected by an antenna discharge unit.

(b) Location. Antenna discharge units shall be located outside the building or inside the building between the point of entrance of the lead-in and the radio set or transformers, and as near as practicable to the entrance of the conductors to the building. The antenna discharge unit shall not be located near combustible material nor in a hazardous (classified) location as defined in Article 500.

A lightning arrester is not required where the lead-in conductors are enclosed in a continuous metal shield, such as rigid or intermediate metal conduit, electrical metallic tubing, or any metal raceway or metal-shielded cable that is effectively grounded. A lightning discharge will take the path of lower impedance and jump from the lead-in conductors to the metal raceway or shield rather than take the path through the antenna coil of the receiver.

(c) Grounding. The antenna discharge unit shall be grounded in accordance with Section 810-21.

810-21. **Grounding Conductors — Receiving Stations.** Grounding conductors shall comply with (a) through (j) below.

(a) Material. The grounding conductor shall be of copper, aluminum, copper-clad steel, bronze, or similar corrosion-resistant material.

(b) Insulation. Insulation on grounding conductors shall not be required.

(c) Supports. The grounding conductors shall be securely fastened in place and shall be permitted to be directly attached to the surface wired over without the use of insulating supports.

Exception: Where proper support cannot be provided, the size of the grounding conductors shall be increased proportionately.

(d) Mechanical Protection. The grounding conductor shall be protected where exposed to physical damage, or the size of the grounding conductors shall be increased proportionately to compensate for the lack of protection.

(e) Run in Straight Line. The grounding conductor for an antenna mast or antenna discharge unit shall be run in as straight a line as practicable from the mast or discharge unit to the grounding electrode.

(f) Electrode. The grounding conductor shall be connected as follows:

(1) To the nearest accessible location on (1) the building or structure grounding electrode system as covered in Section 250-81, (2) the grounded interior metal water piping system as covered in Section 250-80(a), (3) the power service accessible means external to enclosures as covered in Section 250-71(b), (4) the metallic power service raceway, (5) the service equipment enclosure, or (6) the grounding electrode conductor or the grounding electrode conductor metal enclosures; or

(2) If the building or structure served has no grounding means, as described in (f)(1), to any one of the individual electrodes described in Section 250-81; or

(3) If the building or structure served has no grounding means, as described in (f)(1) or (f)(2), to (1) an effectively grounded metal structure or (2) to any of the individual electrodes described in Section 250-83.

(g) Inside or Outside Building. The grounding conductor shall be permitted to be run either inside or outside the building.

(h) Size. The grounding conductor shall not be smaller than No. 10 copper or No. 8 aluminum or No. 17 copper-clad steel or bronze.

(i) Common Ground. A single grounding conductor shall be permitted for both protective and operating purposes.

The requirements for grounding are in accordance with the provisions of Article 250. Antenna masts are required to be grounded to the same grounding electrode used for the electrical system of the building. This is necessary to ensure that all exposed, dead metal parts are at the same potential. In many cases, masts are incorrectly connected to conveniently located vent pipes, metal gutters, and downspouts. This could create potential differences between various metal parts located in or on buildings and lead-in conductors, resulting in possible shock and fire hazards. Underground gas piping systems are not permitted to be used as the required grounding electrode.

(j) Bonding of Electrodes. A bonding jumper not smaller than No. 6 copper or equivalent shall be connected between the radio and television equipment grounding electrode and the power grounding electrode system at the building or structure served where separate electrodes are used.

This section was revised in the 1990 *Code* to clarify that the bonding requirement applies only to electrodes at the same building or structure. The use of separate radio/television grounding electrodes is not required.

C. Amateur Transmitting and Receiving Stations — Antenna Systems

810-51. **Other Sections.** In addition to complying with Part C, antenna systems for amateur transmitting and receiving stations shall also comply with Sections 810-11 through 810-15.

810-52. **Size of Antenna.** Antenna conductors for transmitting and receiving stations shall be of a size not less than given in Table 810-52.

Table 810-52. **Size of Amateur Station Outdoor Antenna Conductors**

	Minimum Size of Conductors	
	Where Maximum Open Span Length is	
	Less than	Over
Material	150 feet	150 feet
Hard-drawn copper	14	10
Copper-clad steel, bronze, or other high-strength material	14	12

For SI units: one foot = 0.3048 meter.

810-53. **Size of Lead-in Conductors.** Lead-in conductors for transmitting stations shall, for various maximum span lengths, be of a size at least as great as that of conductors for antennas as specified in Section 810-52.

810-54. **Clearance on Building.** Antenna conductors for transmitting stations, attached to buildings, shall be firmly mounted at least 3 inches (76 mm) clear of the surface of the building on nonabsorbent insulating supports, such as treated pins or brackets equipped with insulators having not less than 3-inch (76-mm) creepage and airgap distances. Lead-in conductors attached to buildings shall also comply with these requirements.

Exception: Where the lead-in conductors are enclosed in a continuous metallic shield that is permanently and effectively grounded, they shall not be required to comply with these requirements. Where grounded, the metallic shield shall also be permitted to be used as a conductor.

The creepage distance is measured from the conductor, across the face of the supporting insulator, to the building surface. The air gap distance is measured from the conductor (at its closest point), across the air space (not necessarily in a straight line), to the surface of the building. The exception covers coaxial cable with the shield permanently and effectively grounded.

810-55. **Entrance to Building.** Except where protected with a continuous metallic shield that is permanently and effectively grounded, lead-in conductors for transmitting stations shall enter buildings by one of the following methods: (1) through a rigid, noncombustible, nonabsorbent insulating tube or bushing; (2) through an opening provided for the purpose in which the entrance conductors are firmly secured so as to provide a clearance of at least 2 inches (50.8 mm); or (3) through a drilled window pane.

810-56. **Protection Against Accidental Contact.** Lead-in conductors to radio transmitters shall be so located or installed as to make accidental contact with them difficult.

810-57. **Antenna Discharge Units — Transmitting Stations.** Each conductor of a lead-in for outdoor antennas shall be provided with an antenna discharge unit or other suitable means that will drain static charges from the antenna system.

Exception No. 1: Where protected by a continuous metallic shield that is permanently and effectively grounded.

Exception No. 2: Where the antenna is permanently and effectively grounded.

Where an antenna discharge unit is not installed at a transmitting station, protection against lightning may be provided by a switch that connects the lead-in to ground during the time the station is not in operation.

810-58. **Grounding Conductors — Amateur Transmitting and Receiving Stations.** Grounding conductors shall comply with (a) through (c) below.

(a) **Other Sections.** All grounding conductors for amateur transmitting and receiving stations shall comply with Sections 810-21(a) through (j).

(b) **Size of Protective Grounding Conductor.** The protective grounding conductor for transmitting stations shall be as large

as the lead-in, but not smaller than No. 10 copper, bronze, or copper-clad steel.

(c) **Size of Operating Grounding Conductor.** The operating grounding conductor for transmitting stations shall not be less than No. 14 copper or its equivalent.

D. Interior Installation — Transmitting Stations

810-70. **Clearance from Other Conductors.** All conductors inside the building shall be separated at least 4 inches (102 mm) from the conductors of any electric light, power, or signaling circuit.

Exception No. 1: As provided in Article 640.

Exception No. 2: Where separated from other conductors by raceway or some firmly fixed nonconductor, such as porcelain tubes or flexible tubing.

810-71. **General.** Transmitters shall comply with (a) through (c) below.

(a) **Enclosing.** The transmitter shall be enclosed in a metal frame or grille, or separated from the operating space by a barrier or other equivalent means, all metallic parts of which are effectively connected to ground.

(b) **Grounding of Controls.** All external metal handles and controls accessible to the operating personnel shall be effectively grounded.

(c) **Interlocks on Doors.** All access doors shall be provided with interlocks that will disconnect all voltages of over 350 volts between conductors when any access door is opened.

ARTICLE 820 Community Antenna Television and Radio Distribution Systems

Contents

A. General

820-6. Mechanical Execution of Work.

B. Cables Outside and Entering Buildings

820-10. Outside Cables.
  (a) On Poles.
  (b) Lead-in Clearance.
  (c) Above Roofs.
  (d) Between Buildings.
  (e) On Buildings.
820-11. Entering Buildings.
  (a) Underground Systems.
  (b) Direct Buried Cables and Raceways.

C. Protection

820-33. Grounding of Outer Conductive Shield of a Coaxial Cable.
  (a) Shield Grounding.
  (b) Shield Protection Devices.

D. Grounding Methods

820-40. Cable Grounding.
  (a) Grounding Conductor.
  (b) Electrode.
  (c) Electrode Connection.
  (d) Bonding of Electrodes.
820-41. Equipment Grounding.
820-42. Bonding and Grounding at Mobile Homes.
  (a) Grounding.
  (b) Bonding.

E. Cables within Buildings

820-49. Fire Resistance of CATV Cables.
820-50. Listing, Marking, and Installation of Coaxial Cables.
820-51. Additional Listing Requirements.
  (a) Type CATVP.
  (b) Type CATVR.
  (c) Type CATV.
  (d) Type CATVX.
820-52. Installation of Cables and Equipment.
  (a) Separation from Other Conductors.

  (b) Spread of Fire or Products of Combustion.
  (c) Equipment in Other Space Used for Environmental Air.
  (d) Hybrid Power and Coaxial Cabling.
  (e) Support of Conductors.
820-53. Applications of Listed CATV Cables.
  (a) Plenum.
  (b) Riser.
  (c) Other Wiring within Buildings.
  (d) Cable Substitutions.

A. General

820-1. Scope. This article covers coaxial cable distribution of radio frequency signals typically employed in community antenna television (CATV) systems.

(FPN): Where the installation is other than coaxial, see Articles 770 and 800 as applicable.

820-2. Energy Limitations. The coaxial cable shall be permitted to deliver low-energy power to equipment directly associated with the radio frequency distribution system if the voltage is not over 60 volts and if the current supply is from a transformer or other device having energy-limiting characteristics.

820-3. Definitions. See Article 100. For the purposes of this Article, the following additional definition applies:

Point of Entrance. The point of entrance within a building is the point at which the cable emerges from an external wall, from a concrete floor slab, or from a rigid metal conduit or an intermediate metal conduit grounded to an electrode in accordance with Section 820-40(b).

820-5. Access to Electrical Equipment Behind Panels Designed to Allow Access. Access to equipment shall not be denied by an accumulation of wires and cables that prevents removal of panels, including suspended ceiling panels.

820-6. Mechanical Execution of Work. Community antenna television and radio distribution systems shall be installed in a neat and workmanlike manner.

B. Cables Outside and Entering Buildings

820-10. **Outside Cables.** Coaxial cables, prior to the point of grounding, as defined in Section 820-33, shall comply with (a) through (e) below.

(a) On Poles. Where practicable, conductors on poles shall be located below the electric light or power conductors and shall not be attached to a cross-arm that carries electric light or power conductors.

(b) Lead-in Clearance. Lead-in or aerial-drop cables from a pole or other support, including the point of initial attachment to a building or structure, shall be kept away from electric light or power circuits so as to avoid the possibility of accidental contact.

Exception: Where proximity to electric light or power service conductors cannot be avoided, the installation shall be such as to provide clearances of not less than 12 inches (305 mm) from light or power service drops.

(c) Above Roofs. Cables shall have a vertical clearance of not less than 8 feet (2.44 m) from all points of roofs above which they pass.

Exception No. 1: Auxiliary buildings such as garages and the like.

Exception No. 2: A reduction in clearance above only the overhanging portion of the roof to not less than 18 inches (457 mm) shall be permitted if (1) not more than 4 feet (1.22 m) of communication service drop conductors pass above the roof overhang, and (2) they are terminated at a through-the-roof raceway or support.

Exception No. 3: Where the roof has a slope not less than 4 inches (102 mm) in 12 inches (305 mm), a reduction in clearance to not less than 3 feet (914 mm) shall be permitted.

(d) Between Buildings. Cables extending between buildings and also the supports or attachment fixtures shall be acceptable for the purpose and shall have sufficient strength to withstand the loads to which they may be subjected.

Exception: Where a cable does not have sufficient strength to be self-supporting, it shall be attached to a supporting messenger cable that, together with the attachment fixtures or supports, shall be acceptable for the purpose and shall have sufficient strength to withstand the loads to which they may be subjected.

(e) On Buildings. Where attached to buildings, cables shall be securely fastened in such a manner that they will be separated from other conductors as follows:

(1) Electric Light or Power. The coaxial cable shall have a separation of at least 4 inches (102 mm) from electric light or power conductors not in raceway or cable, or be permanently separated from conductors of the other system by a continuous and firmly fixed nonconductor in addition to the insulation on the wires.

(2) Other Communications Systems. Coaxial cable shall be installed so that there will be no unnecessary interference in the maintenance of the separate systems. In no case shall the conductors, cables, messenger strand, or equipment of one system cause abrasion to the conductors, cable, messenger strand, or equipment of any other system.

(3) Lightning Conductors. Where practicable, a separation of at least 6 feet (1.83 m) shall be maintained between any coaxial cable and lightning conductors.

820-11. **Entering Buildings.**

(a) Underground Systems. Underground coaxial cables in a duct, pedestal, handhole, or manhole containing electric light or power conductors or Class 1 circuits shall be in a section permanently separated from such conductors by means of a suitable barrier.

(b) Direct Buried Cables and Raceways. Direct buried coaxial cable shall be separated at least 12 inches (305 mm) from conductors of any light or power or Class 1 circuit.

Exception No. 1: Where electric service conductors or coaxial cables are installed in raceways or have metal cable armor.

Exception No. 2: Where electric light or power branch-circuit or feeder conductors or Class 1 circuit conductors are installed in a raceway or in metal-sheathed, metal-clad, or Type UF or Type USE cables; or the coaxial cables have metal cable armor or are installed in a raceway.

C. Protection

820-33. **Grounding of Outer Conductive Shield of a Coaxial Cable.** Where coaxial cable is exposed to lightning or to accidental contact with lightning arrester conductors or power conductors operating at a voltage of over 300 volts to ground, the outer conductive shield of the coaxial cable shall be grounded at the building premises as close to the point of cable entry as practicable. For purposes of this section, the point at which the exposed cable enters shall be considered to be the point of emergence through an exterior wall, a concrete floor slab, or from a rigid or intermediate metal conduit grounded to an electrode in accordance with Section 820-40(b).

For purposes of this section, grounding located at mobile home service equipment located in sight from and no more than 30 feet (9.14 m) from the exterior wall of the mobile home it serves, or at a mobile home disconnecting means grounded in accordance with Section 250-24 and located in sight from and not more than 30 feet (9.14 m) from the exterior wall of the mobile home it serves, shall be considered to meet the requirements of this section.

(FPN): Selecting a grounding location to achieve the shortest practicable grounding conductor will help limit potential differences between CATV and other metallic systems.

(a) Shield Grounding. Where the outer conductive shield of a coaxial cable is grounded, no other protective devices shall be required.

(b) Shield Protection Devices. Grounding of a coaxial drop cable shield by means of a protective device that does not interrupt the grounding system within the premises shall be permitted.

This section permits the use of a shield protective device that does not interrupt the grounding system within the premises. This permits protection against overheating for the CATV service-drop cable. Overheating can occur due to neutral fault currents in the power and lighting system. Such a protective device would have to maintain the integrity of the coaxial system to prevent RF leakage. An ordinary fuse, for example, would not be suitable.

D. Grounding Methods

820-40. **Cable Grounding.** Where required by Section 820-33, the shield of the coaxial cable shall be grounded as specified in (a) through (d) below.

(a) Grounding Conductor.

(1) Insulation. The grounding conductor shall be insulated and shall be listed as suitable for the purpose.

(2) Material. The grounding conductor shall be copper or other corrosion-resistant conductive material, stranded or solid.

(3) Size. The grounding conductor shall not be smaller than No. 14; it shall have a current-carrying capacity approximately equal to that of the outer conductor of the coaxial cable.

(4) Run in Straight Line. The grounding conductor shall be run to the grounding electrode in as straight a line as practicable.

(5) Physical Protection. Where subject to physical damage, the grounding conductor shall be adequately protected. Where the grounding conductor is run in a metal raceway, both ends of the raceway shall be bonded to the grounding conductor or the same terminal or electrode to which the grounding conductor is connected.

(b) Electrode. The grounding conductor shall be connected as follows:

(1) To the nearest accessible location on (1) the building or structure grounding electrode system as covered in Section 250-81, (2) the grounded interior metal water piping system as covered in Section 250-80(a), (3) the power service accessible means external to enclosures as covered in Section 250-71(b), (4) the metallic power service raceway, (5) the service equipment enclosure, (6) the grounding electrode conductor or the grounding electrode conductor metal enclosure, or (7) to the grounding conductor or to the grounding electrode of a building or structure disconnecting means that is grounded to an electrode as covered in Section 250-24; or

(2) If the building or structure served has no grounding means as described in (b)(1), to any one of the individual electrodes described in Section 250-81; or

(3) If the building or structure served has no grounding means as described in (b)(1) or (b)(2), to (1) an effectively grounded metal structure or (2) to any one of the individual electrodes described in Section 250-83.

(c) Electrode Connection. Connections to grounding electrodes shall comply with Section 250-115.

(d) Bonding of Electrodes. A bonding jumper not smaller than No. 6 copper or equivalent shall be connected between the antenna systems grounding electrode and the power grounding electrode system at the building or structure served where separate electrodes are used.

This section requires bonding of CATV and power grounding electrodes at the same building or structure. There are no requirements for separate grounding electrodes for CATV.

Exception: At mobile homes as covered in Section 820-42.

(FPN No. 1): See Section 250-86 for use of lightning rods.

(FPN No. 2): Bonding together of all separate electrodes will limit potential differences between them and between their associated wiring systems.

The most common error made in grounding CATV systems is to connect the coaxial cable sheath to a ground rod driven by the CATV installer at a convenient location near the point of cable entry to the building. This is permitted by the *Code* only if the building or structure has none of the grounding means described in Sections 820-40(b)(1) or 820-40(b)(2), which is rare. The *Code* does not require that these grounding means be readily available; if they exist, they are required to be used.

Proper bonding of the CATV system coaxial cable sheath to the electrical power ground is needed to prevent potential fire and shock hazards. The earth cannot be used as an equipment grounding conductor or bonding conductor, as it does not have the low-impedance path required. See Section 250-91(c).

Both CATV systems and power systems are subject to current surges as a result, for example, of induced voltages from lightning in the vicinity of the usually extensive outside distribution systems. Surges also result from switching operations on power systems. If the grounded conductors and parts of the two systems are not bonded by a low-impedance path, such line surges can raise the potential difference between the two systems to many thousands of volts. This can result in arcing between the two systems; for example, wherever the coaxial cable jacket contacts a grounded part, such as a metal water pipe or metal structural member, inside the building.

If an individual is the interface between the two systems and the bonding has not been done in accordance with the *Code*, the high-voltage surge could result in electric shock. More common, however, is burnout of the TV tuner, as this part is almost always an interface between the two systems. The tuner is connected to the power system ground through the grounded neutral of the power supply, even if the TV set itself is not provided with an equipment grounding conductor.

Also see commentary following Sections 250-71(b)(3) and 820-33(b).

820-41. **Equipment Grounding.** Unpowered equipment and enclosures or equipment powered by the coaxial cable shall be considered grounded where connected to the metallic cable shield.

820-42. **Bonding and Grounding at Mobile Homes.**

(a) Grounding. Where there is no mobile home service equipment located in sight from and not more than 30 feet (9.14 m) from the exterior wall of the mobile home it serves, or there is no mobile home disconnecting means grounded in accordance with Section 250-24 and located within sight from and not more than 30 feet (9.14 m) from the exterior wall of the mobile home it serves, the coaxial cable shield ground, or surge arrester ground, shall be in accordance with Sections 820-40(b) (2) and (3).

(b) Bonding. The coaxial cable shield grounding terminal, surge arrester grounding terminal, or grounding electrode shall be bonded to the metal frame or available grounding terminal of the mobile home with a copper grounding conductor not smaller than No. 12 under any of the following conditions:

(1) Where there is no mobile home service equipment or disconnecting means as in (a) above, or

(2) Where the mobile home is supplied by cord and plug.

E. Cables within Buildings

820-49. **Fire Resistance of CATV Cables.** Coaxial cables installed as wiring within buildings shall be listed as being resistant to the spread of fire in accordance with Sections 820-50 and 820-51.

820-50. **Listing, Marking, and Installation of Coaxial Cables.** Coaxial cables in a building shall be listed as being suitable for the purpose, and cables shall be marked in accordance with Table 820-50. The cable voltage rating shall not be marked on the cable.

(FPN): Voltage markings on cables may be misinterpreted to suggest that the cables may be suitable for Class 1, electric light and power applications.

Exception No. 1: Voltage markings shall be permitted where the cable has multiple listings and voltage marking is required for one or more of the listings.

Exception No. 2: Listing and marking shall not be required where the cable enters the building from the outside and is run in rigid metal conduit or intermediate metal conduit, and such conduits are grounded to an electrode in accordance with Section 820-40(b).

Exception No. 3: Listing and marking shall not be required where the length of cable within the building does not exceed 50 feet (15.2 m) and the cable enters the building from the outside and is terminated at a grounding block.

Table 820-50. Cable Markings

Cable Marking	Type	Reference
CATVP	CATV plenum cable	Sections 820-51(a) and 820-53(a)
CATVR	CATV riser cable	Sections 820-51(b) and 820-53(b)
CATV	CATV cable	Sections 820-51(c) and 820-53(c)
CATVX	CATV cable, limited use	Sections 820-51(d) and 820-53(c), Exception Nos. 1, 2, and 3

(FPN No. 1): Cable types are listed in descending order of fire-resistance rating.

(FPN No. 2): See the referenced sections for listing requirements and permitted uses.

820-51. **Additional Listing Requirements.** Cables shall be listed in accordance with (a) through (d) below.

(a) **Type CATVP.** Type CATVP community antenna television plenum cable shall be listed as being suitable for use in ducts, plenums, and other space used for environmental air and shall also be listed as having adequate fire-resistant and low-smoke-producing characteristics.

(FPN): One method of defining low-smoke-producing cables is by establishing an acceptable value of the smoke produced when tested in accordance with the Test for Fire and Smoke Characteristics of Wires and Cables, NFPA 262-1990 (ANSI), to a maximum peak optical density of 0.5 and a maximum average optical density of 0.15. Similarly, one method of defining fire-resistant cables is by establishing maximum allowable flame travel distance of 5 feet (1.52 m) when tested in accordance with the same test.

See commentary following Section 725-51(a), FPN.

(b) **Type CATVR.** Type CATVR community antenna television riser cable shall be listed as being suitable for use in a vertical run in a shaft or from floor to floor and shall also be listed as having fire-resistant characteristics capable of preventing the carrying of fire from floor to floor.

(FPN): One method of defining fire-resistant characteristics capable of preventing the carrying of fire from floor to floor is that the cables pass the requirements of the Standard Test for Flame Propagation Height of Electrical and Optical-Fiber Cable Installed Vertically in Shafts, ANSI/UL 1666-1986.

See commentary following Section 725-51(b), FPN.

(c) **Type CATV.** Type CATV community antenna television cable shall be listed as being suitable for general purpose CATV use, with the exception of risers and plenums, and shall also be listed as being resistant to the spread of fire.

(FPN): One method of defining resistant to the spread of fire is that the cables do not spread fire to the top of the tray in the "Vertical-Tray Flame Test" in the Reference Standard for Electrical Wires, Cables and Flexible Cords, ANSI/UL 1581-1985.

Another method of defining resistant to the spread of fire is for the damage (char length) not to exceed 4 feet 11 inches (1.5 m) when performing the "Vertical Flame Test—Cables in Cable Trays," as described in Test Methods for Electrical Wires and Cables, CSA C22.2 No. 0.3-M-1985.

See commentary following Section 725-51(c), FPN.

(d) **Type CATVX.** Type CATVX limited-use community antenna television cable shall be listed as being suitable for use in dwellings and for use in raceway and shall also be listed as being flame-retardant.

(FPN): One method of determining that cable is flame-retardant is by testing the cable to the "VW-1 (Vertical-Wire) Flame Test" in the Reference Standard for Electrical Wires, Cables and Flexible Cords, ANSI/UL 1581-1985.

See commentary following Section 725-51(d), FPN.

820-52. **Installation of Cables and Equipment.** Beyond the point of grounding, as defined in Section 820-33, the cable installation shall comply with (a) through (e) below.

(a) Separation from Other Conductors.

(1) Open Conductors. Coaxial cable shall be separated at least 2 inches (50.8 mm) from conductors of any electric light or power circuits or Class 1 circuits.

Exception No. 1: Where the electric light or power or Class 1 or coaxial cable circuit conductors are in a raceway, or in metal-sheathed, metal-clad, nonmetallic-sheathed, or Type UF cables.

Exception No. 2: Where the conductors are permanently separated from the conductors of the other circuits by a continuous and firmly fixed nonconductor, such as porcelain tubes or flexible tubing, in addition to the insulation on the wire.

(2) In Enclosures and Raceways.
 a. Other Power-Limited Circuits. Coaxial cables shall be permitted in the same raceway or enclosure with jacketed cables of any of the following:
  1. Class 2 and Class 3 remote-control, signaling, and power-limited circuits in compliance with Article 725.
  2. Power-limited fire protective signaling systems in compliance with Article 760.
  3. Communications circuits in compliance with Article 800.
  4. Optical fiber cables in compliance with Article 770.
 b. Electric Light or Power Circuits. Coaxial cable shall not be placed in any raceway, compartment, outlet box, junction box, or other enclosures with conductors of electric light or power or Class 1 circuits.

Exception No. 1: Where the conductors of the different systems are separated by a permanent barrier.

Exception No. 2: Conductors in outlet boxes, junction boxes, or similar fittings or compartments where such conductors are introduced solely for power supply to the coaxial cable system distribution equipment or for power connection to remote-control equipment.

The electric light, power, and Class 1 circuit conductors and nonpower-limited fire protective signaling circuit conductors shall be routed within the enclosure to maintain a minimum 0.25-inch (6.35-mm) separation from the coaxial cable.

(3) In Shafts. Coaxial cables run in the same shaft with conductors of electric light or power shall be separated from electric light or power conductors by not less than 2 inches (50.8 mm).

Exception No. 1: Where the conductors of either system are encased in metal raceway.

Exception No. 2: Where the electric light or power conductors are in raceway, or in metal-sheathed, metal-clad, nonmetallic-sheathed, or Type UF cables.

(b) Spread of Fire or Products of Combustion. Installations in hollow spaces, vertical shafts, and ventilation or air-handling ducts shall be so made that the possible spread of fire or products of combustion will not be substantially increased. Openings around penetrations through fire-resistance-rated walls, partitions, floors, or ceilings shall be firestopped using approved methods.

(c) Equipment in Other Space Used for Environmental Air. Section 300-22(c) shall apply.

(d) Hybrid Power and Coaxial Cabling. The provisions of Section 780-6 shall apply for listed hybrid power and coaxial cabling in closed-loop and programmed power distribution.

(e) Support of Conductors. Raceways shall not be used as a means of support for coaxial cables.

820-53. **Applications of Listed CATV Cables.** CATV cables shall comply with (a) through (d) below.

(a) Plenum. Cables installed in ducts, plenums, and other spaces used for environmental air shall be Type CATVP.

Exception: Types CATVP, CATVR, CATV, and CATVX cables installed in compliance with Section 300-22.

(b) Riser. Cables installed in vertical runs and penetrating more than one floor, or cables installed in vertical runs in a shaft, shall be Type CATVR. Floor penetrations requiring Type CATVR shall contain only cables suitable for riser or plenum use.

Exception No. 1: Types CATV and CATVX cables encased in metal raceway or located in a fireproof shaft having firestops at each floor.

Exception No. 2: Types CATV and CATVX cables in one- and two-family dwellings.

(FPN): See Section 820-52(b) for the firestop requirements for floor penetrations.

(c) Other Wiring within Buildings. Cables installed in building locations other than the locations covered in (a) and (b) above shall be Type CATV.

Exception No. 1: Type CATVX cable enclosed in raceway.

Exception No. 2: Type CATVX cable in nonconcealed spaces where the exposed length of cable does not exceed 10 feet (3.05 m).

Exception No. 3: Type CATVX cables that are less than .375 inch (9.52 mm) in diameter and installed in one- or two-family dwellings.

Exception No. 4: Type CATVX cables that are less than .375 inch (9.52 mm) in diameter and installed in nonconcealed spaces in multifamily dwellings.

(d) Cable Substitutions. The substitutions for community antenna television cables listed in Table 820-53 shall be permitted.

Table 820-53.   Coaxial Cable Substitutions

Cable Type	Permitted Substitutions
CATVP	MPP, CMP
CATVR	CATVP, MPP, CMP, MPR, CMR
CATV	CATVP, MPP, CMP, CATVR, MPR, CMR, MPG, MP, CMG, CM
CATVX	CATVP, MPP, CMP, CATVR, MPR, CMR, CATV, MPG, MP, CMG, CM

9

Tables and Examples

Contents

A. Tables

Notes to Tables

B. Examples

4(a). Multifamily Dwelling

4(b). Optional Calculation for Multifamily Dwelling

5(a). Multifamily Dwelling Served at 208Y/120 Volts, Three Phase

5(b). Optional Calculation for Multifamily Dwelling Served at 208Y/120 Volts, Three Phase

6. Maximum Demand for Range Loads

8. Motors, Conductors, Overload, and Short-Circuit and Ground-Fault Protection

9. Feeder Size Determination for Generator Field Control

10. Determining Conductor Ampacity for a Group of Six Elevators on a Single Feeder Using Adjustable Speed Drive

A. Tables

Notes to Tables

1. Tables 3A, 3B, and 3C apply only to complete conduit or tubing systems and are not intended to apply to sections of conduit or tubing used to protect exposed wiring from physical damage.

Tables 3A, 3B, and 3C provide the user with a set of precalculated conduit fill values so that a calculation is not required for each installation.

2. Equipment grounding or bonding conductors, where installed, shall be included when calculating conduit or tubing fill. The actual dimensions of the equipment grounding or bonding conductor (insulated or bare) shall be used in the calculation.

Some aluminium building wire in types THW, THWN/THHN, and XHHW is compact stranded. Table 5A provides appropriate dimensions for these types of wire.

3. Where conduit or tubing nipples having a maximum length not to exceed 24 inches (610 mm) are installed between boxes, cabinets, and similar enclosures, the nipple shall be permitted to be filled to 60 percent of its total cross-sectional area, and Article 310, Note 8(a) of Notes to Ampacity Tables of 0-2000 Volts need not apply to this condition.

Tables are not provided with precalculated conduit fill for conductors larger than 750 kcmil or for combinations of conductors. For these installations, Tables 4 through 8 must be used.

4. For conductors not included in Chapter 9, such as multi-conductor cables, the actual dimensions shall be used.

5. See Table 1 for allowable percentage of conduit or tubing fill.

Example: Three 15-kV single conductors are to be installed in conduit. The outside diameter of each conductor measures $1\frac{5}{8}$ inch ($1\frac{5}{8}$ inch = 1.62 inch).

$$1.62 \times 1.62 \times .7854 \times 3 = 6.18 \text{ sq in.}$$

Table 1 allows 40 percent conduit fill for three or more conductors. Table 4 indicates that 40 percent of a 5-inch conduit is 8.00 square inch, thus accommodating three 15-kV single conductors.

The percentage fills of Table 1 for conduit and tubing are to be used where any conflict occurs in Tables 3A, 3B, or 3C and also where various conductor sizes are to be installed in the same conduit.

An example of computing the conduit size for various conductor sizes follows:

Number	Wire size and type	Table 5 cross-sectional area (ea.)	Subtotal cross-sectional area
4	12 THWN	0.0117	0.0468
3	8 TW	0.0471	0.1413
3	6 THW	0.0819	0.2457
Total cross-sectional area			0.4338

The 40 percent column (three or more conductors) of Table 4 indicates that 40 percent of a $1\frac{1}{4}$-inch conduit is 0.60 square inches, the required conduit size for these 10 conductors.

An example based on Note 3 (decimal fractions) to determine how many No. 12 THWN conductors are permitted in a $\frac{3}{4}$ inch conduit. Table 1 permits a 40 percent fill (three or more conductors); hence, from Table 4, 40 percent of a $\frac{3}{4}$-inch conduit is 0.21 inches, and, from Table 5, the cross-sectional area of a No. 12 THWN conductor is 0.0117 square inches.

$$0.21 \div 0.117 = 17.9$$

Eighteen such conductors are permitted in a $\frac{3}{4}$-inch conduit. [Since the decimal (0.9) is more than 0.8, it is increased to the next higher whole number. If the decimal had been less than 0.8, the decimal would have been dropped.]

(FPN): Table 1 is based on common conditions of proper cabling and alignment of conductors where the length of the pull and the number of bends are within reasonable limits. It should be recognized that for certain conditions a larger size conduit or a lesser conduit fill should be considered.

Tables 3A, 3B, and 3C provide for the maximum allowable number of conductors that may be enclosed in complete systems of conduit or tubing (based on the percentage fill of Table 1) and do not apply to short sections of conduit or tubing used for the physical protection of conductors and cables. Cables are commonly protected from physical damage by conduit or tubing sleeves sized to enable the cable to be passed through with relative ease without injuring or abrading the protective jacket of the cable. However, a fitting is required on the end(s) of the conduit or tubing to protect the conductors or cables from abrasion. See Section 300-15(b), Exception No. 4.

Conduit nipples, not exceeding 24 inches in length, may be filled to 60 percent of their capacity and the derating factors of Note 8(a) of the Notes to Ampacity Tables of 0 to 2000 Volts need not be applied.

All conductors occupy space in a raceway, and they must therefore all be counted, including equipment grounding of bonding conductors (insulated, bare, or covered) and neutral or grounded conductors (insulated, bare, or covered). The only exception to this rule is the addition of an uninsulated grounding conductor permitted within $\frac{3}{8}$-inch flexible metal conduit (see footnote to Table 350-3). The dimensions of bare conductors are given in Table 8.

For conductors not included in Chapter 9, such as high-voltage types, the cross-sectional area may be calculated in the following manner, using the actual dimensions of each conductor:

D = outside diameter of a conductor (including insulation)

CM = circular mils

1 inch = 1,000 mils (1 mil = 0.001 in.)

CM = $[\pi (3.1416) \div 4]$ = 0.7854 of a square mil

Diameter in mils squares × 0.7854 = cross-sectional area

Table 1. Percent of Cross Section of Conduit and Tubing for Conductors
(See Table 2 for Fixture Wires)

Number of Conductors	1	2	3	4	Over 4
All conductor types except lead-covered	53	31	40	40	40
Lead-covered conductors	55	30	40	38	35

Note 1. See Tables 3A, 3B, and 3C for number of conductors all of the same size in trade sizes of conduit or tubing $\frac{1}{2}$ inch through 6 inch.

Note 2: See Table 5B for number of compact conductors all of the same size in trade sizes of conduit or tubing $\frac{1}{2}$ inch through 4 inch.

Note 3. For conductors larger than 750 kcmil or for combinations of conductors of different sizes, use Tables 4 through 8, Chapter 9, for dimensions of conductors, conduit, and tubing.

Note 4. Where the calculated conductors, all of the same size (total cross-sectional area including insulation), include a decimal fraction, the next higher whole number shall be used where this decimal equals 0.8 or larger.

Note 5. Where bare conductors are permitted by other sections of this Code, the dimensions for bare conductors in Table 8 of Chapter 9 shall be permitted.

Note 6. A multiconductor cable of two or more conductors shall be treated as a single conductor cable for calculating percentage conduit fill area. For cables that have elliptical cross section, the cross-sectional area calculation shall be based on using the major diameter of the ellipse as a circle diameter.

Table 2. Maximum Number of Fixture Wires in Trade Sizes of Conduit or Tubing
(40 Percent Fill Based on Individual Diameters)

Conduit Trade Size (Inches) Wire Types	½ 18	16	14	12	10	¾ 18	16	14	12	10	1 18	16	14	12	10	1¼ 18	16	14	12	10	1½ 18	16	14	12	10	2 18	16	14	12	10
PTF, PTFF, PGFF, PGF, PFF, PF, PAF, PAFF, ZF, ZFF	23	18	14			40	31	24			65	50	39			115	90	70			157	122	95			257	200	156		
TFFN, TFN	19	15				34	26				55	43				97	76				132	104				216	169			
SF-1	16					29					47					83					114					186				
SFF-1	15					26					43					76					104					169				
TF	11	10				20	18				32	30				57	53				79	72				129	118			
RFH-1	11					20					32					57					79					129				
TFF	11	10				20	17				32	27				56	49				77	66				126	109			
AF	11	9	7	4	3	19	16	12	7	5	31	26	20	11	8	55	46	36	19	15	75	63	49	27	20	123	104	81	44	34
SFF-2	9	7	6			16	12	10			27	20	17			47	36	30			65	49	42			106	81	68		
SF-2	9	8	6			16	14	11			27	23	18			47	40	32			65	55	43			106	90	71		
FFH-2	9	7				15	12				25	19				44	34				60	46				99	75			
RFH-2	7	5				12	10				20	16				36	28				49	38				80	62			
KF-1, KFF-1, KF-2, KFF-2	36	32	22	14	9	64	55	39	25	17	103	89	63	41	28	182	158	111	73	49	248	216	152	100	67	406	353	248	163	110

Table 2 through Table 3A

Table 3A. Maximum Number of Conductors in Trade Sizes of Conduit or Tubing
(Based on Table 1, Chapter 9)

Conduit or Tubing Trade Size (Inches)		$^1/_2$	$^3/_4$	1	1 $^1/_4$	1 $^1/_2$	2	2 $^1/_2$	3	3 $^1/_2$	4	5	6
Type Letters	Conductor Size AWG/kcmil												
TW, XHHW	14	9	15	25	44	60	99	142					
(14 through 8)	12	7	12	19	35	47	78	111	171				
RH (14 + 12)	10	5	9	15	26	36	60	85	131	176			
	8	2	4	7	12	17	28	40	62	84	108		
RHW and RHH	14	6	10	16	29	40	65	93	143	192			
(without outer	12	4	8	13	24	32	53	76	117	157			
covering),	10	4	6	11	19	26	43	61	95	127	163		
RH (10 + 8) THW, THHW	8	1	3	5	10	13	22	32	49	66	85	133	
TW,	6	1	2	4	7	10	16	23	36	48	62	97	141
	4	1	1	3	5	7	12	17	27	36	47	73	106
THW,	3	1	1	2	4	6	10	15	23	31	40	63	91
	2	1	1	2	4	5	9	13	20	27	34	54	78
	1		1	1	3	4	6	9	14	19	25	39	57
FEPB (6 through 2),	1/0		1	1	2	3	5	8	12	16	21	33	49
RHW and RHH	2/0		1	1	1	3	5	7	10	14	18	29	41
(without outer	3/0		1	1	1	2	4	6	9	12	15	24	35
covering)	4/0			1	1	1	3	5	7	10	13	20	29
	250			1	1	1	2	4	6	8	10	16	23
	300			1	1	1	2	3	5	7	9	14	20
	350				1	1	1	3	4	6	8	12	18
	400				1	1	1	2	4	5	7	11	16
RH, THHW	500				1	1	1	1	3	4	6	9	14
	600					1	1	1	3	4	5	7	11
	700					1	1	1	2	3	4	7	10
	750					1	1	1	2	3	4	6	9

Note 1. This table is for concentric stranded conductors only. For cables with compact conductors, the dimensions in Table 5A shall be used.
Note 2. Conduit fill for conductors with a -2 suffix is the same as for those types without the suffix.

Table 3B. Maximum Number of Conductors in Trade Sizes of Conduit or Tubing
(Based on Table 1, Chapter 9)

Type Letters	Conductor Size AWG/kcmil	¹/₂	³/₄	1	1¹/₄	1¹/₂	2	2¹/₂	3	3¹/₂	4	5	6
THWN,	14	13	24	39	69	94	154						
	12	10	18	29	51	70	114	164					
	10	6	11	18	32	44	73	104	160				
	8	3	5	9	16	22	36	51	79	106	136		
THHN,	6	1	4	6	11	15	26	37	57	76	98	154	
FEP (14 through 2),	4	1	2	4	7	9	16	22	35	47	60	94	137
FEPB (14 through 8),	3	1	1	3	6	8	13	19	29	39	51	80	116
PFA (14 through 4/0)	2	1	1	3	5	7	11	16	25	33	43	67	97
PFAH (14 through 4/0)	1		1	1	3	5	8	12	18	25	32	50	72
Z (14 through 4/0)	1/0		1	1	3	4	7	10	15	21	27	42	61
XHHW (4 through	2/0		1	1	2	3	6	8	13	17	22	35	51
500 kcmil)	3/0		1	1	1	3	5	7	11	14	18	29	42
	4/0		1	1	1	2	4	6	9	12	15	24	35
	250			1	1	1	3	4	7	10	12	20	28
	300			1	1	1	3	4	6	8	11	17	24
	350			1	1	1	2	3	5	7	9	15	21
	400				1	1	1	3	5	6	8	13	19
	500				1	1	1	2	4	5	7	11	16
	600				1	1	1	1	3	4	5	9	13
	700					1	1	1	3	4	5	8	11
	750					1	1	1	2	3	4	7	11
XHHW	6	1	3	5	9	13	21	30	47	63	81	128	185
	600				1	1	1	1	3	4	5	9	13
	700					1	1	1	3	4	5	7	11
	750					1	1	1	2	3	4	7	10

Note 1. This table is for concentric stranded conductors only. For cables with compact conductors, the dimensions in Table 5A shall be used.
Note 2. Conduit fill for conductors with a -2 suffix is the same as for those types without the suffix.

Table 3C. Maximum Number of Conductors in Trade Sizes of Conduit or Tubing (Based on Table 1, Chapter 9)

Conduit or Tubing Trade Size (In.)		¹/₂	³/₄	1	1¹/₄	1¹/₂	2	2¹/₂	3	3¹/₂	4	5	6
Type Letters	**Conductor Size AWG/kcmil**												
RHW,	14	3	6	10	18	25	41	58	90	121	155		
	12	3	5	9	15	21	35	50	77	103	132		
	10	2	4	7	13	18	29	41	64	86	110		
	8	1	2	4	7	9	16	22	35	47	60	94	137
RHH	6	1	1	2	5	6	11	15	24	32	41	64	93
	4	1	1	1	3	5	8	12	18	24	31	50	72
(with	3	1	1	1	3	4	7	10	16	22	28	44	63
outer	2		1	1	3	4	6	9	14	19	24	38	56
covering)	1		1	1	1	3	5	7	11	14	18	29	42
	1/0		1	1	1	2	4	6	9	12	16	25	37
	2/0			1	1	1	3	5	8	11	14	22	32
	3/0			1	1	1	3	4	7	9	12	19	28
	4/0			1	1	1	2	4	6	8	10	16	24
	250				1	1	1	3	5	6	8	13	19
	300				1	1	1	3	4	5	7	11	17
	350				1	1	1	2	4	5	6	10	15
	400				1	1	1	1	3	4	6	9	14
	500				1	1	1	1	3	4	5	8	11
	600					1	1	1	2	3	4	6	9
	700					1	1	1	1	3	3	6	8
	750						1	1	1	3	3	5	8

Note 1. This table is for concentric stranded conductors only. For cables with compact conductors, the dimensions in Table 5A shall be used.
Note 2. Conduit fill for conductors with a -2 suffix is the same as for those types without the suffix.

Tables 4 through 8, Chapter 9.   Tables 4 through 8 give the nominal size of conductors and conduit or tubing for use in computing size of conduit or tubing for various combinations of conductors. The dimensions represent average conditions only, and variations will be found in dimensions of conductors and conduits of different manufacture.

Table 4.   Dimensions and Percent Area of Conduit and of Tubing
Areas of Conduit or Tubing for the Combinations of Wires Permitted in Table 1, Chapter 9.

Trade Size	Internal Diameter Inches	Area — Square Inches								
		Total 100%	Not Lead-Covered			Lead-Covered				
			2 Cond. 31%	Over 2 Cond. 40%	1 Cond. 53%	1 Cond. 55%	2 Cond. 30%	3 Cond. 40%	4 Cond. 38%	Over 4 Cond. 35%
¹/₂	.622	.30	.09	.12	.16	.17	.09	.12	.11	.11
³/₄	.824	.53	.16	.21	.28	.29	.16	.21	.20	.19
1	1.049	.86	.27	.34	.46	.47	.26	.34	.33	.30
1¹/₄	1.380	1.50	.47	.60	.80	.83	.45	.60	.57	.53
1¹/₂	1.610	2.04	.63	.82	1.08	1.12	.61	.82	.78	.71
2	2.067	3.36	1.04	1.34	1.78	1.85	1.01	1.34	1.28	1.18
2¹/₂	2.469	4.79	1.48	1.92	2.54	2.63	1.44	1.92	1.82	1.68
3	3.068	7.38	2.26	2.95	3.91	4.06	2.21	2.95	2.80	2.58
3¹/₂	3.548	9.90	3.07	3.96	5.25	5.44	2.97	3.96	3.76	3.47
4	4.026	12.72	3.94	5.09	6.74	7.00	3.82	5.09	4.83	4.45
5	5.047	20.00	6.20	8.00	10.60	11.00	6.00	8.00	7.60	7.00
6	6.065	28.89	8.96	11.56	15.31	15.89	8.67	11.56	10.98	10.11

Table 5. Dimensions of Rubber-Covered and Thermoplastic-Covered Conductors

Size AWG kcmil	Types RFH-2, RH, RHH,*** RHW-2, RHW,*** SF-2 Approx. Diam. Inches	Approx. Area Sq. In.	Types TF, THW†, TW, THHW Approx. Diam. Inches	Approx. Area Sq. In.	Types TFN, THHN, THWN Approx. Diam. Inches	Approx. Area Sq. In.	Types**** FEP, FEPB, FEPW, TFE, PF, PFA, PFAH, PGF, PTF, Z, ZF, ZFF Approx. Diam. Inches	Approx. Area Sq. In.	Types XHHW, ZW††, XHHW-2 Approx. Diam. Inches	Approx. Area Sq. In.	Types KF-1, KF-2, KFF-1, KFF-2 Approx. Diam. Inches	Approx. Area Sq. In.
Col 1	Col 2	Col 3	Col 4	Col 5	Col 6	Col 7	Col 8	Col 9	Col 10	Col 11	Col 12	Col 13
18	.146	.0167	.106	.0088	.089	.0062	.081	.0052	...	....	.065	.0033
16	.158	.0196	.118	.0109	.100	.0079	.092	.0066	...	....	.070	.0038
14	30 mils .171	.0230	.131	.0135	.105	.0087	.105 .105	.0087 .0087	...	....	.083	.0054
14	45 mils .204*	.0327*	...	....	...	....	... ...	....	...	....	...	....
14	....	....	.162†	.0206†	...	....	... ...	....	.129	.0131	...	....
12	30 mils .188	.0278	.148	.0172	.122	.0177	.121 .121	.0115 .0115	...	....	.102	.0082
12	45 mils .221*	.0384*	...	....	...	....	... ...	....	...	....	...	....
12	....	....	.179†	.0252†	...	....	... ...	....	.146	.0167	...	....
10	.242	.0460	.168	.0222	.153	.0184	.142 .142	.0158 .0158	...	....	.124	.0121
10	....	....	.199†	.0311†	...	....	... ...	....	.166	.0216	...	....
8	.328	.0845	.245	.0471	.218	.0373	.206 .186	.0333 .0272	...	....	...	....
8	....	....	.276†	.0598†	...	....	... ...	....	.241	.0456	...	....
6	.397	.1238	.323	.0819	.257	.0519	.244 .302	.0468 .0716	.282	.0625	...	....
4	.452	.1605	.372	.1087	.328	.0845	.292 .350	.0670 .0962	.328	.0845	...	....
3	.481	.1817	.401	.1263	.356	.0995	.320 .378	.0804 .1122	.356	.0995	...	....
2	.513	.2067	.433	.1473	.388	.1182	.352 .410	.0973 .1320	.388	.1182	...	....
1	.588	.2715	.508	.2027	.450	.1590	.420 ...	.1385	.450	.1590	...	....
1/0	.629	.3107	.549	.2367	.491	.1893	.462 ...	.1676	.491	.1893	...	....
2/0	.675	.3578	.595	.2781	.537	.2265	.498 ...	.1948	.537	.2265	...	....
3/0	.727	.4151	.647	.3288	.588	.2715	.560 ...	.2463	.588	.2715	...	....
4/0	.785	.4840	.705	.3904	.646	.3278	.618 ...	.3000	.646	.3278	...	....
250	.868	.5917	.788	.4877	.716	.4026	....	....	.716	.4026	...	....
300	.933	.6837	.843	.5581	.771	.4669	....	....	.771	.4669	...	....
350	.985	.7620	.895	.6291	.822	.5307	....	....	.822	.5307	...	....
400	1.032	.8365	.942	.6969	.869	.5931	....	....	.869	.5931	...	....
500	1.119	.9834	1.029	.8316	.955	.7163	....	....	.955	.7163	...	....
600	1.233	1.1940	1.143	1.0261	1.058	.8791	....	....	1.073	.9043	...	....
700	1.304	1.3355	1.214	1.1575	1.129	1.0011	....	....	1.145	1.0297	...	....
750	1.339	1.4082	1.249	1.2252	1.163	1.0623	....	....	1.180	1.0936	...	....
800	1.372	1.4784	1.282	1.2908	1.196	1.1234	....	....	1.210	1.1499	...	....
900	1.435	1.6173	1.345	1.4208	1.259	1.2449	....	....	1.270	1.2668	...	....
1000	1.494	1.7530	1.404	1.5482	1.317	1.3623	....	....	1.330	1.3893	...	....
1250	1.676	2.2062	1.577	1.9532	...	....	....	....	1.500	1.7671	...	....
1500	1.801	2.5475	1.702	2.2751	...	....	....	....	1.620	2.0612	...	....
1750	1.916	2.8832	1.817	2.5930	...	....	....	....	1.740	2.3779	...	....
2000	2.021	3.2079	1.922	2.9013	...	....	....	....	1.840	2.6590	...	....

* The dimensions of Types RHH and RHW with outer covering.
† Dimensions of THW in sizes No. 14 through No. 8. Nos. 6 THW and larger are the same dimension as TW.
*** Dimensions of RHH and RHW without outer covering are the same as THW No. 18 through No. 10, solid; No. 8 and larger, stranded.
**** In Columns 8 and 9, the values shown for size Nos. 1 through 4/0 are for TFE and Z only. The right-hand values in Columns 8 and 9 are for FEPB, Z, ZF, and ZFF only.
†† No. 14 through No. 2.

Table 5 through Table 5A

Table 5A. Compact Aluminum Building Wire Nominal Dimensions* and Areas

Bare Conductor			Type THW and THHW		Type THHN		Type XHHW		
Size AWG or kcmil	Number of Strands	Diam. Inches	Approx. Diam. Inches	Approx. Area Sq. In.	Approx. Diam. Inches	Approx. Area Sq. In.	Approx. Diam. Inches	Approx. Area Sq. Inches	Size AWG or kcmil
8	7	.134	.255	.0510	—	—	.224	.0394	8
6	7	.169	.290	.0660	.240	.0452	.260	.0530	6
4	7	.213	.335	.0881	.305	.0730	.305	.0730	4
2	7	.268	.390	.1194	.360	.1017	.360	.1017	2
1	19	.299	.465	.1698	.415	.1352	.415	.1352	1
1/0	19	.336	.500	.1963	.450	.1590	.450	.1590	1/0
2/0	19	.376	.545	.2332	.495	.1924	.490	.1885	2/0
3/0	19	.423	.590	.2733	.540	.2290	.540	.2290	3/0
4/0	19	.475	.645	.3267	.595	.2780	.590	.2733	4/0
250	37	.520	.725	.4128	.670	.3525	.660	.3421	250
300	37	.570	.775	.4717	.720	.4071	.715	.4015	300
350	37	.616	.820	.5281	.770	.4656	.760	.4536	350
400	37	.659	.865	.5876	.815	.5216	.800	.5026	400
500	37	.736	.940	.6939	.885	.6151	.880	.6082	500
600	61	.813	1.050	.8659	.985	.7620	.980	.7542	600
700	61	.877	1.110	.9676	1.050	.8659	1.050	.8659	700
750	61	.908	1.150	1.0386	1.075	.9076	1.090	.9331	750
1000	61	1.060	1.285	1.2968	1.255	1.2370	1.230	1.1882	1000

* Dimensions are from industry sources.

Most aluminum building wire in types THW, THWN/THHN, and XHHW is compact stranded. Table 5A provides appropriate dimensions for these types of wire.

Table 5B. Maximum Number of Compact Conductors in Trade Sizes of Conduit or Tubing

Insulation Type — each conduit size lists THW·THHW | THHN | XHHW

Conductor Size AWG or kcmil	1 in. THW/THHW	1 in. THHN	1 in. XHHW	1¼ in. THW/THHW	1¼ in. THHN	1¼ in. XHHW	1½ in. THW/THHW	1½ in. THHN	1½ in. XHHW	2 in. THW/THHW	2 in. THHN	2 in. XHHW	2½ in. THW/THHW	2½ in. THHN	2½ in. XHHW	3 in. THW/THHW	3 in. THHN	3 in. XHHW	3½ in. THW/THHW	3½ in. THHN	3½ in. XHHW	4 in. THW/THHW	4 in. THHN	4 in. XHHW	Conductor Size AWG or kcmil
6	5	7	6	9	13	11	12	18	15																6
4	4	4	4	7	8	8	9	11	11	15	18	18													4
2	3	3	3	5	6	6	7	8	8	11	13	13													2
1				3	4	4	5	6	6	8	10	10	11	14	14										1
1/0				3	3	3	4	5	5	7	8	8	9	12	12	12	15	15							1/0
2/0				3	3		3	4	4	5	7	7	8	10	10	10	13	13							2/0
3/0							3	3	3	5	6	6	7	8	8	10	13	13	12	14	14				3/0
4/0							3	3		4	5	5	6	7	7	9	10	10	12	14	14				4/0
250										3	4	4	4	5	5	7	8	8	9	11	11	10	12	12	250
300										3	3	3	4	4	4	6	7	7	8	9	10	10	12	12	300
350													3	3	3	5	6	6	7	8	8	9	11	11	350
400													3	3	4	5	5	6	6	7	8	8	9	10	400
500													3	3		4	4	5	5	6	6	7	8	8	500
600																3	4	4	4	5	5	6	6	7	600
700																3	3	3	4	4	4	5	6	6	700
750																3	3	3	4	4	4	5	5	5	750
1000																			3	3	3	4	4	4	1000

Definition: Compact stranding is the result of a manufacturing process where the standard conductor is compressed to the extent that the interstices (voids between strand wires) are virtually eliminated.

Table 6. Dimensions of Lead-Covered Conductors Types RL, RHL, and THHW

Size AWG/kcmil	Single Conductor Diam. Inches	Single Conductor Area Sq. In.	Two Conductor Diam. Inches	Two Conductor Area Sq. In.	Three Conductor Diam. Inches	Three Conductor Area Sq. In.
14	.28	.062	.28 × .47	.115	.59	.273
12	.29	.066	.31 × .54	.146	.62	.301
10	.35	.096	.35 × .59	.180	.68	.363
8 sol.	.41	.132	.41 × .71	.255	.82	.528
8 str.	.43	.145	.43 × .75	.282	.86	.581
6	.49	.188	.49 × .86	.369	.97	.738
4	.55	.237	.54 × .96	.457	1.08	.916
2	.60	.283	.61 × 1.08	.578	1.21	1.146
1	.67	.352	.70 × 1.23	.756	1.38	1.49
1/0	.71	.396	.74 × 1.32	.859	1.47	1.70
2/0	.76	.454	.79 × 1.41	.980	1.57	1.94
3/0	.81	.515	.84 × 1.52	1.123	1.69	2.24
4/0	.87	.593	.90 × 1.64	1.302	1.85	2.68
250	.98	.754	....	....	2.02	3.20
300	1.04	.85	....	....	2.15	3.62
350	1.10	.95	....	....	2.26	4.02
400	1.14	1.02	....	....	2.40	4.52
500	1.23	1.18	....	....	2.59	5.28

The above cables are limited to straight runs or with nominal offsets equivalent to not more than two quarter bends.

Note: No. 14 through No. 10, solid conductors; No. 8, solid or stranded conductors; Nos. 6 and larger, stranded conductors.

Table 8. Conductor Properties

| Size AWG/ kcmil | Area Cir. Mills | Conductors | | | | DC Resistance at 75°C (167°F) | | |
| | | Stranding | | Overall | | Copper | | Aluminum |
		Quantity	Diam. In.	Diam. In.	Area In.²	Uncoated ohm/kFT	Coated ohm/kFT	ohm/kFT
18	1620	1	—	0.040	0.001	7.77	8.08	12.8
18	1620	7	0.015	0.046	0.002	7.95	8.45	13.1
16	2580	1	—	0.051	0.002	4.89	5.08	8.05
16	2580	7	0.019	0.058	0.003	4.99	5.29	8.21
14	4110	1	—	0.064	0.003	3.07	3.19	5.06
14	4110	7	0.024	0.073	0.004	3.14	3.26	5.17
12	6530	1	—	0.081	0.005	1.93	2.01	3.18
12	6530	7	0.030	0.092	0.006	1.98	2.05	3.25
10	10380	1	—	0.102	0.008	1.21	1.26	2.00
10	10380	7	0.038	0.116	0.011	1.24	1.29	2.04
8	16510	1	—	0.128	0.013	0.764	0.786	1.26
8	16510	7	0.049	0.146	0.017	0.778	0.809	1.28
6	26240	7	0.061	0.184	0.027	0.491	0.510	0.808
4	41740	7	0.077	0.232	0.042	0.308	0.321	0.508
3	52620	7	0.087	0.260	0.053	0.245	0.254	0.403
2	66360	7	0.097	0.292	0.067	0.194	0.201	0.319
1	83690	19	0.066	0.332	0.087	0.154	0.160	0.253
1/0	105600	19	0.074	0.373	0.109	0.122	0.127	0.201
2/0	133100	19	0.084	0.419	0.138	0.0967	0.101	0.159
3/0	167800	19	0.094	0.470	0.173	0.0766	0.0797	0.126
4/0	211600	19	0.106	0.528	0.219	0.0608	0.0626	0.100
250	—	37	0.082	0.575	0.260	0.0515	0.0535	0.0847
300	—	37	0.090	0.630	0.312	0.0429	0.0446	0.0707
350	—	37	0.097	0.681	0.364	0.0367	0.0382	0.0605
400	—	37	0.104	0.728	0.416	0.0321	0.0331	0.0529
500	—	37	0.116	0.813	0.519	0.0258	0.0265	0.0424
600	—	61	0.099	0.893	0.626	0.0214	0.0223	0.0353
700	—	61	0.107	0.964	0.730	0.0184	0.0189	0.0303
750	—	61	0.111	0.998	0.782	0.0171	0.0176	0.0282
800	—	61	0.114	1.03	0.834	0.0161	0.0166	0.0265
900	—	61	0.122	1.09	0.940	0.0143	0.0147	0.0235
1000	—	61	0.128	1.15	1.04	0.0129	0.0132	0.0212
1250	—	91	0.117	1.29	1.30	0.0103	0.0106	0.0169
1500	—	91	0.128	1.41	1.57	0.00858	0.00883	0.0141
1750	—	127	0.117	1.52	1.83	0.00735	0.00756	0.0121
2000	—	127	0.126	1.63	2.09	0.00643	0.00662	0.0106

These resistance values are valid ONLY for the parameters as given. Using conductors having coated strands, different stranding type, and, especially, other temperatures changes the resistance.

Formula for temperature change: $R_2 = R_1 [1 + \alpha(T_2 - 75)]$ where: $\alpha_{cu} = 0.00323$, $\alpha_{AL} = 0.00330$.

Conductors with compact and compressed stranding have about 9 percent and 3 percent, respectively, smaller bare conductor diameters than those shown. See Table 5A for actual compact cable dimensions.

The IACS conductivities used: bare copper = 100%, aluminum = 61%.

Class B stranding is listed as well as solid for some sizes. Its overall diameter and area is that of its circumscribing circle.

(FPN): The construction information is per NEMA WC8-1976 (Rev 5-1980). The resistance is calculated per National Bureau of Standards Handbook 100, dated 1966, and Handbook 109, dated 1972.

Table 9. AC Resistance and Reactance for 600 V Cables, 3-Phase 60, Hz, 75°C (167°F) — Three Single Conductors in Conduit

	XL (Reactance) for All Wires		AC Resistance for Uncoated Copper Wires			AC Resistance for Aluminum Wires			Effective Z at .85 PF for Uncoated Copper Wires			Effective Z at .85 PF for Aluminum Wires			
Size AWG/ kcmil	PVC, Al. Conduits	Steel Conduit	PVC Conduit	Al. Conduit	Steel Conduit	PVC Conduit	Al. Conduit	Steel Conduit	PVC Conduit	Al. Conduit	Steel Conduit	PVC Conduit	Al. Conduit	Steel Conduit	Size AWG/ kcmil
14	.058	.073	3.1	3.1	3.1	—	—	—	2.7	2.7	2.7	—	—	—	14
12	.054	.068	2.0	2.0	2.0	3.2	3.2	3.2	1.7	1.7	1.7	2.8	2.8	2.8	12
10	.050	.063	1.2	1.2	1.2	2.0	2.0	2.0	1.1	1.1	1.1	1.8	1.8	1.8	10
8	.052	.065	0.78	0.78	0.78	1.3	1.3	1.3	0.69	0.69	0.70	1.1	1.1	1.1	8
6	.051	.064	0.49	0.49	0.49	0.81	0.81	0.81	0.44	0.45	0.45	0.71	0.72	0.72	6
4	.048	.060	0.31	0.31	0.31	0.51	0.51	0.51	0.29	0.29	0.30	0.46	0.46	0.46	4
3	.047	.059	0.25	0.25	0.25	0.40	0.41	0.40	0.23	0.24	0.24	0.37	0.37	0.37	3
2	.045	.057	0.19	0.20	0.20	0.32	0.32	0.32	0.19	0.19	0.20	0.30	0.30	0.30	2
1	.046	.057	0.15	0.16	0.16	0.25	0.26	0.25	0.16	0.16	0.16	0.24	0.24	0.25	1
1/0	.044	.055	0.12	0.13	0.12	0.20	0.21	0.20	0.13	0.13	0.13	0.19	0.20	0.20	1/0
2/0	.043	.054	0.10	0.10	0.10	0.16	0.16	0.16	0.11	0.11	0.11	0.16	0.16	0.16	2/0
3/0	.042	.052	0.077	0.082	0.079	0.13	0.13	0.13	0.088	0.092	0.094	0.13	0.13	0.14	3/0
4/0	.041	.051	0.062	0.067	0.063	0.10	0.11	0.10	0.074	0.078	0.080	0.11	0.11	0.11	4/0
250	.041	.052	0.052	0.057	0.054	0.085	0.090	0.086	0.066	0.070	0.073	0.094	0.098	0.10	250
300	.041	.051	0.044	0.049	0.045	0.071	0.076	0.072	0.059	0.063	0.065	0.082	0.086	0.088	300
350	.040	.050	0.038	0.043	0.039	0.061	0.066	0.063	0.053	0.058	0.060	0.073	0.077	0.080	350
400	.040	.049	0.033	0.038	0.035	0.054	0.059	0.055	0.049	0.053	0.056	0.066	0.071	0.073	400
500	.039	.048	0.027	0.032	0.029	0.043	0.048	0.045	0.043	0.048	0.050	0.057	0.061	0.064	500
600	.039	.048	0.023	0.028	0.025	0.036	0.041	0.038	0.040	0.044	0.047	0.051	0.055	0.058	600
750	.038	.048	0.019	0.024	0.021	0.029	0.034	0.031	0.036	0.040	0.043	0.045	0.049	0.052	750
1000	.037	.046	0.015	0.019	0.018	0.023	0.027	0.025	0.032	0.036	0.040	0.039	0.042	0.046	1000

Ohms to Neutral per 1000 feet

Notes:

1. These values are based on the following constants: UL-type RHH wires with Class B stranding, in cradled configuration. Wire conductivities are 100% IACS copper and 61% IACS aluminum, and aluminum conduit is 45% IACS. Capacitive reactance is ignored, since it is negligible at these voltages.

These resistance values are valid only at 75°C (167°F) and for the parameters as given, but are representative for 600-volt wire types operating at 60 Hz.

2. "Effective Z" is defined as R cos(theta) + X sin(theta), where "theta" is the power factor angle of the circuit. Multiplying current by effective impedance gives a good approximation for line-to-neutral voltage drop. Effective impedance values shown in this table are valid only at .85 power factor.

For another circuit power factor (PF), effective impedance (Zc) can be calculated from R and X_L values given in this table as follows: $Zc = R \times PF + X_L \sin[\arccos(PF)]$.

Table 9 through Example No. 1(a)

Table 10. Expansion Characteristics of PVC Rigid Nonmetallic Conduit Coefficient of Thermal Expansion = 3.38×10^{-5} in./in./°F

Temperature Change in Degrees F	Length Change in Inches per 100 ft. of PVC Conduit	Temperature Change in Degrees F	Length Change in Inches per 100 ft. of PVC Conduit	Temperature Change in Degrees F	Length Change in Inches per 100 ft. of PVC Conduit	Temperature Change in Degrees F	Length Change in Inches per 100 ft. of PVC Conduit
5	0.2	55	2.2	105	4.2	155	6.3
10	0.4	60	2.4	110	4.5	160	6.5
15	0.6	65	2.6	115	4.7	165	6.7
20	0.8	70	2.8	120	4.9	170	6.9
25	1.0	75	3.0	125	5.1	175	7.1
30	1.2	80	3.2	130	5.3	180	7.3
35	1.4	85	3.4	135	5.5	185	7.5
40	1.6	90	3.6	140	5.7	190	7.7
45	1.8	95	3.8	145	5.9	195	7.9
50	2.0	100	4.1	150	6.1	200	8.1

B. Examples

Selection of Conductors. In the following examples, the results are generally expressed in amperes. To select conductor sizes, refer to the 0 to 2000 volt ampacity tables of Article 310, and the Notes that pertain to such tables.

Voltage. For uniform application of Articles 210, 215, and 220, a nominal voltage of 120, 120/240, 240, and 208Y//120 volts shall be used in computing the ampere load on the conductor.

Fractions of an Ampere. Except where the computations result in a major fraction of an ampere (0.5 or larger), such fractions shall be permitted to be dropped.

Ranges. For the computation of the range loads in these examples, Column A of Table 220-19 has been used. For optional methods, see Columns B and C of Table 220-19. Except where the computations result in a major fraction of a kilowatt (0.5 or larger), such fractions shall be permitted to be dropped.

SI Units: For SI units: one square foot = 9.093 square meter; one foot = 0.3048 meter.

In the following examples, loads are assumed to be properly balanced on the system. Where loads are not properly balanced, additional feeder capacity may be required.

Example No. 1(a). One-Family Dwelling

The dwelling has a floor area of 1500 sq. ft., exclusive of unoccupied cellar, unfinished attic, and open porches. Appliances are a 12-kW range and a 5.5 kW, 240-volt dryer. Assume range and dryer kW ratings equivalent to kVA ratings in accordance with Sections 220-18 and 220-19.

Computed Load [see Section 220-10(a)]:

General Lighting Load:

1500 sq. ft. at 3 volt-amperes per sq. ft = 4500 volt-amperes.

Minimum Number of Branch Circuits Required [see Section 220-4(b)]:

General Lighting Load:

4500 volt-amperes ÷ 120 volts = 37.5 A: This requires three 15 A 2-wire or two 20 A 2-wire circuits

Small Appliance Load: Two 2-wire 20 A circuits [see Section 220-3(b)]

Laundry Load: One 2-wire 20 A circuit [see Section 220-4(c)]

Minimum Size Feeder Required [see Section 220-10(a)]:

General Lighting............................	4500 volt-amperes
Small Appliance Load......................	3000 volt-amperes
Laundry	1500 volt-amperes
Total General Light and Small Appliance............................	9000 volt-amperes
3000 volt-amperes at 100%	3000 volt-amperes
9000 − 3000 = 6000 volt-amperes at 35%....................................	2100 volt-amperes
Net General Lighting and Small Appliance Load.......................	5100 volt-amperes
Range Load (see Table 220-19)...........	8000 volt-amperes
Dryer Load (see Table 220-18)	5500 volt-amperes
Total Load................................	18,600 volt-amperes

For 120/240-volt 3-wire single-phase service or feeder, 18,600 volt-amperes ÷ 240 volts = 77.5 A.

Net computed load exceeds 10kVA. Service conductors shall be 100 amperes [see Section 230-42(b)(2)].

Neutral for Feeder and Service

Lighting and Small Appliance Load	5100 volt-amperes
Range Load 8000 volt-amperes at 70%	5600 volt-amperes
Dryer Load 5500 volt-amperes at 70%	3850 volt-amperes
Total	14,550 volt-amperes

14,550 volt-amperes ÷ 240 volts = 60.6 amperes

The general lighting and general-use receptacle load is computed from the outside dimensions of the building, apartment, or other area involved. For a dwelling unit(s), the computed floor area is not to include open porches, garages, or unused or unfinished spaces unadaptable for future use. See Section 220-3(b).

Example: A two-story dwelling measures 30 feet × 30 feet for the first floor and 30 feet × 20 feet for the second floor.

30 ft × 30 ft = 900 sq ft (first floor)
30 ft × 20 ft = 600 sq ft (second floor
Total area = 1,500 sq ft

Example No. 1(b). One-Family Dwelling

Same conditions as Example No. 1(a), plus addition of one 6-ampere 230-volt room air-conditioning unit and one 12-ampere 115-volt room air-conditioning unit,* one 8-ampere 115-volt rated disposal and one 10-ampere 120-volt rated dishwasher.* See Article 430 for general motors and Article 440, Part G, for air-conditioning equipment. Motors have nameplate ratings of 115 V and 230 V for use on 120 V and 240 V nominal voltage systems.

From previous Example No. 1(a), feeder current is 78 amperes (3-wire, 240 volts).

	Line A	Neutral	Line B
Amperes from Example No. 1(a)	78	61	78
One 230-V air conditioner	6	—	6
One 115-V air conditioner and 120-V dishwasher	12	12	10
One 115-V disposal	—	8	8
25% of largest motor (Section 430-24)	3	3	2
Amperes per line	99	84	104

*For feeder neutral, use largest of the two appliances for unbalance.

Example No. 2(a). Optional Calculation for One-Family Dwelling, Heating Larger than Air Conditioning
[See Section 220-30(a) and Table 220-30.]

Dwelling has a floor area of 1500 sq. ft., exclusive of unoccupied cellar, unfinished attic, and open porches. It has a 12-kW range, a 2.5-kW water heater, a 1.2-kW dishwasher, 9 kW of electric space heating installed in five rooms, a 5-kW clothes dryer, and a 6-ampere 230-volt room air-conditioning unit. Assume range, water heater, dishwasher, space heating, and clothes dryer kW ratings equivalent to kVA.

Air conditioner kVA is 6 × 230 ÷ 1000 = 1.38 kVA

1.38 kVA is less than the connected load of 9 kVA of space heating; therefore, the air conditioner load need not be included in the service calculation (see Section 220-21).

1500 sq. ft. at 3 volt-amperes	4500 volt-amperes
Two 20-ampere appliance outlet circuits at 1500 volt-amperes each	3000 volt-amperes
Laundry circuit	1500 volt-amperes
Range (at nameplate rating)	12,000 volt-amperes
Water heater	2500 volt-amperes
Dishwasher	1200 volt-amperes
Clothes dryer	5000 volt-amperes
	29,700 volt-amperes

First 10 kVA of other load at 100% = 10,000 volt-amperes	
Remainder of other load at 40% (19.7 kVA × .4) =	7900 volt-amperes
Total of other load =	17,900 volt-amperes
9 kVA of heat at 40% (9 × .4) =	3600 volt-amperes
Total load =	21,500 volt-amperes

Calculated load for service size

21.5 kVA = 21,500 volt-amperes
21,500 VA ÷ 240 volts = 90 amperes

Therefore, this dwelling shall be permitted to be served by a 100-ampere service.

Feeder Neutral Load, per Section 220-22:

1500 sq. ft. at 3 volt-amperes	4500 volt-amperes
Three 20-amp. circuits at 1500 volt-amperes	4500 volt-amperes
Total	9000 volt-amperes

3000 volt-amperes at 100%	3000 volt-amperes
9000 VA –3000 VA = 6000 volt-amperes at 35%.......................................	2100 volt-amperes
	5100 volt-amperes
Range — 8 kVA at 70%	5600 volt-amperes
Clothes dryer — 5 kVA at 70%	3500 volt-amperes
Dishwasher...................................	1200 volt-amperes
Total	15,400 volt-amperes

15,400 VA ÷ 240 volts = 64.2 amperes

Example No. 2(b). Optional Calculation for One-Family Dwelling, Air Conditioning Larger than Heating

[See Section 220-30(a) and Table 220-30.]

Dwelling has a floor area of 1500 sq. ft., exclusive of unoccupied cellar, unfinished attic, and open porches. It has two 20-ampere small appliance circuits, one 20-ampere laundry circuit, two 4-kW wall-mounted ovens, one 5.1-kW counter-mounted cooking unit, a 4.5 kW water heater, a 1.2-kW dishwasher, a 5-kW combination clothes washer and dryer, six 7-ampere 230-volt room air-conditioning units, and a 1.5-kW permanently installed bathroom space heater. Assume wall-mounted ovens, counter-mounted cooking unit, water heater, dishwasher, and combination clothes washer and dryer kW ratings equivalent to kVA.

Air Conditioning kVA Calculation:

Total amperes 6 × 7 = 42.00 amperes
42 × 240 ÷ 1000 = 10.08 kVA of air-conditioned load; assume P.F. = 1.0

The air-conditioning load is calculated at 100 percent, and this load is calculated separately in order to comply with requirements of Section 220-30 and Table 220-30.

Load included at 100%:

Air Conditioning (See below)

Space heater (omit, see Section 220-21)

Other Load:

1500 sq. ft. at 3 volt-amperes	4500 volt-amperes
Two 20-amp. small appliance circuits at 1500 volt-amperes......................	3000 volt-amperes
Laundry circuit................................	1500 volt-amperes
Two ovens....................................	8000 volt-amperes
One cooking unit.............................	5100 volt-amperes
Water heater.................................	4500 volt-amperes

Dishwasher...................................	1200 volt-amperes
Washer/dryer.................................	5000 volt-amperes
Total other load	32,800 volt-amperes
1st 10 kVA at 100%.........................	10,000 volt-amperes
Remainder at 40% (22.8 kVA × .4)	9120 volt-amperes
Total other load	19,120 volt-amperes
Other load.................................	19,120 volt-amperes
Air conditioning..........................	10,080 volt-amperes
	29,200 volt-amperes

29,200 volt-amperes ÷ 240 V = 122 amperes (service rating)

Feeder Neutral Load, per Section 220-22:

(It is assumed that the two 4-kVA wall-mounted ovens are supplied by one branch circuit, the 5.1-kVA counter-mounted cooking unit by a separate circuit.)

1500 sq. ft. at 3 volt-amperes	4500 volt-amperes
Three 20-amp. circuits at 1500 volt-amperes....................................	4500 volt-amperes
Total....................................	9000 volt-amperes
3000 volt-amperes at 100%	3000 volt-amperes
9000 VA – 3000 VA = 6000 volt-amperes at 35%....................................	2100 volt-amperes
	5100 volt-amperes
Two 4-kVA ovens plus one 5.1-kVA cooking unit totals 13.1 kVA	
Table 220-19 permits 55% demand factor 13.1 kVA × .55 = 7.2 kVA feeder capacity 7200 VA × 70% for neutral load	5040 volt-amperes
Clothes washer/dryer — 5 kVA × 70% for neutral load	3500 volt-amperes
Dishwasher	1200 volt-amperes
Total	14,840 volt-amperes

14,840 VA ÷ 240 V = 61.83, use 62 amperes

Example No. 2(c). Optional Calculation for One-Family Dwelling with Heat Pump Single-Phase, 240/120-Volt Service

(See Section 220-30.)

Dwelling has a floor area of 2000 sq. ft., exclusive of unoccupied cellar, unfinished attic, and open porches. It has a 12-kW range, a 4.5-kW water heater, a 1.2-kW dishwasher, a 5-kW clothes dryer, and a 2½-ton (24-ampere) heat pump with 15 kW of back-up heat.

Heat pump kVA is 24 × 240 ÷ 1000 = 5.76 kVA. 5.76 kVA is less than 15 kVA of the back-up heat; therefore, the heat pump load need not be included in the service calculation. (See Table 220-30.)

2000 sq. ft. at 3 volt-amperes...............	6000 volt-amperes
Two 20-ampere appliance outlet circuits at 1500 volt-amperes each..............	3000 volt-amperes
Laundry circuit...............................	1500 volt-amperes
Range (at nameplate rating)	12,000 volt-amperes
Water heater.................................	4500 volt-amperes
Dishwasher	1200 volt-amperes
Clothes dryer	5000 volt-amperes
	33,200 volt-amperes

First 10 kVA of other load at 100% = 10,000 volt-amperes

Remainder of other load at

40% (23,200 volt-amperes × 0.4) = 9,280 volt-amperes

Total of other load = 19,280 volt-amperes

Heat pump and supplementary heat*

240 × 24 = 5760 volt-amperes

15-kW electric heat: 5760 volt-amperes + 15,000 volt-amperes = 20,760 volt-amperes

or = 20.76 kVA

20.76 kVA at 65% = 13.49 kVA

*If supplementary heat is not on at same time as heat pump, heat pump kVA need not be added to total.

Totals:

Other load...................................	19,280 volt-amperes
Heat pump and supplementary heat	13,490 volt-amperes
Total.....................................	32,770 volt-amperes

32.77 kVA ÷ 240 V = 136.5 amperes

Therefore, this dwelling unit shall be permitted to be served by a 150-ampere service.

Example No. 3. Store Building

A store 50 ft. by 60 ft., or 3000 sq. ft., has 30 ft. of show window. There are a total of 80 duplex receptacles. The service is 120/240-volt, single-phase (3-wire service). Actual connected lighting load: 8500 volt-amperes.

Computed Load (Section 220-10):

Noncontinuous Loads:

Receptacle Load (Section 220-13)

80 receptacles at 180 volt-amperes = 14,400 volt-amperes	
10,000 VA at 100%......................	10,000 volt-amperes

(14,400–10,000) VA at 50%..............	2200 volt-amperes
Total.....................................	12,200 volt-amperes

Continuous Loads:

General Lighting Load:*

3000 sq. ft. at 3 volt-amperes per sq. ft..	9000 volt-amperes

Show Window Lighting Load:

30 ft. at 200 volt-amperes per ft.........	6000 volt-amperes

Outside sign circuit 1200 volt-amperes

[Section 600-6(c)]	1200 volt-amperes
	16,200 volt-amperes

Total noncontinuous loads plus continuous loads......................................	28,400 volt-amperes

Minimum Number of Branch Circuits Required:

General Lighting Load: Branch circuits need only be installed to supply the actual connected load [Section 220-4(d)].

8500 volt-amperes × 1.25 = 10,625 volt-amperes

10,625 volt-amperes ÷ 240 volts = 44 amperes for 3-wire, 120/240.

The lighting load shall be permitted to be served by 2-wire or 3-wire 15- or 20-ampere circuits with combined capacity equal to 44 amperes or greater for 3-wire circuits or 88 amperes or greater for 2-wire circuits. The feeder capacity as well as the number of branch-circuit positions available for lighting circuits in the panelboard must reflect the full calculated load of 9000 volt-amperes × 1.25 = 11,250 volt-amperes.

Show Window:

6000 volt-amperes × 1.25 = 7500 volt-amperes

7500 volt-amperes ÷ 240 volts = 31 amperes for 3-wire, 120/240.

The show window lighting shall be permitted to be served by 2-wire or 3-wire circuits with a capacity equal to 31 amperes or greater for 3-wire circuits or 62 amperes or greater for 2-wire circuits.

Receptacles required by Section 210-62 are assumed to be included in the receptacle load above if these receptacles do not supply the show window lighting load.

Receptacles:

Receptacle Load: 14,400 volt-amperes ÷ 240 volts = 60 amperes for 3-wire, 120/240.

The receptacle load shall be permitted to be served by 2-wire or 3-wire circuits with a capacity equal to 60 amperes or greater for 3-wire circuits or 120 amperes or greater for 2-wire circuits.

Minimum Size Feeder (or Service) Overcurrent Protection

[Section 220-10(b) or Section 230-90(a)]:

Total noncontinuous loads..................	12,200 volt-amperes
Total continuous load @ 125%	
16,200 × 1.25...........................	20,250 volt-amperes
Total load	32,450 volt-amperes

32,450 volt-amperes ÷ 240 volts = 135 amperes

The next higher standard size is 150 amperes. (Section 240-6).

Minimum Size Feeders (or Service Conductors) Required

[Sections 215-3, 220-10(b), 230-42(a)]:

For 120/240-volt, 3-wire system:

28,400 volt-amperes ÷ 240 volts = 118 amperes

Service or feeder conductor is No. 1 Cu per Table 310-16 (with 75°C terminations). The No. 1 Cu wire is protected by the 150-ampere overcurrent setting per Sections 215-3 [or Section 230-90(a), Exception No. 2] and 240-3(b).

In the example, 125 percent of the actual connected lighting load (8500 volt-amperes × 1.25 = 10,625 volt-amperes) is less than 125 percent of the load from Table 220-3(b), so the minimum lighting load from Table 220-3(b) is used in the calculation. Had the actual lighting load been greater than the value computed from Table 220-3(b), 125 percent of the actual connected lighting load would have been used.

Example No. 4(a). Multifamily Dwelling

Multifamily dwelling having 40 dwelling units.

Meters in two banks of 20 each and individual subfeeders to each dwelling unit.

One-half of the dwelling units are equipped with electric ranges not exceeding 12 kW each. Assume range kW rating equivalent to kVA rating in accordance with Section 220-19. Other half of ranges are gas ranges.

Area of each dwelling unit is 840 sq. ft.

Laundry facilities on premises available to all tenants. Add no circuit to individual dwelling unit. Add 1500 volt-amperes for each laundry circuit to house load and add to the example as a "house load."

Computed Load for Each Dwelling Unit (Article 220):

General Lighting Load:

840 sq. ft. at 3 volt-amperes per sq. ft . .	2520 volt-amperes

Special Appliance Load:

Electric Range (Section 220-19).........	8000 volt-amperes

Minimum Number of Branch Circuits Required for Each Dwelling Unit (Section 220-4):

General Lighting Load: 2520 volt-amperes ÷ 120 volts = 21 amperes or two 15-ampere, 2-wire circuits; or two 20-ampere, 2-wire circuits.

Small Appliance Load: Two 2-wire circuits of No. 12 wire. [See Section 220-4(b).]

Range Circuit: 8000 volt-amperes ÷ 240 = 33 amperes or a circuit of two No. 8 conductors and one No. 10 conductor as permitted by Section 220-22. (See Section 210-19.)

Minimum Size Subfeeder Required for Each Dwelling Unit (Section 215-2):

Computed Load (Article 220):

General Lighting Load.......................	2520 volt-amperes
Small Appliance Load, two 20-ampere	
circuits.....................................	3000 volt-amperes
Total Computed Load (without ranges)..	5520 volt-amperes

Application of Demand Factor:

3000 volt-amperes at 100%	3000 volt-amperes
2520 volt-amperes at 35%	882 volt-amperes
Net Computed Load (without ranges)....	3882 volt-amperes
Range Load	8000 volt-amperes
Net Computed Load (with ranges)	11,882 volt-amperes

Size of Each Subfeeder (see Section 215-3):

For 120/240-volt, 3-wire system (without ranges):

Net Computed Load, 3882 volt-amperes ÷ 240 volts = 16.2 amperes.

For 120/240-volt, 3-wire system (with ranges):

Net Computed Load, 11,882 volt-amperes ÷ 240 volts = 49.5 amperes.

Subfeeder Neutral:

Lighting and Small Appliance Load	3882 volt-amperes
Range Load, 8000 volt-amperes at 70%	
(see Section 220-22)	5600 volt-amperes
(Not included for apartments without	
electric range)	
Net Computed Load (neutral).........	9482 volt-amperes

9482 volt-amperes ÷ 240 volts = 39.5 amperes

Minimum Size Feeders Required from Service Equipment to Meter Bank (For 20 Dwelling Units — 10 with Ranges):

Total Computed Load:

Lighting and Small Appliance Load:

20 × 5520 volt-amperes	110,400 volt-amperes

Application of Demand Factor:

3000 volt-amperes at 100%	3000 volt-amperes
107,400 volt-amperes at 35%	37,590 volt-amperes
Net Computed Lighting and Small Appliance Load.................................	40,590 volt-amperes
Range Load, 10 ranges (less than 12 kVA, Col. A, Table 220-19)	25,000 volt-amperes
Net Computed Load (with ranges)	65,590 volt-amperes

For 120/240-volt, 3-wire system:

Net Computed Load, 65,590 volt-amperes ÷ 240 volts = 273 amperes.

Feeder Neutral:

Lighting and Small Appliance Load	40,590 volt-amperes
Range Load: 25,000 volt-amperes at 70% (see Section 220-22)......................	17,500 volt-amperes
Computed Load (neutral).................	58,090 volt-amperes

58,090 volt-amperes ÷ 240 volts = 242 amperes.

Further Demand Factor (Section 220-22):

200 amperes at 100%	200 amperes
42 amperes at 70%..........................	29 amperes
Net Computed Load (neutral)	229 amperes

Minimum Size Main Feeder (or Service Conductors) Required (less house load). (For 40 Dwelling Units — 20 with Ranges):

Total Computed Load:

Lighting and Small Appliance Load:

40 × 5520 volt-amperes..................	220,800 volt-amperes

Application of Demand Factor:

3000 volt-amperes at 100%	3000 volt-amperes
117,000 volt-amperes at 35%	40,950 volt-amperes
100,800 volt-amperes at 25%	25,200 volt-amperes
Net Computed Lighting and Small Appliance Load............................	69,150 volt-amperes
Range Load, 20 ranges (less than 12 kVA, Col. A, Table 220-19)	35,000 volt-amperes
Net Computed Load	104,150 volt-amperes

For 120/240-volt, 3-wire system:

Net Computed Load, 104,150 volt-amperes ÷ 240 volts = 434 amperes.

Feeder Neutral:

Lighting and Small Appliance Load	69,150 volt-amperes
Range Load: 35,000 volt-amperes at 70% (see Section 220-22).....................	24,500 volt-amperes
Computed Load (neutral)....................	93,650 volt-amperes

93,650 volt-amperes ÷ 240 volts = 390 amperes.

Further Demand Factor (see Section 220-22):

200 amperes at 100%	200 amperes
190 amperes at 70%........................	133 amperes
Net Computed Load (neutral)	333 amperes

See Tables 310-16 through 310-31, Notes 8 and 10.

Example No. 4(b). Optional Calculation for Multi-family Dwelling

Multifamily dwelling equipped with electric cooking and space heating or air conditioning and having 40 dwelling units.

Meters in two banks of 20 each plus house metering and individual subfeeders to each dwelling unit.

Each dwelling unit is equipped with an electric range of 8-kW nameplate rating, four 1.5-kW separately controlled 240-volt electric space heaters, and a 2.5-kW 240-volt electric water heater. Assume range, space heater, and water heater kW ratings equivalent to kVA.

A common laundry facility is available to all tenants [Section 210-52(f), Exception No. 1].

Area of each dwelling unit is 840 sq. ft.

Computed Load for Each Dwelling Unit (Article 220):

General Lighting Load:

840 sq. ft. at 3 volt-amperes per sq. ft......	2520 volt-amperes
Electric Range................................	8000 volt-amperes
Electric Heat 6 kVA..........................	6000 volt-amperes
(or air conditioning if larger)	
Electric Water Heater	2500 volt-amperes

Minimum Number of Branch Circuits Required for Each Dwelling Unit:

General Lighting Load: 2520 volt-amperes ÷ 120 volts = 21 amperes or two 15-ampere 2-wire circuits or two 20-ampere 2-wire circuits.

Small Appliance Loads: Two 2-wire circuits of No. 12 [see Section 220-4(b)].

Range circuit: 8000 volt-amperes × 80% ÷ 240 volts = 27 amperes on a circuit of three No. 10 conductors as permitted in Column C of Table 220-19.

Space Heating 6000 volt-amperes ÷ 240 volts = 25 amperes
No. of circuits (see Section 220-4).

Minimum Size Subfeeder Required for Each Dwelling Unit
(Section 215-2):

Computed Load (Article 220):

General Lighting Load	2520 volt-amperes
Small Appliance Load, two 20-ampere circuits	3000 volt-amperes
Total Computed Load	5520 volt-amperes
(without range and space heating)	
Application of Demand Factor:	
3000 volt-amperes at 100%	3000 volt-amperes
2520 volt-amperes at 35%	882 volt-amperes
Net Computed Load	3882 volt-amperes
(without range and space heating)	
Range Load	6400 volt-amperes
Space Heating (Section 220-15)	6000 volt-amperes
Water Heater	2500 volt-amperes
Net Computed Load for individual dwelling unit	18,782 volt-amperes

For 120/240-volt, 3-wire system
Net Computed Load 18,782 volt-amperes ÷ 240 volts = 78 amperes

Subfeeder Neutral (Section 220-22)

Lighting and Small Appliance Load	3882 volt-amperes
Range Load: 6400 volt-amperes at 70% (see Section 220-22)	4480 volt-amperes
Space and Water Heating (no neutral) 240 volt	0 volt-amperes
Net Computed Load (neutral)	8362 volt-amperes

8362 volt-amperes ÷ 240 volts = 35 amperes

Minimum Size Feeder Required from Service Equipment to Meter Bank for 20 Dwelling Units:

Total Computed Load:

Lighting and Small Appliance Load 20 × 5520	110,400 volt-amperes
Water and Space Heating Load 20 × 8500	170,000 volt-amperes
Range Load 20 × 8000 volt-amperes	160,000 volt-amperes
Net Computed Load (20 dwelling units)	440,400 volt-amperes

Net Computed Load Using Optional Calculation (Table 220-32):

440,400 volt-amperes × .38	167,352 volt-amperes

167,352 volt-amperes ÷ 240 volts = 697 amperes

Minimum Size Main Feeder Required (less house load) for 40 Dwelling Units:

Total Computed Load:

Lighting and Small Appliance Load 40 × 5520	220,800 volt-amperes
Water and Space Heating 40 × 8500	340,000 volt-amperes
Range Load 40 × 8000 volt-amperes	320,000 volt-amperes
Net Computed Load (40 dwelling units)	880,800 volt-amperes

Net Computed Load Using Optional Calculation (Table 220-32):

880,800 volt-amperes × .28	246,624 volt-amperes

246,624 volt-amperes ÷ 240 volts = 1028 amperes

Feeder Neutral Load for Feeder from Service Equipment to Meter Bank for 20 Dwelling Units:

Lighting and Small Appliance Load:

20 × 5520 volt-amperes	110,400 volt-amperes
First 3000 volt-amperes at 100%	3000 volt-amperes
107,400 volt-amperes at 35%	37,590 volt-amperes
Subtotal	40,590 volt-amperes
20 Ranges = 35,000 volt-amperes at 70%	24,500 volt-amperes
(See Table 220-19 and Section 220-22.)	
Total	65,090 volt-amperes

65,090 volt-amperes ÷ 240 volts = 271 amperes

Further Demand Factor (Section 220-22):

First 200 amperes at 100%	200 amperes
Balance: 71 amperes at 70%	50 amperes
Total	250 amperes

Feeder Neutral Load of Main Feeder (less house load) for 40 Dwelling Units:

Lighting and Small Appliance Load:

40 × 5520 volt-amperes	220,800 volt-amperes
First 3000 volt-amperes at 100%	3000 volt-amperes
120,000 volt-amperes − 3000 volt-amperes = 117,000 volt-amperes at 35%	40,950 volt-amperes
220,800 volt-amperes − 120,000 volt-amperes = 100,800 volt-amperes at 25%	25,200 volt-amperes

Net Computed Lighting and Small Appliance Load	69,150 volt-amperes
40 Ranges = 55,000 volt-amperes at 70%	38,500 volt-amperes

(See Table 220-19 and Section 220-22)

Total	107,650 volt-amperes

107,650 volt-amperes ÷ 240 volts = 449 amperes

Further Demand Factor (Section 220-22):

First 200 amperes at 100%	200 amperes
Balance: 249 amperes at 70%	174 amperes
Total	374 amperes

Example No. 5(a). Multifamily Dwelling Served at 208Y/120 Volts, Three Phase

All conditions and calculations the same as for Multifamily Dwelling [Example No. 4(a)] served at 120/240 volts, single phase except as follows:

Service to each dwelling unit shall be two phase legs and neutral.

Minimum Number of Branch Circuits Required for Each Dwelling Unit (Section 220-4):

Range Circuit: 8000 volt-amperes ÷ 208 volts = 38 amperes or a circuit of two No. 8 conductors and one No. 10 conductor as permitted by Section 220-22.

Minimum Size Subfeeder Required for Each Dwelling Unit (Section 215-2):

For 120/208-volt, 3-wire system (without ranges)

Net Computed Load: 3882 volt-amperes ÷ 2 legs ÷ 120 volts/leg = 16.2 amperes

For 120/208-volt, 3-wire system (with ranges)

Net Computed Load: range, 8000 volt-amperes ÷ 208 volts = 38.5 amperes

Total load: range plus lighting = 54.7 amperes

Subfeeder neutral: range, 5600 volt-amperes ÷ 208 volts = 26.9 amperes

Total load: range plus lighting = 43.1 amperes

Minimum Size Feeders Required from Service Equipment to Meter Bank (For 20 Dwelling Units — 10 with Ranges):

For 208Y/120-volt, 3-phase, 4 wire system

Ranges: Maximum number between any two phase legs = 4

2 × 4 = 8. Table 220-19 Demand = 23,000 volt-amperes.

Per phase demand: 23,000 volt-amperes ÷ 2 = 11,500 volt-amperes

Equivalent 3-phase load = 34,500 volt-amperes

Net Computed Load (total): 40,590 volt-amperes + 34,500 volt-amperes = 75,080 volt-amperes

75,080 volt-amperes ÷ (208)(1.732) = 208.4 amperes

Feeder Neutral Size

40,590 volt-amperes + 34,500 volt-amperes at 70% = 64,700 volt-amperes

Net Computed Neutral Load:

64,700 volt-amperes ÷ (208)(1.732) = 179.6 amperes

Minimum Size Main Feeder (less house load)

(For 40 Dwelling Units — 20 with Ranges):

For 208Y/120-volt, 3-phase, 4-wire system

Ranges: Maximum number between any two phase legs = 7

2 × 7 = 14. Table 220-19 Demand = 29,000 volt-amperes.

Per phase demand: 29,000 ÷ 2 = 14,500 volt-amperes

Equivalent 3-phase load = 43,500 volt-amperes

Net Computed Load (total): 69,150 volt-amperes + 43,500 volt-amperes = 112,650 volt-amperes

112,650 volt-amperes ÷ (208)(1.732) = 312.7 amperes

Main Feeder Neutral Size

69,150 volt-amperes + 43,500 volt-amperes at 70% = 99,600 volt-amperes

99,600 volt-amperes ÷ (208)(1.732) = 276.5 amperes

Further Demand Factor (Section 220-22)

200 amperes at 100%	200.0 amperes
76.5 amperes at 70%	53.6 amperes
Net Computed Load	253.6 amperes

Example No. 5(b). Optional Calculation for Multifamily Dwelling Served at 208Y/120 Volts, Three Phase

All conditions and calculations the same as for Optional Calculation for Multifamily Dwelling [Example No. 4(b)] served at 120/240 volts, single phase except as follows:

Service to each dwelling unit shall be two phase legs and neutral.

Minimum Number of Branch Circuits Required for Each Dwelling Unit (Section 220-4):

Range Circuit: 8000 volt-amperes at 80% ÷ 208 volts = 30.7 amperes or a circuit of two No. 8 and one No. 10 as permitted by Section 220-22.

Space Heating: 6000 volt-amperes ÷ 208 volts = 28.8 amperes. Two 20-ampere, 2-pole circuits required, No. 12 conductor.

Minimum Size Subfeeder Required for Each Dwelling Unit.

Computed Load (120/208-volt, 3-wire circuit)

Net Computed Load: 18,782 volt-amperes ÷ 208 volts = 90.3 amperes

Net Computed Load: Lighting (line to neutral)

3882 volt-amperes ÷ 2 legs ÷ 120 volts/leg	16.2 amperes
Line to line:	
14,900 volt-amperes ÷ 208 volts	71.6 amperes
Total load:	87.8 amperes

Minimum Size Feeder Required for Service Equipment to Meter Bank (For 20 dwelling units):

Net Computed Load: 167,352 volt-amperes ÷ (208)(1.732) = 464.9 amperes

Feeder Neutral Load:

65,080 volt-amperes ÷ (208)(1.732) = 180.67 amperes

Minimum Size Main Feeder Required (less house load)

(For 40 dwelling units):

Net Computed Load: 246,624 volt-amperes ÷ (208)(1.732) = 685.1 amperes

Main Feeder Neutral Load:

107,650 volt-amperes ÷ (208)(1.732) = 298.8 amperes

Further Demand Factor (Section 220-22)

200 amperes at 100%	200.0 amperes
98.8 amperes at 70%	69.2 amperes
Net Computed Load	269.2 amperes

Example No. 6. Maximum Demand for Range Loads

Table 220-19, Column A applies to ranges not over 12 kW. The application of Note 1 to ranges over 12 kW (and not over 27 kW) and Note 2 to ranges over 8¾ kW (and not over 27 kW) is illustrated in the following examples:

A. Ranges all the same rating (Table 220-19, Note 1).

Assume 24 ranges, each rated 16 kW.

From Column A, the maximum demand for 24 ranges of 12 kW rating is 39 kW.

16 kW exceeds 12 kW by 4.

5% × 4 = 20% (5% increase for each kW in excess of 12).

39 kW × 20% = 7.8 kW increase.

39 + 7.8 = 46.8 kW: value to be used in selection of feeders.

B. Ranges of unequal rating (Table 220-19, Note 2).

Assume 5 ranges, each rated 11 kW.

2 ranges, each rated 12 kW.

20 ranges, each rated 13.5 kW.

3 ranges, each rated 18 kW.

5 × 12 = 60 use 12 kW for range rated less than 12.

2 × 12 = 24

20 × 13.5 = 270

$$\frac{3 \times 18 = 54}{30 \qquad 408 \text{ kW}}$$

408 ÷ 30 = 13.6 kW (average to be used for computation).

From Column A, the demand for 30 ranges of 12 kW rating is

15 + 30 = 45 kW.

13.6 exceeds 12 by 1.6 (use 2).

5% × 2 = 10% (5% increase for each kW in excess of 12).

45 kW × 10% = 4.5 kW increase.

45 + 4.5 = 49.5 kW: value to be used in selection of feeders.

Example No. 8. Motors, Conductors, Overload, and Short-Circuit and Ground-Fault Protection

(See Sections 240-6, 430-6, 430-7, 430-22, 430-23, 430-24, 430-32, 430-34, 430-52, and 430-62 and Tables 430-150 and 430-152.)

Determine the conductor size, the motor overload protection, the branch-circuit short-circuit and ground-fault protection and the feeder protection, for one 25-horsepower squirrel-cage induction motor (full voltage starting nameplate current 31.6 amperes, service factor 1.15, Code letter F), and two 30-horsepower wound-rotor induction motors (nameplate primary current 36.4 amperes, nameplate secondary current 65 amperes, 40°C rise), on a 460-volt, 3-phase, 60-Hertz supply.

Conductor Loads

· The full-load current value used to determine the ampacity of conductors for the 25-horsepower motor is 34 amperes [Section

430-6(a) and Table 430-150]. A full-load current of 34 amperes × 1.25 = 42.5 amperes (Section 430-22). The full-load current value used to determine the ampacity of primary conductors for each 30-horsepower motor is 40 amperes [Section 430-6(a) and Table 430-150]. A full-load primary current of 40 amperes × 1.25 = 50 amperes (Section 430-22). A full-load secondary current of 65 amperes × 1.25 = 81.25 amperes [Section 430-23(a)].

The feeder ampacity will be 125 percent of 40 plus 40 plus 34, or 124 amperes (Section 430-24).

Overload and Short-Circuit and Ground-Fault Protection

Overload. Where protected by a separate overload device, the 25-horsepower motor, with nameplate current of 31.6 amperes, shall have overload protection of not over 39.5 amperes [Sections 430-6(a) and 430-32(a)(1)]. Where protected by a separate overload device, the 30-horsepower motor, with nameplate current of 36.4 amperes, shall have overload protection of not over 45.5 amperes [Sections 430-6(a) and 430-32(a)(1)]. If the overload protection is not sufficient to start the motor or to carry the load, it shall be permitted to be increased according to Section 430-34. For a motor marked "thermally protected," overload protection is provided by the thermal protector [see Sections 430-7(a)(12) and 430-32(a)(2)].

Branch-Circuit Short-Circuit and Ground-Fault. The branch circuit of the 25-horsepower motor shall have branch-circuit short-circuit and ground-fault protection of not over 300 percent of a nontime-delay fuse (Table 430-152) or 3.00 × 34 = 102 amperes. The next smaller standard size fuse is 100 amperes (Section 240-6). Since a 100-ampere fuse is adequate to carry the load, Section 430-52(a), Exception No. 1 does not apply. If a time-delay fuse is to be used, see Section 430-52(a), Exception No. 2b. Where the 100-ampere fuse will not allow the motor to run, the value for a nontime-delay fuse shall be permitted to be increased to the next larger standard size, or 110 amperes. If these fuses are not sufficient to start the motor, the value for a nontime-delay fuse shall be permitted to be increased to 400 percent [See Section 430-52(a), Exception No. 2a.]

Feeder Circuit. The maximum rating of the feeder short-circuit and ground-fault protection device is based on the sum of the largest branch-circuit protective device (100-ampere fuse) plus the sum of the full-load currents of the other motors or 100 + 40 + 40 = 180 amperes. The nearest standard fuse that does not exceed this value is 175 amperes [Section 430-62(a)].

Example No. 9. Feeder Size Determination for Generator Field Control

Determining conductor ampacity for a group of six elevators on a single feeder.

(See Sections 620-15, 620-13, 430-26, and 430-24 and Tables 620-15 and 430-150.

Determine the conductor ampacity for a feeder supplying the six elevators. The system is generator field control. The ac drive motor horsepower rating of the largest MG set for one elevator is 40 horsepower, and the remaining elevators each have a 30-horsepower ac drive motor rating for their MG sets. Each controller draws 10 amperes to operate relays, power supplies, and the door operator. The line power supply is 460 volts, 3-phase, 60 Hz ac. The MG sets are rated continuous.

Conductor ampacity is determined as follows:

(a) Per Table 430-150, the full-load current for a 30-horsepower ac motor at 460 volts is 40 amps; for a 40-horsepower ac motor at 460 volts, 52 amps.

(b) Per Section 430-24, Exception No. 1 determine the ampere rating for each motor used for other than continuous duty from Table 430-22(a), Exception.

(c) Per Table 430-22(a), Exception, for intermittent duty using a continuous rated motor, the percentage of nameplate current rating to be used is 140%.

(d) For the 30-horsepower ac drive motors, 1.4 × 40 amps = 56 amps.

For the 40-horsepower ac drive motors, 1.4 × 52 amps = 73 amps.

(e) Per Section 430-24, the total conductor ampacity is:
1.25 × largest motor current + the sum of the remaining motor currents = (1.25 × 73) + (5 × 56) = 371 amps.

(f) Per Section 620-15 and Table 620-15, the conductor (feeder) ampacity shall be permitted to be reduced by the use of a demand factor. For six elevators, the demand factor is .79. The feeder motor ampacity is, therefore, .79 × 371 amps = 293 amps.

(g) The total feeder ampacity is the sum of the motor diverse current and the controller (constant) current. I total = 293 + (6 × 10) = 353 amps.

(h) This total ampacity shall be permitted to be used to select the wire size.

The basic requirement of Section 430-52 is to place a top limit on the rating of the branch-circuit short-circuit and ground-fault protective device for the value calculated. Where the calculated value does not correspond to the standard sizes or ratings of fuses, nonadjustable circuit breakers or thermal protectors, it is necessary to round down to the next lower standard size. In the example, the calculated value for the branch-circuit short-circuit and ground-fault protection is 102 amperes. Use of a 100-ampere device (the next smaller standard size) is acceptable. It provides better protection and permits use of smaller, and usually less expensive, fuses and fuse-holding equipment. If the smaller device is not adequate to carry the load, the next higher standard sized device may be used.

Example No. 10. Determining Conductor Ampacity for a Group of Six Elevators on a Single Feeder Using Adjustable Speed Drive

(See Sections 620-14, 620-15, and 430-26 and Table 620-15.)

Determine the conductor ampacity for a feeder supplying six identical elevators. The system is adjustable speed SCR dc drive. The transformers are external to the drive cabinet. Each drive has an ac nameplate rating of 204 amps. Each transformer is rated 85 kVA with a 300V secondary; efficiency is 90%. The ac line voltage is 460 volts, 3-phase, 60 Hz.

Conductor ampacity is determined as follows:

(a) Per 620-14(b), calculate the nameplate current rating of the transformer:

$$I = \frac{85 \times 1000}{\sqrt{3} \times 460 \times 0.9} = 119 \text{ amps}$$

(b) Per Section 620-14(b), calculate the drive input current reflected to the transformer primary:

$$I = 204 \text{ A} \times 300 \text{ V}/460 \text{ V} = 133 \text{ amps}$$

(c) Per 620-14(b), the larger current is 133 amps.

(d) For six elevators, the total conductor ampacity is 6×133 amps = 798 amps.

(e) Per Section 620-15 and Table 620-15, the conductor (feeder) ampacity shall be permitted to be reduced by the use of a demand factor. For six elevators, the demand factor is .79. The feeder ampacity is, therefore, $.79 \times 798$ amps = 630 amps.

(f) This ampacity shall be permitted to be used to select the wire size subject to Section 430-26.

Appendix A

Extracts

This appendix identifies those *NEC* figures, tables, or actions (first column) that are identified in the *NEC* by a superscript letter "x" (e.g., 515-2ˣ = A-515-2) and the NFPA document (second column) and section, or equivalent (third column), from which the material in the *NEC* was extracted.

Requests for interpretations or proposed revisions of the extracted text will be referred to the NFPA committee responsible for the document from which the text was extracted.

(See Section 90-3, Paragraph 4)

A-500-3(b)(1)	Classification of Gases, Vapors, and Dusts for Electrical Equipment in Hazardous (Classified) Locations, NFPA 497M-1991	Chapter 3, Class II Materials— Dusts
A-500-3(b)(2)	Classification of Gases, Vapors, and Dusts for Electrical Equipment in Hazardous (Classified) Locations, NFPA 497M-1991	Chapter 3, Class II Materials— Dusts
A-514-2	Automotive and Marine Service Station Code, NFPA 30A-1990	Section 7-3
A-Table 514-2	Automotive and Marine Service Station Code, NFPA 30A-1990	Table 7
A-Fig. 514-2	Automotive and Marine Service Station Code, NFPA 30A-1990	Figure 7-1
A-Fig. 514-5(b)	Automotive and Marine Service Station Code, NFPA 30A-1990	Section 9-5.4
A-Fig. 514-5(c)	Automotive and Marine Service Station Code, NFPA 30A-1990	Section 9-5.3
A-515-2	Flammable and Combustible Liquids Code, NFPA 30-1990	Paragraph 5-3.5.3
A-Table 515-2	Flammable and Combustible Liquids Code, NFPA 30-1990	Table 5-3.5.3
A-516-2(a)(1)	Standard for Spray Application Using Flammable and Combustible Materials, NFPA 33-1989	Section 1-2 Spray Area
A-516-2(a)(2)	Standard for Spray Application Using Flammable and Combustible Materials, NFPA 33-1989	Section 1-2 Spray Area
A-516-2(a)(3)	Standard for Spray Application Using Flammable and Combustible Materials, NFPA 33-1989	Section 1-2 Spray Area
A-516-2(a)(4)	Standard for Dipping and Coating Processes Using Flammable or Combustible Liquids, NFPA 34-1989	Section 1-2, Vapor Source, and Paragraph 6-2.2

A-516-2(a)(5)	Standard for Dipping and Coating Processes Using Flammable or Combustible Liquids, NFPA 34-1989	Paragraph 6-2.1		A-516-5	Standard for Spray Application Using Flammable and Combustible Materials, NFPA 33-1989	Chapter 10
A-516-2(a)(6)	Standard for Dipping and Coating Processes Using Flammable or Combustible Liquids, NFPA 34-1989	Figure 6-1(b)		A-516-6	Standard for Spray Application Using Flammable and Combustible Materials, NFPA 33-1989	Chapter 13
A-516-2(b)(1)	Standard for Spray Application Using Flammable and Combustible Materials, NFPA 33-1989	Paragraph 4-7.1		A-517-10, Exception No. 3	Standard for Health Care Facilities, NFPA 99-1990	Section 16-2, Exception; Paragraph 17-3.3.2, Exception
A-516, Fig. 1	Standard for Spray Application Using Flammable and Combustible Materials, NFPA 33-1989	Figure 1		A-517-15	Standard for Health Care Facilities, NFPA 99-1990	3-5.2.1.6
A-516-2(b)(2)	Standard for Spray Application Using Flammable and Combustible Materials, NFPA 33-1989	Paragraph 4-7.2		A-517-25	Standard for Health Care Facilities, NFPA 99-1990	Paragraphs 3-2.2.1, 3-4.2.3.2, 3-4.2.4.1
A-516, Fig. 2	Standard for Spray Application Using Flammable and Combustible Materials, NFPA 33-1989	Figure 2		A-517-30(b)(1)	Standard for Health Care Facilities, NFPA 99-1990	Paragraph 3-4.2.2.1
A-516-2(b)(3)	Standard for Spray Application Using Flammable and Combustible Materials, NFPA 33-1989	Paragraph 4-7.3		A-517-30(b)(2)	Standard for Health Care Facilities, NFPA 99-1990	Paragraph 3-4.2.2.1
A-516-2(b)(4)	Standard for Spray Application Using Flammable and Combustible Materials, NFPA 33-1989	Paragraph 4-7.4		A-517-30(b)(3)	Standard for Health Care Facilities, NFPA 99-1990	Paragraph 3-4.2.2.1
A-516, Fig. 3	Standard for Spray Application Using Flammable and Combustible Materials, NFPA 33-1989	Figure 3		A-517-30(b)(4)	Standard for Health Care Facilities, NFPA 99-1990	Paragraph 3-4.2.2.1
A-516-2(b)(5)	Standard for Dipping and Coating Processes Using Flammable or Combustible Liquids, NFPA 34-1989	Paragraphs 6-2.3 and 6-2.4		A-517-31	Standard for Health Care Facilities, NFPA 99-1990	Paragraphs 3-4.2.2.2(a), 3-5.1.2.1(a)
A-516-2(b)(6)	Standard for Dipping and Coating Processes Using Flammable or Combustible Liquids, NFPA 34-1989	Section 6-3		A-517-32	Standard for Health Care Facilities, NFPA 99-1990	Paragraph 3-4.2.2.2(b)
A-516, Fig. 4	Standard for Dipping and Coating Processes Using Flammable or Combustible Liquids, NFPA 34-1989	Figure 6-1(a)		A-517-33(a)	Standard for Health Care Facilities, NFPA 99-1990	Paragraph 3-4.2.2.2(c)
A-516-3(b)	Standard for Spray Application Using Flammable and Combustible Materials, NFPA 33-1989	Section 4-5		A-517-34	Standard for Health Care Facilities, NFPA 99-1990	Paragraph 3-4.2.2.3(b)
				A-517-34(a)	Standard for Health Care Facilities, NFPA 99-1990	Paragraph 3-4.2.2.3(c)
A-516-3(d)	Standard for Spray Application Using Flammable and Combustible Materials, NFPA 33-1989	Section 4-9		A-517-34(b)	Standard for Health Care Facilities, NFPA 99-1990	Paragraph 3-4.2.2.3(d)
A-516-4	Standard for Spray Application Using Flammable and Combustible Materials, NFPA 33-1989	Chapter 9		A-517-35(a)	Standard for Health Care Facilities, NFPA 99-1990	Paragraph 3-3.2.1.2
				A-517-35(b)	Standard for Health Care Facilities, NFPA 99-1990	Paragraph 3-3.2.1.3
				A-517-41(a)	Standard for Health Care Facilities, NFPA 99-1990	Paragraph 3-4.2.3.2
				A-517-41(b)	Standard for Health Care Facilities, NFPA 99-1990	Paragraph 3-4.2.3.2
				A-517-42	Standard for Health Care Facilities, NFPA 99-1990	Paragraphs 3-4.2.3.3, 3-5.1.2.1(b)
				A-517-43	Standard for Health Care Facilities, NFPA 99-1990	Paragraph 3-4.2.3.4

A-517-44(a)	Standard for Health Care Facilities, NFPA 99-1990	Paragraph 3-3.2.1.2
A-517-44(b)	Standard for Health Care Facilities, NFPA 99-1990	Paragraphs 3-3.2.1.3, 16-3.3.2.1, 17-3.3.2.1
A-517-50(a)	Standard for Health Care Facilities, NFPA 99-1990	Paragraphs 14-3.3.2, 15-3.3.2, 18-3.3.2
A-517-50(b)	Standard for Health Care Facilities, NFPA 99-1990	Paragraph 3-4.2.4.2
A-517-50(c)(1)	Standard for Health Care Facilities, NFPA 99-1990	Paragraph 3-4.2.4.3
A-517-50(c)(2)	Standard for Health Care Facilities, NFPA 99-1990	Paragraph 3-5.1.2.1(c)
A-517-50(c)(3)	Standard for Health Care Facilities, NFPA 99-1990	Paragraph 3-5.1.2.1(c)

A-517-60(a)(1)	Standard for Health Care Facilities, NFPA 99-1990	Section 2-2, Hazardous Area in Flammable Anesthetizing Location
A-517-61(a)(1)	Standard for Health Care Facilities, NFPA 99-1990	Paragraph 12-4.1.3.2
A-517-61(a)(3)	Standard for Health Care Facilities, NFPA 99-1990	Paragraphs 3-4.1.2.1(e)(2) 7-5.1.2.4, 7-5.1.2.5
A-517-64	Standard for Health Care Facilities, NFPA 99-1990	Paragraph 7-5.1.2.3
A-517-160(a)(2)	Standard for Health Care Facilities, NFPA 99-1990	Paragraph 3-4.3.1.2
A-517-160(b)	Standard for Health Care Facilities, NFPA 99-1990	Paragraph 3-4.3.3

Appendix B

B-310-15(b)(1) . Formula Application Information. This appendix provides application information for ampacities calculated under engineering supervision.

The data in Appendix B is based on calculations using the Neher-McGrath formula found in Section 310-15(b). See commentary following that section.

B-310-15(b)(2) . Typical Applications Covered by Tables.

Typical ampacities for conductors rated 0 through 2000 volts are shown in Tables B-310-1 through B-310-10. Underground electrical duct bank configurations, as detailed in Figures B-310-3, B-310-4, and B-310-5, are utilized for conductors rated 0 through 5000 volts. In Figures B-310-2 through B-310-5, where adjacent duct banks are used, a separation of 5 feet (1.52 m) between the centerlines of the closest ducts in each bank or 4 feet (1.22 m) between the extremities of the concrete envelopes is sufficient to prevent derating of the conductors due to mutual heating. These ampacities were calculated as detailed in the basic ampacity paper, "The Calculation of the Temperature Rise and Load Capability of Cable Systems," by J. H. Neher and M. H. McGrath, AIEE Paper 57-660. For additional information concerning the application of these ampacities, see Power Cable Ampacities, IEEE/ICEA Standard S-135/P-46-426.

Typical values of thermal resistivity (Rho) are as follows:

Polyethylene (PE) = 450	Concrete = 55
Polyvinyl Chloride PVC = 650	Very Dry Soil (rocky or
Rubber and Rubber-like = 500	sandy) = 120
Paper Insulation = 550	Damp Soil
Average Soil (90 percent of	(coastal areas, high
USA) = 90	water table) = 60

Thermal resistivity, as used in this appendix, refers to the heat transfer capability through a substance by conduction. It is the reciprocal of thermal conductivity and is normally expressed in the units °C-cm/watt. For additional information on determining soil thermal resistivity (Rho), see IEEE *Guide for Soil Thermal Resistivity Measurements*, ANSI/IEEE Standard 442-1981.

B-310-15(b)(3). Criteria Modifications.

Where values of load factor and Rho are known for a particular electrical duct bank installation and they are different from those shown in a specific table or figure, the ampacities shown in the table or figure can be modified by the application of factors derived from the use of Figure B-310-1.

A soil resistivity higher than 90 will reduce ampacities below those in the underground ampacity Tables B-310-5, B-310-6, B-310-7, B-310-8, B-310-9, and B-310-10 where other factors remain the same. Conversely, a load factor of less than 100 percent will increase ampacities where other factors remain the same. See Section B-310-15(b)(7).

Where two different ampacities apply to adjacent portions of a circuit, the higher ampacity can be used beyond the point of transition, a distance equal to 10 feet (3.05 m) or 10 percent of the circuit length figured at the higher ampacity, whichever is less.

This information is the same as that found in the exception to Section 310-15(c). See commentary following this exception.

Where the burial depth of direct burial or electrical duct bank circuits are modified from the values shown in a figure or table, ampacities can be modified as shown in (1) and (2), which follow.

(1) Where burial depths are increased in part(s) of an electrical duct run to avoid underground obstructions, no decrease in ampacity of the conductors is needed, provided the total length of parts of the duct run increased in depth to avoid obstructions is less than 25 percent of the total run length.

See Figure B-1.

(2) Where burial depths are deeper than shown in a specific underground ampacity table or figure, an ampacity derating factor of 6 percent per increased foot (305 mm) of depth for all values of Rho can be utilized. No rating change is needed where the burial depth is decreased.

For example, in accordance with Table B-310-7 and Figure B-310-2, the ampacity of six paralleled runs of 500 kcmil Type XHHW copper conductors (Rho = 90, Detail 3) is $6 \times 273 = 1638$ amperes at a depth measuring no greater than 30 inches to the top duct in the bank. If the burial depth is 6 feet, the ampacity is $1638 - (3.5 \times 0.06 \times 1638) = 1294$ amperes.

Figure B-1. *If that portion deeper than 30 inches does not exceed 25 percent of the total run length, no decrease in ampacity is required, even though part of the run is more than 30 inches deep, which is the maximum depth assumed in Figure B-310-2, Note 1, in order to maintain the accuracy of the tables.*

B-310-15(b)(4). Electrical Ducts.
The term electrical duct(s) is defined in Section 310-15(d).

B-310-15(b)(5). Tables B-310-6 and B-310-7.

(1) To obtain the ampacity of cables installed in two electrical ducts in one horizontal row with 7.5-inch (191-mm) center-to-center spacing between electrical ducts, similar to Detail 1, Figure B-310-2, multiply the ampacity shown for one duct in Tables B-310-6 and B-310-7 by 0.88.

(2) To obtain the ampacity of cables installed in four electrical ducts in one horizontal row with 7.5-inch (191-mm) center-to-center spacing between electrical ducts, similar to Detail 2, Figure B-310-2, multiply the ampacity shown for three electrical ducts in Tables B-310-6 and B-310-7 by 0.94.

The underground ampacity tables are based on the 7.5-inch center-to-center spacing illustrated in Figure B-310-2. Although moving directly buried cables or electrical ducts further apart will increase ampacities, the effect is surprisingly small. One calculation indicates that two side-by-side electrical ducts buried 30 inches below grade would have to be spaced about 5 feet apart before they could be considered single electrical ducts as shown in Detail 1, Figure B-310-2. Decreasing the burial depth, decreasing the thermal resistivity of the earth or other surrounding medium, and decreasing the load factor have a much greater effect in increasing ampacity than increasing the horizontal spacing.

B-310-15(b)(6) . **Electrical Ducts Utilized in Figure B-310-2.**
If spacing between electrical ducts, as shown in Figure B-310-2, is less than specified in Figure B-310-2, where electrical ducts enter equipment enclosures from underground, the ampacity of conductors contained within such electrical ducts need not be reduced.

B-310-15(b)(7) . **Examples Showing Use of Figure B-310-1 for Electrical Duct Bank Ampacity Modifications.** Figure B-310-1 is used for interpolation or extrapolation for values of Rho and load factor for cables installed in electrical ducts. The upper family of curves shows the variation in ampacity and Rho at unity load factor in terms of I_1, the ampacity for Rho = 60, and 50 percent load factor. Each curve is designated for a particular ratio I_2/I_1, where I_2 is the ampacity at Rho = 120 and 100 percent load factor.

The lower family of curves shows the relationship between Rho and load factor that will give substantially the same ampacity as the indicated value of Rho at 100 percent load factor.

As an example, to find the ampacity of a 500 kcmil copper cable circuit for six electrical ducts as shown in Table B-310-5: At the Rho = 60, LF = 50, I_1 = 583; for Rho = 120 and LF = 100, I_2 = 400. The ratio I_2/I_1 = 0.686. Locate Rho = 90 at bottom of chart and follow the 90 Rho line to the intersection with 100 percent load factor where the equivalent Rho = 90. Then follow the 90 Rho line to I_2/I_1 ratio of 0.686 where F = 0.74. The desired ampacity = 0.74 × 583 = 431, which agrees with the table for Rho = 90, LF = 100.

To determine the ampacity for the same circuit where Rho = 80 and LF = 75, using Figure B-310-1, the equivalent Rho = 43, F = 0.855, and the desired ampacity = 0.855 × 583 = 498 amperes. Values for using Figure B-310-1 are found in the electrical duct bank ampacity tables of this appendix.

Where the load factor is less than 100 percent and can be verified by measurement or calculation, the ampacity of electrical duct bank installations can be modified as shown. Different values of Rho can be accommodated in the same manner.

Table B-310-1. Ampacities of Two or Three Insulated Conductors, Rated 0 through 2000 Volts, within an Overall Covering (Multiconductor Cable), in Raceway in Free Air Based on Ambient Air Temperature of 30°C (86°F)

Size	Temperature Rating of Conductor. See Table 310-13.						Size
	60°C (140°F)	75°C (167°F)	90°C (194°F)	60°C (140°F)	75°C (167°F)	90°C (194°F)	
AWG kcmil	TYPES TW, UF	TYPES RH, RHW, THHW, THW, THWN, XHHW, ZW	TYPES THHN, THHW, THW-2, THWN-2, RHH, RWH-2, USE-2, XHHW XHHW-2, ZW-2	TYPE TW	TYPES RH, RHW, THHW, THW, THWN, XHHW	TYPES THHN, THHW, THW-2, THWN-2, RHH, RWH-2, USE-2, XHHW, XHHW-2, ZW-2	AWG kcmil
	COPPER			ALUMINUM OR COPPER-CLAD ALUMINUM			
14	16†	18†	21†	. . . .	. . . .	. . . .	14
12	20†	24†	27†	16†	18†	21†	12
10	27†	33†	36†	21†	25†	28†	10
8	36	43	48	28	33	37	8
6	48	58	65	38	45	51	6
4	66	79	89	51	61	69	4
3	76	90	102	59	70	79	3
2	88	105	119	69	83	93	2
1	102	121	137	80	95	106	1
1/0	121	145	163	94	113	127	1/0
2/0	138	166	186	108	129	146	2/0
3/0	158	189	214	124	147	167	3/0
4/0	187	223	253	147	176	197	4/0
250	205	245	276	160	192	217	250
300	234	281	317	185	221	250	300
350	255	305	345	202	242	273	350
400	274	328	371	218	261	295	400
500	315	378	427	254	303	342	500
600	343	413	468	279	335	378	600
700	376	452	514	310	371	420	700
750	387	466	529	321	384	435	750
800	397	479	543	331	397	450	800
900	415	500	570	350	421	477	900
1000	448	542	617	382	460	521	1000

Ambient Temp. °C	For ambient temperatures other than 30°C (86°F), multiply the ampacities shown above by the appropriate factor shown below.						Ambient Temp. °F
21-25	1.08	1.05	1.04	1.08	1.05	1.04	70-77
26-30	1.00	1.00	1.00	1.00	1.00	1.00	79-86
31-35	.91	.94	.96	.91	.94	.96	88-95
36-40	.82	.88	.91	.82	.88	.91	97-104
41-45	.71	.82	.87	.71	.82	.87	106-113
46-50	.58	.75	.82	.58	.75	.82	115-122
51-55	.41	.67	.76	.41	.67	.76	124-131
56-60	. . . .	.58	.71	. . . .	.58	.71	133-140
61-70	. . . .	.33	.58	. . . .	.33	.58	142-158
71-80	. . . .	. . . .	.41	. . . .	. . . .	.41	160-176

†Unless otherwise specifically permitted elsewhere in this Code, the overcurrent protection for conductor types marked with an obelisk (†) shall not exceed 15 amperes for No. 14, 20 amperes for No. 12, and 30 amperes for No. 10 copper; or 15 amperes for No. 12 and 25 amperes for No. 10 aluminum and copper-clad aluminum.

Table B-310-2. Ampacities of Two or Three Single Insulated Conductors, Rated 0 through 2000 Volts, Supported on a Messenger, Based on Ambient Air Temperature of 40°C (104°F)

Size	Temperature Rating of Conductor. See Table 310-13.				Size
	75°C (167°F)	90°C (194°F)	75°C (167°F)	90°C (194°F)	
AWG kcmil	TYPES RH, RHW, THHW, THW, THWN, XHHW, ZW	TYPES THHN, THHW, THW-2, THWN-2, RHH, RWH-2, USE-2, XHHW, XHHW-2, ZW-2	TYPES RH, RHW, THW, THWN, THHW, XHHW	TYPES THHN, THHW, RHH, XHHW, RHW-2, XHHW-2, THW-2, THWN-2, USE-2, ZW-2	AWG kcmil
	COPPER		ALUMINUM OR COPPER-CLAD ALUMINUM		
8	57	66	44	51	8
6	76	89	59	69	6
4	101	117	78	91	4
3	118	138	92	107	3
2	135	158	106	123	2
1	158	185	123	144	1
1/0	183	214	143	167	1/0
2/0	212	247	165	193	2/0
3/0	245	287	192	224	3/0
4/0	287	335	224	262	4/0
250	320	374	251	292	250
300	359	419	282	328	300
350	397	464	312	364	350
400	430	503	339	395	400
500	496	580	392	458	500
600	553	647	440	514	600
700	610	714	488	570	700
750	638	747	512	598	750
800	660	773	532	622	800
900	704	826	572	669	900
1000	748	879	612	716	1000
Ambient Temp. °C	For ambient temperatures other than 40°C (104°F), multiply the ampacities shown above by the appropriate factor shown below.				Ambient Temp. °F
21-25	1.20	1.14	1.20	1.14	70-77
26-30	1.13	1.10	1.13	1.10	79-86
31-35	1.07	1.05	1.07	1.05	88-95
36-40	1.00	1.00	1.00	1.00	97-104
41-45	.93	.95	.93	.95	106-113
46-50	.85	.89	.85	.89	115-122
51-55	.76	.84	.76	.84	124-131
56-60	.65	.77	.65	.77	133-140
61-70	.38	.63	.38	.63	142-158
71-80	. . . .	.45	. . . .	.45	160-176

Table B-310-3. Ampacities of Multiconductor Cables with not more than Three Insulated Conductors, Rated 0 through 2000 Volts, in Free Air. Based on Ambient Air Temperature of 40°C (104°F) (For TC, MC, MI, UF, USE, and SNM cables)

Size	Temperature Rating of Conductor. See Table 310-13.								Size
AWG kcmil	60°C (140°F)	75°C (167°F)	85°C (185°F)	90°C (194°F)	60°C (140°F)	75°C (167°F)	85°C (185°F)	90°C (194°F)	AWG kcmil
	COPPER				ALUMINUM OR COPPER-CLAD ALUMINUM				
18				11†					18
16				16†					16
14	18†	21†	24†	25†					14
12	21†	28†	30†	32†	18†	21†	24†	25†	12
10	28†	36†	41†	43†	21†	28†	30†	32†	10
8	39	50	56	59	30	39	44	46	8
6	52	68	75	79	41	53	59	61	6
4	69	89	100	104	54	70	78	81	4
3	81	104	116	121	63	81	91	95	3
2	92	118	132	138	72	92	103	108	2
1	107	138	154	161	84	108	120	126	1
1/0	124	160	178	186	97	125	139	145	1/0
2/0	143	184	206	215	111	144	160	168	2/0
3/0	165	213	238	249	129	166	185	194	3/0
4/0	190	245	274	287	149	192	214	224	4/0
250	212	274	305	320	166	214	239	250	250
300	237	306	341	357	186	240	268	280	300
350	261	337	377	394	205	265	296	309	350
400	281	363	406	425	222	287	317	334	400
500	321	416	465	487	255	330	368	385	500
600	354	459	513	538	284	368	410	429	600
700	387	502	562	589	306	405	462	473	700
750	404	523	586	615	328	424	473	495	750
800	415	539	604	633	339	439	490	513	800
900	438	570	639	670	362	469	514	548	900
1000	461	601	674	707	385	499	558	584	1000

Ambient Temp. °C	For ambient temperatures other than 30°C (86°F), multiply the ampacities shown above by the appropriate factor shown below.								Ambient Temp. °F
21-25	1.32	1.20	1.15	1.14	1.32	1.20	1.15	1.14	70-77
26-30	1.22	1.13	1.11	1.10	1.22	1.13	1.11	1.10	79-86
31-35	1.12	1.07	1.05	1.05	1.12	1.07	1.05	1.05	88-95
36-40	1.00	1.00	1.00	1.00	1.00	1.00	1.00	1.00	97-104
41-45	.87	.93	.94	.95	.87	.93	.94	.95	106-113
46-50	.71	.85	.88	.89	.71	.85	.88	.89	115-122
51-55	.50	.76	.82	.84	.50	.76	.82	.84	124-131
56-60	....	.65	.75	.77	....	.65	.75	.77	133-140
61-70	....	.38	.58	.63	....	.38	.58	.63	142-158
71-80	....	....	.33	.44	....	....	.33	.44	160-176

† Unless otherwise specifically permitted elsewhere in this Code, the overcurrent protection for conductor types marked with an obelisk (†) shall not exceed 15 amperes for No. 14, 20 amperes for No. 12, and 30 amperes for No. 10 copper; or 15 amperes for No. 12 and 25 amperes for No. 10 aluminum and copper-clad aluminum.

Table B-310-4. Ampacities for Bare or Covered Conductors Based on 40°C (104°F) Ambient, 80°C (176°F) Total Conductor Temperature, 2 Feet (610 mm) per Second Wind Velocity

Bare Copper Conductors		Covered Copper Conductors	
AWG kcmil	AMPS	AWG kcmil	AMPS
8	98	8	103
6	124	6	130
4	155	4	163
2	209	2	219
1/0	282	1/0	297
2/0	329	2/0	344
3/0	382	3/0	401
4/0	444	4/0	466
250	494	250	519
300	556	300	584
500	773	500	812
750	1000	750	1050
1000	1193	1000	1253

Bare AAC Aluminum Conductors		Covered AAC Aluminum Conductors	
AWG kcmil	AMPS	AWG kcmil	AMP
8	76	8	80
6	96	6	101
4	121	4	127
2	163	2	171
1/0	220	1/0	231
2/0	255	2/0	268
3/0	297	3/0	312
4/0	346	4/0	364
266.8	403	266.8	423
336.4	468	336.4	492
397.5	522	397.5	548
477.0	588	477.0	617
556.5	650	556.5	682
636.0	709	636.0	744
795.0	819	795.0	860
954.0	920		
1033.5	968	1033.5	1017
1272	1103	1272	1201
1590	1267	1590	1381
2000	1454	2000	1527

Table B-310-5. Ampacities of Single Insulated Conductors, Rated 0 through 2000 Volts, in Nonmagnetic Underground Electrical Ducts (One Conductor per Electrical Duct) Based on Ambient Earth Temperature of 20°C (68°F), Electrical Duct Arrangement per Figure B-310-2, Conductor Temperature 75°C (167°F)

Size	3 Electrical Ducts (Fig. B-310-2 Detail 2)			6 Electrical Ducts (Fig. B-310-2 Detail 3)			9 Electrical Ducts (Fig. B-310-2 Detail 4)			3 Electrical Ducts (Fig. B-310-2 Detail 2)			6 Electrical Ducts (Fig. B-310-2 Detail 3)			9 Electrical Ducts (Fig. B-310-2 Detail 4)			Size
	TYPES RHW, THHW, THW, THWN, XHHW, USE			TYPES RHW, THHW, THW, THWN, XHHW, USE			TYPES RHW, THHW, THW, THWN, XHHW, USE			TYPES RHW, THHW, THW, THWN, XHHW, USE			TYPES RHW, THHW, THW, THWN, XHHW, USE			TYPES RHW, THHW, THW, THWN, XHHW, USE			
kcmil	COPPER									ALUMINUM OR COPPER-CLAD ALUMINUM									kcmil
	RHO 60 LF 50	RHO 90 LF 100	RHO 120 LF 100	RHO 60 LF 50	RHO 90 LF 100	RHO 120 LF 100	RHO 60 LF 50	RHO 90 LF 100	RHO 120 LF 100	RHO 60 LF 50	RHO 90 LF 100	RHO 120 LF 100	RHO 60 LF 50	RHO 90 LF 100	RHO 120 LF 100	RHO 60 LF 50	RHO 90 LF 100	RHO 120 LF 100	
250	410	344	327	386	295	275	369	270	252	320	269	256	302	230	214	288	211	197	250
350	503	418	396	472	355	330	446	322	299	393	327	310	369	277	258	350	252	235	250
500	624	511	484	583	431	400	545	387	360	489	401	379	457	337	313	430	305	284	500
750	794	640	603	736	534	494	674	469	434	626	505	475	581	421	389	538	375	347	750
1000	936	745	700	864	617	570	776	533	493	744	593	557	687	491	453	629	432	399	1000
1250	1055	832	781	970	686	632	854	581	536	848	668	627	779	551	508	703	478	441	1250
1500	1160	907	849	1063	744	685	918	619	571	941	736	689	863	604	556	767	517	477	1500
1750	1250	970	907	1142	793	729	975	651	599	1026	796	745	937	651	598	823	550	507	1750
2000	1332	1027	959	1213	836	768	1030	683	628	1103	850	794	1005	693	636	877	581	535	2000
Ambient Temp. °C	For ambient temperatures other than 20°C (68°F), multiply the ampacities shown above by the appropriate factor shown below.																		Ambient Temp. °F
6-10	1.09			1.09			1.09			1.09			1.09			1.09			43-50
11-15	1.04			1.04			1.04			1.04			1.04			1.04			52-59
16-20	1.00			1.00			1.00			1.00			1.00			1.00			61-68
21-25	.95			.95			.95			.95			.95			.95			70-77
26-30	.90			.90			.90			.90			.90			.90			79-86

Table B-310-6. Ampacities of Three Insulated Conductors, Rated 0 through 2000 Volts, within an Overall Covering (Three-Conductor Cable) in Underground Electrical Ducts (One Cable per Electrical Duct) Based on Ambient Earth Temperature of 20°C (68°F), Electrical Duct Arrangement per Figure B-310-2, Conductor Temperature 75°C (167°F)

Size AWG kcmil	1 Electrical Duct (Fig. B-310-2 Detail 1) TYPES RHW, THHW, THW, THWN, XHHW, USE			3 Electrical Ducts (Fig. B-310-2 Detail 2) TYPES RHW, THHW, THW, THWN, XHHW, USE			6 Electrical Ducts (Fig. B-310-2 Detail 3) TYPES RHW, THHW, THW, THWN, XHHW, USE			1 Electrical Duct (Fig. B-310-2 Detail 1) TYPES RHW, THHW, THW, THWN, XHHW, USE			3 Electrical Ducts (Fig. B-310-2 Detail 2) TYPES RHW, THHW, THW, THWN, XHHW, USE			6 Electrical Ducts (Fig. B-310-2 Detail 3) TYPES RHW, THHW, THW, THWN, XHHW, USE			Size AWG kcmil
	COPPER									ALUMINUM OR COPPER-CLAD ALUMINUM									
	RHO 60 LF 50	RHO 90 LF 100	RHO 120 LF 100	RHO 60 LF 50	RHO 90 LF 100	RHO 120 LF 100	RHO 60 LF 50	RHO 90 LF 100	RHO 120 LF 100	RHO 60 LF 50	RHO 90 LF 100	RHO 120 LF 100	RHO 60 LF 50	RHO 90 LF 100	RHO 120 LF 100	RHO 60 LF 50	RHO 90 LF 100	RHO 120 LF 100	
8	58	54	53	56	48	46	53	42	39	45	42	41	43	37	36	41	32	30	8
6	77	71	69	74	63	60	70	54	51	60	55	54	57	49	47	54	42	39	6
4	101	93	91	96	81	77	91	69	65	78	72	71	75	63	60	71	54	51	4
2	132	121	118	126	105	100	119	89	83	103	94	92	98	82	78	92	70	65	2
1	154	140	136	146	121	114	137	102	95	120	109	106	114	94	89	107	79	74	1
1/0	177	160	156	168	137	130	157	116	107	138	125	122	131	107	101	122	90	84	1/0
2/0	203	183	178	092	156	147	179	131	121	158	143	139	150	122	115	140	102	95	2/0
3/0	233	210	204	221	178	158	205	148	137	182	164	159	172	139	131	160	116	107	3/0
4/0	268	240	232	253	202	190	234	168	155	209	187	182	198	158	149	183	131	121	4/0
250	297	265	256	280	222	209	258	184	169	233	207	201	219	174	163	505	144	132	250
350	363	321	310	340	267	250	312	219	202	285	252	244	267	209	196	245	172	158	350
500	444	389	375	414	320	299	377	261	240	352	308	297	328	254	237	299	207	190	500
750	552	478	459	511	388	362	462	314	288	446	386	372	413	314	293	374	254	233	750
1000	628	539	518	579	435	405	522	351	321	521	447	430	480	361	336	433	291	266	1000

Ambient Temp. °C	For ambient temperatures other than 20°C (68°F), multiply the ampacities shown above by the appropriate factor shown below.						Ambient Temp. °F
6-10	1.09	1.09	1.09	1.09	1.09	1.09	43-50
11-15	1.04	1.04	1.04	1.04	1.04	1.04	52-59
16-20	1.00	1.00	1.00	1.00	1.00	1.00	61-68
21-25	.95	.95	.95	.95	.95	.95	70-77
26-30	.90	.90	.90	.90	.90	.90	79-86

Table B-310-7. Ampacities of Three Single Insulated Conductors, Rated 0 through 2000 Volts, in Underground Electrical Ducts (Three Conductors per Electrical Duct) Based on Ambient Earth Temperature of 20°C (68°F), Electrical Duct Arrangement per Figure B-310-2, Conductor Temperature 75°C (167°F)

Size	1 Electrical Duct (Fig. B-310-2 Detail 1) TYPES RHW, THHW, THW, THWN, XHHW, USE			3 Electrical Ducts (Fig. B-310-2 Detail 2) TYPES RHW, THHW, THW, THWN, XHHW, USE			6 Electrical Ducts (Fig. B-310-2 Detail 3) TYPES RHW, THHW, THW, THWN, XHHW, USE			1 Electrical Duct (Fig. B-310-2 Detail 1) TYPES RHW, THHW, THW, THWN, XHHW, USE			3 Electrical Ducts (Fig. B-310-2 Detail 2) TYPES RHW, THHW, THW, THWN, XHHW, USE			6 Electrical Ducts (Fig. B-310-2 Detail 3) TYPES RHW, THHW, THW, THWN, XHHW, USE			Size
AWG kcmil	COPPER									ALUMINUM OR COPPER-CLAD ALUMINUM									AWG kcmil
	RHO 60 LF 50	RHO 90 LF 100	RHO 120 LF 100	RHO 60 LF 50	RHO 90 LF 100	RHO 120 LF 100	RHO 60 LF 50	RHO 90 LF 100	RHO 120 LF 100	RHO 60 LF 50	RHO 90 LF 100	RHO 120 LF 100	RHO 60 LF 50	RHO 90 LF 100	RHO 120 LF 100	RHO 60 LF 50	RHO 90 LF 100	RHO 120 LF 100	
8	63	58	57	61	51	49	57	44	41	49	45	44	47	40	38	45	34	32	8
6	84	77	75	80	67	63	75	56	53	66	60	58	63	52	49	59	44	41	6
4	111	100	98	105	86	81	98	73	67	86	78	76	79	67	63	77	57	52	4
3	129	116	113	122	99	94	113	83	77	101	91	89	83	77	73	84	65	60	3
2	147	132	128	139	112	106	129	93	86	115	103	100	108	87	82	101	73	67	2
1	171	153	148	161	128	121	149	106	98	133	119	115	126	100	94	116	83	77	1
1/0	197	175	169	185	146	137	170	121	111	153	136	132	144	114	107	133	94	87	1/0
2/0	226	200	193	212	166	156	194	136	126	176	156	151	165	130	121	151	106	98	2/0
3/0	260	228	220	243	189	177	222	154	142	203	178	172	189	147	138	173	121	111	3/0
4/0	301	263	253	280	215	201	255	175	161	235	205	198	219	168	157	199	137	126	4/0
250	334	290	279	310	236	220	281	192	176	261	227	218	242	185	172	220	150	137	250
300	373	321	308	344	260	242	310	210	192	293	252	242	272	204	190	245	165	151	300
350	409	351	337	377	283	264	340	228	209	321	276	265	296	222	207	266	179	164	350
400	442	376	361	394	302	280	368	243	223	349	297	284	321	238	220	288	191	174	400
500	503	427	409	460	341	316	412	273	249	397	338	323	364	270	250	326	216	197	500
600	552	468	447	511	371	343	457	296	270	446	373	356	408	296	274	365	236	215	600
700	602	509	486	553	402	371	492	319	291	488	408	389	443	321	297	394	255	232	700
750	632	529	505	574	417	385	509	330	301	508	425	405	461	334	309	409	265	241	750
800	654	544	520	597	428	395	527	338	308	530	439	418	481	344	318	427	273	247	800
900	692	575	549	628	450	415	554	355	323	563	466	444	510	365	337	450	288	261	900
1000	730	605	576	659	472	435	581	372	338	597	494	471	538	385	355	475	304	276	1000

Ambient Temp. °C	For ambient temperatures other than 20°C (68°F), multiply the ampacities shown above by the appropriate factor shown below.						Ambient Temp. °F
6-10	1.09	1.09	1.09	1.09	1.09	1.09	43-50
11-15	1.04	1.04	1.04	1.04	1.04	1.04	52-59
16-20	1.00	1.00	1.00	1.00	1.00	1.00	61-68
21-25	.95	.95	.95	.95	.95	.95	70-77
26-30	.90	.90	.90	.90	.90	.90	79-86

Table B-310-8. Ampacities of Two or Three Insulated Conductors, Rated 0 through 2000 Volts, Cabled within an Overall (Two- or Three-Conductor) Covering, Directly Buried in Earth Based on Ambient Earth Temperature of 20°C (68°F), Arrangement per Figure B-310-2, 100 Percent Load Factor, Thermal Resistance (RHO) of 90

Size	1 Cable (Fig. B-310-2 Detail 5)		2 Cables (Fig. B-310-2 Detail 6)		1 Cable (Fig. B-310-2 Detail 5)		2 Cables (Fig. B-310-2 Detail 6)		Size
	60°C (140°F)	75°C (167°F)	60°C (140°F)	75°C (167°F)	60°C (140°F)	75°C (167°F)	60°C (140°F)	75°C (167°F)	
	TYPES		TYPES		TYPES		TYPES		
AWG kcmil	UF	RHW, THHW, THW, THWN, XHHW, USE	UF	RHW, THHW, THW, THWN, XHHW, USE	UF	RHW, THHW, THW, THWN, XHHW, USE	UF	RHW, THHW, THW, THWN, XHHW, USE	AWG kcmil
	COPPER				ALUMINUM OR COPPER-CLAD ALUMINUM				
8	64	75	60	70	51	59	47	55	8
6	85	100	81	95	68	75	60	70	6
4	107	125	100	117	83	97	78	91	4
2	137	161	128	150	107	126	110	117	2
1	155	182	145	170	121	142	113	132	1
1/0	177	208	165	193	138	162	129	151	1/0
2/0	201	236	188	220	157	184	146	171	2/0
3/0	229	269	213	250	179	210	166	195	3/0
4/0	259	304	241	282	203	238	188	220	4/0
250		333		308		261		241	250
350		401		370		315		290	350
500		481		442		381		350	500
750		585		535		473		433	750
1000		657		600		545		497	1000
Ambient Temp. °C	For ambient temperatures other than 20°C (68°F), multiply the ampacities shown above by the appropriate factor shown below.								Ambient Temp. °F
6-10	1.12	1.09	1.12	1.09	1.12	1.09	1.12	1.09	43-50
11-15	1.06	1.04	1.06	1.04	1.06	1.04	1.06	1.04	52-59
16-20	1.00	1.00	1.00	1.00	1.00	1.00	1.00	1.00	61-68
21-25	.94	.95	.94	.95	.94	.95	.94	.95	70-77
26-30	.87	.90	.87	.90	.87	.90	.87	.90	79-86

For ampacities of UF cable in underground electrical ducts, multiply the ampacities shown in the table by 0.74.

Table B-310-9. Ampacities of Three Triplexed Single Insulated Conductors, Rated 0 through 2000 Volts, Directly Buried in Earth Based on Ambient Earth Temperature of 20°C (68°F), Arrangement per Figure B-310-2, 100 Percent Load Factor, Thermal Resistance (RHO) of 90

Size	See Fig. B-310-2 Detail 7		See Fig. B-310-2 Detail 8		See Fig. B-310-2 Detail 7		See Fig. B-310-2 Detail 8		Size
	60°C (140°F)	75°C (167°F)	60°C (140°F)	75°C (167°F)	60°C (140°F)	75°C (167°F)	60°C (140°F)	75°C (167°F)	
AWG	TYPES		TYPES		TYPES		TYPES		AWG
kcmil	UF	USE	UF	USE	UF	USE	UF	USE	kcmil
	COPPER				ALUMINUM OR COPPER-CLAD ALUMINUM				
8	72	84	66	77	55	65	51	60	8
6	91	107	84	99	72	84	66	77	6
4	119	139	109	128	92	108	85	100	4
2	153	179	140	164	119	139	109	128	2
1	173	203	159	186	135	158	124	145	1
1/0	197	231	181	212	154	180	141	165	1/0
2/0	223	262	205	240	175	205	159	187	2/0
3/0	254	298	232	272	199	233	181	212	3/0
4/0	289	339	263	308	226	265	206	241	4/0
250		370		336		289		263	250
350		445		403		349		316	350
500		536		483		424		382	500
750		654		587		525		471	750
1000		744		665		608		544	1000
Ambient Temp. °C	For ambient temperatures other than 20°C (68°F), multiply the ampacities shown above by the appropriate factor shown below.								Ambient Temp. °F
6-10	1.12	1.09	1.12	1.09	1.12	1.09	1.12	1.09	43-50
11-15	1.06	1.04	1.06	1.04	1.06	1.04	1.06	1.04	52-59
16-20	1.00	1.00	1.00	1.00	1.00	1.00	1.00	1.00	61-68
21-25	.94	.95	.94	.95	.94	.95	.94	.95	70-77
26-30	.87	.90	.87	.90	.87	.90	.87	.90	79-86

Table B-310-10. Ampacities of Three Single Insulated Conductors, Rated 0 through 2000 Volts, Directly Buried in Earth Based on Ambient Earth Temperature of 20°C (68°F), Arrangement per Figure B-310-2, 100 Percent Load Factor, Thermal Resistance (RHO) of 90

Size	See Fig. B-310-2 Detail 9		See Fig. B-310-2 Detail 10		See Fig. B-310-2 Detail 9		See Fig. B-310-2 Detail 10		Size
	60°C (140°F)	75°C (167°F)	60°C (140°F)	75°C (167°F)	60°C (140°F)	75°C (167°F)	60°C (140°F)	75°C (167°F)	
AWG	TYPES		TYPES		TYPES		TYPES		AWG
kcmil	UF	USE	UF	USE	UF	USE	UF	USE	kcmil
	COPPER				ALUMINUM OR COPPER-CLAD ALUMINUM				
8	84	98	78	92	66	77	61	72	8
6	107	126	101	118	84	98	78	92	6
4	139	163	130	152	108	127	101	118	4
2	178	209	165	194	139	163	129	151	2
1	201	236	187	219	157	184	146	171	1
1/0	230	270	212	249	179	210	165	194	1/0
2/0	261	306	241	283	204	239	188	220	2/0
3/0	297	348	274	321	232	272	213	250	3/0
4/0	336	394	309	362	262	307	241	283	4/0
250		429		394		335		308	250
350		516		474		403		370	350
500		626		572		490		448	500
750		767		700		605		552	750
1000		887		808		706		642	1000
1250		979		891		787		716	1250
1500		1063		965		862		783	1500
1750		1133		1027		930		843	1750
2000		1195		1082		990		897	2000
Ambient Temp. °C	For ambient temperatures other than 20°C (68°F), multiply the ampacities shown above by the appropriate factor shown below.								Ambient Temp. °F
6-10	1.12	1.09	1.12	1.09	1.12	1.09	1.12	1.09	43-50
11-15	1.06	1.04	1.06	1.04	1.06	1.04	1.06	1.04	52-59
16-20	1.00	1.00	1.00	1.00	1.00	1.00	1.00	1.00	61-68
21-25	.94	.95	.94	.95	.94	.95	.94	.95	70-77
26-30	.87	.90	.87	.90	.87	.90	.87	.90	79-86

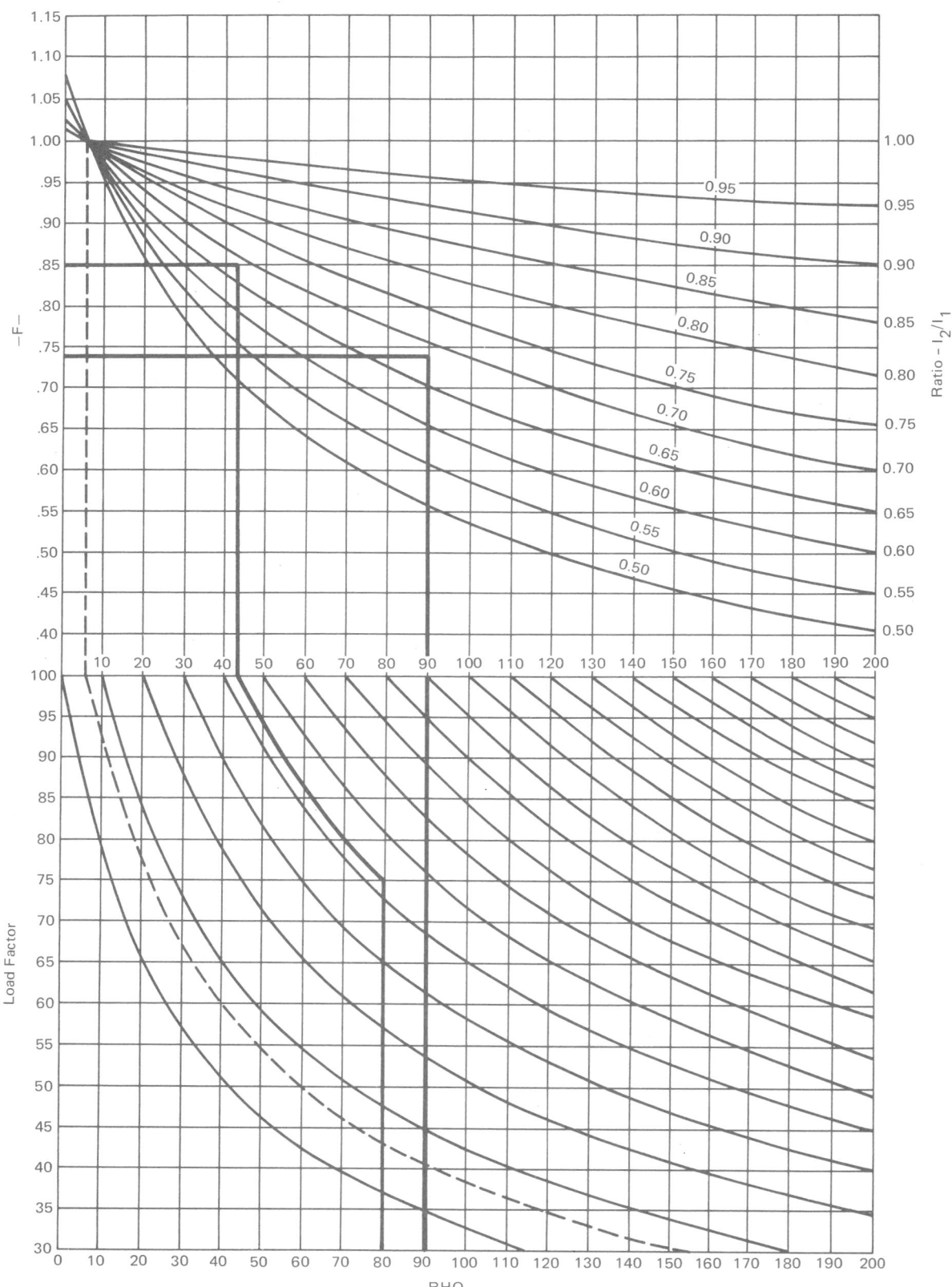

Figure B-310-1. *Interpolation Chart for Cables in a Duct Bank* I_1 *= Ampacity for Rho - 60, 50 LF;* I_2 *= Ampacity for Rho-120, 100 LF; Desired Ampacity = F X* I_1

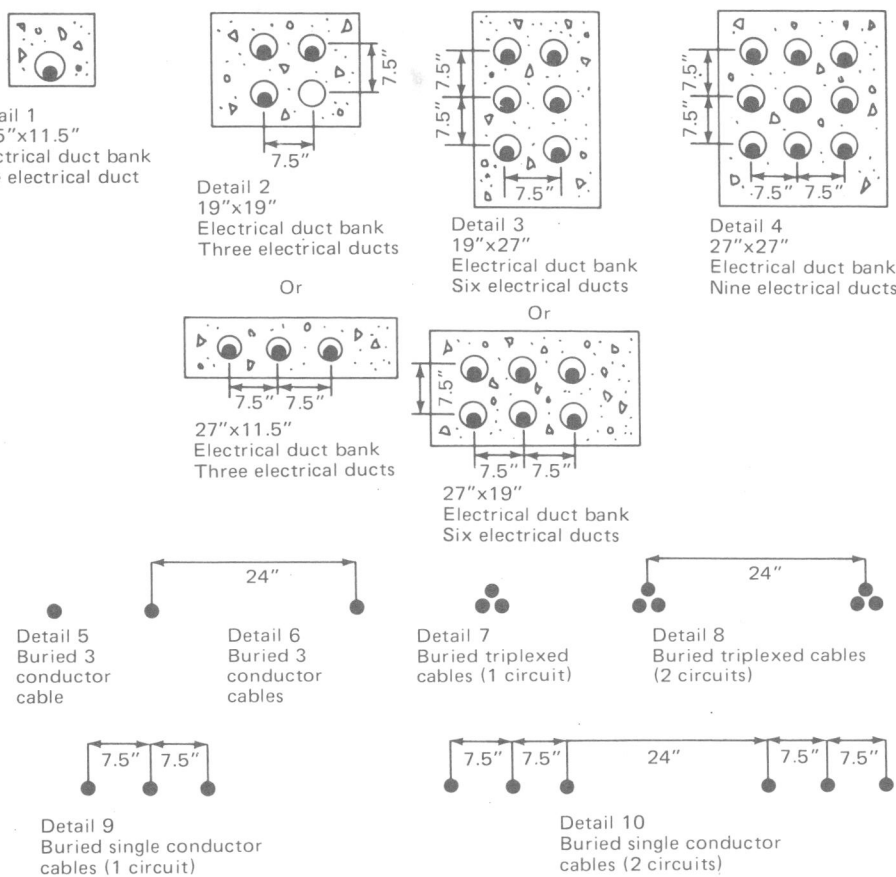

Figure B-310-2. Cable Installation Dimensions for Use with Tables B-5 through B-10

Detail 1
11.5"x11.5"
Electrical duct bank
One electrical duct

Detail 2
19"x19"
Electrical duct bank
Three electrical ducts

Or

Detail 3
19"x27"
Electrical duct bank
Six electrical ducts

Or

Detail 4
27"x27"
Electrical duct bank
Nine electrical ducts

27"x11.5"
Electrical duct bank
Three electrical ducts

27"x19"
Electrical duct bank
Six electrical ducts

Detail 5
Buried 3
conductor
cable

Detail 6
Buried 3
conductor
cables

Detail 7
Buried triplexed
cables (1 circuit)

Detail 8
Buried triplexed cables
(2 circuits)

Detail 9
Buried single conductor
cables (1 circuit)

Detail 10
Buried single conductor
cables (2 circuits)

Notes for all details:
1. Minimum burial depths to top electrical ducts or cables shall be in accordance with Section 300–5. Maximum depth to the top of electrical duct banks shall be 30 inches and maximum depth to the top of direct buried cables shall be 36 inches.

2. For two and four electrical duct installations with electrical ducts installed in a single row, see Section B-310-15(b)(5).

3. For SI units: one inch = 25.4 millimeters; one foot = 305 millimeters.

Legend

▢ Backfill
(earth or concrete)

◯ Electrical duct

● Cable or cables

Figure B-310-3. Ampacities of Single Insulated Conductors Rated 0 through 5000 Volts in Underground Electrical Ducts (Three Conductors per Electrical Duct) Nine Single-Conductor Cables per Phase Based on Ambient Earth Temperature of 20°C (68°F), Conductor Temperature 75°C (167°F)

Design Criteria
Neutral and Electrical Grounding
Conductor (EGC) Duct = 6 inch
Phase Ducts = 3 to 5 inch
Conductor Material = Copper
Number of Cables per Duct =3
Number of Cables per Phase = 9
Rho Concrete = Rho Earth − 5
Rho PVC Duct = 650
Rho Cable Insulation = 500
Rho Cable Jacket = 650

NOTES:

Neutral configuration per Section 300-5(i), Exception No. 2 for isolated phase installations in nonmagnetic ducts.

Phasing is A, B, C in rows or columns. Where magnetic electrical ducts are used, conductors are installed A, B, C per electrical duct with the neutral and all equipment grounding conductors in the same electrical duct. In this case, the 6-inch trade size neutral duct is eliminated.

Maximum harmonic loading on the neutral conductor cannot exceed 50 percent of the phase current for the ampacities shown in the table.

Metallic shields of Type MV-75 cable shall be grounded at one point only where using A, B, C phasing in rows or columns.

For SI units: one inch = 25.4 millimeters.

Size	Types			Size
	RHW, THHW, THW, THWN, XHHW, USE, OR MV-75			
kcmil	Total Per Phase Ampere Rating			kcmil
	RHO EARTH 60 LF 50	RHO EARTH 90 LF 100	RHO EARTH 120 LF 100	
250	2340 (260A/Cable)	1530 (170A/Cable)	1395 (155A/Cable)	250
350	2790 (310A/Cable)	1800 (200A/Cable)	1665 (185A/Cable)	350
500	3375 (375A/Cable)	2160 (240A/Cable)	1980 (220A/Cable)	500

Ambient Temp. °C	For ambient temperatures other than 20°C (68°F), multiply the ampacities shown above by the appropriate factor shown below.					Ambient Temp. °F
6-10	1.09	1.09	1.09	1.09	1.09	43-50
11-15	1.04	1.04	1.04	1.04	1.04	52-59
16-20	1.00	1.00	1.00	1.00	1.00	61-68
21-25	.95	.95	.95	.95	.95	70-77
26-30	.90	.90	.90	.90	.90	79-86

Figure B-310-4. **Ampacities of Single Insulated Conductors Rated 0 through 5000 Volts in Nonmagnetic Underground Electrical Ducts (One Conductor per Electrical Duct) Four Single-Conductor Cables per Phase Based on Ambient Earth Temperature of 20°C (68°F), Conductor Temperature 75°C (167°F)**

Design Criteria
Neutral and Electrical Grounding
Grounding Conductor Duct = 6 inch
Phase Ducts = 3 inch (min.)
Conductor Material = Copper
Number of Cables per Duct = 1
Number of Cables per Phase = 4
Rho Concrete = Rho Earth − 5
Rho PVC Duct = 650
Rho Cable Insulation = 500
Rho Cable Jacket = 650

NOTES:

Neutral configuration per Section 300-5(i), Exception No. 2.

Maximum harmonic loading on the neutral conductor cannot exceed 50 percent of the phase current for the ampacities shown in the table.

Metallic shields of Type MV-75 cable shall be grounded at one point only.

For SI units: one inch = 25.4 millimeters.

Size	Types RHW, THHW, THW, THWN, XHHW, USE, OR MV-75			Size
	Total Per Phase Ampere Rating			
kcmil	RHO EARTH 60 LF 50	RHO EARTH 90 LF 100	RHO EARTH 120 LF 100	kcmil
750	2520 (750A/Cable)	1860 (465A/Cable)	1680 (420A/Cable)	750
1000	3300 (825A/Cable)	2140 (535A/Cable)	1920 (480A/Cable)	1000
1250	3700 (925A/Cable)	2380 (595A/Cable)	2120 (530A/Cable)	1250
1500	4060 1015A/Cable	2580 (645A/Cable)	2300 (575A/Cable)	1500
1750	4360 (1090A/Cable)	2740 (685A/Cable)	2460 (615A/Cable)	1750

Ambient Temp. °C	For ambient temperatures other than 20°C (68°F), multiply the ampacities shown above by the appropriate factor shown below.				Ambient Temp. °F
6-10	1.09	1.09	1.09	1.09	1.09	43-50
11-15	1.04	1.04	1.04	1.04	1.04	52-59
16-20	1.00	1.00	1.00	1.00	1.00	61-68
21-25	.95	.95	.95	.95	.95	70-77
26-30	.90	.90	.90	.90	.90	79-86

Appendix B

Figure B-310-5. Ampacities of Single Insulated Conductors Rated 0 through 5000 Volts in Nonmagnetic Underground Electrical Ducts (One Conductor per Electrical Duct) Five Single-Conductor Cables per Phase Based on Ambient Earth Temperature of 20°C (68°F), Conductor Temperature 75°C (167°F)

Design Criteria
Neutral and Electrical Grounding
Conductor (EGC) Duct = 6 inch
Phase Ducts = 3 inch (min.)
Conductor Material = Copper
Number of Cables per Duct =1
Number of Cables per Phase = 5
Rho Concrete = Rho Earth – 5
Rho PVC Duct = 650
Rho Cable Insulation = 500
Rho Cable Jacket = 650

NOTES:

Neutral configuration per Section 300-5(i), Exception No. 2.

Maximum harmonic loading on the neutral conductor cannot exceed 50 percent of the phase current for the ampacities shown in the table.

Metallic shields of Type MV-75 cable shall be grounded at one point only.

For SI units: one inch = 25.4 millimeters.

Size	Types RHW, THHW, THW, THWN, XHHW, USE, OR MV-75			Size
kcmil	Total Per Phase Ampere Rating			kcmil
	RHO EARTH 60 LF 50	RHO EARTH 90 LF 100	RHO EARTH 120 LF 100	
2000	5575 (1115A/Cable)	3375 (675A/Cable)	3000 (600A/Cable)	2000

Ambient Temp. °C	For ambient temperatures other than 20°C (68°F), multiply the ampacities shown above by the appropriate factor shown below.					Ambient Temp. °F
6-10	1.09	1.09	1.09	1.09	1.09	43-50
11-15	1.04	1.04	1.04	1.04	1.04	52-59
16-20	1.00	1.00	1.00	1.00	1.00	61-68
21-25	.95	.95	.95	.95	.95	70-77
26-30	.90	.90	.90	.90	.90	79-86

Table B-310-11. Adjustment Factors for More than Three Current-Carrying Conductors in a Raceway or Cable with Load Diversity

Number of Current-Carrying Conductors	Percent of Values in Tables as Adjusted for Ambient Temperature if Necessary
4 through 6	80
7 through 9	70
10 through 24*	70
25 through 42*	60
43 and above*	50

*These factors include the effects of a load diversity of 50 percent.

(FPN): This table is based on the following formula:

$A_2 = \dfrac{\sqrt{0.5\,N}}{E} \times (A_1)$ where

A_1 = Table ampacity multiplied by factor from Article 310, Notes to Ampacity Tables of 0 to 2000 Volts, Note 8(a)

N = Total number of conductors used to obtain factor from Article 310, Notes to Ampacity Tables of 0 to 2000 Volts, Note 8(a)

E = Desired number of energized conductors

A_2 = Ampacity limit for energized conductors

Part 2
Supplements

The following supplements are included in this *Handbook* to provide additional background information for *Code* users. Since they are not part of the *Code*, they are printed in black.

Supplement 1: Model Law Providing for Inspection of Electrical Installations

NOTICE: All questions or other communications relating to this document should be sent to NFPA Headquarters, addressed to the attention of the Electrical Department.

Foreword

This Model Law Providing for the Inspection of Electrical Installations was prepared by the Electrical Field Service Advisory Committee of the NFPA as a guide for those jurisdictions that do not have formalized electrical inspection procedures and those that desire to amend their electrical inspection laws, and as a guide to adoption of the *National Electrical Code®*. The Model Law is *intended for use by a state as well as a municipality. The first edition was adopted by the Association on May 15, 1973. This second edition supersedes the first edition. It was approved by the Electrical Field Service Advisory Committee on March 27, 1987.*

The development and periodic revision of the *National Electrical Code*, the nationally recognized safety standard for electrical installations, represents an enormous effort in the public interest by the electrical utilities, contractors, manufacturers, journeymen, inspectors, and other interested parties.

In order that the application of the *National Electrical Code* be mandatory, it usually must be incorporated in a law, or a law must be passed authorizing a governmental agency or board to adopt it. To facilitate drafting such a law, as well as establishing the accompanying inspection and enforcement procedures, NFPA offers this Model Law as a basis for the preparation of such legislation. It may require modification in order to comply with the stature-writing rules of the adopting political jurisdiction.

Three alternative methods of adopting the requirements of the *National Electrical Code* for electrical installations are presented in the Model Law. Circumstances in a particular jurisdiction determine which alternate is most appropriate. Less comprehensive provisions may be entirely adequate for smaller political subdivisions. Certain financial items such as budgeting, disposition of fees, and appropriation are not covered by these guidelines.

In the following pages the text of the Model Law is given in the left-hand column. Explanatory comments are presented in the right-hand column.

The following tables indicate the suggested arrangement of the law text for each of the three alternative adoption methods.

Alternate I: The Board Method

Sec. 1 (Common to all Methods)
Sec. 2
Sec. 3
Sec. 4
Sec 5-18   (Common to all Methods)

Alternate II: The Prima Facie Method

Sec. 1 (Common to all Methods)
Sec. 2
Sec. 3
Sec. 4
Sec 5-18   (Common to all Methods)

Alternate III: The Periodic Adoption Method

Sec. 1 (Common to all Methods)
Sec. 2
Sec. 3
Sec. 4
Sec 5-18   (Common to all Methods)

Alternate I: The Board Method

Title: An Act to Safeguard Persons and Property; to Provide for the Inspection of Electrical Installations; to Create an Electrical Administrative Procedure; to Exempt Certain Political Subdivisions Under Specific Conditions and to Prescribe Penalties Under the Provision of this Act.

Section 1. Application of the Provisions of this Act

COMMENT: This Section defines the general scope of the application of the law.

    a. The provisions of this Act apply to:

        (1) Installations of electric conductors and equipment within or on public and private buildings or other structures, including mobile homes, recreational vehicles, and floating buildings; and other premises such as yards, carnival, parking and other lots, and industrial substations.

        (2) Installation of conductors that connect to the supply of electricity.

COMMENT: This Section follows the corresponding wording in the edition of the *National Electrical Code* in effect at the time of the preparation of the text of this Model Law setting forth electrical installations "covered" and "not covered."

        (3) Installations of other outside conductors on the premises.

        (4) Installations of optical fiber cable.

    b. The provisions of this Act do not apply to:

        (1) Installations in ships, watercraft other than floating buildings, railway rolling stock, aircraft, or automotive vehicles other than mobile homes and recreational vehicles.

        (2) Installations underground in mines.

        (3) Installations of railways for generation, transformation, transmission, or distribution of power used exclusively for operation of rolling stock or installations used exclusively for signaling and communication purposes.

        (4) Installations of communication equipment under exclusive control of communication utilities, located outdoors or in building spaces used exclusively for such installations.

        (5) Installations under the exclusive control of electric utilities for the purpose of communication, or metering; or for the generation, control, transformation, transmission and distribution of electric energy located in buildings used exclusively by utilities for such purposes or located outdoors on property owned or leased by the utility or on public highways, streets, roads, etc., or outdoors by established rights on private property.

The electrical inspector having jurisdiction may grant exception for the installation of conductors and equipment, not under the exclusive control of the electric utilities and used to connect the electric utility supply system to the service-entrance conductors of the premises served, provided such installations are outside a building or terminate immediately inside a building wall.

COMMENT: It is the intent of this Section that it covers all premises' wiring or wiring other than utility owned metering equipment, on the load side of the service point of buildings, structures, or any other premises not owned or leased by the utility. Also, it is the intent that this Section covers installations in buildings used by the utility for purposes other than listed in (5), such as office buildings, warehouses, garages, machine shops, and recreational buildings which are not an integral part of a generating plant, substation, or control center.

Section 2. Creation of Electrical Board

There is hereby created the Electrical Board of the _____ of _____ hereinafter designated as the Board. Members shall be residents appointed by the Governor with the advice and consent of the Senate (or by the Mayor with the advice and consent of the Council, or the equivalent).

Members of the Board shall be chosen as to represent a well-balanced representation of qualified individuals from the groups below including at least one member representing the public who is not affiliated with any other designated group represented on the Board.

COMMENT: The Electrical Board has the authority to provide for the safe use of appropriate electrical safety standards where such exist, and to establish appropriate requirements where they do not exist to cover electrical installations; to classify locations where installations are made; and through appropriate procedures administer the provisions of this Act.

Other members of the Board shall be selected from among the following affected persons and interests:

    (a) The Fire Marshal (or Fire Chief).

(b) The Chief Electrical Inspector of a municipality.[1]

(c) An electrical contractor operating in the jurisdiction.

(d) A licensed professional engineer engaged primarily in the design or maintenance of electrical installations.

(e) A representative of the property/casualty insurance industry, if available.

(f) A master (supervising) electrician.

(g) A journeyman wireman.

(h) A representative of an electric power utility operating in the jurisdiction.

(i) A representative of electrical manufacturers primarily and actively engaged in producing materials, fittings, devices, appliances, fixtures, or apparatus used as a part of or in connection with electrical installations.

COMMENT: Composition of the Board will vary according to the availability of qualified personnel and the need to keep the size of the Board commensurate with the size and complexity of the jurisdiction.

To the extent that is feasible, appointments to membership on the Board shall be selected from the above categories so that the Board will not be dominated by a single or by collusive interests.

COMMENT: A properly constituted Board will usually have the advantages of continuity, sustained interest and freedom from undue influence or pressure.

The Chief Electrical Inspector authorized in Section 3a(2) shall be an ex-officio member of the Board and shall not have a vote. Of the members first appointed, 2 shall be appointed for a term of 1 year, 2 for a term of 2 years, 3 for a term of 3 years, and 3 for a term of 4 years, and thereafter each appointment shall be for a term of 4 years or until a successor is appointed. In the event of a vacancy during a term, the appointing authority may appoint a replacement to fulfill the unexpired portion of the term. The Board shall elect for a 1-year term one of its members to act as the Chairman who shall have a vote on all matters before the Board. Any appointed member may, for cause and after a hearing, be removed from office by the appointing authority.

COMMENT: In order that the Chief Electrical Inspector authorized in Section 3a(2) execute the decisions of the

Board accurately and for good communication, the Chief Electrical Inspector should be an ex-officio member of the Board.

Staggered terms of members on the Board are preferable so that there will be a high degree of continuity.

Each appointed member shall receive the sum of _____ dollars ($ _____) for each day during which the member attends a meeting of the Board and, in addition thereto, shall be reimbursed for all expenses in attending such meetings, except loss of compensation from regular employment.

COMMENT: Per diem remuneration for appointed members is specified in order to attract individuals who otherwise may be reluctant to give up time from their regular business.

_____ members of the Board present at any meeting shall constitute a quorum for the transaction of business. The Chairman of any meeting of the Board including the temporary Chairman may vote. The Board shall hold such meetings as are necessary to carry out the purposes of this Act. The Chairman or a majority of the members of the Board shall have the authority to call meetings of the Board.

Review of Decisions.

Any person, firm or corporation may register an appeal with the Board for a review of any decision of the Board or of the Chief Electrical Inspector or of any Electrical Inspector, provided that such appeal is made in writing within fifteen (15) days after such person, firm or corporation shall have been notified of such decision by the Chief Electrical Inspector or an Electrical Inspector. Upon receipt of such appeal, said Board shall, if requested by the person making the appeal, hold a public hearing and proceed to determine whether the action of the Board, or of the Chief Electrical Inspector or of the Electrical Inspector complies with this law and, within fifteen (15) days after receipt of the appeal or after holding the hearing, shall make a decision in accordance with its findings.

COMMENT: In order to safeguard the public against any possible unfairness or partiality, any person who feels that an injustice has been done to that person by any action of an Inspector, or the Board itself, should be free at any time to present that person's grievance to the Board and should be given a hearing.

Section 3. Duties and Authority of the Electrical Board

COMMENT: As the administrative authority, the Board is charged with the duty of enforcing and administering the law.

[1]This appointment is applicable in the case of a Board operating at the state level.

The specific duties of the Board are listed in this Section; these being chiefly to appoint a Chief Electrical Inspector, Inspectors and other personnel, to examine applicants for certificates of qualification, issue certificates and to revoke or suspend such certificates for cause, and to establish procedures for recognition of electrical safety standards and acceptance of equipment conforming to these standards.

a. It shall be the duty of the Board to:

(1) Adopt the necessary rules and regulations to administer and enforce this Act;

(2) Appoint a Chief Electrical Inspector and employ Electrical Inspectors and other necessary personnel, and establish their qualifications, duties and responsibilities.

(3) At least every six months, conduct examinations of persons who apply for inspector's certificates of qualification; and to grant certificates to qualifying applicants who have paid the prescribed fee.

The Board may delegate to the Chief Electrical Inspector the authority to conduct examination of applicants for inspector's certificates of qualification and to issue such certificates.

COMMENT: Authority to conduct examinations and issue certificates may be delegated to the Chief Electrical Inspector.

(4) To revoke or suspend any Inspector's certificate on the grounds set forth in Section 13 of this Act;

(5) After advance notice to the public of hearings and the execution of such hearings, the Board is authorized to establish and update the provisions for the safety of electrical installations to conform with the current edition of the National Electrical Code (NFPA 70) and other nationally recognized safety standards for electrical installations.

COMMENT: After a public hearing, the Board shall establish requirements for the safety of electrical installations and equipment.

This being a law to provide for safety to electrical installations, it is of fundamental importance that standards be adopted that will afford proper protection to the public. The requirements prescribed by the *National Electrical Code* are adopted by a majority of the states and by practically all municipalities in the USA where electrical ordinances are in force. Therefore, it would appear appropriate that the provisions adopted by the Board closely follow the *National Electrical Code.*

The *National Electrical Code* is revised every three years by its sponsor, the National Fire Protection Association, and is designated as NFPA 70. Upon approval by NFPA, each edition is submitted to the American National Standards Institute for approval as an American National Standard. After such approval is carries the designation ANSI/NFPA 70.

(6) Establish procedures for recognition of electrical safety standards and acceptance of equipment conforming to these standards and acceptance of equipment conforming to these standards as specified in Section 4; and

COMMENT: This provision is intended to supplement the *National Electrical Code* Section 90-6, "Examination of Equipment for Safety."

(7) Take such other action as the Board may find necessary for carrying out the provisions of this Act.

Section 4. Standards for Electrical Equipment and its Installation

a. The equipment covered by this Act are the types of electrical equipment and their ratings for which suitable electrical safety standards have been established and which have been listed by a qualified electrical testing laboratory.

The standards to be adopted as criteria for the safety of such equipment shall be those designated and recognized as safety standards, are publicly available, and have a broad level of public acceptance selected from among the following:

(1) American National Standards (ANSI);

(2) Standards of a qualified technical society, trade association, agency, or other organization of national scope and recognition; and

(3) Federal, state or local government safety standards.

COMMENT: Suitable standards for electrical equipment should be established in order (a) that the Inspector may legally reject equipment, the use of which would be hazardous, (b) that the electrical contractor may know what products may be used, and (c) that the manufacturer may have full knowledge of what products are acceptable within the jurisdiction.

In addition, the standards shall be consonant with the installation and equipment requirements of the *National Electrical Code.*

The testing laboratory for determining compliance with these standards shall be properly equipped and qualified for experimental testing, inspections of run of goods at factories, and service/value determination through field inspections. It shall operate as a third-party testing/inspection body.

Conformity with standards noted above shall be evidenced by the listing[2] or labeling[3] of such equipment by such a laboratory.

COMMENT: The public and the industry can best be served by the national acceptance of uniform electrical safety standards. Before such standards can be made effective, facilities must also be provided for testing electrical equipment to determine conformity with the standards, for certifying such conformity and for frequent rechecks to make sure that the quality of the sample originally tested is maintained in the commercial product.

b. Establish electrical safety requirements for electrical equipment where no applicable nationally recognized electrical safety standards exists.

COMMENT: A provision in the law should establish the basis on which the inspector should act when considering the acceptability of equipment in categories not covered by a qualified testing laboratory.

Section 5. Local Requirements

(This Section is applicable only in the case of a State Law providing for electrical inspections.)

Application of the provisions of Sections 2 and 3 of Alternate I; Sections 2,3 and 4 of Alternate II; Sections 2, 3 and 4 of Alternate III; and Sections 1, 12, 14, 15, 16, 17 and 18 of this Act shall

not be mandatory[4] within the jurisdiction of any county, city, village, or township which has adopted or hereafter adopts an ordinance providing requirements of electrical wiring and its installation that are not less than those prescribed by the Electrical Board or by this statute and further provides by resolution or ordinance for the inspection of electrical installations within the limits of such a subdivision by a qualified person. No person other than the holder of an Electrical Inspector's certificate of qualification shall be appointed to act as Electrical Inspector and to enforce the provisions of this Act and any applicable resolution or ordinance within his or her jurisdiction.

COMMENT: Enabling state legislation often delegates to governmental subdivisions the authority to adopt their own electrical inspection regulations. When they do so, it is necessary for the safety of the public in such localities that the technical provisions are at least at a level of safety equal to the state's provisions and that the Electrical Inspectors are qualified by having been certified by the state Board.

In order to avoid interfering with existing arrangements, a city, town, village, county, or other political subdivision of the state, having adopted a local inspection ordinance, may operate its own electrical inspection service.

If, however, the amount of inspection work to be done in such a locality is insufficient to warrant the full-time employment of a qualified inspector, it may be advantageous for the state to perform this service. Where the local authorities take no action to provide for inspection, the service is provided by the state. If the inspection service is provided by the state, and if the locality adopts an ordinance providing standards for electrical wiring and its installation not less than prescribed by the Board or state statute, the inspectors should enforce the local ordinance and the law should be reworded to so state.

Section 6. Authority of Chief Electrical Inspector and Other Inspectors

The Chief Electrical Inspector and every Electrical Inspector having jurisdiction shall have the right, in accordance with existing law, during reasonable hours, to enter any building or premises in the discharge of his or her official duties including the making of any inspections, reinspections or test of the electric equipment contained therein or its installation.

---

[2] Listed. Equipment or materials included in a list published by an organization acceptable to the authority having jurisdiction and concerned with product evaluation, that maintains periodic inspection of production of listed equipment or materials, and whose listing states either that the equipment or material meets appropriate standards or has been tested and found suitable for use in a specified manner.

NOTE: The means for identifying listed equipment may vary for each organization concerned with product evaluation, some of which do not recognize equipment as listed unless it is also labeled. The authority having jurisdiction should utilize the system employed by the listing organization to identify a listed product.

[3] Labeled. Equipment or materials to which has been attached a label, symbol, or other identifying mark of an organization acceptable to the authority having jurisdiction and concerned with product evaluation, that maintains periodic inspection of production of labeled equipment or materials and by whose labeling the manufacturer indicates compliance with appropriate standards or performance in a specified manner.

These definitions are contained in the *National Electrical Code* but are included as a provision of the law to make it more self-contained.

---

[4] A jurisdiction may on its own choose to apply such provision.

COMMENT: In order to enforce this Act, every inspector must have the right to enter any building or premises in the discharge of his or her official duties. An Inspector may order the disconnection of any electrical equipment which is found to be hazardous to persons or property and, in an emergency, may cause the cutting or otherwise the disconnection of wires.

When the use of any electrical equipment or its installation shall be found to be dangerous to human life or property, the Chief Electrical Inspector, or an authorized Electrical Inspector, is hereby empowered to condemn it and/or cause it to be disconnected from its source of electric supply, except that the service equipment and/or utility service drop and/or service lateral wires shall not be disconnected unless said service equipment, service lateral and/or utility wires in themselves constitute a hazard to life and/or property. When such equipment or installation has been so condemned and/or disconnected, a notice shall be placed thereon listing the causes for the condemnation and/or disconnection and the penalty under Section 14 for the unlawful use thereof, and written notice of such condemnation and/or disconnection and the causes therefore shall be given within 24 hours to the owners and/or the occupant of such building, structure, or premises.

It shall be unlawful for any person to remove the said notice and/or reconnect the electric equipment to its source of electric supply, and/or to use or permit to be used electric power in any such electric equipment until such causes for the condemnation and/or disconnection have been remedied to the satisfaction of the inspection authorities.

COMMENT: New developments or unusual conditions may make it desirable to permit installations that employ wiring methods, equipment and devices differing in certain respects from the methods recognized in the current edition of the *National Electrical Code*. This paragraph sets up an orderly procedure to be followed where the Electrical Inspector decides that a certain special wiring method conforms with all fundamental requirements for safety and that experience with its use under actual working conditions will contribute to the progress of the electrical industry.

The Chief Electrical Inspector shall, with the concurrence of the Electrical Board, have the authority to allow the installation and use of special equipment, material, wiring methods and installations if in his or her judgment they are reasonably safe for the intended use.

Section 7. Permits

In any political subdivision which has provided for electrical inspection in accordance with the provisions of this Act, no electric equipment shall be installed within or on any building, structure or premises, publicly or privately owned, nor shall any alteration or addition be made in any such existing equipment without first securing a permit therefor from the Electrical Inspector, except as provided in Section 9 and except that no permit will be required to execute any of the classes of electrical work specified in the following paragraphs:

a. Installation or replacement of equipment such as plug-in lamps, electric utilization equipment approved for connection to suitable permanently installed receptacles. Replacement of flush or snap switches, fuses, lamp sockets and receptacles, and other minor maintenance and repair work, such as replacing worn cords and tightening connections on a plug.

b. The process of manufacturing, testing, servicing, or repairing of electric equipment or apparatus.

COMMENT: The permit system or its equivalent has been found a necessary feature of electrical inspection requirements. The system provides the Inspector with an orderly record of work in progress and completed work, and facilitates the scheduling of inspections at proper times. Certain classes of work are exempted from the permit requirements because no useful purpose would be served by requiring permits in these cases.

Annual Permits. In lieu of an individual permit for each installation or alteration, an annual permit shall, upon application therefor, be issued to any person, firm or corporation regularly employing one or more journeyman wiremen for the installation, alteration, and maintenance of electric equipment in or on buildings or premises owned or occupied by the applicant for the permit. Upon application, an electrical contractor as agent for the owner or tenant shall be issued an annual permit. The applicant shall keep records of all work done and such records shall be transmitted periodically to the Electrical Inspector.

COMMENT: Where one or more journeyman wiremen are permanently employed by a concern to do electrical work on the premises owned or occupied by such concern, it usually is not practical to require that a permit be obtained for each individual piece of work.

Provisions should therefore be made for the issuing of annual permits to such concerns, with the understanding that they keep records of all work done, such records to be available to the Inspector.

Permits — Outside Territory. The Board shall establish requirements similar to the preceding requirements of this Section in any territory where an Electrical Inspector has been authorized to make inspections and shall authorize said inspector to issue such permits.

Section 8. Fees for Permits

Any political subdivision which has provided for electrical inspection in accordance with the provisions of this Act may establish fees which shall be paid by the applicant for a permit before the permit is issued.

COMMENT: To provide for the expense of inspecting electrical installations, municipalities and counties are empowered to establish inspection fees. Such fees should be reasonable and should not be so high as to produce more than is required to cover the cost of the inspection service.

Where inspection service is provided outside the political subdivision that has adopted the *National Electrical Code*, the Board is directed to establish a schedule of inspection fees which shall be uniformly applied. The fee system is recognized as a practicable method of securing sufficient revenue to meet the cost of administering electrical inspection procedures.

Where any Electrical Inspector has been authorized by the Board to make inspections outside the territorial limits of any political subdivision where electrical inspection has not been established by the local governing body as set forth in Section 5, such inspector shall collect fees for permits according to a schedule of fees which shall be established by the Board and which shall be uniformly applied Such fees shall be paid by the inspector to the political subdivision adopting the *National Electrical Code*.

Section 9. Inspection and Certificates of Inspection

Upon the completion of any installation of electric equipment which has been made under a permit other than an annual permit, it shall be the duty of the person, firm or corporation making the installation to notify the Electrical Inspector having jurisdiction, who shall inspect the work within a reasonable time.

Where the Inspector finds the installation to be in conformity with the statutes of all applicable local ordinances, and all rules and regulations, the Inspector shall issue to the person, firm or corporation making the installation a certificate of approval, with

duplicate copy for delivery to the owner, authorizing the connection to the supply of electricity and shall send written notice of such authorization to the supplier of electric service. When a certificate of temporary approval is issued authorizing the connection of an installation, such certificates shall be issued to expire at a time to be stated therein and shall be revocable by the Electrical Inspector for cause.

COMMENT: The complete routine of inspection of new installations is covered by this Section as follows:

a. Notification to the Inspector that the work is ready for inspection. So far as practicable, no wiring may be concealed from view until it has been inspected.

b. Inspection.

c. Issuance of a certificate of approval, if the installation is in conformity with the legal requirements or notification to the installer of defects found if the installation does not meet the requirements. A duplicate copy of the certificate of approval should be forwarded to the owner of the building as tangible evidence that the Inspector has rendered the service for which the inspection fee was paid. A special form of certificate may be issued, giving temporary authorization for the use of an installation for a limited time.

d. Authorization to the supplier of electricity to make service connections.

When any electric equipment within the jurisdiction of an Electrical Inspector is to be hidden from view by the permanent placement of parts of the building, the person, firm or corporation installing the equipment shall notify the Electrical Inspector having jurisdiction, and such equipment shall not be concealed until is has been approved by the Electrical Inspector or until a reasonable time shall have elapsed from the time of such notification; provided that on large installations, where the concealment of equipment proceeds continuously, the person, firm or corporation installing the equipment shall give the Electrical Inspector due notice in advance, and inspections shall be made periodically during the progress of the work.

At regular intervals, the Electrical Inspector having jurisdiction shall visit all buildings and premises where work may be done under annual permits and shall inspect all electric equipment installed under such permits since the date of the previous inspection. The Electrical Inspector shall issue a certificate of approval for such work as is found to be in conformity with the provisions of this Act and all applicable ordinances, orders, rules and regulations, after payments of all required fees.

COMMENT: Where work is done under annual permits, the Inspector should, as often as may be necessary, visit the premises and inspect all installations since the time of his or her last previous inspection.

If, upon inspection, any installation is found not to be fully in conformity with the provisions of this Act, and all applicable ordinances, rules and regulations, the Inspector making the inspection shall at once forward to the person, firm or corporation making the installation a written notice stating the defects which have been found to exist.

Section 10. Connection to Electricity Supply

COMMENT: In order to avoid unnecessary delay it is provided that if the Inspector is notified of the completion of an installation and, within five (5) business days, neither authorizes the supplier of electricity to connect nor instructs the supplier not to connect because of defects in the installation, the supplier has full authority to make service connections. It is then the intention that the Inspector shall visit the premises at a later date and, if the installation is not found to be in conformity with the legal requirements, the installer must, within fifteen (15) business days after notification, remedy all defects found by the inspector. If the necessary corrections are not made within fifteen (15) business days or a longer period which may be specified by the Board, the Board may order the supplier of electricity to discontinue service.

Except where work is done under an annual permit and except as otherwise provided in this Section, it shall be unlawful for any person, firm or corporation to make connection from a supply of electricity or to supply electricity to any electric equipment installation of which a permit is required or which has been disconnected or ordered to be disconnected by the Electrical Inspector having jurisdiction, without the authorization of the Electrical Inspector having jurisdiction.

If, within five (5) business days after the Electrical Inspector is notified of the completion of an installation of electric equipment other than a temporary approval installation, the Electrical Inspector has neither authorized connection nor disapproved the installation, the supplier of electricity is authorized to make connections and supply electricity to such installation.

If an installation or electric equipment is located in any territory where an Electrical Inspector has not been authorized to make inspections, the supplier of electricity is authorized to make connections and supply electricity to such installations.

Where a connection is made to an installation which has not been inspected, as outlined in the preceding paragraphs of this Section, the supplier of electricity shall immediately report such connection to the Chief Electrical Inspector. If, upon subsequent inspection, it is found that the installation is not in conformity with the provisions of this Act, the Chief Electrical Inspector shall notify the person, firm, or corporation making the installation to rectify the defects and, if such work is not completed within fifteen (15) business days or a longer period which may be specified by the Board, the Board shall have the authority to cause the disconnection of that portion of the installation that is not in conformity.

Section 11. Inspector's Certificate of Qualification

No person shall be employed as an Electrical Inspector unless that person is the holder of an Electrical Inspector's certificate of qualification issued by the Board, except that any person who on the date on which this law went into effect was serving as a legally appointed Electrical Inspector of _____ shall, upon application and payment of the prescribed fee and without examination, be issued a special certificate permitting him or her to continue to serve as an Electrical Inspector in the same territory.

COMMENT: In order that the inspection of electrical installations may be effective, it is obvious that the Inspectors must be properly qualified. It is, therefore, provided that before any person may be appointed as an Electrical Inspector, that person must have a thorough knowledge of the nationally accepted standards as embodied in the *National Electrical Code* and must have had sufficient experience and training to make him or her familiar with the standard materials and methods used in electrical installations and with the practical application of the standards to such installations. To determine the qualifications of an applicant for appointment as an Inspector, the applicant must be examined by the Electrical Board or by the Chief Electrical Inspector, or other authorized body, and if successful in passing this examination, the applicant is given an Electrical Inspector's certificate of qualification.

Inspectors serving at the time the law goes into effect may be allowed to retain their positions without examination.

Except as provided above, in order to obtain an Electrical Inspector's certificate of qualification an applicant shall be of good moral character; shall be possessed of such executive ability as is requisite for the performance of his or her duties; shall have a thorough knowledge of the standard materials and methods used in the installation of electric equipment; shall be well versed in the approved methods of construction for safety to persons and property, the statutes of _____ relating to electrical work and the *National Electrical Code*, as approved by the American National Standards Institute; shall have had at least five (5) years experience as an Electrical Inspector or in the installation of electrical equipment or, in lieu of such experience, shall be a graduate in electrical and mechanical engineering, or of a similar scientific curriculum of a college or university considered by the Board as having suitable requirements for graduation and shall have had two (2) years practical electrical experience; and shall have passed an examination given by the Board, or if authorized by the Board, the Chief Electrical Inspector.

Examinations shall be in writing, and a complete record of every examination given shall be kept on a file until three (3) years after the date of the examination. Each application for a certificate of qualification shall be made in writing to the Board, stating the applicant's name and address and such other information as the Board may request.

The Board may recognize the results of the individual modules (Electrical One- and Two-Family Dwelling, Electrical Inspector General and Electrical Plan Review) of the National Certification Program for Construction Code Inspectors administered by the Educational Training Service, Princeton, NJ.

COMMENT: The Construction Code Inspector Certification Examinations have been developed by several model code groups, national inspection organizations and several states in collaboration with Educational Testing Service, Princeton, NJ. These organizations have joined together to establish a testing program that will provide nationally recognized evidence of competence and professionalism in construction code enforcement.

Before an Electrical Inspector's certificate of qualification is issued to any applicant, the applicant shall pay to the Board a fee, the amount of which is to be established by the Board.

Each Electrical Inspector's certificate of qualification shall continue in force until suspended or revoked by the Board or until a period of twelve (12) months has elapsed during which time the holder of the certificate shall not have been employed as an Electrical Inspector, in which case the certificate shall automatically expire at the end of such twelve-month period.

Section 12. Records of the Electrical Board

Records of the meetings of the Board shall be open to the public for inspection at all reasonable times. The Board shall keep a record of all certificates issued by it.

Section 13. Revocation and Suspension of Certificate of Qualification

No inspector's certificate of qualification issued in accordance with the provisions of this Act shall be assignable or transferable.

COMMENT: It is always possible that, even though a person apparently meets the qualifications specified in Section 11 and passes the required examination, the holder of an inspector's certificate of qualification may fail to perform his or her duties in a satisfactory manner. In such a case, the Board should have the power to suspend or revoke the certificate; otherwise, the provisions of Section 10 would not be fully effective.

Any Inspector's certificate of qualification may, after the inspector has a hearing, be suspended for a definite length of time or revoked by the Board if the holder of such a certificate fails to perform his or her duties properly as an Inspector in conformity with the provisions of this Act.

Section 14. Penalties

Any person, firm, or corporation who shall willfully violate any of the applicable provisions of this Act shall be guilty of a misdemeanor and, upon conviction thereof, shall be punished by a fine of not less than _____ dollars ($ _____) nor more than _____ dollars ($ _____) for each offense, together with the costs of prosecution and/or imprisonment for not less than _____ (_____) days nor more than _____ (_____) days.

COMMENT: These are routine provisions which are customarily included in a law of this character.

Section 15. Liability for Damages

This Act shall not be construed to affect the responsibility or liability of any party owning, operating, controlling, or installing any electric equipment for damages to persons or property caused by any defect therein, nor shall the _____ nor any of its employees be held as assuming any such liability by reason of the inspection, re-inspection, or other examination authorized herein, or by reason of the certificate of approval issued as herein provided, or by reason of the approval or disapproval of any equipment authorized herein.

COMMENT: These are routine provisions which are customarily included in a law of this character.

Section 16. Validity

If any section, subsection, sentence, clause, or phrase of this Act is for any reason held to be unconstitutional, such decision shall not affect the validity of the remaining portions of this Act.

COMMENT: These are routine provisions which are customarily included in a law of this character.

Section 17. Repeal of Conflicting Acts

All Acts or parts of Acts in conflict with the provisions of this Act are hereby repealed.

COMMENT: These are routine provisions which are customarily included in a law of this character.

Section 18. Effective Date

This Act shall take effect _____ (_____) days after its passage and publication.

COMMENT: These are routine provisions which are customarily included in a law of this character.

Alternate II: The Prima Facie Method

Title: An Act to Safeguard Persons and Property; to Provide for the Inspection of Electrical Installations; to Create an Electrical Administrative Procedure; to Exempt Certain Political Subdivisions Under Specific Conditions and to Prescribe Penalties Under the Provisions of this Act.

Section 1. Application of the Provisions of this Act.

(The Law Text for this Section is identical to Section 1, Alternate I.)

Section 2. Standards for Electrical Equipment and Its Installation

All installations of electrical equipment shall be reasonably safe to persons and property and in conformity with the provisions of this law, and all orders, rules, and regulations issued by the authorities established by this Act.

COMMENT: This being a law to provide for safety of electrical installations, it is of fundamental importance that standards be adopted which will afford proper protection to the public. The requirements prescribed by the *National Electrical Code* are adopted by a majority of the states and by practically all municipalities in the USA where electrical ordinances are in force. Therefore, it would appear appropriate that the provisions adopted by the Electrical Board (see Section 3) closely follow the *National Electrical Code*.

The *National Electrical Code* is revised every three years by its sponsor, the National Fire Protection Association, and is designated as NFPA 70. Upon approval by NFPA, each edition is submitted to the American National Standards Institute for approval as an American National Standard. After such approval, it carries the designation ANSI/NFPA 70.

Attempts have been made to adopt the *National Electrical Code* by means of some simple form of statement such as "The *National Electrical Code* is hereby made a part of this ordinance." The general legal consensus is, however, that any such wording constitutes a delegation of power to an organization over which the state has no jurisdiction, and therefore is unconstitutional. It is considered by competent legal counsel that this difficulty can be avoided by the application of the prima facie reference to the *National Electrical Code*.

This method of reference involves the establishment or adoption of a common law standard of duty to the effect that all installations of electrical equipment shall be reasonably safe to persons and property and in conformity with the applicable statutes of the state. The standard of duty imposed has a well-defined meaning in law as the common law test of safety, and any installation of equipment made under its provisions would have to be safe for the use intended at the time the installation was made. That common law test is certain, definite and fixed and does not depend in any way upon any codes or regulations of private bodies. Legally speaking, it is an unchanging test. Compliance with the *National Electrical Code* is merely prima facie evidence that the installation meets the definite common law standard of duty imposed. In other words the prima facie clause merely specifies one type of evidence which a party may use to show compliance with the standard imposed by the legislative body. This method effectuates the use of the current edition of the *National Electrical Code*.

Conformity of installations of electrical equipment with applicable requirements set forth in the *National Electrical Code*, shall be prima facie evidence that such installations are reasonably safe to persons and property.

Conformity to standards noted below shall be evidenced by the listing[5] or labeling[6] of such equipment by a qualified laboratory as described herein.

COMMENT: Suitable standards for electrical equipment should be established in order (a) that the inspector may legally reject equipment, the use of which would be hazardous, (b) that the electrical contractor may know what products may be used, and (c) that the manufacturer may have full knowledge of what products are acceptable within the jurisdiction.

The standards to be adopted as criteria for the safety of such equipment shall be those designated and recognized as safety standards, are publicly available, and have a broad level of public acceptance selected from among the following:

(a) American National Standards (ANSI);

(b) Standards of a qualified technical society, trade association, agency, or other organization of national (or international) scope and recognition; and

(c) Federal, state or local government safety standards.

COMMENT: The public and the industry can best be served by the national acceptance of uniform electrical safety standards. Before such standards can be made effective, facilities must also be provided for testing electrical equipment to determine conformity with the standards, for certifying such conformity and for frequent rechecks to make sure that the quality of the sample originally tested is maintained in the commercial product.

In addition, the standards shall be consonant with the installation and equipment requirements of the *National Electrical Code*.

The testing laboratory for determining compliance with the standard shall be properly equipped and qualified for experimental testing, inspection of runs of goods at factories, and service/value determinations through field inspections. It shall operate as a third-party testing/inspection body.

Section 3. Creation of Electrical Board

(The Law Text for this Section is identical to Section 2, Alternate I.)

Section 4. Duties and Authority of the Electrical Board

(The Law Text of this Section is identical to Section 3, Alternate I, except Clause 5 is omitted.)

Section 5.* Local Requirements

Section 6.* Authority of Chief Electrical Inspector and Other Inspectors

Section 7.* Permits

Section 8.* Fees for Permits

Section 9.* Inspection and Certificates of Inspection

Section 10.* Connection to Electricity Supply

---

[5] Listed. Equipment or materials included in a list published by an organization acceptable to the authority having jurisdiction and concerned with product evaluation, that maintains periodic inspection of production of listed equipment or materials, and whose listing states either that the eqipment or material meets apporpriate standards or has been tested and found suitable for use in a specified manner.

NOTE: The means for identifying listed equipment may vary for each organization concerned with product evaluation, some of which do not recognize equipment as listed unless it is also labeled. The authority having jurisdiction shall utilize the system employed by the listing organization to identify a listed product.

[6] Labeled. Equipment or materials to which has been attached a label, symbol, or other identifying mark of an organization acceptable to the authority having jurisdiction and concerned with product evaluation, that maintains periodic inspection of production of labeled equipment or materials and by whose labeling the manufacturer indicates compliance with appropriate standards or performance in a specified manner.

These definitions are contained in the *National Electrical Code* but are included as a provision of the law as to make it more self-contained.

---

*The Law Text for each section is identical to that of the corresponding section in Alternate I.

Section 11.* Inspector's Certificate of Qualification

Section 12.* Records of the Electrical Board

Section 13.* Revocation and Suspension of Certificate of Qualification

Section 14.* Penalties

Section 15.* Liability for Damages

Section 16.* Validity

Section 17.* Repeal of Conflicting Acts

Section 18.* Effective Date

Alternate III: The Periodic Adoption Method

Title: An Act to Safeguard Persons and Property; to Provide for the Inspection of Electrical Installations; to Create an Electrical Administrative Procedure; to Exempt Certain Political Subdivisions Under Specific Conditions and to Prescribe Penalties Under the Provisions of this Act.

Section 1. Application of the Provisions of this Act

(The Law Text of this Section is identical to Section 1, Alternate I.)

COMMENT: This method involves adoption of a specific edition of the *National Electrical Code* which is considered appropriate by many competent legal counsels. However, it is cumbersome because each time a new edition of the *National Electrical Code* is promulgated, which is generally every three years, it becomes necessary to amend the law in order to adopt the new edition. To overcome this problem, attempts have been made to adopt future editions of the *National Electrical Code*. The

general legal consensus is, however, that such delegation of legislative authority to an organization over which the political subdivision has no jurisdiction is unconstitutional.

Section 2. Standards for Electrical Equipment and Its Installation

All installations of electrical equipment shall be in conformance with the applicable provisions set forth in the _____ (year) edition of the *National Electrical Code*.

(The remaining Law Text of this Section is identical to Section 4, Alternate I.)

COMMENT: This being a law to provide for safety of electrical installations, it is of fundamental importance that standards be adopted which will afford proper protection to the public. The requirements prescribed by the *National Electrical Code* are widely recognized throughout the United States.

The *National Electrical Code* is revised every three years by its sponsor, the National Fire Protection Association, and is designated as NFPA 70. Upon approval by NFPA, each edition is submitted to the American National Standards Institute for approval as an American National Standard. After such approval, it carries the designation ANSI/NFPA 70.

Section 3. Creation of Electrical Board

(The Law Text for this Section is identical to Section 2, Alternate I.)

Section 4. Duties and Authority of the Electrical Board

(The Law Text for this Section is identical to Section 3, Alternate I, except Clause 5 is ommitted.)

Section 5.* Local Requirements

Section 6.* Authority of Chief Electrical Inspector and Other Inspectors

Section 7.* Permits

---

*The Law Text for each section is identical to that of the corresponding section in Alternate I.

*The Law Text for each section is identical to that of the corresponding section in Alternate I.

Section 8.* Fees for Permits

Section 9.* Inspection and Certificates of Inspection

Section 10.* Connection to Electricity Supply

Section 11.* Inspector's Certificate of Qualification

Section 12.* Records of the Electrical Board

Section 13.* Revocation and Suspension of Certificate of Qualification

Section 14.* Penalties

Section 15.* Liability for Damages

Section 16.* Validity

Section 17.* Repeal of Conflicting Acts

Section 18.* Effective Date

———————

*The Law Text for each section is identical to that of the corresponding section in Alternate I.

Supplement 2: Sample Calculations

Interrupting Rating

Sections 110-9, 110-10, and 230-65 require that devices intended to break current must be capable of safely interrupting the fault current that they might be called upon to interrupt. Under fault conditions, (L-L-L. . . . L-L. . . L-G. . . . L-N) fuses and circuit breakers can be subject to very high values of current. Devices that do not have adequate interrupting ability can violently rupture, resulting in serious injury to personnel and damage to the equipment.

Sections 110-10, 250-51, 250-70, and 250-75 require that equipment must be protected so as not to allow extensive damage, and that grounding and bonding conductors have capacity to conduct safely any fault current likely to be imposed on the conductors. The FPNs to Section 250-1 also reference ground fault currents. It is important to know the levels of fault current.

It is beyond the scope of this text to discuss fault current calculations in detail. The following example is a simple, three-phase fault current calculation.

Fault currents are calculated in a number of ways using pocket calculators and computer software programs. Simple methods are used by electrical inspectors, plan checkers, contractors, engineers, and others to calculate "worst-case conditions" to determine if the installation "meets *Code*." The following shows one such simple method. Utilities also are more than happy to furnish available fault currents at the point where they connect to the customer's service entrance equipment.

Calculate Available Fault Current

Step 1. Calculate Transformer Secondary Full Load Amps (FLA)

A 167 kVA, 3-phase, 208/120 volt, impedance 2% transformer.

Transformer:
167 kVA
208/120 volt
3-phase, 4-wire
2% impedance
FLA 464 amp

Available fault current at secondary of transformer:
23,200 amp

One 500 kcmil copper conductor per phase in steel conduit. Length of conductors is 20 ft.

Available fault current at line-side terminals of main disconnect switch:
19,766 amp

Feeders to other locations in building

Figure 1.

$$I = \frac{kVA \times 1000}{E \times 1.73} = \frac{167 \times 1000}{208 \times 1.73} = 464 \text{ amperes FLA.}$$

Step 2. Find transformer impedance (Z) on nameplate. This is given in percentage.

Transformer nameplate shows 2 percent impedance.

Step 3. Determine the maximum fault current available at the secondary terminals of the transformer. This method assumes that the utility can furnish an "infinite" amount of fault current on the primary. Using the 3-phase transformer illustrated in Step 1 above, 500 kcmil copper in steel conduit.

$$I_{sca} = \frac{\text{Transformer FLA} \times 100}{\text{Transformer Impedance}}$$

$$= \frac{464 \times 100}{2} = \frac{46,400}{2} = 23,200 \text{ ASC}$$

ASC = amperes short-circuit current rms symmetrical.

Step 4. Using the point-to-point method, calculate the three-phase fault current available at the line-side terminals of the main switch located 20 feet from the transformer. This calculation uses a multiplier "M." The multiplier is determined by a formula using an "f" factor. The formula includes a "C" value obtainable from manufacturers' technical literature based on the size and type of conductors used and the type of raceway (steel or aluminum) or direct burial cables, etc.

Only one "C" value for the 500 kcmil copper conductor is shown in this calculation (22,185), merely to show how the calculation is done. "C" values equal one (1) over the impedance (Z) per foot of the conductor. "N" represents the number of conductors per phase.

For 3-phase circuits:

$$\text{"f" factor} = \frac{1.73 \times L \times I}{N \times C \times E_{L-L}}$$

$$= \frac{1.73 \times 20 \times 23,200}{1 \times 22,185 \times 208} = 0.174.$$

$$\text{"M" multiplier} = \frac{1}{1 + f}$$

$$= \frac{1}{1 + 0.174} = 0.852.$$

The available short circuit current at the end of the run of "L" feet equals the short circuit current at the beginning of the run times "M." In the above example:

23,200 × 0.852 = 19,766 amperes fault current (rms) at the line-side terminals of the main disconnect switch.

The interrupting rating of the overcurrent devices in the main switch must be capable of safely interrupting 19,766 amperes rms symmetrical. The bus bracing in the equipment must also be capable of withstanding the 19,766 amperes of fault current. Knowing the "C" values, distances, and wiring methods for other feeders running from the main disconnect switch will allow for the calculation of available fault currents throughout the system.

Sizing Conductors

The following two examples are based on Section 110-14(c), Exception No. 1.

Conductor Size

Determine the size conductors required to supply a 75-ampere nonmotor load. The device terminations are rated at 75°C. Conductor type is THHN copper.

Table 310-16, 90°C column, No. 6 AWG = 75 amperes. Since the device terminal is rated at 75°C, the values listed in the 75°C column are applicable. No. 6 AWG = 65 amperes, and is not suitable.

The ampacity for No. 4 AWG under the 75°C column is 85 amperes and, therefore, is adequate to carry the 75-ampere load.

Conductor Size with Derating Factors

The conditions for this example are the same as in the example above except that there are six conductors in the same raceway and the load is 65 amperes. Adjustment factors from Note 8(a) of Notes to Ampacity Tables of 0-2000 Volts are applicable.

Number of current carrying conductors = 6.
Percent of value in ampacity tables = 80%.

65 amperes ÷ 0.80 = 81.25 amperes.
Table 310-16, 75°C Column, No. 4 AWG = 85 amperes.

Therefore, No. 4 AWG is suitable for six conductors in the same raceway supplying the 65-ampere load.

Proof: No. 4 AWG THHN ampacity = 95 amperes.
       0.80 × 95A = 76 amperes.

No. 4 AWG is capable of carrying a load of 76 amperes under the conditions specified.

Size of Grounded Conductor

Determine the minimum size of the grounded conductor required to be installed in each service raceway. The service consists of four parallel sets of 750 kcmil copper conductors supplied from a 480-volt, 3-phase, 4-wire system. The system is grounded at the utility distribution transformer secondary.

Section 250-23(b) requires the grounded conductor to be routed with the phase conductors and be sized not less than the grounding electrode conductor in accordance with Table 250-94. Where the phase conductors are larger than 1100 kcmil, the grounded conductor cannot be less than 12.5 percent of the cross-sectional area of the largest phase conductor, or equivalent area for parallel conductors.

Section 220-22 provides requirements for sizing a service neutral conductor based on calculated neutral load. This rule must be satisfied as well as Section 250-23(b).

Total cross-sectional area of largest phase conductor is then

4 × 750 kcmil = 3000 kcmil.

12.5% of 3000 kcmil = 375 kcmil.

Since the *Code* requires the grounded conductor to be routed with the phase conductors, the total cross-sectional area of a grounded conductor can be divided between the four raceways.

375 kcmil ÷ 4 = 93.75 kcmil.

93.75 kcmil × 1000 = 93,750 circular mils.

Using Table 8 in Chapter 9, the next higher circular mil area is 105,600; therefore, the minimum size grounded conductor permitted in each raceway is 1/0 copper.

Note: Section 310-4 does not permit conductors smaller than 1/0 to be connected in parallel.

Overcurrent Protection of Transformers Rated 600 Volts or Less

Primary

For a dry type transformer rated:
— 480 volts primary
— 208/120 volts secondary
— 3-phase
Primary overcurrent protection only, use Section 450-3(b)(1).

Transformer rated primary current =

$$\frac{112.5 \text{ kVA} \times 1000}{1.73 \times 480\text{V}} = 135 \text{ A.}$$

Section 450-3(b)(1), Exception No. 1, permits the next higher standard size overcurrent device to be used in accordance with the standard ampere ratings listed in Section 240-6.

$$125\% \text{ of } 135 \text{ A} = 169 \text{ A;}$$

therefore, the next higher size permitted in accordance with Section 240-6 is 175 amperes.

Primary and Secondary

Transformer rating same as above.
Primary and secondary overcurrent protection, Section 450-3(b)(2).

Transformer rated primary current =

$$\frac{112.5 \text{ kVA} \times 1000}{1.73 \times 480\text{V}} = 135 \text{ A.}$$

Section 450-3(b)(2) allows the primary overcurrent device to be no greater than 250 percent of transformer primary rated current. Therefore,

$$250\% \text{ of } 135 \text{ A} = 338 \text{ A}.$$

The *Code* does not provide an exception to allow increasing the overcurrent device to the next higher rating. Therefore, the primary overcurrent device can be any size equal to or less than 337.5 amperes.

The secondary overcurrent device must be rated not greater than 125 percent of the transformer secondary rated current.

Transformer rated secondary current =

$$\frac{112.5 \text{ kVA} \times 1000}{1.73 \times 208\text{V}} = 313 \text{ A}.$$

Section 450-3(b)(2), Exception, permits the next higher standard overcurrent device to be used in accordance with the standard ampere ratings listed in Section 240-6.

$$125\% \text{ of } 313 \text{ A} = 391 \text{ A}.$$

The maximum highest size overcurrent device in accordance with 240-6 is 400 amperes.

Number of Conductors Permitted

Metal Wireways

The metal wireway is 6 in. × 6 in. square. Determine the maximum number of No. 6, THHN conductors allowed in the wireway when supplying power circuits.

Section 362-5 limits conductor fill to not more than 20 percent of the interior cross-sectional area of the wireway where not more than 30 conductors are installed.

Total cross-sectional area of wireway =

$$6 \text{ in.} \times 6 \text{ in.} = 36 \text{ sq. in.}$$

$$20\% \text{ of } 36 \text{ sq. in.} = 7.2 \text{ sq. in.}$$

Cross-sectional area of No. 6, THHN conductor from Chapter 9, Table 5, is .0519 sq. in.

$$7.2 \text{ sq. in.} \div 0.0519 \text{ sq. in.} = 139 \text{ No. 6, THHN}$$
conductors.

The derating factors specified in Article 310, Note 8(a) of Notes to Ampacity Tables of 0-2000 Volts do not apply to the 30 current-carrying conductors at 20 percent fill. See Exception Nos. 1, 2, and 3.

Cable Trays—Single Conductors

Determine the maximum number of 500 kcmil, THWN single conductors permitted to be installed in an 18-inch wide-ladder or ventilated-trough cable tray. The conductors are rated 2000 volts or less.

Section 318-10(a)(2) requires that the sum of the cross sectional area does not exceed the maximum allowable fill given in Column 1 of Table 318-10.

Using Table 318-10, Column 1, 19.5 sq. in. of conductors are allowed in an 18-inch wide cable tray.

Using Table 5 of Chapter 9, the cross-sectional area of a 500 kcmil, THWN conductor is 0.7163 sq. in.

Number of conductors allowed =

$$\frac{19.5 \text{ sq. in.}}{0.7163 \text{ sq. in.}} = 27 \text{ conductors.}$$

Section 318-11(b)(2) requires the ampacity of the above cables to be based on 65 percent of the ampacities in Tables 310-17 and 310-19 for uncovered cable trays.

Cable Trays—Multiconductor Cable

Determine the maximum number of multiconductor cables rated 2000 volts or less, 4/0 or larger, installed in a ladder or ventilated-trough cable tray 18 inches wide.

The cables to be installed are three conductor 4/0 cable assemblies.

Section 318-9(a)(1) limits the number of conductors based on the sum of their diameters not exceeding the width of the cable tray where installed in a single layer.

Obtain outside dimension of cables from the manufacturers or use actual measurements.

Assuming that a three conductor 4/0 cable outside diameter is 1.50 inches:

$$18 \text{ in.} \div 1.5 \text{ in.} = 12 \text{ cables.}$$

Section 318-11(a) requires the ampacity of the above cables to be based on Tables 310-16 and 310-18. Note 8(a) to the 0 to 2000 volt tables applies only where the number of current-carrying conductors within the cable exceeds three.

Supplement 3: Electrical Issues Covered in Other NFPA Documents

Requirements extracted from other NFPA documents and included in the *NEC* are listed in Appendix A. The following are some related sources of electrical information found in other NFPA documents.

NFPA 99, 1990 Edition
Standard for Health Care Facilities

3-3.2.1.6	Service transformers are not permitted in an emergency generator room.
3-4.1.2.4 (b) Exception No. 1	Receptacles are not required in bathrooms or toilet rooms.
3-4.2.2.4(b)(1)	Branch circuit overcurrent devices are required to be readily accessible to nursing and other authorized personnel.
3-5.1.2.4(a)	Main and feeder circuit breakers are to be tested regularly.
3-5.2.2.1(d)	Receptacle retention in patient care areas is to be tested.

NFPA 303, 1990 Edition
Fire Protection Standard for Marinas and Boatyards

3-5.2	Phase loads are required to be balanced.
3-5.3	System power is not to exceed 250 volts phase-to-phase (with exceptions).
3-5.6	Service equipment is to be protected against access to unauthorized persons.
3-6.2	No. 12 insulated grounding conductor is required.
3-12.2	Wiring is to be installed underground (with exceptions).
3-12.3(d)	Warning signs are required if wiring is overhead.
3-13.2	Circuit breakers with thermal elements are prohibited where exposed to direct rays of the sun.
3-16.1	Disconnects are to be readily available for each boat. Electrical equipment is to be located so as not to interfere with mooring lines.
Appendix B	Configurations of locking and grounding receptacles are found in Appendix B.

NFPA 20, 1990 Edition
Standard for the Installation of Centrifugal Fire Pumps

6-3.1.2	Pump room wiring is to be rigid conduit, IMC, or liquidtight flexible metal conduit if part of pump electrical system.
6-4.1	Transformer may need to be increased in size. References NFPA 70 [see Section 450-3(d)].
6-5.1.1	Fire-resistive MI cable is required to be attached in accordance with its listing (see UL building materials directory). Motors are to be specifically listed for fire pump service.
6-7.1	Generator is not required to carry locked rotor current.
6-7.4	Transfer switch is to be located within the pump room.

NFPA 32, 1990 Edition
Standard for Drycleaning Plants

1-6.1	Plans are required for remodeling or change of solvents.
2-1	Plants are classified in accordance with the type of solvent used.

2-3.1.1	Electric heat is not permitted in some dry-cleaning plants.
2-4.6.1	For static electricity problems see NFPA 77, Recommended Practice on Static Electricity.

NFPA 33, 1989 Edition
Standard for Spray Application Using Flammable & Combustible Materials

4-3	Space heating appliances are not to be located in spray areas, under certain conditions.
12-1	Automobile undercoating is generally exempt from spray applications requirements, if adequately ventilated.
13-4(c)	Special grounding is required around powder operations.

NFPA 34, 1989 Edition
Standard for Dipping & Coating Processes Using Flammable or Combustible Liquids

5-5.6	Bonding is required between metal containers or process tanks and a nozzle that is dispensing a Class I liquid.
9-2.5	A sign is required indicating the safe distance from electrodes of electrostatic apparatus.
9-4	Electrically conductive objects in the area of electrostatic apparatus, such as paint containers, wash cans, guards, etc., are required to be grounded. A sign indicating the need for such grounding is required.

NFPA 79, 1991 Edition
Electrical Standard for Industrial Machinery

5-8	Machine disconnect is to be *within* or *adjacent to* the control enclosure.
5-11	An attachment plug and receptacle is permitted as disconnecting means, under specified conditions.
7-2	Control circuit voltage is not to exceed 120 volts.

10-1(b)	Pipelines, tubing, or devices for handling air, gases, or liquids are not permitted in control enclosures.
12-1(a)	Receptacles external to the control enclosure rated more than 20 amperes are required to be locking type.
12-3(f)	Machine work lights are not permitted to contain switches or receptacles where exposed to liquids or condensing mists unless identified for the purpose.
Table 13-5(a)	Special allowable ampacities are permitted for machine wiring.
14-1	Color coding of conductors is required.
15-2	Raceways can be filled to 50 percent.

NFPA 30A, 1990 Edition
Automotive & Marine Service Station Code

Table 7	Pits and below grade work areas of quick lube facilities are unclassified when ventilated in accordance with Section 5-1.3.

NFPA 497A, 1992 Edition
Recommended Practice for Classification of Class I Hazardous (Classified) Locations for Electrical Installations in Chemical Process Areas

Figure 3-4.24	Area around drum filling stations containing flammable liquids is classified.

NFPA 780, 1992 Edition
Lightning Protection Code

2-16.2	Electrical system grounding electrodes are not to be used as a lightning protection ground rod.

NFPA 75, 1992 Edition
Standard for the Protection of Electronic Computer/Data Processing Equipment

3-1.3	Computer "areas" as well as computer rooms are required to be separated from other occupancies within a building. (See Figure B-1 of NFPA 75.)
10-4	A disconnect is required for the computer "area" as defined in Figure B-1 of NFPA 75.

Supplement 4: Cross-Reference Between 1990 and 1993 Editions of the NEC

1990	1993
90-5	90-6
90-6	90-7
90-7	90-8
90-8	90-9
110-1	90-5
Definitions Part A	
AC General-Use Snap Switch*	Deleted
AC-DC General Use Snap Switch*	Deleted
Anesthetizing Location*	Deleted
Block (City, Town, or Village)*	Deleted
Branch-Circuit, FPN	Deleted
Branch-Circuit Selection Current*	Deleted
Cell (As applied to Raceways)*	Deleted
Control Circuit*	Deleted
Current-Limiting Overcurrent Protective Device*	Deleted
Disconnecting Means, FPN	Deleted
Dust-Ignitionproof*	Deleted
Duty: Varying Duty, FPN	Deleted
Duty Cycle (Welding)*	Deleted
Explosionproof Apparatus, FPN	New
Festoon Lighting*	Deleted
Grounded, Effectively	Moved to Part A
Hazardous (Classified) Locations*	Deleted

1990	1993
Header*	Deleted
Hermetic Refrigerant Motor-Compressor*	Deleted
Neutral Conductor*	Deleted
Nonincendive Circuit and FPN	New
Overload, FPN*	Deleted
Projector, Nonprofessional*	Deleted
Projector, Professional*	Deleted
Rated-Load Current*	Deleted
Separately Derived System	New
Welder, Electric:*	
Actual Primary Current*	Deleted
Rated Primary Current*	Deleted
X-Ray:*	
Long-Time Rating*	Deleted
Momentary Rating*	Deleted
Definitions Part B	
Grounded, Effectively	Moved to Part A
110-1	90-5
110-3(a)(1) (1st sentence retained for '93 ed)	110-3(a)(1), FPN
None	110-10, FPN
110-11, FPN	110-11, FPN No. 1
None	110-11, FPN No. 2
None	110-12(c)
None	110-14(c)
110-16(e), Exc.	Deleted
110-16(f), Exc.	110-16(f), Exc. No. 1
None	110-16(f), Exc. No. 2
None	110-31, FPN No. 3

*These definitions were not complete but only referenced other sections of Code.

1990	1993	1990	1993
None	210-4(a), FPN	230-95(a), Exc. No. 1	230-95, Exc. No. 1
None	210-6(c)(2)	230-95(a), Exc. No. 2	230-95, Exc. No. 2
210-6(c)(2)	210-6(c)(3)	230-200, Service Point	Article 100
210-6(c)(3)	210-6(c)(4)	230-205(a), FPN	Deleted
210-6(c)(4)	210-6(c)(5)	240-3, Exc. No. 1	Deleted
210-6(c)(5)	210-6(c)(6)	240-3, Exc. No. 2	Deleted
210-8(b)	210-8(b)(1)	240-3, Exc. No. 3	240-3(a)
None	210-8(b)(2)	None	240-3(a), FPN
210-9, Exc. No. 2	210-9, Exc. No. 1	240-3, Exc. No. 4	240-3(b)
None	210-9, Exc. No. 2	None	240-3(c)
210-9, FPN	Deleted	240-3, Exc. No. 5	240-3(d)
210-9, Exc. No. 1	Deleted	240-3, Exc. No. 6	240-3(e)
None	210-21(b)(1), Exc.	240-3, Exc. No. 6	240-3(f)
210-24, Exc.	Deleted	240-3, Exc. No. 6	240-3(g)
None	210-52(b)(1), Exc. No. 4	240-3, Exc. No. 6	240-3(h)
None	210-52(b)(1), Exc. No. 5	240-3, Exc. No. 2	240-3(i)
None	210-52(c), FPN	240-3, Exc. No. 7	240-3(j)
None	220-3(c)(5) and Exc.	240-3, Exc. No. 8	240-3(k)
220-3(c)(5)	220-3(c)(6)	240-3, Exc. No. 1	240-3(l)
220-22, FPN	220-22, FPN No. 1	None	240-3(m)
None	220-22, FPN No. 2	240-6, Paragraph 1	240-6(a)
225-8	225-8(a)	240-6, Exc.	240-6(a), Exc.
230-84(a)	225-8(b)	240-6, Paragraph 2	240-6(b)
230-84(a), Exc. No. 1	225-8(b), Exc. No. 1	240-6, Exc. and FPN to Paragraph 2	240-6(b), Exc. and FPN
230-84(a), Exc. No. 2	225-8(b), Exc. No. 2	240-21, Exc. No. 1	Deleted
230-84(b)	225-8(c)	None	240-21(a)
230-84(b), Exc.	225-8(c), Exc.	240-21, Exc. No. 2	240-21(b)
None	225-8(d)	240-21, Exc. No. 3	240-21(c)
None	225-9, FPN	240-21, Exc. No. 4	240-21(n)
None	225-19(a), Exc. No. 4	240-21, Exc. No. 5	240-21(f)
230-201	230-10	240-21, Exc. No. 6	240-21(h)
None	230-24, Exc. No. 4	240-21, Exc. No. 7	240-21(g)
None	230-28, FPN	240-21, Exc. No. 8	240-21(d)
None	230-66	240-21, Exc. No. 9	240-21(i)
None	230-82, FPN	240-21, Exc. No. 10	240-21(e)
230-91(b)	Deleted	240-21, Exc. No. 11	240-21(j)
230-91(c)	230-91(b)	None	240-21(k)
		None	240-21(m)

1990	1993	1990	1993
None	240-24(c), FPN	310-5, Exc. No. 10	310-5, Exc. No. 9
None	240-24(e)	310-7, FPN	Deleted
None	250-5, FPN	None	310-7, FPN No. 1
None	250-7(c)	None	310-7, FPN No. 2
None	250-32, Exc.	None	310-11(d)
None	250-33, Exc.	None	310-11(d), FPN
None	250-43(l)	310-12(a), Exc. No. 1	Deleted
250-53(b), Exc.	250-53(b), Exc. No. 2	310-12(a), Exc. No. 2	310-12(a), Exc. No. 1
None	250-53(b), Exc. No. 1	310-12(a), Exc. No. 3	310-12(a), Exc. No. 2
None	250-57(b), Exc. No. 3	310-12(a), Exc. No. 4	310-12(a), Exc. No. 3
250-57(b), Exc. No. 3	250-57(b), Exc. No. 4	310-12(a), Exc. No. 5	310-12(a), Exc. No. 4
250-81, Exc.	250-81, Exc. No. 1	None	310-12(c), Exc.
None	250-81, Exc. No. 2	None	310-15, FPN
None	250-81(a), Exc.	310-15(b), FPN No. 1	310-15(b), FPN
None	250-114, Exc.	310-15(b), FPN No. 2	Deleted
300-3(b), Exc. to (a) and (b)	300-3(b), Exc. No. 3 to (a) and (b)	310-15(b), FPN No. 3	Deleted
None	300-3(b), Exc. No. 1	None	310-15(c), FPN
None	300-3(b), Exc. No. 2 to (b)	None	Appendix B, Table B-310-11 Chart - Notes to Ampacity Tables of 0 to 2000 Volts, Note 8(a), Column A, single and double asterisk notes, and FPN
None	300-6(c), Exc.	None	Notes to Ampacity Tables of 0 to 2000 Volts, Note 8(a), Exc. No. 5 and FPN
None	300-10, Exc. No. 3		
300-15(b), Exc. No. 3	Deleted		
300-15(b), Exc. No. 4	300-15(b), Exc. No. 3	Table 310-65	Deleted
300-15(b), Exc. No. 5	300-15(b), Exc. No. 4	Table 310-66	Deleted
300-15(b), Exc. No. 6	300-15(b), Exc. No. 5	None	Table 310-67
300-15(b), Exc. No. 7	300-15(b), Exc. No. 6	None	Table 310-68
300-15(b), Exc. No. 8	300-15(b), Exc. No. 7	318-3(b)(1), Exc.	318-3(b)(1), Exc. No. 1
300-15(b), Exc. No. 9	300-15(b), Exc. No. 8	None	318-3(b)(1), Exc. No. 2
None	300-15(d)	None	318-6(a), FPN
None	300-21, FPN	None	318-6(j)
None	300-23	None	318-6(j), FPN
None	300-37	None	318-11(a), FPN
None	305-4(i)	None	318-11(b)(4), FPN
310-13, Exc. No. 1	Deleted	None	330-16
310-13, Exc. No. 2	Deleted	None	331-3(7)
None	310-3, Exc.		
310-5, Exc. No. 8	Deleted		
310-5, Exc. No. 9	310-5, Exc. No. 8		

1990	1993	1990	1993
None	331-11, Exc.	None	349-17
None	Article 333, New Part Title, A. General	350-3, Exc. No. 1	Deleted
		350-3, Exc. No. 2	350-3, Exc. No. 1
None	Article 333, New Part Title, B. Installation	350-3, Exc. No. 3	350-3, Exc. No. 2
None	Article 333, New Part C. Construction Specifications	350-3, Exc. No. 4	350-3, Exc. No. 3
		350-3, Exc. No. 5	350-3, Exc. No. 4
		350-3, Exc. No. 6	350-3, Exc. No. 5
333-3	333-22	None	374-9(f)
333-6(a)	333-3	380-17, FPN	Deleted
333-4	333-19	None	384-4, FPN No. 4
333-5	333-20	Notes to Table 400-4	Notes to Table 400-4
333-5, Exc.	333-20, Exc.	Note 2	Deleted
333-6(b)	333-4	Note 3	Note 2
None	333-7, Exc. No. 4	Note 4	Note 3
None	333-21	Note 5	Note 4
None	334-10(a), Exc. No. 1	Note 6	Note 5
None	334-10(a), Exc. No. 2	Note 7	Note 6
None	334-10(f)	Note 8	Note 7
None	334-10(g)	Note 9	Note 8
334-13, Exc.	334-13, Exc. No. 1	Note 10	Note 9
None	334-13, Exc. No. 2	Table 400-4	Table 400-4
None	336-15, FPN	Type AFC	Deleted
None	338-1(b), Exc.	Type AFPD	Deleted
338-1(b), FPN	338-1(b), FPN No. 1	Type AFS	Deleted
None	338-1(b), FPN No. 2	Type AFSJ	Deleted
Article 344	Deleted	Type DP	Deleted
None	Article 343, Preassembled Cable in Nonmetallic Conduit	None	Type ETP
		None	Type SEOO
		None	Type SJEOO
None	345-12, FPN	None	Type SVEOO
346-5, Exc. No. 1	Deleted	Table following 400-5, Column A, Notes, and FPN	Deleted
346-5, Exc. No. 2	346-5, Exc.		
None	346-12	None	400-5, Exc. No. 1
347-1, FPN	Deleted	None	400-5, FPN
None	347-3(b), Exc.	Table 400-5(A)	Table 400-5(A)
None	347-9, Exc.	"Asbestos Types" Column	Deleted
None	347-17, Exc.	*Note	Deleted
348-5, Exc. No. 1	Deleted	**Note	*Note
348-5, Exc. No. 2	348-5, Exc.	***Note	**Note

1990	1993	1990	1993
Note, Ultimate Insulation Temperature	400-5, Paragraph 2	None	364-11, Exc. (text from 1990 paragraph)
Table 400-5(B), Note, Ultimate Insulation Temperature	400-5, Paragraph 2	364-25, Exc.	364-25, Exc. (to Paragraph 1)
400-6	400-6(a)	None	364-25, FPN
None	400-6(b)	None	370-5
None	400-6(b), FPN	370-5	370-15
None	402-9(c)	370-6	370-16
None	402-9(c), FPN	None	370-16, Exc.
Table 402-3	Table 402-3	Table 370-6(a)	Table 370-16(a)
None	Type ZHF	Table 370-6(b)	Table 370-16(b)
None	410-15(b)(1), Exc.	370-7	370-17
410-16(h), FPN	410-16(h), FPN No. 1	370-8	370-18
None	410-16(h), FPN No. 2	370-9	370-19
None	410-56(i)	370-10	370-20
None	410-30(c), Exc.	370-11	370-21
None	410-56(i), Exc.	370-12	370-22
Article 410, Part O	Article 410, Part N	370-13	370-23
None	350-9	370-13(g)	Deleted
None	350-10	370-13(h)	370-23(g)
None	351-4(a)(3)	370-14	370-24
None	351-11	370-15	370-25
None	351-23(b)(4), Exc.	370-17	370-27
351-24, Exc.	351-24, Exc. No. 1	370-18	370-28
None	351-24, Exc. No. 2	370-19	370-29
None	351-24, Exc. No. 3	370-20	370-40
351-27	351-28	None	370-40(b), Exc. No. 1 and Exc. No. 2
None	351-29		
None	351-30	370-21	370-41
None	352-9	370-22	370-42
None	352-28	370-23	370-43
None	352-28, FPN	370-24	370-44
None	352-29	370-50	370-70
None	Article 362, New Part Title, A. Metal Wireways	370-51	370-71
		370-52	370-72
None	Article 362, New Part, B. Nonmetallic Wireways	410-73, Exc. to (e)	410-73(e), Exc. No. 1
		None	410-73(e), Exc. No. 2
		None	410-73(e), Exc. No. 3
364-11	364-11 (New Text)	None	410-73, FPN

1990	1993
410-85(a)	410-85
410-85(b)	410-85, Exc.
422-8(d)(3), Exc.	422-8(d)(3), Exc. No. 1
None	422-8(d)(3), Exc. No. 2
None	422-8(d)(3), Exc. No. 3
None	422-29
424-22(c), FPN (to Paragraph 2)	424-22(c), FPN No. 2
None	424-22(c), FPN No. 1
426-27(c)	Deleted
None	426-53
None	426-54
430-1, FPN No. 1	430-1, Exc. No. 2
430-1, FPN No. 2	430-1, FPN
None	430-1, Exc. No. 1
430-7(d)	430-7(d)(1)
	430-7(d)(2)
430-7(e)	Deleted
430-19	Deleted
430-22(b)	Deleted
430-22(c)	430-22(b)
430-24(a), Paragraph 2, and 430-24(a)(1), (2), and (3)	430-24, Exc. No. 1
430-25(a), Exc.	430-24, Exc. No. 2
430-24, Exc.	430-24, Exc. No. 3
430-24(b)	455-6
430-25(a)	Deleted
430-25(b)	430-25
430-25(c)	Deleted
430-25(a), Exc.	430-24, Exc. No. 2
None	430-28, Exc. (g)
None	430-34, FPN
430-52(c)	Deleted
None	430-62(a), Exc.
430-64	Deleted
430-83	430-83(a)
None	430-83(b)
None	430-83(b), FPN
430-86 and FPN	Deleted

1990	1993
Table 430-91, Enclosure Type No. 11	Deleted
None	Article 430, Part H
Article 430, Part H	Article 430, Part I
430-101(c)	Deleted
None	430-107(1)
None	430-107(2)
None	430-107(3)
430-110(d)	430-107, Exc.
	Deleted
440-4(c), FPN	440-2 Definitions Branch-Circuit Selection Current Rated-Load Current
440-4(a), FPN	450-3, FPN No. 1
450-3, FPN	450-3, FPN No. 2
None	450-3(d)
None	450-21(b), Exc. No. 1
450-21(b), Exc. No. 1 to (b)	450-21(b), Exc. No. 2
450-21(b), Exc. No. 2 to (b)	Article 455
None	500-3(a), FPN No. 2
500-3, FPN No. 2	500-3(b), FPN No. 2
	500-3, FPN No. 2
500-3, FPN No. 3	500-3, Paragraph 2
500-3, FPN No. 4	500-3, FPN to Pararaph 2
	500-3, Exc.
None	500-3(a)
None	500-3(a)(1)
500-3, FPN No. 5	500-3(a)(2)
500-3, FPN No. 6	500-3(a)(2), Exc. No. 1
500-3, FPN No. 9	500-3(a)(2), Exc. No. 2
500-3, FPN No. 10	500-3(a)(3)
500-3, FPN No. 7	500-3(a)(4)
500-3, FPN No. 8	500-3(a)(4), Exc.
None	500-3(a), FPN No. 4
500-3, FPN No. 11	500-3(a), FPN No. 1
500-3, FPN No. 12	500-3(a), FPN No. 3
500-3, FPN No. 16	500-3(b)
None	

1990	1993	1990	1993
500-3, FPN No. 13	500-3(b)(1)	None	504-2, Definition, Different Intrinsically Safe Circuits
500-3, FPN No. 17	500-3(b)(1), FPN	None	504-50(c)
500-3, FPN No. 14	500-3(b)(2)	None	504-50(c), Exc.
None	500-3(b)(2), FPN	504-60	504-60(a)
500-3, FPN No. 15	500-3(b)(3)	None	504-60(b)
None	500-3(b)(3), FPN No. 1	None	504-70, FPN
500-3, FPN No. 18	500-3(b)(3), FPN No. 3	504-80(b), FPN No. 1	504-80(c)
500-3(a)	500-3(c)	None	504-80(b), Exc.
500-3(b)	500-3(d)	504-80(b), FPN No. 2	504-80(b), FPN No. 1
500-3(c)	500-3(e)	504-80(b), FPN No. 3	504-80(b), FPN No. 2
500-3(d)	500-3(f)	None	511-3(b), Exc.
Table 500-3(b)	Table 500-3(d)	None	514-5(b)
Table 500-3(d)	Table 500-3(f)	None	514-5(c)
None	501-4(b), FPN	None	514-5(c), FPN
501-5, FPN	501-5, FPN No. 1	516-2(b)(5)	516-2(b)(5)
None	501-5, FPN No. 2		516-2(b)(6)
None	501-5(d), Exc.	None	516-2(b)(6), Exc.
501-8(b), FPN	501-8(b), FPN No. 1	516-2(b)(6)	516-2(c) and Exc.
None	501-8(b), FPN No. 2	516-2(c)	516-2(d)
None	501-10(b)(1)b, Exc.	516-2(d)	516-2(e)
None	501-16, Exc.	516-4(d)	516-4(j)(1)
501-17	501-17(a)	516-4(e)	516-4(d)
None	501-17(b)	516-4(f)	516-4(e)
None	501-18	516-4(g)	516-4(f)
None	501-18, Exc.	516-4(h)	516-4(g)
None	502-1, FPN to Paragraph 2	None	516-4(h)
None	502-4(a)(2), FPN	None	516-4(i)
502-4(b), Exc.	502-4(b), Exc. No. 1	None	516-4(j)
None	502-4(b), Exc. No. 2	None	516-4(j)(2)
None	502-16(a), Exc.	517-3	517-2
None	502-18	517-2, Definitions	517-3, Definitions
None	502-18, Exc.	None	Limited Care Facility
None	503-3(a)(2), FPN	None	Patient Bed Location
None	503-16(a), Exc.	None	Patient Care Area
504-4	504-2	Patient Care Areas	Patient Care Areas of a Hospital
504-2	504-4		

1990	1993	1990	1993
Residential Custodial Care Facility	Deleted (Replaced by Limited Care Facility in Article 517)	520-68	520-68(a)
		None	520-68(b)
517-15(a)	Deleted	None	520-68(b), Exc.
517-15(b)	Deleted	None	530-2, Definitions
None	517(a), FPN	None	Portable Equipment
517-20(1)	517-20(a)	None	Plugging Box
None	517-20(a), Exc.	None	AC Power Distribution Box
517-20(2)	517-20(b)		
517-30(a), Exc.	Deleted	None	530-17(b)
None	517-30(c)(3), Exc. No. 4	None	530-18(e)
		530-18(e)	530-18(f)
517-63(b)a	517-63(b)(1)	None	530-21(1)
517-63(b)b	517-63(b)(2)	None	530-21(2)
517-63(b)c	517-63(b)(3)	None	530-21(3)
517-63(b)d	517-63(b)(4)	None	530-22
517-63(c)a	517-63(c)(1)	None	547-5(a)
527-63(c)b	517-63(c)(2)	None	547-5(b)
517-63(c)c	517-63(c)(3)	None	547-5, FPN
517-63(c)d	517-63(c)(4)	550-5, Exc.	550-5, Exc. No. 1
517-80, FPN No. 1	517-80, FPN	None	550-5, Exc. No. 2
517-80, FPN No. 2	Deleted	550-8(f)	550-8(f)(1)
517-160(b)(1), FPN	Deleted	None	550-8(f)(2)
518-4, Exc. No. 1	Deleted	550-23(a), Exc.	550-23(a), Exc. No. 1
518-4, Exc. No. 2	518-4, Exc.	None	550-23(a), Exc. No. 2
None	518-5	None	550-23(g)
None	520-4, Exc. No. 3	None	550-24(a), Exc.
None	520-8	551-70, Definitions	551-2, Definitions
None	520-44, Exc.	Recreational Vehicle Park	551-2
520-45(1)	Deleted	Recreational Vehicle Site	551-2
520-45(2)	Deleted	Recreational Vehicle Site Feeder Circuit Conductors	551-2
None	Table 520-44		
None	520-53(k)	Recreational Vehicle Site Supply Equipment	551-2
520-53(k)	520-53(l)		
520-53(l)	520-53(m)	Recreational Vehicle Stand	551-2
520-53(m)	520-53(n)	None	551-30(d), FPN
520-53(n)	520-53(o)	551-30(f)	Deleted
None	520-53(p)	551-46(e), Exc.	551-46(e), Exc. No. 1
None	520-53(p), Exc.	None	551-46(e), Exc. No. 2

1990	1993	1990	1993
551-70, Definition, Power-Supply Assembly	Deleted	None	675-8(b), Exc.
None	551-72, FPN	None	680-5(c), Exc. No. 4
None	551-76(a), Exc.	680-20(d)(1), (2), (3)	Deleted
None	555-4, FPN	680-20(d)(4)	680-20(d)(1)
None	555-7(b), Exc.	680-25(c), Exc. No. 5	Deleted
None	555-10	680-26(a), FPN	680-26(a), FPN No. 1
None	600-2(a), Exc. No. 1		680-26(a), FPN No. 2
600-2(a), Exc.	600-2(a), Exc. No. 2		680-26(a), FPN No. 3
None	600-31(a), FPN	None	680-32, Exc.
None	610-11, Exc. No. 5	None	680-41(d)(4), Exc.
None	610-21, Exc. No. 1, FPN	None	680-42
None	610-21, Exc. No. 7	None	690-4(d)
620-22	620-22(a)	None	690-8(c)
None	620-22(b)	None	690-13, Exc.
620-37, Exc.	620-37, Exc. No. 1	None	690-13, FPN
None	620-37, Exc. No. 2	700-8	700-8(a)
None	620-51(a), FPN	None	700-8(b)
None	620-51(b)(4)	701-9	701-9(a)
None	620-54	None	701-9(b)
None	620-61(b)(4)	702-8	702-8(a)
620-71, Exc.	620-71, Exc. No. 1	None	702-8(b)
None	620-71, Exc. No. 2	None	710-2, Definition, High Voltage
620-72, Exc.	620-72, Exc. No. 1		
None	620-72, Exc. No. 2	710-2	710-3
None	620-84	710-3	710-4
None	620-85	Table 710-3(b)	Table 710-4(b)
None	645-5(d)(5)	710-4	710-5
645-11, Exc.	645-11, Exc. No. 1	None	725-6
None	645-11, Exc. No. 2	725-38(a)(1),(2),(3),(4)	725-52(a)(1),(2),(3),(4)
645-15, FPN	645-11, FPN No. 1	725-38(b)(1),(2),(3),(4)	725-52(b)(1),(2),(3),(4)
None	645-11, FPN No. 2	None	725-42(1)
670-4(a), FPN No. 1	Deleted	None	725-42(2)
670-4(a), FPN No. 2	670-4(a), FPN	None	725-52
None	670-4(b), Exc. to Paragraph 2	None	725-52(c)
		None	725-52(c), Exc.
None	670-5	None	725-53(b), FPN
None	670-5, Exc.	None	725-53(f)
		725-53(f)	725-53(g)
		None	760-7

1990	1993	1990	1993
None	760-17(e)(3), FPN	None	800-51(c)
760-17(e)(4), Exc.	760-17(e)(4), Exc. No. 1	None	800-52(c), FPN
None	760-17(e)(4), Exc. No. 2	800-51(c)	800-51(d)
None	760-52(c)	800-51(d)	800-51(e)
None	760-53(b), FPN	800-51(e)	800-51(f)
770-6	770-4	800-51(f)	800-51(g)
770-4	770-5	800-51(h)	800-51(i)
None	770-5, Exc.	800-52(a)(2)c2	Deleted
None	770-5, FPN	800-52(a)(2)c3, Exc. No. 1	800-52(a)(2)c1, Exc. No. 1
770-5	770-6	None	800-52(a)(2)c1, Exc. No. 2
None	770-7	800-52(a)(2)c3	800-52(a)(2)c2
None	770-49	None	800-52(a)(2)c2, Exc. No. 1
None	770-51(c)	None	800-52(a)(2)c2, Exc. No. 2
None	770-51, FPN	None	800-52(e)
None	770-51(e)	None	800-53(b), FPN
None	770-51(f)	800-53(d)	800-53(c)
None	770-53(b), FPN	800-53(d), Exc.	800-53(c), Exc.
None	800-2 Definition, Point of Entrance	800-53(c)	800-53(d)
None	800-3, FPN	800-53(c), Exc. Nos. 1,2,3,4,5	800-53(d), Exc. Nos. 1,2,3,4,5
800-51(i)	800-4	None	800-53(e)
800-51(i), FPN	800-4, FPN	800-53(e)	800-53(f)
800-51(i), Exc.	800-4, Exc. No. 1	None	810-5
	800-4, Exc. No. 2	None	820-3, Definition, Point of Entrance
None	800-5	None	820-5
None	800-6	None	820-6
800-10(a)(4), FPN	Deleted	820-11	820-11(a)
None	800-30(a), FPN No. 4	820-11	820-11(b)
None	800-31, FPN	820-11, Exc.	820-11(b), Exc. No. 2
None	800-32, FPN No. 1	None	820-11(b), Exc. No. 1
None	800-32, FPN No. 2	None	820-40(d), Exc.
800-40(b)(3), Exc.	Deleted	None	820-42
None	800-49	None	820-49
800-50, Exc. No. 3, FPN	800-50, Exc. No. 3, FPN No. 1	None	820-50, Exc. No. 2
None	800-50, Exc. No. 3, FPN No. 2	820-50, Exc. No. 2	820-50, Exc. No. 3
None	800-51, FPN		

1990	1993	1990	1993
None	820-52(e)	Table 1, Note 3	Table 1, Note 4
None	820-52(b), Exc. No. 2, FPN	Table 1, Note 5	Table 1, Note 6
None	820-53(c), Exc. No. 4	None	Table 3A, Note 2
None	Table 1, Note 2	Table 3A, Note	Table 3A, Note 1
Table 1, Note 2	Table 1, Note 3	None	Example No. 9
		None	Example No. 10
		None	Table B-310-11

Supplement 5: Summary of Changes to the 1993 *National Electrical Code*

ARTICLE 90—Introduction

Sections 90-2(a)(2) and (3): Revised by inserting "and equipment" to improve clarity and to recognize that the *NEC* covers the installation of both conductors and equipment.

Section 90-2(b)(2): Revised to provide appropriate coverage for structural surface installations and other surface mining applications and to clarify that self-propelled surface mining equipment and its trailing cable are not covered.

Section 90-5: This section was previously identified as Section 110-1.

Section 90-6: This section was previously identified as Section 90-5.

Section 90-7: This section was previously identified as Section 90-6.

Section 90-7 (FPN No. 1): Revised to match title of Section 110-3.

Section 90-8: This section was previously identified as Section 90-7.

Section 90-9: This section was previously identified as Section 90-8.

Chapter 1—General

ARTICLE 100—Definitions

A. General

AC General-Use Snap Switch: Term and cross-reference have been deleted to conform with the scope of Article 100.

AC-DC General-Use Snap Switch: Term and cross-reference have been deleted to conform with the scope of Article 100.

Anesthetizing Location: Term and cross-reference have been deleted to conform with the scope of Article 100.

Block (City, Town, or Village): Term and cross-reference have been deleted to conform with the scope of Article 100.

Branch Circuit (FPN): FPN has been deleted to conform with the scope of Article 100.

Branch Circuit Selection Current: Term and cross-reference have been deleted to conform with the scope of Article 100.

Cell (As applied to Raceways): Term and cross-reference have been deleted to conform with the scope of Article 100.

Circuit Breaker (FPN): Cross-reference has been deleted to conform with the scope of Article 100.

Circuit Breaker, Adjustable: Revised to conform to *NEC Style Manual*.

Circuit Breaker, Setting: Revised to conform to *NEC Style Manual*.

Conduit Body: Cross-reference has been deleted to conform with the scope of Article 100.

Control Circuit: Term and cross-reference have been deleted to conform with the scope of Article 100.

Controller: Cross-reference has been deleted to conform with the scope of Article 100.

Current-Limiting Overcurrent Protective Device: Term and cross-reference have been deleted to conform with the scope of Article 100.

Disconnecting Means (FPN): FPN has been deleted to conform with the scope of Article 100.

Dust-Ignitionproof: Term and cross-reference have been deleted to conform with the scope of Article 100.

Duty, Varying Duty (FPN): FPN has been deleted to conform with the scope of Article 100.

Duty Cycle (Welding): Term and cross-reference have been deleted to conform with the scope of Article 100.

Explosionproof Apparatus (FPN): FPN has been added to clarify definition for this type of apparatus.

Festoon Lighting: Term and cross-reference have been deleted to conform with the scope of Article 100.

Garage (FPN): FPN revised to conform with *NEC Style Manual*.

Grounded (Effectively Grounded Communication System): Term and cross-reference have been deleted to conform with the scope of Article 100.

Grounded (Effectively): Definition has been moved from Part B of Article 100 so it will apply to systems that are both under and over 600 V.

Grounding Conductor, Equipment: Revised to conform with *NEC Style Manual*.

Grounding Electrode Conductor: Revised to conform with *NEC Style Manual*.

Hazardous (Classified) Locations: Term and cross-reference have been deleted to conform with the scope of Article 100.

Header: Term and cross-reference have been deleted to conform with the scope of Article 100.

Hermetic Refrigerant Motor-Compressor: Term and cross-reference have been deleted to conform with the scope of Article 100.

Identified (FPN): Cross-references have been deleted to conform with the scope of Article 100.

Listed: Revised by adding "designated" to clarify intent.

Neutral Conductor: Term and cross-reference have been deleted to conform with the scope of Article 100.

Nonincendive Circuit: New definition and FPN have been added to be consistent with the scope of Article 100.

Outline Lighting: Definition revised to address all electric-discharge lighting, including fluorescent lighting.

Overload (FPN): FPN has been deleted to conform with the scope of Article 100.

Panelboard: Revised by adding "equipped" for clarity.

Premises Wiring (System): Revised to create consistent terminology within the *NEC*.

Projector, Nonprofessional: Term and cross-reference have been deleted to conform with the scope of Article 100.

Projector, Professional: Term and cross-reference have been deleted to conform with the scope of Article 100.

Raceway (FPN): Revised by adding "cablebus" to be consistent with Section 365-1.

Rated-Load Current: Term and cross-reference have been deleted to conform with the scope of Article 100.

Separately Derived System: New definition has been added to be consistent with the scope of Article 100.

Service Point: New definition has been added to Part A, so that the definition applies to systems both under and over 600 volts.

Switches, AC General-Use Snap Switch: Term and cross-reference have been deleted to conform with the scope of Article 100.

Switches, AC-DC General-Use Snap Switch: Term and cross-reference have been deleted to conform with the scope of Article 100.

Utilization Equipment: Revised to clarify that suitably listed electronic computer/data processing equipment is covered by this definition.

Welder, Electric, Actual Primary Current: Term and cross-reference have been deleted to conform with the scope of Article 100.

Welder, Electric, Rated Primary Current: Term and cross-reference have been deleted to conform with the scope of Article 100.

X-ray, Long-Time Rating: Term and cross-references have been deleted to conform with the scope of Article 100.

X-ray, Momentary Rating: Term and cross-references have been deleted to conform with the scope of Article 100.

B. Over 600 Volts, Nominal

Introduction: Revised editorially by changing "ones" to "definitions" for clarity.

Grounded, Effectively: Definition has been moved to Part A of Article 100 so it will apply to systems that are both under and over 600 V.

Switching Device: Revised to conform with *NEC Style Manual*.

Oil Cutout (Oil-Filled Cutout)): Revised grammatically.

ARTICLE 110—Requirements for Electrical Installations

Section 110-1: Moved to Section 90-5, since it is clearly introductory material.

Section 110-11 (FPN. No. 2): Added to warn that some cleaning and lubricating compounds can cause deterioration of some plastic insulators and structural components of electrical equipment.

Section 110-12(c): Added to require cleanup or replacement of damaged or contaminated electrical components.

Section 110-14(c): Added to bring attention to the temperature limitations associated with conductor terminations. Exceptions have been added to allow the use of some higher temperature ratings.

Section 110-16(a): Revised to make it clear that work space in front of electrical equipment shall be clear both vertically and horizontally from the floor to $6\frac{1}{2}$ feet in height.

Section 110-16(a), Exception No. 2: Now allows smaller spaces for voltages of 42 volts peak, instead of RMS, and also 60 volts dc.

Section 110-16(e), Exception: Deleted to recognize the need for illumination for all service equipment or panelboards in dwelling units.

Section 110-16(e) (FPN): Added to clarify that additional lighting fixtures are not required where an adjacent light source will provide the necessary illumination.

Section 110-16(f), Exception No. 1: Now allows only service equipment or panelboards not exceeding 200 amperes in existing dwelling units to have reduced headroom.

Section 110-22: Now requires identified replacement component marking on enclosures for series rated systems.

Section 110-31: Revised for clarity and fence height reduced to 7 feet. FPN No. 3 was added to explain that the 7-foot fence can be composed of 6 feet of fence material plus an extension of 1 foot or more utilizing three or more strands of barbed wire.

Section 110-33, Exception No. 2: "Panelboard" has been deleted and replaced with "control panels."

Sections 110-34(b) and (c): The word "energized" was changed to "live" to be consistent with the new definition of "live" in the *NEC Style Manual*. The warning signs were required to be labeled "Danger—High Voltage—Keep Out" to be consistent with Sections 230-203, 710-43, and 710-45.

Chapter 2—Wiring and Protection

ARTICLE 210—Branch Circuits

Section 210-2: Revised to bring attention to other specific-purpose branch circuit applications included in the *NEC*.

Section 210-3: Revised to replace "classification" with "rating," since this is the term used in other sections of the Code.

Section 210-4(a)(FPN): New FPN added to address possible high harmonic neutral currents of computer systems.

Section 210-4(d)(FPN): Section references added to remind *Code* users that the color orange is already designated for high leg marking.

Section 210-6(c)(2): Added to create enforceable requirements for autotransformer sizing, thermal limits, overcurrent protection, and listing.

Section 210-7(c): Revised editorially to (1) include other wiring methods and (2) to use proper term from Article 100.

Section 210-7(d): Second paragraph added to require replacement receptacles to be GFCI protected if required to be GFCI protected elsewhere in this *Code*.

Section 210-7(d), Exception: In second to last sentence, "-type receptacle" deleted because ground-fault protection need not be exclusively a receptacle-type GFCI.

Receptacles protected by GFCIs are required to be marked "GFCI protected."

Section 210-8(a)(2), Exception No. 2: Revised to exclude single or duplex receptacles for a stationary, cord- and plug-connected appliance from requiring GFCI protection where located within a dedicated space in a garage.

Section 210-8(a)(3): First paragraph revised by deleting "dwelling unit and," since a receptacle located outdoors at grade level must be protected by a GFCI even if the house is elevated on pilings.

Section 210-8(a)(4): New paragraph added to define unfinished basements.

Section 210-8(a)(5): Revised to require GFCI protection of wet bar sinks.

Section 210-8(b)(1): First paragraph revised to encompass all bathrooms located in other than dwelling units. Second paragraph revised to provide the definition of a bathroom pertaining to the entire Article 210.

Section 210-8(b)(2): Added to require GFCI protection of receptacles on roofs.

Section 210-9 and Exception No. 1: Revised to improve syntax by incorporating the first exception into the body of the requirement.

Section 210-9(FPN): Deleted.

Section 210-9, Exception No. 2: Added to address autotransformers in industrial occupancies and allow the connection to supply 600 volts from a 480-volt system or 480 volts from a 600-volt system under qualified maintenance.

Section 210-10: Revised to include references for double-pole switched lampholders and for electric-discharge lamp auxiliary equipment switching devices.

Section 210-21(b)(1), Exception: Added to allow the use of a receptacle with a lower ampere rating than the branch-circuit rating for motor circuits consisting of portable motors rated at $1/3$ horsepower or less.

Section 210-22(a): Revised to conform with *NEC Style Manual*.

Section 210-22(c): Revised to note that 125 percent of the continuous load plus the noncontinuous load applies only to the overcurrent device.

Section 210-24: Revised to clarify usage limitations of dwelling unit branch circuits. Public or common area lighting, central alarm, signal, communications, or other needs shall not be supplied from a dwelling unit panelboard.

Table 210-24: Unnecessary insulation types were removed from the table heading.

Section 210-50(c): Heading revised to apply to all appliance outlets in addition to laundry outlets. "Receptacle" inserted between "appliance" and "outlets" to indicate that receptacle outlets are the type covered.

Section 210-52(a): Revised to include railings among fixed room dividers.

Section 210-52(b)(1), Exception No. 4: Added to allow a circuit to feed a receptacle for motor loads in the small appliance area.

Section 210-52(b)(1), Exception No. 5: Added to allow ignition systems and clock timers for ranges to be fed from the small appliance circuits.

Section 210-52(c): Revised to clarify receptacle locations for counter tops, islands, and peninsular counter areas and to prohibit their installation in a face-up position in counter tops.

Section 210-52(d): Revised to require a receptacle adjacent to each basin in a bathroom.

Section 210-52(e): Revised to address need for two outdoor receptacles, front and back, in one- and two-family dwellings.

Section 210-63: "Rooftop" added to heading. Dimension revised from 75 feet to 25 feet.

Section 210-70(a): Deleted "only" in the second paragraph to allow a lighting outlet controlled by a light switch to be installed for any attic, underfloor space, utility room, or basement, whether or not it is used for storage or contains equipment requiring servicing.

Section 210-70(a)(FPN): Revised to clarify that a vehicle door in any garage is not an outdoor entrance and does not require a lighting outlet.

Section 210-70(c): Revised to require any serviceable equipment to have illumination. "Light" replaced by "wall" in the second sentence to clarify the intent to require a wall switch at the point of entry to the attic or underfloor space.

ARTICLE 215—Feeders

Sections 215-2 and 215-(2)(b): "Lower" changed to "less" for conformance with Section 215-2(a).

Section 215-8: Revised because the conductor is grounded, not neutral.

Section 215-10, Exception: Revised to comply with the mandatory rule requirement of Section 90-5.

ARTICLE 220—Branch-Circuit, Feeder, and Service Calculations

Article 220, Title: Revised to include "service."

Section 220-1: Scope revised to conform to new article title.

Section 220-3(c)(5): Added to reference Section 410-102, which provides requirements for track lighting circuit calculations.

Section 220-22 and (FPN No. 2): Section revised to prohibit reduction in ampacity of a grounded conductor in a 3-wire circuit supplied from a 4-wire, 3-phase, wye-connected system. Former FPN is now FPN No. 1. New FPN No. 2 added to address possible high harmonic neutral currents found in computers and other similar electronic loads.

Section 220-36: Deleted "and sub-feeder," since this term is not defined.

Table 220-36: Revised by adding "remainder" to Table 220-36. The calculation method now requires loads up to 325 kVa to be figured at 80 percent for total electric or 100 percent for those that aren't total electric, and any loads in excess of 325 kVa shall be figured at 50 percent demand for total electric or 70 percent for those not total electric.

ARTICLE 225—Outside Branch Circuits and Feeders

Section 225-1: Scope revised for grammar and clarity and to more clearly reflect intent and content of Article 225.

Section 225-8: Restructured by relocating former text to Section 225-8 (a) and adding new Sections 225-8(b) and (c), which were formerly Section 230-84. The require-

ments of Sections 230-71 and 230-72 were added to require grouping of the disconnects on a particular feeder.

Section 225-9 and (FPN): Revised to address all Article 240 feeder overcurrent protection requirements. FPN added to reference overcurrent device access.

Section 225-18: "Overhead spans" added to clarify the requirement is for clearance for overhead conductors. "Open multiconductor cables" was added to cover cables used for overhead drops. The new wording added to the 12-foot clearance requirement now includes residential property.

Section 225-19(a): Revised for specificity and to conform with Section 225-18 revisions.

Section 225-19(a), Exception No. 4: Added to allow a vertical clearance of 3 feet for the final conductor span attached to the side of a building.

Section 225-19(d): Second paragraph added to ensure that overhead branch circuits and feeders shall not be installed beneath openings where materials are moved.

Section 225-26: Revised to clarify that no vegetation, live or dead, shall be used for support of overhead wires.

ARTICLE 230—Services

Section 230-9: First paragraph revised to clarify that requirement applies to windows designed to be opened. Second paragraph revised by adding word "overhead" to define the type of service conductors.

Section 230-10: Former Section 230-201 moved to indicate that the service point applies to all services, both above and below 600 V.

Section 230-23(c): "(Neutral)" deleted because requirement applies to any grounded conductor in a service drop.

Section 230-24(a): Revised to clarify that the 8-foot measurement to the service-drop conductors is from the roof surface.

Section 230-24(a), Exception No. 3: Revised to increase flexibility for service-drop terminations by allowing up to 6 feet of service-drop conductors (4 feet horizontally) to pass above the roof overhang.

Section 230-24(a), Exception No. 4: Added to allow a vertical clearance of 3 feet for the final conductor span attached to the side of a building.

Section 230-24(b): Revised to conform with Section 225-18, since requirements are identical and consistent with that section.

Section 230-28(FPN): Added to clarify that only power service-drop conductors may be attached to an electrical service mast.

Section 230-31(c): Deleted "(neutral)," since requirement applies to any grounded conductor in a service lateral.

Section 230-42(a), Exception: Term "ampacity" replaced by "current" to comply with the *NEC Style Manual* definition.

Sections 230-42(b)(1) and (2): Revised to clarify intent that a 3-wire system be installed.

Section 230-42(c): Deleted "(neutral)," since requirement applies to any grounded conductor in a service entrance.

Section 230-43: "Liquidtight flexible metal conduit" added to allow its use as a wiring method used to enclose service-entrance conductors. Section references deleted to avoid confusion caused by referencing only some applicable *Code* sections.

Section 230-54(e): "Openings" used to accommodate slot-type openings. "Different potential" rather than "opposite polarity" used to describe conductors of different phases.

Section 230-66: Added to address the need for marking service equipment as being suitable for use as service equipment.

Section 230-82(FPN): Added to clarify that individual meter socket enclosures are not required to be suitable for use as service equipment.

Section 230-84: Moved to become revised Section 225-8.

Section 230-90(a), Exception No. 3: Revised to clarify that up to six disconnects are permitted, provided the calculated load in accordance with Article 220 does not exceed the ampacity of the service conductors and that the sum of the six disconnecting means is permitted to exceed the ampacity of the service conductors.

Sections 230-91(b) and (c): Section 230-91(b) deleted, since provisions apply to branch circuits and feeders and are covered by Section 225-9.

Section 230-92: "Readily" added to correlate with Section 240-24(a) and to clarify that these branch-circuit overcurrent devices must be capable of being reached quickly for operation, renewal, or inspections.

Section 230-95, Exception Nos. 1 and 2: Relocated from Section 230-95(a) to Section 230-95, since these exceptions apply to the entire section.

Section 230-200: Definition of service point moved to Article 100.

Section 230-201: "Service Conductors" moved to become new Section 230-10 to apply to both over 600 volts and 600 volts or less.

Section 230-205(a), Exception: "Service" replaced by "feeder" to identify these conductors as feeders.

Section 230-205(a)(FPN): Deleted due to redundancy.

Section 230-205(b): Requires the service disconnecting means to be capable of closing and withstanding the maximum short-circuit current available the supply terminals.

Section 230-208(b)(2): "Service" replaced by "feeder" to identify these conductors as feeders.

Section 230-209: Revised so that arrester location is determined by electrical design engineers.

Section 230-211: "Wood" replaced by "combustible" to broaden application and to correlate with Section 384-7.

ARTICLE 240—Overcurrent Protection

Section 240-3: Rewritten and reorganized to convert important exceptions into direct requirements for better understanding. Additional revision permits fire protective signaling circuits to be protected against overcurrent in accordance with Article 760.

Section 240-6: Revised editorially and rearranged to conform with other areas of the *Code* and correspond with *NEC Style Manual*.

Section 240-8, Exception: "Approved" replaced by "listed," to ensure the fuses or circuit breakers that are factory-assembled in parallel are also listed as a unit.

Section 240-20(b), Exception: Revised to clarify that, in grounded systems, individual circuit breakers with handle ties are permitted for line-to-line loads on single-phase circuits, 3-wire dc circuits, or lighting or appliance branch circuits for 4-wire, 3-phase systems having a grounded neutral.

Section 240-21: Rewritten and reorganized to convert exceptions into direct requirements. Exception No. 1, which covered the protection of smaller conductors, was deleted.

Section 240-21(c): Feeder taps not over 25 feet long no longer requires tap conductors to be not less than ⅓ of the rating of conductors from which they are tapped. Also, tap conductors are permitted to be enclosed in a raceway or protected from physical damage.

Section 240-21(e): Feeder taps over 25 feet long was revised similarly to Section 240-21(c).

Section 240-21(j): The sum of the ratings of the overcurrent devices is not permitted to exceed the ampacity of the secondary conductors.

Section 240-21(m): This new section permits outside conductors tapped to a feeder or connected to a transformer secondary to be protected by the disconnect and overcurrent device at the building.

Section 240-24(c)(FPN): Added to provide further information on exposure to physical damage from deteriorating agents.

Section 240-24(e): Added to clarify that overcurrent devices shall not be located in bathrooms.

Section 240-32: Revised to correlate with Section 373-2(a). The ¼-inch air space requirement and the damp or wet location identification requirement was deleted from this section, since Section 373-2(a) already contains this information.

Section 240-60(a), Exception: Revised to allow these fuses on single-phase circuits where the line-to-neutral voltage does not exceed 300 volts.

Section 240-83(e)(FPN): Revised for clarification, and to ensure that breakers are not used in circuits that exceed the circuit breaker's voltage rating.

ARTICLE 250—Grounding

Section 250-1(FPN No. 1): Second sentence revised to clarify that a low impedance path for fault current is necessary to facilitate the operation of overcurrent devices from the point of the fault through an equipment grounding conductor to the system grounded conductor back to the system supply.

Section 250-1(FPN No. 2): Revised to emphasize that bonding and grounding are separate and distinct operations, but that both are necessary for safety.

Section 250-5(FPN): Added to provide a direct reference to the use of a corner-grounded delta system transformer connection.

Section 250-5(b)(3): Revised by adding "winding."

Sections 250-6(a)(1) and (b)(2): Revised editorially to conform with *NEC Style Manual*.

Section 250-7(c): Added to reference that in accordance with Article 668, electrolytic cell circuits are not required to be grounded.

Sections 250-21(b) and (b)(1): Revised to emphasize that not all of the grounding connections can be discontinued and that an effective grounding path must still be provided.

Section 250-23(b)(FPN): Revised to conform with *NEC Style Manual*.

Sections 250-24(c)(1), (2), and (3) and Exception No. 1: "Second" replaced by "separate," since more than two buildings may be involved in the installation. Section 250-24(c)(3) revised, since it is not necessary to install a junction box for grounding if another appropriate enclosure, such as a panelboard or switchboard, is located properly and can be used for the required grounding.

Section 250-24(d): Revised to include bonding requirements of enclosures for grounding electrode conductors as covered in Section 250-92(b).

Section 250-26(a): Revised to include Section 250-23(a), Exception No. 5, to ensure that where a panelboard or switchboard has a wire or busbar main bonding jumper from the neutral to the equipment grounding bar or bus, the appropriate connection to the system grounding conductor is to the grounding terminal block so that ground-fault detection is not desensitized.

Section 250-26(a), Exception No. 1: Revised to include Class 2 and Class 3 circuits.

Section 250-26(b), Exception No. 1: Revised to include Class 2 and Class 3 circuits, and editorially for clarity.

Section 250-27(b): Second paragraph added for sizing neutral conductors for high-impedance grounding systems.

Section 250-32, Exception: Added to allow underground metal elbows that are at least 18 inches deep and enclosing service conductors to be ungrounded.

Section 250-33, Exception No. 4: Added to allow underground metal elbows that are at least 18 inches deep and enclosing other than service conductors to be ungrounded.

Section 250-43: First paragraph clarified to avoid conflict with Section 250-43(k), since submersible pumps are not normally exposed, and a new Section 250-43(l) added.

Section 250-43(a), Exception: Revised by adding "from ground" for clarification.

Section 250-43(l): Added to require that metal well casings be bonded to the pump circuit equipment grounding conductor.

Section 250-45(c): Revised to define application of grounding for various types of tools.

Section 250-45(d): Revised to define application of grounding for various types of tools.

Section 250-45(d), Exception No. 2: Revised to more clearly define the types of tools that are not required to be grounded.

Section 250-50, Exception: Revised to permit the grounding conductor of a grounding-type receptacle outlet to be grounded to any accessible point on the grounding electrode system, in accordance with Section 250-81, and no longer allows this connection to the water piping system unless connected within 5 feet of the point of entrance of the water system to the building.

Section 250-51: Deleted last three words in first paragraph, which were redundant.

Section 250-53(a)(FPN): Revised to conform with *NEC Style Manual*.

Section 250-53(b) and Exception Nos. 1 and 2: Section was revised to specify that the service-disconnect enclosure and the equipment grounding conductor must be connected to the grounded conductor at each service disconnect. Exception No. 1 was added to allow a single grounded conductor to be run to an assembly that has multiple disconnects and is listed for use as service equipment. The grounded conductor must be bonded to the assembly enclosure. Former Exception No. 1 was renumbered as Exception No. 2.

Section 250-57(b), Exception Nos. 3 and 4: New Exception No. 3 added to permit equipment grounding conductors to run separately from the circuit conductors, as provided in the exception to Sections 250-50(a) and (b). Former Exception No. 3 renumbered as Exception No. 4 and revised editorially to address the concept of more than one equipment grounding conductor in a multiconductor cable.

Section 250-71(a)(1): Revised to add "cablebus framework" as another wiring method for services.

Section 250-71(a)(3): New second sentence added to require bonding at each end of a metallic raceway or armor enclosing a grounding electrode conductor and at all intervening boxes or enclosures.

Section 250-71(b)(3): Existing paragraph revised to specify bonding material as copper or other corrosion-resistant material. New second paragraph added to also require the accessible intersystem bonding means at separate buildings or mobile homes where the electrical system is not a service.

Section 250-72(b): Revised editorially for clarity.

Section 250-74, Exception No. 4: Revised to specify that termination of the isolated equipment grounding conductor is to be within the same building or structure.

Section 250-74, Exception No. 4(FPN): Revised to include "outlet box."

Section 250-75, Exception: Revised to clarify that only an equipment enclosure supplied by a branch circuit is permitted to be isolated and that the listed nonmetallic raceway fittings must be located at the point of attachment of the raceway to the enclosure. Other wiring, raceways, or equipment beyond that equipment is not permitted.

Section 250-79(b): Revised to clarify that a screw is required to be identified with green color where a main bonding jumper is a screw only.

Section 250-79(d): Last sentence revised to include bonding of cable armor and moved to a separate paragraph to clarify that the bonding jumper addressed is not the same nor is it necessarily sized the same as the one specified in the first sentence of Section 250-79(d).

Section 250-81 and Exception Nos. 1 and 2: New sentence added to prohibit the use of interior metal water piping located more than 5 feet from the point of entrance of the building as a conductor to interconnect electrodes and the grounding electrode conductor. Section 250-92(b) now included for further requirements for bonding of enclosures for grounding electrode conductors. Former exception is now Exception No. 1 and is revised to allow two splicing methods. In addition, the restriction of this exception to commercial and industrial locations has been deleted. New Exception No. 2 added to allow industrial/commercial locations with qualified maintenance personnel to connect to the water piping system along the entire length if the piping system is exposed.

Section 250-81(a) and Exception: Deleted interior metal water piping as a bonding connection for the supplemental electrode. New exception added to allow the connection of the supplemental electrode to the interior metal water piping system as covered in Section 250-81, Exception No. 2.

Section 250-81(c): Revised to clarify that bare, zinc galvanized, or electrically conductive coated rebars are suitable.

Section 250-83(c)(2): Revised to clarify that stainless steel rods of less than $\frac{5}{8}$ inch must be listed.

Section 250-86(FPN No. 1): Revised to conform with *NEC Style Manual.*

Section 250-91(a), Exception No. 3: Revised to clarify that a splice is permitted using listed irreversible compression-type connectors or exothermic welding processes. In addition, the commercial/industrial location restriction has been deleted.

Section 250-91(b)(7): Revised by adding "copper" to correlate with Section 330-22.

Section 250-91(b), Exception No. 1: First paragraph revised to require listed products. Revised item a to limit total combined length of flexible metallic raceways in a ground return path to 6 feet.

Section 250-91(b), Exception No. 2: First paragraph revised to required listed products and to clarify that the total combined length of liquidtight flexible metal raceways in a ground return path is limited to 6 feet.

Section 250-92(a): Second paragraph revised to clarify that neither insulated or bare aluminum conductors shall be used in direct contact with masonry, earth, or corrosive conditions.

Section 250-92(b): Revised by adding "electrode" to match heading.

Table 250-94(FPN): Revised to conform with *NEC Style Manual.*

Section 250-95: Second and fourth paragraphs revised to include cables. Fifth paragraph revised to a permissive rather than a mandatory statement.

Section 250-95, Exception No. 3: Revised to include other section requirements.

Section 250-114, Exception: Added so the isolated equipment grounding conductors permitted by Section 250-74, Exception No. 4 are not required to be connected to the box or the other equipment grounding conductors.

Section 250-115: Revised by replacing "fitting" with "electrode" for consistency and use of correct term.

Section 250-118: Revised to allow connection of the equipment grounding conductor by a device designed so cleaning of the surface is not necessary.

Chapter 3—Wiring Methods and Materials

ARTICLE 300 — Wiring Methods

Section 300-1(a), Exception No. 1: Revised to conform with *NEC Style Manual.*

Section 300-3(b), Exception Nos. 1 and 2: New Exception No. 1 added to address conductors of single-conductor Type MI cable. New Exception No. 2 added to address column-type panelboards. Former exception renumbered as Exception No. 3.

Section 300-3(c)(1): First sentence revised for clarity and to conform with *NEC Style Manual.* Second sentence revised to clarify that the conductors shall have an insulation rating equal to the maximum voltage applied to any conductor.

Section 300-3(c)(1)(FPN): Reference updated.

Section 300-4(b): Heading revised to specify that the type of cable covered was nonmetallic-sheathed cable.

Section 300-4(b)(1): New heading added.

Section 300-4(b)(2): New heading added.

Table 300-5: First column, sixth-row revised to clarify that the burial depth is for dwelling driveways used for dwelling-related purposes. Fourth column (now labeled "3") heading revised for clarity and to specify approved raceway. Column numbers added for ease of identification. Note 4 revised by replacing "conduit" with "wiring method."

Section 300-6(c): Revised to clarify that requirement is for exposed installations.

Section 300-6(c), Exception: Added to clarify when airspace is not needed.

Section 300-10, Exception No. 1: Reference updated.

Section 300-10, Exception No. 3: Added to correlate with Section 250-75 for reduction of electrical noise.

Section 300-11(a): New second and third paragraphs clarify support wire specifications of fire-rated and non-fire-rated floor or roof/ceiling assemblies.

Section 300-11(b), Exception No. 3: Reference updated.

Section 300-15(a), Exception No. 1: References updated.

Section 300-15(b), Exception No. 3: Deleted, since rosettes were deleted from the 1990 Code. Subsequent exceptions renumbered.

Section 300-15(b), Exception No. 6: Former Exception No. 7 renumbered and references updated.

Section 300-15(d): Added to allow listed integral junction boxes or wiring compartments in lieu of a separate box.

Section 300-19(a): Revised to clarify that intermediate support of conductors must be provided.

Section 300-21(FPN): Added to clarify listing limitations and to provide further assistance in complying with firestop requirements.

Section 300-22(FPN): Reference updated.

Section 300-22(c), Exception No. 5: Deleted "or equipment" to clarify that only wiring may pass through these spaces.

Section 300-23: Added to require access be provided behind panels designed to allow access, such as suspended ceiling panels.

Section 300-37: Added to clarify burial depth as required by Section 710-4(b).

ARTICLE 305—Temporary Wiring

Section 305-4(b): Revised by deleting "multiconductor" to better correlate with Table 400-4, since single conductor cords or cables are available.

Section 305-4(g): Revised by changing "metal-jacketed" to "metal-sheathed."

Section 305-4(i): Added to require that cables entering enclosures containing devices be secured to the box with the proper fittings.

Section 305-6(a): New last sentence added for GFCI protection for receptacles that are part of the permanent wiring work but used for temporary electric power.

ARTICLE 310—Conductors for General Wiring

Section 310-3, Exception Nos. 1 and 2: Replaced by exception that makes general reference to where permitted or required elsewhere in the Code.

Section 310-4, Exception No. 3: Revised editorially for clarity.

Section 310-4: Fourth paragraph revised editorially.

Section 310-5: Revised editorially.

Section 310-5, Exception No. 8: Deleted to conform with Table 310-13 since asbestos-type insulation was deleted from the 1990 *NEC*. Subsequent exceptions renumbered.

Section 310-7(FPN No. 1): Former FPN information now included in new FPN Nos. 1 and 2 to Section 310-7, since this section pertains to direct burial conductors.

Section 310-10(FPN): Revised to indicate that there are now allowable ampacity tables and true ampacity tables, including tables in Appendix B, in which losses and factors are considered.

Section 310-11(d) and (FPN): Added to allow optional markings for special characteristics of cable materials.

Section 310-12(a), Exception No. 1: Deleted, since product is no longer manufactured. Subsequent exceptions renumbered.

Section 310-12(b), Exception No. 2c: Editorially revised to add "colored."

Section 310-12(c), Exception: Added to reference Section 200-7 to indicate that ungrounded conductors can also be white for certain applications.

Section 310-13: Table references updated.

Table 310-13: Replaced "Heat-Resistant Rubber" with "Heat-Resistant Cross-Linked Synthetic Polymer" to recognize currently available material. Insulation Type XHH added. Type V cable deleted. Second sentence of triple obelisk footnote deleted, due to redundancy. In mineral insulation (metal sheathed) section, under the "AWG or kcmil" column, thickness changed from 3-250 to 3-500, and new thickness 18-16 added with a footnote to define the circuit types covered. For Types RH, RHH, RHW, and RHW-2, "rubber" replaced by "cross-linked synthetic polymer."

Section 310-15: Former Section 310-15(b), FPN No. 3, which deals with voltage drop considerations, has been expanded and now follows the first paragraph of Section 310-15. Section 310-15(a) has introduced allowable ampacity of Tables 310-16 through 310-19 as application tables for use in determining conductor sizes based upon load calculations in accordance with Article 220.

310-15(c)(FPN): Reference to Section 110-14(c) for conductor termination limitations has been added.

Table 310-16: Table heading revised to reflect use of allowable ampacities. Insulation Types MI, RHW-2, THW-2, THWN-2, USE-2, XHH, XHHW-2, and ZW-2 added. Type V cable and its entire column deleted, since product is no longer manufactured. Temperature ratings in °F column under correction factors revised to cover complete temperature ranges.

Table 310-17: Table heading revised to reflect use of allowable ampacities. Insulation Types THW-2, THWN-2, USE-2, XHH, and ZW-2 added. Temperature ratings in °F column under correction factors revised to cover complete temperature ranges. Type MI insulation deleted from aluminum or copper-clad aluminum, since it is only available in copper. Type V cable and its entire column deleted, since product is no longer manufactured.

Table 310-18: Table heading revised to reflect use of allowable ampacities. Temperature ratings in °F column under correction factors revised to cover complete temperature ranges.

Table 310-19: Table heading revised to reflect use of allowable ampacities. Temperature ratings in °F column under correction factors revised to cover complete temperature ranges.

Notes to Ampacity Tables of 0 to 2000 Volts:

Note 3 and Table: Revised to include feeders and service lateral conductors and to clarify that services are not always in dwelling units. Conductors utilized as service-entrance conductors, service lateral conductors, and feeders that supply the total load to a dwelling unit may use the conductor sizes shown in the table. Deleted "service" in third column heading in table to broaden application.

Note 7 (FPN): Revised by adding "allowable" to indicate that the referenced table does not contain true ampacities, which consider loading factors, loss factors, and all other thermal factors.

Note 8: Deleted the term "amapcity" in the title.

Note 8(a) and Table: Added the term "current-carrying," to the table to cover only those conductors actually carrying current. Column A has been moved to new Table B-310-11 as referenced in the new FPN following Exception No. 5. Exception No. 5 allows the use of Table B-310-11 under engineering supervision. The FPN for the former Column A formula is also part of Table B-310-11. Former Column B is now the new table for Note 8(a), with the number of conductors no longer limited to 60.

Note 10: Note 10 (a) revised for clarity. Note 10(c) revised to comply with Section 220-22; "nonlinear loads" added for specificity.

Table 310-65: Deleted, since product is no longer manufactured.

Table 310-66: Deleted, since product is no longer manufactured.

Table 310-67: Added a medium-voltage ampacity table to cover cables triplexed in air.

Table 310-68: Added a medium-voltage ampacity table to cover cables triplexed in air.

ARTICLE 318—Cable Trays

Section 318-2: Added "and raceways" for consistency with Section 318-3(a)(1) and to recognize that cable trays often do support raceways.

Section 318-3(a)(1): Expanded and revised to clarify which wiring methods are permitted to be used with a cable support system.

Section 318-3(b): Revised editorially for consistency throughout Article 318.

Section 318-3(b)(1): Section 318-3(b) allows any size cables listed for cable tray use to be used in ventilated cable tray. Deleted "or in a ventilated trough" cable tray in the second sentence of Section 318-3(b)(1) to avoid conflict between the two sections.

Section 318-3(b)(1), Exception Nos. 1 and 2: Former exception renumbered Exception No. 1. New Exception No. 2 added to allow single conductors as small as No. 4, used as equipment grounding conductors, to be installed in ladder cable tray.

Section 318-6(a)(FPN): Added to clarify that cable trays are not required to be installed as a complete system and often are not continuous between separate trays or between trays and the equipment. Adequate bonding must still be provided.

Section 318-6(j) and (FPN): New Section 318-6(j) added to allow incidental support for raceways from cable trays. FPN added for raceway support restrictions. The cable tray system must be designed such that it will physically support these attached raceways.

Section 318-7(b)(3): Deleted "-type," since it is redundant.

Section 318-9: "Nominal" deleted.

Section 318-9(d): Heading revised to comply with *NEC Style Manual*.

Table 318-10: In second asterisk note, "MCM" changed to "kcmil" for *NEC* consistency.

Section 318-10: "Nominally" deleted.

Section 318-10(a)(4): Revised grammatically.

Section 318-10(b): Revised editorially for consistency throughout Article 318, and to include 3-inch ventilated channel cable trays.

Section 318-11: Text, excluding heading, relocated as new first sentence of Section 318-11(b) so that it applies only to multiconductor cables and not to single-conductor cables.

Section 318-11(a), Exception No. 2 and (FPN): Exception No. 2 revised to clarify ampacity limitations. FPN added to reference Table B-310-3.

Section 318-11(b): New first sentence was formerly introductory paragraph of Section 318-11.

Section 318-11(b)(4) and (FPN): Section 310-15(b) referenced and FPN reference to Table B-310-2 added.

Section 318-12: "Nominally" deleted.

Section 318-13(b)(3): New Tables 310-67 and 310-68 referenced for allowable ampacities. These new tables provide the ampacity values of single-conductor, medium-voltage cables (2-35 kV) where installed triplexed in uncovered cable tray with maintained spacing. The ampacity limit of 105 percent is no longer required, since it was a factor used with Tables 310-71 and 310-72 and specific tables have been provided in the current Code.

ARTICLE 320—Open Wiring on Insulators

Section 320-6: Deleted "rosette" to comply with deletion of term in the 1990 *NEC*.

Section 320-7: Revised editorially.

Section 320-13(FPN): Revised editorially to conform with *NEC Style Manual*.

ARTICLE 321—Messenger Supported Wiring

Section 321-3(a): Revised editorially.

Section 321-3(b)(1): Revised editorially.

ARTICLE 325—Integrated Gas Spacer Cable Type IGS

Section 325-22: Revised editorially.

ARTICLE 326—Medium Voltage Cable Type MV

Section 326-2: Revised editorially.

ARTICLE 328—Flat Conductor Cable Type FCC

Section 328-6(a): Revised editorially.

Section 328-35(b): Revised grammatically by adding "shall" to ensure that this is a requirement.

ARTICLE 330—Mineral-Insulated, Metal-Sheathed Cable Type MI

Section 330-13: First paragraph revised editorially. New Sections 330-13(1) and (2) added for bend radii determinations. Section 330-13(2) now covers bending radius of ten times the diameter for conductors larger than 250 kcmil.

Section 330-16: Added to require grouping of all phase conductors and neutral conductors when using single-conductor cables to minimize induced voltage on the sheath. Also, where single-conductor cables enter ferrous enclosures, it is necessary to comply with Section 300-20 to prevent heating from induction.

ARTICLE 331—Electrical Nonmetallic Tubing

Section 331-3(1): Revised to better identify that ENT can be installed either exposed or concealed within walls, floors, or ceilings in any building not exceeding three floors above grade.

Section 331-3(2): Revised to indicate that, in any building exceeding three floors, ENT shall be concealed behind a thermal barrier with at least a 15-minute finish rating.

Section 331-3(5): Added new wording that clarifies that ENT installed above a suspended ceiling in a building that does not exceed three floors above grade is permitted to be installed without a thermal barrier in a building.

Section 331-3(7): New section added to allow ENT to be installed in wet locations indoors or in a concrete slab on or below grade.

Section 331-4(7): Revised to reference new Section 331-3(7) for wet locations.

Section 331-5(b): Dimension revised to permit the use of ENT sizes to a maximum of 2 inches.

Section 331-11 and Exception Nos. 1 and 2: New Exception No. 1 added to allow ENT to be supported at least every 3 feet by openings through framing members. New

Exception No. 2 added to allow ENT to be used in lengths not exceeding 6 feet from a fixture terminal for tap connections to lighting fixtures.

Section 331-13: Added "device boxes" to conform with previous Article 370 revisions.

Section 331-15: Added new last sentence for tubing with limited-smoke-producing characteristics.

ARTICLE 333—Armored Cable Type AC

Entire Article: Text reordered and new part titles added for clarity.

New Part Title: A. General

Section 333-1: Reference updated.

Section 333-3: Former text moved to new Section 333-22. New Section 333-3 is former Section 333-6(a) covering permitted uses of Type AC cable. Type ACL cable deleted, since it is no longer manufactured.

Section 333-4: Former text moved to new Section 333-19. New Section 333-4 is former Section 333-6(b) covering uses not permitted for Type AC cable.

Section 333-5 and Exception: Moved to new Section 333-20.

Section 333-6: Now covered in new Sections 333-3 and 333-4.

New Part Title: B. Installation

Section 333-7: Revised editorially for clarity.

Section 333-7, Exception No. 4: Added to reference Section 318-8(b) where Type AC cable is installed in cable trays.

Section 333-8: Heading revised to correlate with text subject.

Section 333-10: Heading and text revised to clarify that AC cable installed parallel to framing members must also comply with Section 300-4.

Section 333-12(b): Heading and text revised to address AC cable installed parallel to framing members.

New Part Title: C. Construction Specifications

Section 333-19: Former Section 333-4.

Section 333-20 and Exception: Former Section 333-5 and exception.

Section 333-21: Added to require an adequate path for equipment grounding as required by Section 250-51.

Section 333-22: Moved from Section 333-3.

ARTICLE 334—Metal-Clad Cable Type MC

Section 334-10(a), Exception Nos. 1 and 2: Exception No. 1 added to require MC cable used as branch circuits to be secured within 12 inches from every outlet box, junction box, cabinet, or fitting in a dwelling unit. Exception No. 2 added to allow Type MC cable to be fished.

Section 334-10(f): Added to require compliance with Section 300-4.

Section 334-10(g): Added to provide reference for accessible attic or roof space installations.

Section 334-13, Exception Nos. 1 and 2: Former exception renumbered as Exception No. 1. New Exception No. 2 added to reference Table 402-5 for No. 18 and No. 16 conductors.

ARTICLE 336—Nonmetallic-Sheathed Cable Types NM and NMC

Section 336-10: Revised for correlation among articles with respect to the support of nonmetallic-sheathed cables.

Section 336-10(b): Revised to include Schedule 80 PVC rigid nonmetallic conduit for protection against physical damage.

Section 336-11: Revised to require compliance for Types NM and NMC cable protection as covered in Section 300-4.

Section 336-12: Revised to reference Section 300-4(d), and to delete "faces of the joists," since unfinished basements are subject to remodeling.

Section 336-15 and (FPN): Revised by adding "cable ties" to allow nonmetallic-sheathed cable to be secured by cable ties. Added last two sentences to prohibit two conductor cables from being stapled on edge and to require that cable be considered supported where run through holes in wooden joists, rafters, or studs. Added new FPN to reference Section 370-17(c) for support where nonmetallic boxes are used.

ARTICLE 337—Shielded Nonmetallic-Sheathed Cable Type SNM

Section 337-8: Revised editorially to conform with *NEC Style Manual*.

ARTICLE 338—Service-Entrance Cable Types SE and USE

Section 338-1: Revised grammatically.

Section 338-1(b), Exception: Added to clarify that Type USE cable is permitted for service laterals above ground outside of buildings to feed from below ground to a meter base above ground.

Section 338-1 (FPN Nos. 1 and 2): Former FPN renumbered as FPN No. 1 and revised to conform with *NEC Style Manual*. Added new FPN No. 2 to reference Section 330-5(d) for protection from physical damage.

Section 338-3(b): Deleted "interior" in second paragraph, since Type SE cable can be used in wet locations.

ARTICLE 340—Power and Control Tray Cable Type TC

Section 340-4: Added new Item (5) to permit Type TC cable for nonpower-limited fire protective signaling circuits, where in compliance with Section 760-16.

Section 340-7: Revised reference from "Section 400-5" to "Section 402-5," since it is more appropriate.

ARTICLE 343—Preassembled Cable in Nonmetallic Conduit

Article 343: New article added to address preassembled cable-in-conduit. Since the cable is removable after the conduit installation, the conduit must comply with all requirements for conductor fill and number of bends in a run.

ARTICLE 344—Underplaster Extensions

Entire Article: Deleted; its intent is now outdated or covered by other *NEC* articles.

ARTICLE 345—Intermediate Metal Conduit

Section 345-8: Conversion revised for proper translation.

Section 345-12 and (FPN): Former text revised for clarity and consistency with other conduit support language.

Added new last sentence to increase fastening distance to 5 feet where there is structural interference. Added new FPN to explain that support is provided by a bored or punched hole in a framing member.

Section 345-14: Added "device boxes" to reflect Article 370 title change.

ARTICLE 346—Rigid Metal Conduit

Section 346-1(b), Exception: Revised grammatically.

Section 346-5, Exception Nos. 1 and 2: Deleted Exception No. 1 for underplaster extensions due to deletion of Article 344. Exception No. 2 is now unnumbered.

Section 346-7(b): Conversion revised for proper translation.

Section 346-12 and (FPN): Former text revised for clarity and consistency with other conduit support language. Added new last sentence to increase fastening distance to 5 feet where there is structural interference. Added new FPN to explain that support is provided by a bored or punched hole in a framing member.

Section 346-14: Added "device boxes" to reflect Article 370 title change.

ARTICLE 347—Rigid Nonmetallic Conduit

Section 347-1: Revised to allow conduits that are listed for the purpose to be installed underground in continuous lengths from a reel.

Section 347-1(FPN): Deleted.

Section 347-2: Revised to require the use of listed conduit and fittings.

Section 347-3(a): Revised editorially and to reference Section 503-3(a), which also includes rigid nonmetallic conduit requirements for Class III locations.

Section 347-3(b), Exception: Added to permit, with restrictions, rigid nonmetallic conduit to support nonmetallic conduit bodies. These conduit bodies are not permitted to contain devices or support fixtures.

Section 347-8: Revised for clarity and consistency. Added last sentence to allow for thermal expansion and contraction.

Section 347-9, Exception: Added so that if the expansion or contraction is .25 inches or less in a straight run

between securely mounted items, an expansion joint is not required.

Section 347-16: Added "device boxes" to reflect Article 370 title change.

Section 347-17 and (FPN): Added new last sentence to section to permit surface marking for special characteristics. Added FPN to provide examples of these special markings.

ARTICLE 348—Electrical Metallic Tubing

Section 348-1: Added new item (5) to clarify that electrical metallic tubing is not permitted for the support of fixtures or other equipment.

Section 348-5(a), Exception Nos. 1 and 2: Deleted Exception No. 1 deleted for underplaster extensions due to deletion of Article 344. Exception No. 2 is now unnumbered.

Section 348-6(FPN): Revised editorially.

Section 348-9: Revised editorially.

Section 348-12: Revised for consistency with other articles that address support. "Fitting" was replaced with "termination," since couplings are defined in Article 100 as a fitting and supports 3 feet on either side of a coupling are not necessary.

Section 348-12, Exception: Revised to permit fastening of unbroken lengths to be increased in distance to 5 feet where structural members do not permit the 3-foot fastening.

Section 348-14: Added "device boxes" to reflect Article 370 title change.

ARTICLE 349—Flexible Metallic Tubing

Section 349-17: Added to address splices and taps and to reference Article 370 installation requirements.

ARTICLE 350—Flexible Metal Conduit

Section 350-2: Added new item (7) to prohibit the use of flexible metal conduit where subject to physical damage.

Section 350-3, Exception Nos. 1,2,3,4, and 5: Deleted Exception No. 1 for underplaster extensions due to deletion of Article 344 . Remaining exceptions renumbered.

Section 350-5, Exception No. 1: Added "an equipment" to help maintain consistency throughout the *Code*.

Section 350-5, Exception No. 2: Added "listed" to emphasize the requirement for listed flexible metal conduit as a grounding means.

Section 350-6: Moved second paragraph to Section 350-8, since angle connectors are fittings.

Section 350-8: Revised to include second paragraph of Section 350-6.

Section 350-9: Added to address trimming/finishing requirements for cut ends except where fittings that thread into the convolutions are used.

Section 350-10: Added to address splice and tap requirements.

ARTICLE 351—Liquidtight Flexible Metal Conduit and Liquidtight Flexible Nonmetallic Conduit

Section 351-4(a): Revised editorially to clarify that liquidtight flexible metal conduit is not required to be marked for exposed and concealed work.

Section 351-4(a)(3): Added to require liquidtight flexible metal conduit intended for direct burial to be listed and marked for that purpose.

Section 351-4(b)(2): Revised to conform with *NEC Style Manual*.

Section 351-7: Revised to include second paragraph from Section 351-10, since angle connectors are fittings.

Section 351-9, Exception No. 1: Revised editorially to specify the type of grounding conductor by adding "equipment."

Section 351-9, Exception No. 2: Added "listed" to allow only listed liquidtight flexible metal conduit as a grounding means, since the listed type has a copper shorting across the convolutions.

Section 351-10: Moved second paragraph to Section 351-7, since angle connectors are fittings.

Section 351-11: Added to address splice and tap requirements.

Section 351-23(b)(3), Exception: Revised to permit longer lengths where essential for required degree of flexibility.

Section 351-23(b)(4), Exception: Added to reference Section 600-31(a), Exception requirements for electric signs over 600 V.

Section 351-24, Exception Nos. 1, 2, and 3: Former exception now Exception No. 1. Added new Exception No. 2 to recognize safe use of ³/₈ inch liquidtight flexible nonmetallic conduit, with restrictions. Added new Exception No. 3 to allow ³/₈ inch for electric sign conductors on insulators where in accordance with Section 600-31(a).

Section 351-26: Revised to include angle connectors, since they are fittings.

Section 351-28: Former Section 351-27.

Section 351-29: Added to address splice and tap requirements.

Section 351-30: Added to address bend limitations.

ARTICLE 352—Surface Metal Raceways and Surface Nonmetallic Raceways

Section 352-9: Added to require a means for connecting an equipment grounding conductor when providing a transition from other wiring methods.

Section 352-21: Added new last sentence to recognize limited-smoke characteristics.

Section 352-28 and (FPN): Added new section for surface nonmetallic raceway extensions through dry walls, dry partitions, and dry floors. Added FPN to reference Section 353-3 for multioutlet assemblies.

Section 352-29: Added to address splice and tap requirements.

ARTICLE 362—Metal Wireways and Nonmetallic Wireways

Article 362: Title revised and new Part titles A and B added to address both metal and nonmetallic wireways.

New Part Title: A. Metal Wireways

Section 362, Exception: Revised editorially to conform with *NEC Style Manual*.

Section 362-5, Exception Nos. 2 and 3: Revised editorially.

Section 362-5(FPN): Revised editorially.

Section 362-11: Revised to permit cord pendant extensions.

New Part Title: Added "B. Nonmetallic Wireways" to cover nonmetallic wireways that are flame-retardant troughs with removable covers. It covers uses permitted and not permitted, size of conductors allowed, deflection of insulated conductors installed in the wireway, splices and taps within the wireway, support, expansion joint requirements, extensions from the wireway using any wiring method in Chapter 3, and the required marking with manufacturer's name and the cross-sectional area.

ARTICLE 363—Flat Cable Assemblies Type FC

Section 363-11: Revised to correct terminology for surface metal raceways.

ARTICLE 364—Busways

Section 364-4(a), Exception No. 1a: Revised to expand intent to include not only fixtures but also other loads.

Section 364-8: Revised first sentence to include "liquidtight flexible metal conduit" and "listed bus drop cable" as branch options. Revised second sentence both editorially and to specify that the length of the flexible cord assembly not exceed 6 feet from the busway plug-in device to the tension take-up device.

Section 364-10: Deleted "subfeeders" in the heading, since they are not defined in the *Code*.

Section 364-11 and Exception: Revised to require overcurrent protection where busways are reduced in ampacity. Added exception for industrial establishments and then only if the reduced ampacity busway does not exceed 50 feet and is at least $\frac{1}{3}$ the rating or setting of the overcurrent device feeding the busway.

Section 364-12: Revised heading and text by replacing "subfeeder" with "feeder," since the former term is not defined in the *Code*.

Section 364-14: Revised editorially for clarity and to conform with *NEC Style Manual*.

Section 364-25, Exception and (FPN): Relocated exception to follow first paragraph, since it applies only to the first paragraph. Added FPN to reference Section 300-21 firestopping requirements.

ARTICLE 370—Outlet, Device, Pull and Junction Boxes, Conduit Bodies and Fittings

Section 370-1: Deleted last sentence , since fittings such as capped elbows and service-entrance elbows are conduit bodies and should be subjected to the same requirements.

Section 370-5: Renumbered former Section 370-5 as Section 370-15. Added new Section 370-5 to address restrictions/requirements for short radius conduit bodies.

Section 370-15 and (FPN No. 1): Formerly Section 370-5. Updated cross-reference in FPN No. 1.

Section 370-16: Formerly Section 370-6. Updated cross reference in third paragraph.

Section 370-16(a): Updated table and section references.

Section 370-16(a)(1) and Exception: Updated table references. Revised second sentence to include "or equipment" for consistency with Section 210-4(b). Added new exception to address fixture canopy requirements.

Section 370-16(a)(2): Updated table and section references. Revised text to allow the deductions to be based on the largest conductor connected to the device or equipment supported by the yoke or strap.

Section 370-16(b): Updated table and section references. Revised text to allow the same deductions as in Section 370-16(a)(2).

Section 370-16(c): Revised first paragraph to exclude short radius conduit bodies, as described in Section 370-5, from requirement. Revised second paragraph to clarify that, if a splice or tap is to be made, the conduit body must be marked appropriately, and revised further to permit the use of the provisions in Section 370-16(b) for the maximum number of conductors allowed.

Section 370-17: Formerly Section 370-7.

Section 370-17(b): Deleted last sentence, since fittings such as capped elbows and service-entrance elbows are conduit bodies and should be subjected to the same requirements.

Section 370-17(c), Exception: Added new last sentence to clarify that multiple cable entries in a single knockout opening are permitted where using 2½ inch × 4 inch non-metallic boxes.

Sections 370-18, 370-19, 370-20, and 370-21: Formerly Sections 370-8, 370-9, 370-10, and 370-11, respectively.

Section 370-22 and Exception: Formerly Section 370-12. Revised exception editorially to clarify intent.

Section 370-23: Formerly Section 370-13. Updated reference from 370-13(h) to 370-23(g). Deleted Section 370-13(g), since material is covered adequately in (renumbered) Sections 370-23(d) and (e).

Section 370-23(d): Revised to clarify intent of support for the enclosure.

Section 370-23(e): Added "shall be considered to be adequately supported" to clarify the meaning of support for the enclosure.

Section 370-23(g): Formerly Section 370-13(h).

Sections 370-24, 370-25, 370-26, 370-27, and 370-28: Formerly Sections 370-14, 370-15, 370-17, and 370-18, respectively.

Section 370-28(a): Revised to address No. 4 or larger conductors, without specifying trade size.

Section 370-28(a)(3): Revised to include "conduit body(ies)," since the provisions of this section include conduit bodies.

Section 370-40: Formerly Section 370-20.

Section 370-40(b) and Exception Nos. 1 and 2: Added "zinc box" in the same category as aluminum. Added Exception Nos. 1 and 2 to allow thinner designs where based on appropriate testing and listing.

Section 370-41: Formerly Section 370-21. Revised to require listing where the cover is provided separately and is not part of box or fitting assembly, or is not made of the same material as the box or fitting.

Section 370-70: Updated cross-references.

Sections 370-71 and 370-72: Formerly Sections 370-51 and 370-52, respectively.

ARTICLE 373—Cabinets, Cutout Boxes, and Meter Socket Enclosures

Article Title: Revised to include meter socket enclosures.

Section 373-11(c): Replaced "subfeeder" with "feeder," since "subfeeder" is not defined in the *Code*.

ARTICLE 374—Auxiliary Gutters

Section 374-9(f): Added to reference Article 250 for grounding requirements.

ARTICLE 380—Switches

Section 380-4: Added new second sentence to prohibit a switch from being installed in a tub or shower space unless part of a listed assembly.

Section 380-8(a), Exception No. 3: Revised to allow height requirement to exceed 6½ feet for a hookstick operable isolating switch.

Section 380-10(b): Updated cross-reference.

Section 380-11: Revised to include reference to Section 240-83 for marking requirements.

Section 380-12: Added new last sentence to require metal face plates to have adequate grounding.

Section 380-14(b)(2): Revised editorially.

Section 380-17 and (FPN): FPN deleted and incorporated into the text to conform with *NEC Style Manual*.

ARTICLE 384—Switchboards and Panelboards

Section 384-3(d): Revised to clarify that not only load terminals but any terminal in a switchboard or panelboard is covered by requirement.

Section 384-4(FPN No. 4): Added to clarify that working space provisions in accordance with Section 110-16 still apply and prohibit equipment from occupying the space specified as working space.

Section 384-11, Exception: Revised for technical accuracy and specificity.

Section 384-16(c), Exception: Revised for consistency with Article 100 terminology; replaced "approved" with "listed."

Chapter 4—Equipment for General Use

ARTICLE 400—Flexible Cords and Cables

Table 400-4: Revised as follows: Cable Types AFC, AFPD, AFPO, AFS, and AFSJ deleted, since asbestos cords are no longer available. Type DP cable deleted, Type ETP elevator traveling cable added, since it is still manufactured; cable Types SEOO, SJEOO, and SVEOO added to include these listed flexible cords; for Types ET, ETLB, and ETT, outer covering requirements revised to allow protection equivalent to specified cotton; Types SC, SCE, and SCT cables added for flexible stage and lighting power (** footnote added for outer covering requirements).

Notes to Table 400-4:

Note 1: Deleted Type AFPO, since it is no longer available; revised editorially.

Note 2: Deleted former note , due to deletion of data processing cable, Type DP; former Note 3 is now Note 2; renumbered subsequent notes.

Note 3: Formerly Note 4.

Note 4: Formerly Note 5. Revised to include Types SC, SCE, and SCT cables, which were added to Table 400-4 for flexible stage and lighting power; and to include Type SEOO, which was added to Table 400-4, since it is a UL-listed flexible cord.

Note 5: Formerly Note 6. Revised to include ETP elevator traveling cable, as it appeared in NFPA 70-1987 and earlier editions; revised further to address optical fibers.

Note 6: Formerly Note 7. Revised to use consistent terminology throughout *NEC*.

Note 7: Formerly Note 8. Deleted cable Types AFC, AFPD, AFPO, AFS, and AFSJ, since they are no longer available.

Note 8: Formerly Note 9. Revised to include Type SEOO, which was added to Table 400-4. Revised editorially.

Note 9: Formerly Note 10.

Section 400-5: Revised first paragraph to indicate that Table 400-5(A) is for allowable ampacities and Table 400-5(B) is for ampacities. In the table following Section 400-5, Column A has been moved to Table B-310-11. Revised Column B, left side, last line, by changing "41 through 60" to "41 and above"; deleted Column B heading; asterisk notes, FPN, and formula to simplify procedures for adjusting the ampacity of multiple conductors in raceways and cables. Added second paragraph to address ultimate insulation temperature [formerly a note to Tables 400-5(A) and (B)]. Added exception to reference Section 310-15(b) for other loading conditions. Added FPN for other adjustment factors. Former second paragraph, now third, revised to clarify when a neutral conductor is not a current-carrying conductor. Former third paragraph, now fourth, revised editorially. Former fourth paragraph, now fifth, revised to correlate with changes to Section 220-22 in 1990 *NEC*. Former fifth and sixth paragraphs are now sixth and seventh, respectively.

Table 400-5(A): Revised title and obelisk note to indicate that these are allowable ampacities without all factors figured. Deleted asbestos types column and former single-asterisk note, since asbestos cords are no longer listed in these types. Remaining asterisk footnotes revised accordingly. Added FPN to clarify table's intent. "Note" relocated as new second paragraph of Section 400-5.

Table 400-5(B): Revised title and first footnote to include cable Types SC, SCE, and SCT for flexible stage and lighting power. First footnote further revised to ensure correct use of the term "ampacity." "Note" relocated as new second paragraph of Section 400-5.

Section 400-6: Revised heading to comply with *NEC Style Manual*.

Section 400-6(a): Revised text of former Section 400-6 and added new heading "(a) Standard Markings." Revised second paragraph to include Types SC, SCE, and SCT for flexible stage and lighting power and to include Types SEOO and SJEOO, since they are UL-listed flexible cords.

Section 400-6(b) and (FPN): Added for optional markings. FPN provides examples.

Section 400-11: Revised to include Types SEOO and SJEOO.

Section 400-23: Revised heading and text to include "equipment grounding conductor," which conforms with *NEC* terminology.

Section 400-24: Revised to include "equipment grounding conductor," which conforms with standard *NEC* terminology.

Section 400-31(c): Revised heading and text to include "equipment grounding conductor," which conforms with standard *NEC* terminology.

ARTICLE 402—Fixture Wires

Table 402-3: Added "high temperature modified ETFE." Alphabetized fixture wire list in table.

Section 402-5: Added the term "allowable," since not all factors are figured into the ampacity.

Section 402-9(c) and (FPN): Added for optional marking. FPN provides examples.

ARTICLE 410—Lighting Fixtures, Lampholders, Lamps, and Receptacles

Section 410-4(c)(FPN): Revised to conform with *NEC Style Manual*.

Sections 410-8(d)(1),(2),(3), and (4): Replaced "area" with "space" for consistency with Section 410-8(a) definition and for clarity. Revised Sections 410-8(d)(2), (3), and (4) grammatically.

Figure 410-8: Deleted FPN. Figure now is captioned directly.

Section 410-12: Deleted "rosette." This term was deleted from the 1990 *NEC*.

Section 410-15(a): Deleted "rosettes." This term was deleted from the 1990 *NEC*.

Section 410-15(b)(1), Exception: Added to permit omission of handhole, with restrictions, where pole has hinged base. Added new last sentence to reference Section 250-75 bonding requirements.

Section 410-16(h)(FPN Nos. 1 and 2): Former FPN is now FPN No. 1. Added new FPN No. 2 to reference Section 300-5(d) for protection of direct buried cables.

Section 410-24(b)(FPN No. 1): Revised to reference Section 402-5 rather than Table 402-5.

Section 410-29(a)(FPN): Added "equipment" to reflect title of Table 250-95.

Section 410-30(c)(1) and Exception and Sections 410-30(c)(2) and (3): Three paragraphs of former Section 410-30(c) now numbered separately. Section 410-30(c)(1) further revised to permit cord connections for *listed* fixtures or fixture assemblies. Added exception to allow listed fixtures or fixture assemblies incorporating a cord and canopy to be exempt from requiring a cord cap at the termination end.

Section 410-56(c): Added "(electromagnetic interference)" to include same information found in Section 250-74, Exception No. 4.

Section 410-56(i) and Exception: Added to require receptacles in raised covers to be secured by more than one screw unless part of an assembly listed for such use.

Section 410-57(b), Exception: Revised to clarify that the covers that are weatherproof only when not in use are acceptable only for use with portable tools or portable equipment normally connected to the outlet when attended.

Part Title, N. Construction of Flush and Recessed Fixtures: Formerly Part O. Revised to "N" per *NEC Style Manual*.

Section 410-73(e), Exception Nos. 1,2, and 3: Former exception is now Exception No. 1, and revised to specify fluorescent fixtures with straight tubular lamps. Added Exception No. 2 for exit fixture ballasts and Exception No. 3 for emergency egress lighting.

Section 410-73(f): Deleted "recessed" from heading, and revised text so that remote ballasts must be thermally protected, whether or not the fixtures are recessed.

Section 410-73(f)(FPN): Added to allow thermal protection to be accomplished by means other than a thermal protector.

Section 410-77(c): Deleted last sentence, since its deletion does not alter the intent of the section.

Section 410-80(b): Added "or on" to clarify intent that it is not permissible to install open-circuit voltage exceeding 1000 volts *on* a dwelling.

Section 410-80(c): Revised terminology to conform with *NEC Style Manual*.

Section 410-85 and Exception: Deleted Section 410-85(a) heading and Section 410-85(b) to clarify intent. Reworded exception.

Section 410-101(c): Revised item (8) to recognize low-voltage track lighting.

ARTICLE 422—Appliances

Sections 422-8(d)(1) and (2): Deleted specific cord types, thus permitting utilization of suitable new cord types as they are developed.

Section 422-8(d)(3), Exception Nos. 1, 2, and 3: Renumbered former exception as Exception No. 1 and revised by deleting the requirement for factory-installed GFCI protection for spray washers if protected by double insulation and supplied with permanent warning to be connected to a receptacle that is GFCI protected. New Exception No. 2 allows a high-pressure spray washer rated for a 3-phase supply not to be GFCI protected. New Exception No. 3 allows a high-pressure spray washer rated over 250 volts not to be GFCI protected.

Section 422-23(FPN): Revised to conform with *NEC Style Manual*.

Section 422-29: Added to require listing for cord- and plug-connected pipe heating assemblies that are used to prevent freezing of piping.

ARTICLE 424—Fixed Electric Space Heating Equipment

Section 424-3: Replaced "approved" with "listed" to avoid having suitable equipment rejected by AHJ.

Section 424-9: Added second paragraph to this section with a reference to Section 210-50(b) so that the application of electric baseboard heaters equipped with factory-installed receptacle outlets will cover location of receptacle outlets in other than dwelling units, since outlet spacing requirements are not applied for other than dwelling units.

Section 424-19(b)(1): Revised to allow the branch-circuit switch or circuit breaker to serve as the disconnecting means if located within sight from the heater or if it is capable of being locked in the open position.

Section 424-22(c)(FPN Nos. 1 and 2): Former FPN following second paragraph is now FPN No. 2 and was revised to conform with *NEC Style Manual*. Added FPN No. 1 to reference Section 240-10 for supplementary overcurrent protection.

Section 424-99(c)(4): Revised to clarify that products identified for this use are acceptable.

ARTICLE 426—Fixed Outdoor Electric Deicing and Snow-Melting Equipment

Sections 426-27(a) and (c): Added "shall be bonded together" to Section 426-27(a). Deleted Section 426-27(c), since bonding and grounding requirements are now covered in Section 426-27(a).

Section 426-40: Revised to use "current" as the proper terminology instead of "ampacity."

Section 426-44(FPN): Revised to conform with *NEC Style Manual*.

Section 426-53: Added to require ground-fault protection of equipment for branch circuits supplying fixed outdoor electric deicing and snow-melting equipment.

Section 426-54: Added to require listing for cord- and plug-connected deicing and snow-melting equipment.

ARTICLE 427—Fixed Electric Heating Equipment for Pipelines and Vessels

Section 427-26: Revised to clarify that secondary winding of an isolation transformer connected to the pipeline or vessel being heated shall not have an output voltage greater than 30 volts ac.

Section 427-30: Deleted "rated."

Section 427-48(FPN): Revised to conform with *NEC Style Manual*.

ARTICLE 430—Motors, Motor Circuits, and Controllers

Section 430-1: Former text and FPN No. 1 replaced by new text and Exception Nos. 1 and 2 to clarify scope of article and address motor control centers. Former FPN No. 2 is now unnumbered.

Section 430-5: Revised to delete "phase converters," which are now covered by new Article 455. Revised list of articles to include new material.

Section 430-6(c): Revised editorially to delete "and/or" to comply with *NEC Style Manual*.

Section 430-7(d): Paragraphs now numbered. Updated reference in Section 430-7(d)(1).

Section 430-7(e): Deleted; phase converters are now covered in new Article 455.

Section 430-10(b): Deleted second paragraph; information now covered in new Part H, Motor Control Centers, Section 430-97(c).

Section 430-12: Deleted "phase converter" from title; now covered by new Article 455.

Section 430-12(e): Deleted "phase converter" ; now covered by new Article 455.

Section 430-19: Deleted; phase converters now covered by new Article 455.

Section 430-21(FPN No. 1): Revised to conform with *NEC Style Manual*.

Section 430-22(a): Revised editorially and to require that the selection of branch-circuit conductors between the controller and the motor be based on the current rating of the winding(s).

Sections 430-22(b) and (c): Deleted former Section 430-22(b); phase converters are now covered by new Article 455. Former Section 430-22(c) is now Section 430-22(b).

Section 430-24: Revised to simplify the rules for determining conductor ampacity for several motors or a motor and other loads. Phase converter requirements deleted; now covered by new Article 455.

Section 430-25: Revised to correlate with Section 430-24 revisions. Deleted Section 430-25(c); phase converters now covered by new Article 455.

Section 430-26: Revised "may" to "shall be permitted to" to conform with *NEC Style Manual*. Updated reference.

Section 430-28: Revised item (1) to set ampacity ratio at a 10:1 maximum for increased safety and to comply with Section 240-21(b)(5).

Section 430-28, Exception: Added item g to require that the tap be not less than 30 feet from the floor to comply with Section 240-21(e)(7).

Section 430-34(FPN): Added to explain that higher class overload relays will provide a longer motor acceleration and may preclude selection of a higher trip current.

Section 430-37: Deleted "thermal cutouts;" they are no longer covered by *NEC*.

Section 430-37: Deleted "thermal cutouts." Revised to include 1-phase motors on 3-phase systems.

Section 430-38: Deleted "thermal cutouts;" they are no longer covered by *NEC*.

Section 430-52(a): Deleted "phase converters"; now covered by new Article 455. Revised second paragraph to require instantaneous trip circuit breaker and combination controller criteria. Revised exception to second paragraph to permit trip settings above 700 percent where proved necessary by engineering evaluation. Revised FPN editorially. Revised fifth paragraph to allow solid-state motor controller systems to use suitable fuses in lieu of devices listed in Table 430-152.

Section 430-52(a), Exception No. 1: Revised to require that values first be rounded down where the values do not correspond to a standard overcurrent device, and then, if the device is unable to carry the load, round up.

Section 430-52(c): Deleted; phase converters now covered by new Article 455.

Sections 430-53(c)(1),(2), and (5)(FPN): Revised to conform with *NEC Style Manual*.

Section 430-62(a) and Exception: Revised text to clarify basis for sizing maximum permitted value for the protective device. Added exception so that where instantaneous trip circuit breakers are used for motor branch-circuit short-circuit and ground-fault protection, the maximum rating for the feeder SCGFP shall be a rating not exceeding the size allowed for the type of device employed. This is based on the assumed value for the largest value on the branch SCGFP for the same type as the feeder plus the sum of the full-load current of the other motors in the group.

Section 430-64: Deleted; phase converters now covered by new Article 455.

Section 430-71(FPN): Revised to conform with *NEC Style Manual*.

Section 430-73: Revised to clarify that an accidental ground in the remote-control device must not bypass manually operated shutdown devices or automatic safety shutdown devices.

Section 430-74(a), Exception No. 1: Replaced "live" with "energized" to conform with *NEC Style Manual*.

Section 430-82(a): Replaced "stalled" with "locked" for consistency with the terminology of Articles 430 and 440.

Section 430-82(c)(2): Replaced "value" with "rate."

Sections 430-83(a) and (b): Former text is now Section 430-83(a) with new heading. Added Section 430-83(b) to require that a controller be applied only in a circuit in which the nominal voltage to ground does not exceed the controller's voltage rating.

Section 430-86 and (FPN): Deleted; phase converters now covered by new Article 455.

Section 430-91: Revised to conform with *NEC Style Manual*.

Table 430-91: Enclosure Type No. 11 deleted; it is no longer manufactured. Revise obelisk note to no longer exempt Type No. 1 from marking.

H. Motor Control Centers: Added new Part H to provide a definition and comprehensive coverage of requirements for motor control centers installed for the control of motors, lighting, and power circuits. It covers overcurrent protection requirements, use as service equipment, grounding, phase arrangement, support and arrangement of busbars and conductors, barriers, and marking.

I. Disconnecting Means: Formerly Part H.

Section 430-102(a) and Exception No. 1: Revised to clarify requirement for controller disconnecting means. Revised Exception No. 1 editorially for clarity to indicate the disconnecting means for a controller be capable of being locked in an open position.

Section 430-102(c): Deleted; phase converters now covered by new Article 455.

Section 430-103: Deleted second paragraph ; requirement now contained in new Article 455.

Section 430-106: Revised editorially to conform with *NEC Style Manual*.

Section 430-109: Deleted "(nonautomatic circuit interrupter)"; it is no longer relevant to disconnect function. Listing now required.

Section 430-109, Exception No. 7: Added to allow an instantaneous trip circuit breaker as disconnecting means if the breaker is part of a listed combination motor controller.

Section 430-110(c)(1): Revised to conform with *NEC Style Manual*.

Section 430-110(d): Deleted; phase converters now covered by new Article 455.

Section 430-141: Replaced "live" with "energized" to conform with *NEC Style Manual*.

Section 430-145(b): Revised editorially. New second paragraph allows liquidtight flexible nonmetallic conduit and rigid nonmetallic conduit to enclose motor leads if grounding conductor is connected to motor and box.

Table 430-151: Added reference for phase converters, Section 455-8(c).

ARTICLE 440—Air-Conditioning and Refrigerating Equipment

Section 440-2: Revised to include definitions for branch-circuit selection current and rated-load current; relocated from the FPNs to Sections 440-4(a) and (c).

Section 440-4(a)(FPN): Relocated definition to Section 440-2.

Section 440-4(c)(FPN): Relocated definition to Section 440-2.

Section 440-12(b): Revised to conform with the *NEC Style Manual*. Resistance heaters deleted.

Section 440-12(b)(1)b: Revised to include resistance heaters as an example.

ARTICLE 450—Transformers and Transformer Vaults (Including Secondary Ties)

Section 450-3: Revised to allow up to six circuit breakers or sets of fuses on the secondary side of a transformer where the total of all devices does not exceed the allowed value of a single overcurrent device.

Section 450-3 (FPN Nos. 1 and 2): Former FPN is now FPN No. 1 with added reference to Section 240-21 to clarify need for overcurrent protection. Added FPN No. 2 to warn that nonlinear loads can increase the heat in a transformer.

Section 450-3(a)(1): Revised to allow electronically-actuated fuses that are set to open in accordance with settings for circuit breakers.

Section 450-3(b): Revised for clarity with a new introduction to the section.

Section 450-3(c) and FPN: Deleted "potential." Updated FPN and revised per *NEC Style Manual*.

Section 450-3(d): Added to address fire pump installations so that where the transformer is dedicated to supply power to the fire pump, secondary overcurrent protection can be deleted. Primary OCP must still be based on Section 450-3(a) or 450-3(b) and must be able to carry the locked-rotor currents of the fire pump motor and associated fire pump accessory equipment indefinitely.

Section 450-8(c): Revised to clarify that the rule applies to equipment operating voltage of 600 volts or less.

Section 450-11: Revised to require marking for clearance of transformers with ventilating openings.

Section 450-12: Updated table reference.

ARTICLE 455—Phase Converters

Article 455: Added new article to cover the installation and use of phase converters, both static and rotary.

ARTICLE 460—Capacitors

Section 460-2(a): Revised to clarify that a limit of 3 gallons of flammable liquid applies to any single unit in an installation of capacitors.

Chapter 5—Special Occupancies

ARTICLE 500—Hazardous (Classified) Locations

Section 500-2: Revised "are" to "shall be" in first paragraph to reflect scope requirements. Revised "prevent" to "minimize" in fourth paragraph, since it is not possible to prevent the passage of gases or vapors.

Section 500-2(FPN No. 2): Added references for more guidance on adequate ventilation.

Section 500-2(FPN No. 4): Revised to include NFPA 820-1992(ANSI).

Section 500-3: Revised to make group classifications mandatory. Section reorganized for clarity and conformance with *NEC Style Manual*.

Section 500-3(b): Revised to remove resistivity as a means to classify.

Section 500-6(a)(FPN): Revised to specify only Group E dusts as electrically conductive for classification purposes.

ARTICLE 501—Class I Locations

Section 501-3(a)(FPN): Updated NFPA reference.

Section 501-3(b)(1), Exception, item c: Deleted "i.e., are nonincendive" and revised to read "c. In nonincendive circuits. . ."

Section 501-3(b)(4): Updated table reference.

Section 501-4(b): Revised to exclude "armored cable with approved fittings."

Section 501-4(b)(FPN): Added reference for flexible conduit grounding requirements.

Section 501-4(b), Exception: Revised to more specifically address nonincendive circuits by using that term.

Section 501-5(FPN Nos. 1 and 2): Former FPN is now FPN No. 1. Added FPN No. 2 to recognize that gas or vapor leakage and propagation of flames may occur through the interstices between the strands on larger than No. 2 conductors. It also recognizes that strand compacting or sealing the individual strands reduces the leakage and prevents propagation of flames.

Section 501-5(a)(2)(FPN): Updated FPN.

Section 501-5(b)(2), Exception Nos. 1 and 2: First paragraph of former exception is now Exception No. 1. The second paragraph of that exception is now Exception No. 2 dealing with conduits terminating at an outdoor unclassified area.

Section 501-5(d), Exception: Added to specify that multiconductor cables can be used as single conductors for sealing purposes, no longer requiring that the outside jacket be removed to seal around individual conductors where the end of the cable is sealed.

Section 501-8(b): Revised to clarify requirements for exposed surface of space heaters, including approval marking.

Section 501-8(b)(FPN Nos. 1 and 2): Former FPN now FPN No. 1. Added FPN No. 2 to address risk of ignition due to currents arcing across discontinuities and overheating of parts.

Section 501-10(b)(1)b, Exception: Added to allow electrical resistance heat tracing approved for Class I, Division 2 locations.

Section 501-11: Revised to permit extension of flexible cord within a suitable raceway between a wet pit and power source. Added new paragraph allowing electric mixers that travel into and out of open-type mixing tanks or vats to be considered portable.

Section 501-14(b)(1), Exception, item c: Deleted "i.e., are nonincendive" and revised to read "c. In nonincendive circuits. . ."

Section 501-16(a), Exception: Added to clarify specific bonding means shall only be required to the point of grounding at *that* building disconnecting means.

Section 501-16(a)(FPN): Revised to conform with *NEC Style Manual.*

Sections 501-17(a) and (b): Restructured and revised former Section 501-17 as Sections 501-17(a) and (b). Section 501-17(a) clarifies Class I, Division 1 requirements for surge arresters. Section 501-17(b) expands Class I, Division 2 requirements. General-purpose enclosures are permitted and surge arresters must be nonarcing.

Section 501-18 and Exception: Added for multiwire branch circuit grounding.

ARTICLE 502— Class II Locations

Section 502-1: Revised second paragraph so as not to permit the entrance of any dust. Deleted resistivity specification and Group F dusts in last paragraph.

Section 502-1(FPN): Added for further information on dust-ignitionproof enclosures.

Section 502-4(a)(2): Revised to reference Section 502-12 for flexible cord requirements.

Section 502-4(a)(2)(FPN): Added for flexible conduit grounding requirements.

Section 502-4(b): Expanded list of acceptable wiring methods.

Section 502-4(b), Exception: Revised for clarity to specify nonincendive circuits.

Section 502-5: Revised "will not be required" to "shall not be required" to conform with *NEC Style Manual.*

Section 502-8(b): Updated section reference.

Section 502-14(b)(1), Exception: Revised to specify nonincendive circuits.

Section 502-16(a), Exception: Added to clarify that specific bonding means shall only be required to the point of grounding at that building disconnecting means.

Section 502-16(a)(FPN): Revised to conform with *NEC Style Manual.*

Section 502-16(b), Exception: Revised editorially for clarity.

Section 502-18 and Exception: Added for multiwire branch circuit grounding.

ARTICLE 503—Class III Locations

Section 503-3(a)(2) and (FPN): Revised text to conform with Section 503-10. Added FPN for flexible conduit grounding.

Section 503-16(a), Exception: Added to specify that bonding means is only required to the point of grounding at that building disconnecting means.

Section 503-16(a)(FPN): Revised to conform with *NEC Style Manual.*

Section 503-16(b), Exception: Revised editorially for clarity.

ARTICLE 504—Intrinsically Safe Systems

Section 504-1: Revised to include "systems" to clarify scope.

Section 504-2: Formerly Section 504-4 (former Section 504-2 is now Section 504-4.). Revised to include definition for different intrinsically safe circuits as referenced in Section 504-30(b).

Section 504-4: Formerly Section 504-2, relocated to conform with *NEC Style Manual.*

Section 504-30(a)(3)(FPN No. 2): Revised to add another acceptable physical barrier type.

Section 504-50(a): Deleted former text and replaced with grounding requirement for intrinsically safe apparatus, associated apparatus, and raceways.

Section 504-50(c) and Exception: Added to require shielded conductor grounding.

Sections 504-60(a) and (b): Former text is now Section 504-60(a) for hazardous locations. Added Section 504-60(b) for nonhazardous locations.

Section 504-70 and (FPN): Revised to be consistent with Section 500-2. Added FPN to clarify that an explosion-proof seal is not intended.

Section 504-80(b)(FPN Nos. 1, 2, and 3): Moved FPN No. 1 to new Section 504-80(c); FPN Nos. 2 and 3 renumbered as FPN Nos. 1 and 2, respectively.

Section 504-80(b), Exception: Added to require underground circuit identification where the circuits become accessible after emergence from the ground.

Section 504-80(c): Added for color coding of intrinsically safe conductors. This was former Section 504-80, FPN No. 1.

ARTICLE 511—Commercial Garages, Repair and Storage

Section 511-3(b), Exception: Added to require classification of lubrication and service rooms in accordance with Table 514-2.

Section 511-3(c): Revised heading to clarify intent.

Section 511-6(a): Expanded list of acceptable fixed wiring methods.

Section 511-10: Deleted "automotive," since other diagnostic equipment can be used with same degree of hazard.

ARTICLE 513—Aircraft Hangars

Section 513-4(a): Revised "metallic" to "metal" to conform with *NEC Style Manual*.

Sections 513-4(b) and (c): Added "equipment," since flexible cords include an equipment grounding conductor.

Section 513-4(d): Revised "raceway" to "wiring," since other wiring methods are permitted.

Section 513-11(b): Deleted "to the raceway system," since other wiring methods are permitted.

ARTICLE 514—Gasoline Dispensing and Service Stations

Section 514-1: Revised to include "approved containers," to conform with NFPA 30A.

Table 514-2: NFPA and ANSI/UL references are new FPNs to conform with *NEC Style Manual*. Table updated to correlate with Table 7 of NFPA 30A. "Lubrication or Service Room — without Dispensing" revised to conform with new material in Table 7 of NFPA 30A.

Section 514-5(b): Added requirements for an emergency control for attended self-service stations to be located not more than 100 feet from the dispensers.

Section 514-5(c): Added requirements for an emergency control for unattended self-service stations to be located more than 20 feet but less than 100 feet from the dispensers. Controls are required to shut off all power to all dispensing equipment at the station and must be manually resettable in a manner approved by the authority having jurisdiction.

ARTICLE 515—Bulk Storage Plants

Section 515-2: Revised to correlate with revised NFPA 30 text.

Section 515-2(FPN): Updated to conform with *NEC Style Manual*. Revised "area" to "space."

Table 515-2: Revised reference to NFPA 30 to conform with *NEC Style Manual*.

ARTICLE 516—Spray Application, Dipping, and Coating Processes

Section 516-2(a)(4): Revised to conform with NFPA 34, Sections 1-2 and 6-2.2 by requiring a 5-foot radial dimension from the source.

Section 516-2(a)(5): Revised to conform with NFPA 34, Section 6-2.1.

Section 516-2(b)(5): Revised to conform with NFPA 34, Section 6-2.3. Deleted "and for other hazardous operations" and now requires Division 2 classification for 3 feet surrounding the Class I, Division 1 area.

Section 516-2(b)(6): Added to conform with NFPA 34, Section 6-2.4. This provides classification extending

20 feet horizontally in all directions from the Class I, Division 1 location.

Section 516-2(b)(6) Exception: Added to declassify locations where the vapor source is 5 square feet or less and where the contents do not exceed 5 gallons. In addition, the vapor concentration must not exceed 25 percent of the lower flammable limit outside the Class I location specified in Section 516-2(a)(4).

Section 516-2(c) and Exception: Formerly Section 516-2(b)(6). Revised to conform with NFPA 34, Section 6-3.2. The section was moved into an exception and a new sentence added to the section, which provides that the space adjacent to an enclosed coating and dipping operation is considered nonclassified except as indicated in the exception.

Sections 516-2(d) and (e): Formerly Sections 516(c) and (d), respectively.

Section 516-4: Revised to conform with current wording of NFPA 33, Chapter 9 and *NEC Style Manual*. Added wording to include robotic devices. Where robotic programming procedures involve manual manipulation of the robot arm while spraying with the high voltage on, Section 516-5 for hand operations shall apply. Electrostatic spray equipment is required to be listed or approved.

Section 516-4(b) requires electrodes and atomizing heads to be insulated from ground and adequately supported. New Section 516-4(h) requires signs to be conspicuously posted to restrict the area to qualified personnel only, and identify the grounding requirements of all electrically conductive objects in the spray area. New Section 516-4(i) requires all insulators to be kept clean and dry. New Section 516-4(j) provides direction for equipment classified as nonincendive. Conveyers and hangers must maintain a distance of at least twice the sparking distance, and warnings defining this distance must be posted. An automatic shutdown must be employed if the distance between the goods and an electrode or a spray head falls below that required.

Section 516-7(a): Revised grammatically.

ARTICLE 517—Health Care Facilities

Section 517-2: Formerly Section 517-3.

Section 517-3: Revised former Section 517-2. Definition for Health Care Facilities now conforms with NFPA 99. Added definitions for Limited Care Facility (replacing deleted Residential Custodial Care Facility), Patient Bed Location, and Patient Care Area (with FPN added for nonpatient care areas). Existing definition of Patient Care Areas revised to apply to hospitals only and to correlate with NFPA 99 revisions. Revised definition of Reference Grounding Point for clarity. X-Ray Installation (Mobile) revised to conform with *NEC Style Manual*.

Deleted "design" from heading; the *Code* is not intended for design specifications.

Section 517-10, Exception No. 3c: Deleted "battery" to conform with NFPA 99 and to apply power to operate all alarm systems.

Section 517-13(b): Expanded list of acceptable methods to include those types of raceways permitted by Section 250-91(b). Deleted verification of ground path integrity, as it may impair/degrade an otherwise acceptably installed system.

Section 517-14: Revised to require the bonding between more than two panels serving the same patient vicinity to be continuous from panel to panel but can be broken to allow termination at each panel.

Section 517-15: Deleted.

Section 517-17(a): Revised to include feeder disconnecting means to be ground-fault protected where required to be protected by Section 215-10 and also the additional level of Ground Fault Protection in the next downstream feeder disconnecting means.

Section 517-17(a)(FPN): Added to clarify that additional levels of ground-fault protection are not intended on the load side of an essential electrical system transfer switch, between the on-site generator and the essential system transfer switch, or on electrical systems that are not solidly grounded wye systems with greater than 150 volts to ground.

Section 517-18(a): Deleted "inpatient care."

Section 517-18(c): Revised heading and text to delete psychiatric locations, since tamper resistance is intended to protect children.

Section 517-19(a): Deleted requirement for all emergency branch circuits to originate in the same panelboard, to increase the reliability of the emergency circuit at the patient bed location.

Section 517-19(c): Revised heading to clarify intent that this patient grounding point is an option and is no longer a requirement.

Section 517-19(c)(FPN): Revised to correlate with deletion of Section 517-15.

Section 517-19(d)(1): Revised to clarify that the bonding jumper shall be connected to the junction point of the raceway or the ground bus of the panel.

Section 517-19(e): Added "(Optional)" to heading to avoid creating performance criteria.

Sections 517-20(a) and Exception, and (b): Revised structurally to conform with *NEC Style Manual*; Former Sections 517-20(1) and (2) now Sections 517-20(a) and (b), respectively. Exception to Section 517-20(a) added to allow branch circuits supplying only fixed-in-place listed therapeutic and diagnostic equipment not to be GFCI protected under certain conditions.

Section 517-25: Updated terminology to cover limited care facilities.

Section 517-30(a), Exception: Deleted, since the reorganization of Article 517 now makes these references unnecessary.

Section 517-30(b)(4): Added "or systems" to conform with NFPA 99 and reference to Diagram 517-30(3).

Diagram 517-30(3): Revised to include "150 kVA or less" to comply with Section 517-30(b)(4).

Section 517-30(c)(3), Exception No. 4: Added to allow Schedule 40 PVC where encased in not less than 2 inches of concrete except for branch circuits serving patient care areas.

Section 517-32(c): Revised to conform with NFPA 99 by deleting electrical water-flow alarm devices connected to sprinkler systems and automatic fire or smoke detection devices from the life safety branch.

Section 517-32(e): Revised to cover task illumination battery charges for emergency battery-powered lighting fixtures.

Sections 517-33(a)(8) and item a and (9): Revised to conform with NFPA 99 to cover selected receptacles and selected power circuits. It also covers general care bed locations.

Sections 517-40(a), (b), and (c) and (FPN): Terminology updated for new limited care facilities.

Section 517-41(a): Terminology updated for new limited care facilities.

Section 517-41(b): Added "or systems" to conform with NFPA 99 and reference to Diagram 517-41(3).

Diagram 517-41(3): Revised to include "150 kVA or less" to clarify Section 517-41(b).

Section 517-42(c)(1): Revised to conform with NFPA 99 to include only fire alarms.

Section 517-61(c)(1): Expanded list of approved metal raceways to include those types of raceways permitted by Section 250-91(b).

Section 517-62: Deleted "or portable", since it is performance criteria. Deleted "X" denoting extracted material.

Sections 517-63(b)(1), (2), (3), and (4) and Exception: Revised from former Sections 517-63(b), items a, b, c, and d to conform with *NEC Style Manual*.

Section 517-73(a)(2): Revised to permit more realistic requirements for sizing conductors and overcurrent protective devices based on experience while maintaining substantial safety factors.

Section 517-78(c): Revised to correlate with deletion of Section 517-15.

Section 517-80 and (FPN No. 2): Deleted "grounding" from text. Deleted FPN No. 2 to clarify intent. Former FPN No. 1 now unnumbered.

Section 517-160(b)(1): Revised to make *Code* language uniform for mandatory requirements.

Section 517-160(b)(1)(FPN): Deleted due to improper text for an FPN.

ARTICLE 518—Places of Assembly

Section 518-5: Added for portable supply requirements for power in a place of assembly.

ARTICLE 520—Theaters, Audience Areas of Motion Picture and Television Studios, and Similar Locations

Article Title: Revised to include audience areas of studios and complete cross-references between Articles 520 and 530.

Section 520-1: Revised to include audience areas of studios.

Section 520-4, Exception No. 2: Revised "reproduction" to "recording."

Section 520-4, Exception No. 3: Added to allow wiring methods in Section 518-4, Exception No. 1 in similar areas of studios.

Section 520-8: Added for branch-circuit requirements.

Section 520-23: Revised to clarify that a separate overcurrent device is not required for each receptacle.

Section 520-27(c): Added new second paragraph for supply capacity computations for switchboards.

Section 520-44(b) and Exception: Revised text to specify only listed extra-hard usage cable. Section 400-5 is now referenced for ampacity. Added exception for listed multiconductor extra-hard usage type cords not in direct contact with heat-producing equipment to be allowed to use ampacities from Table 520-44.

Table 520-44: Added for allowable ampacity of listed extra-hard usage cords and includes a table for derating when more than three current-carrying conductors are in the cable.

Section 520-45: Deleted continuous/noncontinuous load requirements. Added reference to Article 400.

Section 520-46: Revised to reference Section 520-44(b) for supply cables for connector strips and drop boxes.

Section 520-48: Revised to require curtain machines to be listed.

Section 520-49: Revised to increase accessibility/visibility to involved equipment.

Section 520-51: Added "power" before "outlets" for correct usage of term as defined in Article 100.

Section 520-53: Revised to include new material.

Section 520-53(h): Revised to specify only listed extra-hard usage cord or cable. Revised single conductor sizing for portable supply cable sets to not smaller than No. 2 and No. 6 for an equipment grounding conductor. Expanded grounding and grounded identification requirements.

Section 520-53(k): Added for single-pole separable connector requirements. Former Section 520-53(k) and subsequent parts relettered.

Section 520-53(o): Formerly Section 520-53(n). Revised to conform with *NEC Style Manual* and to add requirement for single-conductor feeder cables not installed in raceways are used on multiphase circuits to size the grounded conductor to an ampacity of 130 percent of the ungrounded conductors.

Section 520-53(p) and Exception: Added to require that only qualified personnel perform electrical work.

Section 520-61: Revised to specify that listed extra-hard usage cord and cable be used for interconnecting cord sets and interconnecting cords and cables.

Section 520-62(b): Revised to allow only that listed extra-hard usage cord or cables.

Sections 520-68(a), (b) and Exception: Former Section 520-68(a) is now Section 520-68. Revised to specify only listed extra-hard usage cords or cables. Deleted list of flexible cords and cables. Added Section 520-68(b) and exception for conductor ampacity requirements.

ARTICLE 530—Motion Picture and Television Studios and Similar Locations

Section 530-2: Added to provide definitions for portable equipment, plugging box, and ac power distribution box.

Sections 530-17(a) and (b): Former Section 530-17 is now Section 530-17(a). Revised to address portable carbon arc lamp requirements. Added Section 530-17(b) for portable noncarbon arc electric-discharge lamp fixtures.

Section 530-18: Revised to include new material added in (e).

Section 530-18(e): Added to address ac power distribution box requirements. Former Section 530-18(e) is now Section 530-18(f).

Section 530-18(f): Formerly Section 530-18(e). Revised to apply restriction only to portable cords connected to deplugging boxes.

Table 530-19(a): Revised wording in first column for clarity.

Section 530-21: Revised and expanded to clarify ratings and connector requirements.

Section 530-22: Added for branch-circuit requirements for stage set lighting loads.

ARTICLE 545—Manufactured Building

Section 545-1: Revised "and/or" to "and" to conform with *NEC Style Manual*.

Section 545-7: Revised to reference Section 230-70(a) for service equipment location requirements.

Section 545-11: Deleted "and/or" to conform with *NEC Style Manual*.

ARTICLE 547—Agricultural Buildings

Sections 547-1 and (a) and (b): Revised to clarify intent to include nontraditional animal confinement areas.

Section 547-4: Revised to permit wiring methods in Article 347 and Article 351, Part B.

Sections 547-5(a) and (b) and (FPN): Added new Section 547-5(a) to require dustproof and weatherproof enclosures, and Section 547-5(b) to require watertight, corrosion-resistant enclosures. FPN addresses corrosion of cast aluminum and magnetic steel.

Section 547-7(c): Deleted "and/or" to conform with *NEC Style Manual*.

Section 547-8(a), Exception No. 1b: Revised to clarify equipment grounding conductor is required to be the same size if of same material as supply conductors and to require sizing in accordance with Table 250-95 if of different materials.

Section 547-8(d): Deleted the use of motors fully insulated from ground, since these types of motors do not comply with Section 250-43(k).

ARTICLE 550—Mobile Homes and Mobile Home Parks

Section 550-2: Deleted "and/or" from definition for Laundry Area to conform with *NEC Style Manual*. Revised Mobile Home definition and FPN to include manufactured homes and specify that the difference between a manufactured home and a mobile home is that a mobile home does not have a permanent foundation.

Section 550-2(a), Exception Nos. 1 and 2: Former exception is now Exception No. 1. Added Exception No. 2 to reference Section 550-23(a), Exception No. 2 for manufactured homes, which allows the service to be located on or in the home with certain restrictions or "under certain conditions."

Section 550-6(a) and FPN: Revised third paragraph to include clothes closets as unacceptable for distribution panelboards. Delete "and/or" from FPN to conform with *NEC Style Manual*.

Section 550-7(b): Revised to require that small appliance branch circuits be installed in accordance with Section 210-52(b).

Section 550-8(b): Deleted "and/or" and "tub/shower" to conform with *NEC Style Manual*.

Section 550-8(d): Revised to clarify intent is to require installation of required outlets.

Section 550-8(d), Exception No. 2: Corrected terminology, since these receptacles are not concealed but are not readily accessible.

Sections 550-8(f)(1) and (2): Former Section 550-8(f) is now Section 550-8(f)(1). Added Section 550-8(f)(2) to prohibit installation of receptacles in a face-up position in any counter top.

Section 550-10(f): Added requirement for tubing to be reamed to remove rough edges.

Section 550-11: Revised to read "grounded circuit conductor (neutral)" for correct terminology.

Section 550-15(b): Deleted "and/or" to conform with *NEC Style Manual*.

Section 550-23(a), Exception Nos. 1 and 2: Former exception now Exception No. 1. Revised for clarity and to emphasize that all of Section 250-24 applies. Added

Exception No. 2 to allow the service to be located on or in the manufactured building if the service equipment is installed by the manufacturer of the structure, complies with Article 230, and means are provided for connection of a grounding electrode conductor to the service equipment routed outside the structure.

Section 550-23(g): Added for marking requirements.

Section 550-24(a) and Exception: Deleted "continuous." Added exception to correlate with Section 550-23(a) provisions.

ARTICLE 551—Recreational Vehicles and Recreational Vehicle Parks

Section 551-2: Revised definition for Power-Supply Assembly to clarify grounding conductor types addressed. Added definitions from Section 551-70 for Recreational Vehicle Park, Recreational Vehicle Site, Recreational Vehicle Site Feeder Circuit Conductors, Recreational Vehicle Site Supply Equipment, and Recreational Vehicle Stand.

Section 551-4(b): Revised voltage to conform with Section 551-2 definition for low voltage.

Section 551-10(c)(5): "AWG" deleted to conform with *NEC Style Manual*.

Section 551-20(f): Deleted "and/or" to conform with *NEC Style Manual*. Replaced "connector" with "receptacle" to correct terminology.

Section 551-30(d)(FPN): Added to reference NFPA 501C for generator compartment construction requirements.

Section 551-30(e): Revised to include enclosed transfer switches as an acceptable point of first termination.

Section 551-30(f): Deleted. Generator compartment construction requirements are now referenced in new FPN for Section 551-30(d).

Section 551-40(c): Deleted "and/or" to conform with *NEC Style Manual*.

Section 551-41(c)(3): Revised to require a receptacle located in an area with a toilet, a shower, a tub, or any combination thereof.

Section 551-45(a): Revised editorially to clarify that grounded conductor termination bar be isolated from the enclosure.

Section 551-46(a)(1): Revised to use attachment plug instead of receptacle for correct terminology.

Section 551-46(c)(1): Revised reference from Section 551-10(a) to Section 551-42(a).

Section 551-46(e), Exception Nos. 1 and 2: Former exception now Exception No. 1. Added Exception No. 2 to allow the point of entrance of a power-supply assembly to be located more than 15 feet from the rear of the vehicle for greater flexibility. Where this occurs, the cord also must be extended the same distance.

Section 551-47(b): Revised to require tubing to be reamed to remove rough edges.

Section 551-47(n): Revised to allow greater design flexibility by allowing other raceways or cables identified for outdoor or underchassis wiring.

Section 551-47(r)(2): Deleted "and/or" to conform with *NEC Style Manual*.

Section 551-60(a): Revised to use technically correct terminology of ungrounded and grounded conductors.

Section 551-60(b): Revised "live" to "ungrounded" to conform with *NEC Style Manual*.

Section 551-70: Deleted. Relocated definitions to Section 551-2.

Section 551-71: Deleted reference to 15 amperes to correlate with Figure 551-46(c) and Section 551-81 that requires the receptacle to be 20 amperes, 125 volts.

Section 551-72(FPN): Added to explain that on 120/240-volt, 3-wire, single-phase services or feeders, the neutral cannot be reduced in size if there aren't any 240-volt loads since, the neutral will carry the same current as the ungrounded conductors.

Section 551-73(a): Second paragraph added for sizing loads to other amenities such as service buildings, recreational buildings, and swimming pools.

Section 551-73(d): Revised to require that the grounded conductors have the same ampacity as the ungrounded conductors.

Table 551-73: Added "site" to title to clarify that the table is intended to cover site feeders and service entrance conductors.

Section 551-76(a), Exception: Added for location of electrical supply equipment in pull-through sites.

ARTICLE 553—Floating Buildings

Section 553-7(b): Revised to expand list of acceptable wiring methods for feeders to include liquidtight flexible metal and nonmetallic conduit and extra-hard usage portable power cable listed for wet locations and sunlight resistance.

ARTICLE 555—Marinas and Boatyards

Section 555-3(FPN No. 3): Revised to reference NFPA 303 (ANSI) for establishment of datum plane.

Section 555-4(FPN): Added to warn that supplying receptacles with voltages other than the voltages marked on the receptacle may cause overheating or malfunctioning of connected equipment.

Section 555-6: Revised to expand list of acceptable wiring methods to include extra-hard usage portable power cable listed for wet locations and sunlight resistance.

Section 555-6(FPN No. 2): Revised to provide information for establishment of datum plane.

Section 555-7(b), Exception: Added to permit the equipment grounding conductor of Type MI cable to be identified at terminations.

Section 555-10: Added to require service equipment for floating docks or marinas to be located adjacent to, but not on or in, the floating structure.

Chapter 6—Special Equipment

ARTICLE 600—Electric Signs and Outline Lighting

Section 600-2(a), Exception Nos. 1 and 2: Added new Exception No. 1 to not require disconnecting means for an exit directional sign connected to a circuit within scope of Article 700. Former exception is now Exception No. 2, revised to include outline lighting in requirements.

Section 600-8(e): Revised to include aluminum in requirement. Revised "thickness of dimensions" to conform with third party certification requirements.

Section 600-9: Revised to include "sections" so parts of signs can be covered.

Section 600-9(b): Revised to delete the list of cord types and simply require 3-conductor junior hard service or hard service types as designated in Table 400-4, with one conductor grounded as provided in Section 600-9(a).

Section 600-11: Revised to ensure protection of the power-supply cord and connection points by requiring factory-installed GFCI protection either in the attachment plug or within 12 inches of the plug.

Part Title, B. 1000 Volts, Nominal, or Less: Deleted "600 volts" in heading and replaced with "1000 volts," since this is the established voltage level for higher voltage signs.

Part Title, C. Over 1000 Volts, Nominal: Deleted "600 volts" in heading and replaced with "1000 volts," since this is the established voltage level for higher voltage signs.

Section 600-31(a)(FPN): Added to reference Section 600-5 for grounding requirements.

Section 600-31(f): Revised to require that free-hanging conductors that are isolated from combustible material and not subject to physical damage be insulated for the voltage.

Section 600-32(b): Third paragraph revised to make 60 milliamperes the maximum instead of 30 milliamperes.

Section 600-32(d), Exception No. 2: Revised to clarify that small portable sign transformers are permitted to be connected in series if listed for the purpose and equipped with secondary leads permanently attached to the secondary winding within the transformer enclosure.

Section 600-34(b): Revised to resolve conflict with Section 600-34(a), which allows insulation in lieu of spacing.

ARTICLE 604—Manufactured Wiring Systems

Sections 604-6(a)(1) and (2) and Exception Nos. 1 and 2: Revised to permit No. 10 copper-insulated conductors and to require that the equipment grounding conductor be equivalent in size to the ungrounded conductor.

ARTICLE 610—Cranes and Hoists

Section 610-11, Exception No. 5: Added to permit a cord suitable for the purpose to be used, with limitations, where flexibility is required for power or control to moving parts.

Section 610-12: Revised heading to correlate with 1990 *NEC* to include cable terminal fittings.

Section 610-14(e)(2): Deleted "circuit," since only conductors have ampacity.

Section 610-42(a), Exception No. 2: Revised to add "conductor" since tap conductors as well as the tap have ampacity.

Section 610-57: Revised "alive" to "energized."

ARTICLE 620—Elevators, Dumbwaiters, Escalators, Moving Walks, Wheelchair Lifts, and Stairway Chair Lifts

Section 620-2: Revised to include wheelchair and stairway chair lifts in the requirement.

Section 620-3: Revised to require that all live parts of runways and machinery spaces of wheelchair and stairway chair lifts also be enclosed.

Section 620-11: Revised to include wheelchair and stairway chair lifts in the requirement.

Section 620-11(c): Revised to require that all conductors in the runways and machinery spaces of wheelchair and stairway chair lifts also have flame-retardant insulation.

Section 620-11(d): Revised to permit hoistway cable as an acceptable conductor. Revised grammatically.

Section 620-12: Revised to include wheelchair and stairway chair lifts.

Section 620-13: Revised to include wheelchair and stairway chair lifts. Deleted reference to Section 620-13(c).

Section 620-14: Revised to include wheelchair and stairway chair lifts.

Section 620-21: Revised to permit Type AC cable and include wheelchair lifts, stairway chair lift runways, and machinery spaces.

Section 620-21, Exception No. 1 and (FPN): Revised exception to permit liquidtight flexible metal conduit and to clarify where cables in Class 2 power-limited circuits can be installed, with limitations. Added FPN to clarify that "signal fixtures" include audible and visible equipment such as gongs, chimes, lights, and displays that convey information to the user.

Section 620-21, Exception No. 2: Revised to permit liquidtight flexible metal conduit.

Section 620-21, Exception No. 4: Revised to permit liquidtight flexible metal conduit and to prohibit Type AC cable. Revised to permit flexible metal conduit or liquidtight flexible metal conduit not exceeding 6 feet in length between control panels and disconnecting means.

Section 620-21, Exception No. 5: Revised to permit liquidtight flexible metal conduit of 3/8 inch trade size.

Section 620-21, Exception No. 6: Revised to permit flexible metal conduit and liquidtight flexible metal conduit, and also to permit them as flexible connections for elevators. Revised to reference Section 620-72, Exception Nos. 1 and 2.

Section 620-21, Exception No. 7: Added to allow various wiring methods to be permitted on the counterweight assembly, in lengths not exceeding 6 feet with some restrictions.

Sections 620-22(a) and (b): Revised to harmonize with *Canadian Electrical Code*. Expanded to require a dedicated branch circuit for car lighting, accessories, heating, and air conditioning on each elevator car.

Section 620-34: Revised to clarify that attachment to the escalator or moving walk truss or to runway construction is allowed. Revised to include wheelchair and stairway chair lift runways.

Section 620-37: Revised to include machine rooms in requirements. Relocated first sentence as the last.

Section 620-37, Exception Nos. 1 and 2: Former exception is now Exception No. 1. Added new Exception No. 2 to permit feeders inside the hoistway for elevators with driving machine motors located in the hoistway or on the car or counterweight.

Section 620-38: Revised to include wheelchair and stairway chair lifts.

Section 620-39: Revised to include rigid nonmetallic conduit and liquidtight flexible nonmetallic conduit as acceptable for sidewalk elevators.

Section 620-41: Revised to require that traveling cables be so suspended at a counterweight end that strain on the individual conductors is kept to a minimum.

Section 620-44: Revised to include counterweight, where applicable, in requirement.

Section 620-51: Revised to include wheelchair and stairway chair lifts.

Section 620-51(a) and (FPN): Revised to clarify restrictions and requirements for disconnecting means. Added FPN to reference AMSE/ANSI A17.1 for additional information.

Section 620-51(b)(4): Added to address disconnecting means for wheelchair lifts and stairway chair lifts.

Section 620-53: Revised to include "accessories" to reflect industry practice and to harmonize with the *Canadian Electrical Code.*

Section 620-54: Added to require that elevators shall have a single means to disconnect all ungrounded car heating and air conditioning supply conductors for each unit. Where there is equipment for more than one car in the equipment room, the disconnecting means must be numbered according to the car number and must be capable of being locked in the open position.

Sections 620-61(b)(1),(2), and (3): Revised to correct terminology from "overcurrent" to "overload."

Section 620-61(b)(4): Added to require wheelchair lift and stairway chair lift driving machine motors to be classed as intermittent duty. These motors are required to be protected against overload in accordance with Section 430-33.

Section 620-71, Exception Nos. 1 and 2: Former exception is now Exception No. 1 revised to include wheelchair and stairway chair lifts and to allow disconnecting means to be an integral part of, as well as adjacent to, the motor controller. Revised further to clarify motor controller cabinet requirements and locations for escalators and moving walks. Disconnecting means, where integral to the controller, must be operable without opening the cabinet. Added Exception No. 2 to permit elevator motor controllers and driving machines to be outside specified spaces, with certain restrictions.

Section 620-72, Exception Nos. 1 and 2: Former exception is now Exception No. 1 revised to permit the waiving of the clearance requirements for the disconnecting means where the entire panel and disconnecting means

are arranged to be readily removable from the machine space and flexible leads are provided for all external connections. New Exception No. 2 addresses similar permissions for elevator motor control panel and disconnecting means.

Section 620-84: Added to reference Article 250 for escalator, moving walk, wheelchair lift, and stairway chair lift grounding requirements.

Section 620-85: Added to require GFCI protection for personnel for all 125-volt, single-phase, 15- and 20-ampere receptacles installed in machine rooms, machinery spaces, pits, and elevator car tops.

ARTICLE 630—Electric Welders

Sections 630-11(a) and (b): Deleted "rated," since conductor ampacity is not rated.

Sections 630-21(a) and (b): Deleted "rated," since conductor ampacity is not rated.

Sections 630-31(a)(1) and (2) and (b): Deleted "rated," since conductor ampacity is not rated.

ARTICLE 645—Electronic Computer/Data Processing Equipment

Section 645-5(d)(2): Revised to permit the use of rigid nonmetallic conduit for enclosing branch-circuit supply conductors.

Section 645-5(d)(5) and Exception Nos. 1, 2, and 3 and (FPN): Added to require cables, other than those in Section 645-5(d)(2), to be listed as Type DP, for fire resistance. Added Exceptions for (1) interconnecting cables enclosed in conduit or raceway or (2) listed with equipment manufactured prior to July 1, 1994 and (3) other acceptable cable type designations. Added FPN to provide method to define fire resistance.

Section 645-10: Revised to clarify that the control for the disconnecting means shall be grouped and identified at a readily accessible location at the principal exit doors.

Section 645-11, Exception Nos. 1 and 2: Former exception is now Exception No. 1. Added Exception No. 2 so that a disconnecting means is not required for certain sizes of UPS systems or where the battery circuits are integral to the electronic equipment.

Section 645-15: First sentence revised and last sentence deleted to clarify grounding requirements.

Section 645-15(FPN Nos. 1 and 2): Former FPN is now FPN No. 1. Added FPN No. 2 to clarify that listed equipment specified provides the bonding and grounding requirements of Article 250.

ARTICLE 660—X-RAY Equipment

Section 660-1(FPN): Revised to conform with *NEC Style Manual*.

ARTICLE 665—Induction and Dielectric Heating Equipment

Section 665-23: Revised to that require that signs that read "DANGER—HIGH VOLTAGE—KEEP OUT" be attached to the equipment and be plainly visible where unauthorized persons might come in contact with energized parts.

ARTICLE 670—Industrial Machinery

Section 670-3(a): Revised to require the maximum ampere rating of the short-circuit and ground-fault protective device to be included on the permanent nameplate.

Section 670-4(a)(FPN), and (b) and Exception: Revised heading and Section 670-4(b) expanded to address overcurrent protection. Section 670-4(b) now includes rules for sizing the motor branch-circuit protective devices for industrial machinery, with an exception added for calculations where one or more instantaneous trip circuit breakers or motor short-circuit protectors are used. Deleted Section 670-4(a)(FPN No. 1); former FPN No. 2 is now unnumbered and "ratings" deleted, since conductors are not rated.

Section 670-5: Added to allow clearance to be 2½ feet where conditions of maintenance and supervision assure only qualified persons will service the installation. The doors of the equipment must be able to open at least 90 degrees or be removable.

Section 670-5, Exception: The clearances are permitted to be less than 2½ feet where the enclosure requires a tool to open it and only troubleshooting and testing is involved on parts operating at not over 150 volts, line-to-line.

ARTICLE 675—Electrically Driven or Controlled Irrigation Machines

Section 675-4(c): Deleted "which shall be designed" to conform with *NEC Style Manual*.

Section 675-8(b), Exception: Added to permit circuit breakers without marked horsepower ratings when in accordance with Section 430-109.

Sections 675-11(a), (b), and (c): Replaced "ampacity" with "current rating," since collector rings have a current rating rather than an ampacity. Revised Section 675-11(c) to correlate with Section 675-11(a).

Section 675-13: Revised second sentence to require the equipment grounding conductor to be sized not less than the largest supply conductor in each cord, cable, or raceway.

ARTICLE 680—Swimming Pools, Fountains, and Similar Installations

Section 680-1(FPN): Revised to clarify that the term "fountain" does not include drinking water fountains.

Section 680-3(FPN): Updated reference.

Section 680-4: Deleted "metal" in definitions for Forming Shell and Wet-Niche Lighting Fixture, allowing for use of new nonmetallic materials.

Section 680-5(a): Revised to require the transformer to be an isolated winding type, and that the branch circuit supplying the primary include a grounded circuit conductor and be protected by a GFCI.

Section 680-5(c) and Exception No. 3: Replaced "conduit" with "raceway" to allow other acceptable wiring methods.

Section 680-5(c), Exception No. 4: Added to allow grounding conductors to occupy the same raceway, box, or enclosure with GFCI-protected conductors.

Section 680-6: Revised heading to include ceiling fans.

Section 680-6(a)(1) and Exception: Revised to require receptacles to be located at least 10 feet from a fountain except for receptacles used to power water pumps for a permanently installed fountain, with some restrictions.

Section 680-6(a)(2): Deleted "convenience" to correct *Code* terminology.

Section 680-6(b)(1) and Exception No. 2: Revised to address ceiling fans where mounted above or near swimming pools and to clarify that no part of the lighting fixture or ceiling fan be less than 12 feet above the maximum water level.

Section 680-6(c): Revised to clarify that the required distance for switching devices from the edge of the pool is measured horizontally.

Section 680-8, Exception No. 1: Revised editorially and to no longer specify that the supply lines or service drops be utility-owned, operated, and maintained.

Section 680-20(a)(2): Revised to add "on supply circuits" to clarify intent.

Section 680-20(b)(1): Deleted "approved metal" to allow for nonmetallic materials for forming shells, and "threaded" is no longer specified for conduit entries into these forming shells.

Section 680-20(d): Revised to allow no-niche fixtures that are listed for the purpose and installed in accordance with Section 680-20(b). Where connection to a forming shell is required, the connection must be to the mounting bracket.

Section 680-21(a): Revised to include no-niche fixture mounting brackets.

Section 680-21(a)(1): Revised to include a nonmetallic hub listed for the purpose of a junction box connected to a conduit.

Section 680-21(b): Revised to include no-niche fixture mounting brackets.

Section 680-21(b)(1): Revised to include a nonmetallic hub listed for the purpose.

Section 680-21(b)(4): Revised to require a height of 4 inches above the pool deck of an enclosure connected to a forming shell or to a no-niche fixture and to locate it at least 8 inches above maximum water level.

Section 680-21(d): Revised to include no-niche fixture mounting brackets.

Section 680-22(a)(2): Revised to include no-niche fixture mounting brackets.

Section 680-22(a)(6), Exception No. 1: Revised to require that the steel tie wires for bonding the rebar together be made tight.

Section 680-22(b): Revised to permit stainless steel clamps for bonding the pool parts into a bonding grid.

Section 680-24: Revised to include no-niche fixtures in grounding requirements.

Section 680-25(b)(1): Expanded to require dry niche and no-niche fixtures to be connected to the equipment grounding conductor.

Sections 680-25(b)(2) and (3): Revised to include no-niche fixtures.

Section 680-25(c), Exception No. 3: Revised to specify insulated or covered equipment grounding conductor for a pool motor equipment grounding conductor.

Section 680-25(c), Exception No. 5: Deleted, since double-insulated pool motors were originally listed only for storable pools and are not intended for use on permanent pools.

Section 680-25(d)(FPN): Revised to conform with *NEC Style Manual*.

Section 680-26(a)(FPN Nos. 1, 2, and 3): Revised and restructured former FPN to conform with *NEC Style Manual* and relocated information into two new FPNs.

Section 680-32(5), Exception: Added to allow lighting assemblies without transformers to be cord- and plug-connected for storable pools with certain restrictions.

Section 680-41(b)(1) and Exception No. 1: Revised to include ceiling fans in requirements for spas and hot tubs.

Section 680-41(d)(4), Exception: Added to exempt from bonding requirements those small conductive surfaces not likely to become energized, such as air and water jets and drain fittings, if they are not connected to metal piping, towel bars, mirror frames, etc.

Section 680-42: Added to require spa and hot tub GFCI protection by January 1, 1994.

Section 680-52(b)(FPN): Updated reference.

Section 680-56(b): Revised to specify only hard-service cord rather than specific types, as designated in Table 400-4.

Section 680-70: Deleted GFCI protection requirement for the circuit.

ARTICLE 685—Integrated Electrical Systems

Section 685-2: Revised list to include Ground-Fault Protection of Equipment, Section 240-13, Exception No. 1.

ARTICLE 690—Solar Photovoltaic Systems

Diagram 690-1: Caption revised to clarify that grounding system is not shown.

Section 690-4(d): Added to require inverters or motor generators to be identified for use in solar photovoltaic systems.

Section 690-8(b)(2): Revised to specify "short-circuit" current rating be included in the circuit current computation.

Section 690-8(c): Added to address systems with multiple dc voltages.

Section 690-13, Exception: Added to prohibit the switch or circuit breaker used as a disconnecting means from having a pole in the grounded conductor where a circuit grounding connection is not designed to be automatically interrupted as part of the ground-fault protection system required by Section 690-5.

Section 690-13(FPN): Added to clarify that the grounding conductor is permitted to have a bolted or terminal disconnecting means to allow maintenance or troubleshooting by qualified personnel.

Section 690-15: Deleted "(live)" to conform with *NEC Style Manual.*

Section 690-31(b): Revised to include Types SE and USE conductor cable as acceptable for photovoltaic source circuits. Where directly exposed to sun rays, Type UF cable identified as sunlight-resistant or Type USE cable must be used.

Chapter 7—Special Conditions

ARTICLE 700—Emergency Systems

Section 700-1: Deleted "and/or" to conform with *NEC Style Manual.*

Sections 700-8(a) and (b): Former text is now Section 700-8(a) Emergency Sources. Added Section 700-8(b) to require a sign at the grounding location where the grounded circuit conductor connected to the emergency source is connected to a grounding electrode conductor remote from the emergency source. The sign must identify all emergency and normal sources connected at that location.

Section 700-9(b): Revised second sentence to clarify intent and relocated to follow exceptions to avoid misinterpretation, since exceptions apply only to first sentence of Section 700-9(b).

Section 700-12: Revised third paragraph to require that emergency circuits be designed and located to minimize hazards that might cause failures.

Section 700-12(f): Revised first paragraph to conform with *NEC Style Manual.* Revised second paragraph to require that the branch-circuit feeding unit equipment be clearly identified at the distribution panel.

Section 700-26: Revised to clarify that the alternate source for emergency systems is not required to have ground-fault protection of equipment with automatic disconnecting means. Ground-fault indication is required in accordance with Section 700-7(d).

ARTICLE 701—Legally Required Standby Systems

Section 701-1: Revised to conform with *NEC Style Manual.*

Section 701-9: Former text is now Section 701-9(a) Mandated Standby. Added Section 701-9(b) to require a sign at the grounding location where the grounded circuit conductor connected to the emergency source is connected to a grounding electrode conductor remote from the emergency source. The sign must identify all emergency and normal sources connected at that location.

Section 701-11: Revised first paragraph to include Section 701-11(f) for acceptable system type. Deleted "and/or" in third paragraph to conform with *NEC Style Manual.*

Section 701-11(f): Deleted "and/or" to conform with *NEC Style Manual.*

ARTICLE 702—Optional Standby Systems

Section 702-6: Revised to require that the transfer equipment, located on the load side of branch-circuit protection, be permitted to contain supplementary overcurrent protection having an interrupting rating sufficient for the available fault current the generator can deliver.

Sections 702-8(a) and (b): Former text is now Section 702-8(a) Standby. Added Section 702-8(b) to require a sign at the grounding location where the grounded circuit conductor connected to the emergency source is connected to a grounding electrode conductor remote from the emergency source. The sign must identify all emergency and normal sources connected at that location.

ARTICLE 705—Interconnected Electric Power Production Sources

Section 705-50: Revised editorially so that all applicable parts of Article 250 are included.

ARTICLE 710—Over 600 Volts, Nominal General

Section 710-2: Added to provide definition for "high voltage" as more than 600 volts, nominal.

Section 710-3: Formerly Section 710-2.

Section 710-4: Formerly Section 710-3.

Section 710-4(b): Updated table reference.

Table 710-4(b): Formerly Table 710-3(b). Revised title to clarify definition of "cover."

Section 710-5: Formerly Section 710-4.

(FPN): Updated section reference.

Section 710-32: Updated section reference.

Section 710-43: Revised required marking to "DANGER—HIGH VOLTAGE—KEEP OUT" for uniform *Code* language.

Section 710-45: Revised required marking to "DANGER—HIGH VOLTAGE—KEEP OUT" for uniform *Code* language.

ARTICLE 720—Circuits and Equipment Operating at Less than 50 Volts

Section 720-1, Exception: Revised to include references to Articles 551, 669, and 690.

ARTICLE 725—Class 1, Class 2, and Class 3 Remote-Control, Signaling, and Power-Limited Circuits

Section 725-5: Revised to require that the cables be listed as communications cables or multipurpose cables.

Section 725-6: Added to require that access to electrical equipment behind panels designed to allow access not be hampered by accumulations of wire and cable.

Section 725-16(b): Alphabetized conductor type list.

Tables 725-31(a) and (b): Added "source" to titles to clarify that it is the power source, not the circuit itself, that is to be limited to the values indicated; tables further revised for editorial consistency.

Notes for Tables 725-31(a) and (b): Revised Note 1 to make "VA_{max}" a separate paragraph, since it applies to both I_{max} and VA_{max}.

Section 725-38: Deleted Sections 725-38(a) and (b) and added reference to new Section 725-52 for installation requirements.

Sections 725-42, (1), and (2): Revised requirements to include exposure to lightning on interbuilding circuits on the same premises. Section 725-42(1) addresses other-than-coaxial conductors. Section 725-42(2) addresses coaxial conductors.

Sections 725-50 and (a): Revised heading and Section 725-50(a) to include "installation" to correlate with Sections 770-50, 800-50, and 820-50.

Table 725-50 and (FPN No. 1): Reorganized table hierarchically and revised to include reference to Section 725-53(b), Exception No. 2 for Types CL2, CL2X, CL3, and CL3X. Revised FPN No. 1 to specify that Class 3 cables are listed above Class 2, since Class 3 may substitute for Class 2.

Section 725-51(c): Revised to include ducts and any space used for environmental air, for consistency with Sections 725-51(a) and 300-22.

Section 725-52: Added for the installation of conductors and equipment on the load side of overcurrent protection, transformers, and current-limiting devices. Included are requirements for separation, for conductors of different circuits in the same cable, enclosure, or raceway, and the requirement that raceways not be used as a means of support for Class 2 or 3 conductors.

Section 725-53: Revised to include Section 725-53(g) for compliance requirements.

Section 725-53(a), Exception: Revised to specify that listed wires and cables be used in this application.

Section 725-53(b), Exception No. 1: Revised to reference Table 725-53 and listed wiring methods of Chapter 3 to clarify intent.

Section 725-53(b)(FPN): Added to reference Section 300-21 for firestop requirements for floor penetrations.

Section 725-53(e), Exception No. 1: Revised to specify Type CL2X or CL3X installed in a raceway, or other wiring methods in Chapter 3.

Section 725-53(f): Added to require that CL2 or CL3 wire or cable shall be used for cross-connect arrays.

Section 725-53(g): Formerly Section 725-53(f).

Table 725-53: Revised editorially to create hierarchical order of substitutions and to include cable Types MPG and CMG.

Figure 725-43: Replaced "may" with "shall be permitted to" to conform with *NEC Style Manual*. Revised section reference to include Section 760-51(g) for coaxial cables. Revised "residential" to "dwellings" to conform with Section 725-53 terminology. Cable Types MPG and CMG now included.

ARTICLE 760—Fire Protective Signaling Systems

Section 760-1(FPN No. 1): Revised to include NFPA 72, the consolidated signaling systems standard.

Section 760-7: Added to require that access to electrical equipment behind panels designed to allow access not be hampered by accumulations of wire and cable.

Section 760-17(c)(6): Revised to include ducts and other space used for environmental air.

Section 760-17(e)(2), Exception No. 2: Revised to include conductors in compliance with Section 760-16(c) and encased in metal raceway.

Section 760-17(e)(3), Exception No. 1: Revised for clarity and to include cables that are in compliance with Section 760-16(c) and encased in metal raceway.

Section 760-17(e)(3)(FPN): Added to reference Section 300-21 for firestop requirements for floor penetrations.

Section 760-17(e)(4), Exception Nos. 1 and 2: Former exception is now Exception No. 1 revised to emphasize Section 760-16(c). Added Exception No. 2 to permit Type NPLFP or NPLFR cables.

Section 760-18(a): Revised to correlate with Section 725-17(a).

Sections 760-18(b)(1) and (2): Revised to correlate with Section 760-18(a).

Tables 760-21(a) and (b): Added "source" to titles to clarify that it is the power source, not the circuit itself, that is to be limited to the values indicated; further revised tables for editorial consistency.

Section 760-22: Revised to clarify that the equipment must be marked to indicate each circuit that is power limited.

Section 760-28(b)(1): Revised to prohibit raceways from being used as a means of support for power-limited fire protective signaling circuit conductors.

Section 760-50: Revised heading and text to include installation requirements and to reference Section 760-52 requirements.

Section 760-51(f): Revised to include ducts and other space used for environmental air, for consistency with Section 760-51(d).

Section 760-51(f)(FPN): Added second paragraph to provide another method of defining "resistant to the spread of fire."

Section 760-52(a)(2), Exception No. 1: Replaced "partition" with "barrier" for consistent *Code* language.

Section 760-52(a)(2), Exception No. 2: Revised first paragraph to clarify nonpower-limited *circuit* conductors are intended. Added second paragraph to clarify routing and separation requirements.

Sections 760-52(b) and (b)(1): Revised heading and text to include communications circuits.

Section 760-53(a), Exception: Revised to allow Type FPLP cable.

Section 760-53(b)(FPN): Added to reference Section 300-21 for firestop requirements for floor penetrations.

Section 760-53(c), Exception No. 2: Revised to allow cables specified in Chapter 3 that meet the requirements of Sections 760-51(a) and (b) and are installed in nonconcealed spaces for not more than 10 feet.

Section 760-53(d): Revised to include conductor requirements of Section 760-51(g) for coaxial cables.

Table 760-53: Revised editorially to create hierarchical order of substitutions and to include cable Types MPG and CMG.

Figure 760-53: Replaced "may" with "shall be permitted to" to conform with *NEC Style Manual*. Revised section reference to include Section 760-51(g) for coaxial cables. Revised "residential" to "dwellings" to conform with Section 760-53 terminology. Cable Types MPG and CMG now included.

ARTICLE 770—Optical Fiber Cables and Raceways

Article Title: Revised to clarify that optical fiber raceways are also covered in this article.

Section 770-1: Scope clarified and revised to include installation of raceways but also to exclude the construction of optical fiber cables and raceways.

Section 770-4: Formerly Section 770-6.

Section 770-4(c): Revised "hybrid" to "composite" for technical consistency among standards developers.

Section 770-5: Formerly Section 770-4. Revised to require that where optical fiber cables are installed in a raceway, the raceway must be of a type permitted by, and installed in accordance with Chapter 3.

Section 770-5, Exception: Added for listed optical fiber raceway.

Section 770-5(FPN): Added to warn of plastic innerduct's fire safety level for use within buildings.

Section 770-6: Formerly Section 770-5. Revised to reference Table 770-50 cable types.

Section 770-7: Added to require that access to electrical equipment behind panels (and suspended ceiling panels) designed to allow access not be hampered by accumulations of wire and cable.

Section 770-49: Added to require fire resistance of optical fiber cables installed within a building.

Section 770-50: Added "installation" to heading, since this section also includes installation requirements. Revised text to clarify intent.

Table 770-50: Revised to include cable marking Types OFNG and OFCG.

Table 770-50(FPN No. 1): Revised editorially to clarify intent.

Section 770-51: Revised heading to address listing requirements for optical fiber cables and raceways. Revised text to include Section 770-51(d) for cable listing requirements and Sections 770-51(e) and (f) for raceways.

Section 770-51(c) and (FPN): Added for Types OFNG and OFCG. Added FPN to provide a method for defining "resistance to the spread of fire."

Section 770-51(d): Formerly Section 770-51(c). Revised to address space used for environmental air.

Section 770-51(e): Added for plenum optical fiber raceway requirements.

Section 770-51(f): Added for riser optical fiber raceway requirements.

Section 770-52(a): Revised "hybrid" to "composite."

Section 770-53: Revised heading to include "raceways."

Section 770-53(a): Revised second paragraph to clarify that listed plenum optical fiber raceways are intended to be used.

Section 770-53(a), Exception: Revised to include Types OFNG and OFCG.

Section 770-53(b): Revised second paragraph to clarify that listed riser optical fiber raceways are intended.

Section 770-53(b), Exception Nos. 1 and 2: Revised to include Types OFNG and OFCG.

Section 770-53(b)(FPN): Added to reference Section 300-21 for firestop requirements for floor penetrations.

Section 700-53(c): Revised to include Types OFNG and OFCG.

Table 770-53: Revised and reorganized to include Types OFNG and OFCG for permitted substitutions.

Figure 770-53: Revised to include Types OFNG and OFCG.

Chapter 8—Communications Systems

ARTICLE 800—Communications Circuits

Section 800-2: Revised to reference Article 100 for definitions. Added definition for "point of entrance," a term

Table 760-53 through Table 800-50 and (FPN No. 1)

used in Article 800. Relocated definition for "wire" to its correct alphabetical location.

Section 800-3(FPN): Added for other hybrid power and communications cable applications.

Section 800-4: Former Section 800-51(i).

Section 800-5: Added to require that access to electrical equipment behind panels designed to allow access not be hampered by accumulations of wire and cable.

Section 800-6: Added to require communications circuits and equipment to be installed in a neat and workman-like manner.

Sections 800-10 and (a)(1),(2),(3), and (b): Revised to address requirements for overhead communications wires and cables.

Section 800-10(a)(4)(FPN): Deleted due to nonexistence of reference.

Sections 800-11 and (a): Revised to address requirements for underground communications wires and cables.

Section 800-12: Revised to specify primary protectors.

Section 800-12(a): Revised to address requirements for communications wires and cables without a metallic shield, and to specify primary protectors.

Section 800-12(b): Revised to address requirements for communications wires and cables in accordance with Section 800-12(a) on buildings.

Section 800-12(c): Revised to address requirements for communications wires and cables entering buildings, and to specify primary protectors.

Section 800-30(a): Revised to specify primary protectors and to require that, where a lightning exposure exists, each interbuilding circuit on a premises be protected by a listed primary protector at each end of the interbuilding circuit.

Section 800-30(FPN No. 1): Revised to define "premises" as used in this article.

Section 800-30(FPN No. 3): Revised to specify primary protector. Deleted second sentence to avoid conflict with Section 800-30 revisions.

Section 800-30(FPN No. 4): Added to clarify where interbuilding circuits are not considered to have a lightning exposure.

Section 800-30(a)(1) and a., b., c., e., and (a)(2),(b), (b)(FPN), and (c): Revised to specify primary protectors.

Section 800-31: Revised to specify primary protector.

Section 800-31(FPN): Added to provide a way to determine applicable requirements for a listed primary protector.

Section 800-32: Revised to specify primary protector within secondary protector requirements.

Section 800-32(FPN No. 1): Added to provide a way to determine applicable requirements for a listed secondary protector.

Section 800-32(FPN No. 2): Added to clarify that secondary protectors on exposed circuits are not intended for use without primary protectors.

Section 800-40: Revised to specify primary protectors.

Section 800-40(b)(1): Second paragraph added to require that mobile home service equipment or disconnecting means, as described in Section 80-30(b), be considered accessible.

Section 800-40(b)(3), Exception: Deleted to conform with Section 800-41(a).

Sections 800-41 and (a) and (b): Revised to specify primary protector.

Section 800-49: Added for fire resistance of communications wires and cables.

Section 800-50: Revised to correlate with Sections 725-50, 760-50, 770-50, 800-50, and 820-50.

Section 800-50, Exception No. 2: Revised to emphasize that the conduit must be unbroken.

Section 800-50, Exception No. 3: Revised to specify primary protectors.

Section 800-50(FPN Nos. 1 and 2): Former FPN is now FPN No. 1. Added FPN No. 2 to clarify that, if practical, it is the intent to place the primary protector closer to the entrance, than 50 feet.

Table 800-50 and (FPN No. 1): Revised CMUC type to "undercarpet communications wire and cable" to correlate with Section 800-51(f). Updated reference to Section 80-53(c) to 800-53(d). Added Types CMG and MPG. Revised FPN No. 1 for clarity.

Section 800-51 and (FPN): Revised to address addition of new material and added FPN to reference Section 800-4 for equipment listing requirements.

Section 800-51(c) and (FPN): Added to provide requirements for Type CMG cable. Added FPN to provide a method for defining "resistant to the spread of fire."

Sections 800-51(d),(e), and (f): Formerly Sections 800-51(c), (d), and (e), respectively.

Section 800-51(g): Formerly Section 800-51(f). Revised to reference Section 760-51(g) for coaxial cables and to add cable Types CMG and MPG.

Section 800-51(h): Formerly Section 800-51(g).

Section 800-51(i): Formerly Section 800-51(h). Revised by moving one- and two-family dwelling requirement to new Section 800-53(e). Former 800-51(i) relocated as new Section 800-4.

Section 800-52: Revised to address installation of communications wires and cables.

Section 800-52(a)(1) and Exception Nos. 1 and 2: Revised to address installation of communications wires and cables and to include nonpower-limited fire protective signaling circuits.

Section 800-52(a)(2)a: Revised "power-limited" to "limited energy" to correlate with Article 725.

Section 800-52(a)(2)b: Added last sentence to require cables to be listed as communications cables or multipurpose cables.

Section 800-52(a)(2)c: Reorganized and revised to address separation rules for nonpower-limited fire alarm circuits. Updated terminology. Deleted Section 800-52(a)(2)c2. Former Section 800-52(a)c3 is now Section 800-52(a)(2)(c)2.

Section 800-52(d): Revised to specify which cables are permitted to be installed in cable trays.

Section 800-52(e): Added to prohibit raceways from supporting communications wires and cables.

Section 800-53: Revised to include Types CMG and MPG.

Section 800-53: Revised to include Section 800-53(f) requirements.

Section 800-53(a), Exception: Revised to include Type CMG and to create a hierarchical order.

Section 800-53(b)(FPN): Added to reference Section 800-52(b) for firestop requirements for floor penetrations.

Section 800-53(c) and Exception: Formerly Section 800-53(d). Revised title to "Distributing Frames and Cross-Connect Arrays." Revised exception to include Type CMG and to create a hierarchical order.

Section 800-53(d) and Exception Nos. 2 and 4: Formerly Section 800-53(c). Revised to address section reorganization and to include Type CMG. Deleted "listed" in Exception Nos. 2 and 4, since exceptions apply whether or not wires and cables are listed.

Section 800-53(e): Added to include listing and installation requirements for hybrid power and communications cable.

Section 800-53(f): Formerly Section 800-53(e).

Figure 800-53: Replaced "may" with "shall be permitted to" to conform with *NEC Style Manual*. Revised "residential" to "dwellings" to correlate with Section 800-53 terminology. Reference now includes Section 760-51(g). Added Types MPG and CMG.

ARTICLE 810—Radio and Television Equipment

Section 810-2: Revised to require that coaxial cable wiring for television receiving complies with Article 820.

Section 810-5: Added to reference Article 100 for definitions.

ARTICLE 820—Community Antenna Television and Radio Distribution Systems

Section 820-3: Added to reference Article 100 for definitions and to include a definition for "point of entrance."

Section 820-5: Added to require that access to electrical equipment behind panels designed to allow access not be denied by accumulations of wire and cable that prevent removal of panels, including suspended ceiling panels.

Section 820-6: Added to require systems to be installed in a neat and workmanlike manner.

Sections 820-11(a) and (b) and Exception Nos. 1 and 2: Revised and reorganized former Section 820-11 and Exception to clarify requirements for cables entering buildings.

Section 820-33: Added second paragraph for mobile home service equipment grounding requirement.

Section 820-40(a)(1): Revised to require the grounding conductor to be insulated and listed for the purpose.

Section 820-40(a)(5): Revised for consistency and compatibility with Section 800-40(a)(5).

Section 820-40(d), Exception: Added to reference Section 820-42 for mobile homes.

Sections 820-42(a) and (b)(1) and (2): Added to provide bonding and grounding requirements at mobile homes.

Section 820-49: Added to provide fire resistance requirements for CATV cables.

Section 820-50: Revised heading to include installation requirements and to specify coaxial cables. Revised text to correlate with new Section 820-49.

Section 820-50, Exception Nos. 2 and 3: Former Exception No. 2 revised and is now Exception No. 3. Added new Exception No. 2 to not require listing and marking where the cable enters the building from outside and is run in rigid metal conduit or IMC and the conduits are grounded.

Section 820-52: Revised to include through Section 820-52(e) for requirements.

Section 820-52(a)(2)b, Exception No. 2: Added second paragraph for routing and separation requirements.

Section 820-52(e): Added to require that raceways not be used as a means of support for coaxial cable.

Section 820-53(a), Exception: Revised to include Type CATVP cable.

Section 820-53(b), Exception No. 1: Added cable types CATV and CATVX to correlate with Exception No. 2.

Section 820-53(b)(FPN): Added to reference Section 820-52(b) for firestop requirements for floor penetrations.

Section 820-53(c), Exception No. 1: Added cable type CATVX to correlate with Exception Nos. 2 and 3.

Section 820-53(c), Exception Nos. 3 and 4: Revised Exception No. 3 and added Exception No. 4 to correlate

with Article 800. Exception No. 3 now applies only to one- and two-family dwellings. Exception No. 4 applies to nonconcealed spaces in multifamily dwellings.

Table 820-53: Added "coaxial" to title for clarity. Added Types MPP and CMP as substitutes for Type CATVP. Added Types MPG, CMG, MP, and CM as permitted substitutions for Type CATV; Types MPR and CMR for CATVR.

Chapter 9—Tables and Examples

Note 4: Deleted compact conductors.

Table 1, Note 2: Added new note to reference the compact conductor conduit fill criteria in Table 5B. The remainder of the notes were renumbered.

Table 1, Note 4: Revised editorially to clarify that it applies to the physical size of the wire, including insulation, for its size.

Table 3A: Revised first column to clarify that it applies to conduit or tubing. Added Types RH and THHW.

Tables 3B and 3C: Revised first column to clarify that it applies to conduit or tubing. Added Note 2 to clarify that conductors with the suffix "-2" have the same dimensions as conductors without the suffix.

Table 5: Added Types THHW and XHHW-2.

Table 5A: Revised title to clarify that it applies to compact strand conductors.

Table 5B: Revised to apply to tubing as well as conduit.

Table 6: Added Type THHW.

Table 8: Revised "MFT" to "kFT."

B. Examples: Revised "may" to "shall be permitted" in the introduction to the examples.

Example Nos. 1, 2(c), 3, and 8: Revised "may" to "shall be permitted to be."

Example No. 3: Revised to reflect the deletion of the second paragraph of Section 220-10(b) in the 1990 *Code*. Added a breakdown of the calculations for continuous loads to clarify how the figures were derived.

Example No. 8: Revised to comply with the change to Section 430-52.

Example Nos. 9 and 10: Added to provide examples of elevator installations.

Supplement 6: Schedule for the 1996 *National Electrical Code*

November 5, 1993 (5 p.m. EST)
Final date for receipt of proposals from the public for revision of the 1993 *National Electrical Code* preparatory to the issuance of the 1996 edition. Proposals should be forwarded to the Secretary of the Standards Council, National Fire Protection Association, 1 Batterymarch Park, P.O. Box 9101, Quincy, MA 02269-9101.

January 10-22, 1994
Code-Making Panels meeting to consider proposals for *Code* changes.

May 9-13, 1994
Correlating Committee reviews the report submitted by the Code-Making Panels. Establishes that no conflicts exist, that satisfactory correlation is achieved among the recommendations of the Code-Making Panels, and that the Committee's activities have been conducted in accordance with the Regulations Governing Committee Projects and the NEC Operating Procedures.

June 17, 1994
National Electrical Code Technical Committee Report (NEC-TCR or "Preprint") for the 1996 *National Electrical Code* published for distribution to the National Electrical Code Committee and other interested parties.

June 17-October 21, 1994
Period of study by interested parties and submittal of recommendations for modifying report to the Secretary of the Standards Council, NFPA.

October 21, 1994 (5 p.m. EST)
Closing date for comments.

December 5-17, 1994
Code-Making Panels meet to act on public comments.

March 6-10, 1995
Correlating Committee Meeting to review the Code-Making Panel action on comments.

April 14, 1995
NFPA prints and distributes the *National Electrical Code Technical Committee Documentation* (NEC-TCD) to the National Electrical Code Committee and other interested parties.

May 22-25, 1995
Action by NFPA Annual Meeting (Denver, Colorado).

July 19-21, 1995
Action by NFPA Standards Council.

September 1995
Publication of the 1996 *National Electrical Code*.

Index